Program of the

Eleventh Annual Conference of the Cognitive Science Society

16-19 August 1989
Ann Arbor, Michigan

New York London

First Published by
Lawrence Erlbaum Associates, Inc., Publishers
10 Industrial Avenue
Mahwah, New Jersey 07430

Transferred to Digital Printing 2009 by Psychology Press
270 Madison Ave, New York NY 10016
27 Church Road, Hove, East Sussex, BN3 2FA

Distributed by

ISBN 0-8058-0684-9

Publisher's Note
The publisher has gone to great lengths to ensure the quality of this reprint but points out that some imperfections in the original may be apparent.

The Eleventh Annual Conference of the Cognitive Science Society

August 16 - 19 1989

Ann Arbor, Michigan

Conference Co-Chairs

Gary M. Olson
Edward E. Smith

Reviewers

Lawrence Barsalou
Richard Belew
Daniel Bobrow
Lashon Booker
Mark Burstein
Charles Clifton
Allan Collins
Gary Cottrell
Gary Dell
Edmund Durfee
Jeffrey Elman
Jerome Feldman
Janet Fodor
Susan Gelman
Dedre Gentner
Mark Gluck
Kristian Hammond
James Hendler
Keith Holyoak
David Kieras
Walter Kintsch
John Laird
Jill Larkin
Robert Lindsay
Steven Lytinen
James McClelland
Douglas Medin
David Meyer
Nelson Morgan
Richard Nisbett
Donald Norman
J. Terry Nutter
Gary Olson
Judith Olson
Peter Polson
Brian Reiser
Chas Rosenberg
Brian Ross
David Rumelhart
Colleen Seifert
Jeff Shrager
Edward Smith
Keith Smith
Paul Smolensky
Elliot Soloway
Andreas Stolcke
David Swinney
Paul Thagard
Kurt VanLehn
Neff Walker
Terry Weymouth
J. Frank Yates
David Zipser

Proceedings of the
Eleventh Annual Conference of the Cognitive Science Society
Ann Arbor, Michigan - August 16 - 19, 1989

PAPER PRESENTATIONS

POSTER PRESENTATIONS

Author Listing

Liane H. Acker
University of Texas, Austin
Department of Computer Sciences
Taylor Hall
Austin, TX 78712

David W. Aha
University of California, Irvine
Department of Computer Science
Irvine, CA 92717

Woo-Kyoung Ahn
University of Michigan
Department of Psychology
Perry Building
Ann Arbor, MI 48109

Venkatramana G. Ajjanagadde
University of Pennsylvania
Dept. of Computer & Information Science
200 South 33rd Street
Philadelphia, PA 19104-6389

Michael J. Almeida
The Pennsylvania State University
Department of Computer Science
University Park, PA 16802

P. Anandan
Yale University
Computer Science Department
51 Prospect St.
New Haven, CT 06520-2158

John R. Anderson
Carnegie Mellon University
Department of Psychology
Pittsburgh, PA 15213

Sven Anderson
Indiana University
Computer Science Department
101 Lindley Hall
Bloomington, IN 47405-4101

A. G. Baker
McGill University
Department of Psychology
1205 Docteur Penfield
Montreal, Quebec
Canada H3A 1B1

Serge Baudet
University of Paris VIII
U.R.A. au C.N.R.S. No 218
2, rue de la Liberte
93526 St Denis Cedex 02
FRANCE

William Bechtel
Georgia State University
Department of Philosophy
University Plaza
Atlanta, GA 30303

Douglas A. Behrend
University of Michigan
Developmental Psychology
4333 Mason Hall
Ann Arbor, MI 48109

Richard K.Belew
University of California, San Diego
Cognitive Computer Sci. Research Group
Computer Science and Engineering Dept.
La Jolla, CA 92093

Leonid V. Belyaev
University of California, Los Angeles
Artificial Intelligence Laboratory
Computer Science Department
Los Angeles, CA 90024

Thomas Bever
University of Rochester
Department of Psychology
Rochester, NY 14627

Kate Bielaczyc
University of California, Berkeley
Graduate School of Education
Education in Mathematics, Science, & Tech.
Berkeley, CA 94720

Lawrence Birnbaum
Yale University
Department of Computer Science
P.O. Box 2158
New Haven, CT 06520

Gordon H. Bower
Stanford University
Department of Psychology
Jordan Hall; Bldg. 420
Stanford, CA 94305

Lawrence E. Brainerd
Memphis State University
Department of Psychology
Memphis, TN 38152

L. Karl Branting
University of Texas, Austin
Department of Computer Sciences
Taylor Hall 5.120
Austin, TX 78712

Timothy J. Breen
Boeing Computer Services
Advanced Technology Center
P.O. Box 24346, MS 7L-64
Seattle, WA 98124-0346

Michael Brent
MIT AI Lab
545 Technology Square
Cambridge, MA 02139

Olivier Brousse
University of Colorado at Boulder
Department of Computer Science
Institute of Cognitive Science
Boulder, CO 80309-0430

Gordon D. A. Brown
University College of North Wales
Department of Psychology
Bangor Gwynedd LL57 2DG
ENGLAND

Jerome R. Busemeyer
Purdue University
Department of Psychological Sciences
West Lafayette, IN 47907

Stephen Casner
Carnegie Mellon University
Department of Psychology
Pittsburgh, PA 15213

Chiu-Shui Chan
1239 Gibbs Avenue
Falcon Heights, MN 55108

Yves Chauvin
Stanford University
Department of Psychology
Stanford, CA 94305

Patricia W. Cheng
University of California at Los Angeles
Department of Psychology
Franz Hall
Los Angeles, CA 90024-1573

William J. Clancey
Institute for Research on Learning
2550 Hanover Street
Palo Alto, CA 94304

Paul R. Cohen
University of Massachusetts
Department of Computer & Information
Sys.Experimental Knowledge Systems Lab.
Amherst, MA 01003

Tim Converse
The University of Chicago
Department of Computer Science
1100 East 58th St.
Chicago, IL 60637

Garrison W. Cottrell
University of California, San Diego
Dept. of Computer Science and Engineering
La Jolla, CA 92093

Richard E. Cullingford
Georgia Institute of Technology
School of ICS
Atlanta, GA 30332

Kathleen Dahlgren
IBM Corporation
Los Angeles Scientific Center
Dept. 60G/3rd Floor
11601 Wilshire Blvd.
Los Angeles, CA 90025-1738

Gary S. Dell
University of Rochester
Language and Cognition Program
Intercampus Drive/Meliora Hall
Rochester, NY 14627

Guy Denhiere
University of Paris VIII
U.R.A. au C.N.R.S. No 218
2, rue de la Liberte
93526 St Denis Cedex 02
FRANCE

John Dinsmore
Southern Illinois University at Carbondale
Department of Computer Science
Carbondale, IL 62901

Stephanie Doane
University of Colorado, Boulder
Institute of Cognitive Science
Campus Box 345
Boulder, CO 80309-0345

Bonnie J. Dorr
MIT Artificial Intelligence Laboratory
545 Technology Square
Room 810
Cambridge, MA 02139

Barry B. Druhan
Louisiana State University
Department of Psychology
Baton Rouge, LA 70803-5501

Kevin Dunbar
McGill University
Department of Psychology
1205 Dr. Penfield Ave.
Montreal, Quebec
Canada H3A 1B1

Michael G. Dyer
University of California, Los Angeles
Artificial Intelligence Laboratory
Computer Science Department
Los Angeles, CA 90024

Jeffrey L. Elman
University of California, San Diego
Department of Cognitive Science
Cognitive Science C-015
La Jolla, CA 92093

Daniel J. Engelberg
McGill University
Stewart Biological Sciences Bldg.
1205 Dr. Penfield Avenue
Montreal, QC, H3A 1B1 CANADA

Eithan Ephrati
Hebrew University
Department of Computer Science
Jerusalem 91904
ISRAEL

Kanaan A. Faisal
Washington University
Campus Box 1045, Bryan 509
One Brookings Drive
St. Louis, MO 63130-4899

Frank Fallside
Cambridge University
Engineering Department
Trumpington Street
Cambridge, CB2 1PZ
ENGLAND

Richard G. Feifer
University of California at Los Angeles
Graduate School of Education
145 Moore Hall
Los Angeles, CA 90024

Douglas Fisher
Vanderbilt University
Computer Science Department
Box 1679, Station B
Nashville, Tennessee 37235

Margot Flowers
University of California at Los Angeles
Computer Science Department
Artificial Intellligence Laboratory
Los Angeles, CA 90024

Kenneth Forbus
University of Illinois
Beckman Institute
Qualitative Reasoning Group
405 North Mathews Street
Urbana, IL 61801

David R. Forster
University of Massachusetts
Department of Computer and
Information Science
Amherst, MA 01003

Deborah Frisch
University of Oregon
Department of Psychology
College of Arts and Sciences
Eugene, OR 97403-1227

Maria E. Fuenmayor
University of California, Los Angeles
Artificial Intelligence Laboratory
Computer Science Department
Los Angeles, CA 90024

Michael Gasser
Indiana University
Computer Science Department
Bloomington, Indiana 47405

Dedre Gentner
University of Illinois at Urbana
Psychology Department
1304 W. Springfield Avenue
Urbana, IL 61801

Mark A. Gluck
Stanford University
Department of Psychology
Jordan Hall; Bldg. 420
Stanford, CA 94305

Robert L. Goldstone
University of Illinois at Urbana-Champaign
603 E. Daniel St.
Champaign, IL 61820

Arthur C. Graesser
Memphis State University
Department of Psychology
Memphis, TN 38152

Lawrence Guentert
Purdue University
Department of Psychological Sciences
West Lafayette, IN 47907

Leo Gugerty
Educational Testing Service
Division of Cognitive and Assessment
Research
Princeton, NJ 08541

Robert F. Hadley
Simon Fraser University
School of Computing Science
Faculty of Applied Sciences
Burnaby, BC, Canada V5A 1S6

Sandra Hale
Washington University
Department of Psychology
St. Louis, Missouri 63130

Kristian J. Hammond
The University of Chicago
Department of Computer Science
1100 East 58th St.
Chicago, IL 60637

Gilbert Harman
Princeton University
Cognitive Science Laboratory
221 Nassau Street
Princeton, NJ 08542

Catherine Harris
University of California at San Diego
Department of Cognitive Science
Cognitive Science C-015
La Jolla, CA 92093

Michael R. Hee
Stanford University
Department of Psychology
Jordan Hall; Bldg. 420
Stanford, CA 94305

Darold Hemphill
Memphis State University
Department of Psychology
Memphis, TN 38152

Lora Hersberger
Purdue University
Department of Psychological Sciences
West Lafayette, IN 47907

Phil A. Hetherington
McGill University
Department of Psychology
1205 Docteur Penfield
Montreal PQ Canada H3A 1B1

Stephen C. Hirtle
University of Pittsburgh
Department of Information Science
LIS Building
Pittsburgh, PA 15260

Jack B. Hodges
University of California, Los Angeles
Artificial Intelligence Laboratory
Computer Science Department
Los Angeles, CA 90024

Edward Hoenkamp
University of California at Los Angeles
Artificial Intelligence Laboratory
3531 Boelter Hall
Los Angeles, CA 90024-1596

Douglas R. Hofstadter
Indiana University
Center for Res. on Concepts & Cognition
510 North Fess
Bloomington, Indiana 47408

Bettina Horster
University of Dortmund
FB Informatik
D-4600 Dortmund 50
WEST GERMANY

Heidi M. Horstmann
University of Michigan
Department of Physical Medicine & Rehab.
1C335 University Hospital
Ann Arbor, MI 48109-0023

Eduard Hovy
University of Southern California
Information Sciences Institute
4676 Admiralty Way, Suite 1001
Marina del Rey, CA 90292-6695

Edwin L. Hutchins
University of California - San Diego
Department of Psychology
La Jolla, CA 92093

Stephen Jackson
MRC Applied Psychology Unit
15 Chaucer Road
Cambridge, CB2 2EF
ENGLAND

Eric C. Johnson
Lehigh University
Department of Psychology
Chandler-Ullmann Hall 17
Bethlehem, Pennsylvania 18015

Bruce F. Katz
University of Illinois
Beckman Institute for
Advanced Science and Technology
Urbana, IL 61801

Walter Kintsch
University of Colorado, Boulder
Institute of Cognitive Science
Campus Box 345
Boulder, CO 80309-0345

Kenneth R. Koedinger
Carnegie Mellon University
Department of Psychology
Pittsburgh, PA 15213

Kyunghee Koh
University of Rochester
Center for Visual Science
274 Meliora Hall
Rochester, NY 14627

Janet L. Kolodner
Georgia Institute of Technology
School of ICS
Atlanta, GA 30332

Sarit Kraus
University of Maryland
Institute for Computer Studies and
Dept. of Computer Science
College Park, MD 20742

Stan C. Kwasny
Washington University
Campus Box 1045, Bryan 590
One Brookings Drive
St. Louis, MO 63130-4899

Trent E. Lange
University of California, Los Angeles
Artificial Intelligence Laboratory
Computer Science Department
Los Angeles, CA 90024

Jill H. Larkin
Carnegie Mellon University
Department of Psychology
Pittsburgh, PA 15213

David B. Leake
Yale University
Department of Computer Science
P.O. Box 2158 Yale Station
New Haven, CT 06520-2158

Geunbae Lee
University of California at Los Angeles
Computer Science Department
Artificial Intellligence Laboratory
Los Angeles, CA 90024

Daniel Lehmann
Hebrew University
Department of Computer Science
Jerusalem 91904
ISRAEL

James C. Lester
University of Texas, Austin
Department of Computer Sciences
Austin, TX 78712

Stanley Letovsky
Carnegie Mellon University
Computer Science Department
Pittsburgh, PA 15213

James A. Levin
University of Illinois at Urbana-Champaign
Department of Educational Psychology
210 Education Bldg.
1310 South Sixth St.
Champaign, IL 61820-6990

Lori Levin
Carnegie Mellon University
Center for Machine Translation
Pittsburgh, PA 15213-3890

Simon P. Levine
University of Michigan
Department of Physical Medicine & Rehab.
1C335 University Hospital
Ann Arbor, MI 48109-0023

Richard L. Lewis
Carnegie Mellon Univeristy
Computer Science Department
Pittsburgh, PA 15213

Yunn-wen Lien
University of California at Los Angeles
Department of Psychology
Franz Hall
Los Angeles, CA 90024-1573

Susan D.Lima
University of Wisconsin-Milwaukee
Department of Psychology
P.O. Box 413
Milwaukee, WI 53201

Robert K. Lindsay
University of Michigan
Artificial Intelligence Laboratory
162 ATL Bldg., 1101 Beal Avenue
Ann Arbor, MI 48109-2110

Cynthia L. Loiselle
University of Massachusetts
Department of Computer & Information Sys.
Experimental Knowledge Systems Lab.
Amherst, MA 01003

James W. Lundell
Hewlett-Packard
3404 E. Harmony Road
Fort Collins, CO 80525

Steven L. Lytinen
University of Michigan
Artificial Intelligence Laboratory
Ann Arbor, MI 48109

Barbara C. Malt
Lehigh University
Department of Psychology
Chandler-Ullmann Hall 17
Bethlehem, Pennsylvania 18015

Virginia Marchman
University of California-San Diego
Department of Psychology
La Jolla, CA 92093

Mitchell Marks
The University of Chicago
Department of Computer Science
1100 East 58th St.
Chicago, IL 60637

Charles Martin
Yale University
Computer Science Department
New Haven, CT 06520

Michael E. J. Masson
University of Victoria
P.O. Box 1700
Victoria, B.C.
Canada, V8W 2Y2

Robert C. Mathews
Louisiana State University
Department of Psychology
Baton Rouge, LA 70803-5501

Dwight Mazmanian
Concordia University
Department of Psychology
Montreal, Quebec
Canada H3A 1B1

Kathleen F. McCoy
University of Deleware
Department of Computer Science
Newark, DE 19716

Dale M. McNulty
University of California, Irvine
Department of Computer Science
Irvine, CA 92717

Douglas L. Medin
University of Michigan
Department of Psychology
Perry Building
Ann Arbor, MI 48109

Janet Metcalfe
University of California, San Diego
Department of Psychology
La Jolla, CA 92093

David E. Meyer
University of Michigan
Department of Psychology
330 Packard Road
Ann Arbor, MI 48109

Melanie Mitchell
Indiana University
Center for Res. on Concepts & Cognition
510 North Fess
Bloomington, Indiana 47408

Naomi Miyake
Aoyama Gakuin Women's College
Tokyo, Japan

John M. Miyamoto
University of Washington
Department of Psychology
Seattle, WA 98195

Yoshiro Miyata
Bell Communications Research
445 South Street
Room 2D336
Morristown, NJ 07960-1910

Eric Mjolsness
Yale University
Computer Science Department
51 Prospect St.
New Haven, CT 06520-2158

Paul Monro
University of Pittsburgh
Department of Information Science
LIS Building
Pittsburgh, PA 15260

Carol E. Moon
University of Michigan
Artificial Intelligence Laboratory
Ann Arbor, MI 48109

Steven Morris
University of California, Irvine
Information and Computer Science Dept.
Irvine, CA 92717

Joel Myerson
Washington University
Department of Psychology
St. Louis, Missouri 63130

In Jae Myung
Purdue University
Department of Psychological Sciences
West Lafayette, IN 47907

D. Navinchandra
Carnegie Mellon University
The Robotics Institute
Schenley Park
Pittsburgh, PA 15213-3890

Nancy J. Nersessian
Princeton University
Program in History of Science
Princeton, NJ 08544

Allen Newell
Carnegie Mellon Univeristy
Computer Science Department
Pittsburgh, PA 15213

Denis Newman
BBN Systems and Technologies Corp.
10 Moulton Street
Cambridge, MA 02238

Paul Nielsen
General Electric
Corporate Research & Development
P.O. Box 8
Schenectady, NY 12345

Paul O'Rorke
University of California, Irvine
Information and Computer Science Dept.
Irvine, CA 92717

Padraig G. O'Seaghdha
University of Rochester
Language and Cognition Program
Intercampus Drive/Meliora Hall
Rochester, NY 14627

Christopher Owens
Yale University
Computer Science Dept.
P.O. Box 2158 Yale Station
New Haven, CT 06520

Caroline Palmer
Ohio State University
142 Townshend Hall
1885 Neil Ave.
Columbus, Ohio 43210

H. Van Dyke Parunak
Industrial Technology Institute
Computer and Information Sciences Center
2901 Hubbard
P.O. Box 1485
Ann Arbor, MI 41806

R. Pascale
Virginia Polytechnic Inst. and State University
Department of Computer Science
562 McBryde Hall
Blacksburg, VA 24061-0106

Michael J. Pazzani
University of California, Irvine
Department of Information
and Computer Science
Irvine, CA 92717

Robert R. Peterson
University of Rochester
Language and Cognition Program
Intercampus Drive/Meliora Hall
Rochester, NY 14627

Peter Pirolli
University of California, Berkeley
Graduate School of Education
Education in Mathematics, Science, & Tech.
Berkeley, CA 94720

Kim Plunkett
University of Aarhus
Institute of Psychology
Asylvej 4
8240 Risskov
DENMARK

Thad A. Polk
Carnegie Mellon Univeristy
Computer Science Department
Pittsburgh, PA 15213

Peter Polson
University of Colorado, Boulder
Institute of Cognitive Science
Campus Box 345
Boulder, CO 80309-0345

Robert Port
Indiana University
Computer Science Department
101 Lindley Hall
Bloomington, IN 47405-4101

Bruce W. Porter
University of Texas, Austin
Department of Computer Sciences
Austin, TX 78712

Zenon Pylyshyn
University of Western Ontario
Centre for Cognitive Science
Department of Psychology
London, Ontario
CANADA N6A 5C2

William J. Rapaport
State University of New York at Buffalo
Department of Computer Science
226 Bell Hall
Buffalo, NY 14260

Michael Redmond
Georgia Institute of Technology
School of ICS
Atlanta, GA 30332

John F. Reeves
University of California, Los Angeles
Artificial Intelligence Laboratory
Computer Science Department
Los Angeles, CA 90024

Lauren B. Resnick
University of Pittsburgh
Learning Research and Development Center
Pittsburgh, PA 15260

John Roach
Virginia Polytechnic Inst. and State University
Department of Computer Science
562 McBryde Hall
Blacksburg, VA 24061-0106

Tony Robinson
Cambridge University
Engineering Department
Trumpington Street
Cambridge, CB2 1PZ
ENGLAND

Daniel E. Rose
University of California, San Diego
Cognitive Computer Sci. Research Group
Computer Science and Engineering Dept.
La Jolla, CA 92093

Dirk Ruiz
Carnegie Mellon University
Department of Psychology
Pittsburgh, PA 15213

Kathryn E. Sanders
Brown University
Department of Computer Science
Box 1910
Providence, RI 02912

David Schulenburg
University of California, Irvine
Department of Information
and Computer Science
Irvine, CA 92717

Richard Schweickert
Purdue University
Department of Psychological Sciences
West Lafayette, IN 47907

Mark S. Seidenberg
McGill University
Department of Psychology
1205 Docteur Penfield
Montreal, PQ Canada H3A 1B1

Colleen Seifert
The University of Michigan
Department of Pschology
330 Packard
Ann Arbor, MI 48104

Amanda J. C. Sharkey
University of Exeter
Center for Connection Science
Department of Computer Science
Exeter EX4 4PT Devon
ENGLAND

Noel E. Sharkey
University of Exeter
Center for Connection Science
Department of Computer Science
Exeter EX4 4PT Devon
ENGLAND

Lokendra Shastri
University of Pennsylvania
Dept. of Computer & Information Science
200 South 33rd Street
Philadelphia, PA 19104-6389

Hideo Shimazu
NEC Corporation
1-1 Miyazaki 4-chome
Miyamae-ku, Kawasaki
Kanagawa 213
JAPAN

Jeff Shrager
Xerox PARC
3333 Coyote Hill Road
Palo Alto, CA 94304

Thomas R. Shultz
McGill University
Department of Psychology
Stewart Biological Sciences Bldg.
1205 Dr. Penfield Ave.
Montreal, QC H3A 1B1 CANADA

Jane Silber
Vanderbilt University
Management of Technology
Nashville, Tennessee 37235

Gordon Skorstad
University of Illinois
Beckman Institute
Qualitative Reasoning Group
405 North Mathews Street
Urbana, IL 61801

Paul Smolensky
University of Colorado at Boulder
Department of Computer Science
Institute of Cognitive Science
Boulder, CO
80309-0430

Art Souther
University of Texas, Austin
Department of Computer Sciences
Austin, TX 78712

James C. Spohrer
Yale University
Department of Computer Science
51 Prospect Street
New Haven, Ct 06520-2158

Rohini K. Srihari
State University of New York at Buffalo
Department of Computer Science
226 Bell Hall
Buffalo, NY 14260

Andreas Stolcke
International Computer Science Institute
1947 Center St., Suite 600
Berkeley, CA 94704

Ron Sun
Brandeis University
Computer Science Dept.
Waltham, MA 02254

Katia P. Sycara
Carnegie Mellon University
The Robotics Institute
Schenley Park
Pittsburgh, PA 15213-3890

Yosuke Takashima
NEC Corporation
1-1 Miyazaki 4-chome
Miyamae-ku, Kawasaki
Kanagawa 213
JAPAN

Hideto Tomabechi
Carnegie Mellon University
Center for Machine Translation
Pittsburgh, PA 15213-3890

David Touretzky
Carnegie Mellon University
School of Computer Science
Pittsburgh, PA 15213

David J. Townsend
Montclair State College
Department of Psychology
Upper Montclair, NJ 07043

Lana Trick
University of Western Ontario
Centre for Cognitive Science
Department of Psychology
London, Ontario
CANADA N6A 5C2

Fu-Sheng Tsung
University of California, San Diego
Department of Computer Science and Engineering
La Jolla, CA 92093

Shihfen Tu
University of Washington
Department of Psychology
Seattle, WA 98195

Elise H. Turner
Georgia Institute of Technology
School of ICS
Atlanta, GA 30332

Roy M. Turner
Georgia Institute of Technology
School of ICS
Atlanta, GA 30332

Timothy J. van Gelder
Indiana University
Department of Philosphy
Sycamore Hall 026
Bloomington, Indiana 47405

Kurt VanLehn
Carnegie Mellon University
Dept. of Psychology
Pittsburgh, PA 15213

R. S. Virkar
Virginia Polytechnic Inst. and State University
Department of Computer Science
562 McBryde Hall
Blacksburg, VA
24061-0106

Stella Vosniadou
University of Illinois at Urbana/Champaign
174 Children's Research Center
51 Gerty Drive
Champaign, IL 61820

Joseph P. Vybihal
McGill University
School of Computer Science
Montreal, QC H3A 1B1
CANADA

Nigel Ward
University of California at Berkeley
Computer Science Division
Berkeley, CA 94720

Michael Waugh
University of Illinois at Urbana-Champaign
Department of Secondary Education
Education Bldg.
1210 S. Sixth St.
Champaign, IL 61820

Susan Hollbach Weber
University of Rochester
Computer Science Department
734 Computer Study Bldg.
Rochester, NY 14620

Stefan Wermter
University of Massachusetts at Amherst
Department of Computer and Information Sci.
Lederle Graduate Research Center
Amherst, MA 01003

Barbara Y. White
BBN Laboratories
10 Moulton Street
Cambridge, MA 02138

Edward J. Wisniewski
University of Illinois at Urbana -Champaign
Department of Psychology
603 East Daniel Street
Champaign, IL 61820

Dekai Wu
University of California at Berkeley
Computer Science Division
Berkeley, CA
94720

Philip David Zelazo
McGill University
Stewart Biological Sciences Bldg.
1205 Dr. Penfield Avenue
Montreal, QC, H3A 1B1
CANADA

Ingrid Zukerman
Monash University
Department of Computer Science
Clayton, Victoria 3168
AUSTRALIA

Chunking in a Connectionist Network

David S. Touretzky

School of Computer Science
Carnegie Mellon University
Pittsburgh, PA 15213

Incremental performance improvement with accumulated experience has been measured in human beings for a wide variety of cognitive, perceptual, and motor tasks (Newell, 1987). "Chunking" produces similar performance improvements in symbolic computer programs, such as the SOAR production system (Laird et al., 1987). Chunking takes place in SOAR by observing the working memory trace associated with a sequence of rule firings, and abstracting from this trace a chunk which in the future will produce the same results in a single step.

This paper presents a rule-following connectionist system that also improves its efficiency through chunking. It differs from symbolic production systems in several respects. Although connectionist networks may exhibit rule-following behavior, they do not necessarily contain explicit symbolic rules (Rumelhart & McClelland, 1986; Smolensky, 1988; Pinker & Prince, 1988). The system reported here learns its initial set of behaviors by back propagation from examples. Chunks are then created by a mechanism that observes input/output behavior as the network runs. The chunker is not told which features of the input were responsible for a particular output. In SOAR terminology, it has no access to a working memory trace.

The task the connectionist network is performing is string manipulation based on an abstract version of generative phonology. It was while working on a connectionist approach to phonology that I hypothesized chunking might play a role in the linguistic development of humans. Some speculations on the interaction between a chunker and the Language Acquisition Device appear at the end of this paper.

A Rule-Following Connectionist Network

Figure 1 shows part of a connectionist network that manipulates strings according to context-sensitive rewrite rules. The rewrite rules are an abstract version of classical generative phonology rules, and are shown here using classical notation. Rule R1 below says "change C to E in environments where it precedes a D." Similarly, rule R2 says "change A to B when it precedes an E."

```
R1:  C  -->  E  /  _ D
R2:  A  -->  B  /  _ E
```

Application of R1 to the string ABCD yields ABED. Figure 1 shows how this is accomplished. The input buffer, rule module, and change buffer form a three-layer feed-forward network. Symbols are sequentially shifted into the input buffer. Rule units read the buffer state and generate an output pattern in the change buffer describing the changes that are to be made to the input. (Each input buffer segment has a corresponding change buffer segment.) Three types of changes are possible: *mutation* of input tokens, *deletion* of input tokens, and *insertion* of new tokens. A String Editing Network, not shown, reads the input and change buffer patterns and generates an updated input pattern in which the specified changes have been made. The design of the String Editing Network is explained in (Touretzky, 1989).

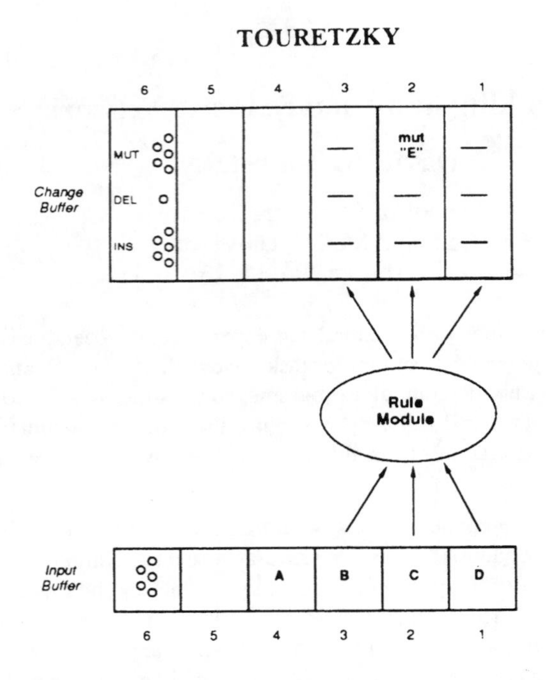

Figure 1: Part of a connectionist network for applying rewrite rules to strings.

The symbols from which strings are composed are binary feature vectors. The experiment reported here uses a representation with five "phonetic" features organized as one group of two features and one of three features. (In real phonology there are many more features; they encode the place and manner of articulation of sounds.) Features within a group are mutually exclusive. There are a total of six legal symbols, labeled A through F. The change buffer patterns use an eleven-element code for each segment: one for signaling deletion, five for describing a mutation, and five for specifying an insertion. Symbols are always inserted to the right of the corresponding input buffer segment.

Change buffer patterns are tri-state: 0 means "no change," +1 means "turn the corresponding bit in the input buffer on," and -1 means "turn the corresponding bit off." For deletion and insertion operations, -1 is treated like zero. The use of tri-state patterns causes the change buffer units to adopt the "no change" case as the default in the absence of input. Tri-state outputs are obtained using the symmetric sigmoid activation function $\sigma(x) = 2/[1 + \exp(-x)] - 1$.

The initial rules are installed by applying backpropagation to a training set of input pattern/change pattern pairs. The rule module serves as the hidden layer during learning. Once the initial rule set has been acquired, there is no supervised learning in the model. To acquire chunks, sequences of typical inputs are run through the input buffer. As it applies its rewrite rules, the model formulates chunks when two rules fire in succession, and trains itself using backprop to predict a chunked action in the appropriate context. Chunking may therefore be regarded as "self-supervised" learning, since the model is serving as its own teacher. The chunking mechanism is explained further after the next section.

Position-Independent Rules

Rules are always learned in "standard position," where the rightmost element of the rule's environment is the rightmost element of the input buffer. However, downstream feeding relationships may require rules to apply in other positions. Consider what happens when the string ACD is shifted into the input buffer one segment at a time. The network does nothing with the initial substrings A and AC. After shifting in the D, ACD is converted to AED by rule R1. R2 should then apply to produce BED, but the AE environment for R2 is not aligned with the right edge of the input buffer; it is one segment downstream.

To allow rules to apply independent of position, we make several downstream copies of the primary rule module and constrain the link weights in each copy to be equal to the corresponding primary module weights, as shown in Figure 2. This way rules need only be learned in standard position, but they can apply anywhere they are needed. The reason for using a change description as the output representation should now be clear: the outputs of all the rule modules can be superimposed by addition at the change buffer units. If each rule module were to directly map the input string to an updated string, the outputs of multiple rule modules could not be combined.

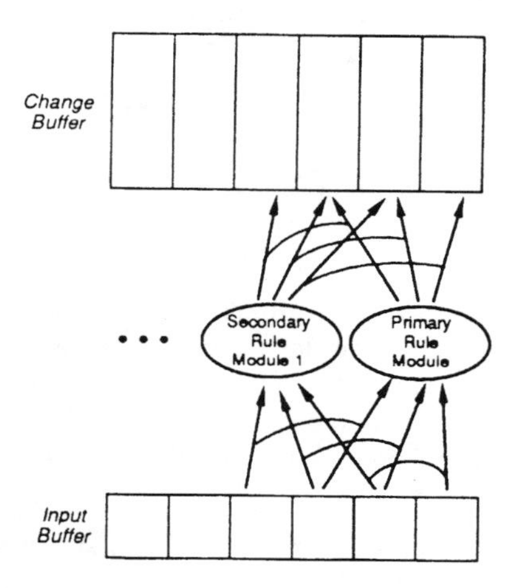

Figure 2: Link-equality constraints cause secondary rule modules to replicate the behavior of the primary module at various positions downstream.

The Chunking Mechanism

Figure 3 shows how chunking is accomplished. The model has two change buffers. The α connections, which control the Current Change Buffer, are created by back propagation learning on an initial training set supplied by the teacher. The β connections control the Chunked Change Buffer, which the network uses to teach itself new chunks.

Chunking occurs continuously as the network processes patterns flowing through its input buffer. Each time a symbol is shifted into the input buffer and a forward pass is performed, the α connections produce a Current Change Buffer pattern. If the pattern is all zeros, meaning no α rule fired, the β connections are taught to produce the same result. If the pattern is non-zero, meaning some α rule did fire, the chunker makes a note of the change buffer pattern, and the string editing network makes the requested change

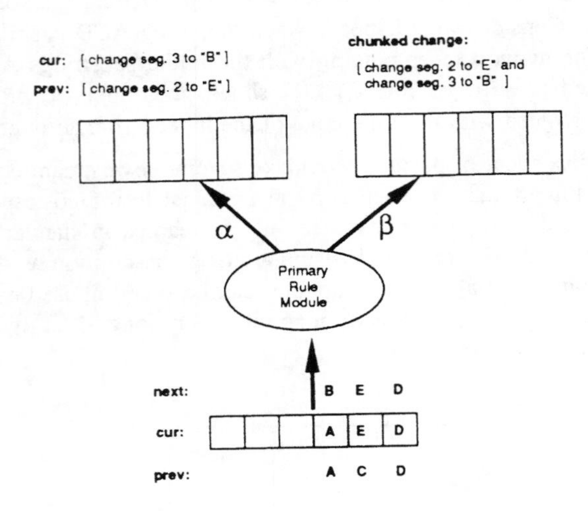

Figure 3: Chunking of rules R1 and R2 by training β connections to produce the composition of the two rules' change buffer patterns.

and updates the input buffer. After a second forward pass, if no more α rules fire, there is no sequence to be chunked. In this case the β connections are taught to imitate the change pattern produced by the single α rule. If an α rule does fire on the second forward pass, a chunk can be composed from the remembered change buffer pattern of the first rule plus the change buffer pattern of the second rule. The β connections are then taught to output this composite change pattern in the context that caused the first α rule to fire.

This training regimen ensures that the β rules will be an essential superset of the α rules. The only α rules not duplicated on the β side will be those that never fire in isolation, but only to feed another rule or as a result of a feeding rule. These non-essential α rules will be replaced by chunks. More commonly, chunked and unchunked versions of rules coexist on the β side.

A number of fine points in the training of the model need to be explained. In a chunking network the connections to rule and change buffer units should remain plastic. Plasticity can be lost if units are allowed to get too far out on the tails of the sigmoid, where the derivative goes to zero. Several steps are taken to prevent loss of plasticity. In standard back propagation the error signal of an output unit is defined to be the difference between the actual and desired outputs multiplied by the derivative of the output function (Rumelhart et al., 1986). In the chunking network the derivative term is omitted for output units.

In addition, weights must not be allowed to grow too large during training, as this can also hinder future learning. To keep the weights small and the rule units from getting too far out on the tails of the sigmoid, the model uses output training targets of +0.5 and -0.5 rather than +1 and -1. When updating the input buffer, any change buffer value greater than +0.3 is treated as +1, and any value less than -0.3 is treated as -1.

Although change buffer units use a symmetric sigmoid, rule units use the standard sigmoid. I conjecture that rules may be learned more easily this way. Rule units are feature detectors, so when a feature is not present the unit's output should be zero. This is easily achieved with the standard sigmoid by supplying a substantial negative bias that can be counteracted only by an appropriate pattern of input features. With tri-state units it is not possible hold the output steady at zero over the entire set of inputs that aren't supposed to trigger a rule.

Finally, it should be noted that in order to learn the environments in which new chunks apply, rule units must modify not only their β output connections, but also their input connections. But this alters the rule unit's response to subsequent inputs, so it may interfere with the continued production of correct patterns in the Current Change Buffer. To prevent the model from leading itself astray, it is programmed to continually rehearse its α behaviors as it trains the β connections. Rehearsal is another instance of self-supervised learning. Each pattern the α units generate in the Current Change Buffer is "idealized" by treating all values greater than +0.3 as +0.5, all values less than -0.3 as -0.5, and all other values as 0. The difference between the actual α outputs and the idealized outputs generates an error signal that helps to readjust the input weights on each presentation, countering the disruptive effect training the β units has on the input weight pattern. The α and β sides of the model are thereby forced to compromise on an input weight pattern that allows each side to do its job.

Complex Rule Interactions

Composing a chunk from two mutation rules is easy: one simply inclusive-or's the change buffer patterns (using tri-state logic), giving the second rule priority in the case of a $+1/-1$ conflict. Composing chunks from other types of rules is slightly more complex. If the first rule inserts or deletes a segment, some portion of the second rule's change buffer pattern will need to be shifted to take this change into account before inclusive-oring the two together. If the second rule mutates a segment that was inserted by the first, the second rule's mutation pattern must be combined (with priority) with the first rule's insert pattern, not its mutation pattern. If the second rule deletes a segment that was inserted by the first rule, the first rule's insertion must be suppressed in the composed chunk. This can be accomplished by setting the insertion bits to zero.

In the simulation, chunked change buffer patterns were composed by a Lisp version of the above algorithm. However, it would be easy to construct a connectionist network to do the same task. The input would be the current and previous change buffer patterns; the output would be the composed change.

A limitation of this particular rewrite-rule architecture is that only one symbol can be inserted between each pair of symbols in the input buffer. Therefore one cannot chunk two rules if they both insert something at the same input position. In practice this situation does not seem to come up in segmental phonology, although there are multi-segment insertions at the morphological level.

Experimental Results

The initial chunker simulation used an input buffer of length six, and three rule modules, each of which looked at three adjacent input segments. The primary rule module was taught rules R1 and R2 by backpropagation on a small training set. (The training set consisted of some environments in which the rules should apply, plus some additional environments in which no rule should fire.) The following example shows the results of this training. R2 and then R1 applies, independently, in standard position, as the string AEFCD is shifted through the input buffer. Underscores denote null segments (all zeros.)

```
* (demo '(a e f c d))
    Shift A into input buffer:    _ _ _ _ _ A
    Shift E into input buffer:    _ _ _ _ A E
      Change due to rule firing:  _ _ _ _ B E        (rule R2)
    Shift F into input buffer:    _ _ _ B E F
    Shift C into input buffer:    _ _ B E F C
    Shift D into input buffer:    _ B E F C D
      Change due to rule firing:  _ B E F E D        (rule R1)
```

We next consider an example of downstream feeding of R2 by R1, which never occurred in the training data. Note that after the last symbol is shifted in, the input buffer changes twice. This is the condition allowing a chunk to be composed.

```
* (demo '(a c d))
    Shift A into input buffer:    _ _ _ _ _ A
    Shift C into input buffer:    _ _ _ _ A C
    Shift D into input buffer:    _ _ _ A C D
      Change due to rule firing:  _ _ _ A E D        (rule R1)
      Change due to rule firing:  _ _ _ B E D        (rule R2)
```

Running the network on sequences such as ACD allows it to learn chunks in self-supervised mode, by observing its own behavior. The chunk for turning ACD into BED consists of R1 plus a shifted version of R2, since R2 is applying one segment downstream. The rule units must learn to pay attention to the third segment of the buffer, whereas for R1 and R2 in isolation only the first two segments are important.

The result of chunking is shown below for the string ACDCD. (To actually use the learned chunks we replace the α weights with the learned β weights.) The ACD to BED portion of the example demonstrates the existence of the R1-R2 chunk; the CD to ED portion that follows demonstrates the preservation of R1 on the β side as an independent rule. Other inputs verified that R2 was also preserved.

```
* (demo '(a c d c d))
    Shift A into input buffer:    _ _ _ _ _ A
    Shift C into input buffer:    _ _ _ _ A C
    Shift D into input buffer:    _ _ _ A C D
      Change due to rule firing:  _ _ _ B E D        (chunk R1-R2)
    Shift C into input buffer:    _ _ B E D C
    Shift D into input buffer:    _ B E D C D
      Change due to rule firing:  _ B E D E D        (rule R1)
```

Additional experiments confirm that the network can chunk insertion and deletion rules as well as mutations. It can also combine a learned chunk with another rule to form a bigger chunk.

As long as the model's behavior is governed solely by the α connections, it will not be able to apply the chunks it has learned. An initial, brute-force solution to this problem is to simply copy the β weights to the α connections whenever the β training error is low enough. But such a drastic, global weight change is admittedly unnatural. We are currently exploring more fluid ways of exchanging knowledge between the α and β sides. One scheme we have tried is to maintain running confidence levels for each side, and with each new input symbol, stochastically choose either the α or β change buffer pattern based on relative confidence values. Initially the β confidence is low. When the α side has successfully trained the β side, the network begins to execute a mix of α and β actions, including some learned chunks. As the β side in turn tries to teach new chunks to the α side, the α confidence level drops and the β rules take over until the new α chunks have been learned.

Interesting Chunking Phenomena

A number of interesting questions are raised by this work. One is the order in which larger chunks should be formed. Consider the feeding rule chain R1-R2-R3-R4. If the model builds at most one chunk before shifting a new symbol into its buffer, the chain will be chunked in the order (((R1 R2) R3) R4). This approach is compatible with the power law of practice cited by Newell. If the model builds a chunk whenever any pair of unchunked rules fire in sequence, the order of chunk creation will be ((R1 R2) (R3 R4)). It is not yet known which order is more compatible with the way the learning algorithm creates rule representations.

A second question is what representation the model will develop for rules that participate in multiple feeding chains. Consider a case where, for one class of inputs there is a chunk R1-R2-R3, and for another class a chunk R1-R4-R5. Since R1 is shared by both chunks and may also apply in isolation, the representations of the two chunks and the original rule should be similar, and will probably share units.

A related issue is the formation of variable-length chunks from self-feeding rules, such as this deletion rule:

```
R6:  E --> Ø / _ F
```

R6 applies three times in succession to the string BEEEF to derive BF. After chunking, BF should be obtained in a single rule firing. If the chunker is exposed to sequences of form $\{E\}^{+}F$ of varying length, it should build a collection of related chunks. The degree and nature of the overlap in representations of these chunks is worth investigating.

Finally there is the issue of variables appearing in rules. Variables serve either to narrow the domain of application of a rule (when the same variable appears twice on the left hand side), or to copy a value from one place to another (when the variable appears once on the left and at least once on the right hand side.) In phonology it is not too expensive to expand a variable-containing rule into a set of variable-free rules, because variables can take on only a few values. In more general symbol processing tasks this may not be feasible. It may be possible to teach a backpropagation network to implement rules with variables by encoding the value in the hidden layer activation pattern. Such a scheme would probably require a more complex hidden layer than in the present model.

Chunking and Language

The segmental phonology of any human language can be expressed by sequences of simple rewrite rules on strings. These rules are highly constrained, so that, for example, reversing the segments of a word is not possible in human phonology (Pinker & Prince, 1988). Another constraint is that there is no metathesis (switching) of non-adjacent segments. The regularity and degree of constraint of phonological processes is striking, and cries out for scientific explanation. The hypothesis motivating the work reported here is that the Language Acquisition Device may only be able to hypothesize very simple rules. The rules can interact to produce lengthy derivations, and they are extensively chunked during development to arrive at adult linguistic performance. But chunking is the only source of complex rules; they cannot be created *de novo* by the LAD.

Why have rules at all in a connectionist theory? Rules separate *policy* (what Chomsky calls linguistic "switch settings") from *mechanism* (the fundamental ability to do insertions, deletions, and mutations.) If a mechanism such as the String Editing Network is universal and genetically determined, then the LAD's job is tremendously easier: it can concentrate on learning just the policies of the speaker's language.

This paper makes no assumption that policies require explicit symbolic representations in speakers' heads. Rather, it shows that chunking can occur even when there is no working memory trace available and new rules cannot be constructed symbolically. The connectionist chunker acquires its rules incrementally, through self-supervised backpropagation and rehearsal of prior knowledge. Further experiments are planned to analyze the representations the chunker develops.

Acknowledgments

This work was supported by a contract with Hughes Research Laboratories, by National Science Foundation Grant EET-8716324, and by the Office of Naval Research under contract number N00014-86-K-0678. I thank Deirdre Wheeler, Marco Zagha, Michael Witbrock, and George Lakoff for discussions that contributed to this work, and Gillette Elvgren for help with the simulations.

References

Newell, A. (1987) The 1987 William James Lectures: Unified Theories of Cognition. Given at Harvard University.

Laird, J. E., Newell, A., and Rosenbloom, P. S. (1987) Soar: An architecture for general intelligence. *Artificial Intelligence* 33(1):1-64.

Pinker, S., and Prince, A. (1988) On language and connectionism: analysis of a parallel distributed processing model of language acquisition. In S. Pinker & J. Mehler (eds.), *Connections and Symbols*. MIT Press.

Rumelhart, D. E., Hinton, G. E., and Williams, R. J. (1986) Learning internal representations by error propagation. In D. E. Rumelhart and J. L. McClelland and (eds.), *Parallel Distributed Processing: Explorations in the Microstructure of Cognition*, volume 1. MIT Press.

Rumelhart, D. E., and McClelland, J. L. (1986) On learning the past tense of English verbs. In J. L. McClelland and D. E. Rumelhart (eds.), *Parallel Distributed Processing: Explorations in the Microstructure of Cognition*, vol. 2. MIT Press.

Smolensky, P. (1988) On the hypotheses underlying connectionism. *Behavioral and Brain Sciences* **11**(1).

Touretzky, D. S. (1989) Towards a connectionist phonology: the "many maps" approach to sequence manipulation. *Proceedings of the Eleventh Annual Conference of the Cognitive Science Society*. Lawrence Erlbaum Associates.

A PDP model of sequence learning that exhibits the power law

Yoshiro Miyata
Bell Communications Research

ABSTRACT

This paper examines some characteristics of the learning process in a model of skill learning (Miyata, 1987) in which performance of executing sequential actions becomes increasingly more efficient as a skill is practiced. The model is a hierarchy of sequential PDP networks which was designed to model a shift from a slow, serial performance of a novice to a fast, parallel performance of an expert in tasks such as typing. The network develops representation of a set of sequences as it tries to produce the sequences faster. The model was found to yield the power law of learning (Newell and Rosenbloom, 1981). In addition, it exhibited a frequency effect on substitution errors similar to what was found in typing (Grudin, 1983).

INTRODUCTION

Learning has intrinsic importance to the study of skilled performance because the nature of performance dramatically changes as a skill develops. However, study of skill learning is difficult because one has to explain not only what processing structure underlies skilled performance in a particular task domain, but also what mechanism enables us to build such structures as a result of experience in many different tasks. The approach taken in this work is to look for phenomena that are observed across a wide range of tasks and to try to develop a model of action learning that attempts to account for what seem to be quite general phenomena.

I have previously proposed a model of skill learning in which performance of sequential actions becomes faster as a skill is practiced (Miyata, 1987). This model successfully accounted for some effects of presentation frequency in typing, specifically the effect on speed (Grudin & Larochelle, 1982) and on a class of execution errors (Sellen, 1986). This paper reports on some additional experiments which revealed some interesting characteristics of the learning process in the model. In particular, the model is shown to exhibit the power law of learning. In addition, it exhibited a frequency effect on error patterns similar to typing errors at the keystroke level as well as at the sequence level as previously shown (Miyata, 1987). I will start by describing an example of the power law to illustrate the kind of skills being modeled in this work.

The Power Law

Probably the most general phenomenon we know about learning is that practice makes performance faster. However, more specific regularities seem to exist. For a wide variety of tasks, the learning curve (i.e., a plot of the time to perform the task versus the number of trials) produces approximately a straight line in log-log coordinates (Newell & Rosenbloom, 1981). This has been generally called the power law because it indicates that the time is a power function of the number of trials. Figure 1 shows a learning curve of a beginning typist in a typing class studied by Gentner (1983) with the median interstroke interval plotted against the number of weeks of study on a log-log scale.

THE HS MODEL

Consider a person learning to type: first, a novice who has just started to learn typing. Suppose the learner has an intention to type the word "type". He would first find the key "t" on the keyboard and then hit the key. (Note that even a novice typist has the skill to hit a key by moving a finger.) Only after this is finished will he proceed to find and hit the next key "y". Performance is serial and slow. Compare this with an expert who no longer has to work letter by letter, but can deal with several keystrokes simultaneously. In fact, skilled typists seem to achieve their speed by overlapping their finger movements for successive keystrokes (Gentner, Grudin & Conway, 1980). As the typists learn to type faster, their finger movement patterns change so as to take into account the context of each character (Gentner, 1983). Performance becomes parallel and fast.

The model to be presented here, called the HS model (for Hierarchical-Sequential Model), was designed to account for this kind of change from a novice to an expert. The HS model, like many other hierarchical models (Miller, Galanter & Pribram 1960; MacKay, 1982; Laird, Rosenbloom, & Newell 1986; Anderson, 1982, for example), assumes a hierarchical control structure, where higher level representation holds more abstract, longer range information, whereas more concrete, short term information is represented at lower levels. Thus, an intention to perform a sequence is represented at the top level and is converted to representations at successively lower levels until it is finally converted into actual physical body movements at the lowest level. For example, the highest level might specify an intention to type a sequence of letters (word, phrase, or sentence), and the intermediate levels might represent letter subsequences, or individual letters, that constitute the whole sequence. Consequently, higher level representation stays relatively stable whereas representations at lower levels changes more rapidly: an intention to type a word stays unchanged at the top level while the lowest level goes through a sequence of action components, eg., finger movements. The HS model differs, however, from the previous hierarchical models in that there is no fixed a priori relations between levels of representation and the levels in the hierarchy of the model, except at the highest and the lowest levels. The relations change as the system learns what level of information each level in the model should represent in order to achieve more efficient performance.

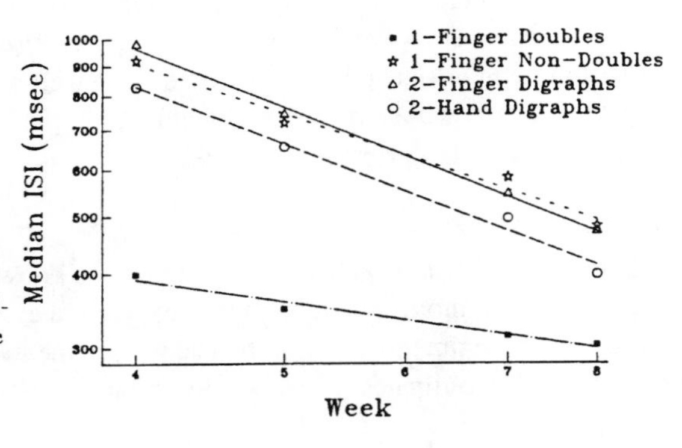

Figure 1. Learning curves for one of the typists studied by Gentner (1983). The median interstroke intervals are plotted against the number of weeks in a beginning typing class on a log-log scale. The four curves correspond to four different digraph classes that differ in their motoric requirements, but the specific effects of digraph classes are not important for the current discussion.

In this framework, the learning process from a novice to an expert described above can be characterized as follows: in the novice case, lower, more "motoric" levels have not developed representations of long sequences but have representations only of small action components, such as "hitting a key". This means that the representation of an intention must be broken down into smaller components at relatively higher levels in the hierarchy. However, as the system becomes expert, representations of chunks of these components (such as small letter sequences) are developed at intermediate levels. Such chunks are broken down into their constituents at lower levels, closer to physical movements. If we only assume that it takes a constant time to execute a chunk at an intermediate level, forming chunks of longer subsequences leads to a faster performance because fewer chunks are required to represent each sequence,

The Network Architecture

A special case of the HS model, in which there are three levels of representation, has been implemented and tested as a PDP network. Since the model was described fully in Miyata (1987, 1988), I will only briefly review the model and summarize the findings previously reported. In the next section, I will describe new findings about the model's learning process. Figure 2 shows the architecture of the network. The highest level, labeled *Intention*, contains a conceptual representation of the action sequence to be performed. The lowest level, labeled *Action* represents individual components to be executed. The middle level, *Plan* mediates the mapping between *Intention* and *Action*. The operation of the model involves two mappings, implemented by two subnetworks: The subnetwork Planning-Net maps from an *Intention* vector to a sequence of *Plan* vectors. The subnetwork Execution-Net maps from a *Plan* vector

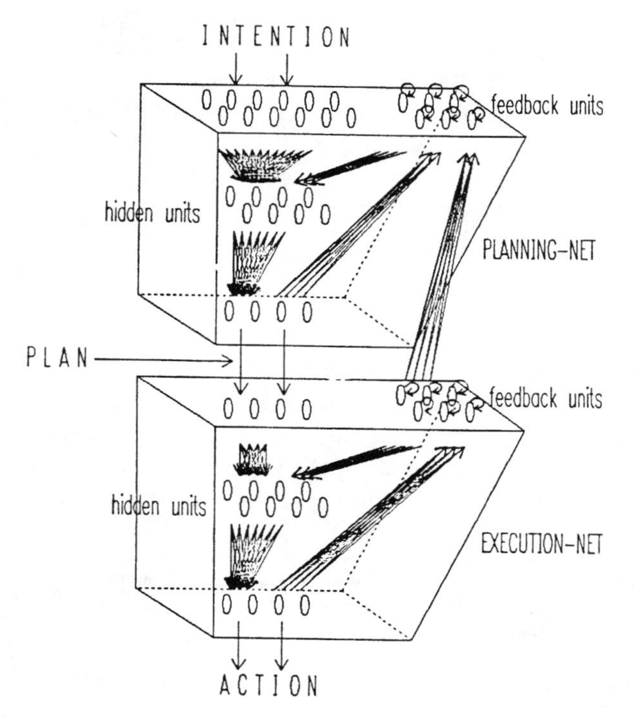

Figure 2. The architecture of the HS model with three levels of representation. *Intention* is a conceptual representation of the action sequence to be performed. *Action* represents individual action components to be executed. *Plan* is an intermediate representation that mediates the mapping between *Intention* and *Action*. A single *Intention* vector is mapped to a sequence of *Plan* vectors by Planning-Net, and each *Plan* vector is mapped to a sequence of *Action* vectors by Execution-Net. The two mappings are implemented by two Jordan networks. The output of Planning-Net is directly fed to the plan units of Execution-Net. The feedback units of the Execution-Net are connected to the feedback units of the Planning-Net.

to a sequence of *Action* vectors.

Each subnetwork was Jordan's sequential network (Jordan, 1986) in order to generate a sequence of output vectors from a single input vector. In addition to a feedforward three-layer architecture with one layer of hidden units, a Jordan network has a set of feedback units with recurrent self-connections which acts as a memory of a temporal context of past output vectors stored as an exponentially decaying trace of past output vectors: The sequence of vectors $X = (\vec{x}_1, \vec{x}_2, \cdots, \vec{x}_T)$, where $\vec{x}_t$ is the output vector at time t, is stored as $\sum_{t=1}^{T} \alpha^{T-t} \vec{x}_t$, where α is the decay factor ($0<\alpha<1$). At each time step, the next output vector is determined both by its input vector (which does not change during the sequence), and by the feedback vector (which changes at each time step).

In the HS model, a set of connections from the feedback units of the Execution-Net to the feedback units of the Planning-Net allowed the latter to keep track of what the former was doing. Also, note that Planning-Net operated at a slower rate than Execution-Net: Planning-Net is updated only once in every three steps (in this particular simulation) of updating Execution-Net.

In the simulation reported here, there were 4 possible actions A, B, C and D, each represented by one of 4 output units of Execution-Net. Each *Intention* vector represented a sequence of three actions.

Pre-Training

The back-propagation algorithm (Rumelhart, Hinton, & Williams, 1986) was used to train the network. However, before the system could start learning, the elementary skill of a novice, such as the ability to find and hit a key, must be somehow realized in the system. This prior knowledge was modeled by pre-training the network so that it could perform in a manner analogous to a novice typist, before the actual training of the task itself started. As the result of pre-training, the network could perform the task but only slowly. Figure 3 illustrates the time course of the operation of the network after the pre-training. It was trained to use 4 *Plan* vectors, each representing one of the 4 possible actions. In order to generate the sequence *ABC*, for example, Planning-Net was pre-trained to generate a sequence of three *Plan* vectors, (*Plan*1, *Plan*2, and *Plan*3) one representing A, one for B, and one for C. Execution-Net was pre-trained to respond to each *Plan* by turning on the corresponding output unit (shown in the figure by the upright rectangle in the action sequence) at the first time step and then turn off all output for the next two time steps.[1]

The network was trained to produce the 64 possible sequences of three components, each component being one of four actions.

Training

In the actual training, a procedure was used that forced the network to gradually speed up its performance. Suppose the network was to produce the sequence *ABC*. Each action produced by the network was compared against a target and the weights modified so as to reduce the error. The target was always the next component in the sequence to be produced. Initially, the target was the first component *A*. The target stayed the same until the *Action* vector matches the target.[2] Thus, if the network generates a wrong action, e.g., *B*, or *C*, instead of *A*, the target continues to be *A*. When the action matches the target,

---

1 The choice of the representational formats for the *Intention* vectors and for the initial *Plan* vectors are mostly arbitrary. In this simulation, a local representation, in which each unit represented a particular action at a particular point in time, was used to avoid any unwanted effects of similarity structures embedded in the representation.

2 Which action the network has produced was decided by choosing the most active output unit.

however, the target is changed to the next component in the sequence, in this case, *B*. A property of this procedure is that the faster the sequence is produced, the smaller the overall error becomes. Figure 4 shows the response of the network generating the sequence *ABC* after 1600 presentations of all 64 patterns. Only one *Plan* was necessary to specify the sequence to Execution-Net, from which Execution-Net generated the whole sequence ABC. All other sequences were also completed with one *Plan* vector. Thus, the network developed a representational format that could encode all 64 sequences of three actions in *Plan* vector.

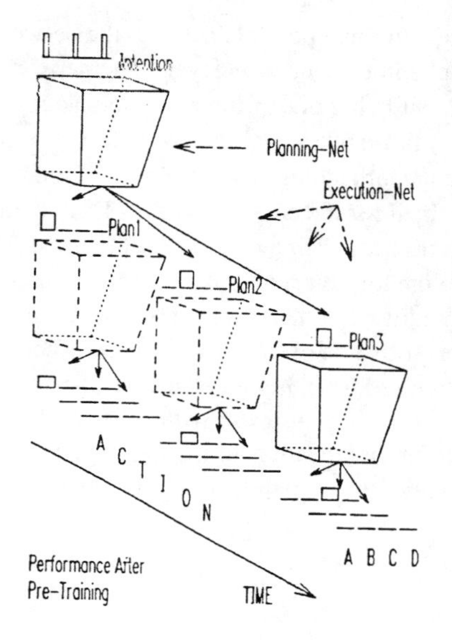

Figure 3. The time course of updating the state of the network. Planning-net maps from an *Intention* to a sequence of three *Plan* vectors. Execution-net maps from each *Plan* to a sequence of three *Output* vectors. The figure shows the response of the network after the pre-training phase. Execution-Net could generate only one action component from a *Plan*. In order to generate the sequence *ABC*, Planning-Net has to generate a sequence of three *Plan* vectors representing *A*, *B*, and *C*. After the pre-training, the network could produce all 64 sequences of three actions but only slowly. It takes seven time steps to complete each sequence.

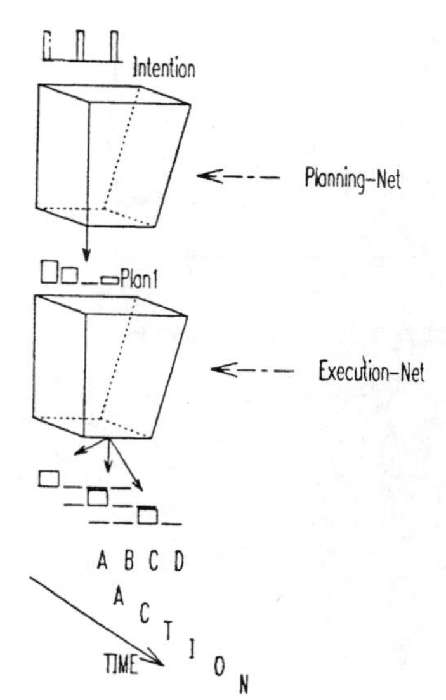

Figure 4. Response of the network after the training phase to the same input as in Figure 3. Only one *Plan* vector is needed to specify the sequence *ABC*. All 64 sequences were each represented by a single *Plan* vector and thus completed in three steps. The *Plan* units which, before the training, could represent only one action component at a time, have learned to represent the entire sequence. Before the training, Execution-Net did only a simple mapping of one *Plan* to one *Action*, and much of the work was done by Planning-Net that mapped an *Intention* to a sequence of *Plans*. The training reversed the situation: the mapping from *Intention* to *Plan* is now one-to-one, and the mapping from *Plan* to *Action* is one-to-sequence. From Planning-Net's viewpoint, the task has changed from a serial one to a highly parallel one.

ANALYSES AND DISCUSSION

The HS model was designed so as to model a certain characteristic of the change from a novice performance to an expert performance. When its learning process was examined more closely, it revealed some other interesting characteristics that are also known for human skill learning, some of which were reported in Miyata (1987). I will describe here some recent findings.

The Learning Curve

To obtain the learning curve, an HS network was tested with three possible actions: the network had three units each in the *Action*, and *Plan* layers and nine units in the *Intention* layer. The network was trained on all the possible sequences of three outputs, each output being one of three possible actions. There are 27 such sequences. Eight networks, with different initial random weights, were trained, and the duration (number of time steps) to generate each sequence was recorded during the training. Figure 5-(a) shows the learning curves, plotted in log-log coordinates, obtained for the eight networks. Each datum is obtained by averaging over a period of 10 training trials, each trial consisting of the 27 sequences. The straight line in each plot shows the best fit linear regression in the log-log space. The learning curves tend to lie along a straight line, and the deviations from the linearity do not seem to show any systematic pattern, except for the apparently asymptotic leveling at the end of some of the curves. This effect will be discussed below. In fact, when these curves were averaged (Figure 5-(b)), it yielded a very good fit to a straight line. (r^2=0.99 by averaging in the original raw data. A very similar result with r^2=0.97 when averaged in the log scale.) This suggests that the deviations from the linearity (in the log-log space) seen in each learning curve are not systematic across different networks. In human learning, the learning rate

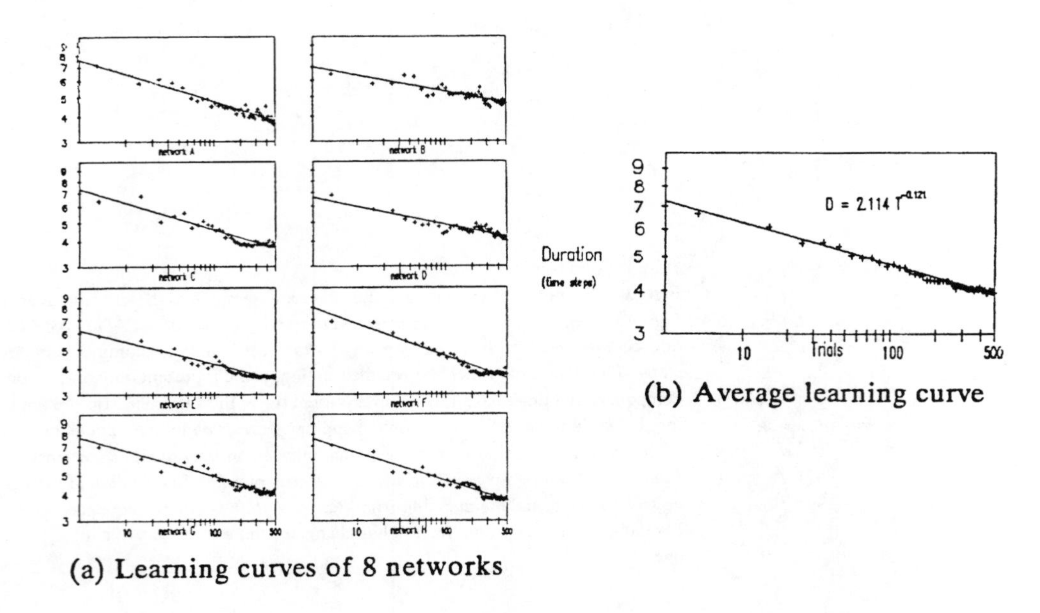

Figure 5. The learning curves in log-log coordinate for the eight networks (a), and the average learning curve (b). The best fit linear regression line is also shown.

(the slope of the line) has been found to vary with the task (Newell & Rosenbloom, 1981; MacKay, 1982), with individual subjects, and with different motoric components in typing (Gentner, 1983). For the 15 data sets analyzed by Newell and Rosenbloom, the value of the learning rate varied from 0.06 to 0.81. For the eight networks shown in Figure 5-(a), it ranged from 0.079 to 0.157.

Asymptotic deviation from linearity such as observed in some of the data in Figure 5-(b) were observed in many of the data sets examined by Newell and Rosenbloom (1981) and by MacKay (1982). The slope of the learning curve often diminished at the end; the beginning of the curve sometimes slightly deviated from linearity (usually downward). Gentner (1983) pointed out that the learning rate of the beginning typist shown in Figure 1 could not continue indefinitely: such typist would be typing at 370 words per minute after 4 year. The improvement must have some asymptotic level eventually.

When the learning rate parameter in the HS network which determines the magnitudes of weight changes in proportion to the errors was varied, the learning curve remained approximately linear for a wide range of parameter values. (The data presented here was obtained with the parameter value of 0.05.) For a very small learning parameter (below 0.01), however, the learning curve deviated downward from a straight line at the beginning.

The shape of the learning curve of the HS model can be understood, at least qualitatively, as follows. Note that in order to achieve a performance speed of kS_0, where S_0 is the initial speed, the *Plan* units have to learn to represent all N_a^k sequences of k primitive actions, where N_a is the number of the primitives (assuming an exponential environment where all combinations of the primitives must be learned, and uniform learning across sequences.) If we take as the measure of difficulty of learning the number of new subsequences to be learned by the *Plan* units in order to achieve a constant amount of speed up, we see that learning becomes exponentially more difficult as the performance becomes faster. In order to derive the learning curve, however, we need a better understanding of the behavior of the learning algorithm itself to relate this measure to the time it takes to learn.

Laird, Rosenbloom, and Newell (1986) showed that their Chunking Theory can account for the power law in a variety of tasks. Currently, the HS model deals with only one of three components in the framework of the Chunking Theory, namely the decoding process in which a representation of a response sequence is decoded into its constituents. Consequently, in order to apply the HS model to the wide range of tasks that the power law has been observed, it needs to be combined with models of the other two components, encoding of stimuli and connection between the encoding and decoding processes (for example, Miyata, 1988b; see Miyata 1988a, for a preliminary discussion).

Frequency effect on substitution errors

A strong effect of frequency on errors in typing has been found at the level of individual letters by Grudin (1983) who examined the confusion matrix (a table showing the frequency with which a letter is typed in place of another for every combination of letters) compiled by Lessenberry (1936) as well as his own data. When homologous errors (striking the key occupying the "mirror-image" position on the keyboard with respect to the correct one) and adjacent errors (striking a key adjacent to the correct one) were analyzed, it was found that higher-frequency letters were more likely to replace lower-frequency letters. When a Jordan network (a simplest case of the HS model) was trained to produce a set of sequences such that each component was presented with different frequency, its error patterns also showed a strong effect of frequency. For all 13 pairs of components with different frequencies, the probability of replacing the lower-frequency component with the high-frequency one was higher than the probability of replacing in the opposite direction.

CONCLUSION

I have described a PDP model of skill learning that readily accounted for the increase in speed and the shift from serial to parallel performance. The learning was achieved by incrementally modifying the mappings in the network so that the internal *Plan* units represented gradually longer subsequences. It is encouraging that the model has yielded, as emergent properties, a number of phenomena that are found in human skill learning. It remains to be studied what factors in the model and the task affect the learning curve, eg., its slope and deviation from linearity, and how. (One possibility is that the learning rate increases with the number of plan units used to represent the sequences, and decreases with the number of sequences that must be learned by the network.) Such study can be compared against subject's performance in similar situations.

REFERENCES

Anderson, J. R. (1982). Acquisition of cognitive skill. *Psychological Review, 89*, 369-406.

Gentner, D. R., Grudin, J., & Conway, E. (May 1980). *Finger movements in transcription typing* (Report No. 8001). Institute for Cognitive Science, University of California San Diego.

Gentner, D. R. (1983). The acquisition of typewriting skill. *Acta Psychologica, 54*, 233-248.

Grudin, J. T. (1981). *The organization of serial order in typing*. Unpublished doctoral dissertation, University of California at San Diego.

Grudin, J. T., & Larochelle, S. (1982). *Digraph frequency effects in skilled typing* (Tech. Rep. No. 110). Center for Human Information Processing, University of California, San Diego.

Grudin, J. T. (1983). Error patterns in skilled and novice transcription typing. In W. E. Cooper (Ed.), *Cognitive aspects of skilled typewriting* (pp. 95-120). New York: Springer-Verlag.

Jordan, M. I. (1986). Attractor dynamics and parallelism in a connectionist sequential machine. In *Proceedings of the eighth annual conference of the Cognitive Science Society* (pp. 531-546).

Laird, J., Rosenbloom, P. & Newell, A. (1986). *Universal Subgoaling and Chunking: the automatic generation and learning of goal hierarchies*. Kluwer Academic Publishers.

MacKay, D. G. (1982). The problems of flexibility, fluency, and speed-accuracy trade-off in skilled behavior. *Psychological Review, 89*, 483-506.

Miller, G. A., Galanter, E., & Pribram, K. H. (1960). *Plans and the structure of behavior*. New York: Holr, Rinehart, & Winston.

Miyata, Y. (1987). Organization of action sequences in motor learning: a connectionist approach. In *Proceedings of the ninth annual conference of the Cognitive Science Society* (pp. 496-507). Seattle, WA. Also, Tech. Rep. No. 8707, Institute for Cognitive Science, UC San Diego. La Jolla, CA.

Miyata, Y. (1988a). *The learning and planning of actions*. PhD Thesis, Psychology Department, also Tech. Rep. No. 8802, Institute for Cognitive Science, University of California, San Diego.

Miyata, Y. (1988b). An unsupervised PDP learning model for action planning. In *Proceedings of the tenth annual conference of the Cognitive Science Society* (pp. 223-229). Montreal.

Newell, A., & Rosenbloom, P. S. (1981). Mechanisms of skill acquisition and the law of practice. In J. R. Anderson (Ed.), *Cognitive Skills and their Acquisition*. Hillsdale, NJ: Erlbaum.

Rumelhart, D. E., Hinton, G. E., & Williams, R. J. (1986). Learning internal representation by error propagation. In D. E. Rumelhart, J. L. McClelland (Ed.), *Parallel distributed processing: Explorations in the microstructure of cognition. Vol. 1: Foundations*. Cambridge, MA: MIT Press/Bradford Books.

Sellen, A. J. (1986). *An experimental and theoretical investigation of human error in a typing task*. Unpublished Master's thesis, University of Toronto.

Structured Representations and Connectionist Models

Jeffrey L. Elman
Department of Cognitive Science
University of California, San Diego

ABSTRACT

Recent descriptions of connectionist models have argued that connectionist representations are unstructured, atomic, and bounded (e.g., Fodor & Pylyshyn, 1988). This paper describes results with recurrent networks and distributed representations which contest these claims. Simulation results are described which demonstrate that connectionist networks are able to learn representations which are richly structured and open-ended. These representations make use both of the high dimensional space described by hidden unit patterns, as well as trajectories through this space in time, and posses a rich structure which reflects regularities in the input. Specific proposals are advanced which address the *type/token distinction*, the *representation of hierarchical categories in language*, and the representation of *grammatical structure*.

INTRODUCTION

It seems clear that to be viable, a model of cognition should be able to represent information in a way which captures the structure of that information. Given the recent interest in connectionist models, it is natural to wonder whether such models can support structured representations of the sort that might be needed (for example) in the service of language processing.

Fodor and Pylyshyn (1988) have in fact recently argued that Classical theories, but not connectionist theories, (1) are "committed to 'complex' mental representations", and (2) have representations that reflect combinatorial structure, such that they enable structure-sensitive mental processes (p. 13). These are the principle differences. In addition, Fodor and Pylyshyn describe connectionist representations as (3) atomic, and therefore (given the limited resources available to support them) (4) finite in number (pp. 22-24).

These are strong claims. Fodor and Pylyshyn are quite right that any cognitive theory worth its salt will support complex mental representations, will reflect both the combinatorics and componentiality of thought, and will enable an open-ended number of representations. What is not self-evident is that these desiderata can only be achieved by the so-called Classical theories, or by connectionist models which are simply implementational variants. In this paper, I present results which suggest that connectionist representations can exhibit rich structure; that the representations may be complex (i.e., not atomic) and capable of reflecting both general patterns and ideosyncratic differences. Furthermore, these representations may in principle open-ended.

I begin with a brief description of the network architecture employed. I will then report results of two sets of simulations. The first explores the development of lexical categories; the second demonstrates the ability to encode syntactic information, including agreement and embedding.

ARCHITECTURE

The work which follows utilizes an architecture inspired by a model studied by Jordan (1986). Jordan demonstrated the utility of allowing recurrent connections from output units. In the form of the network I have been studying, shown in Figure 1, in addition to the usual input units, output units, and hidden units, there are a set of context units which hold a copy of the hidden unit activations (on a one-to-one basis) from the prior cycle. These context units then feed back into the hidden units (on a fully distributed basis) on the next cycle. The hidden units have the task of mapping the input to the output, and because the input now includes their own prior states, they must

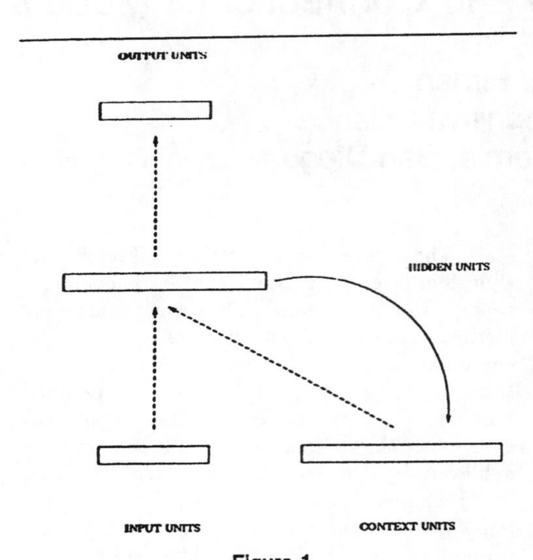

Figure 1.
Network with recurrent connections from hidden units to context units.

develop representations which serve as memory as well. Note that this approach to memory relies on distributed rather than localist representations. Memory is not associated with individual nodes but rather with the state vector on the context units. Furthermore, this notion of memory is highly task specific.

This architecture, which I will call a **Simple Recurrent Network** (SRN) has been studied in Elman (1988, 1989); Hare, Corina, & Cottrell (1988); and Servan-Schreiber, Cleeremans, & McClelland (1988), and will be used for the two simulations I report here. It is particularly relevent in the domain of language, since it allows for the processing of serial inputs. Thus, language can be processed naturally on an element-by-element basis.

DISCOVERING LEXICAL CATEGORIES

One area of language which exhibits rich structure is lexical categorization. Lexical categorization is manifested in a number of ways; in English, one of these manifestations is word order. Not all classes of words may appear in any position. Furthermore, certain classes of words, e.g, transitive verbs, tend to co-occur with other words, e.g., nouns as direct objects (although as will be relevant in the next simulation, the co-occurrence facts may be complex).

The goal of the first simulation was to see if a network could learn the lexical category structure which is implicit in a language corpus. The overt form of the lexical items was arbitrary; however, the behavior of the lexical items — defined as their co-occurrence restrictions — reflected their membership in implicit classes and subclasses. The question was whether the network could induce these classes.

Stimuli, Task, and Network

A lexicon of 29 nouns and verbs was chosen. Words were represented as 31-bit binary vectors (two extra bits were reserved for another purpose); each word was randomly assigned a unique vector in which only one bit was turned on. A sentence-generating program was then used to create a corpus of 10,000 2- and 3-word sentences. The sentences reflected certain properties of the words; for example, only animate nouns occurred as the subject of the verb eat. Finally, the words in successive sentences were concatenated, so that a stream of 27,354 vectors was created. This was the input set.

The task was simply for the network to take successive words from the input stream and to predict the subsequent word (by producing it on the output layer). After each word was input, the output was compared with the actual next word, and the backpropagation of error algorithm (Rumelhart, Hinton, & Williams, 1986) was used to adjust weights. Words were presented in order, with no breaks between sentences. The network was trained on 6 passes through the corpus.

Results

Because the sequence is non-deterministic, short of memorizing the sequence, the network cannot succeed in exact predictions. Nonetheless, the network does learn to approximate the expected frequency of occurrence of successor words. The rms error, using the empirically derived probability of occurrence of successors, was 0.053; the cosine of the angle between output vector and likelihood vectors (which normalizes for length differences) was 0.916, indicating a close match.

Discussion

I would like to focus on *how* the network accomplishes the task. One way to do this is to see what sorts of internal representations the network develops in the process of trying to carry out the prediction task. These representations are captured by the pattern of hidden unit activations which are evoked in response to each word in its context. These patterns were saved during a testing phase, and then subjected to hierarchical clustering analysis. Figure 2 shows the tree constructed from the hidden unit patterns for the 30 lexical items, where each item is the average of for a word across all the contexts in which it occurrs in the testing data.

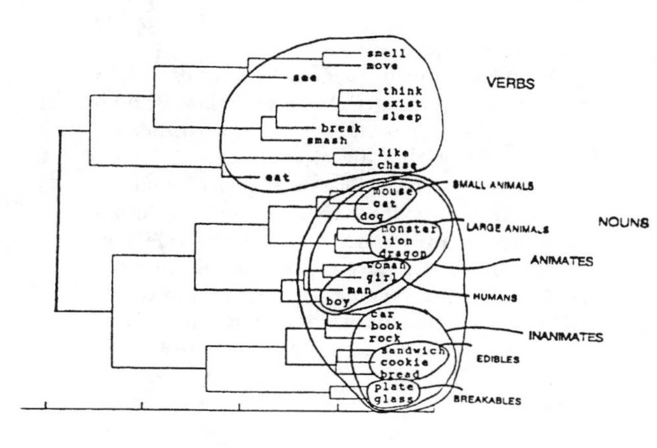

Figure 2.
Hierarchical cluster analysis of the average hidden unit activation patterns for each of the 29 unique words in the word-prediction simulation.

The network has discovered that there are several major categories of words. One large category corresponds to *verbs*; another category corresponds to *nouns*. The verb category is broken down into groups which take animate subjects; which are intransitive or take optional objects, and which require direct objects. The noun category breaks down into major groups for *inanimates* and *animates*; the animates are divided into *large animals* and *small animals*, and *humans*. Inanimates are divided into *breakables*, *edibles*, and miscellaneous.

This category structure reflects facts about the possible sequential ordering of the inputs. The network is not able to predict the precise order of words, but it recognizes that (in this corpus) there is a class of inputs (viz., verbs) which typically follow other inputs (viz., nouns). This knowledge of class behavior is quite detailed; from the fact that there is a class of items which always precedes chase, break, smash, it infers a category we might call *aggressors*.

Several points should be emphasized. First, the category structure is hierarchical. The hierarchicality is achieved through the organization of the representational space described by hidden unit patterns, with higher-level categories corresponding to larger and more general regions of space. Second, the categories are not discrete. Category boundaries are smooth, and category membership may be marginal or ambiguous (although it may also be clear and unambiguous). Finally, the content of the categories is not known to the network. The network has no information available which would "ground" the structural information in the real world. In this respect, the simulation has much less information to work with than is available to real language learners.

Types and tokens. The tree shown in Figure 2 was constructed of activation patterns averaged across context. When the context-sensitive hidden unit patterns are clustered, it is found that the large-scale structure of the tree is identical to that shown in Figure 2. However, each terminal branch now continues with further arborization for all occurrences of the word (no instance of any lexical item appears in the branch of another.

This is an important finding. It verifies that the representation of each lexical item, wherever it occurs, reflects the constraints to which the item is subject *as a lexical type*. The representations clearly mark typehood. But the patterns also individuate the different tokens of types. No two tokens are precisely identical. They are different because they have occurred in different contexts, and the representations are ***highly context-sensitive***.

Even more interesting is that there is a fine sub-structure to the various tokens of a type. For instance, tokens of boy which occur in subject position tend to cluster together, and apart from tokens of boy in object position. The same pattern occurs among the representations of tokens of other nouns. This detailed sub-grouping makes it possible for the network to distinguish ***tokens*** of a ***type***, as well as different ***types***. Usefully, the tokens are themselves organized in a manner which reflects systematic facts about the context in which they occur.

S -> NP VP "."
NP -> PropN | N | N RC
VP -> V (NP)
RC -> *who* NP VP | *who* VP (NP)
N -> *boy* | *girl* *cat* | *dog* |
boys | *girls* *cats* | *dogs*
V -> *hit* | *feed* | *see* | *hear* | *walk* | *live* |
hits | *feeds* | *sees* | *hears* | *walks* | *lives*

Additional restrictions:

- **number agreement between N and V within clause, and (where appropriate) between head N and subordinate V**
- **verb arguments:**
  hit, feed —> **require a DO**
  see, hear —> **optionally take DO**
  walk, live —> **preclude a DO**
- **(observed also for head/verb relations in relative clauses)**

Table 1

REPRESENTATION OF SYNTACTIC STRUCTURE

In the previous simulation there was little interesting grammatical structure. Sentences were short and simple and most of the patterning was explained at the level of properties of individual lexical items. In the next simulation we develop representations which reflect more complex syntactic structure. A phrase structure grammar, shown in Table 1, was used to generate training corpora. Each word was represented by a localist 26-bit vector in which each bit stood for a different word. Training proceded incrementally. A network similar to that shown in Figure 1 was trained on the prediction task. The training data consisted of an initial set of 10,000 sentence corpus of simple sentences; the percentage of complex sentences was gradually altered over the course of training from 0% to 75%. Mean sentence length of the final training set was 5.3 words (range: 3 to 13 words). This simulation superficially resembles the previous one, except that the sentences were more complex and reflected a variety of syntactic constraints. Specifically, it was necessary that the network to learn the following:

- Agreement. Subject nouns agree in number with their verbs.
- Verb arguments. One class of verbs requires a direct object; a second class optionally permits a direct object; and a third class never occurs with a direct object.
- Relative clauses. The presence of relative clauses requires that the network maintain agreement and verb argument relations within the appropriate clause, and despite the presence of intervening clausal material. In dogs who boy feeds see cat, agreement occurs between N1 and V2, and between N2 and V1. Similarly, because this sentence involves an object-headed relative clause, the network is required to learn that although the verb feeds normally is followed by a direct object, that position has already been filled by the prior word dogs.
- Sentence completion. The network is required to develop a sense of what are candidates for complete grammatical sentences, by predicting when a sentence ending (".") may occur.

At the conclusion of training, network performance was measured by comparing the outputs with the empirically derived conditional probability of occurance for each possible word; the mean cosine of the angle between the vectors was 0.92 (SD: 0.19). Network predictions in various contexts are illustrated in Figure 3. As can be seen, the network succeeds in predicting the class of words which appropriately follows in each context. This is true even in complex sentences where relative clauses render useless any generalization based on the linear order of words in simple sentences.

Again, we may ask how the network has achieved this performance. For these purposes, it is important to be able to look at the time-varying states of the network as it processes various sentence types. This information is not easily revealed in hierarchical clustering, so the following procedure involving principal component analysis was developed.

The final training set was passed through the network a final time, and hidden unit patterns were saved. The covariance matrix of these vectors was calculated; the eigenvectors of this matrix were then used as the basis for describing hidden unit vectors. This basis tends to provide a somewhat more interpretable (and localist) view of the hidden units' distributed representations. Furthermore, the dimension are ordered (using the eigenvalues) by decreasing importance in accounting for variability. Thus, we can chose to look at only a few of the dimensions (the principal components, or PC's) and plot the movement through this reduced space as the network processes sentences of interest.

Figure 4 displays state trajectories which illustrate the representation of verb-argument structure. Trajectectories through PC 1x3 space are shown for the three sentence fragments **boy hits** .... (**hits** requires a direct object), **boy sees** ...., (**sees** optionally takes a direct object) and **boy walks** .... (**walks** never occurs with a direct object). The initial state after processing the first word is the same for all three sentences. However, there is a systematic displacement in PC 1x3 space which corresponds to the expectation of a direct object. This pattern holds true over a wide variety of contexts and more complex syntactic structures. Figure 5 shows the manner in which embedding is represented. There is a basic trajectory in PC 1x11 space which is associated with simple sentences; this trajectory is replicated and shifted in space to indicate subordinate clauses.

CONCLUSIONS

Several things may be said about the results of these simulations.

First, it is quite apparent that connectionist representations may be quite rich. They need not be atomic, but may instead possess structure which reflects the systematic patterns which are immanent in the primary data. The representational structure is embodied in the state of the network; different states are associated with different syntactic structures.

Second, the representations in these simulations are highly context-sensitive. This sensitivity co-exists comfortably with the ability to capture systematic patterns which are more generally true. Indeed, the same mechanism is responsible for both aspects of representation. As a consequence, connectionist representations bind the semantics of reference with the syntax of representation. Classical theories have long grappled -- with less than satisfactory results, in the view of many -- with the tension that is produced when one insists that syntactic and semantic representations be kept distinct and that there be no direct interaction between them. It is a natural consequence of connectionist representations that there be a common language which simultaneously supports syntax and semantics. This suggests the distinctions between the syntax and semantics may be quantitative in nature and do not stem from any deep distinctions.

Third, we have seen how the distributed representations which are developed at the hidden unit level make use of state space and state dynamics. The representational space is organized to reflect the structure that is implicit in the primary data. The further dimension of time, captured in the notion of recurring trajectories through space, adds to the representational power and permits statements to be made about syntagmatic relations. Furthermore, we have found that although the representations are highly distributed, this does not mean that they are unanalyzable. It is possibly to insightfully characterize the organization of the representational space, and to discover regularities in patterns of temporal movement through that space.

Fourth, the representational system has itself been inferred from the data. The architecture ultimately *limits* the representational power of a network, of course, but it does not *specify* the representational form. We do not begin with notions of lexical categories or grammatical patterns. These concepts are present in the data and are learned by the network. These results of course do not deny the importance of evolutionary mechanisms in constraining the mechanisms which support language processing. The findings here simply suggest that a simple but powerful learning algorithm such as backpropagation is capable of extracting rather more information from raw input than one might have supposed.

Fifth, the representational system is relatively open-ended. Just as it was not necessary to stipulate categories or structures prior to learning, it was not necessary to place an upper limits on the number of categories or depth of structure.

We have seen how these characteristics can lead to solutions of the *type/token* distinction, to the discovery and representation of *lexical categories,* and to the representation of certain aspects of *syntactic structure.* These are important problems in language theory, and the approach suggested here is highly encouraging. However, language presents many problems of a highly complex nature, and the simple successes obtained here should not cause us to forget just how difficult those problems can be.

There are also serious limitations to the work here which must be pointed out. The most basic has to do with the nature of the task. The prediction task has been useful in these simulations. The appeal of this task is that it makes minimal assumptions about prior knowledge on the part of the learner (or network). But while prediction or anticipation may be a plausible activity during language comprehension, it can hardly be the primary basis for learning language.

It is not clear what an appropriate task is, but there have been recent suggestions which go in the right direction. St. John and McClelland (1988) have described a system in which sentence inputs are used to construct an interpretation of events in the world. This is a far more plausible view of what is involved in processing language than suggested by the prediction task. One question that remains unanswered in the St. John and McClelland model is where the primitive notions such as *patient* and *agent* come from (these figure importantly as built-in constructs in their network), and how to extend the task to complex sentences. Strikingly, these are just the sorts of questions which are addressed by the present approach. It is appealing to think that the two approaches might be combined.

In conclusion, the simulations described here explore a new approach to the representation of language. While there are many deep and important questions to be answered, this approach provides a glimpse of the sort of representational power which a connectionist theory of language could have.

ACKNOWLEDGEMENTS

I would like to thank Jay McClelland, David Rumelhart, and Mary Hare for many useful discussions. This work was supported by contract N00014-85-K-0076 from the Office of Naval Research and contract DAAB-07-87-C-H027 from Army Avionics, Ft. Monmouth.

REFERENCES

Elman, J.L. (1988). Finding structure in time. CRL Technical Report 8801. Center for Research in Language, University of California, San Diego.

Elman, J.L. (1989). Structured representations and connectionist models. CRL Technical Report 8901. Center for Research in Language, University of California, San Diego.

Fodor, J., & Pylyshyn, Z. (1988). Connectionism and cognitive architecture: A critical analysis. In S. Pinker & J. Mehler (Eds.), *Connections and Symbols* (pp. 3-71). Cambridge, Mass.: MIT Press.

Hare, M., Corina, D., & Cottrell, G. (1988) Connectionist perspective on prosodic structure. CRL Newsletter, Vol. 3, No. 2. Center for Research in Language, University of California, San Diego. D.E. Rumelhart & J.L. McClelland (Eds.). (1986). *Parallel distributed processing: Explorations in the microstructure of cognition. Volume II: Psychological and biological models* Cambridge, Mass.: MIT Press.

Rumelhart, D.E., Hinton, G.E., & Williams, R.J. (1986). Learning internal representations by error propagation. In D.E. Rumelhart & J.L. McClelland (Eds.), *Parallel distributed processing: Explorations in the microstructure of cognition* (Vol. 1) (pp. 318-362). Cambridge, Mass.: MIT Press. D.E. Rumelhart & J.L. McClelland (Eds.). (1986). *Parallel distributed processing: Explorations in the microstructure of cognition. Volume I: Foundations* Cambridge, Mass.: MIT Press.

Servan-Schreiber, D., Cleeremans, A., & McClelland, J.L. (1988). Encoding sequential structure in simple recurrent networks. CMU Technical Report CMU-CS-88-183. Computer Science Department, Carnegie-Mellon University.

St. John, M., & McClelland, J.L. (1988). Learning and applying contextual constraints in sentence comprehension. Technical Report. Department of Psychology. Carnegie-Mellon University.

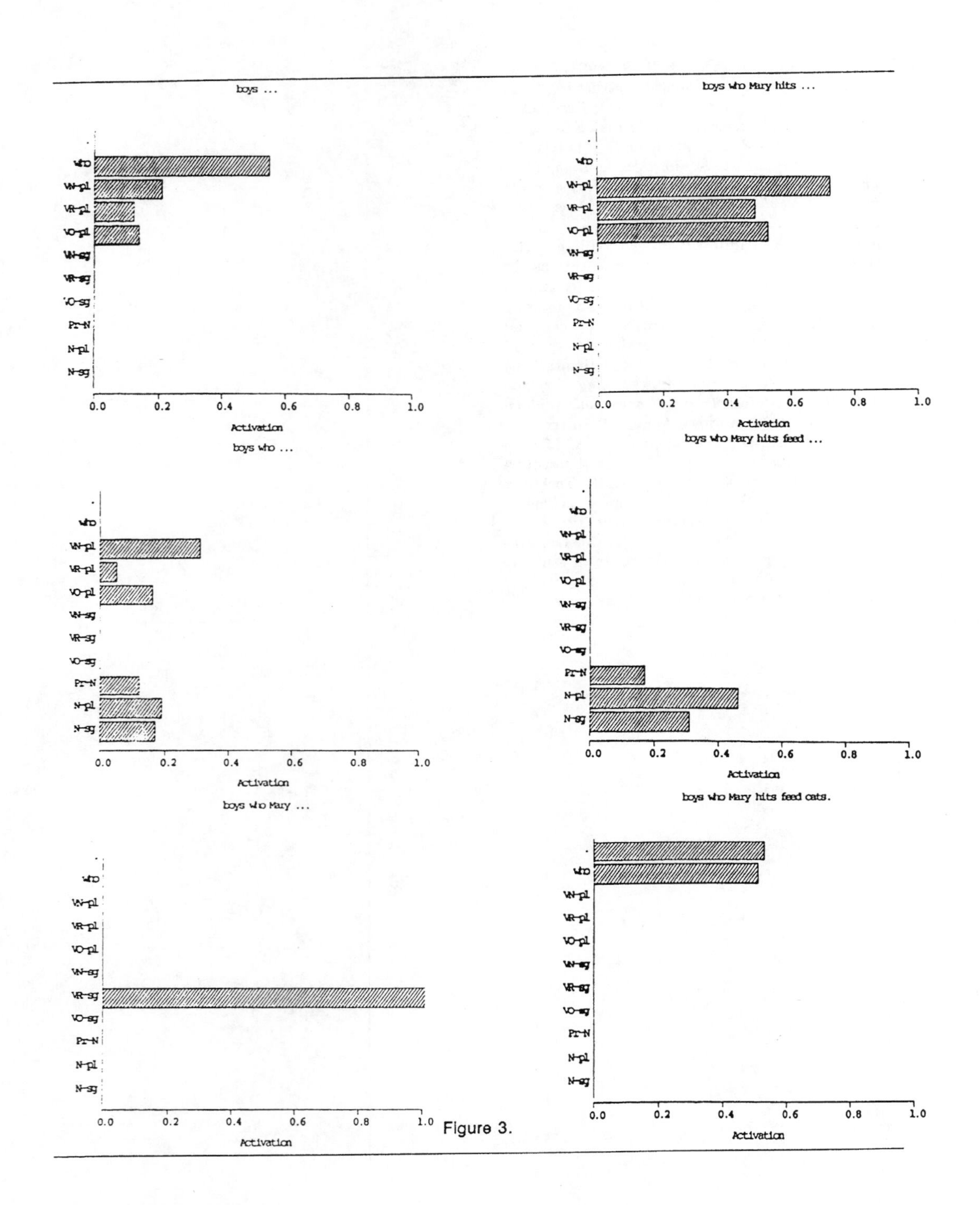
boys ...
boys who ...
boys who Mary ...
boys who Mary hits ...
boys who Mary hits feed ...
boys who Mary hits feed cats.
.
who
VN-pl
VR-pl
VO-pl
VN-sg
VR-sg
VO-sg
Pr-N
N-pl
N-sg
0.0
0.2
0.4
0.6
0.8
1.0
Activation

Figure 3.

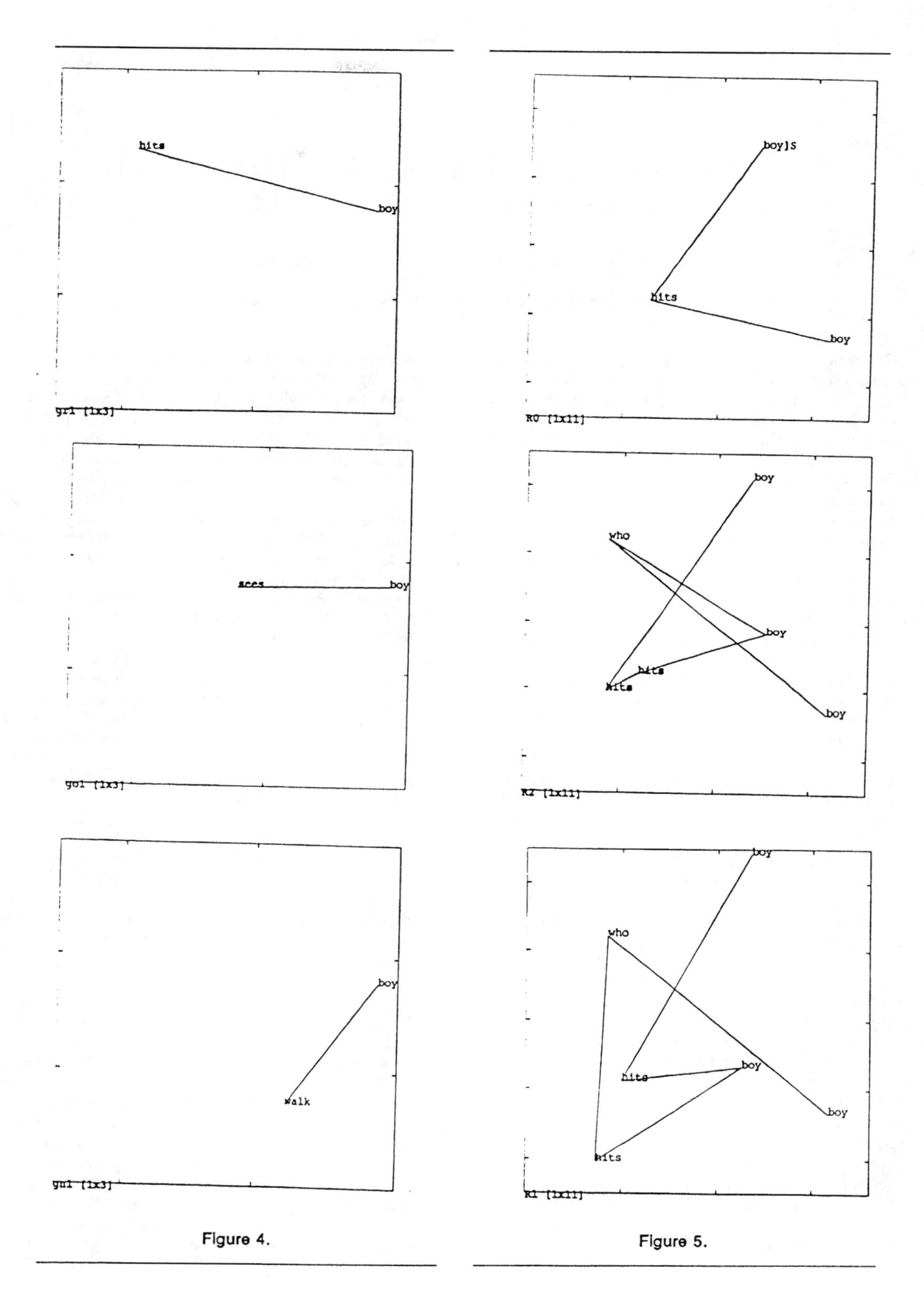

Figure 4.

Figure 5.

Is There "Catastrophic Interference" in Connectionist Networks?

Phil A. Hetherington & Mark S. Seidenberg

Department of Psychology, McGill University

Concern has recently developed regarding the possibility that parallel distributed processing models will exhibit massive amounts of retroactive interference. McCloskey & Cohen (in press) have suggested that such models exhibit "catastrophic interference" under realistic training conditions; they conclude that PDP models may not be able to simulate basic aspects of human performance. In this paper we report replications and extensions of simulations on which these claims were based. The new simulations suggest that "catastrophic interference" may be less of a problem than McCloskey & Cohen suggest; specifically, it is related to the use of a rigid training scheme that bears little resemblance to how children actually learn.

Learning in parallel distributed processing models involves changes to the weights on connections between units as a consequence of feedback or "experience." One of the main properties of these models is that the effects of learning are superimposed on one another; a model's performance is determined by the aggregate effects of the ensemble of training experiences. This property of PDP models is thought to be theoretically important; for example, it enables Seidenberg and McClelland's (in press) model of word recognition to simulate the effects of inconsistent spelling-sound correspondences on tasks such as naming and lexical decision, and Rumelhart and McClelland (1986) have argued that it is critical to an account of facts about the child's acquisition of past tense morphology. Recently, however, it has been noted that this property of PDP models may have some negative side effects. Two issues have arisen. First there is the problem of retroactive interference: events later in the training regime may result in poorer performance on previously-learned items. For example, a word pronunciation model (e.g., Sejnowski & Rosenberg, 1986; Seidenberg & McClelland, in press) might be trained to generate the correct pronunciation of a word such as GAVE; subsequent training on a word such as HAVE might result in changes to the weights that have a negative impact on performance on GAVE, yielding incorrect output or "unlearning".

A second, related issue concerns the regimes used in training PDP models. Most training schemes to date have involved what McCloskey and Cohen (in press; hereafter MC) have termed "concurrent" schedules: there is a set of target patterns to be learned, and training proceeds by sampling from the entire set. This contrasts with what MC term "sequential" regimes, in which target patterns are introduced at different times. Sequential regimes are thought to be more realistic in terms of peoples' actual experience. In learning to read, for example, children are exposed to different words at different times, whereas in the Sejnowski and Rosenberg (1986) and Seidenberg and McClelland (in press) models, all words are available for training at all times.

Given the fact that learning can produce retroactive interference, it is clear that the performance of PDP models will be highly dependent on the type of training scheme that is used. MC have conjectured that PDP models may be incapable of simulating human learning under realistic training conditions. Specifically, their claim is that there is a retroactive interference problem that can only be overcome by using concurrent training schemes. When the more realistic sequential schemes are utilized, such models exhibit "catastrophic" interference: learning on later trials results in grossly impaired performance on previously-learned items. MC illustrated this problem by analyzing some simulations of the task of learning simple arithmetic.

The MC paper raises important issues concerning learning in PDP models; Pinker and Prince (1988) and Lachter and Bever (1988) present similar concerns. MC's simulations demonstrate that there are conditions under which PDP models exhibit behavior that does not relate well to human performance. However, the scope of the "catastrophic" interference problem is unclear; in this paper we report simulations that examine the issue further. Our main conclusion is that catastrophic interference is not as general a problem for PDP models as MC suggest; in fact, replications of their simulations with slight changes in the training procedure yield very different results than they reported. Our simulations provide a

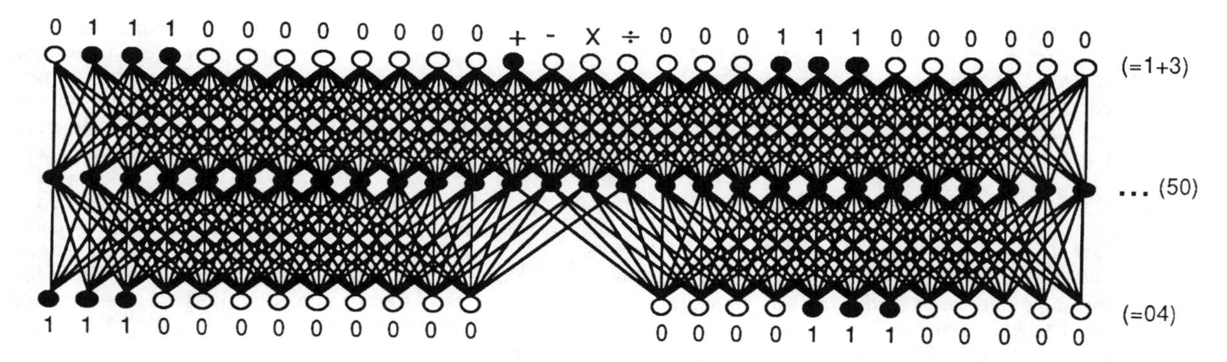

Figure 1: The Model (Input on Top; Output on Bottom)

broader perspective on the conditions that do and do not yield excessive retroactive interference, and why.

BACKGROUND: MODEL AND TASK

MC report several simulations using a two-layer model (i.e., a model with two layers of connections), trained using the backpropagation algorithm (Rumelhart, Hinton, & Williams, 1986). The model consisted of 28 input units, 50 hidden or association (Rosenblatt, 1962) units, and 24 output units (Figure 1), with full connectivity between adjacent layers. The model was trained to perform simple addition and multiplication problems; for example, given the input [3+2], the model was to produce the output [5]. Each of the two digits in an equation was encoded by 12 input units. The remaining four input units encoded which operation was to be performed (+, -, x, ÷). The first 12 output units represented the tens column of the answer; the second 12 coded the digits column. Figure 1 illustrates the problem [1 + 3 = 04]. The input and output representations were distributed; each of the numbers from 0 to 9 was encoded by three units. This method is similar to the thermometer coding scheme used by Anderson (1983) and by Viscuso, Anderson, and Spoehr (in press) to code continuous values in qualitative physics and mathematics. This distributed representation can represent any pair of operands and their sums or products, yet the individual units and connections do not represent the numbers themselves.[1]

MC's simulations were concerned with the task of learning simple arithmetic problems. Consider, for example, the set of simple addition problems involving the digits 1-9. MC show that the model is able to learn the target set of patterns when it is trained using a concurrent method. During the training phase, the model was presented with problems from the target set. Problems were randomly sampled from the set; all problems were available to be sampled at all times. Thus, the model might be trained on [1+3], then [2+9], then [8+7], etc. Under these conditions, the network learned to successfully map all pairs of operands to their respective sums; it also learned the mapping from the operands to their products.

Very different results were obtained using a sequential training method, however. The model was initially trained on addition problems involving 1's (see "Simulation 1: Replication" below); training continued until the model performed without error on these items. The model was then trained on problems involving 2's. The primary motivation for this training scheme was the intuition that it more closely resembles the experience of children learning arithmetic. Children are not exposed to all problems in a random order; they learn the simpler problems and then move to more complex ones. With the sequential method, the model learned to compute the 2's problems; however, performance on the 1's

1. The scheme used to encode digits was not entirely arbitrary. Each digit was encoded by 3 consecutive input units. The first 3 units were used to encode 0, the second 3 units encoded 1, the third 3 units, 2. Thus, digits that differ by one shared 2 encoding units; digits that differ by 2 shared 1 encoding unit, and digits that differ by more than 2 shared no units in common.

problems greatly deteriorated. For example, performance on the 1's decreased from 100% to 57% correct after a single run through the 2's, and to 30% correct after two such runs. "Catastrophic interference" refers to this decrement in performance on earlier-trained items.

SIMULATION 1: REPLICATION

Our first step was to replicate MC's basic findings. We constructed a network exactly like theirs, using the same parameter settings.[2] The simulation was run 5 times, and the data that we report are averaged over these runs (MC reported data averaged over 2 runs). The model was trained on the 1's and 2's problems in sequence. The 1's set included 16 problems: 1+1, 1+2, 1+3, ... 1+9; 3+1, 4+1, ... 9+1. There were no problems containing 0's (as in the MC simulations), and the 2+1 problem was excluded because it occurred in the 2's set. Similarly, the 2's set included 16 problems; 1+2 was excluded because it occurred in the 1's set. Hence the two problem sets were mutually exclusive.

Training involved a series of epochs, where each epoch refers to the presentation of all problems within a set in random order. For example, 40 epochs of training on the 1's set involved presenting 40 sets of the 16 1's problems, each in a different random order. Performance was evaluated in two ways. First, for each problem we calculated an error sum of squares (**E**); this was the sum of the squared differences between computed and target values over all output units:

$$\mathbf{E} = \sum_i (o_i - e_i)^2$$

This score provides a general quantitative measure of performance. Below we report the error scores for the correct answers averaged across all problems within a set and across all 5 runs. However, it is also necessary to determine how often the correct answer to a given problem provided the best fit to the computed output. That is, the error score indicates how closely the computed output matched the pattern for the *correct* answer; we also need to know how often the correct answer produced the lowest error score (what MC term the "best match" criterion). For a given problem, we calculated a set of error scores by comparing the computed pattern of activation to the patterns corresponding to all possible answers. We then determined how often the best fit (lowest error score) was provided by the correct answer.

The training procedure followed MC's sequential method. The model was trained on the 1's problems for 40 epochs. (MC trained their network until all of the output units had activations within .1 of the target activation levels, which took approximately 35 epochs.) The model was then trained on the 2's problems for 40 epochs. We tested the model's performance on the 1's during the training on the 2's. These test trials did not involve additional learning on the 1's; thus, we could examine how training on the 2's affected performance on the 1's. The 1's were tested after each of the first 5 epochs of training on the 2's; thereafter they were tested after every 5 epochs of training until the 40th epoch. Starting at epoch 40, the 1's were tested after each of 5 additional epochs, and then at 5 epoch intervals until the 80th epoch. All that changed across simulations was the order in which the problems were presented within an epoch and the initial random values assigned to the weights.

Results and Discussion

The model learned the 1's set very quickly. After 15 epochs of training, the average error score was .144, and no errors were made (i.e., for all problems, the correct answer provided the best fit to the computed output). Error scores continued to decrease with additional training. However, performance on the 1's decreased drastically once training on the 2's began. In only one epoch, the mean error for the 1's increased from .038 to .734, more than an order of magnitude. After five epochs, the mean error reached 1.41. The best match criterion yielded similar results: the mean number of correct responses fell from 16 to 8.6 in one epoch. By five epochs, the mean number of correct responses was a catastrophic 2.8. Thus, learning the 2's problems interfered with performance on the 1's.

---

2. The simulations were implemented using the McClelland and Rumelhart (1988) software running on an IBM PS/2 Model 80 computer. Except where noted in the text, the simulations followed MC's procedure exactly. The learning rate was set to .25. MC consider this to be a conservative rate although McClelland & Rumelhart's (1988, p. 107) recommendation to use a rate equal to the inverse of the number of input units would result in a much smaller value (.036). Weights on connections between units were assigned initial random values between +/- .3. Target activation values were set to .9 for units that should be on, and .1 for units that should be off. Finally, all hidden and output units were given a random bias.

On the basis of similar results, MC concluded, "to the extent that one is interested in using connectionist networks to model human learning and memory, this sort of disruption would appear to be a significant problem" (p. 14). The question to be addressed is this: how serious is the "catastrophic interference" problem? In particular, how closely is it related to the particular conditions studied by MC, and how do these conditions relate to the ones experienced by children in learning arithmetic and other skills?

SIMULATION 2: SAVINGS

Under the sequential training procedure studied by MC and in Simulation 1, performance on the 1's deteriorates drastically during the learning of the 2's. The decrement in performance is seen in the increasing error scores for the 1's, and the decrease in the proportion of correct answers. Hence it appears that the solutions to the 1's problems were unlearned. If this is correct, the model's performance differs greatly from that of humans; as MC note, unlearning (e.g., in verbal learning experiments) is virtually never complete (see, e.g., Postman & Underwood, 1973). It is possible, however, that the solutions to the 1's problems were not completely unlearned; the weights on connections between units could still have encoded information relevant to these problems despite the seemingly poor level of performance. This issue can be examined by determining whether there is any *savings* (Ebbinghaus, 1885) when the 1's problems are relearned. Consider the following procedure: we train the model as in Simulation 1, producing poor performance on the 1's once the 2's are introduced. We then retrain the model on the 1's, and introduce a new set of problems, the 3's. If the 1's have been completely unlearned due to "catastrophic interference," they should be relearned at the same rate as the entirely new problem set. Faster relearning on the 1's would indicate memory savings, because the 1's problems had not been completely unlearned. Savings would indicate that the network had retained information relevant to computing the correct answers, facilitating relearning.

In the second simulation, we examined whether savings would occur. We first replicated Simulation 1. The 1's were trained for 40 epochs, followed by the 2's for 40 epochs. This procedure results in poor performance on the 1's. We then trained the model on a set of problems involving 1's and 3's. This set of 30 problems contained all of the unique 1's and 3's problems (i.e., the 3+1 problem was excluded from the 1's set, and the 1+3 and 2+3 problems were excluded from the 3's set). The model was trained for 40 epochs on this larger set. This period, epochs 80-120, will be termed the retraining phase. The model's performance on the 1's and 3's problems was tested after each of the first 5 retraining epochs, and every 5 epochs thereafter. The data we report are averaged over the 10 independent simulation runs.

Results and Discussion

The primary results are presented in Figure 2. Over the first 5 epochs of the retraining phase, the model performed similarly on the 1's and 3's. However, looking at the longer trend over the first 25 epochs of retraining, learning of the 3's was slower than relearning of the 1's. Using the mean error scores as the dependent measure in an analysis of variance, there was a main effect of problem set, $\mathbf{F}(1,18) = 43.42$, $\mathbf{p}<.001$. The same effect was found using the best match criterion: the 1's produced significantly fewer errors over the first 25 epochs of training, $\mathbf{F}(1,18) = 46.77$, $\mathbf{p}<.001$. Hence there was savings in the relearning of the 1's, indicating that they had not been completely unlearned.

Since the 1's and 3's problems were similar in terms of complexity, they should have been equally easy to learn. Hence, the improved performance on the 1's appears to have been due to savings—prior experience with the 1's that was not completely erased by exposure to the 2's. To be certain that both problem sets were equally easy to learn, we ran a control

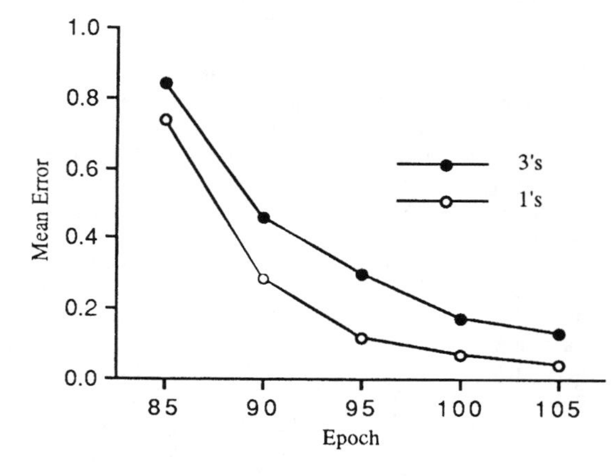

Figure 2: Learning 3's vs Relearning 1's

simulation in which the model was trained from the first epoch on the 1's-and-3's set. The model was then tested on both the 1's and 3's problems at 5 epoch intervals; there were no statistically significant differences between the two problem sets, in terms of either error scores or percentage of correct responses.

This simulation demonstrates that under the "catastrophic" interference conditions studied by MC, the 1's are not entirely unlearned. Because the network retains information relevant to these problems, they are relearned more quickly than a novel set of problems. The simulation illustrates that global measures such as mean squared error or number of correct answers may not fully capture all that a model has learned. The existence of savings is especially important because it bears on the scope of the "catastrophic interference" problem. If there is significant savings, then the "catastrophic" performance of the 1's might be dramatically improved by a small number of relearning trials. That is, catastrophic interference may critically depend on the *blocking* of training trials. When the model is trained on a block of 1's problems, and then on a block of 2's problems, performance on the 1's declines. If, instead of following this strict blocking scheme, there is some minimal retraining on the 1's, performance will rapidly improve due to savings. In the present case, we retrained the model on the 1's after exposure to the 2's (starting at epoch 80). After only 3 epochs of retraining, performance improved from a mean error of 1.73 and 12.5% correct to a mean error of 0.23 and 86.3% correct. After 5 epochs, the error was .11 and 97.5% were correct.

Rapid relearning can also be illustrated in the context of Seidenberg and McClelland's (in press) model of word naming. The model was trained on a set of 2897 monosyllabic words. The model takes a spelling pattern as input and produces a phonological code as output. After 250 epochs of training, the model performs this task with a high degree of accuracy. For a word such as TINT, for example, the best fit to the computed output is provided by the correct phonological code /tint/. Consider now what would happen if we trained the model on a block of trials involving the word PINT, which is spelled like TINT but pronounced differently. Training on PINT will affect the weights in a way that has a negative impact on TINT, producing retroactive interference. Figure 3 illustrates this effect. After 250 epochs of training, TINT produced an error score of 8.92. The model was then trained on 20 PINT trials, with TINT retested after each trial. As the figure illustrates, training on PINT increases the error score for TINT, indicating poorer performance or "unlearning." However, the figure also shows the effects of additional learning trials on TINT. With only 2 additional trials, the error score falls below the level that had been achieved prior to training on PINT. In sum, a small number of retraining or "reminding" trials is sufficient to overcome the interfering effects of prior learning.

It is clear, then, that retroactive interference in simple PDP nets depends on the properties of the training regime. MC's main point is that the concurrent regime used in most simulations is unrealistic. However, the scheme they introduced is equally unrealistic. Their scheme is not merely sequential; it involves strictly blocking trials by type. Consider how this blocking scheme relates to the child's experience in learning arithmetic. It can be seen from any arithmetic primer that children are not taught 1's problems, then 2's, then others in strict blocks. In fact, children's problems are typically ordered in terms of the magnitudes of sums, not operands, with considerable overlap across problem sets. In learning multiplication tables, new problems are typically embedded in written practice sheets along with problems introduced earlier (e.g., Campbell & Graham, 1985). The problem sets are indeed ordered—small-number problems are usually taught earlier—but these problems are also drilled and practiced when new ones are introduced.

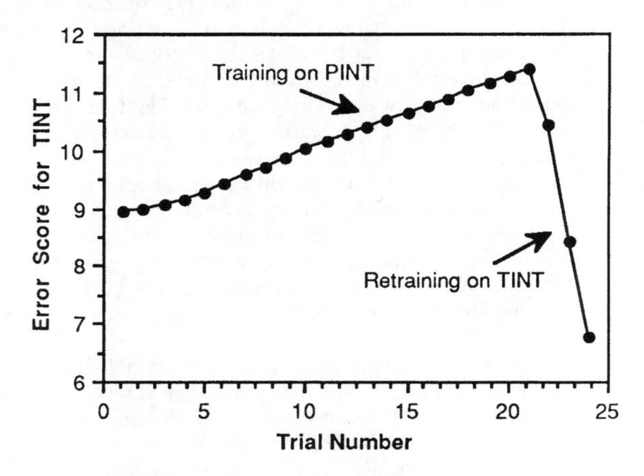

Figure 3: Retraining on TINT after Training on PINT.

Our main point is that a more realistic training regime—one that does not involve strict blocking by type—would take advantage of the savings illustrated in Simulation 2. As long as the child (or model) experiences a small number of relearning trials, the learning of new problems should not result in massive interference. The next simulation examined this issue empirically.

SIMULATION 3: A MORE REALISTIC TRAINING REGIME

As we have noted, addition problems are not taught using mutually exclusive sets of problems. If the 1's are taught first, followed by the 2's, the set of 2's usually contains some of the 1's as reminder or refresher trials. From the teacher's intuitive perspective, the purpose of these trials is to consolidate or reinforce prior learning. The simulation models provide a computational way to construe this "consolidation" process: the reminding trials are necessary in order to reduce the interfering effects of new learning. We examined this process in a new simulation involving 5 stages. The main idea was to use a sequential training regime in which we used overlapping problem sets. The effect of this regime was to slowly introduce new problems while slowly phasing out old ones. Each of the five stages was 10 epochs long. The first stage involved training the model on two sets of 1's problems. During each epoch in the second stage, the model was trained on two sets of 1's and one set of 2's. In the third stage, the model was trained on one set of 1's, two sets of 2's, and one set of 3's. In the fourth stage, the model was trained on one set of 1's, two sets of 2's, two sets of 3's, and one set of 4's. Finally, the fifth stage included one set of 2's, two sets of 3's, two sets of 4's, and one set of 5's. No 1's were presented in the final stage.

As can be seen from this description, the training procedure involved fading in new problems while fading out old ones. Thus, the training regime was not strictly concurrent (all problems were not available for training simultaneously) but it was not as rigidly sequential as the MC procedure. All sets of problems were defined as before; they were constructed so as to contain 13 problems that did not occur in any other set (e.g., 1+3 occurred in the 1's set, not the 3's set). The simulation was replicated 5 times; the data are averaged across all 5 runs.

Results and Discussion

The primary data concern performance on the 1's as a function of exposure to other problems (Figure 4). The data in the figure were averaged over two consecutive epochs. During the first stage, the model learned the 1's problems. Introduction of the 2's during stage two initially caused a small decrement in performance (epochs 12-14), but there was rapid recovery (epochs 16-18). Similar effects were obtained at stages three and four, with a notable decrease in magnitude in stage four. Thus, training on other problems produced diminishing amounts of interference on the 1's. Data concerning the average number of correct responses showed a similar pattern. During stage 5, when there was no additional training on the 1's, the error scores for these problems began to increase again. Note, however, that the increase was still relatively small, and the model still averaged less than one error per problem set. After 75 epochs—35 epochs after the network was last trained on the 1's set and following 2730 trials on other problems—the mean error score for the 1's was .32 and the mean number of correct responses was 11.8/13 (91%). In sum, the model did not exhibit catastrophic interference.

GENERAL DISCUSSION

Our findings can be summarized as follows. MC are correct in observing that there is massive retroactive interference in a simple PDP model of arithmetic learning when the problem sets are strictly blocked (Simulation 1). Earlier problems are not completely unlearned, however, as evidenced by the savings

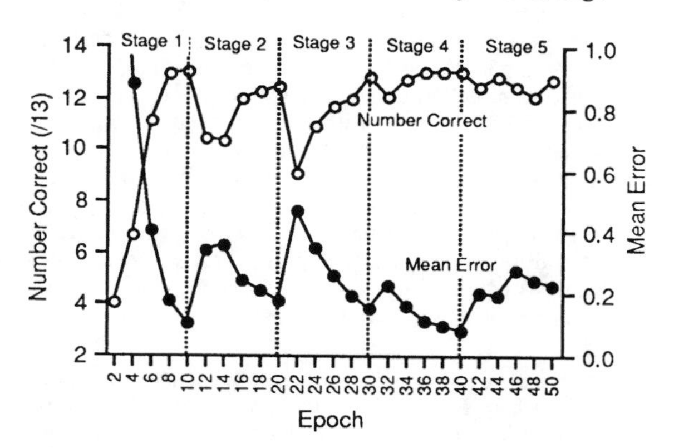

Figure 4: Performance on the 1's Problems During Five Stages of Training

observed in Simulation 2. Taking advantage of this savings merely requires relaxing the strict blocking of training trials by type (Simulation 3). This does not involve the "concurrent" procedure that MC consider unrealistic; rather, it involves a training sequence more like the ones used in the actual teaching of arithmetic. Thus, in Simulation 3, the model was able to learn the 1's problems and this knowledge was not eliminated by a large amount of training on subsequent problems.

The main point of our simulations has been to suggest that it would be a mistake to overinterpret MC's results, since very small changes to their procedures yield very different results. We should stress, however, that our simulations by no means resolve any of the important questions concerning retroactive interference in PDP models. Our simulations—as well as MC's—provide empirical data concerning a relatively small subset of cases. These simulations represent individual points in a very large multidimensional space of possible models. This space of possibilities is defined by the range of possible architectures (e.g., number of units, patterns of connectivity, encoding schemes), learning procedures, and training regimes. Empirical demonstrations such as ours and MC's can be useful in identifying potential problems and solutions. However, they do not provide a definitive basis for identifying principled limitations of the PDP approach.[3]

It will be important to understand the scope of retroactive interference problems in PDP networks in a more rigorous way. There seem to be two fruitful ways to pursue this issue in future research. One is to perform more systematic analyses of the properties of various PDP models, with the goal of identifying the principles that govern their behavior. This type of analysis is difficult to perform, but it is clear that there is beginning to be significant progress in this regard (see, e.g., papers in Touretzky, 1989). Certainly Minsky and Papert's (1969) celebrated analysis of perceptrons provides a model for this type of analysis. A second alternative is to develop more realistic models that provide a systematic account of a broad range of behavioral data. The problem with demonstrations such as MC's (and our own) is that they do not attempt to simulate a realistic learning task or account for detailed aspects of human performance. In the area of arithmetic learning, for example, there is a large amount of behavioral data, several accounts of which have already been proposed (e.g., Groen & Parkman, 1972; Siegler & Shrager, 1984). A reasonable goal would be to attempt to develop simulation models that address such nontrivial phenomena in detail. Again, examples of PDP models with broad scope and coverage of the data are beginning to appear (e.g., Seidenberg & McClelland, in press; Dell, 1986).

Ratcliff (1989) presents an impressive example of the second approach. He explored whether a connectionist model could simulate an extensive set of findings concerning recognition memory performance, and systematically explored several modelling variables (MC also report simulations of some of these phenomena). Interestingly, all of Ratcliff's models produced behaviors unlike humans'. Analyses such as Ratcliff's contribute to understanding where there is and is not a good match between the properties of connectionist models and those of human behavior. The failure of Ratcliff's simulation models suggests that this type of recognition memory performance cannot be construed in terms of learning in multilayer nets via backpropagation. Several characteristics of these recognition memory phenomena appear to be critical to understanding why the simulations failed. Unlike most learning, the typical recognition memory experiment does involve strict sequencing of trials, as well as rapid stimulus presentation that limits the use of rehearsal or other learning strategies, and very simple, unrelated stimuli, such as lists of letters or words. The question then is whether other types of learning exhibit the characteristics that apparently make the connectionist approach so inapplicable in this case.

Consider in this light the question of retroactive interference in learning simple arithmetic. Our simulations suggest that the seriousness of this problem depends in part on questions concerning the learning regime: is it strictly concurrent, is it strictly blocked, or is it neither of these extremes? We suggest that it is more concurrent than MC recognize, and less sequential than in the case of recognition memory experiments. This is simply an empirical

3. We did explore one other factor, the number of hidden units, which we thought would be important on the basis of previous research (e.g., Seidenberg & McClelland, in press) and a reviewer's comments. However, essentially similar results were obtained using 13, 25, and 50 hidden units.

question, however. With a more realistic characterization of the task and the learning environment, it should then be possible to determine whether, in fact, there is a serious retroactive interference problem or not. It is doubtful, however, whether this substantive issue can be decided on the basis of demonstration programs like MC's. One of the main lessons of research in traditional, symbol-processing artificial intelligence was that general principles cannot be uncovered by studying toy problems. There is no reason to think that anything different should obtain in the case of PDP.

REFERENCES

Anderson, J.A. (1983). Cognitive and psychological computations with neural networks. *IEEE Transactions on Systems, Man, and Cybernetics, SMC-13*, 799-815.

Campbell, J.I.D., & Graham, D.J. (1985). Mental multiplication skill: Structure, process, and acquisition. *Canadian Journal of Psychology, 39*(2), 338-366.

Dell, G., (1986). A spreading activation theory of retrieval in sentence production. *Psychological Review, 93*, 283-321.

Ebbinghaus, H. (1885). *Ueber das gedächtnis: Untersuchen zur experimentellen psychologie* ("On memory") (H.A. Ruger & C.E. Bussenius, trans.). New York: Dover, 1964.

Groen, G.J., & Parkman, J.M. (1972). A chronometric analysis of simple addition. *Psychological Review, 79*, 329-343.

Lachter, J., & Bever, T.G. (1988). The relationship between linguistic structure and associative theories of language learning—A constructive critique of some connectionist learning models. *Cognition, 28*, 195-247.

McClelland, J.L., & Rumelhart, D.E. (1988). *Parallel distributed processing: A handbook of models, programs, and exercises. Volume 3.* Cambridge MA.: MIT Press.

McCloskey, M., & Cohen, N.J. (in press). Catastrophic interference in connectionist networks: The sequential learning problem. Paper to appear in G.H. Bower (Ed.), *The psychology of learning and motivation: Volume 23.* New York: Academic Press.

Minsky, M.L., & Papert, S.A. (1969). *Perceptrons.* Cambridge, MA: The MIT Press.

Pinker, S., & Prince, A. (1988). On language and connectionism: Analysis of a parallel distributed processing model of language acquisition. *Cognition, 28*, 73-194.

Postman, L., & Underwood, B.J. (1973). Critical issues in interference theory. *Memory and Cognition, 1*, 19-40.

Ratcliff, R. (1989). *Connectionist models of recognition memory: Constraints imposed by learning and forgetting functions.* Unpublished manuscript.

Rosenblatt, F. (1962). *Principles of neurodynamics.* Washington: Spartan Books.

Rumelhart, D.E., Hinton, G.E., & Williams, R.J. (1986). Learning internal representations by error propagation. In D.E. Rumelhart & J.L. McClelland (Eds.), *Parallel distributed processing: Explorations in the microstructure of cognition. Volume 1* (pp. 318-362). Cambridge MA.: MIT Press.

Rumelhart, D.E., & McClelland, J.L. (1986). On learning the past tenses of English verbs. In J.L. McClelland & D.E. Rumelhart (Eds.), *Parallel distributed processing: Explorations in the microstructure of cognition. Volume 2* (pp. 216-271). Cambridge MA.: MIT Press.

Seidenberg, M.S., & McClelland, J.L. (in press). A distributed developmental model of word recognition and naming. *Psychological Review.*

Sejnowski, T., & Rosenberg, C. (1986). *NETtalk: A parallel network that learns to read aloud.* Baltimore, MD: Johns Hopkins University EE and CS Technical Report JHU/EECS-86/01.

Siegler, R.S., & Shrager, J. (1984). Strategy choices in addition and subtraction: How do children know what to do? In C. Sophian (Ed.), *Origins of Cognitive skills.* Hillsdale, NJ. Lawrence Erlbaum Associates.

Touretzky, D.S., Ed. (1989). *Advances in neural information processing systems 1.* San Mateo, CA: Morgan Kaufmann.

Viscuso, S.R., Anderson, J.A., & Spoehr, K.T. (in press). Representing simple arithmetic in neural networks. In *Advanced cognitive science: Theory and applications.*

This research was supported by NSERC grant A7924 and a grant from the Quebec Ministry of Education. MSS is also affiliated with the Canadian Institute for Advanced Research Artificial Intelligence and Robotics Program.
E-mail: INMK@MUSICB.MCGILL.CA

Compositionality and the Explanation of Cognitive Processes

Tim van Gelder
Department of Philosophy
Indiana University

Abstract: Connectionist approaches to the modeling of cognitive processes have often been attacked on the grounds that they do not employ compositionally structured representations (e.g., Fodor & Pylyshyn 1988). But what exactly is compositional structure, and how does such structure contribute to cognitive processing? This paper clarifies these questions by distinguishing two different styles of compositionality, one characteristic of connectionist modeling and the other essential to mainstream symbolic or "Classical" approaches. Given this distinction, it is clear that connectionist models can employ compositionally structured representations while remaining, both conceptually and in practice, quite distinct from the Classical approach; moreover, it can be shown that certain central aspects of cognition, such as its *systematicity*, are at least in principle amenable to Connectionist explanation.

1. STYLES OF COMPOSITIONALITY

One point of general agreement among cognitive scientists of diverse theoretical persuasions is that sophisticated cognitive processing requires the internal representing of complex structured items or situations. To give an obvious example, engaging in conversation requires, at some level, the ability to represent the sentences used. It is generally agreed, moreover, that it is not sufficient merely to represent such items as a whole; it is essential that the internal *structure* of the items be represented and hence accessible to the system. Thus there is generally little point in representing a sentence with a single letter, for this in itself conveys no information about the syntactic structure of the sentence, and so is of almost no help in determining how the sentence should be processed.

One approach, perhaps the most obvious, to the problem of representing structured items is to use representations that themselves exhibit a compositional structure. In the most general sense, any representation is appropriately said to have a compositional structure when it is built up, in a systematic way, out of regular parts drawn from a certain determinate set; those parts are then the primitive *constituents* of the representation. Constituents are set in systematic correspondence with parts or features of the item to be represented, and various relationships among those parts or features are indicated by the structural relationships among the representation's constituents.

Though this description may have seemed transparent enough, there are in fact a number of fundamentally different ways in which a representation can be "built up" out of parts, and a number of corresponding notions of "part" or "constituent". In particular, we can distinguish the compositional formal structure of the representation itself, which is a fact about its concrete physical design, from a wider sense of compositionality that we get if we consider only its constituency relations (i.e., the constituents the representation happened to be constructed out of and into which it could in turn be broken down), disregarding the particular internal formal configuration of the representation token itself.

To make this more precise: a compositional representation is one that belongs to a compositional scheme, where a compositional scheme is one that satisfies the following conditions:

(a) There is a (typically finite) set of primitive types $\{P_1, ..., P_n\}$; for each type P_i, there is an unbounded number of tokens of each type, p_i.

(b) There is a (typically unbounded) set of expression types R_i; for each type R_i, there is an unbounded number of tokens of those types, r_i.

(c) There is a set of abstract transitive and non-reflexive *constituency* relations over these primitive and expression types. $C(R_i, R_j)$ means, for example, that expressions of type R_j have as constituents expressions of type R_i.

Since in most interesting cases of compositional schemes there is an unbounded number of expression types, *specifying* such a scheme requires recursive rules determining the allowable expression types in terms of their constituency relations; a set of rules of this kind is a *grammar* for the scheme.

Note that these conditions are framed primarily in terms of primitive and expression *types*, and do not yet say anything at all about how *tokens* are actually to be instantiated. In other words, they place no constraints on the formal *sign design* of representations in the scheme. This is a matter needing further specification. Given that there is an unbounded number of expression types to deal with, how is it possible to specify what tokens of each type should look like? Clearly this task must also be carried out recursively. The way in which it is standardly done is by providing (1) actual *samples* of each primitive class, which implicitly (or "ostensively") provide criteria for any physical item's counting as an instance of that primitive class; and (2) a concrete *mode of combination*, which, operating in conformity with the abstract grammatical rules, is used to construct expression tokens out of sets of primitive tokens. Consequently, knowing what kinds of things count as tokens of the primitives, and knowing the systematic effects of the mode of combination, we can determine the characteristic physical makeup of any arbitrary expression.

It is now possible to make an important distinction among kinds of compositional scheme, according to the manner in which they construct expression tokens. Most compositional schemes we are familiar with also satisfy the following two further conditions:

(d) Primitive tokens are *symbols*, i.e., instantiate a distinct physical pattern, such that primitive token classes are disjoint and digitally separable;

(e) The mode of combination is concatenative.

A concatenative mode of combination is, intuitively speaking, one that preserves primitive symbol tokens in the expression itself. More precisely, suppose the set of constituents of an expression type R_j is the set of primitives or expressions $\{\alpha_i: C(\alpha_i, R_j)\}$. Then a necessary condition for a mode of combination to be concatenative is that any token r_j generated using that mode must literally contain a token of every α_i, in the sense that some part or feature of r_j satisfies the identity criteria for each constituent α_i. Since the set $\{\alpha_i\}$ includes the primitive symbolic constituents, it must be the case that some part or feature of any token r_j must satisfy the criteria for counting as an instance of each of the symbols of which r_i is constructed.

Representations in such a scheme therefore have a characteristic formal structure; they are appropriately described as *symbolic*, since they are built up out of primitive symbols in a very direct sense. An excellent example of a symbolic scheme in this sense is the space of expressions of standard propositional logic. Primitive symbols are the letters "P", "&", "(" etc., and expressions take the form "(P&Q)", "((P&Q)&R)" and so on. Note that expression tokens contain within their boundaries instances of their constituents, including in particular their primitive symbolic constituents, and that this is just a blunt fact about their physical configuration. Just about every compositional scheme we are familiar with is symbolic in this sense; this includes natural languages (by and large), the various formal languages of logic, mathematics and computer science, and knowledge representation formalisms in artificial intelligence.

Symbolic schemes should however be contrasted with schemes that are merely *functionally* compositional. Such schemes relax condition (e); they do not require the use of any concatenative mode of combination, and so are not constrained to preserving tokens of symbolic constituents in expression tokens.[1] For such schemes to count as genuinely compositional however it is crucial that they do at least satisfy the following condition:

(e') there are general, effective and reliable processes for (i) generating expression tokens from their constituents and (ii) decomposing those expressions into their constituents again.

Designing and implementing such processes, without relying on simple concatenation of symbol tokens, is - to say the least - a challenging engineering problem; this is one reason why concatenative languages are so pervasive.

A graphic (albeit for a number of reasons quite impractical) example of a formal scheme that is compositional but non-concatenative, and hence non-symbolic in this strong sense, is "Gödelese" - the numerals corresponding to the Gödel numbers of the expressions of propositional logic. Imagine that instead of writing down expressions in their normal notation we chose to write down their corresponding Gödel numerals instead. Since under a Gödel numbering scheme every expression is assigned a unique natural number, this new scheme is expressively equivalent to propositional logic; moreover, it is functionally compositional, since there are simple recipes for generating the Gödel numerals of expressions from those of their constituents and vice versa, on the basis of which one can design and implement the relevant composition and decomposition processes. Yet it is a simple fact about the concrete shape of the numerical tokens themselves that, in general, a "complex" Gödelese numeral does not contain within its physical boundaries tokens of its Gödelese constituents. Suppose, for example, that gn(~) = 3 and gn(P) = 5, then gn(~P) = $2^3.3^5$ = 1944. In Gödelese, then, the expression *1944* has, as constituents, *3* and *5*. Yet it is just a blunt fact about the shapes of the ink marks on the page that no part or feature of the token *1944*

[1] There are interesting consequences that follow from relaxing condition (d) as well: see Smolensky (1987b, 1988)

counts, by any reasonable criteria, as a token of either *3* or *5*.[1] Gödelese expressions are built up by multiplication, not concatenation.

Expressions in a merely functionally compositional scheme typically do have formal (i.e., non-semantic) structure of a kind. Indeed, their possessing a certain systematic internal physical configuration is essential to the possibility of real, implementable generation and decomposition processes. Still, the crucial point is that they are without formal *symbolic* structure, since they do not in general contain tokens of their constituents.[2]

2. COMPOSITIONALITY AND COGNITIVE PROCESSES

This distinction between strictly concatenative compositionality on the one hand and merely functional compositionality on the other can be used to clarify the difference between mainstream symbolic or "Classical" approaches to cognitive modeling and the emerging connectionist alternatives. Briefly put, while Classical approaches are committed, in both theory and practice, to concatenative compositionality, connectionists tend to abjure such strict constraints.

For example, according to Newell and Simon in their classic formulation of the symbolic approach, it is both necessary and sufficient for a system to exhibit intelligent behavior that it be a *Physical Symbol System*, where

> A physical symbol system consists of a set of entities, called symbols, which are physical patterns that can occur as components of another type of entity called an expression (or symbol structure). Thus a symbol structure is composed of a number of instances (or tokens) of symbols related in some physical way (such as one being next to another). At any instant of time the system will contain a collection of these symbol structures...[3]

This definition encapsulates conditions (a) through (e). In particular, it is manifestly committed to (e) rather than (e') because symbol structures are composed of *tokens* of symbols that are *related in some physical way*. Since there can be no relations without relata, the symbol tokens must be present themselves, and not merely extractable by further processing (which would take us to some *further* instant of time). This strong view has recently received further authoritative endorsement from Fodor & Pylyshyn, who claim that

> In the Classical machine, the objects to which the content A&B is ascribed (viz., tokens of the expression 'A&B') literally contain, as proper parts, objects to which the content A is ascribed (viz., tokens of the expression 'A')....In short, it is characteristic of Classical systems...to exploit arrays of symbols some of which are atomic (e.g., expressions like

[1] This point is not at all impugned by the fact that it always takes some finite amount of work for us to *determine* whether or not there are any instances of the symbol *5* in tokens of the expression *1944*, and that some *idiot savant* might, with the same amount of effort, be able to extract the prime factors and hence produce (in his mind or elsewhere) some *other* token of *5*. What matters here is simply the physical shape (and hence the causal properties) of the tokens themselves. All *5* inscriptions have a flat top, and nothing in *1944* has a flat top.

[2] We should not be misled by the fact that Gödel numerals *are* constructed concatenatively from the tokens "0", "1", ... "9". The crucial point is that these tokens are not properly described as the constituents in the Gödel numeral scheme. The essentially orthographic rules of numeral construction are entirely different from the grammatical rules governing generation of the space of *Gödel* numeral expressions.

[3] Newell and Simon 1975 p.40.

'A') but indefinitely many of which have other symbols as syntactic and semantic parts (e.g. expressions like 'A&B').[1]

The presence of symbolic structure in the current strong sense is essential to the conception of cognitive processing which underlies the symbolic approach, for it is symbols which mediate between the semantic and the physical constraints on the behavior of the system. On one hand, the law-governed physical behavior of the system is explained by reference to the *causal* role of symbol tokens themselves, while on the other the system is *interpreted* by means of semantic assignments to those symbols. This is just the classical conception of computation, and the symbolic approach to cognitive modeling asserts that cognition *is* computation.[2]

Does this analysis confuse properties of representations at the cognitive level (the level of the *functional* architecture of the system) with details of the actual implementation? Might not a symbolic theorist be satisfied with merely functionally compositional representations at the implementation level? Suggestions like this do a disservice to the symbolic approach by conceding too much. Classical theorists have always insisted on the concreteness of their concatenatively structured symbolic representations. Thus, for Newell and Simon, symbol structures are physical entities within which symbol *tokens* are related "in some physical way;" Fodor & Pylyshyn, likewise, have stressed that the combinatorial structure of Classical representations must be mapped directly onto structures in the brain. It is this fact which makes possible the Classical explanation of cognitive processes by reference to the causal role of the internal syntactic structure of the representations themselves. If you deny that representations are concatenative at the implementation level, you must have up your sleeve an *independent* explanation of how cognitive processes are engineered. But, according to the true symbolic theorist, you will not - as a matter of contingent, empirical fact - be able to provide such an explanation.

The theoretical framework governing connectionist approaches is by comparison almost completely undeveloped, but we can nevertheless discern an increasing tendency in more recent work to reject precisely this commitment of the mainstream approach. Some relatively well-known work utilizing compositional but non-symbolic methods of representation are Smolensky's tensor product formalism, Hinton's techniques for the representation of hierarchical structures via reduced descriptions, and Pollack's Recursive Auto-Associative Memory (RAAM).[3]

Pollack, for example, devised a way to represent variable-sized data structures such as standard linguistic sequences in the form of stacks, where each stack is a distinct pattern of activity over a bank of hidden units in a three layer (i.e., one hidden layer) network. These stack representations exhibit functional compositionality since elements of a sequence can be stored and recovered, in appropriate order, quite reliably. Yet careful analysis of the stack representations themselves (the patterns over the hidden units) does *not* reveal features that could possibly count as

---

1 Fodor & Pylyshyn 1988 p.16.

2 Pylyshyn 1984.

3 Smolensky 1987a, Hinton 1988, Pollack 1988.

tokens of the various primitive elements of the original sequence (nor those of any other symbolic scheme). Constituents of the represented sequences are effectively *stored* in stacks without being *instantiated* there. Consequently, while it is certainly appropriate to say that stacks are compositional representations *of* symbolic structures, they are not, strictly speaking, symbolic representations themselves. Pollack is therefore being somewhat misleading when he describes his stack representations as "compositional in the strictest sense;"[1] they are compositional, but only functionally so, not in the stricter concatenative sense.

One way to understand the disagreement here is to see that for the Classical theorist, any non-trivial representation of a complex structured item must itself have a parallel structural complexity in its internal compositional configuration. ("Non-trivial" means that the details of the internal *structure* of the item, and not just the item as a whole, are being effectively represented.) Connectionist representations, by contrast, eschew such internal compositionality in favor of a merely functional substitute. Insofar as we are concerned with *compositional* formal internal structure, then, the general point can be put in terms of the following handy slogan: for the connectionist, representations of structure need not be structured representations.

3. IS CLASSICAL COMPOSITIONALITY NECESSARY?

If it is true that connectionism is properly characterized as utilizing compositional but non-symbolic representations, a number of important consequences follow. First, as Smolensky has already pointed out, it is clear that connectionists can employ compositional representations without thereby committing themselves to the strict Classical approach.[2] Compositionality, in other words, is by no means the exclusive prerogative of the Classical paradigm.

Second, we can show that connectionism is well-equipped for the task of explaining certain aspects of cognition which, it has been argued, are beyond the explanatory reach of any model which refuses to employ strictly Classical representations and processes. In their recent influential critique, Fodor & Pylyshyn argued that cognition is *systematic*, and that only by postulating Classical representations and processes is there any real hope of explaining this phenomenon. Systematicity consists in such mundane facts as the following: that the ability to entertain one kind of thought always goes along with the ability to entertain systematically related thoughts (if you can think *John loves the girl* you can think *the girl loves John*); and that the ability to perform one kind of inference always goes along with the ability to perform systematically related inferences (if you can infer *P* from *P&Q* you can also infer *P* from *P&Q&R*).

How does utilizing Classical representations help us in generating an explanation of systematicity? Fodor & Pylyshyn summarize as follows:

---

1 p.37.

2 See Smolensky 1987b. Though we agree on this point, we differ in emphasizing different ways in which connectionist representations are non-Classical. As mentioned above, Smolensky focuses on relaxing condition (d) while I focus on condition (e).

> all the arguments we've been reviewing...are really much the same: If you hold the kind of theory that acknowledges structured representations, it must perforce acknowledge representations with *similar* or *identical* structure... So, if your theory also acknowledges mental processes that are structure sensitive, then it will predict that similarly structured representations will generally play similar roles in thought.[1]

By this reasoning, if connectionism is to be able to explain systematicity, it must also utilize representations that can have *similar* or *identical* structures, such that mental processes can be sensitive to that structure. The crucial question, then, is whether such structural relations can obtain among non-Classical representations, or whether *only* strictly symbolic representations can exhibit the relevant structural similarities. Fodor & Pylyshyn, of course, clearly prefer the latter view. Any non-Classical representations, they assume, must be completely unstructured; consequently, there can be no structural similarity relations for mental processes to pick up on, and so these processes must be purely "associationist."[2]

As I pointed out above, however, compositional but non-concatenative representations must be internally structured, though of course they are not *symbolically* structured. The distinctive structure of a given RAAM stack representation for example is found in the particular distribution of activity levels over the hidden units. Somewhat surprisingly, Fodor & Pylyshyn have simply left this whole class of representations out of consideration entirely. Since these representations are structured, it follows that they can stand in structural similarity relations. Indeed, it is increasingly common practice in connectionist modeling to analyze (using e.g. cluster analysis) sets of representations in order to uncover the order of similarity relations among the representations themselves. Further, these similarity relations tend to be systematic in that they reflect the constituency relations of the representations. Representations that were constructed in a grammatically similar fashion end up as neighboring points in the relevant high-dimensional vector space.

Consequently, in this respect connectionists have at least the raw resources for generating an explanation of the systematicity of cognition; their representations exhibit what Fodor & Pylyshyn themselves argue is the essential ingredient in such explanations. The task that remains is to devise processes, implemented in connectionist architectures, for manipulating these representations in a way that is systematically "sensitive to" (i.e., causally influenced by) their internal structure, and thus respects the compositionality-based similarity relations among representations. In this way, non-symbolic connectionist representations can be manipulated in a way that is systematically "sensitive to" (i.e., reflects) the complex structure of the items they represent.

It is important to realize that connectionists have scarcely begun this difficult task. Perhaps the best argument for the strictly Classical approach is that such processes will prove to be infeasible in the general case, i.e., with respect to the eventual goal of accounting for the full systematic complexity of human cognitive performance. Nevertheless it is also important to realize that, as far

[1] 1988 p.48.

[2] See, e.g., p.32. An associationist mental process is one that is sensitive only to prior correlations in experience, and not "to features of the content or the structure of representations per se."

as can reasonably be predicted at this stage, there is (contra Fodor & Pylyshyn) no *principled* barrier to success in that enterprise. Connectionist approaches which are genuinely non-Classical have at least the basic resources to produce systematic performance, and the hypothesis that such representations in fact underlie our cognitive capacities does *not* render the systematicity of thought a mystery.

REFERENCES

Fodor J.A. & Pylyshyn Z.W. (1988) Connectionism and cognitive architecture: A critical analysis. *Cognition*; 28: 3-71.

Hinton G.E. (1988) Representing part-whole hierarchies in connectionist networks. Proceedings of the Tenth Annual Conference of the Cognitive Science Society. Montreal, Quebec, Canada: 48-54.

Newell A. and Simon H. (1975) Computer science as an empirical inquiry. *Communications of the Association for Computing Machinery*; 19: 113-126.

Pollack J. (1988) Recursive auto-associative memory: Devising compositional distributed representations. Proceedings of the Tenth Annual Conference of the Cognitive Science Society. Montreal, Quebec, Canada.

Pylyshyn Z.W. (1984) *Computation and Cognition: Toward a Foundation for Cognitive Science.* Cambridge MA: MIT Press.

Smolensky P. (1987a) On variable binding and the representation of symbolic structures in connectionist systems; Technical Report CU-CS-355-87, Department of Computer Science, University of Colorado.

— (1987b) The constituent structure of mental states: A reply to Fodor and Pylyshyn. *Southern Journal of Philosophy*; 26 Supplement: 137-160.

— (1988) Connectionism, Constituency, and the Language of Thought. Technical Report CU-CS-416-88, Department of Computer Science, University of Colorado.

Learning from Error

Colleen M. Seifert
University of Michigan

Edwin L. Hutchins
University of California - San Diego

Abstract

Distributed systems of cognition are receiving increasing attention in a variety of research traditions. A central question is how the specific features of cognitive functions will be affected by their occurrence within a system of cooperative agents. In this paper, we will examine the less often considered aspects of the organization of cooperative work settings that can become important in terms of error within a system. Specifically, we examine how response to error in a cooperative task can in some ways benefit future task performance. The goal is to facilitate learning from error so that future errors become less likely. The study involved an analysis of observations of several cooperative teams involved in coordinated activity for the navigation of a large ship. The analysis of the team member's activities revealed a surprisingly high rate of errors; yet, the final product of the group work showed that the error had been removed somewhere within the system. Features of the distributed system that facilitated this error removal included the monitoring of other's performance, as constrained by a horizon of observation, limiting exposure to particular subtasks; the distribution of knowledge within the team, such that more knowledgable members were also ones in a position to detect other's errors; and methods of providing feedback. In particular, specific design tradeoffs were found to underlie the functioning of the system. For example, evaluation depends on utilizing objective knowledge of how the product reconciles with the real world; however, separating evaluation from the system means "wasting" the knowledgable potential participant. Thus, the distributed system was found to contain certain properties that can be exploited for their utility in error detection, diagnosis, and correction. The results may be applied to the design of such cooperative tasks, including a role for technology, with the goal of designing cooperative systems that can more easily learn from their errors.

Introduction

Most studies of error focus on its reduction or elimination, and there are many steps that can be taken to avoid or prevent the occurrence of errors. Yet in systems of cooperative work in the real world, there is a fundamental reason why error is inevitable: such systems always rely on learning on the job, and where there is the need for learning, there is potential for error. A naturally situated system of cooperative work must both produce the intended result of its process and reproduce *itself* at the same time. Such cooperative systems may change overtime, be reorganized, change the things they do, and change the technology they utilize to do the job. Even if the tasks and tools could somehow be frozen, changes in personnel are certain over time. Most commonly, relatively expert personnel are gradually lost while relatively inexpert personnel are added. Even if the skills required to do the job can be taught in schools, the interactions that are characteristic of cooperative work can generally only be learned on the job.

Designing for Error

Norman (1983, 1986, 1987) argues that because error is inevitable, it is important to "design for error." Speaking of designers, Norman says, "Inadvertently, they can make it easy to err and difficult or impossible to discover error or to recover from it " (1987, Ch.

5:24). Norman suggests that designers of artifacts should design to minimize the causes of error, make it possible to "undo" errorful actions, and make it easier to discover and correct errors. These same goals are appropriate for designers of cooperative work systems, but here we can go further. Each of Norman's suggestions is aimed at protecting the current task performance, yet in the broader perspective of production and reproduction in cooperative work, it would be nice if the response to error in the current task could also in some way *benefit* future task performance. That is, another aspect of designing for error might be designing systems that can more easily learn from their errors.

That would give us two major classes of design goals with respect to errors. First, design to eliminate, avoid, or prevent errors wherever possible. Second, design to take full advantage of any errors that do occur. The goal is to facilitate learning from errors so that future errors become less likely. As career trajectories take experienced members out of the work group and expertise is lost from the system, the likelihood of error may increase. The potential advantage of designing for error is that this increase in likelihood of error may be offset by the decrease in likelihood of error due to learning by the remaining and new members of the group. The prevention of error is clearly important and has received a great deal of attention in the past. In this paper, we will examine the less often considered aspects of the organization of cooperative work settings that can become important once an error has occurred.

The Navigation Domain

The response of systems of cooperative work to error came to our attention in studies of navigation teams abord large ships (Hutchins, in press). At all times while a naval vessel is underway, a plot of its past and projected movements is maintained. The information gathered and processed by the navigation team supports the decisions of the conning officer who is responsible for the ship's movements. Day and night, whenever a ship is neither tied to a pier nor at anchor, navigation computations are performed. Most of the time, the work of navigation is performed by one person working alone; however, when a ship leaves or enters port or operates in any other environment where maneuverability is restricted, the computational requirements of the task may exceed the capabilities of any individual. In such circumstances, the navigation duties are carried out by a team of individuals working together.

In addition to satisfying the immediate navigation needs of the ship, navigation teams have developed under the constraints of maintaining a working system in a state of readiness, allowing frequent replacements of individual team members and providing a task performance environment in which the job can be learned by actually doing it. These characteristics are shared by many real world settings of cooperative work.

We observed the actual operations of navigation teams aboard several ships operating in both solo and group performance configurations, and made detailed recordings of the behavior during the course of observations, along with audio and video tape recording during some observation periods. In spite of the fact that all of the navigation teams we observed functioned satisfactorily, close examination of their operation revealed surprisingly high rates of error. However, observing only the final output of the teams, one would not suspect that many errors were being made. In fact, while many errors were committed, virtually all of them were detected and corrected within the navigation team itself.

Facilitating Learning from Error

In order to benefit from errors that do occur, these errors must be detected, diagnosed as to their cause, and corrected with useful feedback. The next sections examine these three processes as they are affected by particular system characteristics.

Detecting Error

Error detection may require considerable resources. Our observations about the conditions under which errors are detected indicate that the following elements are necessary for error detection and may play a role in diagnosis and correction as well.

Access: In order to detect an error, the detector must have access to the errorful behavior or some indication of it.

Knowledge/expectation: The detector must have knowledge of the outcome with respect to which the observed process or outcome can be judged discrepant.

Attention: The detecting entity must attend to the errorful behavior and monitor it in terms of expectation.

Perspective: Different perspectives can result in focus of attention on different aspects of the task, consequently affecting the nature of the discrepancies in performance that are noticed.

In the world of navigation, as in many other systems, novices begin by doing the simplest parts of the collaborative work task. As they become more skilled, they move on to more complex duties, making way for less skilled people behind them. This movement defines a career trajectory for individuals through the roles of the work group. An interesting aspect of the navigation setting is that the career trajectory for individuals follows the path of information through the system in the team's most basic computation, *position fixing*. The simplest jobs involve gathering sensed data, and the more complex jobs involve processing that data. As a consequence of this alignment of career trajectory with the path of information through the system, if one has access to an error, one also has knowledge of the processes that may have generated it, because one has already -- at an earlier career stage -- performed all those operations. The overlap of access and knowledge that results from the alignment of career path and data path is not a necessary feature of these systems, nor is it apparently an intentional one here. It does, however, give rise to especially favorable conditions for the detection and diagnosis of error.

The attention required to detect error may be facilitated or even required by the nature of coordinated tasks. Many errors in earlier processing are detected by the plotter when visual bearings are plotted on the chart. In part, this is because the plotting procedure itself is designed to detect error. Any two lines of position define the location of the ship, but a position "fix" always consists of three lines of position, whose intersection forms a small triangle. If any of the three is in error, the triangle will become larger. Thus, the nature of the plotter's task is different than the way the bearing observers think about the bearings: For the bearing observer, the bearing may be no more than a string of three digits read from a scale in a telescopic sight. It is not necessary for the bearing observer to think of the directional meaning of the number. In contrast, the plotter's job is to recover the directional meaning of the reported bearing and combine the meanings of three bearings to fix the position of the ship. Different jobs in the team require attention to different aspects of the computational objects, so different kinds of error are likely to be detected (or not) by different members of the team.

Many errors are detected by team members who are simply monitoring the actions of those around them. Not only is each member of the team responsible for his own job, each seems also to take responsibility for all parts of the process to which he can contribute. Since detection depends upon access, however, the more the activities of the team members are conducted where they can be observed (or overheard) by others, the higher the potential rate of error detection. Detection also requires attention, which may be a scarce resource. One of the consequences of high workloads may be both an increase in the rate of error itself due to the reduction of resources available for monitoring the actions of others.

On some ships, the job of making a global assessment of the quality of the work of the navigation team is institutionalized in the role of the evaluator. This evaluator is a qualified navigation practitioner who is not engaged in the navigational computations themselves, but monitors the process by which the computations are performed and assesses the quality of the product. There is a tradeoff here between using the evaluator's processing power to do the computations themselves, thereby possibly lowering error rates while risking lower error detection rates, versus keeping the evaluator out of the computations, thereby possibly increasing error rates while detecting more of the errors that are committed.

The important structural property of the evaluator role is that the evaluator has access to and knowledge of the performance of the task, but does not participate in its performance. Instead, the evaluator attends to the way the task is done and specifically monitors the performance for error. The evaluator builds into the system some attention to how well the result of the computation fits the physical world it measures, an aspect of the system's behavior that would not otherwise be reliably present. This same strategy is recognizable in the mandated role of the captain of the ship, or that of the senior captain in a commercial airline cockpit. These people are task monitors rather than task performers (Miyake, 1982); as such, they serve an important function in providing an external validation of the process they observe.

Diagnosing Errors

Not all recoveries from error are instructional in intent or consequence. Because some recovery methods are used simply to complete the task, there may be no need to diagnose the cause of the error in order to discover how to recover from it. However, other error recovery strategies involve the diagnosis of the source of the error, and perhaps explicit demonstration of the correct solution. Diagnosing error depends on understanding how the error may have been generated. This appears to occur through the modelling of the reasoning processes of the person who committed the error. This may require modelling of the reasoning processes of the person who committed the error. The *distribution of knowledge* characteristic of the navigation system, in which access to error and the knowledge of its causes are aligned, insures that most errors that are detected will be detected by people who already have experience with the operations that led to the error. Familiarity with the task assists in modelling other's understanding to determine where the generation of the error may have occurred. Errors indicate in very specific ways exactly what information or ability is missing in the current knowledge state of the novice. Consider this example:

> *A novice navigator was asked, "How far west shall we go to get back to harbor at 1600?" The ship was directly west of the harbor entrance (time = 1200). He paused, then measured the distance the ship could go in an hour and marked it with a compass; he then marked four hour-lengths from the harbor entrance on the chart. This position lay far west of the ship's current position. A more*

experienced quartermaster was observing, and said, "If he wants to be back by 1600, he's not going to go west from now until he hits this point!"

In the task of diagnosis, the expert attempts to determine what may be the cause of the novice's error; to do this, he must utilize meta-knowledge about what the task requires and what the novice is likely to know. A solution procedure would be to measure the current distance to land from the ship, subtract the time to return from this location from the four hours, and then split the remainder to continue west for half of it. The novice appears to have part of the solution procedure available for use: to mark the distance travelled with a distance preserving tool (the divider) and compare the distance to a scale on the side of the chart which provides a transformation into miles. However, this procedure is incorrectly applied to the problem when he focuses on the ability of the ship to travel a particular distance within the time interval rather than on determining the particular distance already traveled from the end point. The response of the observer indicates he is modelling the reasoning process of the novice, as he points out that the solution being generated by the novice is not going to solve the stated problem of returning by 1600.

The particular solution generated by the novice also provides information about what information may be lacking or what elements are problematic for him; the expert can utilize the error to gear the explanation to the novice's current knowledge. By modelling the novice's understanding of the task, the expert may be able to determine where the novice went wrong in his reasoning and how to describe the solution in a way that is useful to the learner. For example, in the above problem, the expert may recognize that the novice started out by solving a more familiar problem; namely, "how far are we from location X?" The solution to that problem is related, but the novice did not know how to pose the course recommendation in a form that connected to this solution. By understanding the way in which the novice was attempting to solve the problem, the next step of correction is assisted because the expert can gear the presentation of a better solution in a way that is more understandable and memorable to the novice.

Correcting Errors

Beyond the purpose of correcting an error that has occurred, a consequence of having engaged in the activities of detecting and/or diagnosing the cause of an error may be that the person doing the detecting comes to a new insight about the operation of the system. This is true whether the error was committed by oneself or someone else, and it may be particularly inportant for novices who detect other's errors. Further, every instance of correction is practice in the skills of detection and confirmation of knowledge which may save the system from consequences of future error.

Feedback on how to correct the error is extremely important to the learning process. Without correction, further performance acts to increase familiarity with the error path, thereby increasing the tendency towards error (Anderson et al, 1984). However, if competing solutions are presented as feedback or can be inferred by the learner from the feedback, the error serves to direct the learning focus towards information that has been demonstrated to be missing from the novice's knowledge base. Even when the feedback lacks instructional content, it could contribute to the refinement of understanding task requirements that may not be apparent from correct performance alone. Such corrections help the learner to induce the principles that define correct performance.

This can be especially important with concepts that must be inferred from cases rather than explicitly stated. Because relevant information for a decision may not be explicitly observable or explicable by an expert, novices have to infer the domain information from experience in a variety of situations, guided by error correction on specific failures. Where there is a solution space to be explored, response to error can guide the discovery of the concept underlying the solution. The result may be a directed search through the information about a task guided by the particular errors made by the novice during performance. Thus, the implicit nature of domain knowledge in the navigation task motivates learning through error. Novices are allowed to do their best, and are provided directed instruction on the particular errors they make.

However, feedback with little instructional content may not be as helpful as a more complete demonstration or instruction. In navigation teams, error feedback is sometimes reduced to a contentless complaint or an exhortation to do better. Such limited feedback may be of little use to the person who has committed the error. However, it may be the only response the error detector can provide. Errors are corrected during performance of the task, rather than delayed. Because the detector is also involved in a subtask, they may not have the time, processing resources, or communication channels required for the composition and delivery of appropriate instruction. Further, because of the ongoing nature of the task, these resources must be available to the person providing correction at or near the time that the error is committed in order to fully benefit from the specifics of the error commission setting. This represents a tradeoff between apprentice training systems, where two people perform the task of one, and redundancy within cooperative systems, where each has a separate task to complete but shared knowledge allows some correction of errors.

Learning from one's own mistakes is an obvious case of improvement of future performance from correction. Particularly in the early stages of acquisition, the correction of errors may play a significant role in improving performance. In addition, meta-knowledge about errors may be transferred through the cooperative process. Contentful corrections may help the novice learn recovery strategies that can be applied to self-detected errors. And, through the correction of errors, the novice may internalize the processes of error detection, diagnosis, and correction.

Additional learning opportunities are provided by the errors others make. When an error is detected and corrected in the context of collaborative work, many participants may witness and benefit from the response to error. Depending, again, on the *horizon of observation* (who has access to what behavior of others), error and correction may provide a learning context for many of the participants. The novice has the opportunity to observe others' errors, witness their correction, and participate in detecting the errors of others. Thus the socially distributed task gives a participatory role to the novice in all areas of task performance that he is physically able to perceive. Thus, the value of a response to error for future performances may depend upon the horizon of observations for various members of the team. Witnessing such a correction may be of value as well to those who are already competant in the task in which the error occurs if they will subsequently be in a position to detect and correct such errors. They can learn about how to provide useful feedback by watching the corrections of others, leading to an improvement in subsequent learning for others in the system.

Through errors, novices learn by being corrected and instructed by more advanced members of the team, by self-detecting, diagnosing, and correcting, and by observing the errors and corrections of others in close proximity, by participating in the detection, diagnosis and correction of others. The avenues of knowledge acquisition investigated by novice navigators are much richer as a result. By participating in the process of error-based learning as a performer, an observer, and a teacher, the novice increases the number of learning experiences available for acquisition and deepens understanding of the lesson through interaction in several participatory roles. In addition, other learners provide models of the learning process itself, and this meta-knowledge may be helpful to novices in forming expectations about their own performance.

Discussion

Tradeoffs are prevalent throughout this analysis: designing systems so as to benefit from error that does occur requires maximizing the ability to learn from the errors. However, improving the detection, diagnosis, and correction capabilities within a system often has other consequences for system performance. For example, *perspective* can be affected within a system to improve error detection. The bearing observers frequently take the perspective of "meter readers" in their performance, ignoring the physical world perspective which would give them some top-down expectations regarding the plausibility of the readings. Consequently, they often fail to detect errors that they *could* recognize using a physical direction perspective. Bearing observing *requires* no thought about how the information is used -- the numbers are simply reported. Despite the fact that they *know* the intended use of the number, they have little motivation to think about the number in terms of its meaning in the coordinate space of the chart. Consequently, error is propagated through the system past the point where it could logically be detected and corrected.

However, the task system could be redesigned to encourage the directional perspective in the bearing observers. One method which would improve self-detection of these errors is to remind the observers of how the information will be used by placing an artifact indicating the directional coordinate space into their work environment -- for example, have an indication of the full 360 degree representation available on the gyrocompass instead of the partial display currently provided. Such a cognitive artifact would serve to *remind* the takers of the coordinate space and therefore of the plausibility of the reported number in that space. To the extent that the bearing observer adopts the perspective of "thinking direction", he will be better able to utilize plausibility information to detect his own or other's errors. But there is a tradeoff involved in affecting perspective: knowing the intended use and plausibility of the reading may influence the perception of the reading. The point is that in thisas in many other design decisions, the choice of whether to cut error rates or diminish the separation of perspectives is simply a tradeoff to be decided based upon environmental features or system goals.

The analysis provided other observations of design tradeoffs in cooperative systems; for example, the evaluator observed on one ship served to detect errors but did not participate in the computation. The cost to this separation of evaluation from computation is first that error is often detected much later in the computational process than need be if evaluation were performed as the processing occurred; and secondly, that the computational advantage of including this potential participant is lost. Other tradeoffs include: the horizon of observation, which allows error detection but increases distraction; the distribution of knowledge, which improves diagnosis but increases costs due to redundancy of training; and error rates, which allow opportunities for learning but cost in current task performance, and in resources for detection and recovery. Under some conditions, these costs can be offset to some extent by the benefits derived from the process of learning from errors through detection, diagnosis, and correction of errors. Achieving these benefits is not an automatic result of error, but requires ways to organize systems that are more likely then others to notice, recover from, and change future performance based on errors. At present, we know of no way to quantify the tradeoffs involved; however, recognizing their nature and identifying the properties of cooperative systems that affect them seems like a useful first step.

In conclusion, errors will occur in any system of human behavior; however, design of cooperative systems can be altered so as to benefit from the unavoidable error by facilitating learning from them. The intent of this research was to examine how learning from errors takes place in a natural setting, and in particular, how the cooperative task setting fosters learning within a complicated computational task. The results of the analysis point to design features of the navigational environment that are well-suited to learning from error. The demands on system organization include not only that the task be completed without major error, but that the system replicate itself and train novice team members while participating in the task. The navigation system appears well-suited to allow novices to perform on the job with little prior training, to allow errors to indicate where instruction is necessary, and to allow detection, diagnosis, and correction of errors while avoiding their propagation into the final decision phase of the task. An analysis of the task properties has identified particular features of this successful task environment, and the criteria identified can be used to design, to analyze, and to intervene in problem situations within cooperative task systems.

References

Anderson, J. R., Boyd, C. F., Farrell, R., and Reiser, B. J. (1984). Cognitive principles in the design of computer tutors. Office of Naval Research Technical Report #84-1.

Hutchins, E. L. (In press). Learning to navigate in context. In J. Lave and S. Chaiklin (Eds.), Context, cognition, and activity. Cambridge: Cambridge University Press.

Miyake, N. (1982). Constructive interaction. CHIP technical report # 113, Center for human information processing, University of California, San Diego, La Jolla, CA.

Norman, D. A. (1983). Design rules based on analyses of human error. Communications of the ACM, 4, 254-258.

Norman, D. A. (1986). Cognitive engineering. In D. A. Norman and S. W. Draper (Eds.), User centered system design: New perspectives on human-computer interaction. Hillsdale, NJ: Erlbaum Associates.

Norman, D. A. (1987). The psychology of everyday things. New York: Basic Books.

A STATE-SPACE MODEL FOR PROTOTYPE LEARNING

In Jae Myung and Jerome R. Busemeyer

Department of Psychological Sciences
Purdue University

ABSTRACT

A general state-space model of prototype learning was formulated in terms of a set of internal states and nonlinear input-output mappings. The general model includes several previous models as special cases such as Hintzman's (1986) multiple trace model, Metcalf's (1982) holographic model, and two parallel distributive memory models (Knapp & Anderson, 1984; McClelland & Rumelhart, 1985). Two basic properties common to the three models were defined in terms of this general model--additivity and time invariance. An experiment was conducted to test the basic properties using random spectral patterns as stimuli allowing possible nonlinear input and output distortions. Especially, ordinal tests of additivity were performed with few assumptions about internal features that subjects may use to encode the stimulus information. The results support additivity but time-invariance was clearly violated. Implications of these findings for models of the human memory system are discussed.

INTRODUCTION

One of the most intriguing questions about the structure and organization of human memory is how new experience interacts with old memory to compose an abstraction. For example, when we meet a new person, we form a first impression, and later, this impression is changed and modified with subsequent meetings with the same person. Somehow, later impressions interact with previous experience in memory to establish the current revised impression. What underlying learning processes enable humans to do such an abstraction? Recently, we have witnessed a surge of adaptive neuro-network models of this dynamic learning process. Interestingly, many of the models have a common core of fundamental assumptions. It would be worthwhile to empirically test the validity of these assumptions before we move on to further development of the models.

The purpose of this study was to empirically test these common assumptions. Specifically, the present experiment was designed to test two basic properties of memory structure assumed by several memory models--additivity and time invariance of memory system. The memory models were Hintzman's multiple trace model (1986), Metcalfe's holographic memory model (1982), and parallel distributed memory models (Knapp & Anderson, 1984; McClelland & Rumelhart, 1985). In order to test the basic properties, we chose to study prototype learning using a new experimental paradigm called prototype production (Busemeyer & Myung, 1988). In the prototype production task subjects are shown a sequence of exemplars (e.g., a series of pictures or sounds) generated from one or more prototypes with category labels. Then subjects are given a category label and are asked to produce their prototype estimate of the category (e.g., draw a picture or vocalize a sound that best represents the category). Note that in the prototype production task, abstraction is a task requirement and so the major question is "how does abstraction occur?"

The present article is organized as follows. First, A general state-space model of prototype formation will be presented, followed by definitions of the two basic properties. Then we will discuss the three memory models in relation to the general model, and we will show that all three models satisfy the two basic properties. Finally, we present experimental tests of additivity and time-invariance followed by discussion of implications of the experimental findings.

STATE-SPACE MODEL OF PROTOTYPE EVOLUTION

We begin by distinguishing between representations of images formed by the subject and by the experimenter. On each trial, denoted t, an exemplar image is presented visually (e.g., a photograph) or auditorily (e.g., a tone sequence). We assume that the experimenter records the exemplar image by obtaining a set of physical measurements. This record is represented by a vector denoted $E(t)$. Another vector, denoted $f(t)$, is used to represent the subject's perceptual image of the corresponding physically defined exemplar image $E(t)$. The values of elements of $f(t)$ represent feature strengths. In prototype learning, an exemplar ensemble consists of two components, an image $f(t)$ and category label denoted $g(t)$ as a vector (e.g., the title of a picture). Then the exemplar ensemble can be represented by a vector $h(t)=g(t)|f(t)$ where the symbol | indicates concatenation of two vectors. Any memory task involves some type of retrieval cue which is used to probe memory and retrieve an image. The retrieval cue is denoted by a finite vector $v(t)$ and the output image retrieved by the cue is represented by the finite vector $Y(t)$. Finally, the output mapping of the internal image $Y(t)$ into an observable response $R(t)$ in the experimenter's coordinates is symbolized by a monotonically increasing function J. The diagram below illustrates the relationship among the inputs and outputs. The square box represents the unobservable memory system which is described next. The two functions, V and J, represent nonlinear input and output response functions, respectively.

$$E(t) \xrightarrow{V} \boxed{f(t) \longrightarrow Y(t+1)} \xrightarrow{J} R(t+1)$$

The general memory model that describes the dynamics of the memory system (the square box in above diagram) can be elegantly expressed by the discrete time state space representation of system theory (Csaki, 1977). The model is based on a system of three equations:

$$z(t)=\Theta[h(t)] \qquad (1)$$

$$X(t+1)=\Psi[t,X(t),z(t)] \qquad (2)$$

$$Y(t+1)=U[X(t+1),v(t+1)] \qquad (3)$$

In the first equation, Θ specifies how category label features, $g(t)$, and exemplar image features, $f(t)$, are associated to produce a memory trace, $z(t)$. In other words, the two types of information in $h(t)$ are somehow combined or associated to form a single memory trace, which is subsequently fed into the memory system to preserve an experience. In general, the memory trace, $z(t)$, is some matrix function Θ of $h(t)$. We may interpret the matrix function Θ as the memory encoding process. Later, we will show how the precise form of Θ varies depending on each specific memory model. In the second equation, Ψ is a matrix function that specifies how the memory system is organized and updated. In this sense, Ψ may be interpreted as the learning process used to preserve an experience. Each input $z(t)$ contributes to update the present state of knowledge, represented by the real valued state matrix $X(t)$. In the state space representation, the state matrix $X(t)$ retains all the relevant information obtained from a sequence of exemplars presented up to trial t-1. Thus $X(t)$ is interpreted as the memory of the system.

When subjects are asked to respond to the experimenter's instruction after observing a sequence of exemplar patterns, somehow they have to transform the internal state $X(t)$ into a proper image for output. This process to build the retrieved image $Y(t)$ from the preserved knowledge $X(t)$ upon a given retrieval cue $v(t)$ is characterized by a function, U. The function U can be interpreted as the memory retrieval process.

DEFINITIONS OF THE TWO BASIC PROPERTIES

The two basic properties can be defined in terms of functional characteristics of the updating function Ψ and the retrieval function U.

Additivity

Additive systems are defined by Equation 5 below, which states that the retrieved image can be expressed as a weighted sum of the effects of each of the input memory traces. Equation 5 can be derived from two separate assumptions regarding the functions Ψ and U. The first assumption is that Ψ is a linear dynamic system:

$$X(t+1) = \Psi[t,X(t),z(t)] = \Phi(t)X(t) + H(t)z(t) \quad (4)$$

where $\Phi(t)$ and $H(t)$ are, in general, time dependent matrix functions, which can be interpreted as the system matrix and the weight matrix for new information, respectively.

The second assumption is that the retrieval function U is a linear transformation with respect to the first argument. Then we can derive the retrieved image,

$$Y(t)=U[\Phi(t-1)\cdot\cdot\Phi(0)X(0),v(t)] + \Sigma\ U[Q(t,k)H(k)z(k),v(t)]. \quad (5)$$

Thus, assuming that both Ψ and U are linear, one can express the retrieved image, $Y(t)$, as a weighted sum of the effects of the memory traces $z(k)$ for trials $k = 1, \ldots, t-1$ as in Equation 5.

Time-invariance

Time-invariant systems are systems with updating functions, Ψ, that are not an explicit function of time coordinate, t:

$$X(t+1) = \Psi[X(t),z(t)] \quad (6)$$

where Ψ can be any linear or nonlinear function. If the system defined by Equation 6 is in the same state at two different points in time, and the same input is applied at these two time points, then the same output will be generated at these two time points. In other words, the system does not change solely as a function of time.

MEMORY MODELS

In this section the three memory models will be briefly described and interpreted in terms of the general state-space model. More rigorous derivations will be given elsewhere (Myung & Busemeyer, manuscript under preparation).

Multiple Trace Model

Hintzman's (1986) schema abstraction model assumes that each exemplar presentation produces a separate memory trace, a retrieval cue contacts all traces simultaneously, activating each according to its similarity to the cue, and information retrieved from memory reflects the summed content of all

Table 1: Characteristic functions in equations (1), (3), & (4) assumed by each memory model. The last column only applies to the blocked prototype production task.

Memory Model	$\theta[h(t)]$	$\Phi(t)$	$H(t)$	$U(X,v)$	$w(t-k)$
Multiple Trace	$1(t)h(t)'$	α	γ	$X'(Xv)^3$	$[\gamma\alpha^{t-k}(g'g)]^3$
Holographic Memory	$g(t)*f(t)$	α	γ	$v\#X$	$\gamma\alpha^{t-k}$
Hebb Rule	$g(t)f(t)'$	α	γ	$X'v$	$\gamma\alpha^{t-k}(g'g)$
Delta Rule	$g(t)f(t)'$	$I-\gamma g(t)g(t)'$	γ	$X'v$	$\gamma g'\Phi^{t-k}g$

activated traces responding in parallel.

This model can be represented by the general state-space model as follows. The state matrix $X(t)$ would be a Nxp matrix with a very large N. The θ function is given by $\theta(h(t))=1(t)h(t)'$ where $1(t)$ is a Nx1 row vector with zeros on all locations except row t and an apostrophe represents the transpose of a vector and matrix. The state matrix $X(t)$ is updated according to the following time-invariant linear system ($X(0) = 0$):

$$X(t+1)=\alpha X(t) + \gamma z(t) \tag{7}$$

where $\Phi(t)=\alpha > 0$ and $H(t)=\gamma > 0$ are scalars. Note that $X(t)$ has nonzero elements only up to row t-1 and all zeros afterwards. Therefore, as shown in above equation, each exemplar $h(t)$ is being separately preserved in the state matrix as a distinct row vector. The retrieved image $Y(t)$ can be computed from the state matrix $X(t)$ and the retrieval cue $v(t)$ by the following function:

$$Y(t)=U[X(t),v(t)]=X(t)'[x(t)v(t)]^3 \tag{8}$$

where A^n symbolizes the element-by-element power, $(A^n)_{ij}=(A_{ij})^n$. In general, the retrieval function in above equation is nonlinear for arbitrary Nxp matrices X. But U does satisfy linearity for the special form of $X(t)$ defined in this model.

<u>Holographic Memory Model</u>

Metcalfe's (1982) holographic memory model (CHARM) is an associative memory model based on convolution and correlation algebra. The holographic memory model represents the interactive association between the category label and exemplar features, denoted $g(t)$ and $f(t)$, in the memory encoding step as the convolution of the two vectors, $z(t)=\theta(g(t),f(t))=g(t)*f(t)$.

The resulting memory trace $z(t)$ is used to update the state vector, $X(t)$, according to the same linear time-invariant system as Equation 7.

The retrieved image $Y(t)$ is a correlation of the state matrix $X(t)$ with the cue $v(t)$,

$$Y(t)=U[X(t),v(t)]=v(t)\#X(t) \tag{9}$$

Note that the correlation operation '#' is a linear retrieval U function.

<u>Parallel Distributed Memory Models</u>

Parallel distributed memory models (Knapp & Anderson, 1984; McClelland

& Rumelhart, 1985), assume that each trial involves three events--first an input is presented to the memory system, this input generates an output, and finally this output is compared to a target as a desired output for that trial. Learning is viewed as a gradual change of connectivity strength among basic memory units.

In this model, the associative memory trace on trial t between the i-th input feature $g_i(t)$ and the j-th target feature $f_j(t)$ is the product of the two feature elements, $z_{ij}(t) = g_i(t)f_j(t)$. The collection of $z_{ij}(t)$'s forms a matrix $z(t) = \theta(g(t), f(t)) = g(t)f(t)'$. Then the memory trace $z(t)$ is used to update the state matrix, $X(t)$, called the connection matrix, which represents the present state of connection strengths between the i-th input feature and the j-th output feature. The connection matrix $X(t)$ as a state matrix is assumed to be updated according to either a Hebb rule or a delta rule and the image retrieved by a cue $v(t)$ is a matrix product of $X(t)$ and $v(t)$.

Table 1 summarizes the relations between each of the memory models and the general state-space model. As can be seen in the Table, all of the memory models does satisfy additivity and all but one (the delta rule) satisfy time-invariance. However, for the experimental procedure used in the present study the delta rule also obeys time-invariance (see next section).

APPLICATION OF THE THREE MODELS TO THE PROTOTYPE PRODUCTION TASK

The experiment reported below used a blocked procedure in conjunction with the prototype production task. In the blocked procedure, subjects learn a sequence of exemplar images associated with a single category label within a block of trials, and after completing the block, they move to another block of trials with an unrelated category label. In this situation, the models are greatly simplified. Within each block of trials, the category label features $g(t)$ of the exemplar ensemble $h(t)$ are fixed, $h(t) = g(t)|f(t) = g|f(t)$. Furthermore, the retrieval cue is also fixed to the same category label within a block. Finally, the category labels across blocks are completely unrelated (i.e., orthogonal vectors). For this condition, it can be shown that all three models are consistent with the following special case of (assuming $X(0) = 0$ and $f(0) = 0$) :

$$Y_j(t+1) = \Sigma\, w(t-k)f_j(k), \quad \text{for } k = 1, \ldots, t, \tag{10}$$

where the weight $w(t-k)$ is a scalar function of the lag $(t-k)$ and is shown in Table 1 for each memory model.

As shown in Equation 10, the general definitions of two basic properties given in the earlier section can be reinterpreted in the present task in terms of the relationships between the input and retrieved feature vectors, $f(t)$ and $Y(t)$. This equation states that the exemplar image features from different trials are combined according to an additive composition rule to produce the prototype image. Time-invariance follows from the assumption that the weight $w(t-k)$ depends upon only on the lag or recency $(t-k)$ of the exemplar image.

METHOD

The experiment was conducted on a microcomputer with all the procedures preprogrammed. The stimuli were mass spectra of fictitious chemical samples as shown in Figure 1, where chemical names correspond to category labels $g(t)$ and mass spectra correspond to exemplar patterns $f(t)$. For a given category label, subjects received four different exemplar patterns of the category and

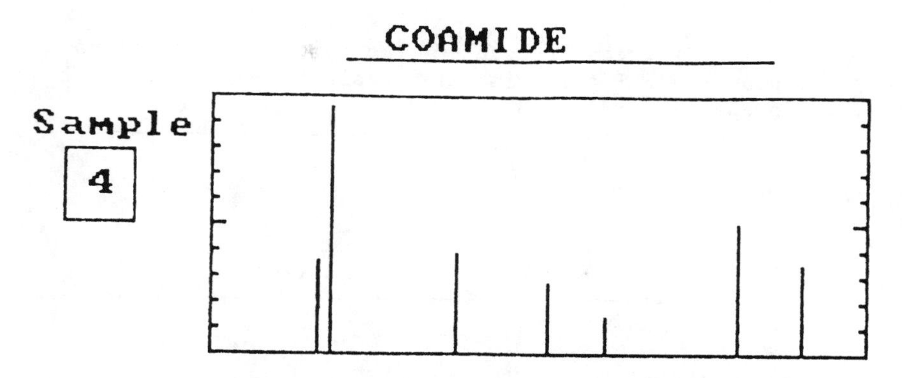

Figure 1. A typical stimulus pattern shown on a video screen.

they were asked to estimate the true pattern for each category based on the four distorted patterns. On each trial, subjects were shown stimulus patterns in the upper half of a video screen, then the pattern was erased and the subjects were asked to draw their estimate of a prototypic spectrum in the lower half of the same screen. After finishing the fourth pattern of a category, they moved to another four trials of a different category. There were two different groups of subjects. One group (Group A) was instructed to provide their estimate after each trial and the other group (Group B) was asked to provide a drawing only at the end of the fourth trial. Each subject received 100 categories (400 exemplar patterns). The subjects were 16 students attending Purdue University. Eight subjects were randomly assigned to each group.

RESULTS

The following results were based on the observed responses averaged across category labels and eight subjects in each group.

Test of Additivity

Additivity (Equation 5) was assessed by testing joint independence properties among patterns. Roberts (1973, p. 210) has described sufficient conditions for an additive system. However, joint-independence is the only property that is empirically testable in the present experiment. Thus, the following joint-independence condition was tested to support or refute additivity.

$$R_{pqrs} > R_{mnrs} \iff R_{pqol} > R_{mnol} \quad (11)$$

where R_{pqrs} represents the prototype estimate after observing a sequence of exemplar patterns, (P_p, P_q, P_r, P_s). Both the prototype estimate and exemplar pattern are recored as 7x1 column vectors where the j-th element is the height of the j-th vertical bar. This relationship should hold for all seven elements of the prototype estimate vector as well as for all trials of prototype production. Note that the test is relatively free of assumptions about how an exemplar pattern is transformed into the subject's internal memory representation. Therefore, additivity across exemplars was tested without mentioning anything about the internal state representation (i.e., the state vector, X(t)) that the memory system actually uses to encode the exemplar information. In this sense, the test of additivity can be considered

Table 2: Test of additivity by counting the number of violations of independence property. Figures in parenthesis indicate the total number of possible independent relations.

Trial (t)	Group A	Group B
2	0 (8)	-
3	0 (72)	-
4	0 (448)	1 (448)

a feature-free test.

All possible joint-independence relations were tested to assess additivity. The result is shown in Table 2, which summarizes the number of significant violations of the joint independence using the confidence interval of α=.05 level. As can be seen in Table 2, no significant violations for Group A and only a single violation for Group B were observed. Considering the fact that the total number of independence relations was 528 for Group A and 448 for Group B, it can be concluded that additivity holds quite well for both conditions. The percentage of violations was still reasonably small even when zero confidence interval was used (5.3% for Group A and 10.7% for Group B).

<u>Test of Time-invariance</u>

Time-invariance was tested by fitting the following model:

$$R(t+1)=J[\Sigma\ w(t,k)f(k)] \quad \text{for } k=1,\ \ldots,\ t. \tag{12}$$

If time-invariance holds, then we should have w(t,k)=w(t-k) for all t and k. Thus, the magnitude of the effect of each exemplar depends only on the lag, (t-k). Both the output response function J and the weights were estimated using a powerful estimation technique called the B-spline method (see DeBoor, 1978). The estimated response function J turned out to be a slightly nonlinear S shaped (not reported in this article). Table 3 contains the estimated weights for different t and k values.

Time-invariance implies that the weight w(t,k) should be solely a function of the lag (t-k), not depending upon the number of exemplars that subjects have seen, that is, trial t. As can be seen in Table 3, time-

Table 3: Test of time-invariance by estimating the weights w(t,k). Figures in parenthesis are predictions from the Hebb rule with time-variable parameters, $\alpha(t)=1-1/t^a$ & $\gamma(t)=1/t^a$ in Equation 7, where the least squares estimate of the exponent was a=.953.

Group Condition	Trial (t)	Lag (t-k) 0	1	2	3
A	2	.49 (.52)	.48 (.48)	-	-
A	3	.41 (.35)	.30 (.34)	.29 (.31)	-
A	4	.28 (.27)	.24 (.26)	.22 (.25)	.26 (.23)
B	4	.26 (.27)	.23 (.26)	.23 (.25)	.26 (.23)

invariance is clearly violated (for example, see the second column at the lag (t-k)=1). In general, as trial t increases, the estimated weights decrease with both primacy and recency effects. The observed data was fit with a time-variable Hebb rule in which the learning rate $\gamma(t)$ can vary according to a power function, i.e., $1/t^a$. Note that a=1 gives the simple arithmetic averaging model. As illustrated in Table 3, the best-fit model was the one with the exponent a=.953. This model accounts for most of qualitative observations except the primacy effect. Allowing $\gamma(t)$ to be an arbitrary function of t can produce both recency and primary effects though it would be less parsimonious.

CONCLUSIONS

The goal of this study was to explore how abstraction occurs in human memory system. Specifically the present experiment was designed to empirically test two basic properties of prototype evolution using the prototype production paradigm-- additivity across exemplars and time-invariance of the memory system. The results indicate that additivity held reasonably well but time-invariance was clearly violated. The additivity result is somewhat surprising because it provides evidence for a linear dynamic memory system. It indicates that we don't have to resort to complex nonlinear dynamic models of memory for understanding prototype abstraction. The violation of time-invariance suggests that adaptive network models need to include a time-varying learning rate parameter of the form $1/t^a$ to simulate the abstraction process.

ACKNOWLEDGEMENTS

This work was supported by NSF Grant BNS # 8710103.

REFERENCES

Busemeyer, J. R., & Myung, I. J. (1988). A new method for investigating prototype learning. Journal of Experimental Psychology: Learning, Memory and Cognition, 14, 3-11.

Csaki, F. (1977). State-space Methods for Control System. Akademiai Kiado, Budapest.

DeBoor, C. (1978). A Practical Guide to Splines. New York: Springer-Verlag.

Hintzman, D. L. (1986). "Schema abstraction" in a multiple-trace model. Psychological Review, 93, 411-428.

Knapp, A. G., & Anderson, J. A. (1984). Theory of categorization based on distributed memory storage. Journal of Experimental Psychology: General, 10, 616-637.

McClelland, J. L., & Rumelhart, D. E. (1985). Distributed memory and the representation of general and specific information. Journal of Experimental Psychology: General, 114, 159-188.

Metcalfe, J. (1982). A composite holographic associative recall model. Psychological Review, 89, 627-661.

Myung, I. J., & Busemeyer, J. R. (1989). A general theory of prototype learning and experimental test of ordinal properties. (manuscript under preparation)

Roberts, F. S. (1979). Measurement theory. Readings, M.A.: Addison-Wesley.

Learning Simple Arithmetic Procedures

Garrison W. Cottrell and Fu-Sheng Tsung
Department of Computer Science and Engineering
Institute for Cognitive Science
University of California, San Diego.

Abstract

Two types of simple recurrent networks (Jordan, 1986; Elman, 1988) were trained and compared on the task of adding two multi-digit numbers. Results showed that: (1) A manipulation of the training environment, called *Combined Subset Training* (CST), was found to be necessary to learn the large set of patterns used; (2) if the networks are viewed as learning simple programming constructs such as conditional branches, while-loops and sequences, then there is a clear way to demonstrate a capacity difference between the two types of networks studied. In particular, we found that there are programs that one type of network can perform that the other cannot. Finally, an analysis of the dynamics of one of the networks is described.

Introduction

One major criticism of artificial neural networks is that there is no obvious method for doing sequential, symbolic processing. Rumelhart, Smolensky, McClelland & Hinton (1986) proposed that symbolic processing may be achieved by **(1)** creating physical representations of the problem, **(2)** processing the representations via pattern association, and **(3)** recording the result of the processing in the physical representation. The example they use is the problem of adding two three digit numbers. First the two numbers are written down in a standard format as on the left:

```
                1
327            327
865            865
-----          -----
                2
```

This is now a pattern recognition problem, with the result being recorded by an action, i.e., writing down the sum of the rightmost column as on the right above. This presents a new pattern, which triggers the writing of a carry and the process repeats. Similarly, they claim that a complex logical problem is solved by breaking it down into simpler problems and applying the above procedure repeatedly. We were interested in just what was involved in implementing the above description, especially when a memory load is added by not explicitly recording the carry.

In order to have a PDP network do sequences of actions, it has to have some way of knowing "where" it is in the sequence. One way of accomplishing this is by explicitly having discrete states in the unit functions which change over time (Feldman & Ballard, 1982). An alternative is to have *recurrence* in the network, so that the state of the network is reflected in the activation levels of the units. We adopt the latter approach, following the work of Jordan (1986) and Elman (1988). Both of these approaches are restricted extensions of the basic feed-forward network used in most back propagation experiments (Rumelhart, Hinton, & Williams, 1986) that nevertheless still allow the use of back propagation learning.

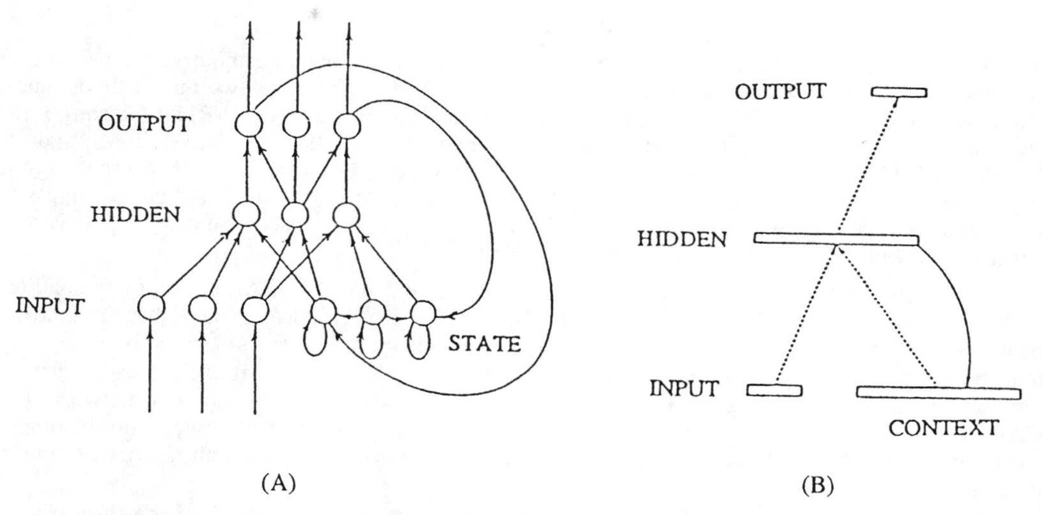

Figure 1. (a) Jordan's recurrent network. The outputs are linearly summed over time in the *state* vector, lower right. (b) Elman's network. The context vector (lower right) is a copy of the hidden units from the previous time step.

In Jordan's approach (see Figure 1(a)), the output vector of the network is linearly averaged into a *state* vector (the same length as the output), which is given to the network as part of the input. We will call these networks "state" networks. The state vector at time t becomes some proportion (*mu*) of its value at time t-1, plus the output vector at time t-1. Thus the network has an exponentially decaying representation of its output history. The other input is called the *plan vector*, that is, an arbitrary representation of the sequence to be produced. This remains constant throughout the processing. State networks can be trained to produce nearly arbitrary sequences.

In Elman's approach (see Figure 1(b)), the hidden unit activations at time t-1 are copied into a *context* vector, which is given as input to the network at time t. This is equivalent to having the hidden units be completely recurrently connected, and back propagating one step in time along the recurrent links. We will call these networks "context" networks. Context networks are typically used to predict their next input, which causes them to represent structural regularities in their environment.

Thus these architectures have typically been applied to very different tasks: The state networks have been used to learn to produce sequences, using a fixed-input plan; the context networks have been used to recognize structural regularities in their input. Hence no comparison of their power has been done. In the following, we apply them both to the same problem: Learning a simple arithmetic procedure. This allows comparison of the two network types. We find that there are procedures that one can perform that the other cannot.

We chose multi-column addition as our symbolic processing task because although it is a simple problem, it is nontrivial for parallel distributed processing (PDP) networks because it involves control processes such as sequential processing and looping that are not traditional PDP tasks. Furthermore, it is an interesting paradigm for generalization, since we can only train the network on a finite set of examples, while there are an infinite number of possible cases. Hence the network must learn the implicit, underlying rule of addition.

Architecture of the models

For both the state and context networks, we assume that the external input to the network at any moment consists of the two digits of the current column. The network has two output fields: an **action** and a **result**. The **action** field is a localist encoding of four possible actions: WRITE the sum of the two digits, note that there is a CARRY, shift the input window to the NEXT column of digits, and DONE. The **result** field only has meaning when the action is WRITE, when it holds the low order digit of the sum of the two inputs. During other actions, the result field is not meaningful and no teaching signal is given to it. One interesting aspect is the NEXT action: The network has control of its inputs and signals when it is ready to move on to the next column of digits.

The program the network must learn is given in Figure 2(A). The CARRY action is conditionally performed, depending on the size of the inputs. Otherwise, it is skipped. Notice that the fact of there being a carry is not represented in the input. That is, the network must learn to "remember" the carry, and must respond differently to identical pairs of digits depending on this. If there was a carry on the previous input, the network should add 1 to the sum, otherwise not. For the state network, a recent CARRY is reflected in its state vector, which averages outputs. The context network, on the other hand, has to learn to recognize the form that its internal state takes when it has output a CARRY on a recent time step.

To reduce the number of basic additions to be learned, we used base 4 instead of decimal. There are thus 16 basic associations for additions, plus the other program elements. The carry complicates the situation, since the net has to respond to each pair differently in the presence of a carry. Worse yet, since the state or context vectors record processing history, the network has essentially an infinite set of unique inputs. Since most of this is irrelevant, one thing the network must learn is to *ignore* its distant history.

Simulations

Training Strategy

The goal is to get the network to learn the addition process for an arbitrary number of digits. Immediate questions are: How to pick a training set? What makes a good one? How many examples are enough for the net to generalize? We somewhat arbitrarily decided to train the network on additions with addends of up to three digits. This set contains all the canonical situations, and therefore should be enough. However, there are 4096 additions (including all 1-digit, 2-digit, 3-digit combinations), and when translated to the network output sequences, there are more than 30,000 individual patterns. Learning is

```
while not done do
begin
    output(WRITE, low_order_digit);
    if sum>radix then
        output(CARRY, ???);
    output(NEXT, ???);
end
if carry_on_previous_input then
    output(WRITE, '01');
output(DONE, ???);
```

(A)

```
while not done do
begin
    output(WRITE, low_order_digit);
    output(NEXT, ???);
    if sum(previous_input)>radix then
        output(CARRY, ???);
end
if carry_on_previous_input then
    output(WRITE, '01');
output(DONE, ???);
```

(B)

Figure 2. (A) The "program" the network learns. There are two output fields, and **action** field and a **result** field. For most outputs, the **result** field is not trained ("???" in the figure). (B) Modified program.

very difficult with such a large training set. To keep the net small (16 hidden units), and the training fairly fast, we tried two training environments. One was a random subset consisting of 1% of the 4096 additions. This was learned within 3 to 5 thousand epochs. However, generalization was poor. We found that if we tried a bigger subset, 8% of the additions, the network would hit a local minima (total sum squared error (tss) of 346 after 5000 epochs). Thus we have the following dilemma: If the training set is small enough to be learned in reasonable time, the network generalizes poorly. If the training set is large enough to insure good generalization, it does not learn in the time we are willing to wait. It seemed that another method of training was needed.

We developed a method we call *combined subset training* (CST)[1] to solve these problems. Initially, a manageable, randomly selected subset is used to train the network with a relatively loose error criterion (stopping condition). Then the training set size is doubled by *retaining the current set* and adding an equal number of other training examples, chosen randomly from the entire set. The error criterion is tightened on the new set by a small fixed amount. Once this is learned successfully, the training set is doubled again in the same fashion. This procedure is repeated until the whole set is included, or until the net is able to generalize to the rest of the original training set. Intuitively, this method should work for the following reason: When the net is only seeing a small subset of the the total training set, many partial solutions adequate for that subset may be possible. Over-training on this set will force the net to choose one of these local solutions, which may not generalize to the global solution desired. Stopping at a higher error criterion leaves the options open by preventing the network from diving too deeply into local minima.

For this experiment, we picked 1% (of the 4096 additions) as our initial set. The networks (both types) are trained to a tss of 1.0, and the training set is doubled to 2% of the total. The total sum squared error (tss) jumps up initially at the introduction of the new examples, but not as high as with the starting weights (see Figure 3a). This shows that the network is already generalizing to some extent. The same behavior was observed when we doubled to 4% and 8%, except that each time, the peak of the error jump is less than the peak before it. At 8% of the training set (close to 3000 individual patterns), we found that

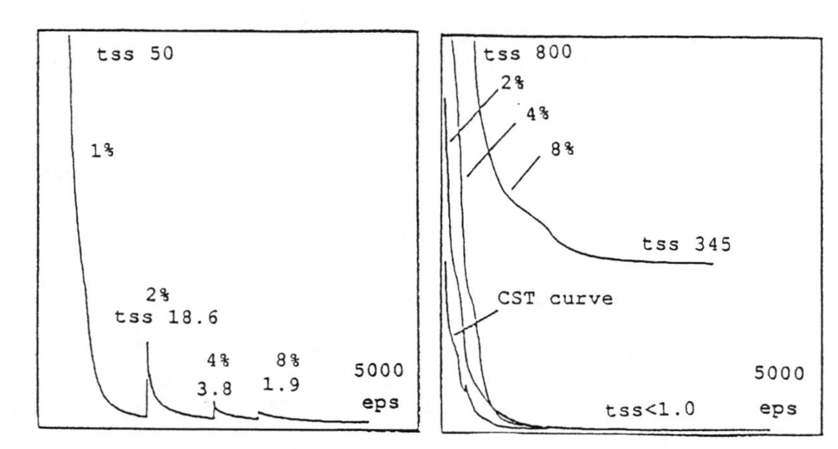

Figure 3. (a) Error curve from combined subset training on the context net. Each jump in tss is where training sets are doubled. Beginning tss: 348.5; final tss: 0.399. (b) Comparison of CST to fixed set training for 2%, 4% and 8% subsets (the y axis is much higher than in (a)).

[1]We report on this method at more length in Tsung & Cottrell (1989).

the net generalizes very well to the rest of the 4096 additions.

In Figure 3(b), we compare the CST procedure outlined above with training on fixed subsets of size 2%, 4% and 8%. Notice that the CST curve falls under all of the others. More to the point, the 8% curve appears to have reached a local minima at tss 346, while the networks trained on fixed subsets of 2% and 4% do not generalize well to the rest of the patterns (data not shown). This illustrates the dilemma stated above: When training on *fixed* subsets, if the training set is small enough for the network to reach criterion, then it doesn't generalize well. With larger training sets, the network does not learn.

We then tested the CST-trained network on longer additions. Even though the network was only trained on additions of up to 3 digits, on tests of 100 longer additions, the miss rate is only 10%. We then trained the net on a part of the test set of longer additions. In general, we found that (see Tsung & Cottrell 1989):

(A) Training on a small part of the test set corrects performance on the rest. This suggests that there only one, or few, classes of errors the net is prone to make.

(B) The network learned to correct the mistakes quickly (within tens of epochs of further training). Furthermore, the extra training does not upset the performance on the 3-digit additions.

(C) Further generalization tests showed very little error, with a miss rate of less than 1%.

From the patterns of error behavior and the observations listed above, it is clear that the network has learned the task, needing only small refinements.

Differences between state and context nets

Both state and context networks behaved similarly on this task. We may ask the question: Is there some task that one can do, and not the other? The answer is yes, and a simple example is found by interchanging two lines in the program the network must learn. Instead of the original sequence of "write result-carry-next", the net is trained to output "write result-next-carry", as in Figure 2 (B). A state network should not be able to solve this problem. This is because the state network has access to only the current input and the *output* history; it keeps no record of previous inputs or the *internal* states of the system. Thus, *a state network cannot "remember" things about its input that are not reflected in its output*. Following the program in Figure 2 (B), after writing the result, the NEXT action shifts the input to the next column of digits. Now, after losing access to the previous input, the state network has to determine whether the previous sum was greater than the radix. The only history the network has reflects only the low order digit of the previous sum. Thus it cannot possibly determine whether the next step should be CARRY or not. The context network, on the other hand, has a transformed version of the input at the hidden layer which is recycled at each time step, thus it should be able to "remember" input that is not reflected in its output.

Simulation results bear this out. The state network does not learn this task, as shown in Figure 4. It achieved a low tss for each subset, but the error curve is not smooth and it does not generalize to the doubled subset. That is, it is memorizing the sequences rather than learning the task. Results with the context network show that this is a harder problem than the original problem, but it did learn it. The context network takes about twice as long to learn this procedure (~10,000 epochs) compared to the previous version.

Initial analysis of the internal representation

To look at the *dynamics* of the network as it moves through the problem, we found the principal components of the 16 hidden unit activations over time, as the context network (using the program in Figure 2 (A)) processed 10 additions from one of the generalization test sets. This analysis gives the directions of highest variance of the hidden unit activations over time. Basically, we can think of this as finding a new coordinate space for the hidden unit vectors, where the coordinate vectors are ordered in terms of how much "action" occurs along each one.

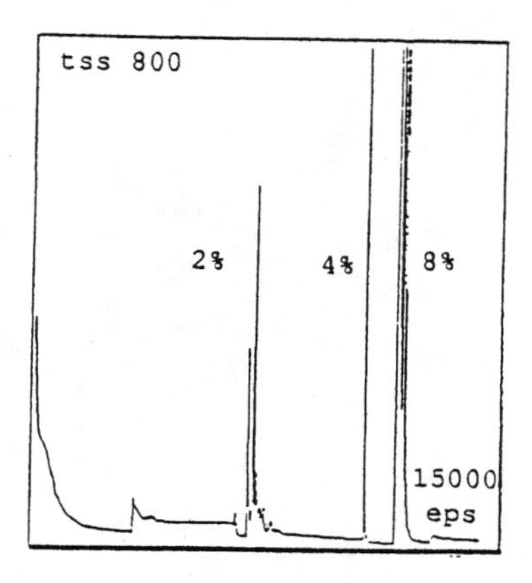

Figure 4. Learning program from Figure 2 (B) with the state network. CST doubling is indicated. The net is learning local solutions, and is unable to generalize.

In Figure 5, we show the projection of the hidden unit vectors onto the plane of the first two principal components as the network is doing a 30 step addition. Each point is labeled by the action that is produced on the output and the step in the entire computation. This shows how the network moves through its internal states as it processes the input. There are several things to notice here. Basically, WRITE result actions (labeled R#) are generally in the right half of the space, NEXTs and CARRYs are

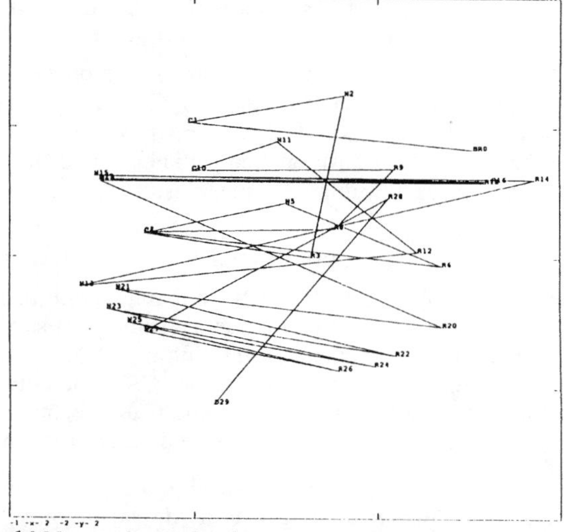

Figure 5. Projections of the hidden units activation vector onto the first two principal components. The number in the point labels corresponds to the step in this addition. R: RESULT, C: CARRY, N: NEXT, D: DONE.

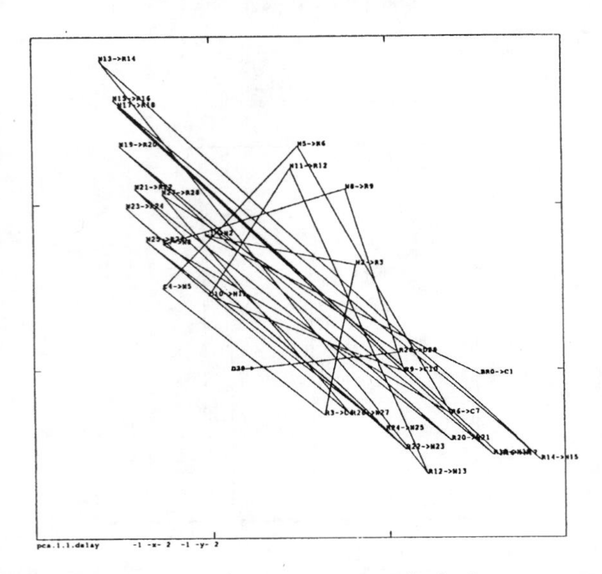

Figure 6. Projection of the hidden unit activation vector onto principal component 1 plotted against itself one time step later.

in the left. Second, in general, the second component is correlated with overall time within this problem. It is interesting that the network represents absolute time even though it is unnecessary for solving the problem. The most striking result that emerges from this analysis is that on the first principal component (the x axis), the network is distinguishing between a NEXT that follows a CARRY, versus one that follows a WRITE. All of the NEXTs following a CARRY are greater than 0 on this axis, all of those following a WRITE are less than 0. The significance of this is that following a NEXT that follows a CARRY, the network must output a result that is one more than the sum of the two inputs. We can thus see the internal state that represents the memory of a carry in this graph.

A second way of viewing the dynamics of the network is to plot the first principal component at time **t** vs. **t+1**. This gives the map from the context vector to the next hidden unit vector, since the context vector at time **t** is the hidden unit vector at time **t-1**. Figure 6 shows this plot for the same problem as in Figure 5. Here points are labeled by the transition being made. Here the separation of the NEXT's following a CARRY is particularly clear, forming a distinct cluster above the main diagonal of the graph.

Conclusions

In this paper we presented a simple model of symbolic manipulation using a connectionist network that learned a procedure for adding two multi-digit numbers. The model served as a catalyst for several other results. The most important one is a method for training networks to learn large training environments via Combined Subset Training. We found that without CST, the networks we studied could not learn the task. Further investigation is necessary to determine if this technique is suitable for other network architectures (such as standard feed-forward networks) and other problem types.

The second result is a clear demonstration of the capacity differences between the type of networks studied by Jordan and those studied by Elman by giving a simple program that one can learn that the other cannot. The basic notion may be stated as follows: Networks with only output histories cannot remember things about their input that are not reflected in their output. This is perfectly clear now; it was not when we started this research.

The third result is a demonstration that networks of this type can learn simple programming constructs that are not nested. In particular, these nets can do simple sequencing, looping, and branching.

Also, values necessary for future processing can be stored over short periods by the context network. Other recurrent network models are more powerful in this regard (Williams & Zipser, 1988), but require a prohibitively large amount of computer time to train. Since remembering a bit takes a long time to learn, this suggests that memory for "variables" requires initial structures subserving this function that are easily refined by learning. We thus have simple versions of all of the mechanisms for a universal computer--except the ability to nest these constructs. We conjecture that nesting will not be able to be carried very deeply (cf. Servan-Schreiber, Cleeremans, & McClelland, 1988).

Fourth, even though the network was not designed to be a psychological model of human learning, it may provide some insight into methods for optimizing human learning in terms of structuring the problem sets of addition facts. Also, this model is fertile ground for exploring other aspects of human procedural learning and symbolic processing.

Finally we have begun an analysis of the network by looking at its state space graph. This type of analysis is necessary when we are using recurrent networks to observe the dynamics of the system. We expect that the use of this kind of analysis will become more commonplace as more researchers study recurrent networks.

REFERENCES

Elman, J. (1988) Finding structure in time. Technical Report 8801, Center for Research in Language, University of California, San Diego, La Jolla, California.

Feldman, J.A. and Ballard, D. (1982) Connectionist Models and their properties. *Cognitive Science, 6*, 205-254.

Jordan, M. (1986) Serial order: A parallel distributed processing approach. Technical Report 8604, Institute for Cognitive Science, University of California, San Diego, La Jolla, California.

Rumelhart, D. E., Hinton, G. E., and Williams, R. J. (1986). Learning internal representations by error propagation. In D. E. Rumelhart, J. L. McClelland, & the PDP Research Group, *Parallel distributed processing: Explorations in the microstructure of cognition. Vol. 1. Foundations.* Cambridge: MIT Press/Bradford. Books.

Rumelhart, D.E., Smolensky, P., McClelland, J.L. and Hinton, G.E. (1986) Schemata and sequential thought processes in PDP models. In McClelland, J.L., Rumelhart, D.E. and the PDP Research Group, *Parallel Distributed Processing: Explorations in the Microstructure of Cognition. Vol. 2: Psychological and Biological Models.* Cambridge: MIT Press/Bradford.

Servan-Schreiber, D., Cleeremans, A., McClelland, J.L. (1988) Encoding sequential structure in simple recurrent networks. CMU-CS-88-183, November 1988. Available from the Department of Computer Science, Carnegie Mellon University, Pittsburgh, PA.

Williams, R. and Zipser, D. (1988) A learning algorithm for continually running fully recurrent neural networks. Technical Report ICS-8805. Institute of Cognitive Science, University of California, San Diego, La Jolla, California.

THIYOS: A Classifier System Model of Implicit Knowledge of Artificial Grammars

Barry B. Druhan and Robert C. Mathews

Louisiana State University

Department of Psychology

ABSTRACT

This study develops a computational model based on the Holland et al.'s (1986) induction theory to simulate the tacit knowledge of artificial grammars acquired from experience with exemplars of the grammar (e.g., Reber, 1969, 1976). The initial application of this model tests the proposition that the rules acquired about an artificial grammar consist of sets of partially valid rules that compete against one another to control response selection. Choices are made and the strength of rules is adjusted based on current levels of strength, specificity, and support among rules having their conditions matched on a particular trial. Verbal instructions generated by two human subjects who developed expertise in discriminating valid from invalid strings through extensive practice on a multiple choice string discrimination task served as inputs into the simulation model. Results show that these sets of rules verbalized by subjects can be represented as sets of condition-action rules. Further, these rules can compete against each other to select valid choices on the string discrimination task as described in the Holland et al. model, resulting in a level of performance very similar to that of human yoked subjects who attempted to use the rules provided by the original subjects. Finally, when the rules are automatically tuned by an optimization algorithm using feedback about correctness of choices, performance of the simulation approaches the level of the original subject. It is concluded that a considerable portion of implicit knowledge that is not verbalized to yoked partners consists of the relative strengths of competing rules.

INTRODUCTION

Learning of artificial grammars has attracted attention in cognitive psychology for two main reasons: First, knowledge about a grammar is acquired as well or better by passive observation of exemplars as compared to deliberate attempts to derive the rules of the grammar (e.g., Reber, 1976; Reber & Allen, 1978). Second, subjects who have acquired knowledge of the grammar implicitly through observing exemplars have a difficult time verbalizing what they have learned (see Reber, in press for a review of this research). Thus researchers have been interested in determining whether this form of learning reflects a unique, subconscious learning mechanism capable of abstracting regularities among exemplars without conscious rule generation.

Recently Mathews, Buss, Stanley, Blanchard-Fields, Cho, and Druhan (in press) performed an extensive series of experiments examining learning of artificial grammars through practice discriminating exemplars from nonexemplars of the grammar. The finite state grammar used in these experiments is illustrated in Figure 1. Each valid string represents one complete path through the grammar, following any allowed set of transitions (arrows) and generating each letter corresponding to the label on each transition chosen. The grammar generates a total of 177 unique valid strings. The Mathews et al. (in press) experiments used a novel teach aloud procedure in which subjects, while learning about the grammar through practice on a multiple choice string discrimination task, periodically attempted to verbalize instructions for another person (yoked subject) to perform the same string discrimination task. On each trial of the string discrimination task original subjects selected one of five alternatives which they

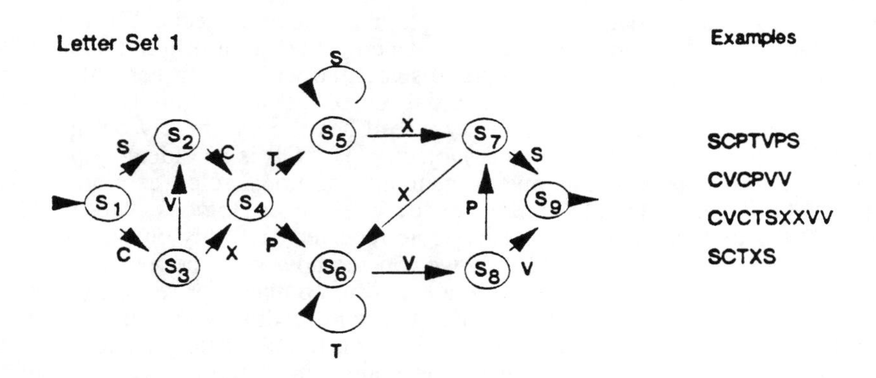

Figure 1.

thought was a valid string. Of the five strings presented, four of them contained "violations" (incorrect letters), and one was correct. They were then given feedback about which was the correct string. These subjects practiced this task 200 trials a week for three weeks. They recorded instructions for their yoked partner after each sequence of ten multiple choice trials. The yoked subjects attempted to perform the same string discrimination task without feedback, using only the current instructions provided by their partner for that trial block.

Several findings from the Mathews et al. experiments are consistent with competitive rule induction models. The instructions verbalized during training resembled sets of condition-action rules such as "select strings that begin with SCT" or "select strings that end in VV". Moreover, the set of rules acquired by different subjects appeared to be different (see Dulany, Carlson, & Dewey, 1984, 1985); and there was no tendency to converge on a common set of rules even after experience with hundreds of exemplars generated by the grammar over an extended period of practice with the task. Thus, as predicted by the Holland et al., (1986) model, learning appeared to involve finding a set of cues to distinguish valid from invalid strings and, once a sufficient set of cues was acquired, learning did not continue (i.e., no additional cues were acquired). In Holland et al. terms learning is completely failure driven. These initially positive results concerning the application of the Holland et al., (1986) framework to implicit learning of artificial grammars encouraged us to develop a formal model to further test the adequacy of this framework for explaining this type of learning.

This paper reports our initial results using a computational model which simulates behavior of our yoked subjects. This model is an implementation of a classifier system in which sets of condition-action rules characterizing original subjects' verbalized instructions compete against each other to control response selection in the string discrimination task. That is, just like our human yoked subjects, THIYOS (for THe Ideal YOked Subject) receives a set of instructions from an original subject for each block of ten trials and then it attempts to select the valid string generated by the grammar from among five choices. In the initial run of the simulation THIYOS gets no feedback about correctness of its choices, so it has to rely entirely on the set of instructions provided by the original subject. THIYOS is an "ideal" yoked subject in the sense that it makes no attempts to generate additional rules, as a human yoked subject might do even in the absence of feedback (Fried & Holyoak, 1984). Also, by giving THIYOS perfect memory for every rule received, not only on the current trial block but on all previous trial blocks, we can see how good performance would be if all of the original subjects' rules were allowed to compete for response selection. Finally, by using additional runs of THIYOS with feedback, we can determine whether an optimization scheme similar to the bucket brigade algorithm is capable of improving THIYOS's performance by tuning the relative strength of the competing rules. One hypothesis tested in this simulation is that part of what original subjects do not verbalize in their instructions for their yoked partners is the relative strengths of competing rules which lead to optimal performance. If we assume that the original subjects' rules have been tuned for optimal application, but the yoked subjects' have not; then THIYOS's performance might improve considerably when sufficient feedback has occurred to optimally tune the strengths of competing rules.

THE MODEL

Classifier systems are a type of production system model with some specific processing assumptions. First, the condition action pairs are composed of strings of equal length, where the elements of the string are restricted to the set {1, 0, #}. This condition action pair is called simply a "classifier". Each element can be thought of as representing a unique feature of the object, or event being described by the classifier. Within this representation, a "1" represents the presence of a feature, a "0" represents its absence, and a "#" is a type of wildcard that will match either case. Complex objects or events can be coded by adding conditions to the condition side of the classifier-- each classifier has only one action. Classifiers operate on "messages" that are similar in format to the condition and action sides of the classifier. Messages reside on a "message list" that represents the current state of the world for the model. The system operates by cycling through the following steps: Process the input interface by putting incoming messages on the message list; compare the condition sides of each classifier to each message on the message list and record all matches; calculate a bid for each classifier that matched and select a set of "highest bidders" to post their messages on a new message list-- the size of the set selected reflects the models' assumptions about working memory limitations; process the contents of the new message list through an output interface which strips off messages tagged for output; replace the old message list with the new one; return to step one. Simple classifier systems such as these can be combined by coupling input and output interfaces to form more complex systems. The performance of the system is regulated by the bidding system, in which a bid is equal to a constant multiplied by the sum of the classifier's strength (past effectiveness), specificity (number of non-"#'s"), and support (number of classifiers on the previous time step that supported the current classifier). (see Holland, et al., 1986).

The computational model described here is essentially a classifier system model with certain assumptions that make it amenable to modeling artificial grammars. Subjects' rules are represented as condition-action pairs, in which both the conditions and the actions are fixed length strings of letters, numbers, "#'s", and "_". The exemplars of the grammar to be learned are represented in a similar fashion such that the lengths of the condition string, the action string, and the exemplar string are all equal. In order to determine whether a rule applies, its condition side is matched position by position against the exemplar string. The "#'s" are a sort of wildcard character that will match anything. In addition, the "#'s" act as variables in that they can pass information through from a message to an action. Consider the following example: if the subject says to choose strings that begin with "SCT", then the corresponding classifier rule would be:

"##SCT########0###00|02CHOOSE_____######".

The pipe or "|" symbol separates the condition side from the action side of the classifier. The five alternative strings are placed on the message list in a similar format. For example, the above rule would match an exemplar on the message list such as: "01SCTVPXVV___#10###". Numbers at the beginning of the strings are tags which differentiate strings coming from the input interface from those going to the output interface. In the exemplar string, the "1" and "0" in the 14th and 15th positions indicate that it is choice number 1 for the given trial, and that it has zero violations. Since the corresponding positions in the condition and action side of the classifier contain "#'s", the "1" and "0" are passed through from the exemplar to the action. Since the action of this classifier is tagged for the output interface, it would tell the system to choose letter string number 1. The execution cycle performs one trial per cycle by iterating through the following steps:

1) Read in the five alternative exemplars from the input interface, and place them on the message list.

2) If at the beginning of a trial block, read in the rules given by the original subject for that trial block.

3) Compare the condition sides of all rules to each message on the message list and record all matches.

4) Select the set of *w* matches involving classifiers with the highest strengths and allow these classifiers to post their messages on an interim message list. (The size of the set selected reflects the models' assumptions about working memory limitations.)

5) Calculate a bid for each classifier on the interim list using the parameters of strength, specificity, and support.

6) Resolve conflicts on the interim list on the basis of the bids from step 5, and place any remaining messages on the new message list.

7) Process the contents of the new message list through an output interface which strips off messages tagged for output. If feedback is turned on, then correct choices cause payoff to be rewarded to all rules on the interim message list supporting the same choice made by the highest bidder. All rules on the interim list payout a portion of their strength. If feedback is off, rules

neither payoff nor payout.

8) Replace the old message list with the new one; return to step one.

This process continues until all trials have been completed.

The performance of the system is regulated by the bidding system, in which a bid is equal to a constant multiplied by the sum of the classifier's strength (past effectiveness), specificity (number of non- "#'s"), and support (number of classifiers that agree to pick the same choice).

Hence, the bid is represented by the following formula:

$$B = (b)[(sw)S+(rw)R+(vw)V]$$

where b is a constant between 0 and 1; S, R, and V are strength, specificity, and support respectively; sw, rw, and vw are weights associated with each parameter. In classifier systems, a rule must pay out an amount proportional to its current strength whenever it is selected to fire, and it receives a payoff whenever it is successful. Within the Induction framework by Holland et. al., it is these two parameters that implement the "bucket brigade algorithm". The algorithm gets its name from the fact that it implements a limited spread of activation by passing strength back to rules, which on the previous time step, supported a classifier in its attempt to post its message. In doing so the system implicitly couples sets of rules that tend to work together in so far as they lead to a successful representation of the environment.

In the current model, since the goal was to simulate a yoked subject, we intended for the rules to operate with some autonomy unless explicitly coupled by the original subject who stated the rules. For example, a subject might say "strings that start with SCT are good rules, and strings that end in VV are good rules". Whereas on another occasion the same subject might deliberately couple the rules: "choose strings that begin with SCT and end in VV". The goal was to have THIYOS strictly adhere to the rules of the original subject. For that reason, there is only one type of action (i.e. to choose one of the alternatives) and all of the actions are tagged for the output interface. The result is that no direct chaining of rules takes place. Tuning the rules when feedback is on changes only the relative strengths of the rules. No additional explicit or implicit (coupled) rules are created by THIYOS. Therefore the tuned rules remain literal representations of the rules provided by the original subject.

In order to benefit from the powerful use of support provided by the bucket brigade algorithm, while adhering to a literal representation, the current model attempts to emulate the algorithm by measuring support as the number of classifiers on a given time step that agreed to pick the same choice, and by giving feedback to all classifiers that supported each other in making a correct selection. Further, an optimal performance measure was sought through the implementation of a double bidding process. The parameters of payoff and payout tend to operate in a manner that causes the strength of rules with average cue validity to remain relatively constant, while those with above average cue validity have their strength increased, and those with below average cue validity have their strength decreased. The double bidding process, the algorithm assures that access to the final competition is limited to the strongest set of applicable rules. Thus overly general rules can not repeatedly enter the final competition through support by stronger more specific rules. Steps three through six of the execution cycle described above implement this two-stage process. In the first stage, all matches are recorded and are considered for placement on the message list. In THIYOS, the competition to move on to the next stage is based on strength alone. In the second stage, if there is a conflict between messages that have been presented to represent the environment, then those items compete on the basis of strength, specificity, and support. In this manner the system is assured of adjusting the strength based on past performance by eliminating the possibility that clusters of bad rules will overcome the stronger rules through mutual support. At the same time, weaker rules are not completely locked out of the system by virtue of the fact that not all of the strongest rules will apply at the same time. Also, the double bidding process effectively implements the system's assumptions about the size of working memory (i.e. the number of rules chosen to enter the second stage), and at same time, implements the system's assumptions about the nature of working memory. That is, that rules enter into working memory automatically based on their strength, and once there, can be consciously manipulated based on their strength, specificity, and support.

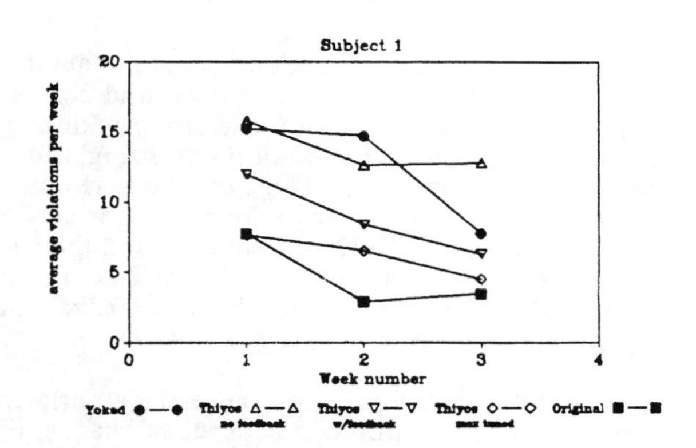

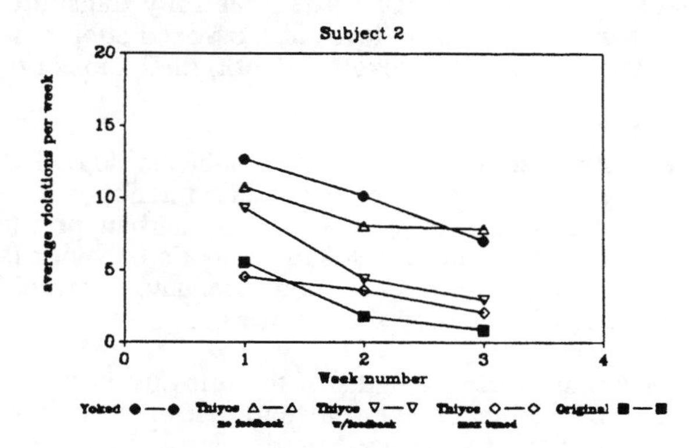

Figure 2.

THE SIMULATION

The data from two human subjects in the Mathews et. al. (in press) letter string task were selected at random for the simulation. Their verbal instructions were translated into classifier rules using the aforementioned representation scheme. The simulation proceeded trial by trial in the same order as the original and yoked subjects, and the rules were presented block by block. There were 600 trials total divided into three weeks of 200 trials per week for each of the original and yoked subjects. In the experiment, verbal instructions were given by the original subjects every 10 trials yielding 60 sets of rules that were read in to THIYOS for each subject. Subjects number one and two stated 104 and 144 unique rules respectively. Rules that were repeated by the subjects were not stored as additional rules, but had their strength increased by a diminishing amount proportional to their current strength (the higher the strength, the less the increase). The set of rules for each subject was run once without feedback, once with feedback, and finally in a "maximum tuning" run in which the system was allowed to continue cycling for three runs through the experiment using the same set of rules until the increase in performance leveled off.

RESULTS AND DISCUSSION

The dependent variable on the string discrimination task is the number of violations in each set of choices in a trial block. Each multiple choice trial consisted of five choices including one valid string (no violations), one string with one violation (one letter which could not occur in a particular position), one string with two violations, one with three, and one with four violations. Thus, chance performance is approximately 20 violations per trial block, and better performance consists of fewer violations. The mean performance of the two original subjects and their human yoked partners is plotted in the upper and lower panels of Figure 2 across the three weeks of practice. Performance of THIYOS without feedback, with feedback, and after three runs with feedback is also plotted on each graph.

The pattern of results is quite clear. Original subjects always perform better than their yoked partners, but both subjects perform much better than chance; implying some but not all of an original subject's knowledge was successfully transmitted to their yoked partner. THIYOS performs at about the level of the yoked subject without feedback, better with feedback, and at nearly the level of the original subject on the third run with feedback.

We conclude from this simulation that the original subjects' knowledge of the grammar can be adequately represented as a set of condition-action rules which compete for control of response selection using strength, specificity and support to determine the winners. We also conclude that a human yoked subject's behavior is reasonably well described as attempts to apply these rules without adequate knowledge of the relative strengths necessary to optimally employ the set of rules.

By allowing feedback to adjust the strengths of the rules using the optimization algorithm, performance of THIYOS came very close to that of the original subject. This result implies that the set of rules verbalized by the original subjects was probably an adequate description of the rules actually used by that subject. However, subjects do not adequately verbalize information about the relative strengths of the competing rules. That is, a large part of the nonverbalized, tacit knowledge acquired about an artificial grammar appears to be the optimal relative strengths of competing rules resulting from the nonconscious rule-tuning implemented by the optimization algorithm.

REFERENCES

Dulany, D. E., Carlson, R. A., & Dewey, G. I. (1984). A case of syntactical learning and judgment: How conscious and how abstract? *Journal of Experimental Psychology: General, 113,* 541-555.

Dulany, D. E., Carlson, R. A., & Dewey, G. I. (1985). On consciousness in syntactical learning and judgment: A reply to Reber, Allen, & Regan. *Journal of Experimental Psychology: General, 114,* 25-32.

Fried, L. S., & Holyoak, K. J. (1984). Induction of category distributions: A framework for classification learning. Journal of Experimental Psychology: Learning, Memory, and Cognition, 10, 234-257.

Holland, J. H., Holyoak, K. J., Nisbett, R. E., & Thagard, P. R. (1986). *Induction: Processes of inference, learning, and discovery.* Cambridge, MA: The MIT Press.

Mathews, R. C., Buss, R. R., Stanley, W. B., Blanchard-Fields, F., Cho, J., and Druhan, B. (in press). The role of implicit and explicit processes in learning from examples: A synergistic effect. *Journal of Experimental Psychology: Learning, Memory, and Cognition.*

Reber, A. S. (1976). Implicit learning of artificial languages: The role of instructional set. *Journal of Experimental Psychology: Human Learning and Memory, 2,* 88-94.

Reber, A. S. (in press). Implicit learning and tacit knowledge. *Journal of Experimental Psychology: General.*

Reber, A. S., & Allen, R. (1978). Analogy and abstraction strategies in synthetic grammar learning: A functionalist interpretation. *Cognition, 6,* 189-221.

ACKNOWLEDGEMENTS

This research was supported in part by National Science Foundation Grant #BNS-8509493 to Robert C. Mathews, Ray R. Buss, and William B. Stanley, and in part by the Louisiana Board of Regents Grant #86-LBR(21)- 021-10 through the Louisiana Quality Education Support Fund to Robert C. Mathews.

We would also like to acknowledge Bernardita Lasquety for her diligence in translating scores of verbal transcripts into regular expressions that could be parsed into classifiers.

LEXICAL CONCEPTUAL STRUCTURE AND GENERATION IN MACHINE TRANSLATION

Bonnie Dorr

M.I.T. Artificial Intelligence Laboratory

ABSTRACT

This paper introduces an implemented scheme for generating target-language sentences using a compositional representation of meaning called *lexical conceptual structure*. Lexical conceptual structure facilitates two crucial operations associated with generation: lexical selection and syntactic realization. The compositional nature of the representation is particularly valuable for these two operations when semantically equivalent source- and target-language words and phrases are structurally or thematically divergent. For example, the English verb ***to stab*** may be translated as the composite Spanish form ***dar cuchilladas a*** (literally, ***to knife*** or ***to give knife-wounds to***). To determine the correct lexical items and syntactic realization associated with the surface form in such cases, the underlying lexical-semantic forms are systematically mapped to the target-language syntactic structures. The model described constitutes a lexical-semantic extension to UNITRAN, a syntactic-based translation system that is bidirectional between Spanish and English.[1]

INTRODUCTION

This paper describes an implemented generation system that matches the underlying conceptual structure of a sentence to the appropriate target-language lexical items and produces the structural realization of the target-sentence by means of syntactic mappings associated with these lexical items. This work represents a shift away from complex, language-specific, syntactic generation without entirely abandoning syntax. Furthermore, this work moves toward a model that employs a well-defined lexical conceptual representation without depending on situational context, expectations, or complex knowledge representations. Two crucial operations, *lexical selection* of target-language terms and *syntactic realization* of target-language forms, will be examined, and structural and thematic divergences that encumber these two operations will be discussed.

Consider the following example of translation from English to Spanish:

(1) I stabbed John ⇒ Yo di cuchilladas a Juan (I gave knife-wounds to John)

Two properties of the system enable it to provide an appropriate translation for cases such as (1). The first is that the system relies on the notion of *compositionality* in order to select target-language terms. For example, because of the inherently compositional nature of the English source-language verb *stab*, the system is able to select the composite Spanish form *dar cuchilladas a* (literally, *to knife* or *to give knife-wounds to*) as the target-language equivalent. The second property of the system is that it relies on an abstraction of lexical-semantic information from syntactic information. For example, the system is able to choose the lexical item *dar* (literally, *give*) as the translation of *stab* without regard to its syntactic realization, and it is able to realize the phrase *a Juan* (literally, *to John*) in place of *John* without regard to its lexical-semantic structure. We will see in the overview section that compositionality and lexical-semantics/syntax abstraction are crucial to the model presented here.

Other generators for machine translation have been either syntactic-based (see McDonald, 1987, McKeown, 1985, and Slocum, 1984) or semantic-based (see Cullingford, 1986, Lytinen, 1987, Nirenburg *et. al.*, 1987, and Schank & Abelson, 1977).[2] We will see that syntactic-based approaches are not adequate for translation in cases such as (1) since they do not take advantage of the lexical-semantic properties that aid the selection process; in addition, we will see that semantic-based approaches are not adequate for this example since they do not take advantage of syntactic information that aids the realization process.[3]

---

[1]See Dorr, 1987.

[2]The reader should note that the division between syntactic and semantic approaches is not as clean-cut as implied here. For example, systems such as MUMBLE (McDonald, 1983, 1987) and TEXT (McKeown, 1985) are not entirely syntactic-based in that they use discourse and focus constraints to derive *messages* (*i.e.*, underlying representational forms); and systems such as SAM (Cullingford, 1981, and Schank & Abelson, 1977) and MOPTRANS (Lytinen, 1987), which rely on the current situational context and expectations, are not entirely semantic-based since they take syntax into account for target-term positioning.

[3]The system described here is implemented in Common Lisp and is currently running on a Symbolics 3600 series machine. Because it translates one sentence at a time, it does not incorporate context or domain knowledge; thus, it

BACKGROUND FOR THE GENERATION SCHEME

The work of Jackendoff (1983) has been the primary influence on the design of UNITRAN's lexical-semantic generator. The representation adopted is *lexical conceptual structure* (henceforth LCS) as formulated by Hale and Laughren (1983) and Hale and Keyser (1986). Each lexical entry has two levels of description: the first is the syntactic description (*i.e.*, θ-roles, category, and hierarchical and linear positioning of each argument associated with a lexical root word) and the second is a lexical-semantic description (*i.e.*, the LCS of the lexical root word).[4] For example, the lexical entry for the word *stab* is:

(2)
```
(DEF-ROOT-WORD (STAB)
  ;; Syntactic description
  :CAT (V)
  :INTERNAL ((Z N GOAL)) or ((Z N GOAL) (Y P INSTRUMENT INANIMATE))
  :EXTERNAL ((X N AGENT ANIMATE))
  ;; LCS description
  :LCS (CAUSE X (GO-TEMP (Y SHARP-OBJECT)
          (FROM (AT (Y SHARP-OBJECT) X)) (TO (AT (Y SHARP-OBJECT) Z)))))
```

The LCS description provides the meaning "X causes a sharp object Y to go (temporally) to Z."[5] Given these two components of a lexical entry, a composed LCS can be constructed from the source-language parse tree (using the lexical-semantic description), and a target-language parse tree can then be generated from the composed LCS (using the syntactic description).[6] Notice that the syntactic level determines which of the arguments at the LCS level will be syntactically realized. For example, the verb *stab* may or may not syntactically realize its instrument argument since the disjunction in the :INTERNAL slot of the root word definition allows for both possibilities. Thus, it would be possible to generate either *he stabbed the robber* or *he stabbed the robber with a knife (scissors, poker, etc.)*. In the next section, we will see how this representation is used in the generation scheme.

OVERVIEW OF THE GENERATION PROCESS

Two top-level generation procedures are activated after a source-language sentence has been parsed. The first is a lexical-semantic composition procedure that maps the source-language syntactic tree into an underlying composed LCS; the second is a syntactic generation routine that maps the underlying composed LCS into a target-language syntactic tree. The lexical-semantic composition task is implemented as a recursive procedure that converts a lexical word (henceforth referred to as the *head*) into its corresponding LCS, and then does the same for each of the arguments of that head. These LCS forms are then composed into a single LCS that underlies the source- and

---

cannot use discourse, situational expectations, or domain information in order to generate a sentence. Consequently, there are a number of capabilities found in systems such as TEXT, MUMBLE, MOPTRANS, and SAM, that cannot be reproduced here including external pronominal reference, paraphrasing, story telling, interactive question-answering, *etc.*

[4]It is possible to use a more general linking strategy that relates variables in the LCS with variables in the syntactic structure (*e.g.*, see Jackendoff, 1989). Such a strategy would allow structural positioning of arguments to be determined independent of the lexical entries. This possibility is currently under investigation.

[5]Appendices A and B have the Spanish and English LCS definitions for the examples used throughout this paper. The lexical-semantic primitives of the system will not be enumerated here. To summarize, I adopt Jackendoff's notions of EVENT and STATE; these are further specialized into such primitives as CAUSE, GO, BE, STAY, and LET. The specialized primitives are placed into Temporal, Possessive, Identificational, Circumstantial, and Existential fields. For example, the primitive GO-TEMP refers to a Temporal (or Locational) GO event (*e.g.*, the meeting went (= GO-TEMP) from 2:00 to 4:00). If the GO event were placed in a Possessive setting, it would become GO-POSS (*e.g.*, Beth received (= GO-POSS) the doll). In addition to EVENTs and STATEs, there are also THINGs (*e.g.*, BOOK, DEFINITE-PERSON, REFERENT *etc.*), PATHs (*e.g.*, TO, FROM, *etc.*), LOCATIONs and TIMEs (*e.g.*, IN, AT, *etc.*), PROPERTYs (*e.g.*, TIRED, HUNGRY, *etc.*), MANNERs (*e.g.*, FORCEFULLY, WELL, *etc.*), and INTENSIFIERs (*e.g.*, VERY, *etc.*). One difference between Jackendoff's representation and the one shown here is that the LOCATIONs are implemented as two-place predicates; thus, the SHARP-OBJECT represented by the variable Y appears both in the FROM PATH and in the TO PATH. Although the system uses only a small set of lexical-semantic primitives, the set is quite adequate for defining a potentially large set of words due to the compositional nature of LCS's. Furthermore, because the set is so small, the search space during the lexical-selection stage of generation is greatly reduced.

[6]Although the examples in this paper describe translation in one direction only, the composed LCS is actually a *pivot* (language-independent form) for translation in either direction.

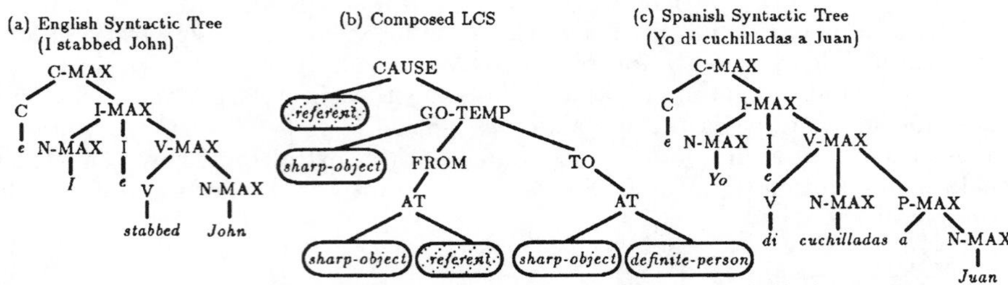

Figure 1: Translation of *I stabbed John* as *Yo di cuchilladas a Juan*

target-language sentences. The syntactic generation task is also a recursive procedure; it maps a node in the composed LCS to an appropriate target-language head, and then does the same for each of the arguments of that node. Each target-language head is then projected to its phrasal (or *maximal*) level and attached according to the positioning requirements of the lexical head that selects it.[7]

We return to our translation example shown in (1). Figure 1 shows three snapshots of the translation from English to Spanish.[8] When the LCS-composition procedure is applied to the parse tree shown in figure 1(a), the heads *I*, *stab*, and *John* are isolated, and the corresponding LCS's are positioned according to the syntax-to-LCS mapping defined in the lexicon. Thus, the internal argument specification `((Z N GOAL))` (see the definition of *stab* in (2)) maps the `N-MAX` projected from *John* to the variable `Z`. Similarly, the external argument specification `((X N AGENT ANIMATE))` maps the `N-MAX` projected from *I* to the variable `X`. The result is the composed LCS shown in figure 1(b).[9]

Notice that the `SHARP-OBJECT` argument is included in the LCS even though the source-language syntactic tree does not realize this argument. Including this argument at the level of LCS allows flexibility in generating the target-language sentence, which may or may not require this argument to be realized. Once this LCS has been composed, the syntactic generation component undertakes the tasks of *lexical selection* and *syntactic realization* to produce the target-language tree. We will now examine these two tasks in more detail before describing the process for the current example.

Lexical Selection: Thematic Divergence

Lexical selection is the task of choosing the target-language words that accurately reflect the meaning of the corresponding source-language words. One of the difficulties of this task is the fact that the equivalent source- and target-language forms are potentially thematically divergent. An example of thematic divergence shows up in the translation of the Spanish word *gustar* to the English word *like*. Although these two verbs are semantically equivalent, their argument structures are not identical: the subject of *like* (*I*) is the *theme* of the action, whereas the subject of *gustar* (*el libro*) is the *agent* of the action.[10] Thus, we have:

(3) Me gusta el libro (The book pleases me) ⇒ I like the book

[7]For discussion of projection to maximal level by the $\overline{X}$ component of the system, see Dorr, 1987. In a nutshell, `X-MAX` refers to the `XP` phrase that has a lexical head of category `X`.

[8]In this case, there is only one possible parse; however, if the structure were ambiguous, other possibilities would be displayed. The *e* elements under `C` and `I` are syntactic positions for which there is no overt lexical material.

[9]The co-referring `REFERENT` nodes have been shaded; this co-reference relation corresponds to the multiple occurrence of `X` in the LCS definition of *stab*. The first occurrence of `X` corresponds to the agent of the `CAUSE` action, and the second occurrence corresponds to the source of the `GO-TEMP` action. Notice that `X` takes on two roles at the level of LCS, but is only associated with one θ-role (agent) at the syntactic level; this distinction allows the θ-criterion to be satisfied at the level of syntax (see Dorr, 1987) while still allowing multiple roles to be assigned at the level of LCS.

[10]In (3), the subject of the source-language sentence has freely inverted into post-verbal position, leaving behind a coindexed *pro* (empty pronominal element). Thus, the post-verbal subject is considered to be the external argument of the main verb. Free subject-inversion is a property of *pro-drop* languages (*i.e.*, languages such as Spanish, Italian, Hebrew, *etc.* that do not require a sentence to have a subject); this property is taken into account during syntactic parsing and generation. For further discussion of the principles and parameters underlying the parser, see Dorr, 1987.

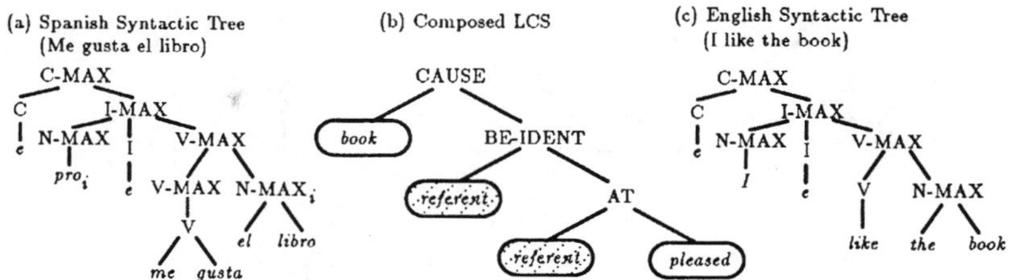

Figure 2: Translation of *Me gusta el libro* as *I like the book*

In a syntactic-based scheme, the semantics of the verb *gustar* would be lost since the literal translation (*to please*) would be selected for the target-language verb. By contrast, a semantic-based system would generally be able to make the correct lexical selection, but it might have difficulty with syntactic realization of the target-language arguments because it has no notion of syntactic argument divergence.

In the LCS approach, the underlying conceptual structure for *gustar* and *like* is identical, but the syntactic mappings associated with these two verbs are language-specific. The LCS reflects the fact that `THING X` is pleasing to `THING Y`. However, the variables `X` and `Y` map to different syntactic positions for Spanish and English:

(4)			
	gustar:	`:INTERNAL ((Y P THEME ANIMATE))`	`:EXTERNAL ((X N AGENT))`
	like:	`:INTERNAL ((X N AGENT))`	`:EXTERNAL ((Y N THEME ANIMATE))`

Thus, the agent of the action becomes the subject (external argument) in Spanish, and the object (internal argument) in English.[11]

At syntactic generation time, lexical selection of a target-language head involves matching the composed LCS to the appropriate lexical head in a target-language possibility set. For example, suppose the system is trying to select the appropriate target-language token for the composed LCS that corresponds to the source-language verb *gustar*. Several target heads (including *like*, *stab*, and many others that use the `CAUSE` LCS) are selected as possible lexical possibilities. Each of these possibilities is then examined for a match: not only must the top-level LCS coincide, but all LCS's under the top-level LCS must also coincide.[12] The system immediately determines that the *like* LCS is a match because it contains a `BE-IDENT` event whose arguments coincide with the arguments of the `BE-IDENT` in the composed LCS.[13] Figure 2 shows the syntactic trees and composed LCS for this example.

Notice that even though the arguments are not syntactically realized in the same way, the lexical selection procedure still succeeds. This is because of the separation between the syntactic description and the conceptual description. LCS descriptions provide the abstraction necessary for lexical selection without regard to syntax. In the next subsection, we will see how syntactic descriptions provide the necessary mechanism for argument realization without regard to conceptual considerations.

[11] Notice also that the syntactic categories of the theme are not the same; this structural divergence shows up during syntactic realization, which will be discussed in the section on syntactic realization.

[12] In general, there are two classes of LCS nodes that are taken into consideration during the matching process of lexical-selection. The more general nodes (*e.g.*, `CAUSE`, `BE-IDENT`, *etc.*) allow the matcher to determine the LCS class of the target-language term; the more specific nodes (*e.g.*, `PLEASED`, `FORCEFULLY`, *etc.*) are used for final convergence on a particular target-language term such as *like* as opposed to *love*, and *force* as opposed to *cause*.

[13] There is still the question of what to do when the LCS-matching procedure does not adequately cut down the target-language possibilities. For example, there are many open-ended classes of words (in particular, noun-phrases, adjectives, and adverbs) that are not distinguishable by their LCS's. If the possibility list is still quite large (*i.e.*, more than two or three lexical items) after LCS-matching routines have finished the lexical selection process, a direct-mapping routine is used here instead for lexicalization. That is, certain lexical-items (*e.g.*, *me*, *I*, *John*, etc.) may be selected on the basis of a direct mapping to the surface form. Pustejovsky and Nirenburg (1987) provide an elegant approach to generation of open-class lexical items based on focus information. Because the system described here does not include a model of discourse, the direct-mapping technique is used for such problematic cases.

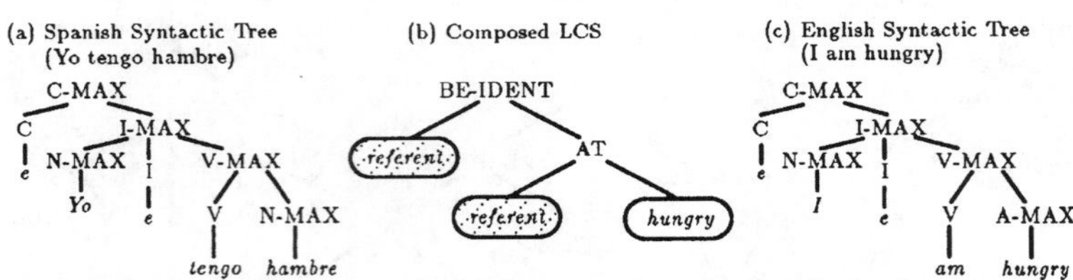

Figure 3: Translation of *Yo tengo hambre* as *I am hungry*

Syntactic Realization: Structural Divergence and Conflation

Syntactic realization is the task of mapping a syntactic description to a surface-syntactic representation. Two problems are associated with this task. The first is that source- and target-language forms are potentially structurally divergent. An example of structural divergence is the realization of arguments in the translation of *tener* to *be* as in (5) (the corresponding argument-structures are included):

	Yo tengo hambre	$[_{\text{V-MAX}}\ [_{\text{V}}\ \text{tener}]\ [_{\text{N-MAX}}\ \text{hambre}]] \Rightarrow$
(5)	(I have hunger)	
	I am hungry	$[_{\text{V-MAX}}\ [_{\text{V}}\ \text{be}]\ [_{\text{A-MAX}}\ \text{hungry}]]$

Here, not only are the predicates *tener* and *be* lexically distinct, but the arguments of these two predicates are structurally divergent: in Spanish, the argument is a noun-phrase, and, in English, the argument is an adjectival-phrase.

As for the lexical-selection of the appropriate predicate, the same LCS procedure that was used in the *stab-dar* case is used to match the LCS's of *tener* and *be*. However, for structural realization of the `PROPERTY` argument `Y`, the system must not only choose the appropriate lexical head, but it must choose the appropriate syntactic structure (*i.e.*, the category that will be projected from the head).

A syntactic-based scheme is inadequate for this example because it would choose the literal translation *hunger* for the source-language word *hambre*. This choice would be semantically awkward, but syntactically correct if the translation were *I have hunger*; however, if the more appropriate predicate *be* were chosen instead of *have*, the translation would be both semantically awkward and syntactically incorrect: *I am hunger*. A semantic-based scheme would make the correct lexical selection (that is, it would probably choose an argument that has a "desire to eat" property associated with it), but it would have no clue as to the syntactic form of the argument.

In the LCS approach, the lexical-selection procedure determines that both *hunger* and *hungry* lexically match the LCS for *hambre* because both are defined as the same LCS `PROPERTY: HUNGRY`. In order to choose between these two possibilities, the system must access the `:INTERNAL` slot of the predicate *be* that was chosen as the top-level lexical head: `((Y A))`. Since an adjective is selected, the nominal possibility is eliminated, the adjective *hungry* is chosen, and the argument is projected up to its maximal level (`A-MAX`). Figure 3 shows the syntactic trees and composed LCS for this example.

The second problem for structural realization is the potential for a divergent degree of *conflation* between the source- and target-language predicates. According to Talmy (1985), verbs may have a semantic representation that is not entirely exhibited at the level of syntactic structure. For example, the verb *enter* incorporates a *conflated* or "understood" particle *into* as part of its meaning structure; this particle manifests itself in the similar composite predicate *break into*. As it turns out, the Spanish equivalent of *break into* (*forzar*) has an additional conflated argument *entrada* (literally, *entry*); this argument is "understood," but not syntactically realized in English:

	Juan forzó la entrada al cuarto	$[_{\text{V-MAX}}\ [_{\text{V}}\ \text{forzar}]\ [_{\text{N-MAX}}\ \text{la entrada}]\ [_{\text{P-MAX}}\ \text{a} \cdots]] \Rightarrow$
(6)	(John forced entry to the room)	
	John broke into the room	$[_{\text{V-MAX}}\ [_{\text{V}}\ \text{break}]\ [_{\text{P-MAX}}\ \text{into} \cdots]]$

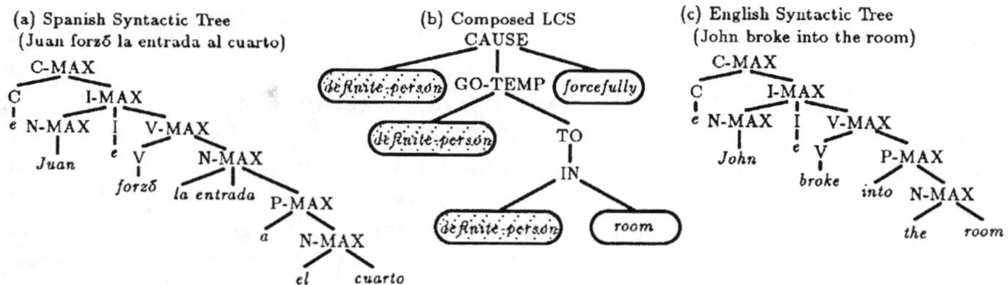

Figure 4: Translation of *Juan forzó la entrada al cuarto* as *John broke into the room*

Thus, there are three difficult tasks in the translation of *forzar* to *break*:[14] selection of the predicate *break*, suppression (conflation) of the *entry* argument, and realization of the particle *into*.[15]

A syntactic-based scheme has no notion of compositionality and would fail immediately in trying to map *forzar* (literally *force*) to *break* (or vice-versa). Furthermore, it would have the problem of choosing the appropriate particle, even if it were able to provide the correct structure (*i.e.*, a prepositional-phrase). On the other hand, a robust semantic-based scheme would have the ability to compose *forzar* and *entrada*, but it would not be able to determine whether the target-language argument was to be left implicit or whether it was to be syntactically realized, since there is no notion of conflation in such a scheme.

The LCS scheme uses compositionality to map *forzar la entrada* to *break*: the LCS for *forzar* contains a `CAUSE`, and the LCS for *entrada* contains a `GO-TEMP`, both of which combine to match the composite LCS for *break*.[16] At this point, the structural realization procedure determines that the `GO-TEMP` LCS is not part of the syntactic mappings of *break*, so it does not get realized (and so fulfills the conflation task). However, the `TO-IN PATH` argument *is* in the syntactic mappings of *break*, so the system matches this argument with the `TO-IN PATH` LCS of *into*, and the phrase *into the room* is realized. Figure 4 shows the syntactic trees and composed LCS for this example.

STAB-DAR REVISITED

We now return to our translation example: *I stabbed John.* Once the LCS for this sentence has been composed (see figure 1(b)), the lexical selection procedure must choose the appropriate Spanish lexical head by matching the composed LCS not only at top level, but at all lower levels. Of the target-language root word possibilities that match the LCS `GO-TEMP`, only the root word *dar* matches. Thus, this root is selected to be the lexical head that will be projected. Next, the system must project the arguments of the selected lexical head *dar*. A recursive call is made to the selection procedure in order to determine the correct lexical head for each of the argument LCS's `SHARP-OBJECT`, `FROM`, and `TO`. Just prior to this recursive call, the system accesses the `:INTERNAL` and `:EXTERNAL` slots of the lexical head *dar* to establish the syntactic category that will be projected for each of these arguments. Notice that unlike the *stab* definition, the *dar* definition requires the `SHARP-OBJECT` and `TO` arguments to be realized at the syntactic level; thus, the system performs an "inverse conflation" in order to arrive at the target-language realization for this example. The lexical heads chosen for LCS's `REFERENT`, `SHARP-OBJECT`, and `TO` are *yo*, *cuchilladas*, and *a*, respectively. As dictated by the syntactic argument slots of the lexical head *dar*, these three heads are maximally-projected as `N-MAX`, `N-MAX`, and `P-MAX`, respectively. Finally, the `DEFINITE-PERSON` LCS is projected

[14] There are three analogous tasks in the reverse direction. That is, translation from English to Spanish requires selection of the predicate *forzar*, realization of the *entry* argument (this is actually an "inverse conflation"), and realization of the particle *a*.

[15] Notice that the LCS definitions of *a* and *into* (see appendix A and appendix B, respectively) both have an `*EXTERNAL*` argument. The `*EXTERNAL*` marker is a place-holder for an LCS that will fill this position by means of lexical-semantic composition. For example, when the LCS associated with *a* is composed with the `GO-TEMP` LCS, the argument that is the theme of the `GO-TEMP` will replace the `*EXTERNAL*` marker of the *a* LCS.

[16] Notice that there are two LCS's for the word *break* (see appendix B); the first is the matching `GO-TEMP` LCS for this example, and the second one is a `GO-IDENT` LCS that corresponds to "breaking an object." The mapping routine of the lexical selection procedure succeeds on the first one and (correctly) fails on the second one for the *break into* example.

as **N-MAX** according to the **:INTERNAL** slot of the lexical head *a*.[17] The final Spanish syntactic tree is in figure 1(c).

SUMMARY

This paper has demonstrated that lexical conceptual structure can be valuable for sentence generation, particularly in the context of machine translation. Two operations, lexical selection and syntactic realization, have been identified; in addition, two potential hazards, structural and thematic divergence, have been isolated. LCS descriptions seem to provide the abstraction necessary for selecting appropriate target-language terms with minimal dependence on syntax. In addition, LCS's provide the necessary mechanism for realizing arguments without regard to conceptual considerations. Although this approach is related to other generation approaches, it differs from syntactic-based approaches in that it avoids the non-compositional, direct-mapping word selection, and it differs from semantic-based approaches in that it does not entirely abandon syntactic considerations for word selection and structural realization. In summary, this paper has shown that the combination of lexical-conceptual description and syntactic description facilitates the lexical-selection and structural realization processes, and it also aids in tackling the associated problems of thematic divergence, structural divergence, and conflation.

A SPANISH DEFINITIONS

```
(DEF-ROOT-WORD (GUSTAR)
  :CAT (V) :EXTERNAL ((X N AGENT)) :INTERNAL ((Y P THEME ANIMATE))
  :LCS (CAUSE X (BE-IDENT Y (AT Y PLEASED))))

(DEF-ROOT-WORD (DAR)
  :CAT (V)
  :EXTERNAL ((X N AGENT ANIMATE))
  :INTERNAL ((W N INSTRUMENT INANIMATE) (Z P GOAL)) or ((Y N THEME INANIMATE) (Z P GOAL))
  :LCS (CAUSE X (GO-TEMP W (FROM (AT W X)) (TO (AT W Z))))
     or (CAUSE X (GO-POSS Y (FROM (AT Y X)) (TO (AT Y Z))))

(DEF-ROOT-WORD (TENER)
  :CAT (V) :EXTERNAL ((X N THEME)) :INTERNAL ((Y N GOAL)) or ((Z N CONDITION))
  :LCS (BE-POSS X (AT X Y)) or (BE-IDENT X (AT X Z)))

(DEF-ROOT-WORD (FORZAR)
  :CAT (V) :EXTERNAL ((X N AGENT ANIMATE)) :INTERNAL ((Z N THEME)) or ((Z C THEME))
  :LCS (CAUSE X Z FORCEFULLY))

(DEF-ROOT-WORD (A) :CAT (P) :INTERNAL ((Y N)) :LCS (TO (AT *EXTERNAL* Y)))

(DEF-ROOT-WORD (CUCHILLADA) :CAT (N) :LCS SHARP-OBJECT)

(DEF-ROOT-WORD (ENTRADA)
  :CAT (N) :INTERNAL ((Y P GOAL LOCATION))
  :LCS (GO-TEMP *EXTERNAL* (TO (IN *EXTERNAL* Y))))

(DEF-ROOT-WORD (HAMBRE) :CAT (N) :LCS HUNGRY)
```

B ENGLISH DEFINITIONS

```
(DEF-ROOT-WORD (LIKE)
  :CAT (V) :EXTERNAL ((Y N THEME ANIMATE)) :INTERNAL ((X N AGENT))
  :LCS (CAUSE X (BE-IDENT Y (AT Y PLEASED))))

(DEF-ROOT-WORD (GIVE)
  :CAT (V)
  :EXTERNAL ((X N AGENT ANIMATE))
  :INTERNAL ((Y N THEME INANIMATE) (Z P GOAL)) or ((Z N GOAL) (Y N THEME INANIMATE))
  :LCS (CAUSE X (GO-POSS Y (FROM (AT Y X) (TO (AT Y Z))))))

(DEF-ROOT-WORD (BE)
  :CAT (V) :EXTERNAL ((X N THEME)) :INTERNAL ((Y A)) or ((W P LOCATION)) or ((W P TIME))
  :LCS (BE-IDENT X (AT X Y)) or (BE-TEMP X (AT X W)))

(DEF-ROOT-WORD (BREAK)
  :CAT (V)
  :EXTERNAL ((X N AGENT ANIMATE))
  :INTERNAL ((Y P GOAL LOCATION)) or ((Z N THEME INANIMATE))
  :LCS (CAUSE X (GO-TEMP X (TO (IN X Y))) FORCEFULLY)
     or (CAUSE X (GO-IDENT Z (TO (AT Z BROKEN)))))
```

---

[17]The proper noun *John* is considered to be a member of one of the many open-ended word classes discussed in footnote 13. Thus, the translation *Juan* is selected on the basis of a direct mapping from the source-language form.

```
(DEF-ROOT-WORD (STAB)
  :CAT (V)
  :EXTERNAL ((X N AGENT ANIMATE))
  :INTERNAL ((Z N GOAL)) or ((Z N GOAL) (Y P INSTRUMENT INANIMATE))
  :LCS (CAUSE X
         (GO-TEMP (Y SHARP-OBJECT)
           (FROM (AT (Y SHARP-OBJECT) X)) (TO (AT (Y SHARP-OBJECT) Z)))))
(DEF-ROOT-WORD (INTO) :CAT (P) :INTERNAL ((Y N LOCATION)) :LCS (TO (IN *EXTERNAL* Y)))
(DEF-ROOT-WORD (HUNGER) :CAT (N) :LCS HUNGRY)
(DEF-ROOT-WORD (HUNGRY) :CAT (A) :LCS HUNGRY)
```

REFERENCES

Cullingford, Richard E. (1986) *Natural Language Processing: A Knowledge-Engineering Approach*, Rowman and Littlefield, Totowa, New Jersey.

Dorr, Bonnie J. (1987) "UNITRAN: A Principle-Based Approach to Machine Translation," AI Technical Report 1000, Master of Science thesis, Department of Electrical Engineering and Computer Science, Massachusetts Institute of Technology.

Hale, Kenneth and M. Laughren (1983) "Warlpiri Lexicon Project: Warlpiri Dictionary Entries," Massachusetts Institute of Technology, Cambridge, MA, Warlpiri Lexicon Project.

Hale, Kenneth and Jay Keyser (1986) "Some Transitivity Alternations in English," Center for Cognitive Science, Massachusetts Institute of Technology, Cambridge, MA, Lexicon Project Working Papers #7.

Jackendoff, Ray S. (1983) *Semantics and Cognition*, MIT Press, Cambridge, MA.

Jackendoff, Ray S. (1989) *Semantic Structure*, unpublished manuscript, Brandeis University.

Lytinen, Steven L. (1987) "Integrating Syntax and Semantics," in *Machine Translation: Theoretical and Methodological Issues*, Sergei Nirenburg (ed.), Cambridge University Press, Cambridge, England.

McDonald, David D. (1987) "Natural Language Generation: Complexities and Techniques," in *Machine Translation: Theoretical and Methodological Issues*, Sergei Nirenburg (ed.), Cambridge University Press, Cambridge, England.

McKeown, Kathleen (1985) *Text Generation: Using Discourse Strategies and Focus Constraints to Generate Natural Language Text*, Cambridge University Press, Cambridge, England.

Nirenburg, Sergei, Victor Raskin, and Allen B. Tucker (1987) "The Structure of Interlingua in TRANSLATOR," in *Machine Translation: Theoretical and Methodological Issues*, Sergei Nirenburg (ed.), Cambridge University Press, Cambridge, England.

Pustejovsky, James and Sergei Nirenburg (1987) "Lexical Selection in the Process of Language Generation," *Proceedings of the 25th Annual Conference of the Association for Computational Linguistics*, Stanford University, Stanford, CA, 201–206.

Schank, Roger C. and Robert Abelson (1977) *Scripts, Plans, Goals, and Understanding*, Lawrence Erlbaum Associates, Inc., Hillsdale, NJ.

Slocum, Jonathan (1984) "METAL: The LRC Machine Translation System," Linguistics Research Center, University of Texas, Austin, Working Paper LRC-84-2.

Talmy, Leonard (1983) "How Language Structures Space," in *Spatial Orientation: Theory, Research, and Application*, Pick, Herbert L., Jr., and Linda P. Acredolo (eds.), Plenum Press, New York.

ACKNOWLEDGEMENTS

This report describes research done at the Artificial Intelligence Laboratory of the Massachusetts Institute of Technology. Support for this research has been provided by NSF Grant DCR-85552543 under a Presidential Young Investigator's Award to Professor Robert C. Berwick. Useful guidance and commentary during this research were provided by Bob Berwick, Michael Brent, Bruce Dawson, Sandiway Fong, and Mike Kashket.

Robust Lexical Selection in Parsing and Generation

Michael Gasser
Computer Science Department, Indiana University

ABSTRACT

A well-known difference between human language understanding and typical computational theories of language understanding is in the degree to which they handle partial or errorful input: computational models are comparatively brittle in the face of input which deviates from the norm. In language generation there is an analogous problem, that of selecting an appropriate lexical entry when there is none in memory which matches the pragmatic/semantic input to generation. This paper presents a localized connectionist model of robust lexical selection for both language understanding and generation. Processing takes the form of pattern completion, where patterns consist of complexes of semantic, morphosyntactic, and pragmatic features. The system is presented with portions of such patterns and retrieves others. In generation the given information is pragmatic/semantic and in understanding mainly morphosyntactic. This approach is not only a natural way of accommodating both understanding and generation but it also fosters the robustness that is characteristic of human language processors.

ROBUSTNESS IN PARSING AND GENERATION

A well-known difference between human language understanding and typical AI language understanding programs is in the degree to which the two systems handle partial or errorful input. AI systems tend to be brittle; when the input to a parser does not conform to any of the patterns stored in memory, the system breaks down. People, on the other hand, are remarkably good at interpreting linguistic input which deviates from the norm. The best-known examples of the robustness of the human parsing mechanism are utterances which are almost completely devoid of syntax, yet remain interpretable on semantic grounds:

(1) *mary paycheck receive go bank deposit*

Yet the phenomenon is more general that this. It includes on the one hand the handling of phonologically degraded input and on the other the recognition and interpretation of lexical items used in non-standard ways. This paper is concerned with the latter type of robustness. Consider the following sentence, a variant of one actually produced by a non-native speaker of English.

(2) *He deposited his property to his friend.*

The intention of the speaker was to describe a situation in which the actor leaves his valuables with a friend for safekeeping while he is away on business. The use of *deposit* in this sentence is decidedly odd, yet a native listener of English would have no trouble understanding it in context.

Less attention has been paid to the corresponding ability in language generation. Consider the process of lexical selection, a central component in generation, though one that has not been the subject of much research (Levelt & Schriefers, 1987). Given a set of semantic/pragmatic features associated with a particular lexical item, one should not expect that all of these features will be present in the input to the lexical selection process. Rather <u>enough</u> of the features need to be present for the appropriate item to be selected. Thus in this sense the input to generation may be incomplete, requiring robustness in the lexical selection process.

Lexical selection is made more difficult when input features <u>conflict</u> with features of lexical entries, that is, when there is no entry in memory which matches all of the features to be conveyed. This would correspond to the problem of having something to say but no completely appropriate way of saying it. Second language speakers often face such problems. In general, speakers seem again to be able to cope; they identify the lexical item which does the job better than any other. Sentence (2) above is a good example. The speaker may know *deposit* only in its sense of transferring money to a financial institution, but it still seems the best available word.

There are good reasons why people are robust understanders and generators. The utterances which one encounters, especially in spoken language, are often deficient in one way or another, and even when they are well-formed, the perceptual apparatus may fail to pick up all of the relevant features. Likewise, speakers are forced to map an infinite variety of potential discourse topics onto a finite set of lexical items and structures. Of necessity the set of semantic/pragmatic features we choose to convey at any given time will rarely match those associated with particular lexical items. In both processes robustness permits the system to cope with the range of potential inputs.

PARSING AND GENERATION AS PATTERN COMPLETION

There is general agreement on the desirability of accommodating both language generation and comprehension within the same system, though there is disagreement on the degree to which knowledge can be shared by the two processes. At the very least, people certainly learn most of what they know about generating language through the process of parsing language, and this fact implies a significant amount of sharing. The processes themselves, while largely the reverse of each other in terms of their inputs and outputs, can both be viewed as a form of **pattern completion**. That is, if linguistic patterns are seen as complexes of semantic, morphosyntactic, and sometimes pragmatic features, the processing system is given some of these and must retrieve others. In parsing what is given is mainly morphosyntactic, and what is retrieved is semantic and pragmatic, though available semantic and/or pragmatic features normally guide the process as well. In generation, the given features are mainly semantic and pragmatic and the retrieved features morphosyntactic. On this view, not only do both parsing and generation consist of the completion of incomplete patterns; both processes make use of the same patterns.

In certain connectionist models (Feldman & Ballard, 1982; Rumelhart, Hinton, & McClelland, 1986) the dominant mode of processing is pattern completion. In these models activation on a set of units representing a portion of a familiar pattern tends to lead to the activation of the other units that take part in the pattern. Thus this approach is ideal for modeling parsing and generation within a single system. For parsing, processing is initiated through the activation of a set of units representing morphosyntactic and possibly also semantic or pragmatic features, and the output consists of the activation of units representing a complete set of semantic and/or pragmatic features. For generation processing is initiated through the activation of a set of units representing primarily pragmatic and semantic features, and the output consists of the activation (in the appropriate sequence) of units representing words. Associations within the network are bidirectional so that activation can spread in either direction.

Pattern completion in connectionist models is designed to find the best characterization in memory for a given set of input features. Thus it is admirably suited to the problem of coping with errors or missing information in the input to understanding and generation.

This paper discusses the robustness of lexical access in the **connectionist lexical memory** (CLM) model of sentence processing, a localized connectionist approach. The model is implemented in a program which generates and parses simple English sentences.

A CONNECTIONIST FRAMEWORK FOR PARSING AND GENERATION

The main features of the CLM model are the following:

1. Memory consists of a network of nodes joined by weighted connections. The system's knowledge is embodied entirely in these connections.
2. Concepts are represented as frames consisting of subnetworks of the memory.

3. The basic units of linguistic knowledge are subnetwork frames associating surface-level form directly with function. These form-function mappings comprise an inventory from which selections are made during generation and parsing.
4. Processing consists in the parallel spread of activation through the network starting with nodes representing inputs. The amount of activation spreading along a connection depends on the connection's weight. Activation on nodes decays over time.
5. Decision making takes the form of competition among sets of mutually inhibiting nodes and the eventual dominance of one over the others.
6. Processing is more interactional than modular. Pragmatic, semantic, and syntactic information may be involved simultaneously in the selection of units of linguistic knowledge.

The system exhibits robustness in that it can find patterns to match input even when there are no perfect matches. Other aspects of human language processing which are modeled include 1) parallelism and competition, 2) priming effects, 3) a combination of top-down and bottom-up processing, 4) flexibility in generation, 5) speech errors involving substitution, and 6) knowledge in the form of tendencies with degrees of associated strength rather than strict rules or constraints. In addition, the model accommodates both generation and parsing. An earlier version of the CLM model is described in detail in Gasser (1988).

Linguistic Memory

Memory in the model is a localized connectionist implementation of a semantic network similar to Fahlman's NETL (1979). In NETL, roles, such as ACTOR, COLOR, and SUBJECT, take the form of nodes rather than links, and links are confined to a small primitive set representing in particular the IS-A, HAS-A, and DISTINCTNESS relations. In the present model, these links are replaced by pairs of weighted, directed connections of a single type, one connection for each direction.

Linguistic knowledge is integrated into the rest of memory. The basic units of linguistic knowledge are generalizations of two types of acts: **illocutions** and **utterances**. In this paper I will be only concerned with the latter. A generalized utterance, or **entry**, is a frame (implemented as a network fragment) associating a morphosyntactic pattern with a set of semantic and possibly also contextual features. Entries include frames for clauses, noun phrases, adjective phrases, and prepositional phrases. They are arranged in a generalization hierarchy with syntactic structures at its more general end and phrasal lexical entries at its more specific end. Thus lexical entries in the model are just a relatively specific type of entry. An entry normally has a node representing the whole phrase, one or more nodes representing constituents of the phrase, and one or more nodes representing semantic or pragmatic aspects of the phrase.

Figure 1 shows a portion of the lexical entry for the verb *deposit* in the sense of 'leaving money in a bank'. Nodes are denoted by rectangles and pairs of connections by lines. For convenience frame boundaries are indicated by fuzzy rectangles with rounded corners, but these boundaries have no significance in processing. Node names likewise are shown for convenience only; they are not accessible to the basic procedures. Names of lexical entries begin with an asterisk, and lower-case names indicate roles. The lexical entry shown in the figure, *DEPOSIT1, associates clauses having a form of the word *deposit* as their main verb with instances of the concept of ABSTRACT-TRANSFER having MONEY as their OBJECT and BANK as their DESTINATION. The frame is represented as a subtype of *ABSTRACT-TRANSFER, the general frame for clauses referring to instances of ABSTRACT-TRANSFER. Other subtypes of this frame include entries such as *GIVE, *SEND, and *STEAL.

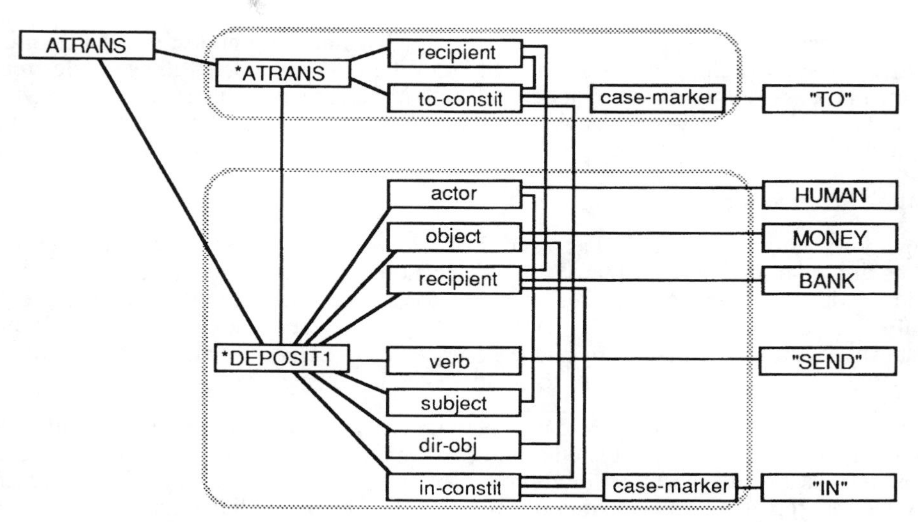

Figure 1: Portion of the entry for *depositi*ng money in a bank

Note that the *DEPOSIT1 entry includes the information needed to associate semantic and synactic roles. For example, there is a connection joining the SUBJECT[1] constituent with the ACTOR of the instance of ABSTRACT-TRANSFER that is being referred to. Likewise the DIRECT-OBJECT and IN-CONSTITUENT (the constituent with *in* as case marker) are associated with the appropriate semantic roles. In the *ABSTRACT-TRANSFER entry only one constituent is shown in the figure, the TO-CONSTITUENT[2] which refers to the RECIPIENT of the transfer. Note how this is linked to the corresponding roles in the *DEPOSIT1 entry.

Processing in General

Each node in the network has at any given time an activation level. When the activation of a node reaches its threshold, the node fires and sends activation along all of its output connections. The firing of a node represents a decision made by the system. For example, the selection of an entry matching an input pattern is represented by the firing of the head node of the entry. Following firing, a node is inhibited for an interval during which its state is unaffected by inputs from other nodes. After this interval has passed, the node recovers with a small amount of positive activation and can be further activated from other nodes. There is also a decay mechanism reflecting the importance of recency in processing: the activation level of all nodes decreases at a fixed rate.

The amount of activation spreading from one node to another is proportional to the weight on the connection from the source to the destination node. In most cases activation from more than one source is required for a node to fire; thus processing is oriented around intersections of paths of activation. Connection weights may also be negative, in which case the relationship is an inhibitory one.

Sometimes we want only one node from a set to fire at a given time. For example, in the generation of a clause, the system should select only one of the set of verb lexical entries. In such

[1]In its present form the entry applies to active clauses only.

[2]The system does not have knowledge of indirect objects, that is, constituents referring to the RECIPIENT (or BENEFACTOR) that take no case marker.

cases the members of the set form a network of mutually inhibiting nodes called a **winner-take-all (WTA) network** (Feldman & Ballard, 1982). When two or more of these nodes receive activation, a process is initiated by which nodes with more activation in effect draw activation from those with less. This usually results eventually in the firing of one of the nodes, at which point the winner-take-all process terminates.

Language Processing

Language processing can be viewed as a series of selections, each made on the basis of a set of factors making quantitative contributions to the decisions. During sentence generation the items selected include general morphosyntactic patterns for the sentence and its constituents (e.g., STATEMENT, COULD-YOU-QUESTION, COUNTABLE-NP) and a set of lexical items to fill the slots in these patterns. During sentence analysis the items selected include word senses, semantic roles to be assigned to referents, and intentions to be attributed to the speaker.

In the CLM model the selection process is implemented in terms of 1) the parallel convergence of activation on one or more candidate nodes and 2) the eventual dominance of one of these nodes over the others as a result of mutual inhibition through a WTA network. Consider the case of lexical selection in generation. Activation converges on a set of candidate lexical entries starting from nodes representing conceptual features of an input. Any number of entries may receive some activation for a given input, but because the entries inhibit each other through a WTA network, only one is selected.

Input to generation consists of a set of firing nodes representing a goal of the speaker. As activation spreads from the input nodes, it converges on nodes representing a general pattern appropriate for the goal type, for example, the STATEMENT pattern, and a set of patterns appropriate for the propositional content of the goal. These include lexical patterns such as *DEPOSIT1 and *MONEY and grammatical patterns such as PAST-CLAUSE and INDEFINITE-NP.

The same basic mechanism works for parsing. Input consists of firing nodes representing words. These are presented to the program at intervals of four time steps. Activation from the word nodes converges on entries for lexical and syntactic patterns. For ambiguous words there are two or more entries which inhibit one another through a WTA network. Lexical selection leads to the firing of conceptual nodes representing the interpretation of the input.

Alongside entry selection, the basic processing mechanism also implements the temporary **role binding** that is necessary for both generation and parsing and the appropriate output **sequencing** of constituents that is required for generation. These aspects of processing are not discussed further in this paper; for details, see Gasser (1988).

AN EXAMPLE

Parsing

Consider first the selection of the verb lexical entry that takes place during the parsing of sentence (2). A more complete version of the entry *DEPOSIT1 is shown in Figure 2. Here an abbreviated notation is used. Connections between head and role nodes are represented by indentation, and connections among roles within the same frame are represented using a caret preceding the name of the role at the other end of a connection. Thus the SOURCE role in *DEPOSIT1 is connected to the ACTOR role within the same frame. The dotted line separates semantic from morphosyntactic features within the entry.

```
(*DEPOSIT1 *ABSTRACT-TRANSFER ABSTRACT-TRANSFER
     (actor HUMAN)
     (object MONEY)
     (source ^actor)
     (recipient BANK)
     (duration TEMPORARY)
     (purpose1 PREVENT                ;;keep money safe
         (object LOSE
             (object ^object)))
     (purpose2 INCREASE-VALUE         ;;earn interest
         (object ^object))))
-------------------------------------------------------------
     (verb "DEPOSIT")
     (subject ^actor)
     (direct-object ^object)
     (in-constituent ^recipient
         (case-marker "IN")))
```

Figure 2: Entry for *deposit*ing money in a bank

The system also has two other entries for the verb *deposit*, one meaning 'the PHYSICAL-TRANSFER of MONEY into a VENDING-MACHINE', the other 'the PHYSICAL-TRANSFER of PARTICULATE-MATTER onto a HORIZONTAL-SURFACE through the action of some NATURAL-FORCE'.

During the parsing process, nodes representing both conceptual and formal features of the input are activated, and these in turn activate roles in various entries as paths of activation intersect there. For sentence (2), the parsing of the subject results in the firing of the ACTOR and SUBJECT roles in *DEPOSIT1 as well as the corresponding roles in all entries with a SUBJECT referring to a HUMAN ACTOR. The recognition of the verb causes the VERB role to fire in the three entries which have *deposit* in this slot. The appearance of the direct object, however, does not strongly activate the DIRECT-OBJECT and OBJECT roles in any of these entries because in sentence (2) the direct object refers not to money or particulate matter but to some unspecified property. The same is true for the IN-CONSTITUENT. In this case the input deviates in two ways from what appears in the *DEPOSIT1 entry: the referent is not a BANK, and the CASE-MARKER in the constituent is not "IN".

At this point, the most strongly competing entries are *DEPOSIT1 and *DEPOSIT2 ('put money in a vending machine'). In both cases the entry head nodes receive activation from their SUBJECT/ACTOR roles (because they are linked to HUMAN) and from their VERB roles (because they are linked to "DEPOSIT"). Here we can imagine a variety of information that a human understander might use in selecting one of the two lexical entries over the other. This system is currently not sophisticated enough to make elaborate inferences, and it needs some help from the context. In this case, we assume that the context has led the system to expect that the actor will want to protect his property. This leads to the firing of the PURPOSE1 role in *DEPOSIT1, providing the extra activation that this entry needs to win out over *DEPOSIT2. Figure 3 illustrates the competition between *DEPOSIT1 and *DEPOSIT2. The fuzzy line denotes an inhibitory connection, the thick black borders firing nodes, and the arrows the path of activation spread.

Once the head node for *DEPOSIT1 has fired, it leads to the firing of more general entries associated with this one, in particular, *ABSTRACT-TRANSFER. *ABSTRACT-TRANSFER contains the information that the constituent referring to the RECIPIENT is normally marked with *to*. The firing of the node for this constituent provides the extra activation needed for the RECIPIENT role in *DEPOSIT1 to fire, allowing the system to recognize that the friend referred to in the phrase

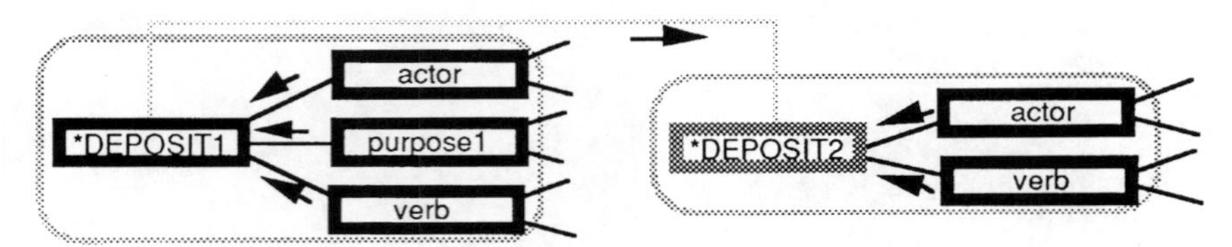

Figure 3: Competition between two entries during parsing

following *to* is the intended recipient of the property. For details on how this temporary role binding process works, see Gasser (1988).

Generation

Consider now the generation of sentence (2). Assume the speaker has an entry like the one in Figure 2 except that she does not know that the appropriate case marker for this sense is *in*.

At the point in generation where the verb entry selection is to take place, a number of nodes representing the input concept will have fired. As activation spreads from these nodes, it will intersect on the roles of some entries. Within *DEPOSIT1, the ACTOR, SOURCE, RECIPIENT, DURATION, and PURPOSE1 (protecting the transferred property) roles will fire, while the OBJECT role, which is an instance of PROPERTY rather than MONEY, and the PURPOSE2 (earning interest) role, which is not applicable in this case, will not fire. The firing roles send activation to the head node of the entry, which also receives activation from ABSTRACT-TRANSFER. The head node competes via a WTA network with other verb lexical entries, including some which will also have significant activation, such as the entry for *give*. The WTA network sees to it that only one of the entry head nodes fires.

The *GIVE entry, like *DEPOSIT1, is associated with the general notion of ABSTRACT-TRANSFER. Like *DEPOSIT1, it includes the information that the ACTOR and SOURCE of the transfer are the same, but for *GIVE there is a tendency for the DURATION of the transfer to be PERMANENT. For the example, *GIVE receives input from ABSTRACT-TRANSFER and from the ACTOR and SOURCE roles. *DEPOSIT1, on the other hand, receives input from its RECIPIENT and DURATION roles (and others not shown in the figure) in addition to ABSTRACT-TRANSFER and the ACTOR and SOURCE roles. *DEPOSIT1 wins out over *GIVE because of the activation received from a greater number of matching roles exactly as this happens among competing entries during parsing.

RELATED WORK

Work on robust parsing within traditional symbolic frameworks has focused on problems of unfamiliar lexical items (e.g., Zernik, 1987) or ungrammaticality (e.g., Fain, Carbonell, Hayes, & Minton, 1985). Within the connectionist paradigm, McClelland & Kawamoto (1986) demonstrated that connectionist models are well suited to the problem of mapping syntactic to semantic case in the presence of novel verbs or missing arguments. In this paper, the focus has been on accessing entries for known lexical items, given input that deviates from that found in the entries. While the model requires refinement and further testing before it can be shown to handle all of the categories of input that these other approaches do, it is felt that these other types of processing difficulties will be accommodated within the single general framework proposed here.

Robustness in generation, on the other hand, has not come up in the literature. The generation work most closely related to the present approach is that of Kukich (1987) and Ward (1988). Kukich trained a connectionist network to associate semantic features with phrasal idioms. While she did not specifically address the issue of robustness, it is clear that her system would be able to handle noisy or incomplete input. However, the fact that there are no roles in her model makes the representation of constituency in concepts and patterns unwieldy if not impossible. Ward uses a spreading activation approach to model generation as a creative process. Thus, as in this paper, he is concerned with the fact that there are often no simple mappings between sets of input features and lexical entries. However, he does not make use of the competition among entries that seems to be required to deal with input features that do not match any entry in a straightforward way.

Unlike the current approach, none of the models discussed here handles lexical selection in both parsing and generation.

CONCLUSIONS AND FUTURE WORK

In this paper I have characterized robustness as a general feature desirable in both language understanding and generation systems and have described a model which handles lexical selection in terms of the general mechanism of pattern completion. This mechanism not only provides a natural way of treating understanding and generation as similar sorts of processes operating on the same memory; it is ideally suited to coping with input that does not correspond precisely to the patterns stored in linguistic memory.

Current work is concerned with transforming the localized memory of the CLM model to a distributed memory. The advantages of distributed representations include the availability of relatively simple learning algorithms; a more efficient use of memory; tolerance to damage to memory; and more direct interaction among the relevant features, one that is not mediated by head nodes and by the levels in is-a hierarchies.

ACKNOWLEDGEMENTS

The research reported on here was conducted partly while the author was at the AI Laboratory, UCLA. It was supported in part by grants from the ITA Foundation and the JTF program of the U.S. Department of Defense.

REFERENCES

Fahlman, S. E. (1979). *NETL: A system for representing and using real-world knowledge.* Cambridge, MA: MIT Press.

Fain, J., Carbonell, J. G., Hayes, P. J., & Minton, S. N. (1985). MULTIPAR: A robust entity-oriented parser. *Seventh Annual Conference of the Cognitive Science Society*, 110-119

Feldman, J. A., & Ballard, D. H. (1982). Connectionist models and their properties. *Cognitive Science, 6,* 205-254.

Gasser, M. (1988). *A connectionist model of sentence generation in a first and second language.* (Technical Report UCLA-AI-88-13). Los Angeles: University of California, Los Angeles, Computer Science Department.

Kukich, K. (1987). Where do phrases come from: Some preliminary experiments in connectionist phrase generation. In G. Kempen (Ed.), *Natural language generation* (pp. 405-421). Dordrecht: Martinus Nijhoff.

Levelt, W. J. M., & Schriefers, H. (1987). Stages of lexical access. In Kempen (Ed.), *Natural language generation.* (pp. 395-404). Dordrecht: Martinus Nijhoff.

McClelland, J. L., & Kawamoto, A. H. (1986). Mechanisms of sentence processing: Assigning roles to constituents of sentences. In J. L. McClelland, D. E. Rumelhart, & the PDP Research Group (Eds.), *Parallel Distributed Processing. Explorations in the microstructures of cognition: Vol. 2: Psychological and biological models* (pp. 272-325). Cambridge, MA: MIT Press.

Rumelhart, D. E., Hinton, G. E., & McClelland, J. L. (1986). A general framework for Parallel Distributed Processing. In D. E. Rumelhart, J. L. McClelland, & the PDP Research Group (Eds.), *Parallel Distributed Processing: Explorations in the microstructures of cognition: Vol.1: Foundations* (pp. 110-149). Cambridge, MA: MIT Press.

Ward, N. (1988). Issues in word choice. *Twelfth International Conference on Computational Linguistics*, 726-731.

Zernik, U. (1987). *Strategies in language acquisition: Learning phrases from examples in context* (Technical Report UCLA-AI-87-1). Los Angeles: University of California, Computer Science Department.

Causal/Temporal Connectives: Syntax and Lexicon

Michael Brent
MIT AI Lab

Abstract
This paper elucidates the linguistic representation of temporal relations among events. It does so by examining sentences that contain two clauses connected by **temporal/causal connectives**, words like *once, by the time, when,* and *before*. Specifically, the data involve the effect of the tenses of the connected clauses on the acceptability of sentences. For example, *Rachel disappeared once Jon had fallen asleep* is fine, but **Rachel had disappeared once Jon fell asleep* is unacceptable. First a theory of acceptability is developed, then its implications for interpretation are discussed. The strategy employed is to factor linguisitic knowledge into a general, syntactic component and a lexical component dependent on the properties of individual connectives. Once the syntactic and lexical components have been teased apart the problem of interpretation becomes clearer. Finally, a computer model of the theory, which serves as a workbench and confirms the theory's behavior, is demonstrated.

Overview

This paper elucidates the linguistic representation of temporal relations among events. It does so by examining sentences that contain two clauses connected **temporal/causal connectives**, words like *once, by the time, when,* and *before*. Specifically, the data involve the effect of the tenses of the connected clauses on the acceptability of such sentences. After a theory of acceptability is developed, then its implications for interpretation are discussed. The questions of acceptability are:

1. What knowledge about the admissible combinations of tenses in connected clauses can be represented in a general way that does not depend on the particular connective? For example, the tenses in (1) seem to be a bad combination independent of the connective.

   (1)   * Rachel disappears { *when, *once, *by the time, *before } Jon will fall asleep

2. What limitations do specific connectives impose on the tenses of the clauses they connect? What lexical knowledge must people have about temporal/causal connectives to identify those limitations? For example, consider (2).[1]

   (2) a. OK Rachel disappeared ONCE Jon had fallen asleep
   b. * Rachel had disappeared ONCE Jon fell asleep
   c. OK Rachel had disappeared BY THE TIME Jon fell asleep
   d. * Rachel disappeared BY THE TIME Jon had fallen asleep

[1] While some speakers accept (2d), (2c) is widely preferred. In this paper sentences that are marginal but are improved by a tense shift are marked with an asterisk — more finely articulated theories of relative grammaticality must await further progress.

To see how factoring out general constraints affects the lexical representations of connectives, consider that under a completely naive, completely lexical approach, the answer to question 2 would be: *For each temporal/causal connective, its lexical entry must represent exactly which subset of all possible combinations of tenses in two clauses the connective is compatible with.* Since English has six simple tenses (see below), a little arithmetic[2] shows that the naive approach allows $2^{36} \approx 68$ billion possible lexical representations for connectives. This paper shows that, in fact, at most 8 different lexical representations are needed to answer question 2. This reduction is achieved by factoring general constraints that do not depend on lexical entries from specific constraints that do, i.e., from answering question 1 first. The factoring depends on a combination of results from Hornstein (in press) with new results not presented elsewhere. Hornstein's representation of tenses and the way they combine, which provides some constraint on the possible combinations, is presented in the next two sections. The remaining sections present new constraint, semantic interpretation, and a computer model.

An outline of the strategy followed in this research, which doubles as an outline of this paper, is provided below.

1. Discover and exploit as much general syntactic constraint as possible.
2. Determine which features of syntactic constructs must be represented in the lexical entries of individual connectives. (This endeavor is called **lexical syntax**.)
3. Attempt to find semantic interpretations of the lexical-syntactic features. (This endeavor is called **lexical semantics**.)
4. Implement a computer model of the theory to verify its behavior and demonstrate potential applications to natural language processing.

The Representation

In order to construct a formal theory explaining which tenses can be combined we need a representation of tense. The representation used here is taken from Hornstein (in press), who bases it on Comrie (1985). It is a Neo-Reichenbachian representation (Reichenbach 1947) in that its simple tense structures (STSs) relate the following three entities: the time of the event named by the verb, denoted by "E", the time of speech, denoted by "S", and a reference time, denoted by "R". The reference time R is used to locate an event with respect to another event in sentences like (2a) and (2c) above. (A mechanism for connecting tenses via the R point will be detailed below.) Each STS consists of a relation between S and R and one between R and E; S and E are not directly related. For any time points X and Y, at most one of four possible syntactic (that is, formal) relations holds between them. These are written as in Table 1.

Initially, Hornstein assumes that "_" is interpreted as temporal precedence and "," as simultaneity. Thus construed, (1) would mean *X precedes Y*, (2) would mean *Y precedes X*, and

[2]Here is the calculation: 6 possible tenses for the matrix clause and six for the adjunct clause gives 36 possible combinations in two-clause sentences; a given temporal/causal connective might be compatible with any subset of the 36 tense combinations. There are 2^{36} such subsets, and therefore at least 2^{36} possible lexical representations for a given connective.

(1) X_Y	(2) Y_X	(3) X,Y	(4) Y,X

Table 1: **The four possible relations between time points X and Y**

past	E,R R_S	(*R. disappeared*)	past perfect	E_R R_S	(*R. had disappeared*)
present	S,R R,E	(*R. disappears*)	present perfect	E_R R,S	(*R. has disappeared*)
future	S_R R,E	(*R. will disappear*)	future perfect	E_R S_R	(*R. will disappear*)

Table 2: **The six STSs that can be expressed in English verbal morphology**

(3) and (4) would mean *X and Y are simultaneous.* Note that although Hornstein gives the same interpretation to (3) and (4), they remain syntactically distinct. For the lexical syntactic endeavor we need not commit to a specific interpretation. It is important, however, that "_" be interpreted as some partial order, call it $<$, and that "," be interpreted as some symmetric relation, call it $=$. Furthermore, $=$ must be such that $X < Y$ and $Y = Z$ together imply $X < Z$. Particular relations for $<$ and $=$ will be considered briefly in the section on lexical semantics.

There are four possible S-R relations and four possible R-E relations for a total of 16 possible simple tense structures. Of these, six[3] can be expressed in English using only verbal morphology (see Table 2). The interpretation of the past STS, for example, would be written $E = R < S$, while that of the past perfect STS would be written $E < R < S$. Under Hornstein's initial interpretation, where $<$ is precedence and $=$ is simultaneity, these STSs yield the intuitively correct ordering of events.

Causal/Temporal Adjunct Clauses

This section and the next correspond to stage 1 of the strategy outlined above, identifying general syntactic constraints.

The tense structure of an adjunct clause is composed with that of its matrix by **identifying** their respective S and R points. **Identifying** two points means treating them as a single entity. Consider sentence (2a). The matrix clause in (2a) is in the past tense and the adjunct clause (the one following the connective) is in the past perfect. We write the combined tense structure (CTS) for a past matrix with a past perfect adjunct as in (3),

```
(3)  E,R R_S (past matrix)
       | | |
     E_R R_S (past perfect adjunct)
```

where the vertical links represent identity. If two points are to be treated as the same point they must stand in the same relationship to all other points. This becomes an issue when more than

[3]Some of the remaining combinations occur when above the tense structures are modified by adverbs and adjuncts. See Hornstein, in press, for details.

one pair of points is identified. For example, consider the CTS (4), which corresponds to sentences like (1).

```
(4) S,R R,E  (present matrix)
    | | |
    S_R R,E  (future adjunct)
```

(4) is ill-formed because the single entity formed out of S_{mat} and S_{adj} stands in two inconsistant relations to the single entity formed out of R_{mat} and R_{adj}. On the upper tier, which comes from the matrix clause's tense, we have S, R; on the lower, adjunct tier we have S_R. In this way the process of tense combination imposes a well-formedness condition on CTSs.

There is one qualification to the well-formedness condition on CTSs discussed above: in the configuration shown in (5)

```
(5) X_Y (matrix)
    | |
    W,Z (adjunct)
```

the adjunct W,Z can be "harmonized" or "coerced" to W_Z. This transformation occurs only when the matrix clause is "_", the adjunct is ",", and linear order is preserved. Such a transformation accounts for the the very widespread coercibility of presents to futures. One example of such coercion is the ability of present tense clauses to be adjoined to futures, as in (6).

(6) Rachel will disappear {when, once, before} Jon falls asleep.

The combined tense structure for (6) is shown in Figure 1. Note that the adjunct clause in (6), although in the present tense, is interpreted as occurring in the future. Another example of such

```
(Recall that future = S_R R,E and present = S,R R,E)

S_R R,E (future matrix)
| | |
S_R R,E (present adjunct)
 |
COERCED
```

Figure 1: **A present tense adjunct coerced to future by a future tense matrix**

coercion, one not involving adjoined clauses this time, is the ability of present tense matrix clauses to be interpreted as futures when occurring with a future adverb, as in (7).

(7) I leave for New York tomorrow

The combination of the RS identification process for composition and the coercion discussed above permit only 16 combined tense structures. The 20 that it rules out are, like (1), clearly bad independent of the connective.[4]

More Constraints

Of the 16 combined tense structures permitted in Hornstein's account, seven seem to be either unattested or infelicitous. These seven are ruled out by the two new constraints proposed below.

Interpretability Constraint

Recall that the only commitment we have made to the interpretation of "_" and "," is that the former be interpreted as some partial order that we call "<", while the latter is interpreted as some equivalence relation that we call "=". With that assumption we can sometimes use transitivity to draw conclusions about the relationship between the matrix event and the adjunct event of a CTS. For example, the CTS in (8)

```
(8)  E_R R_S (past perfect matrix)
       | | |
     E,R R_S (past adjunct)
```

yields the interpretation $E_{mat} < R = E_{adj}$ and the deduction $E_{mat} < E_{adj}$. By contrast, CTSs containing the configuration shown in (9) yield no such deduction.

```
(9)  E_R (matrix)
       |
     E_R (adjunct)
```

(9) receives the interpretation $E_{mat} < R$ and $E_{adj} < R$, but it is completely uninformative about the relationship between E_{mat} and E_{adj}. The **Interpretability Constraint** says that all such CTS are infelicitous, allowing only CTSs where either $E_{adj} < E_{mat}$, $E_{mat} < E_{adj}$, or $E_{adj} = E_{mat}$ is a valid deduction. (10) shows a sentence violating the Interpretability Constraint.[5]

(10) * Rachel had disappeared before Jon had fallen asleep.

This constraint rules out 4 bad CTSs, leaving a total of 12 CTSs still possible.

[4] The identification process and the coercion process are taken from Hornstein (in press, Ch. 2), where they are discussed in slightly different terms.

[5] As usual, (10) is starred because it is not as good as a restatement with the tenses shifted to the simple past. There are certain discourse contexts in which (10) improves, but discourse considerations are beyond the scope of this paper.

Coercion Parameter & Full Interpretation

Because of the coercibility of adjunct S,R to S_R, some CTSs can be formed from more than one pair of simple tense structures. An example is shown in Figure 2. It appears that within a given

```
(Recall that future = S_R R,E and present = S,R R,E)

S_R R,E (future matrix)                          S_R R,E (future matrix)
|  |  |                   is identical to        |  |  |
S_R R,E (FUTURE ADJUNCT)                         S_R R,E (PRESENT ADJUNCT)
                                                  |
                                                COERCED
```

Figure 2: **Two ways of constructing the same CTS**

language either the coerced form of the adjunct or the form that requires no coercion is consistently preferred. In English and German the coerced forms are preferred, while in Romance languages the uncoerced forms are preferred. This suggests a cross-linguistic parameterization. What's more, there seems to be an economy constraint, or perhaps some version of the **principle of full interpretation** (Chomsky 1985) guiding the choice of this parameter. In English and German using uncoerced adjuncts (i.e., future and future perfect) requires an additional auxiliary word (*will*) not required for the use of coerced adjuncts (i.e., present and present perfect). Not surprisingly, the shorter, coerced forms are preferred in English and German. (11) provides an example in English. If some version of economy or full interpretation is at work here, one would

(11) a. OK Rachel will disappear when Jon falls asleep *(present adj.)*
b. * Rachel will disappear when Jon will fall asleep *(future adj.)*

expect that languages requiring the same number of auxiliaries for the coerced and uncoerced forms would choose the coercion parameter freely. This appears to be correct: Romance languages, which require auxiliaries for either present or future, use uncoerced forms.[6]

The coercion parameter rules out three of the remaining 12 CTSs, leaving only the nine acceptable ones.

Lexical Syntactic Features

We now turn from general constraints on all CTSs to the compatibility of particular CTSs with particular temporal/causal connectives. This constitutes stage 2 of the strategy outlined above.

Recall that the **Interpretability Constraint** permits only CTSs that yield one of the following deductions: $E_{adj} < E_{mat}$, $E_{mat} < E_{adj}$, or $E_{adj} = E_{mat}$. It turns out that **the particular**

[6] There is some debate as to whether Chinese has a bona-fide tense system, but if it does, it too has an equal number of tense marking words either way, but chooses the opposite setting as Romance.

	$E_{mat} < E_{adj}$	$E_{adj} < E_{mat}$	$E_{adj} = E_{mat}$
matrix adjunct	past perfect past	past past perfect	past past
matrix adjunct	present perfect present	present present perfect	present present
matrix adjunct	future perfect present	future present perfect	future present

Table 3: **Legal tense combinations arranged by interpretation**

deduction yielded by a given CTS is the only feature that affects its compatibility with a given temporal/causal connective.[7] The complete body of evidence supporting this observation cannot be presented in a paper so a few illustrative examples must suffice.

Consider the connective *once. Once* is compatible with any CTS whose interpretation yields the deduction $E_{adj} < E_{mat}$ (see Table 3).[8] *once* is not compatible with the CTSs where $E_{mat} < E_{adj}$. Sentences (2a,b) demonstrate this. The opposite holds for *by the time*, as shown in (2c,d). *When* and *before* are compatible only with CTSs where $E_{mat} = E_{adj}$.

Since there are only three kinds of CTSs for the purposes of connective compatibility, there are at most $2^3 = 8$ possible lexical representations needed to account for connective compatibility. As noted above, this is a reduction from the $2^{36} \approx 68$ billion such representations without constraint, and $2^{16} \approx 64$ thousand based on the constraint provided by Hornstein's account of temporal adjunction.[9]

Lexical Semantics

This section corresponds to stage 3 of the strategy outlined above, the attempt to assign meaning to the lexical syntactic features introduced above. The following is a brief a outline of issues and possible solutions.

We have posited lexical features that assert the compatibility of a given connective with combined tense structures implying one of the three possible $E_{mat} - E_{adj}$ relations. The interpretation of these features is naturally tied to the interpretation of the $E_{mat} - E_{adj}$ relation itself. As noted above, Hornstein (in press) initially assumes that "<", the interpretation of "_", is temporal precedence and that "=", the interpretation of ",", is simultaneity. This is natural for simple tense structures, but the interpretation of = as simultaneity runs into trouble when $E_{mat} = E_{adj}$ is deduced from CTSs. To see the difficulty, first note that the connective *when* can appear only with CTSs where $E_{mat} = E_{adj}$. Then consider (12).[10] In (12a) the adjunct event precedes (or

[7] But see the caveat on aspectual class below.

[8] *once* is also compatible with $E_{mat} = E_{adj}$, although no examples are shown.

[9] The idea that only the E-E relation matters for connective compatibility was suggested in Hornstein (in press, Ch. 2), but it could not be demonstrated until the Interpretability Constraint and the Coercion Parameter were factored out.

[10] Moens and Steedman (1988) attribute (12) to Ritchie (1979).

(12) When they built the 39th St. Bridge...

a. ...a local architect drew up the plans
b. ...they used the very best materials
c. ...they solved most of the traffic problems

overlaps) the matrix event, in (12b) they overlap, and in (12c) the matrix event precedes the adjunct event. This observation casts doubt on the possibility of interpreting the $E_{mat} = E_{adj}$ deduction, and hence the lexical features that determine connective compatibility, in any simple way. Hornstein (in press, Ch. 2) notes this and suggests that the interpretation of "," is less specific than simultaneity, allowing the connective and other contextual factors to influence it. But that approach is slightly disquieting, since the interpretation of "," as simultaneity was important for the appeal of the simple tense structures of Table 2. One way out would be to maintain simultaneity as the interpretation of ",", while loosening the notion of identification of respective S and R points. The vertical bars in a combined tense structure such as (8) might be interpreted by some relation looser than either identity or simultaneity. In that case both "," and "—" would imply =, but "," would also carry the more specific simultaneity interpretation.[11] One possible interpretation of the vertical bars (and hence of =) is that the points connected by them are temporally near enough to allow immediate causal dependency to hold between them. (See Moens & Steedman, 1988.) Another is that no relevant events intervened between E_{mat} and E_{adj}. These definitions leave the specific time frame dependent on aspectual, pragmatic, and discourse considerations, a degree of flexibility that seems to be required by the data. At the same time they preserve the natural interpretation of "," in the simple tense structures.

The Computer Model

This section represents stage 4 of the strategy outlined above, the development of a computer model to verify the behavior of the theory and demonstrate some potential applications.

The theory presented above was implemented as a computer program. The program operates on parse trees, building complex tense structures out of simple ones and determining whether or not they are grammatical according to the syntactic and lexical constraints of the theory. This program was linked to a simple feature-grammar parser. In addition to building the CTS for a sentence, the program lists the interpretations of the CTSs it accepts and the constraints violated by the CTSs it rejects. It's behavior on some sentences from (1) and (2) is shown below.

```
;;; * Rachel disappears when Jon will fall asleep
(compute-tense-structures
  (parse '(Rachel +s disappear when Jon will fall-asleep)))
((TS
S,R   R,E    PRESENT
| |   |
S_R   R,E    FUTURE
* CTS violates:  economy: prefer S,R   R,E    PRESENT; CDTS))
```

[11] Note that the Interpretability Constraint makes sense only if $<$ is reinterpreted so that $X = Y$ implies that neither $X < Y$ and $Y < X$.

```
;;; OK: Rachel disappeared once Jon had fallen asleep
(compute-tense-structures
  (parse '(Rachel +ed disappear once Jon +ed have +en fall-asleep)))
((TS
E,R   R_S     PAST
  |    | |
E_R   R_S     PAST-PERFECT
interp: E(adj)<E(mat)))

;;; * Rachel had disappeared once Jon fell asleep
(compute-tense-structures
  (parse '(Rachel +ed have +en disappear once Jon +ed fall-asleep)))
((TS
E_R   R_S     PAST-PERFECT
  |    | |
E,R   R_S     PAST
* CTS violates:  connective compatibility))
```

Conclusions

The strategy outlined in the first section has yielded a satisfying explanation of the possible combinations of tenses and temporal/causal connectives. However, one of the stages of that strategy, finding semantic interpretations of the lexical syntactic features, remains to be fully worked out. A second direction in which this research will be pushed is toward verbal aspect, which in some cases affects the acceptability of tense combinations in interesting ways. In particular, some ideas of Hinrichs (1986) might be fruitfully applied to factor in the effect of, for example, stative verbs on the $E_{mat} - E_{adj}$ interpretation.[12] In summary, a major source of constraint on tense combinations in adjoined clauses has been uncovered and partially explored, but exciting new treasures may lie beyond the next bend.

References

Chomsky, N. (1985) *Knowledge of Language.* Praeger, New York.

Comrie, B. (1985) *Tense* Cambridge University Press, Cambridge.

Hinrichs, E. (1986) "Temporal Anaphora in Discourses of English". *Linguistics and Philosophy* 9(1): 63-82.

Hornstein, N. (forthcoming) *As Time Goes By: Tense and Universal Grammar.* MIT Press, Cambridge, MA

Moens, M. and M. Steedman (1988) "Temporal Ontology and Temporal Reference". *Computational Linguistics*, 14(2).

Reichenbach, H. (1947) reprinted 1966 in *The Elements of Symbolic Logic.* The Free Press, New York, NY.

Ritchie, G. (1979) "Temporal Clauses in English". *Theoretical Linguistics* 6:87-115.

Vendler, Z. (1967) "Verbs and Times". Ch. 4 of *Linguistics in Philosophy.* Cornell University Press, Ithaca, NY.

[12]In general, the Vendlerian classes (Vendler, 1967) of verbs may affect the acceptability of tense combinations.

A Critical Look at the Foundations of Autonomous Syntactic Analysis

Lawrence Birnbaum

Yale University
Department of Computer Science
New Haven, Connecticut

I argue that the claim of autonomous syntactic processing is irrefutable if non-determinism is permitted, e.g., by the use of arbitrary choice and backtracking. The vast majority of existing models of syntactic analysis, therefore, cannot support such a claim if it is to be considered an *empirical* claim. More recent deterministic theories of syntactic analysis—in particular, Marcus (1980) and Marcus *et al.* (1983)—seem at first glance more promising. However, by their repeated failure to address many of the problems which make language analysis so difficult in the first place—such as lexical ambiguity and genuine structural ambiguity—these theories too fail to assert or support an empirically significant claim of autonomous syntactic processing. Moreover, the very problems in language analysis that these theories ignore provide strong evidence that such claims are in fact false.

AUTONOMY AND DETERMINISM

The autonomy of syntax—or the lack of it—has long been a contentious issue within the cognitive sciences. Part of the contentiousness has been due to a certain degree of vagueness, probably unavoidable, as to what exactly would constitute "autonomy." A rather modest claim might be that semantics does not dictate the content of syntactic facts, for example the fact that adjectives precede nouns in English noun phrases. While such a claim might be interesting from a linguistic perspective, however, it is the question of whether syntactic *processing* is autonomous that is of greatest interest to artificial intelligence. Within the realm of processing, the claim that is generally identified with syntactic autonomy is the following: That the syntactic structure of linguistic input can and should be determined by a process that makes little or no reference to semantic and contextual information.

Now, whether syntactic analysis *should* be autonomous in this way depends on whether that would, on balance, be the most useful approach. Such utility might be defined with respect to the ability to explain characteristics of human language processing, or more functionally, with respect to facilitating the construction of language processing systems that are more efficient, more easily extended, more robust, etc. The more basic question, however, and the one that is addressed most directly by computational modelling, is this: Is it even *possible* to construct models of syntactic analysis that are autonomous in the sense described above?

On the face of it, obviously, this question seems rather silly. After all, quite a large number of autonomous syntactic analyzers have been written and are in use at the present time. However, the aim of this paper is to show that current models of syntactic analysis in fact fail to support an empirically significant claim of autonomous syntactic processing. My argument will involve making explicit what is in fact required in order for such a claim to be "empirically significant."

The first part of the argument concerns *non-deterministic* models of syntactic analysis, which constitute by far the overwhelming majority of such models. When confronted with a possible or genuine ambiguity in the syntactic analysis of an input, non-deterministic parsers either pursue all possible analyses, or decide which analysis to pursue *arbitrarily,* while making some provision for backtracking should that decision prove erroneous. Leaving aside the obvious issue of computational efficiency, or even tractability, there is a deeper problem with such an approach. For if non-determinism is permitted, then *if it is possible to construct a process model of syntactic analysis at all, it will* always *be possible to construct one that is autonomous:* Whenever a syntactic decision seems to require contextual information of the sort that is forbidden under the assumption of autonomy, a non-deterministic model can always be constructed that simply pursues all possible choices, or else chooses arbitrarily, and then backtracks if that choice proves mistaken. Thus, the claim that the syntactic analysis of linguistic inputs can be accomplished without appeal to semantic or contextual information is *irrefutable* if non-determinism is permitted. As a result, non-deterministic models of syntactic analysis cannot support the claim that syntactic analysis is possible without the use of semantic and contextual information—at least, not if that claim is intended as an empirical one. This includes, to repeat, the vast majority of syntactic analyzers, including obviously all ATN-like models (e.g., Thorne, Bratley, and Dewar, 1968; Bobrow and Fraser, 1969; Woods, 1970; and numerous descendant models), as well as Prolog-based parsers (e.g., Colmerauer, 1978; Pereira and Warren, 1980).

In order to support an empirically meaningful claim of syntactic autonomy, then, a model of syntactic analysis must be *deterministic.* This makes Marcus's (1980) attempt to construct such a model, and subsequent efforts, particularly significant and noteworthy. However, I will argue below—using Marcus's theory as a prototype case—that that these models, too, systematically fail to address issues that must be addressed in order to support an empirically significant claim of autonomous syntactic processing.[1] In particular, I will articulate the functional requirements that must be met by the output of a syntactic analyzer in order to sustain such a claim, show how current theories fail to address those requirements, and show further that there is good evidence that in fact those requirements cannot be met.

One final comment: It is important to be clear that the main point of this paper is *not* to refute the possibility of any empirically significant claim of autonomous syntactic processing being true, although I believe that the preponderence of evidence argues for such a conclusion. Rather, my point is that current models of syntactic analysis simply fail to support such an empirically significant claim.

DETERMINISM AND GENUINE STRUCTURAL AMBIGUITY

Genuine structural ambiguity poses a severe problem to a theory of deterministic, autonomous syntactic analysis. The dedication to autonomy largely forecloses the use of semantic and

[1]My use of Marcus's theory as the prototypical case should not be taken to imply that it suffers from any special problem. Quite the contrary, it reflects my view that his work constitutes the most comprehensive and explicit defense of syntactic autonomy from a computational perspective.

contextual information to resolve such ambiguity within the language analyzer itself, while the dedication to determinism militates against generating all possible analyses automatically. What Marcus (1980) decided to do about this quandary, therefore, was to preserve autonomy, but shift the burden of non-determinism to the language understanding process as a whole. In particular, he proposed that the syntactic analyzer would produce only one analysis of an input sentence at a time—even if others were possible—and that if this analysis proved incorrect, the analyzer would be called on the same input again, with some provision made to block the original, erroneous analysis.

Such an approach does not immediately render the theory empirically insignificant: After all, it might prove impossible to construct a deterministic autonomous analyzer capable of dealing even with those ambiguities that remain. Nevertheless, it is highly questionable for several reasons. First, I think it is fair to say that such an approach greatly reduces the scope of Marcus's claims: His parser no longer needs to be concerned about resolving those potential structural ambiguities that turn out to reflect actual structural ambiguities of the input. Even more, it no longer needs to deal with any subsequent potential ambiguity that might be caused by prior, genuine ambiguity—that is, potential ambiguity that might have arisen if some prior genuine ambiguity had not been resolved, expeditiously, by fiat.[2]

Second, on this account, the rest of the understanding system must in some way be able to prevent the syntactic analyzer from producing the original, and erroneous, analysis, so that some other analysis will be produced instead. But in order to do that, the language understanding process as a whole needs some knowledge of, and access to, the internals of the syntactic processor. It is, of course, exactly to avoid this kind of interaction that autonomous theories are proposed in the first place.

Now, what Marcus (1980) seems to imply, presumably in an attempt to forestall such criticism, is that the rest of the understanding system need not know very *much* in order to control the syntactic analyzer's behavior in this way. All that seems necessary is a communication protocol by which the rest of the understanding system could send a message indicating that the syntactic analyzer should "reparse the input, taking a different analysis path, if the other consistent analyses are desired," (Marcus, 1980, note 10, p. 13). However, the apparent simplicity of such an interaction belies the underlying additional complexity of the syntactic anlyzer which it presupposes. In particular, in order to make such a scheme work, the syntactic processor would need to keep a record of the decisions which, if made differently, would result in an alternate analysis, including its state at each of those decision points, the order in which those decisions arose, and some way of keeping track of which alternatives it had already chosen in producing previous analyses. In a word, that is, it would need all of the machinery that is needed to implement non-determinism.

The main defect of this approach, however, does not lie in the additional costs, in terms of increased complexity, that are imposed on the syntactic processor itself. The real problem here is that the theory is robbing Peter, repeatedly, to pay Paul once: Determinism and autonomy are preserved for the syntactic analyzer at the expense of non-determinism in the language understanding process as a whole. On this account, determining the correct interpretation of

[2]These same objections can be raised about Marcus's failure to address the issue of lexical ambiguity; see Birnbaum (1985).

genuinely ambiguous sentences requires the use of arbitrary choice and backtracking not by the syntactic processor alone, but by the syntactic and semantic processors in conjunction. That is, if the knowledge of and access to the internals of the syntactic analyzer on the part of the understanding system as a whole are to be kept to a minimum—as they must be, in order to uphold the claim of autonomy—then not only can semantic and contextual processes play no role in determining the syntactic analysis of an input utterance, but the only information that they can transmit to the syntactic module about an inappropriate analysis is that it *is* inappropriate. As a result, no information about the particular *way* in which the analysis happens to be inappropriate can be used to help produce the correct analysis. In sum, the cost of minimizing the bandwidth of communication between syntactic processing and other processing in this case is that the language understander as a whole is reduced to the crudest and most expensive possible method for producing an appropriate interpretation of the input, namely, arbitrary choice and backtracking.[3]

Perhaps most troubling, however, is not the fact that Marcus's theory avoids the problems posed by genuine structural ambiguity, but the manner in which it does so. Simply putting such problems aside—shifting the burden of non-determinism to the understanding process as a whole—places this entire approach on a slippery slope. One can, obviously, continue to put aside each problem that seems to require sacrificing either determinism or autonomy, and narrow the scope of the theory further and further—what has been dubbed by one of my colleagues "the incredible shrinking module." But, just as with the use of non-determinism, this leads ultimately to theories which are irrefutable. It is tautological that the subset of syntactic decisions that can be resolved deterministically, using only syntactic information, can in fact be resolved within a deterministic, autonomous model of syntactic analysis. If the claim of autonomy is to have any empirical force, therefore, it is necessary to show that the set of such decisions, and the rules needed to resolve them, can be characterized in advance. And it seems to me that the fact that exactly the same potential ambiguity can, in some cases, be resolved within a sentence on syntactic grounds, and in others leads to genuine structural ambiguity, immediately refutes this possibility in the case of most, if not all, syntactic decisions.

This point also bears on one of the most common arguments made in favor of autonomous syntactic analysis. There is a common-sense grain of truth at the root of the idea, and it is often put as follows: "What's the problem here? You let syntax do what it can deterministically, and then semantics takes care of the rest." Although even this claim is arguable, let's suppose that it were true. It simply does not follow that there must exist an independent syntactic processor which makes those particular decisions that can in fact be made deterministically using only syntactic information. It is perfectly compatible with almost any view of language processing that decisions that don't happen, in a particular instance, to require the use of semantics can be made, in that instance, without such information. Once again, therefore, the fact that particular *instances* of syntactic decisions can be made deterministically using only syntactic information does not support an empirically meaningful claim of autonomous syntactic analysis. What is

[3]It is also worth pointing out that this approach to genuinely ambiguous sentences seems inconsistent with Marcus's account of garden path sentences. That account rests on the claim that people do not backtrack and produce an alternate analysis for an input without becoming consciously aware of that fact. However, this raises the question of why people are not consciously aware of backtracking when confronted with genuinely ambiguous sentences. In any case, Crain and Steedman (1985) have demonstrated that the phenomenon of garden path sentences is crucially dependent upon semantic and pragmatic factors, and that no purely syntactic account, such as Marcus's, can be correct.

necessary is that classes of such decisions, and the rules which are necessary to make them, be characterized and specified in advance as the proper domain of an autonomous syntactic analyzer.

REDEFINING THE OUTPUT

Consider now the problems raised in determining, and representing, the correct role of a prepositional phrase within a sentence—one of the most common instances of genuine structural ambiguity in English, and moreover a problem that is widely acknowledged, even by Marcus, to require heavy use of semantic and contextual information. Because a syntactic analyzer is by itself incapable of correctly determining where to attach a prepositional phrase, Marcus's original parser simply attached all such phrases to the closest available constituent that was syntactically acceptable, regardless of whether or not that is correct (personal communication). For example, it would analyze the sentence "I kissed the girl in the park on the lips," as if the prepositional phrase "on the lips" modified the noun "park."

More recently, Marcus, Hindle, and Fleck (1983) have attempted to face up to this sort of problem by proposing that the output of a syntactic analyzer should not, in fact, be a phrase marker of the sort employed in linguistics. Instead, they propose that it should be something vaguer and less informative, a description corresponding to a set of such phrase markers.[4] In particular, the relation "immediately dominates" in the structural description of a sentence is replaced by the less informative relation "dominates," and constituents are referred to by non-unique names, so that two symbols may—if the facts that are known about the constituents to which they refer are compatible—turn out to refer to the same constituent.

Unfortunately, however, once again no functional justification is offered for this sort of output, other than the fact that it may prove possible to produce it without the use of semantic and contextual information, and once again this failure places the entire approach on a slippery slope. As long as the output of the syntactic analyzer can be redefined to be less informative—without being subject to any constraints of functional utility—whenever the attempt to produce a more informative output appears to threaten either autonomy or non-determinism, then of course it will always be possible to maintain them both. But if the output of a syntactic analyzer is defined as that structural information about a sentence which can be deterministically derived without appeal to semantic or contextual information, then it is once again tautological that deterministic autonomous syntactic analysis is possible. Unless it can be demonstrated that such an output will be functionally useful, the claim of autonomy is without empirical content. Just as much as permitting arbitrary choice and back-up, defining the output in this way results in autonomous theories which are irrefutable. To take this to its logical conclusion, one can quite simply write a deterministic parser that does not require semantics: It need only take in strings and output them without alteration. Without applying the constraints of functional utility, we have no guarantee that the output of a process is anything other than a trivial transformation of the input.

Moreover, although a functionally justified output is a *necessary* condition for an empirically significant claim of autonomy, it is by no means *sufficient*. It must also be shown that the information contained in such an output can actually be exploited without violating the original

[4]A similar proposal was subsequently made by Barton and Berwick (1985). The comments that follow apply equally to this work.

claim of syntactic autonomy, and this is not a foregone conclusion: The utilization of such a representation may itself turn out to require the highly integrated application of syntactic, semantic, and contextual information. That is, even if it were possible to produce useful syntactic representations in a deterministic autonomous fashion, such representations might prove too impoverished to support the application of useful—or even necessary—syntactic rules. Indeed, it is quite possible that a given syntactic rule could sometimes be applied by the syntactic processor—given a simple and unambiguous enough input—while at other times the information necessary to apply the same rule would not be available. If such rules are genuinely useful, then it will be necessary to apply them after sufficient information about the structure of the input has been recovered—which is to say, after semantic and contextual information have been applied. There seems little point to the claim of autonomy under such circumstances.

It is important to understand that the above argument is not merely theoretical. The output produced according to Marcus *et al.* (1983) is in fact insufficiently informative to support the use of the putative syntactic rules constraining pronoun reference cited in Marcus (1984), in response to Schank and Birnbaum (1984), as arguing for the need to compute explicit, independent syntactic representations. Such rules depend on knowing, rather precisely, how high in the structural description of a sentence a noun phrase is with respect to a potentially co-referent noun phrase, and this is exactly the sort of information that has been discarded by Marcus *et al.*'s later theory.

In particular, the rule cited by Marcus (1984) is as follows:[5]

> Given two noun phrases NP1 and NP2 in a sentence, if (1) NP1 precedes NP2 in the sentence, (2) NP1 commands NP2—i.e., the first noun phrase or sentence node above NP1 is also above NP2—and (3) NP2 is not a pronoun, then NP1 and NP2 cannot be coreferential.

The problem here, of course, is with the notion of "command" used in the second condition of this rule. Consider, for example, the following sentence: "I recognized the spirit in him by the boy's behavior." Determining that "him" and "the boy" can be coreferential according to this rule depends on knowing that the prepositional phrase "in him" is attached to the noun phrase "the spirit," while the prepositional phrase "by the boy's behavior" is attached to the verb phrase "recognized." In that case, "him" does not command "the boy," and so the rule permits them to be coreferential—as indeed they seem to be. If instead, for example, they were both attached to the verb phrase, then "him" *would* command "the boy," and coreference would be blocked.[6] However, since prepositional phrase attachment depends on semantic and contextual information, on Marcus *et al.*'s account this determination would not be made by the syntactic analyzer. Thus, if such syntactic rules for pronoun reference were in fact to be applied in understanding, that could only occur *after* semantic and contextual information had been employed to recover sufficiently explicit information about the structure of the input utterance. Indeed, on this account, such syntactic rules would not even seem to be within the province of the syntactic

[5]Marcus references Lasnik's (1976) formulation of this rule. However, the original insight that "precede and command" relations might play a role in explaining pronominal reference is due to Langacker (1966).

[6]This mistaken reading corresponds, as a matter of fact, to what Marcus *et al.* call the "default" interpretation of their representation.

processor itself. Alternatively, one might consider using the above pronominal reference rule to help determine the appropriate syntactic analysis of an input. That, however, would depend on a prior decision as to whether the noun phrases in question should be viewed as coreferential or not—and *that* decision could only be made using semantic and contextual information.

Now the fact is that I don't believe that these rules are completely correct, or that a purely syntactic account of the phenomena in question is actually possible. (A convincing critique of such claims can, in any event, be found in Bolinger, 1979.) Still, I am not sure that I would go so far as to say that syntax plays no role in the matter, and unless Marcus is prepared to say that that is the case, he must concede either (1) that sophisticated syntactic knowledge must exist and be applied outside of the syntactic processor, (2) that semantic and contextual preferences about coreference actively constrain syntactic representations, rather than the other way around as Marcus (1984) contends, or else (3) he must abandon determinism. It is not clear, under these circumstances, what the claim of syntactic autonomy amounts to.

THE NEXT MOVE

It seems clear that job of developing models of language analysis capable of supporting an empirically significant claim of autonomous syntactic processing is far more difficult than has been recognized by proponents of such claims. In particular, the use of vague syntactic representations is not the panacea that it might at first appear to be. One possible alternative is Tomita's (1985) proposal to use a "shared-packed forest" representation as the output of a syntactic analyzer. This proposal shares with Marcus *et al.*'s the idea of an output that represents a set of possible syntactic descriptions rather than just one, but differs radically in the way that it does so. Rather than using a vague description corresponding to a set of possible syntactic analyses, a shared-packed forest representation encodes all of the possible interpretations of an ambiguous sentence in an extremely compact and efficient way. Although Tomita's overall approach has severe limitations as currently formulated—in particular, from both a computational and a linguistic perspective, the restriction to context-free grammars, and from a psychological perspective, the difficulty of accounting for garden path sentences in a model that carries forward all possible analyses[7]—his representation seems superior to Marcus *et al.*'s as far as the application of the coreference rule described above is concerned. That is, it seems quite feasible to apply such rules to a shared-packed forest representation.[8]

The larger point remains, however, that rules of this sort cannot unambiguously be applied as filters to narrow the choices available to semantic and contextual analysis, as Marcus (1984) contends. What they might decide depends on what the correct syntactic analysis is determined to be, and this determination will involve arbitrarily complex inferential processing. Such a decision may, in a given case, make use of potential syntactic constraints on coreference; but then again, it may not. The picture that emerges is one in which syntactic, semantic, and contextual constraints are exploited in an interleaved manner.

[7] Although, in fairness to Tomita, it is not at all clear how Marcus *et al.*'s theory could account for them either.

[8] There is however, some question as to the functional suitability of such representations in a larger language processing system: At least one project attempting to use Tomita's approach was led to discard local ambiguity packing, the most novel aspect of his representation, as being more trouble than it was worth (A. Fano, personal communication).

Acknowledgments: This paper is based on portions of my Ph.D. thesis (Birnbaum, 1986). I owe a special debt to my advisor, Roger Schank, as well as the other members of my committee, Robert Abelson, Drew McDermott, and Elliot Soloway, for their help and support. Chris Riesbeck first taught me about language analysis. I also thank Gregg Collins, Ed Hovy, Steve Lytinen, Mitch Marcus, Charlie Martin, Rod McGuire, and Mallory Selfridge for many spirited discussions on these topics. Special thanks to Eric Jones for helping me to understand the implications of Tomita's "shared-packed forest" representation. This work was supported in part by the Defense Advanced Research Projects Agency, monitored by the Office of Naval Research under contract N0014-85-K-0108.

REFERENCES

Barton, E., and Berwick, R. 1985. Parsing with assertion sets and information monotonicity. *Proceedings of the Ninth IJCAI,* Los Angeles, CA, pp. 769-771.

Birnbaum, L. 1985. Lexical ambiguity as a touchstone for theories of language analysis. *Proceedings of the Ninth IJCAI,* Los Angeles, CA, pp. 815-820.

Birnbaum, L. 1986. Integrated processing in planning and understanding. Research report no. 489, Yale University, Dept. of Computer Science, New Haven, CT.

Bobrow, D., and Fraser, B. 1969. An augmented state transition network analysis procedure. *Proceedings of the First IJCAI,* Washington, DC, pp. 557-567.

Bolinger, D. 1979. Pronouns in discourse. In T. Givon, ed., *Syntax and Semantics, Vol. 12: Discourse and Syntax,* Academic Press, New York, pp. 289-309.

Colmerauer, A. 1978. Metamorphosis grammars. In L. Bolc, ed., *Natural Language Communication with Computers,* Springer, Berlin, pp. 133-189.

Crain, S., and Steedman, M. 1985. On not being led down the garden path: The use of context by the psychological parser. In D. Dowty, L. Karttunen, and A. Zwicky, eds., *Natural Language Parsing: Psychological, Computational, and Theoretical Perspectives,* Cambridge University Press, Cambridge, England.

Langacker, R. 1966. On pronominalization and the chain of command. In W. Reibel and S. Schane, eds., *Modern Studies in English,* Prentice Hall, Englewood Cliffs, NJ.

Lasnik, H. 1976. Remarks on coreference. *Linguistic Analysis,* vol. 2, no. 1.

Marcus, M. 1980. *A Theory of Syntactic Recognition for Natural Language.* MIT Press, Cambridge, MA.

Marcus, M. 1984. Some inadequate theories of human language processing. In T. Bever, J. Carroll, and L. Miller, eds., *Talking Minds: The Study of Language in Cognitive Science,* MIT Press, Cambridge, MA, pp. 253-278.

Marcus, M., Hindle, D., and Fleck, M. 1983. D-theory: Talking about talking about trees. *Proceedings of the 21st ACL Conference,* Cambridge, MA, pp. 129-136.

Pereira, F., and Warren, D. 1980. Definite clause grammars for language analysis—A survey of the formalism and a comparison with augmented transition networks. *Artificial Intelligence,* vol. 13, pp. 231-278.

Schank, R., and Birnbaum, L. 1984. Memory, meaning, and syntax. In T. Bever, J. Carroll, and L. Miller, eds., *Talking Minds: The Study of Language in Cognitive Science,* MIT Press, Cambridge, MA, pp. 209-251.

Thorne, J., Bratley, P., and Dewar, H. 1968. The syntactic analysis of English by machine. In D. Michie, ed., *Machine Intelligence, Vol. 3,* American Elsevier, New York, pp. 281-309.

Tomita, M. 1985. An efficient context-free parsing algorithm for natural languages. *Proceedings of the Ninth IJCAI,* Los Angeles, CA, pp. 756-764.

Woods, W. 1970. Transition network grammars for natural language analysis. *Communications of the ACM,* vol. 13, pp. 591-606.

The Frame of Reference Problem in Cognitive Modeling

William J. Clancey

Institute for Research on Learning

ABSTRACT

Since at least the mid-70's there has been widespread agreement among cognitive science researchers that models of a problem-solving agent should incorporate its knowledge about the world and an inference procedure for interpreting this knowledge to construct plans and take actions. Research questions have focused on how knowledge is represented in computer programs and how such cognitive models can be verified in psychological experiments. We are now experiencing increasing confusion and misunderstanding as different critiques are leveled against this methodology and new jargon is introduced (e.g., "not rules," "ready-to-hand," "background," "situated," "subsymbolic"). Such divergent approaches put a premium on improving our understanding of past modeling methods, allowing us to more sharply contrast proposed alternatives. This paper compares and synthesizes new robotic research that is founded on the idea that knowledge does not consist of objective representations of the world. This research develops a new view of planning that distinguishes between a robot designer's ontological preconceptions, the dynamics of a robot's interaction with an environment, and an observer's descriptive theories of patterns in the robot's behavior. These frame-of-reference problems are illustrated here and unified by a new framework for describing cognitive models.

CHANGE AND CONFLUENCE IN COGNITIVE SCIENCE

What accounts for the regularities we observe in intelligent behavior? Many cognitive scientists would respond, "Mental structures which are representations, symbols of things in the world." Since at least the mid-70's there has been widespread agreement among cognitive science researchers that models of a problem-solving agent should incorporate knowledge about the world and some sort of inference procedure for interpreting this knowledge to construct plans and take actions. Research questions have focused on how knowledge is represented in computer programs and how such cognitive models can be verified in psychological experiments.

We are now experiencing a change in the dominant paradigm, as different critiques are leveled against this methodology and new computational models, based on the idea of neural networks, are introduced. There have been many philosophical arguments against Cognitive Science and AI research over the years; what reason is there to suppose that we are making progress now on these complex issues? Most striking is the convergence of ideas and new approaches over the past 5 years:

o The long-standing criticism of Dreyfus (1972), for example, has been joined by insiders (Winograd & Flores, 1986)(Clancey, 1987)(Rommetveit, 1987);

o Neural net research has reminded us of the extent of the gap between neurobiology and cognitive science models, while new hardware and programming techniques have enabled a resurgence of network modeling (Rumelhart, et al.,1986);

- o Cognitive science itself has flourished and succeeded in including social scientists within the community, and their methods and analyses often starkly contrast with the AI view of human knowledge and reasoning (Suchman, 1987). For example, increasing emphasis is placed on representation construction as an activity within our perceptual space, organized by social interaction, (e.g., Allen, 1988), not something in our memory that precedes speaking, drawing, or action in general.

Criticisms of AI and cognitive science may have often failed to be effective because they aren't sufficiently grounded in computational modeling terminology and may even appear to be compatible with existing programs. For example, the current buzzword "situated" might just mean "conditional on the input data of particular situations"; hence all programs are situated. The discourse of another intellectual tradition may even appear incoherent to cognitive scientists; consider for example, "representation must be based on interactive differentiation and implicit definition" (Suchman, 1987, p. 78). Experienced AI researchers know that an engineering approach is essential for making progress on these issues. Perhaps the most important reason for recent progress and optimism about the future is the construction of alternative cognitive models as computer programs, the field's agreed basis for expressing theories:

- o The AI-learning community is focusing on how a given ontology of internal structures--the designer's prior commitment to the objects, events, and processes in the world--enables or limits a given space of behavior (e.g., the knowledge level analyses of (Dietterich, 1986) (Alexander, et al., 1986)).

- o New robots ("situated automata") demonstrate that a full map of the world isn't required for complex behavior; instead, maintaining a relation between an agent's perceptual state and new sensations enables simple mechanisms to bring about what observers would call search, tracking, avoidance, etc. (Braitenberg, 1984)(Brooks, 1988)(Agre, 1988) (Rosenschein, 1985).

- o Neural networks, incorporating "hidden layers" and using back-propagation learning, provide a new means of encoding input/output training relationships, and are suggestive of how sensory and motor learning may occur in the brain (Rumelhart, et al., 1986).

In essence, this new research reconsiders how the internal representations in an agent derive from the *dynamics of a physical situation*, relegating an observer's later descriptions of the patterns in the agent's behavior (what has been called "the agent's knowledge") to a different level of analysis. That is to say, this new research suggests that we reclassify most existing cognitive models as being *descriptive and relative to an observer's frame of reference*, not structure-function mechanisms internal to the agent that cause the observed behavior.

By systematically analyzing these emerging alternative intelligent architectures, placing them in ordered relation to each other, we should be able to articulate distinctions that the researchers couldn't accomplish alone. The result will be a better understanding of the diverse approaches to "situated cognition" and "neural networks" research, contrasted against conventional AI research. Thus, understanding a new approach and reconceptualizing what a "traditional" approach was about will arise together.

My approach here is to characterize the ontological commitments of the alternative models: What facts about the world are built into each program? Two useful, related questions are: *Who owns the representations* (robot, designer, or observer)? *Where's the knowledge* (in a designer's specification, in robotic memory, in the relation of the robot to its environment, or in our statements as observers)? Throughout, I will use the term "robot" to emphasize that we are dealing with designed artifacts intended to be agents in some known environment. I believe we need to distance ourselves from our programs, so we can better understand our relation to them. "Robot" here means any cognitive model implemented as a computer program, specifically including computational models of people. Our orientation here is not of philosophical discourse in the abstract, but rather trying to find *an appropriate language to describe existing robots and the process by which they are designed,* so the engineering methods for building them are clear enough to order, compare, and improve upon them. In the conclusion, I will reach beyond what has been currently built in order to articulate what designers are attempting to achieve and to relate to other analyses in anthropology, linguistics, and philosophy.

THE PROBLEM: THE ONTOLOGICAL COMMITMENTS OF PLANS

When we examine situated automata research, we find a striking emphasis on the *nature of planning*, focusing on the ontological commitments made by the designer of the computer program. Agre and Kaelbling (Kaelbling, 1988) emphasize the resource and information limitations of real-time behavior--deliberation between alternatives must be extremely limited and many details about the world (e.g., will the next closed door I approach open from the left or the right?) can't be anticipated. Rosenschein found that formal analyses of knowledge bases are problematic--how can they be related in a principled way to the world, when their meaning depends on the designer's changing interpretations of the data structures? Cohen was wedged in a designer's conundrum: Since AARON is supposed to be producing new drawings of people standing in a garden, how could he build in a representation of these drawings before they are made? (Cohen, 1988) Cohen was face to face with the ultimate ontological limit of traditional cognitive models: Any description of the world that he builds in as a designer will fix the space of AARON's drawings. How then can a robot be designed so it isn't limited by its designer's preconception of the world? If such limitations are inevitable for designed artifacts, how can the specification process be accomplished in a principled way? Following are four perspectives on these questions.

Classical Planning -- Knowledge is in the robot's memory

In most AI/cognitive science research to date, the descriptions of regularities in the world and regularities in the robot's behavior are called "knowledge" and located in the robot's memory. A robot preferably uses a declarative map of the world, planning constraints, metaplanning strategies, etc. This view is illustrated especially well by natural language programs, which incorporate in memory a model of the domain of discourse, script descriptions of activities, grammars, prose configuration plans, conversational patterns, etc. Aiming to cope with the computational limits of combinatoric and real-time constraints, some researchers are re-engineering their programs to use parallel processing, partial compilation, failure and alternative route anticipation, etc. These approaches might incorporate further ontological distinctions (e.g., preconceptions of what can go wrong), but adhere to the classical view of planning.

Knowledge is in the designer's specification.

Rosenschein introduces an interesting twist. Besides using efficient engineering (compiling programs into digital circuits), his methodology explicitly views the robot as a designed artifact. He formally specifies robotic behavior in terms of I/O and internal state changes, gaining the advantages of internal consistency and explicitly-articulated task assumptions. The problem of building a robot is viewed as an engineering problem, nicely delineating the designer's relation to the robot and the designed behavior.

Knowledge is not incorporated as data structure encodings; it is replaced by a design description that specifies how the state of the machine and the state of the environment should relate. Thus, knowledge is not something placed in the robot, but is a theoretical construct used by the designer for deriving a circuit whose interactive coupling with its environment has certain desirable properties. These "background constraints . . . comprise a permanent description of how the automaton is coupled to its environment and are themselves invariant under all state changes" (Rosenschein, 1985, p. 12). Regardless of how program structures are compiled or transformed by a learning process, the program embodies the designer's ontology. Rosenschein's formal analysis can be contrasted with Brooks' analogous, but ad-hoc constructive approach (functionally-layered, finite-state automata) (Brooks, 1988); Brooks assembles circuits without spelling out his ontological commitments to world objects, machine states, and relations among them.

Knowledge is the capacity to maintain dynamic relationships.
Agre views the ontological descriptions built into his robot as *indexical* and *functional*. That is, descriptions of entities, representations of the world, are inherently a combination of the robot's viewpoint (what it is doing now) and the role of environmental entities in the robot's activity. For example, the term *the-ice-cube-that-the-ice-cube-I-just-kicked-will-collide-with* combines the indexical perspective of the robot's ongoing activity (the ice cube I just kicked) with a functionally-directed visualization (one role of ice cubes is for destroying bees).

Agre demonstrates that an internal representation of the world needn't be global and objective, in the form of a map, but--for controlling robotic movements at least--can be restricted to ontological primitives that relate the robot's perceptions to its activities. There are two more general points here: The claim that representations are *inherently* indexical and functional (that is, a rejection of the correspondence theory of truth, that representations are objectively about the world) and the claim that the robot can get by with mostly local information about the activity around him. Agre is showing us a new way of talking about knowledge base representations, and demonstrating that a different perspective, that of "dynamics" as opposed to "objective description," can be used for constructing an ontology. It is arguable that Agre's programs aren't fundamentally different from conventional AI architectures; the use of hyphenation just makes explicit that internal names and variables are always interpreted from the frame of reference of the agent, relative to its activities. The important claim is metatheoretical: All representations are indexical, functional, and consequently subjective.

Knowledge is attributed by the observer.
Cohen's work nicely articulates the distinction between designer, robot, behavioral dynamics, and observer's perception that Rosenschein, Agre, and Brooks are all wrestling with.

"AARON draws, as the human artist does, in feedback mode. No line is ever fully planned in advanced: it is generated through the process of matching its current state to a desired end state" (Cohen, 1988). "All higher-level decisions are made in terms of the state of the drawing, so that the use and availability of space in particular are highly sensitive to the history of the program's decisions." Notably, AARON's internal, general representation of objects is sparse; it doesn't plan the details of its drawings; and it maintains no "mental photograph" of the drawing it is producing.

There is no grammar of aesthetics; rather 3-d properties, *as attributed by an observer*, emerge from following simple 2-d constraints like "find enough space." The point is made by Agre, in saying that the purpose of the robot's internal representation is "not to express states of affairs, but to maintain causal relationships to them" (p. 190). The internal representations are not in terms of the "state of affairs" perceived by an observer, but the immediate, "ready-at-hand" dynamics of the drawing process (again, the terms are indexical/functional, e.g., "the stick figure I am placing in the garden now is occluded by the object to its left"). The robot's knowledge is not in terms of an objective description of properties of the resultant drawing, rather the ontology supplied by Cohen characterizes the relation between states of the robot (what it is doing now) and how it perceives the environment (the drawing it is making).

SUMMARY AND CONCLUSION: WHO OWNS THE KNOWLEDGE?

The above analyses demonstrate the usefulness of viewing intelligent machine construction (and cognitive modeling in general) as a *design problem.* That is to say, we don't simply ask "What knowledge structures should be placed in the head of the robot?" but rather, "What sensory-state coupling is desired and what machine specification brings this about?" Figure 1 summarizes the elements of this new perspective.

Briefly, the figure illustrates that a machine specification is a representation that derives from the designer's interpretation of the machine's interaction with its environment. No "objective" descriptions are imputed--how the machine's behavior is described is a matter of selective perception, biased by expectations and purposes. The recurrent behavior attributed to the machine by the observer/designer is a matter of how people talk about and make sense of the world. Furthermore, the specification--usually an external representation in the form of equations and networks--is itself prone to reinterpretation: What the specification means (its "semantics") cannot be described once and for all. The validity of the specification lies in the over-all coherence of the designer's goals, the machine's behavior, and what the designer observes.

Cognitive science research has to date not been driven by such metatheoretic analyses. Most researchers have simply assumed that the world can be exhaustively and uniquely described as theories, and that learning itself involves manipulating theories--a correspondence view of reality. But a radically different point of view has played a central role in methodological analyses in fields as diverse as anthropology and physics. For example, one interpretation of Heisenberg's Uncertainty Principle is that theories are true only with respect to a frame of reference. Bohr himself said, "There is no quantum world. There is only an abstract quantum description. It is wrong to think that the task of physics is to find out how nature *is*. Physics only concerns want we can *say* about nature" (quoted in (Gregory, 1988)). AI and cognitive science research has been based on the contrary point of view that theories (representations and language) correspond to a reality *that can be objectively known* and knowledge consists of theories; consequently, alternative design methodologies have rarely entered the discussion.

Let us recapitulate the emerging alternatives approaches to cognitive modeling. In classical planning, epitomized by present-day expert systems, descriptions of regularities an observer will perceive in the robot's interaction with the world are stored in the **robot's memory**, and interpreted as instructions for directing the robot's behavior. Rosenschein breaks with this idea, instead compiling a state-transition machine from a **designer's specification** of the desired coupling between machine and environment. Agre's work reminds us that regardless of what compilation process is used, a program still embodies a designer's ontological commitments, and these are fruitfully viewed as **indexical and functional with respect to the robot's activity**. As an artist, reflecting on the robot's behavior, Cohen reminds us that this indexical/functional theory is to be contrasted with **an observer's statements** about the robot's behavior. The essential claim is that representations in computer programs are not objective--true because they correspond to the world--but inherently indexical/functional, relationships between the agent and the world that a designer specifies should be maintained. Moving from engineering "knowledge structures" in an agent to designing on the basis of state-sensory coupling constraints is a significant theoretical advance.

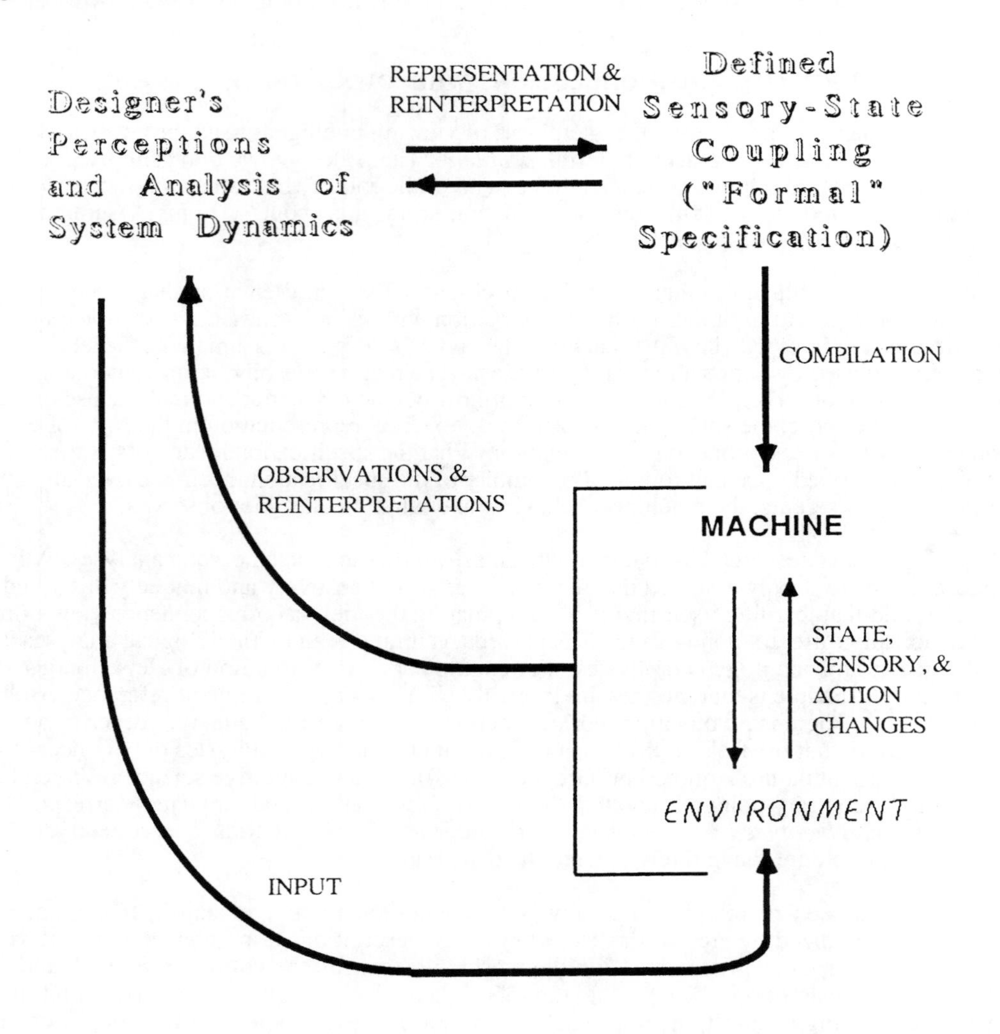

Figure 1. Relation of designer's theory to machine and coupling

However, situated automata research doesn't get to the heart of the matter: Each program still embodies the designer's ontology, which is neither fixed nor objective. Rosenschein in particular continues to speak of an objective physical reality, implying that perception is just a matter of processing data on fixed sensors in axiomatic way (cf. Neisser, 1976). He fails to acknowledge that his coupling specification and background constraints are linguistic entities prone to change under his own interpretation, no less than knowledge structures built into a classical planning system. Formality is not gained by behavioral specification, because these specifications still embody the designer's perceptions of the robot's behavior and his theory of the dynamics of the robot's interactions. Compilation into circuits only changes computational efficiency; the resultant physical structures formally correspond to the designer's original formal notations of "world conditions" and "behavioral correlations." And what these notations mean cannot be objectively specified.

Furthermore, while the robot's structural form is fixed after the design process, the coupling can be modified by human intervention. When a person interprets internal structures during the operation of the program (e.g., providing "input" by responding to the robot's queries), the coupling between robot sensation and action is changed. This interpretation is again an inherently subjective, perceptual process.

Viewing knowledge as relative to an observer/designer's perceptions of dynamic indexical-functional relations between an agent and its environment is indeed a major theoretical reconceptualization of the process of constructing "intelligent agents." However, is a more radical stance possible? Further analysis might focus on the nature of the primitive ontology, specifically to restrict it to sensations inherent in the agent's peripheral sensors (if any) or to primitive perceptual structures that arise in the early developmental interactions of the agent and its environment. From a strict sense, we could claim that the robots described above react to sensors, but never perceive, because they never form new ontologies, new ways of seeing the world. Driving this analysis would be the radical hypothesis that all perceiving is a form of learning and it is dialectically coupled to development of new physical routines. Speaking, for example, is articulating how the world is, conceptualizing, forming perceptions for the first time, not translating internal representations that describe what is about to be said. We must explain how a string like "potentially-attacking-bee" could signify a new way of seeing the world to the robot itself, rather than being a structure that determines its behavior in a fixed, programmatic way. How do we break away from modeling learning by grammatical reshuffling of grammars? For a new beginning, dance, jazz improvisation, drawing, speaking, and ensemble performances of all kinds could be viewed as examples of developing and never fully-definable routines, dialectically coupled to the robot's changing perceptions of own environmental interactions. By this, neural net researchers would move from building in ontologies (however hyphenated or compiled) to finding ways that a process-oriented memory would embody (rather than describe) recurrent interactions the agent has with its world. In short, situated automata research has laid down the gauntlet: How far can we go in removing the observer-designer's commitments from structures built into the machine?

REFERENCES

Allen, C. (1988). Situated Design. Carnegie-Mellon University, Department of Computer Science. Unpublished dissertation for Master of Science in Design Studies.

CLANCEY

Agre, P. E. (1988). The Dynamic Structure of Everyday Life. MIT Doctoral Dissertation.

Alexander, J. H., Freiling, M. J., Shulman, S.J., Staley, J.L., Rehfuss, S., & Messick, M. (1986). Knowledge Level Engineering: Ontological Analysis. *Proceedings of the National Conference on Artificial Intelligence*, pps. 963-968.

Braitenberg, V. (1984). Vehicles--Experiments in Synthetic Psychology. Cambridge: The MIT Press.

Brooks, R.A. (1988). *How to build complete creatures rather than isolated cognitive simulators.* In K. vanLehn (editor), Architectures for Intelligence: The Twenty-Second Carnegie Symposium on Cognition. Hillsdale: Lawrence Erlbaum Associates. (In preparation.)

Clancey, W.J. (1987). Review of Winograd and Flores's "Understanding Computers and Cognition." *Artificial Intelligence*, 31(2), 232-250.

Cohen, H. (1988). How to draw three people in a botanical garden. *Proceedings of the Seventh National Conference on Artificial Intelligence*. Minneapolis-St. Paul, pps. 846-855.

Dietterich, T.G. (1986). Learning at the knowledge level. *Machine Learning* 1(3)287-316.

Dreyfus, H. L. (1972). What Computers Can't Do: A critique of artificial reason. New York: Harper & Row.

Gregory, B. (1988). Inventing Reality: Physics as Language. New York: John Wiley & Sons, Inc.

Kaelbling, L. P. (1988). Goals as parallel program specifications. *Proceedings of the Seventh National Conference on Artificial Intelligence*. Minneapolis-St. Paul, pps. 60-65.

Neisser, U. (1976). Cognition and Reality: Principles and Implications of Cognitive Psychology. New York: W.H. Freeman.

Rommetveit, R. (1987). Meaning, context, an control: Convergent trends and controversial issues in current social-scientific research on human cognition and communication. *Inquiry,* 30:77-79.

Rosenschein, S. J. (1985). *Formal theories of knowledge in AI and robotics*. SRI Technical Note 362.

Suchman, L. A. (1987). Plans and Situated Actions--The Problem of Human-Machine Communication. New York: Cambridge Press.

Winograd, T. & Flores, F. (1986). Understanding Computers and Cognition: A new foundation for design. Norwood: Ablex.

THE MANY USES OF 'BELIEF' IN AI

Robert F. Hadley

School of Computing Science, Simon Fraser University

ABSTRACT

Within AI and the cognitively related disciplines, there exist a multiplicity of uses of 'belief'. On the face of it, these differing uses reflect differing views about the nature of an objective phenomenon called 'belief'. In this paper I distinguish six distinct ways in which 'belief' is used in AI. I shall argue that not all these uses reflect a difference of opinion about an objective feature of reality. Rather, in some cases, the differing uses reflect differing concerns with special AI applications. In other cases, however, genuine differences exist about the nature of what we pre-theoretically call belief. To an extent, the multiplicity of opinions about, and uses of 'belief', echoes the discrepant motivations of AI researchers. The relevance of this discussion for cognitive science arises from the fact that (a) many regard theoretical research within AI as a branch of cognitive science, and (b) even if theoretical AI is not cognitive science, trends within AI influence theories developed within cognitive science. It should be beneficial, therefore, to unravel the distinct uses and *motivations* surrounding 'belief', in order to discover which usages merely reflect differing pragmatic concerns, and which usages genuinely reflect divergent views about reality.

INTRODUCTION

Within AI and the cognitively related disciplines, there exist a multiplicity of uses of 'belief'. On the face of it, these differing uses reflect differing views about the nature of an objective phenomenon called 'belief'. In this paper I distinguish six distinct ways in which 'belief' is used in AI. I shall argue that not all these uses reflect a difference of opinion about an objective feature of reality. Rather, in some cases, the differing uses reflect differing concerns with special AI applications. In other cases, however, genuine differences exist about the nature of what we pre-theoretically call belief. To an extent, the multiplicity of opinions about, and uses of 'belief', echoes the discrepant motivations of AI researchers, some of whom see themselves as simultaneously engaged in both AI and cognitive science, while others make no claims for the generality or cognitive validity of their results.

The relevance of our discussion to cognitive science is twofold. First, some of the theories (and senses) of belief described here are held by researchers who would identify themselves as cognitive scientists (whether or not they work in AI). It should be of use to these people to distinguish among several (though not necessarily all) of the current alternative views of belief. Secondly, research in AI sometimes influences the development of theories by cognitive scientists who do not regard AI as cognitive science. If AI contains conflicting theories of belief, and if (as is often the case) the motivation for these theories is a mixture of scientific and pragmatic concerns, it would be well for us to be aware of which theories are intended *primarily* as cognitive theories, and which are intended primarily as special purpose tools. Unfortunately, researchers in AI are frequently unclear about the degree to which they intend a particular theory or formalism to be taken as a cognitive model. This is especially apparent in the domain of "belief" (cf. Hadley, 1988). It is not unusual to find discussions of belief in AI which reject other treatments of 'belief' for their counter-intuitive features (e.g., logical omniscience) (cf. Levesque, 1984; Fagin and Halpern, 1985). However, when the counter-intuitive features of one's own theory are brought to light, the defense is often made that pragmatic value, rather than cognitive validity, is the issue. In what follows, I shall try to unravel some of the underlying motivations for the varying approaches to belief in AI, and to distinguish their pragmatic value from their cognitive validity.

1. THE SYNTACTIC THEORY

According to the 'syntactic' view of belief, beliefs are syntactic objects (sentences) which are explicitly stored in a special region of an agent's memory, often called a knowledge or belief base. Only those sentences which are explicitly stored are believed. Thus, from the mere fact that an agent believes 'Mary has a brother', it would not follow that the agent believes 'Mary has a male sibling'. In general, the syntactic approach assumes that *no* two distinct sentences express precisely the same belief.

Now, on the face of it, there is a circularity lurking in the above definition, because an appeal is made to the notion of a 'belief' base. One wonders whether the notion of a belief (or knowledge) base can be elucidated without invoking the very concept we are trying to analyse. Upon reflection, however, the circularity may be illusory. For one might attempt to distinguish a belief base from *other* regions of an agent's memory by noting that sentences which are stored in a *belief* base are taken by the agent as grounds for *action*. That is, when a sentence is stored in an agent's belief base, the agent is (usually) willing to act as though the sentence is true. If the sentence is too abstract to act upon directly, then the agent is at least willing to use the sentence as a premise in derivations which lead to action (unless the agent desires to *conceal* his/her beliefs).

If we accept the above suggestion -- that a sentence is in an agent's belief base if and only if the agent is willing (in the absence of concealment motives) to use the sentence as a premise when formulating its plans for action -- then we should accept a precondition of this suggestion, namely, that the agent is able to assign some semantic interpretation to the sentence. For an agent could not act upon the truth of the sentence unless he/she knew how to draw experientially meaningful consequences from the assumption of the sentence's truth, and this seems to presuppose at least *some* ability to interpret the terms occurring in that sentence.

Now, most AI treatments of belief do not confront the question whether the agent can interpret or "understand" (in any full-fledged sense) the sentences it "believes". No doubt this is due, at least in part, to the fact that builders of AI systems expect those systems to be used and *interpreted* by humans. That is, humans provide the semantics for the system. However, since we are here concerned with cognition generally, we cannot resort to an analysis of belief which is parasitic upon human cognition. Having said that, I must now sidestep the thorny question of how a system assigns a semantic interpretation to sentences it believes. The issue receives *some* further attention in our discussion of *intensions*, but for the most part, we must be content merely to acknowledge the existence of the problem.[1] In the remainder of our discussion, we shall assume that agents have the ability to semantically interpret sentences in their belief bases.

Apart from the difficulties just described, the "syntactic approach" has come under attack for a different, though related, reason. Many contend that the syntactic approach is hopelessly fine-grained, since it does not allow that any two syntactically distinct sentences are *necessarily* interchangeable in belief contexts. That is, the syntactic approach concedes that mutual interchangeability (or substitutivity) fails even in cases where we would intuitively judge those sentences to express the same "thought contents", proposition, or information. Now, many who reject the syntactic view would argue that one *could not* believe that Mary has a brother without believing that Mary has a male sibling. This is not to say that whoever believes 'Mary has a brother' could *describe* their belief using expressions like 'male sibling', but rather that the same belief can be *expressed* in words which may or may not be known to an agent who has the belief.

Among those who reject the purely syntactic approach to belief there is disagreement about just how fine-grained the criteria for 'same belief' should be. For example, some would insist that '*p or q*' and '*q or p*' are interchangeable in belief contexts, while others would hesitate to say that belief is closed under *any* logical transformation, however simple. Nevertheless, there are many who believe that belief is not *primarily* a relation between a sentence and an agent, but between an *abstraction* and the agent. The same abstraction is expressible by means of distinct sentences. In the following section we pursue this view of belief.

In defense of the syntactic view of belief, it should be noted that not all its advocates intend the view to be taken as a serious analysis of our ordinary concept of belief. Within AI, at least, the syntactic approach is sometimes adopted as an expedient which permits the construction of planning systems (cf. Haas, 1985, 1986). A robot who knows how to interpret and apply sentences to the world may derive useful plans based upon sentences explicitly written in its belief base. The fact that the *content* of these plans might be represented differently by other agents does not prevent the robot from using the plans it formulates.

---

[1]See, however (Hadley, 1989), and Searle's well known (1980) paper, which addresses these issues in detail.

However, the robot will be limited in its ability to communicate if it cannot conceive that another agent could represent those same plans using different words.

2. THE INTENSIONAL THEORY

As we have noted, a major drawback of the syntactic theory, when viewed as a serious *theory of belief*, is that it fails to account for the fact that *some* distinct sentences seem to express the same thought or belief. The notion of "thought contents" is one which has troubled philosophers for centuries. Beginning with Frege, however, substantial progress has been made in the elucidation of this concept. Nowadays, thought contents are commonly identified with intensions, propositions, and 'information expressed by a sentence'. I shall not attempt to unravel the distinctions among these notions in the space available here. Rather, I attempt to say what they have in common. This commonality, and its relationship to belief, is what I am (somewhat loosely) calling *the intensional theory*.

Most modern philosophers who have proposed theories of intensions, or propositions regard these as *abstract* objects which (roughly) constitute the *meanings* of sentences. Those who adopt Frege's basic approach towards these objects (e.g., Montague, 1970; Lewis, 1976) take intensions (propositions) to be *functions* which map sentences onto the possible worlds in which those sentences are true. Barwise and Perry (1983), however, take propositions to be abstract situation types whose structure is largely reflected in the syntactic structure of sentences which express those propositions. Both the Fregian-based and the situation-based view of propositions take propositions to arise as a result of *compositional* semantics. The composite, structured object expressed by a sentence arises (or is at least *picked out*) by a compositional processes involving *senses* or *sets* attached to the elementary terms occurring in the sentence. This composite, structured object (or, in the Barwise-Perry theory, a particular, situated *instance* of this object) is the appropriate object of belief. It is possible to *represent* this structured object by means of a canonical representation, and such representations are often called the *logical form of a sentence*. What is especially relevant to our present concerns is that all the propositional theories we have been considering associate sentences with such canonical logical forms, and all these theories recognize the existence of *many-to-one* mappings between symbolically distinct sentences and a given logical form. Moreover, all these theories admit the possibility, in principle, of "compilation procedures" by which a given sentence may be compiled into its logical form. It is thus possible, in principle, to ascertain whether two different sentences express the same belief by compiling the sentences into their logical forms. It is commonly recognized both by the neo-Fregian and by the situationists that such compilation processes must be sensitive to the context in which sentences are used.

Now, although the preceding discussion glosses over distinctions between the different theories which I have broadly depicted as "intensional", it has hopefully emerged that these distinct theories share a common motivation and sensitivity to the *structure* of a belief. The multiplicity of such theories partially reflects the difficulty of analysing the notion of 'thought contents'. However, the abundance of intensional theories also arises in consequence of the fact that (for the most part) proponents of these theories are attempting to describe the true nature of belief. That is, they are aiming at a cognitively accurate model rather than a special purpose construct. Within AI, the intensional stance towards belief has been adopted primarily by those concerned with cognitive fidelity and natural language (cf. Wilks & Ballim, 1987; Hadley, 1988).

An obstacle to the selection of a single 'correct' theory seems to be that there is no general consenses about the data to be explained. For example, Moore (1942) denies that the analysis of a concept is usually substitutable for an atomic term expressing that concept in a belief context. Thus, if we allow that 'male sibling' is an analysis of 'brother', Moore would deny that whoever believes that Mary has a brother also believes that Mary has a male sibling. On the other hand, Moore *could* allow that 'Tadpoles swim' and 'Polliwogs swim', express the same belief, because 'tadpole' and 'polliwog' are not only synonymous, but are equally explicit.

Another (*prima facie*) difficulty for the 'intensional' approach arises from the fact that belief *sometimes* seems to be sensitive not only to the *structure* of a sentence, but to the identity of proper names occurring in the sentence. For example, some would argue that (a) 'Mark Twain wrote *Huckleberry Finn*' and (b) 'Sam Clemens wrote *Huckleberry Finn*' convey precisely the same proposition (or information), because the proper names 'Mark Twain' and 'Sam Clemens' denote the same individual, and so have the same meaning (since they are *names* and not descriptions). However, it seems entirely possible that a child (say, Becky) who knew only a little about Mark Twain could believe (a) without believing (b). The syntactic theory, considered earlier, at least has the merit that it could assign a differing belief status to these two sentences.

In defense of the intensional approach, the reply could be made that the sentences in question have both a purely referential (*de re*) reading, and an opaque (*de dicto*) reading. Although 'Mark Twain' and 'Sam Clemens' both denote the same object, one could have different *concepts* or *vivid impressions* associated with these names. Thus, when Becky says 'Mark Twain wrote H. F.' she is normally *conceiving* of Mark Twain in a certain way (e.g., as a famous American author), and this *mode of conception* enters into the content of her proposition. For Becky, (a) and (b) do not convey the same *information*, and this is as it should be. A *context sensitive*, compositional semantics would *not* assign both sentences the same interpretation. To be sure, when 'Mark Twain' and 'Sam Clemens' are both being used in a purely referential mode, (a) and (b) can express the same proposition. In *that* case, however, we have no reason to suppose that Becky does not believe both (a) and (b). The fact that Becky would not assent to (b) is irrelevant when (b) is being used in a *de re* sense.

3. BELIEFS AS INFORMATION

In the previous section the term 'information' was used somewhat narrowly. This restricted use has been fostered by Barwise and Perry (1983), who use 'information' to denote what might also be described as a *structured state of affairs*. On their view, the structure of a state of affairs approximately mirrors the syntax of a sentence which describes that state of affairs. (Thus, information for Barwise and Perry roughly corresponds to *facts* for Wittgenstein, 1921). However, 'information' has other uses (cf. Dretske, 1981; Shannon & Weaver, 1949), and computer scientists are often concerned with the 'information' explicitly or implicitly present in a database. For many applications, one is not especially concerned about the *particular* logical structure of database information. Rather, the concern is with the 'picture of the world' that the information creates. That is, if one were to accept the information in the database as accurate, one would expect the world to be a certain way, independently of the particular syntax used to describe that world. On this use of 'information', one who knows that *if P then Q*, has the same information as one who knows that *if not Q then not P*.

Now, within AI, the practice has arisen of referring to declarative assertions in a database as 'beliefs' of the system. Given this casual use of 'belief', and given a concern for information in a broad sense, it is not surprising that we find AI researchers who regard beliefs as equivalence classes of logically equivalent sentences. We may formalize this use of 'belief' as follows:

Agent X believes S if and only if S is explicitly present in X's belief base, or S is logically equivalent to a sentence which is explicitly present.

Concerns for efficiency have lead some researchers to restrict the equivalence relation to "equivalent in a *computationally tractable* logic" (e.g., Levesque, 1984; Lakemeyer, 1987). However, such computational concerns are extraneous to the primary motivation we are now considering. If two agents have identical information encoded in syntactically different forms, that information will be identical whether or not the equivalence can be proved by a tractable algorithm. If we have chosen to identify the beliefs of a system with information in that system, then we should regard tractability as extraneous to belief as well.

Now, although the sense of 'belief' formulated above is motivated by the specialized concerns of AI researchers, it does accord with *some* of our ordinary uses of 'belief'. For example, if we have recently informed a friend that X and Y are both true, and we see that a sentence Z is an absolutely trivial consequence of X and Y, then we may reasonably conjecture that our friend will soon believe that Z. In cases such as these, we are not usually concerned with the particular *syntax* of the belief that Z, but with the information that our friend acquires. On other occasions however, a much finer-grained sense of belief seems to be at work. Thus, virtually any logic instructor will attest that a student may believe that $p \vee q$ and yet not believe that $\neg(\neg p \wedge \neg q)$.

4. THE LOGISTIC APPROACH TO BELIEF

Since the appearance of Levesque's "A Logic of Implicit and Explicit Belief" (1984), the prevailing approach within AI towards epistemic states has been to model belief by means of epistemic logics. Epistemic logics adopt the *modal* formalism developed by philosophical logicians who were dealing primarily with the concepts of possibility and necessity. However, they are also strongly influenced by Hintikka's (1962) application of modal logics to belief. Due to the influence of Levesque's (1984) results, together with his later arguments (1986), many have been persuaded not only that belief should be modelled via logic, but via *tractable* logics. In part this emphasis on tractability reflects a strong concern for the development of *practical* AI systems which can deliver results in feasible time (cf. Levesque, 1984; Lakemeyer, 1987). But concerns about tractability also arise for those who seek models of cognition which are at least equal in power to the cognitive abilities of humans.

We may summarize the stance towards belief currently adopted by many (though not all) AI researchers as follows:

Agent X believes sentence S if and only if S is explicitly present in X's belief base, or S is derivable, by means of a *tractable* epistemic logic, from a set of epistemic formulae corresponding to a subset of X's explicit belief base.

Now certain difficulties with the above emerge as soon as the thesis is explicitly stated. For example, the epistemic logics cited above do not address the fact that agents acquire beliefs over a period of time. Nor do they address the fact that an agent may, on occasion, validly derive a conclusion from prior beliefs, but *abandon* that conclusion because it conflicts with another of the agent's beliefs. To be sure, if the agent is rational, the conclusion will be abandoned only if the agent also discards at least one premise of the retracted conclusion. Nevertheless, agents often have inconsistent beliefs, and do not automatically "commit to" the conclusions they derive.

Now, the Levesque camp may object that there are many AI *applications* in which agents have only consistent beliefs, and never reject their own conclusions. But, this objection carries little weight. For, apart from the fact that the objection implicitly concedes that the "logistic approach" cannot provide a *general* account of belief, the objection does not begin to address the *temporal* problem. That is, current epistemic logics fail to distinguish between what an agent *now* believes, and what the agent could justifiably come to believe. Indeed, it appears that if the analysis of belief cited above is to have any plausibility, it must be construed not as an analysis of belief, but as an analysis of what an agent could *come to believe* by tractable means. This is brought home by the fact that all epistemic logics so far mentioned require agents to have an *infinite* set of (informationally non-equivalent) beliefs. For example, the logics of Levesque (1984) and Lakemeyer (1987) require that any agent who believes p also believes $p \vee \neg(q \wedge r)$, and an infinity of other disjunctions. However, it seems implausible that an agent with finite resources could *at once* believe an infinity of non-equivalent propositions.

We are lead, therefore, to suppose that the motivation underlying the logistic approach is to provide logics which can characterize what an agent could justifiably come to believe by tractable means. However, the issue is complicated by the fact that the logicians cited above are greatly concerned to avoid a counter-intuitive aspect of Hintikka's epistemic logics, namely, logical omniscience. Logical omniscience is the thesis that an agent believes *all* the logical consequences of the agent's explicitly represented beliefs. Such a thesis is clearly false for finite agents, given our usual concept of belief. But, if we are liberalizing our interpretation of 'belief', and allowing that agents believe things which they are merely (logically) entitled to believe, then it is no longer clear that logical omniscience is an unacceptable doctrine. The fact that many epistemic logicians in AI find this doctrine unacceptable is puzzling, because their own logics demand a liberal interpretation of 'belief'. The situation is further complicated by the fact that creators of these logics often stress the 'intuitive aspects' of their logics.

Now, it may be that the deep reason why logical omniscience is rejected by many within AI, is not that the doctrine is counter-intuitive, but that it involves intractability. But if *tractability* is deemed essential, then it ought to be shown that under *no circumstances* may an agent arrive at new beliefs via intractable reasoning, and *no* beliefs should be stated in an intractable logic. However, it is far from clear that *purely artificial* agents can always meets their needs using only tractable logics. For example, researchers in automated planning, automated programming, and qualitative physics have not shown these domains to be susceptible to tractable methods. Indeed, the consensus seems to be, that *if* formal logic is in fact an appropriate tool for these domains, then something at least as rich as first-order logic *with functions* will be required. And, if formal logic is *not* an appropriate tool for these domains, it is *a-fortiori* possible for agents to arrive at new beliefs (in these domains) without recourse to tractable logics. Moreover, it is known that proofs involving the principle of mathematical induction cannot even be formalized in a language as rich as first-order logic. Are we to say that those who discover theorems via mathematical induction are not acquiring *beliefs*, simply because their reasoning processes cannot be simulated by the application of tractable logics? Difficulties such as these could be dismissed by those concerned merely with restricted applications of AI, but as we have noted, the motivations of those advocating tractable logics in AI are often not clear.

5. BELIEFS AS 'WHAT ONE COULD RAPIDLY DISCOVER'

There is a use of 'belief', in ordinary parlance, according to which one believes not only those things which one *remembers* as true, but those things one could quickly discover. For example, if we ask a friend whether she believes that some carpenters are poets, she may pause a second, and then reply 'Yes'. In all likelihood, our friend has never considered the question, but because she can discover (or infer) the truth of a proposition so quickly, it seems not unnatural to say that she believes the proposition. Note, however, that if a considerable span of time is required for the inference, then we are reluctant to describe the proposition as something our friend believed at the time the question was posed. In certain AI applications, however, it may be reasonable to be flexible about the span of time involved. For in a given application, we may not be as much concerned with preserving the niceties of ordinary usage as we are with finding a convenient label for the things an artificial agent could discover in a given time T. Considerations such as these may have lead Fagin and Halpern (1985) to adopt a liberalization of the 'syntactic approach' described in section one.[2]

In Fagin's and Halpern's system (hereafter, the F & H approach), an agent is said to believe not only formulae explicitly present in the agent's belief base, but any formula which the agent is both 'aware of', and which is derivable from the belief base (by means of a specified logic). F & H allow 'aware of' to be interpreted in a number of ways, depending upon the application. One interpretation they suggest, however, is that an agent is aware of any formula which the agent could derive in time T. Using this extended notion of awareness, in combination with F & H's general approach, we are lead to the following characterization of belief:

Agent X believes S if and only if S is in X's belief base, or X could prove S, using the belief base and a logic L, within time T.

The above formulation permits us the option, in particular applications, of requiring L to be a tractable logic. However, we would remain more faithful to the motivation which underlies this extended use of 'believes' if we do not place a-priori restrictions upon the logic which the agent uses. For, the relevant question is whether the agent can indeed discover the truth of S in time T.[3] Moreover, we should note that the above formulation strays a fair distance from common usage, not only because it permits the interval T to be arbitrarily large, but because it counts as a belief any sentence which an agent *could* derive in time T (even though the agent may in fact never discover S because, for example, the agent is pursuing other lines of thought).

Now, it would be natural to assume that F & H's extended usage of 'belief' is intended merely as a technical convenience, and not as an analysis of 'real belief'. However, there are passages in their (1985) paper which suggest that they may be aiming at a true analysis of belief. For example, they provide 'ordinary language' examples to support their contention that awareness is a necessary component of

---

[2]I am indebted to Bill Demopolous for pointing this out.

[3]Concerning what an agent could derive in time T (where T is less than 10 seconds, say), it should be noted that there now exist surprisingly efficient, tableau-based theorem-provers for first-order logic, which can prove many difficult theorems in short order (cf. Oppacher & Suen, 1987).

belief. They then proceed to use 'awareness' in a number of senses which would be considered unusual, at least. (I have argued this in detail in Hadley, 1988). Moreover, they criticize Levesque (1984) for counter-intuitive aspects of his logic of belief, although they do not make clear which aspects of their theory they take to be intuitively appealing and which are intended merely as technical tools.

6. BELIEF AS DEGREES OF CONFIDENCE

We now consider a usage of 'belief' which is radically different in kind from the foregoing, and which could be viewed as a *qualification* upon each of the previous usages. I refer to Cheeseman's (1988) analysis of belief as a subjective, probability estimate of a proposition's truth. In part, Cheeseman is concerned to defend the use of probability as an AI tool for reasoning with uncertainties. However, he also suggests that we focus upon *degrees of belief* rather than upon an absolute belief/non-belief distinction. Now, there may be considerable merit in concentrating upon probability estimates when reasoning with uncertainties, but that is not our present concern.

However, it does seem true that we sometimes have degrees of belief. But, below a certain (difficult to identify) threshhold of confidence, it seems odd to describe our probability estimates as beliefs. For example, it seems strange to speak of believing a proposition which we regard as only 15% likely. To be sure, it makes sense to say that we *believe* that P is 15% likely, but here 'belief' applies to 'P is 15% likely', and not to P itself. Analogously, every assertion of the form 'P is *x%* likely' may itself become a candidate for belief. If we adopt Cheeseman's analysis of belief, then we must assign a probability estimate to 'P is 15% likely' before we can believe *this* assertion. And if we do assign a probability to this latter assertion, we can raise a similar question about whether this *last* probability estimate is believed. Clearly, if we are to avoid an infinite regress, we must eventually stop assigning probabilities to our judgements, and simply *accept* (or believe) the judgement made.

This is not to deny that we often work with probability judgements, or even to deny that we sometimes form meta-probability judgements. Rather, the point is that we must at some point, and by some mechanism, simply assign and record a probability. It does not matter how this *recording* is implemented, we may still (from a logical standpoint) regard the *record* as an entry made in the agent's belief base, which has the form 'P is *x%* likely'. Once this is recognized, we see that the suggestion that we work with probabilities does not eliminate the need for decisions about whether to accept any of the foregoing analyses of belief. For, we may still raise questions whether an agent believes only those sentences in its belief base, or must also believe equivalent sentences (or other entailed consequences). Thus, it seems plausible that a probabilistic approach to reasoning could be combined with each of the foregoing uses of belief.

CONCLUSION

We have reviewed a number of distinct views and uses of belief. There are important interrelationships among certain of these views. For example, with the possible exception of the probabilistic view of belief, the syntactic approach occurs as an ingredient, in each of the other approaches. Moreover, the 'equivalent information', 'epistemic logic', and 'what could soon be discovered' approaches all involve the use of formal logic. Each of these approaches arises from a different motivation, and gives rise to a distinct use of 'belief'. It is not clear to what extent each of these approaches is commonly *taken* (by AI researchers) to be a *true* theory of belief, but they may be seen as compatible when taken merely as artifices for special AI applications. The 'intensional' approach, by contrast, seems to arise from a genuine concern to formulate a correct theory of belief. Its origins lie in philosophy, rather than AI, but it has found favor with some AI researchers. The probabilistic approach is distinctly a minority view within AI, but, as we have argued, it is possible to reinterpret this approach in such a way that it can be *applied* to each of the foregoing approaches. For example, one might hold that *propositions* are the appropriate *object* of belief, while insisting that in certain contexts it is pragmatically useful to believe propositions of the form 'P is 74% likely'.

In passing, it should be emphasized that the foregoing is not intended as an exhaustive list of views and uses of 'belief' in AI. Rather, my purpose has been to display at least a range of possible approaches to belief, and to show that such approaches *need not* be incompatible. Whether they are in fact incompatible depends upon their intended purpose.

REFERENCES

Barwise, J. and Perry, J. (1983) *Situations and Attitudes*, Cambridge: Bradford Books.

Cheeseman, P. (1988) "An Inquiry Into Computer Understanding", *Computational Intelligence*, Vol. 4, pp.58-66.

Cresswell, M.J. (1985) *Structured Meanings: The Semantics of Propositional Attitudes*, MIT Press, Cambridge, MA.

Dretske, F.I. (1981) *Knowledge and the Flow of Information*, Bradford Books, Cambridge, Mass.

Fagin, R., and Halpern, J. (1985) "Belief, Awareness, and Limited Reasoning", Proceedings of IJCAI, Los Angelos, pp. 491-501.

Frege, G. (1952) "On Sense and Reference", in *Translations from the Philosophical Writings of Gottlob Frege*, Oxford.

Haas, A. (1985) "Possible Events, Actual Events, and Robots". *Computational Intelligence*, Vol. 1, pp. 59-70.

Haas, A. (1986) "A Syntactic Theory of Belief and Action", *Artificial Intelligence*, Vol. 28, 245-292.

Hadley, R.F. (1988) "Logical Omniscience, Semantics and Models of Belief", *Computational Intelligence*, Vol. 4, pp. 17-30.

Hadley, R.F. (1989, to appear) "A Default-Oriented Theory of Procedural Semantics", *Cognitive Science*, Vol. 13, pp. 107-137.

Hintikka, J. (1962) *Knowledge and Belief: An Introduction to the Logic of the Two Notions*, Cornell University Press.

Lakemeyer, G. (1987) "Tractable Meta-Reasoning in Propositional Logics of Belief", Proceedings of IJCAI, Milan, pp. 401-408.

Levesque, H.J. (1984) "A Logic of Implicit and Explicit Belief", Proceedings of the American Association for Artificial Intelligence, Austin, TX., pp. 198-202.

Levesque, H.J. (1986) "Making Believers Out of Computers", *Artificial Intelligence*, Vol. 30, pp. 81-108.

Lewis, D. (1976) "General Semantics", in *Montague Grammar*, (ed.) Partee, B., Academic Press, New York.

Montague, R. (1970) "Universal Grammar", *Theoria* 36.

Moore, G.E. (1942) ""Reply to my critics", In *The philosophy of G.E. Moore*, (Ed.) P. Schilpp. Northwestern University Press, Evanston and Chicago.

Oppacher, F. & Suen, E. (1987) "HARP: a Tableau-Based Theorem Prover", *Journal of Automated Reasoning*, Vol. 3.

Searle, J. (1980) "Minds, Brains, and Programs", *The Behavioural and Brain Sciences*, 3, 111-169.

Wittgenstein, L. (1921) *Tractatus Logico-Philosophicus*, translation by Pears, D.F., and McGuinnes, B.F., reprinted (1963) Routledge & Kegan Paul, London.

Shannon, C.E., and Weaver, W. (1949) *The Mathematical Theory of Communication*, University of Illinois Press, Urbana.

Wilks, Y. & Ballim, A. (1987) "Multiple Agents and Heuristic Ascriptions of Belief", Proceedings of IJCAI, Milan, pp. 118-124.

Using View Types to Generate Explanations in Intelligent Tutoring Systems

Art Souther Liane Acker James Lester Bruce Porter
Department of Computer Sciences
University of Texas at Austin

ABSTRACT

Providing coherent explanations of domain knowledge is essential for a fully functioning Intelligent Tutoring System (ITS). Current ITSs that generate explanations directly from domain knowledge offer limited applicability because they place restrictions on the form and extent of the domain knowledge. Moreover, generating explanations in tutors that are designed to teach the breadth of foundational knowledge conveyed in most introductory college courses poses special problems. These problems arise because this knowledge is complex and contains multiple, highly-integrated viewpoints. To overcome these problems, we propose a method for selecting only the knowledge that is relevant for generating a coherent explanation from a desired viewpoint. This method uses domain-independent knowledge in the form of *view types* to select the appropriate knowledge.

INTRODUCTION

Providing coherent explanations of domain knowledge is essential for a fully functioning Intelligent Tutoring System (ITS). There are two ways to provide coherent explanations: presenting "canned text" and generating explanations directly from the domain knowledge. Generating explanations offers several advantages, including providing explanations for unanticipated questions, tailoring explanations for the current situation and student, and ensuring consistency between the explanations and the knowledge base when the knowledge base changes.

Current ITSs have a limited solution to explanation generation. Their success results from limitations on the form and extent of domain knowledge. These limitations include dedicating the ITS to a single task [Clancey 87, Hollan 84], representing the domain knowledge with a relatively small number of rules or axioms [White 87, vanLehn 80, Brown 82], covering only a small portion of a domain [Brown 73], and explicitly partitioning the knowledge base according to the tasks for which the knowledge will be used [Brown 82, White 87].

There is an important class of tutors, however, that requires a more comprehensive solution to generating explanations. The domain of these tutors is the foundational knowledge conveyed in introductory college courses. For most subjects, this knowledge broadly surveys the domain, contains multiple, highly-integrated viewpoints, and is not reducible to a small number of principles or axioms. Large-scale knowledge bases containing fundamental knowledge pose a serious problem for explanation generation: to answer a question, a generator must efficiently select only the knowledge it needs to present a relevant explanation.

To address this problem, we present a method for selecting information from a knowledge base to answer a question.[1] This method uses viewpoints, which specify the knowledge to be selected. For example, to answer the question, "What is a car?", the viewpoint of a "car as a manufactured artifact" contains different information than a "car as a vehicle for transportation."

The use of viewpoints in organizing knowledge for explanations has been proposed by other researchers [Swartout 83, McKeown 85, Suthers 88]. However, both Swartout and McKeown encode viewpoints explicitly into the representation of the domain knowledge. Viewpoints in Swartout's XPLAIN consist of annotations on elements of domain knowledge. The annotations indicate when a piece of knowledge should be included in an explanation. McKeown also explicitly represents each viewpoint. These viewpoints are represented as separate classification hierarchies, one for each task in the domain. Explicitly representing all possible coherent viewpoints in a large-scale knowledge base is an intractable problem. Our solution is to dynamically generate viewpoints through the use of a small number of *view types* and their associated strategies. Suthers [Suthers 88] has proposed a *View Retriever* which seems to operate like our view type strategies, although the preliminary nature of the work in both cases makes comparison difficult.

REPRESENTING FOUNDATIONAL KNOWLEDGE

To investigate the problem of generating explanations from foundational knowledge, we have constructed a knowledge base in the domain of botanical anatomy, physiology, and development. Although the knowledge base currently contains over 4,000 concepts, it is only a small portion of the information contained in an introductory botany course.

The "backbone" of the knowledge base is a hierarchy of related botanical objects and processes. The relations support the inheritance of facts from general concepts to specific concepts. Each concept is represented by a *node*, and relations between concepts are represented by *arcs*. Figure 1 depicts the current state of the knowledge base with respect to chloroplast photosynthesis. Representing this process requires multiple viewpoints, such as "photosynthesis viewed as photochemical energy transduction" and "photosynthesis viewed as a producer of chemical bond energy." Although the representation is complex, it represents only a small part of the scientific knowledge about chloroplast photosynthesis.

Explanations are subgraphs of the knowledge base which is represented as a semantic network. Although a very large number of subgraphs of the botany knowledge base are possible, most subgraphs correspond to incoherent explanations. Therefore, some means must be provided to limit the nodes and arcs included when explanations are generated.

[1]Once selected, this knowledge constitutes a core from which an ITS's natural language generator may fashion an explanation. However, natural language generation is outside the scope of our current project.

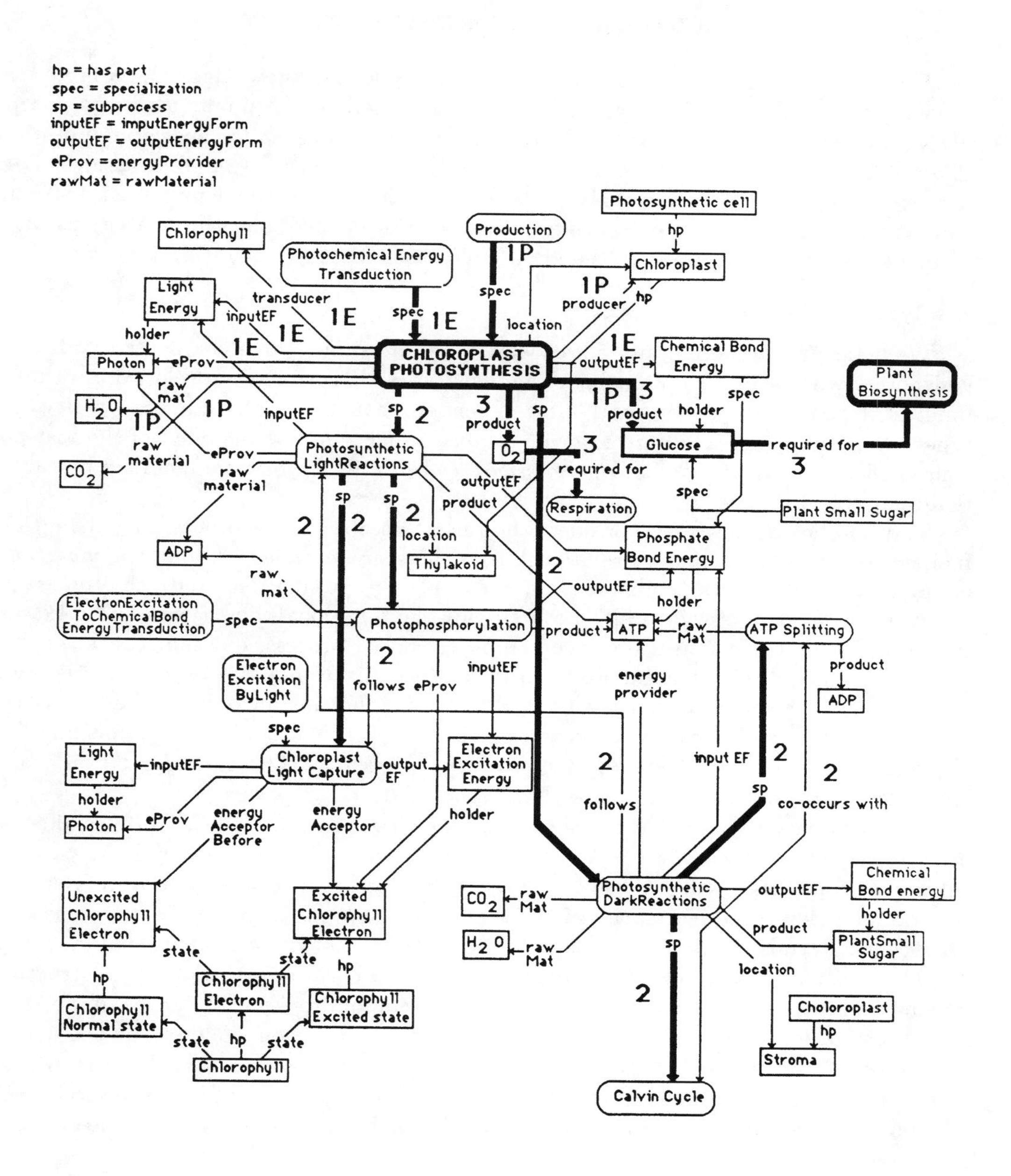

Figure 1: Chloroplast Photosynthesis

SELECTING KNOWLEDGE FOR EXPLANATION GENERATION

This section describes our method for selecting relevant knowledge from a large-scale knowledge base. Rather than explicitly encoding numerous viewpoints for each concept in the knowledge base, our method generates viewpoints as needed for answering questions. The method employs a small number of *view types* and their associated strategies. Each strategy is designed to answer a given class of questions the student might ask.[2] To answer a question about a particular concept, a view type is selected, and the strategy associated with the view type is applied to the knowledge base, thereby generating a viewpoint.

View Types

We believe that a small number of view types are sufficient to characterize all viewpoints within physical domains. The view types that we have developed are the functional, modulatory, structural, class-dependent, attributional, and comparative view types. A view type specifies ***necessary relations***, which must be included in the viewpoints generated by the view type, and ***permissible relations***, which may be included but are not required.

The *functional* view type considers the role of an object in a process. By definition, it includes some kind of *actor in* relationship, such as *producer, agent*, and *raw material.* For example, the viewpoints "pollen as an actor in plant reproduction" and "chloroplast as the producer in plant photosynthesis" both employ the functional view type. These examples illustrate a direct relationship between an object and a process, but sometimes the relationship is indirect. For example, a part or specialization of the object may be an actor in the process specified, rather than the object itself. For instance, it can be said that one of the functions of the seed is to protect the plant embryo, though strictly speaking it is the seed coat, a *part of* the seed, that protects the embryo. The *part of* relation is an example of a permissible relation for functional relationship paths.

The *modulatory* view type considers how one object or process affects (or is affected by) another object or process. An example of a modulatory viewpoint is "sunlight as an influence on plant growth" or "embryo growth as a cause of seed coat rupture." A modulatory viewpoint necessarily includes at least one regulatory relation, such as *causes* or *inhibits.* Permissible relations may also be included, as with the functional view type.

The *structural* view type considers an object or process in terms of its substructures or superstructures. These structures may be either temporal or spatial. An example of a substructural viewpoint is "photosynthesis as the light reactions followed by the dark reactions." An example of a superstructural viewpoint is "seed coat as the part of a seed containing the endosperm and embryo." As illustrated by these examples, a structural viewpoint includes those relations that specify how the temporal or spatial parts are interconnected.

The *class-dependent* view type considers a concept in terms of how it fits into a class hierarchy. There are two subtypes: categorical view type and enumerative view type. The *categorical* view type considers a concept in terms of the properties and relations it inherits

---

[2]These question types are described in [Porter 89].

from one of its generalizations or from a concept of which it is an instance. For example, "flower as reproductive organ" is a categorical viewpoint. The *enumerative* view type considers a class concept in terms of its instances or specializations. An example of an enumerative viewpoint is "plant reproduction as sexual plant reproduction or asexual plant reproduction."

The simplest view type is the *attributional* view type, which considers a concept in terms of properties, such as *color* and *weight*. Properties have values that fall along some range or spectrum.

Finally, the *comparative* view type uses a subordinate view type to compare two concepts. For example, two concepts can be compared according to their structure, their function, or their effects on other concepts. Examples include comparisons between concepts within the same category, as in "the similarities and differences between photosynthesis and chemosynthesis as energy transduction processes," and comparisons of the functional role of two objects, as in "the differences between 'chlorophyll a' and 'chlorophyll b' in photosynthesis."

A view type is instantiated to create a particular viewpoint by specifying a concept of interest and a reference concept. A *concept of interest* is the main topic of an explanation. A *reference concept* is the term to which the concept of interest should be related and is only required for the functional, categorical, and modulatory view types.[3] For example,

- View Type: Functional
- Concept of Interest: Pollen
- Reference Concept: Plant Reproduction

specifies pollen from the viewpoint of its functional role in plant reproduction. Thus a view type, when applied to a concept of interest and a reference concept, generates a specific viewpoint. This generation is guided by explanation strategies as described in the following section.[4]

Explanation Strategies

Explanation strategies select domain knowledge relevant to answering a particular question according to a particular viewpoint. Each strategy selects knowledge about the concept of interest and its relationship to the reference concept. This knowledge constitutes a coherent explanation. To illustrate these strategies we will use the definition question "What is photosynthesis?"

The *definition-generation* strategy for the categorical view type explains how the concept of interest (in this case, Photosynthesis) is a specialization of the reference concept. For the categorical view type, the reference concept can be any generalization of the concept of interest. Two possible choices for reference concept in this case are the knowledge base nodes Production and Photochemical Energy Transduction.

[3]The choice of reference concept depends on the dialogue history, the student's current understanding of the domain, and explanation heuristics.

[4]A more thorough discussion of the explanation strategies for each of the view types is found in [Porter 89].

A system using this strategy first collects all relations and properties that the concept of interest inherits from the reference concept. The relations inherited to Photosynthesis from Production are *producer*, *products*, and *raw materials* (see Figure 1, paths marked **1P**). Thus, the resulting definition contains the information that "Photosynthesis is a kind of production that has a chloroplast as the producer, water and carbon dioxide as the raw materials, and oxygen and glucose as the products." If Photochemical Energy Transduction is chosen as the reference concept instead of Production, the result contains the information "Photosynthesis is a kind of photochemical energy transduction that has chlorophyll as the transducer, a photon as the energy provider, light energy as the input energy form, and chemical bond energy as the output energy form" (Figure 1, paths marked **1E**).

The definition-generation strategy for the structural view type explains the substructural or superstructural relationships for an event or object. A substructural definition reports the values on all substructure arcs (*parts* or *stages* for objects, *subevents* for events). This definition also includes relations that describe the interconnection of parts or the ordering of subevents or stages. For example, a substructural definition of photosynthesis contains the information "Photosynthesis is an event consisting of two subevents: the light reactions followed by the dark reactions. The light reactions consist of chloroplast light capture followed by photophosphorylation. The dark reactions consist of the Calvin cycle and ATP splitting which occur simultaneously" (Figure 1, paths labeled **2**). A superstructural definition is constructed in an analogous manner and contains information about how the object or event is a component of an encompassing object or event.

The definition-generation strategy for the modulatory view type explains how the concept of interest explains how the concept of interest modulates the reference concept, or vice versa. This strategy requires a search for a path from the concept of interest to the reference concept consisting only of modulatory and permissible relations. This limitation on the kinds of arcs that may be traversed constrains search more effectively than general spreading activation. For example, suppose the chosen reference concept is Plant Biosynthesis. The search begins at Photosynthesis, but because no modulatory relations emanate from the concept Photosynthesis, a permissible relation must be chosen. One of the permissible relations is *products*, with values Oxygen and Glucose. Oxygen has a modulatory relation (*required for*) to Respiration, and Glucose has the same relation to Plant Biosynthesis (See Figure 1, paths labeled **3**). The search terminates because Plant Biosynthesis is the reference concept, and the resulting explanation contains the information "Photosynthesis has product glucose, which is required for plant biosynthesis."

CONCLUSION

Generating explanations using a large-scale knowledge base creates a serious problem: selecting relevant and coherent information. Past research on this problem has employed viewpoints to constrain knowledge selection. These viewpoints have been encoded by hand in a domain-dependent manner. However, a large-scale knowledge base, such as the one we have constructed in the domain of botany, requires a very large number of viewpoints. Our method for solving these problems uses view types, which can be used to generate viewpoints.

For each of our six view types, we have developed explanation generation strategies for two different classes of questions: definition requests and comparison questions. Each strategy locates the knowledge required to generate an explanation according to a particular view type. The strategies, either singly or in combination, were sufficient to generate each of 50 definitions selected from a botany textbook.

We are applying our research to the ITS task of presenting domain knowledge to students in a mixed-initiative environment. A question answerer, in conjunction with a pedagogical planner, will use the view types to answer students' questions and to provide instruction in the domain. By accessing a student model and a dialogue history, the system will be able to generate context-specific presentations.

ACKNOWLEDGEMENTS

We appreciate the work of Ken Murray, Karen Pittman, and Tom Jones on the Botany Knowledge Base Project. We are grateful to Ken Murray for helpful comments on previous drafts of this paper.

Support for this research was provided by the Army Research Office under grant ARO-DAAG29-84-K-0060, the National Science Foundation under grant IRI-8620052, and donations from Apple, Texas Instruments, and the Cray Foundation.

REFERENCES

[Brown 82] Brown, J.; Burton, R.; and de Kleer, J. (1982) Pedagogical, natural language, and knowledge engineering techniques in SOPHIE I, II, and III. In Sleeman, D.; and Brown, J. (Eds.) *Intelligent Tutoring Systems.* Academic Press, London.

[Brown 73] Brown, J.; Burton, R.; and Zdybel, F. (1973) A model-driven question-answering system for mixed-initiative computer-assisted instruction. *IEEE Transactions on Systems, Man, and Cybernetics*, vol. 3, 248-257.

[Clancey 87] Clancey, W. (1987) *Knowledge-Based Tutoring: The GUIDON Program.* Cambridge, MA.: MIT Press.

[Hollan 84] Hollan, J.; Hutchins, E.; and Weitzman, L. (1984) STEAMER: An interactive inspectable simulation-based training system. *AI Magazine*, vol. 5, no. 2, 15-27.

[McKeown 85] McKeown, K. (1985). Tailoring Explanations for the User. *Columbia University Technical Report CUCS-172-85.*

[Porter 88] Porter, B.; Lester, J.; Murray, K.; Pittman, K.; Souther, A.; Acker, L.; and Jones, T. (1988) AI Research in the Context of a Multifunctional Knowledge Base Project. *AI Laboratory Technical Report AI88-88.* University of Texas at Austin.

[Porter 89] Porter, B.; Acker, L.; Lester, J.; and Souther, A. (1989) Generating explanations in an intelligent tutor designed to teach fundamental knowledge. *Second Intelligent Tutoring Systems Research Forum.* San Antonio.

[Suthers 88] Suthers, D. (1988). Providing multiple views of reasoning for explanation. *International Conference on Intelligent Tutoring Systems.* Montreal, Canada.

[Swartout 83] Swartout, W. (1983). XPLAIN: A system for creating and explaining expert consulting programs. *Artificial Intelligence*, vol. 21, 285-325.

[vanLehn 80] vanLehn, K.; and Brown, J. (1980) Planning nets: A representation for formalizing analogies and semantic models of procedural skills. In Snow, R.; Frederico, P.; and Montague, W. (Eds.) *Aptitude, Learning, and Instruction: Cognitive Process Analyses.* Hillsdale, NJ: Lawrence Erlbaum Associates.

[White 87] White, B.; and Frederiksen, J. (1987) Qualitative models and intelligent learning environments. In Lawler, R.; and Yazdani, M. (Eds.), *AI and Education.* New York: Ablex Publishing Co.

Relations Relating Relations

Robert L. Goldstone
Dedre Gentner
Douglas L. Medin
University of Illinois at Urbana-Champaign

Abstract

The aim of the current work is to incorporate structural information in judgments of similarity. According to the assumption of feature independence, how one feature affects similarity is independent of the values of the other features present. We present three violations of this assumption, all arising from the influence of relations between features and of relations between relations. A shared relation is more important for similarity judgments if it cooccurs with (A) relations that augment the first relation by "pointing in the same direction" as the first relation, (B) relations which are themselves salient, and (C) salient relations that involve the same objects as the first relation. We interpret these results as suggesting that relations do not have separately determined weights or saliences; the weight of a relation depends the relational structure in which it exists. Relations influence each other by creating higher-order relational structures, and also by affecting processing.

Introduction

Our current interest in structural similarity stems from two sources. First, similarity has been a pivotal, if under-explored, agent in many theories. Problems are said to be easier to solve if similar problems have been previously solved. The transfer of one skill to another is said to be proportional to their degree of similarity. One event reminds us another if they are similar. An object belongs to a category if it is similar to the category's examples or prototype. An account of what makes things similar is essential to our understanding of cognition. Second, it has long been argued, particularly in artificial intelligence, that simple, independent feature representations, inadequately capture most of our knowledge. Propositional representations, explanation based learning, and pattern recognition all point to the need for systems that represent how the units of analysis are related and interconnected in structural descriptions. Thus, separate fields have argued for the importance of structure and for the importance of similarity; at the most general level, our research goal is to consolidate structure and similarity into a single framework.

One of the most important and common assumptions associated with a wide variety of psychological models is that there exists a set of features that are independent of one another. Features are independent if the effect of the value on any one feature does not depend on the value of any other feature. A selection of prominent examples illustrates the prevalence of the feature independence assumption. Tversky 's influential contrast model (1977) makes the explicit assumption that the joint effect of two components in determining similarity is independent of the fixed level of the third component. Posner and Keele (1968) assume that the psychological distance of a dot from its prototypical location is independent of the locations of other dots. Independent-cue prototype models propose that categorization of an example into a group is a function of the feature matches between the example and the group, additively combined in an independent manner. The assumption of feature independence is a powerful simplifying assumption , permitting analyses which would otherwise be unwieldy or impossible. Without the independence assumption, any single feature of a system with ten binary-valued features could produce 1024 different effects; with the independence assumption, the same feature can produce only two effects.

Unfortunately, it is not always true that what makes for a simple and powerful model also makes for an accurate model of human behavior. There is good reason to suppose that cognitive processes are often based on highly interactive features. The feature "gray" does not mean the same thing in "gray hair" as it does in "gray cloud" (Medin & Shoben, 1988). Pomerantz (1986) has shown that in displays such as ")(" the two parentheses are not independently perceived - although they are physically detached, they are psychologically fused, creating emergent properties. Gati and Tversky (1984) present examples in which monotonicity and feature independence are violated because adding certain features causes interactions with the features already present. Indeed, all context effects can be construed as cases of non-independence. In general, there is reason to think that feature independence is the exception rather than the rule - object features often mutually constrain and modulate each other.

It might be thought that admitting feature dependencies into a model would yield an overwhelming number of degrees of freedom and a loss of important constraints. Contrary to this position, we will argue that feature dependence need not be a "counsel of despair." The similarity judgments that this paper investigates are not constrained by feature independence, but they are constrained by specific principles. The central claim will be that the importance of a relation in a scene depends on the quality, quantity, and location of the other relations present.

The general representational system outlined in Dedre Gentner's Structure-mapping Theory (SMT) (Gentner, 1983, 1989) will be used. In Gentner's terminology, a first-order relation is any relation that takes two or more objects as arguments. The relation "DARKER-THAN" is first-order because it takes two objects, two wings for example, and establishes a relation between them. The relation can be propositionally represented as DARKER-

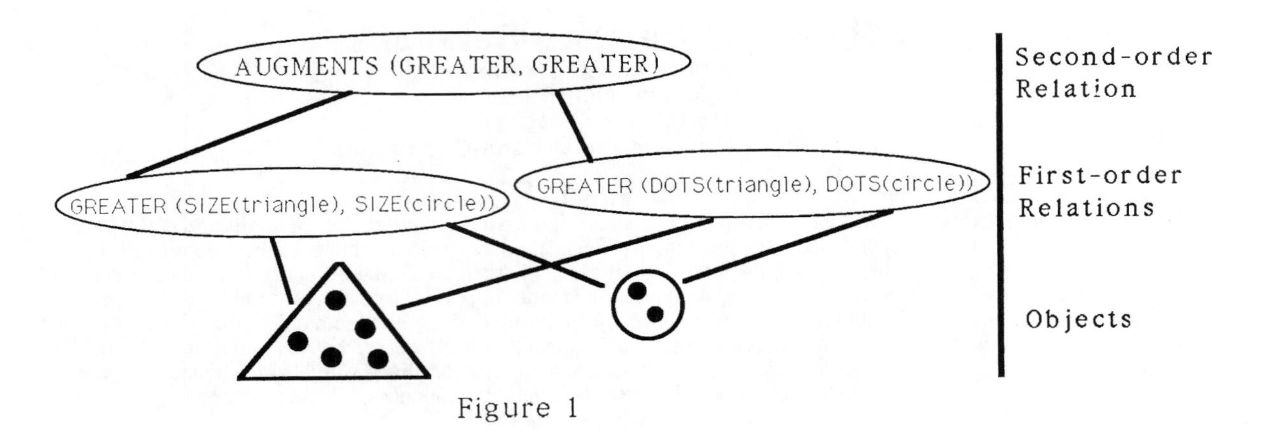

Figure 1

THAN (Wing1, Wing2) (see also Palmer, 1975). A relation is "higher-order" if it takes two or more relations as objects. According to SMT, a common relation is more important for an analogy if it is involved in a common higher-order relation. For the analogy between the solar system and an atom, the relation GREATER (MASS(sun), MASS(planet)) will be more important than the relation GREATER (BRIGHTNESS(sun), BRIGHTNESS(planet)) because it is involved in the higher-order relation CAUSE(GREATER (MASS(sun), MASS(planet)), REVOLVE-AROUND (planet, sun)) . Consequently, according to SMT, the goodness of an analogy depends on the relational correspondences between two domains, and on the relational structure in which these correspondences exist.

Higher-order relations illustrate one case of relations between relations. While the importance of higher-order relations has been shown for causal analogies (Clement & Gentner, 1988; Gentner, 1983; Winston, 1980), we will present demonstrations that suggest the importance of higher-order relations in determining perceptual similarity. All higher-order relations are not treated equally; some higher-order relations serve to highlight the relations that compose them, whereas other potential higher-order relations do not. As such, not only are object features involved in dependencies - the relations themselves display dependencies. A second case of relations between relations is also suggested - even when a true higher-order relation is not formed by two relations, the relations can still influence each other's importance by affecting how each is processed. For example, the perception of one relation may prime individuals to see other similar relations. In general, both cases argue that a person's sensitivity to a relation depends on the other relations with which it is composed.

Determining the Polarity of the Darker-than and Larger-than Relations

While Gentner's work with analogies typically uses causal relations as the higher-order relations that connect first-order relations, the higher-order relations used here will be comparisons of magnitude differences. In doing so, we preserve the basic vocabulary of propositional representation (Palmer, 1978). In Figure 1, the two blocks have the following first-order relations: GREATER-THAN (SIZE(triangle), SIZE(circle))[1] and GREATER-THAN (NUMBER-OF-DOTS (triangle), NUMBER-OF-DOTS (circle)). There is also a relation between these two relations - namely, in both relations, the triangle has the larger quantity. This higher-order relation will be called "AUGMENTATION" because each of the first-order relations augments the effect of the other by "pulling in the same direction" as the other; more technically, the two relations are magnitude relations of the same type, that take the same object arguments in the same order. The opposite of an AUGMENTATION relation is an "OPPOSITION" relation, whereby one relation cancels out the other relation by "pulling in the opposite direction"; more technically, the two relations are magnitude relations of opposite types, that take the same arguments in the same order. If the triangle were taller than the circle, but had fewer dots than the circle, then the relation between the dots and the relation between the sizes would be in an OPPOSITION relation.

To determine whether a higher-order relation is AUGMENTATION (both first-order relations in same objects pointing in the same direction) or OPPOSITION (first-order relations pointing in opposite directions) we must first determine the direction of greater magnitude for each relation. Following the general logic of Smith, Sera, and Goodrich's (in press) procedure for determining the "polarity" of a relation, we asked 18 subjects to label one side of a butterfly "positive" and the other side "negative." Subjects were told to use the words "positive" and

---

[1] GREATER-THAN (SIZE (triangle), SIZE (circle)) is equivalent to the representation LARGER-THAN (triangle, circle). The former can be viewed as an expansion of the latter.

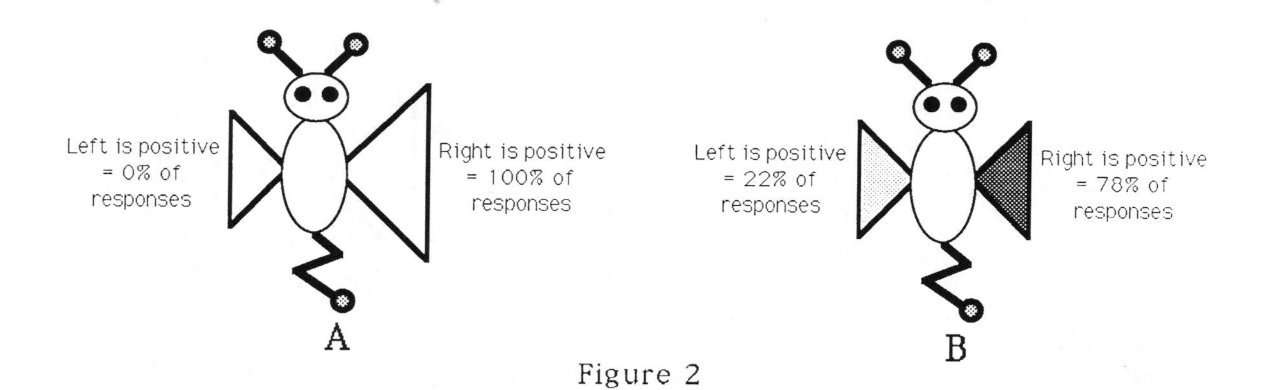

Figure 2

"negative" in a loose or metaphorical sense. The butterflies in Figure 2 tested the polarity of the TALLER-THAN and DARKER-THAN relations.

To control for possible left-right biases, half the subjects received butterflies identical to A and B except that the left and right wings were switched. All 18 subjects thought the larger side of A was positive, supporting the intuition that large is (metaphorically) positive and small is negative. Further, The results of 2B show that for most adults dark is positive and light is negative.[2] When the relational structure of butterflies are later represented, we will treat large wings as being GREATER-THAN small wings, and dark wings as being GREATER-THAN light wings. For example, if the left wing of a butterfly is larger than and darker than the right wing, then these two relations augment each other; if the left wing is larger than and lighter than the right wing, then the relations oppose each other.

General Method

Subjects were shown computer displays containing three butterflies. The butterfly at the top was the comparison butterfly. Subjects were told to either choose the lower left or the lower right butterfly, whichever was more similar to the comparison butterfly. Subjects pressed keys to choose either A or B as more similar to T. The relations used were: SAME-SIZE, LARGER-THAN, SMALLER-THAN, SAME-SHADE, DARKER-THAN, LIGHTER-THAN, and DIFFERENT-SHADE. There is no DIFFERENT-SIZE relation because any pair of wings which are differently sized can be described by the LARGER-THAN or SMALLER-THAN relation. In all experiments, the left/right order of butterflies A and B was randomized.

Higher-order Relations that Increase Relational Responding AUGMENTATION vs. OPPOSITION

Thirty-six University of Illinois undergraduates were presented butterfly triads with two choices, one of which was superficially similar to T and one of which was relationally similar to T. An example of two such triads is shown in Figure 3. For both the left and right cases, if a subject responds that A is more similar to T than is B, then we take this as evidence that they are responding superficially - they are basing their similarity on the gray that both A and T have on their right wings. A response of "B" is labelled a relational response, based on the common relation that B and T share - their right wings are darker than their left wings. A relation which is shared by T and only one of the two choices is called a unique relation. DARKER-THAN (right wing, left wing) is a unique relation, possessed only by T and B. A relation which is possessed by all three butterflies is called an accompanying relation. LARGER-THAN (right wing, left wing) is an accompanying relation for the three butterflies on the left because each of them possesses this relation.

The unique relations used in the experiment were: SMALLER-THAN, LARGER-THAN, DARKER-THAN, and LIGHTER-THAN. Each unique relation was paired with an augmenting and an opposing accompanying relation, yielding a total of eight different butterfly triads. For each triad, the left/right order of the relational and superficial responses were randomized, as was the presentation order of the pictures. Forty-two

[2] These results may seem to be opposed to Smith et al.'s (in press) evidence that adults have some tendency to view lighter objects as positive. One possible resolution is that our stimuli heighten the "dark=positive" effect because of they appear on a computer screen with a white background.

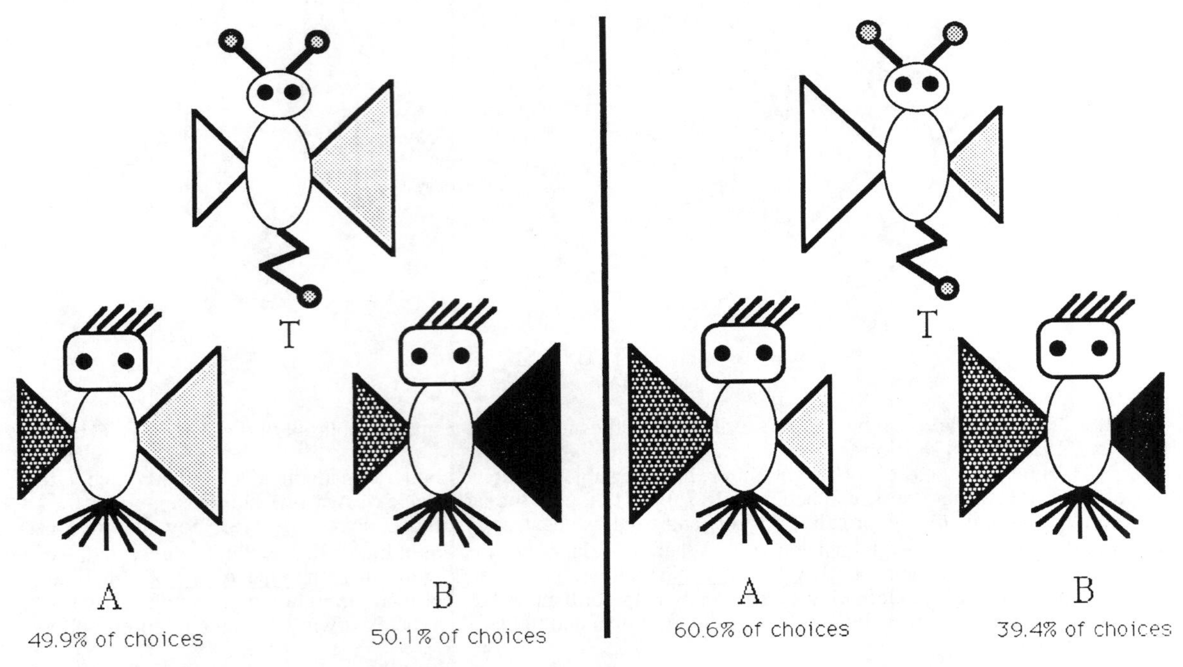

Figure 3

University of Illinois undergraduates were shown each of the eight pictures four times, and were required to make each response within 3.5 seconds.

Our interest is not in the absolute number of superficial and relational responses that subjects give; we are interested in variable that shift subjects' judgments. Here, the manipulated variable of importance is whether the accompanying relation augments or opposes the unique relation. For the three butterflies on the left, the accompanying relation LARGER-THAN (right wing, left wing) augments the unique relation DARKER-THAN (right wing, left wing) because they both are GREATER-THAN relations which take the same arguments in the same order. For the three butterflies on the right, the accompanying relation is SMALLER-THAN (right wing, left wing); this relation opposes the unique relation because SMALLER-THAN is a LESS-THAN relation. If the unique relation pertains to size, then four different accompanying relations are used - one for each shade relation. If the unique relation pertains to shade, then all three size relations are used as accompanying relations.

The question of primary interest is: What proportion of subjects give the relational response (as opposed to the superficial response) when the accompanying relation augments/opposes the unique relation. When the accompanying relation is augmenting, subjects give the relational response (choice B in the above figure) on 50.1% of trials; the proportion of relational responding drops down to 39.4% when the accompanying relation is opposing. This significant difference ($p<.01$) between the amount of relational responding suggests that the salience of a common relation in a similarity judgment is affected by the other relations present in a scene. Two simple explanations of our results will not suffice.

First, our results cannot be explained by simply assuming that some relations are inherently more salient than others. When subjects make choice B over A as most similar to T, they must be doing so because of the unique relation DARKER-THAN (right wing, left wing), since this is the only property that distinguishes A and B that also belongs to T. This relation is the same in the two triads. The only difference between the augmenting and opposing conditions is the wing size relation, which is shared by all three butterflies. Thus, how important the DARKER-THAN relation is for similarity depends on a relation which, by itself, does not distinguish between the two choices.

Second, our results also cannot be explained by saying: "Perhaps there is a general advantage to picking up other relations when the right wing is larger than the left wing." If the unique relation had been DARKER-THAN (left wing, right wing), then the opposite accompanying relation [LARGER-THAN (left wing, right wing)] resulted in a boost to relational responding. It is not the specific quality of a first-order relation considered by itself which results in the increased relational responding - it is the relation between first-order relations which affects the degree of relational responding.

Nonspecific Increases in Responding to Unique Relations Due to Accompanying Relation

Putting aside the specific relation-relation interactions, other results also suggest that some accompanying relations can serve as "universal facilitators," increasing the likelihood of relational responses in general. When the accompanying relation shared by all three butterflies is SAME-SIZE or SAME-SHADE (dimensional identity relations), then responding on the basis of the unique relations is higher than when the accompanying relation is one of the other relations. Figure 4 depicts an example of this effect. For both the left and right triads, the relational choice (B) has the unique relation SMALLER-THAN(LEFT WING, RIGHT WING) that the superficial choice (A) does not. The tendency (non significant if Figure 4 alone is considered, but significant overall) is for subjects to choose the relational choice more when wings have a SAME-SHADE relation. The unique relations include equal numbers of each of the seven relation (four shade relations, three size relations) types. The same subjects used in the preceding study produced the following results:

Accompanying Relation	% of Responding based on Unique Relation
DIFFERENT-SHADE (left wing, right wing)	70%
SAME-SHADE (Left wing, right wing)	76% (significantly greater than 71%)
LIGHTER-THAN or DARKER-THAN (left wing, right wing)	71%
LARGER-THAN or SMALLER-THAN (left wing, right wing)	44%
SAME-SIZE (left wing, right wing)	50% (significantly greater than 44%)

The presence of SAME-SIZE and SAME-SHADE relations within the butterflies causes further relational correspondences between the butterflies to be noticed. It has been suggested (Goldstone, Medin, & Gentner, 1987) that increasing the importance of relational correspondences between two objects will bias the subject to look for further relational matches as opposed to superficial matches. The percentage of responses on the basis of a relation

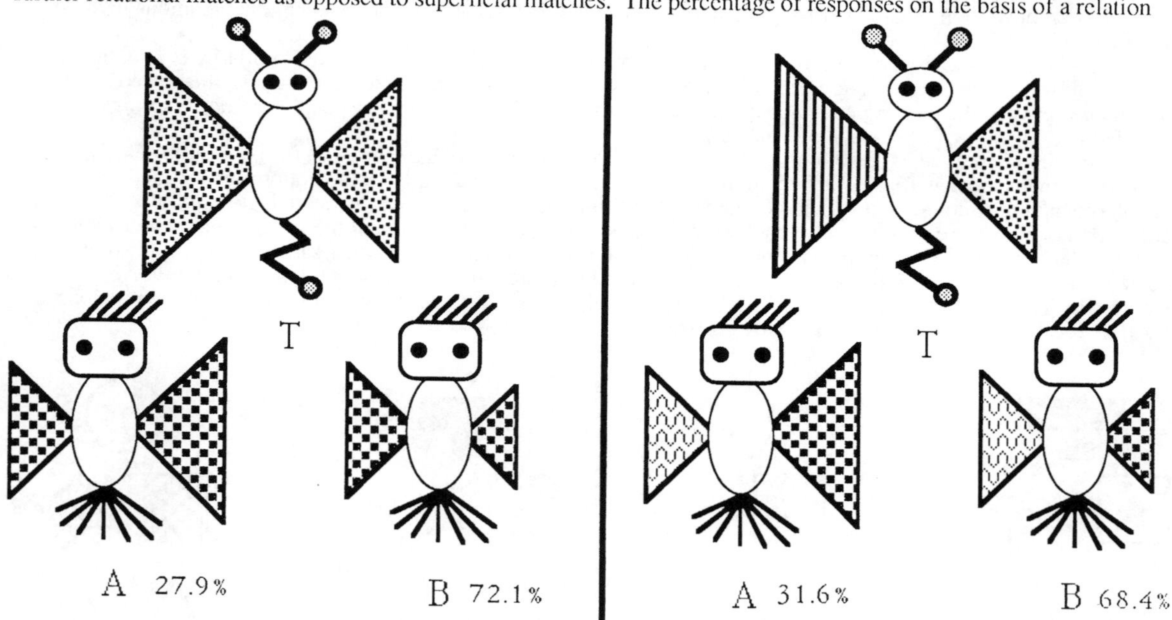

Figure 4

can be increased by either (1) increasing the number and salience of other relations present, or (2) decreasing the number or salience of superficial similarities present. The current results support this suggestion if SAME-SHADE and SAME-SIZE are assumed to be stronger, more noticeable relations than DIFFERENT-SHADE, LIGHTER-THAN, and SMALLER-THAN, so that, as accompanying relations, they call attention to the unique relation. Independent support for this assumption comes from the fact that when the unique relation is SAME-SHADE or SAME-SIZE, the relationally similar butterfly is chosen 72% of the time. Relational responding drops to 61% when the unique relation is one of the other relations. In the current experiments, we find that that a relation which might not be thought to have any influence on judgment (because both of the choices possess it), still influences judgment by highlighting other relations in a non-specific manner. The highlighting is non-specific in that SAME-SIZE and SAME-SHADE relations increase the likelihood of responses based on any other relation. No good higher-order relation results from the juxtaposition of SMALLER-THAN and SAME-SHADE (as in Figure 4). SAME-SHADE's tendency to increase the importance of SMALLER-THAN is due to its general processing facilitation of all relations.

Increased Relational Responding with Relations Associated with the Same Objects

A final demonstration shows a specific influence of relations on relations. Whereas the first demonstration showed an influence specific to the nature of the relations involved, another influence is specific to the structural configuration of the relations. A common pattern is that relations that share objects facilitate each other more than relations that belong to different objects. Thus, a relation will count for more in a similarity judgment if it involves objects that share another strong relation. Subjects rated the similarity of two scenes on a scale from 1 to 9,with 1 referring to very low similarity and 9 referring to very high similarity. Six sets of pictures were given of the same abstract design as Figure 5, intermingled with 30 filler sets. In Figure 5, the left pair (A and B) and the right pair (C and D) have exactly the same shapes and shades in common. Beyond this, they also share the same first-order relations: one SAME-SHAPE, one SAME-SHADE, and several DIFFERENT-SHAPE and DIFFERENT-SHADE relations. The only difference between the left and right pair is that the two SAME relations cooccur in the same objects on the right, whereas they belong to different objects on the left. So, the two triangles of C and D instantiate both the SAME-SHAPE and the SAME-SHADE relation. For A and B, the SAME-SHAPE relation is located with the bottom shapes while the SAME-SHADE relation is stationed in the middle row of shapes. Consistent with the previous demonstration, it will be assumed that relations involving SAME are more salient than relations involving DIFFERENT for these stimuli.

As figure 5 shows, when both of the salient relations belong to the same objects, similarity is rated higher. Five out of the six picture sets show an advantage for the location-coupled relations, and the sixth showed no difference between the coupled and uncoupled relations. The mean difference between the similarity ratings for the coupled and uncoupled sets was .255 ($p < .05$).

Again, alternative explanations of the results do not seem to adequately account for the results. Criticisms such as "perhaps the SAME-SHADE relation is always more salient when it is on the bottom" are refuted by counterbalancing conditions in which the second and third rows of all the scenes are switched. Similar counterbalancings were performed for each of the scenes. The absolute location of the salient relation does not matter; what matters is whether the salient relation is in the same location as the other salient relation. In addition, it does not appear that the two relations have to be similar. In Figure 5, the two salient relations both involve identicality - either of shape or shade. However, in two other sets that yield the same effect, one of the relations is DARKER-THAN while the other is SAME-SHAPE.

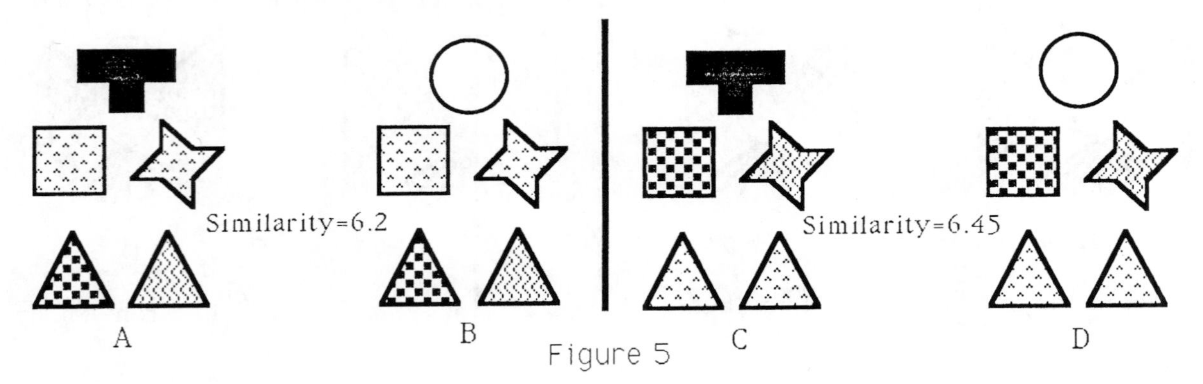

Figure 5

Conclusions

In explaining the three observed relation-relation interactions, we can either 1) posit particular higher-order relations, or 2) posit processing principles. The first observation, that augmenting relations are more likely to be the basis of similarity judgments than opposing relations, is naturally handled by the first strategy - by postulating that people are selectively sensitive to the particular higher-order relation AUGMENTS (LIGHTER-THAN (left wing, right wing), SMALLER-THAN(left wing, right wing)). Consequently, two butterflies with an AUGMENTATION higher-order relation will be perceived as highly similar, whereas two butterflies with an OPPOSITION higher-order relation will not be perceived to be as similar. On the other hand, a processing account might argue that perceiving a relation with one magnitude relation facilitates noticing/evaluating other relations with a relation of the same polarity, without requiring the psychological reality of the actual higher-order relation AUGMENTS.

At the other end of the continuum, the observation that a SAME-SHADE relation (as opposed to DIFFERENT-SHADE) increases the saliency of LARGER-THAN, seems best explained by the processing principle that a salient relation primes people to look for any other relation, even if these relations do not form a compelling higher-order relation. The only higher-order relation shared by SAME-SHADE and LARGER-THAN is DIFFERENT-RELATION, and it is unlikely that this higher-order relation would have psychological salience in our stimulus set. Relations take part in specific interactions with other relations, expressible as higher-order relations; they also interact non-specifically, with highly salient relations acting as "universal facilitators" for the perception of other relations.

To review, the results argue that how important a relation is for similarity depends on the other relations present -relations do not have absolute, intrinsic saliences . First, a relation becomes more important if it cooccurs with a relation which points in the same direction that it does. That is, in order to make a relation clear or noticeable, other relations should be introduced so as to augment, not oppose, the relation at issue. Second, there is also a non-specific interaction between relations, such that a prominent relation (SAME-SIZE or SAME-SHADE) increases the salience of all of the other relations in a scene. To make a relation more likely to be noticed, a good strategy is to put the person into a "relational frame of mind" by adding other salient relations to the object. Third, a relation is more important if it connects objects that are connected by another salient relation; unlike the second effect, the facilitative effect of a relation is focused on other relations with which it coincides; unlike the first effect, this specific facilitation is primarily based on the configuration and not the nature of the relations.

These three points argue for an account of similarity that is not based upon the independent analysis of features, or even the independent analysis of relations between features. The importance of relations between relations precludes any model which simply assigns each matching and mismatching feature/relation a static weight, and counts the weighted features/relations to determine the similarity of two objects. The weight given to a relation cannot be assigned without knowing what other relations are present. Rather than viewing similarity as based on lists of features, similarity is best viewed as being sensitive to the structural relations between features. Even in the domain of visual perception, where the postulation of simple feature detectors is most appealing, we find that the higher-order structural representation of a scene influences the use of lower-order relations, which in turn influence the use of object features.

References

Clement, C., & Gentner, D. (1988). Systematicity as a selection constraint in analogical mapping. In The Tenth Annual Conference of the Cognitive Science Society, (pp. 412-418), Montreal.

Gati, I., & Tversky, A. (1984). Weighting common and distinctive features in perceptual and conceptual judgments. Cognitive Psychology, 16, 341-370.

Gentner, D. (1989). The mechanisms of analogical learning. In S. Vosniadou & A. Ortony (Eds.), Similarity, analogy, and thought. New York: Cambridge University Press.

Gentner, D. (1983). Structure-mapping: A theoretical framework for analogy. Cognitive Science, 7, 155-170.

Goldstone, R., Medin, D., & Gentner, D. (1987). Relational similarity and the non-independence of features in similarity judgments. Address to the Mid-West Psychological Association: Chicago.

Hintzman, D. L. (1986). "Schema abstraction" in a multiple-trace memory model. Psychological Review, 93, 411-429.

Palmer, S. E. (1975). Visual perception and world knowledge. In D. A. Norman & D. E. Rumelhart (Eds.), Explorations in cognition. San Francisco: W. H. Freeman.

Palmer, S. E. (1978). Fundamental aspects of cognitive representation. In E. Rosch & B. B. LLoyd (Eds.), Cognition and categorization. Hillsdale, NJ: Lawrence Erlbaum Associates.

Pomerantz, J. R. (1986). Visual form perception: An overview. In Pattern recognition by humans and machines: Visual perception, Volume 2. New York: Academic Press.

Posner, M. I., & Keele, S. W. (1968). On the genesis of abstract ideas. Journal of Experimental Psychology, 77, 353-363.

Smith, L. B., Sera, M., & Goodrich, T. (1984). A developmental analysis of the polar structure of dimensions. in press.
Tversky, A. (1977). Features of similarity. Psychological Review, 84, 327-352.
Winston, P. H. (1980). Learning and reasoning by analogy. In: Communications of Association for Computing Machinery, 23, 689-703.

Integrating Generalizations with Exemplar-Based Reasoning

L. Karl Branting
Department of Computer Sciences
University of Texas

ABSTRACT

Knowledge represented as generalizations is insufficient for problem solving in many domains, such as legal reasoning, because of a gap between the language of case-descriptions and the language in which generalizations are expressed, and because of the graded structure of domain categories. Exemplar-based representation addresses these problems, but accurate assessment of similarity between an exemplar of a category and a new case requires reasoning both with general domain theory and with the explanation of the exemplar's membership in the category. GREBE is a system that integrates generalizations and exemplars in a cooperative manner. Exemplar-based explanations are used to bridge the gap between case-descriptions and generalizations, and domain theory in the form of general rules and specific explanations is used to explain the equivalence of new cases to exemplars.

INTRODUCTION

In many important domains, knowledge expressed as generalizations is insufficient for such important tasks as determining membership in domain categories and evaluating domain predicates. One reason for the insufficiency of generalizations in such domains is that there may be a "gap" between the language in which cases are described and the language in which generalizations are expressed [PBH89]. A second reason is that domain categories may exhibit a gradient of centrality or typicality [Bar85] which generalizations expressed as rules are ill-suited to represent [SM81].

Both of these factors are illustrated by the domain of legal reasoning. Determining the legal consequences of a set of facts may require determining whether a surgeon acted with "reasonable care," a killer acted with "malice," or an employee was acting "in furtherance of employment," since these terms appear in general legal rules for determining guilt and liability. However, the terms "reasonable care," "malice," and "in furtherance of employment" do not appear in case descriptions, and the domain theory provides no general rules for determining whether such terms are satisfied under the facts of a given case [vdLG84].

Graded structure is illustrated by the category "activities in furtherance of employment." An employee working on an assembly line is clearly acting in furtherance of his employment, but what about an employee carrying equipment from his car to the shop, driving from home to work, or shaving in preparation for work? It is problematical to determine at what point an activity is sufficiently remote from work that it is no longer a category instance. This example illustrates a gradient of possible cases—from clear category instances through unclear cases to clear noninstances—that cannot easily be expressed by any single general rule.

These problems are addressed by an approach to knowledge representation in which full descriptions of known instances, or *exemplars*, of various categories are retained and each new case is analyzed by comparing it to the exemplars that it most closely resembles. Examples of this approach include MEDIATOR [Sim85], Protos [PBH89], Kibler and Aha's systems [KA87], and in the legal reasoning community, HYPO [RA87]. Exemplar-based systems typically use a feature vector representation of cases and assess the degree of similarity between cases by calculating the weighted sum (or product) of features of the exemplar matched by the new case.

An exemplar-based representation makes it possible to reason about categories for which there are insufficient generalizations and is well suited for concepts with graded structure, since there is a range of possible degrees of match with an exemplar. However, determining category membership exclusively as a weighed function of shared features has been criticized on the grounds that it neglects the generalization-based domain theory in which exemplars are embedded [MM85]. Murphy and Medin point out that the relative feature weights that determine degree of similarity depend on the context and task. They conclude that exemplar-based categorization requires knowledge of the relations among features and of the explanatory principles that connect exemplars to the categories of which they are members.

The use of general domain theory to assist in the assessment of similarity between cases was investigated in Protos [PBH89], a learning apprentice for heuristic classification in the domain of clinical audiology. Categories are represented in Protos by exemplars embedded in a network of causal and associational rules derived from explanations of category membership. The similarity of a new case to an exemplar is evaluated by attempting to construct an explanation of featural equivalence between the cases from these rules. Protos demonstrated that use of general domain theory to assist in similarity assessment could lead to high levels of performance in audiology.

Protos is nevertheless inadequate for more complex domains such as legal reasoning. Protos is limited to a feature-vector representation of cases that is unsuited to the complex narratives that constitute the facts of legal cases. In addition, Protos can only apply generalization-based reasoning in assessing similarity between individual case features, and can only apply exemplar-based reasoning to its top-level goal or to infer a new case feature necessary to match an exemplar feature. More complex domains such as legal reasoning require the ability to choose between and combine exemplar-based and generalization-based reasoning more flexibly so that each technique can be used in support of the other.

For example, it is sometimes necessary to use domain generalizations to reformulate a goal into subgoals, some of which are amenable to generalization-based reasoning and others of which require exemplar-based reasoning. Similarly, determining whether a feature of an exemplar is present in a new case can require both generalizations and exemplar-based reasoning.

This paper describes an approach to flexible integration of generalization-based and exemplar-based reasoning. This approach is applicable to complex cases that do not lend themselves to feature-vector representation and permits reasoning steps used in assessing similarity to be reused in subsequent cases.

OVERVIEW OF GREBE

GREBE (Generator of Recursive Exemplar-Based Explanations) is a system that uses knowledge in the form both of generalizations and category exemplars to determine the classification of new cases. GREBE integrates generalization-based knowledge with exemplars in two ways. First, exemplar-based reasoning is used to help evaluate antecedents of legal or common-sense rules for which there are no applicable generalizations. Second, general domain rules and specific explanations of category membership by exemplars are used in the assessment of similarity between cases. In this manner, generalization-based reasoning and exemplar-based reasoning are treated as complementary processes, each of which is necessary for the success of the other.

GREBE uses a semantic network representation of cases in which individual facts correspond to relation/unit/value triples and the facts of an entire case correspond to a labeled graph.

When GREBE is queried about whether a certain conclusion applies to a case, it tries to find the conclusion in the case description. If it is unable to do so, it attempts to construct either of the following types of explanations of the conclusion:

- *Generalization-based explanation.* The conclusion is the consequent of a general domain rule all the antecedents of which are themselves explained. This form of explanation is similar to "explanation as proof" [Moo88] [KC85].
- *Exemplar-based explanation.* The conclusion is justified by the similarity between the new case and the relevant aspects of an exemplar to which the conclusion applied.

In exemplar-based explanation, not all of the facts of an exemplar case are necessarily relevant to a given result. For example, if several explanations apply to an exemplar, it may be that only a subset of the facts are relevant to each explanation. The facts of a case that are used to explain a given result are the exemplar's *criterial facts* with respect to the result. The criterial facts of an exemplar form a labeled subgraph of the graph that represents all the facts of the exemplar.

The criterial facts of an exemplar are necessarily quite specific. Even though it is the pattern of relations and not the particular individuals in a precedent that must be matched in a new case, new cases nevertheless seldom contain exactly the same pattern of relations as any precedent. The solution to the problem posed by the specificity of exemplars is to use generalization-based and exemplar-based explanations to explain how individual criterial facts are matched in a new case. This permits multiple sources of knowledge to be exploited in order to explain the equivalence of a new case to an exemplar.

GREBE assesses the degree of similarity between a new case and an exemplar with respect to a given conclusion by attempting to map the subgraph representing the criterial facts of the exemplar onto the new case.[1] A best-first search is performed among possible mappings between the criterial facts of the exemplar and the new case, using fewest unmatched triples as the evaluation function. GREBE is then called recursively to attempt to infer any facts missing from the new case that are needed for a perfect match.

Missing facts can be inferred by reusing the explanations from previous exemplars. These explanations may be either generalization-based explanations or exemplar-based explanations. For example, if in a previous exemplar a common-sense rule was used to infer a given relation, this common-sense rule is available to infer the same relation in subsequent cases in which the rule's antecedents are met. Similarly, if there is an exemplar of the relation, then the relation can be inferred in any new case that shares the criterial facts of the exemplar.

GREBE's knowledge base currently contains rules and a small (but growing) collection of exemplar cases concerning the compensability under Texas worker's compensation law of injuries to workers traveling outside of the work place. GREBE's rules fall into two distinct categories: legal rules and common-sense rules. Legal rules are rules that are explicitly stated in statutes or judicial opinions. Common-sense rules represent reasoning in judicial opinions that is implicit because it is too obvious (to humans) to need pointing out. An example is the inference that if an activity is a duty of employment, then each step of that activity is a duty of employment as well.

[1]This process resembles the structure mapping of [Gen83]. It differs, however, in that the criterial facts of an exemplar are a part of the domain theory and cannot be recognized *a priori* using syntactic criteria such as relationality or systematicity.

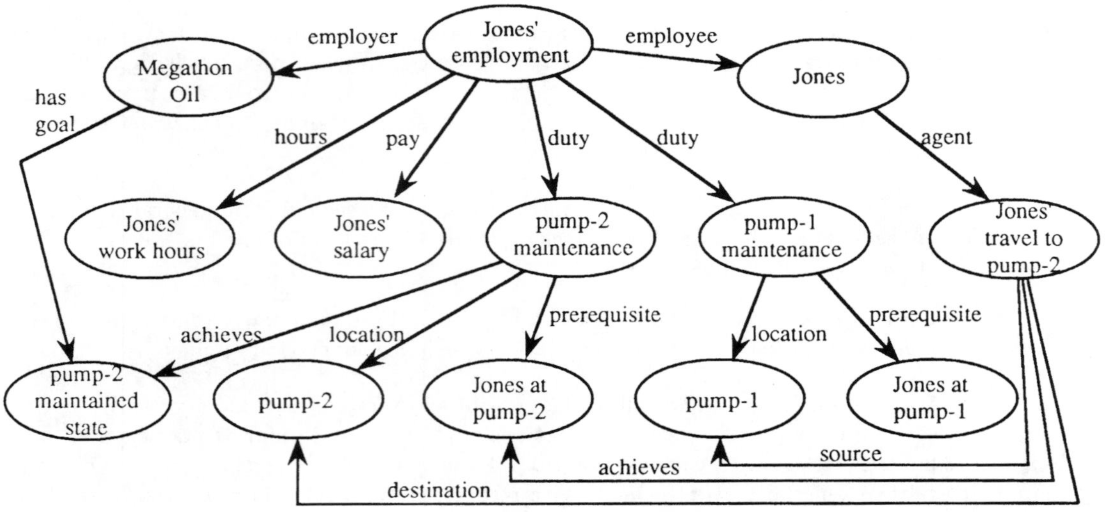

Figure 1: A partial representation of the facts of *Jones.*

USING GENERALIZATIONS AND EXEMPLARS TO ANALYZE A NEW CASE

Consider the following hypothetical case: Jones, a maintenance man employed by Megathon Oil Company, was involved in a one-car accident while driving in his own car from one pumping station where he had performed maintenance duties to a second pumping station where he planned to perform additional maintenance duties. Figure 1 shows a portion of the facts of *Jones.*[2]

If the system is queried whether Megathon is liable to Jones for his injuries, it is able to create a partial generalization-based explanation for Megathon's liability, shown in Figure 2. Megathon's liability to Jones is explained by statutory rule 1 and by the conclusions that Jones was employed by Megathon and that the injury was "sustained in the course" of the job. That the injury was "sustained in the course" of Jones' job follows under statutory rule 2 from the following conclusions: the injury occurred during Jones' travel to pump station 2, this travel was "in furtherance of" Jones' employment, and Jones' injury "originated in" the employment.

The gap between case descriptions and domain generalizations emerges in attempting to determine whether Jones' travel was in furtherance of his employment. There are no general rules for determining whether an activity is in furtherance of employment, so GREBE attempts to construct an exemplar-based explanation of this predicate. First, a promising exemplar of traveling in furtherance of employment, *Jecker v. Western Alliance Ins. Co.,* 369 S.W.2d 776 (Tex. 1963), is identified and retrieved.[3] Then, the degree of similarity between *Jecker* and *Jones* is assessed by attempting to create an exemplar-based explanation using *Jecker* as the exemplar.

Creating an Exemplar-Based Explanation

In constructing an exemplar-based explanation, GREBE begins by mapping the criterial facts of *Jecker* with respect to travel in furtherance of employment onto *Jones.* Figure 3 shows a

[2] Italicized names refer to the case involving the person named, *e.g.*, the *Jones* case, whereas unitalicized names refer to the person himself, *e.g.*, Jones.

[3] Identification and retrieval of appropriate exemplars is performed in a manner similar to Protos' use of difference links [PBH89].

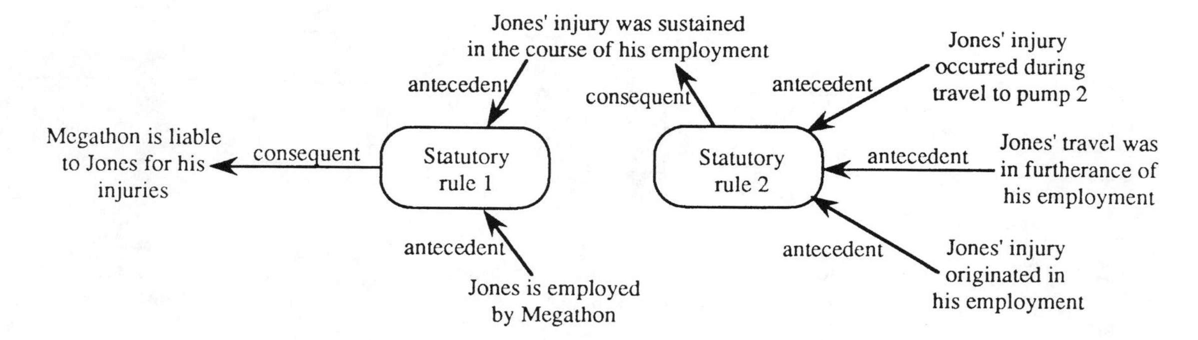

Figure 2: A partial generalization-based explanation of workers' compensation liability.

portion of the mapping from these criterial facts (which actually consist of 31 triples) onto the facts of *Jones*. Since it is the pattern of relationships, and not the particular individuals, of a case that are responsible for its legal consequences, a relation/unit/value triple in the exemplar is considered to match a triple in the new case if the relations are equal and if the unit and value mappings are consistent with those of other matched triples. In Figure 3, each of the triples of *Jecker* shown has a match in *Jones* under the mapping shown except that Jecker's travel was an implied duty of his employment, whereas this relation is not given as part of the *Jones* case. GREBE therefore attempts to infer that Jones had a duty to travel.

GREBE is unable to construct a generalization-based explanation that Jones had a duty to travel, but finds that *Jecker* has an exemplar-based explanation that Jecker's traveling was an implied duty of employment. This exemplar-based explanation was used by the court that decided *Jecker* as part of its explanation of the similarity between *Jecker* and an earlier exemplar in which traveling was an express duty.

GREBE fetches the criterial facts of *Jecker* with respect to this explanation (represented as 19 triples) and performs a mapping from this set of criterial facts onto *Jones*. Under the best mapping (a portion of which is shown in Figure 4) a criterial fact for Jecker's implied duty to travel—that the traveling occurred during his work hours—is unmatched in *Jones*. However, GREBE constructs an explanation that Jones' travel occurred during his work hours (shown in Figure 5) by reusing a common-sense rule from an earlier exemplar, *Brown*. This rule provides that if an employee determines his own hours, then any time he spends performing job duties is, in effect, working hours.

GREBE returns an explanation structure showing that there is an actual or inferrable fact in *Jones* corresponding to each criterial fact of *Jecker* with respect to travel in furtherance of employment, with the sole exception that the maintenance site to which Jones was traveling was not under the employer's direct control. *Jones* is therefore strongly analogous to *Jecker*. The exemplar-based explanation that Jones' travel was in furtherance of his employment satisfies the antecedent of statutory rule 2 (in Figure 2) and completes the explanation that Megathon is liable to Jones for his accident.

If *Jones* were modified to provide that Jones was traveling home from a maintenance site rather than between two maintenance sites, GREBE would find two additional facts to be unmatched: there would be no employment activity performed at Jones' destination, and being at the destination would not be a prerequisite for an employment activity. GREBE's analysis is

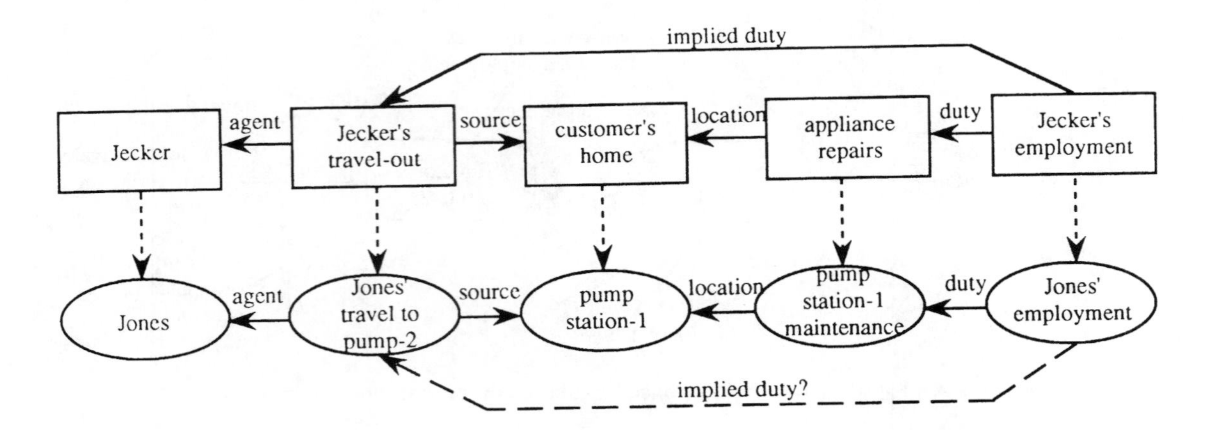

Figure 3: The dashed vertical arrows indicate the mapping from a portion of the criterial facts of *Jecker* with respect to travel in furtherance of employment onto the facts of *Jones*. All the criterial facts shown are matched except for Jones' travel being an implied duty of employment.

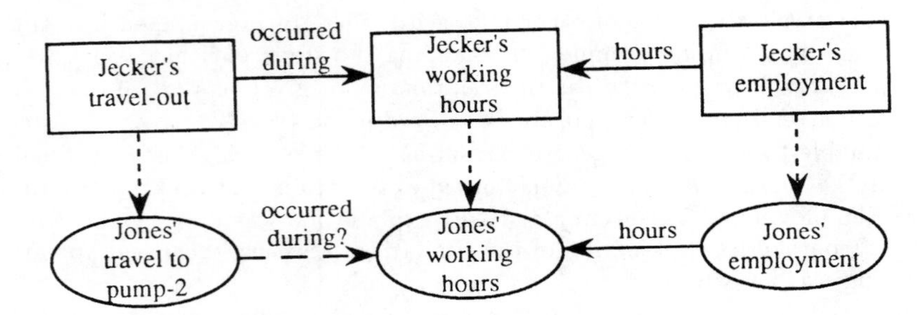

Figure 4: Under the mapping between a portion of the criterial facts of *Jecker* with respect to implied duties and facts of *Jones*, the fact that the travel occurred during working hours is unmatched.

consistent with the assessment of human experts that the original hypothetical is strongly analogous to *Jecker*, but that the modified hypothetical differs significantly from *Jecker* [Bra88].

Explanation Reuse

The accurate assessment of similarity between *Jones* and *Jecker* depended on reuse of the explanation that Jecker's travel was in furtherance of his employment. This example illustrates that exemplar-based explanations can be reused in two ways.

First, knowledge that a particular set of facts of an exemplar is criterial for a given category is reused when a new case is classified on the basis of its match with those criterial facts. For example, knowing the criterial facts of *Jecker* for traveling in furtherance of employment means knowing that Jecker was acting in furtherance of his employment because he was driving from one location where he performed a job duty on a direct route to a second location where he intended to perform a job duty, and the driving was an implied duty under the employment contract. This portion of the explanation is reused in explaining that Jones' travel was in furtherance of his

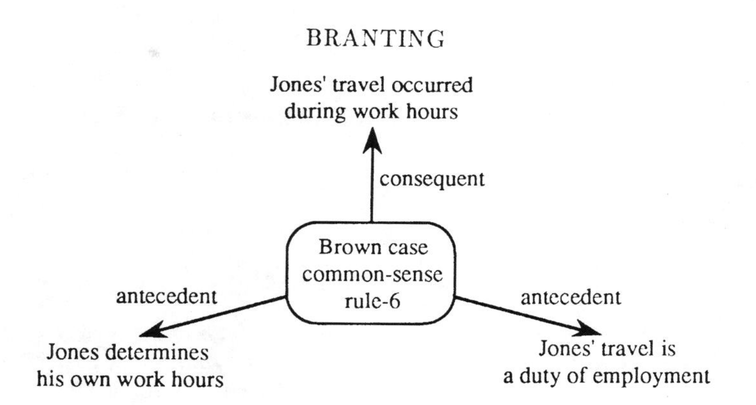

Figure 5: A generalization-based explanation that *Jones'* travel occurred during his work hours.

employment because of the similarity between these criterial facts and the facts of *Jones*.

The second way that exemplar-based explanations can be reused is that explanations of any inferred criterial facts can be reused in subsequent exemplar-based explanations. The exemplar-based explanation for Jecker's implied duty to travel was reused to infer that Jones had an implied duty to travel. Similarly, the generalization-based explanation that the travel in *Brown* occurred during work hours was reused to infer that Jones' travel occurred during his work hours.

Integrating Multiple Explanations

The *Jones* case illustrates how generalization- and exemplar-based explanations drawn from various sources can be integrated by GREBE into a single explanation for the classification of a new case. The explanation of Megathon's liability for Jones' injury combines two statutory rules, exemplar-based explanations involving two different aspects of *Jecker*, and a common-sense rule taken from a second exemplar, *Brown*. Exemplar-based explanation was necessary to satisfy an antecedent of a generalization-based explanation for workers' compensation liability. The assessment of similarity between *Jecker* and *Jones*, in turn, required both generalization-based reasoning and additional exemplar-based reasoning.

Such an explanation could not be produced by a system limited exclusively to generalization- or exemplar-based reasoning. Neither could it be produced by Protos, which is unable to apply generalization-based reasoning to its top-level rule or exemplar-based reasoning to rule antecedents.

CONCLUSION

GREBE integrates generalizations with exemplars in a manner that compensates for the weakness of each form of knowledge representation. Exemplars help bridge the gap between case descriptions and the language of generalizations, and aid in the representation of graded concepts. General domain theory and specific exemplar-based explanations are necessary for accurate assessment of similarity between complex and superficially dissimilar cases.

GREBE represents an advance over previous exemplar-based systems in that it retains and reuses the explanations of category exemplars, uses exemplar-based reasoning recursively to assist in assessment of similarity, and allows both generalization- and exemplar-based reasoning to be freely combined.

ACKNOWLEDGEMENTS

Support for this research was provided by the Army Research Office under grant number ARO DAAG29-84-K-0060.

REFERENCES

[Bar85] Lawrence W. Barsalou. Ideals, central tendency, and frequency of instantiation as determinants of graded structure in categories. *Journal of Experimental Psychology: Learning, Memory, and Cognition*, 11(4):629–649, October 1985.

[Bra88] L. Karl Branting. Protocol analysis of five worker's compensation problems. Unpublished protocol analysis of problem solving by attorneys at the Colorado Court of Appeals, September 1988.

[Gen83] Dedre Genter. Structure mapping: A theoretical framework for analogy. *Cognitive Science*, 7(2):155–170, April-June 1983.

[KA87] Dennis Kibler and David W. Aha. Learning representative exemplars of concepts: an initial case study. In *Proceedings of the 4th International Workshop on Machine Learning*, pages 1–11, 1987.

[KC85] Smadar Kedar-Cabelli. Purpose-directed analogy. In *Proceedings of the 7th Annual Conference of the Cognitive Science Society*, 1985.

[MM85] George L. Murphy and Douglas L. Medin. The role of theories in conceptual coherence. *Psychological Review*, pages 289–316, 1985.

[Moo88] Raymond Mooney. *A General Explanation Based Learning Mechanism and its Application to Narrative Understanding.* PhD thesis, University of Illinois, 1988.

[PBH89] Bruce W. Porter, E. Ray Bareiss, and Robert C. Holte. Knowledge acquisition and heuristic classification in weak-theory domains. Technical Report AI-TR89-96, Artificial Intelligence Laboratory, Department of Computer Sciences, University of Texas at Austin, February 1989.

[RA87] Edwina Rissland and Kevin Ashley. Hypo: A case-based reasoning system. Project memo 18, Department of Computer and Information Sciences, University of Massachusetts, 1987.

[Sim85] Robert L. Simpson. *A Computer Model of Case-based Reasoning in Problem Solving: An Investigation in the Domain of Dispute Mediation.* PhD thesis, Georgia Institute of Technology, 1985.

[SM81] Edward E. Smith and Douglas L. Medin. *Categories and Concepts.* Harvard University Press, 1981.

[vdLG84] Anne van der Lieth Gardner. *An Artificial Intelligence Approach to Legal Reasoning.* PhD thesis, Stanford University, 1984.

Combining Explanation Types for Learning by Understanding Instructional Examples

Michael Redmond
School of Information and Computer Science
Georgia Institute of Technology

Abstract

Learning from instruction is a powerful technique for improving problem solving. It is most effective when there is cooperation between the instructor and the student. In one cooperative scenario, the instructor presents examples and partial explanations of them, based on the perceived needs of the student. An active student will predict the instructor's actions and then try to explain the differences from the predictions. This focuses the learning, making it more efficient. We expand the concept of explanation beyond the provably correct explanations of explanation-based learning to include other methods of explanation used by human students. The explanations can use deductions from causal domain knowledge, plausible inferences from the instructor's actions, previous cases of problem solving, and induction. They involve the goal being pursued and the action taken in support of the goal. The explanations result in improved diagnosis and improved future explanation. This combination of explanation techniques leads to more opportunities to learn. We present examples of these ideas from the system we have implemented in the domain of automobile diagnosis.

INTRODUCTION

People learn much of what they know from instruction. Presentation of examples can be an important part of instruction. LeFevre and Dixon [1986] found that students prefer examples to written text in learning a procedural task. Reder, Charney and Morgan [1986] found that instruction that included examples was more effective. What is it that makes examples effective teaching instruments?

One characteristic that makes them effective is that active students that try to explain the examples learn through the process of explanation. Lancaster and Kolodner [1988] and Chi, Bassok, Lewis, Reimann, and Glaser [in press] have both observed this in protocol studies. This has been our focus - learning from understanding how a teacher solves an example problem.

Figure 1 summarizes the general process. Essentially, the instructor presents the problem, and appropriate actions or solutions. The student uses various types of knowledge to predict the instructor's actions, and then to understand or explain why the instructor's action or solution is appropriate.

The student is testing her ability to diagnose when she predicts what the instructor will do. The same techniques she would use if she were actually diagnosing are used to set up the prediction. In this way, when an opportunity to learn occurs, what is learned will be useful when the student actually goes about diagnosing. The example helps focus the learning.

We have constructed a system that creates explanations using deductions from causal domain knowledge, plausible inferences from the instructor's actions, previous cases of problem solving, and induction. The explanations involve the goal being pursued and the action taken in support of the goal. The explanations result in improved diagnosis and improved future explanation. This combination of explanation techniques leads to more opportunities to learn. This paper discusses the different types of explanations, and how they improve future problem solving and explanation.

---

1. The *instructor* states the problem description.
2. The *student* attempts to generate an appropriate action for the problem and current context.
3. The *instructor* generates a correct action or solution for the problem and current context.
4. The *student* then attempts to explain this action, learning if possible.
5. Continue with step 2 if the problem is not solved.

Figure 1: General Algorithm.

EXPLANATION

In our approach, explanation follows prediction and observation. The first step, therefore, is to compare the prediction with the expert's problem solving. This includes whether the instructor appears to be pursuing the predicted goal, and whether pursuit of the goal leads to the predicted action.

A correct prediction is essentially a successful explanation. Further explanation is required where the prediction isn't met. There can be many different ways of explaining differences. In this paper we discuss explanations involving:

- Inferring the instructor's current goal, and when necessary learning a new goal.
- Inferring the place of the current goal and actions in the diagnosis episode.
- Adjusting the saliency of features for future case retrieval.
- Trying to causally explain actions.

We have also begun to deal with a few other types of explanation that we will not discuss here. For example, explaining differences in implementation detail may rely on differences in car models, available tools, or in the current state of the car.

The types of explanations we make use of overlap with the types of explanations observed by Chi et al [in press]. They observed explanations that:

1. Refine or expand the conditions of an action
2. Explicate or infer different consequences of an action
3. Determine a goal or purpose for an action
4. Give meaning to a set of quantitative expressions.

Their first type of explanation is not a type that we have explored as yet. Our causal chaining explanation type corresponds to their second type, and our inferring the instructor's goal explanation type corresponds to their third type. Their fourth type is not applicable to our domain, though really it is a more specific version of inferring a goal. At a different level, Chi et al [in press] note explanations relating example actions to domain principles and to other example actions. Causal chaining can be seen as relating the observed actions to the domain principles. Inferring the place of the current goal and actions in the current diagnosis episode is one part of relating actions to each other.

In the following sections we will discuss in more detail how explanation of instruction is done, and how it improves the system through what is learned.

INFERRING INSTRUCTOR'S GOAL

Since the instructor's goal is usually not explicitly stated, it must be inferred from her actions. Different goals result in different types of actions being done. The instructor's goal must be inferred so that it can be compared to the predicted goal. The process is focused by the student's prediction of the instructor's goal. The predicted goal is the first goal considered as a possibility. If the instructor's actions are consistent with that goal then it is inferred that that is the goal being used. Otherwise, the goal must be inferred bottom up, with all possible goals being possible. This means that if the student gets lost in the example, she can find actions that make sense and get back to following along from there, and salvage something from the instructional episode.

```
(test (low ^fast-idle-speed))
(do (remove ^air-cleaner))
(do (disconnect ^radiator-fan))
(do (connect ^tachometer ^engine))
(do (plug ^vacuum-advance-hose))
(use (c-4812-2c))
(do (connect c-4812-2c ^choke-cam-follower-pin))
(do (release ^throttle-lever))
(ask ((rpm ^engine-system) nil) ^tachometer (reply 1600))
```

Figure 2: Instructor's Actions. The instructor's actions, entered into the system either interactively or by batch in a variable, are predicate forms specifying the type of action, and the action.

Some possible goals in a diagnostic domain include generating a hypothesis, testing a hypothesis, interpreting a test, fixing a fault, verifying a complaint, and clarifying a complaint. Figure 2 shows a portion of the instructor's actions in a given example. The complaint had been that the engine stalls, and the instructor has just hypothesized that the fast idle speed is set too low. This hypothesis must be tested. The instructor says that she is going to test whether the fast idle speed is low. Then she removes the air cleaner. She disconnects the radiator fan and connects a tachometer, and otherwise prepares for the test. Then using a specific tool specified in a reference book, she carries out the test, reading the value from the tachometer and comparing it to the specifications.

The process of inferring the instructor's goal uses knowledge about the goals stored in their representation. Some goals require particular types of actions. Some action types are inappropriate for some goals. Some action types can occur multiple times in the pursuit of a particular goal, some can only occur once. To give one example of the type of inference involved, testing a hypothesis *must* include an *ask* type action in order for results to be obtained. When it is determined that the predicted goal was not pursued, the other known goals are considered. Once the system knows what goal is being pursued, then the same explaining is done as if the goal had been correctly predicted. The student can recover and resume following the instructor.

If none of the diagnosis-specific goals are appropriate a more general goal can be considered, which could result in a diagnosis-specific specialization of the goal being learned. Figure 3 shows an annotated run of our system CELIA (Cases and Explanations in Learning: an Integrated Approach), reasoning as a student would, realizing that it needs to learn a new goal. For this run of the

```
...
Next Task
G-PREDICT-EXPERTS-ACTION

Next predicted goal
G-REPLACE-FIX
 Mentally Simulating strategy  S-RETRIEVE-MEMORY-PIECE  for goal  G-REPLACE-FIX
 retrieve a piece from memory now
 Matches fragments (pieces) -
    (GEN-REPLACE-FIX-LOW-IDLE                 7.6000004)
    (GEN-REPLACE-FIX-THERM-COIL-CHOKE         5.6)
    (GEN-REPLACE-FIX-LEAN-CHOKE               5.6)
    (GEN-REPLACE-FIX-TOO-RICH                 1.3)
 Simulating based on retrieved piece GEN-REPLACE-FIX-LOW-IDLE
 The fault has been determined to be: (LOW IDLE-SPEED)
 The fix usually done in previous similar experiences was: (INCREASE (POSITION IDLE-SPEED-SCREW))
 The method of doing the fix in previous similar experiences was: ...

Next Task
G-OBSERVE-EXPERTS-ACTION

Expert's next action       ****** NOTE - test if engine is cold when it stalls ******
(TEST (TEMPERATURE ENGINE-SYSTEM (WHEN (STALLS ENGINE-SYSTEM)) COLD))
Expert's next action  :
(DO (DRIVE CAR) UNTIL (STALLS ENGINE-SYSTEM))
Expert's next action  :  ****** NOTE - read engine temperature gauge when car stalls ******
                         ******          engine is cold when it stalls                  ******
(ASK ((TEMPERATURE ENGINE-SYSTEM) NIL) ENGINE-TEMP-GAUGE (REPLY (COLD)))

Next Task
G-EXPLAIN-DIFFERENCE

 Comparing instructors actions to predicted actions
************ He's using a different goal than expected **********
...
************ don't know the goal being used or know it incorrectly ***********
...
He's probably pursuing a specialization of the goal:  G-TEST-DECISION
************ Create that specialization ***********
 NEW GOAL:  G-DIAG-TEST-DECISION
**** Add new goal to tables ****
  modify goal-action table
  modify feature-saliency table
  modify goal hierarchy
  modify goal-slot table
  modify slot-action table
  modify slot-context table
  reacting to observing learned goal  G-DIAG-TEST-DECISION
 making new case piece ...  CASE-DIAG-TEST-DECISION-1
...
```

Figure 3: Realizing the need to Learn a Goal.

program we removed knowledge of the goal G-TEST-HYPOTHESIS from the student. This is equivalent to the novice student observed by Lancaster and Kolodner [1987], who came up with a reasonable hypothesis, then proceeded directly to trying to fix it without testing to see if it was a correct hypothesis. The example picks up after the instructor has made the hypothesis that the idle speed is low. The student retrieves a case piece suggesting the repair to do as a prediction of the instructor's actions. The instructor, however, correctly tests the hypothesis. These actions do not match expected action types for carrying out a repair, and in fact are not consistent with action types expected for any of the student's known diagnostic goals. It does, however, on further inspection, fit with expectations for a more general, cross-domain goal, of testing a decision. This enables learning a new diagnostic goal which will be a specialization of the more general goal.

There seems to be a difference between the goals that Chi et al [in press] talk about being inferred and the goals that our system infers. Specifically, if one looks at a goal as a goal type plus a parameter, our main effort is in inferring the goal type. The goal type would be our goal, for example, G-REPLACE-FIX, and the parameter would be the specific instantiation, for example (INCREASE (POSITION IDLE-SPEED-SCREW)). The parameter comes pretty easily for our system due to the input representation. Chi et al [in press] observed students trying to infer fully instantiated goals where the parameter could be less than obvious. However, the key point is that the student must understand what goal is being pursued in each part of the example as part of explaining the example. Future work can be directed towards inferring the parameter from less well-tailored input.

INFERRING PLACE IN CURRENT DIAGNOSIS

Inferring the place of the current goal and actions in the diagnosis episode is another step toward understanding observed problem solving. It is not only important in understanding what the instructor is doing, it is also necessary for saving the episode in a useful form as a case for case-based reasoning (CBR) [Kolodner and Simpson 1984]. A case will be more useful in the future if it reflects the problem solving done in the episode.

The instructor in most cases diagnoses hierarchically. People doing diagnosis don't hop around between unrelated hypotheses. The experienced mechanic considers a system as a potential source of the problem, then narrows the hypothesis down until a replaceable or fixable unit is determined to be malfunctioning. To a naive observer the hierarchy is not seen, the instructor's actions are sequential, a straight line instead of a tree. The rank novice observed by Lancaster and Kolodner

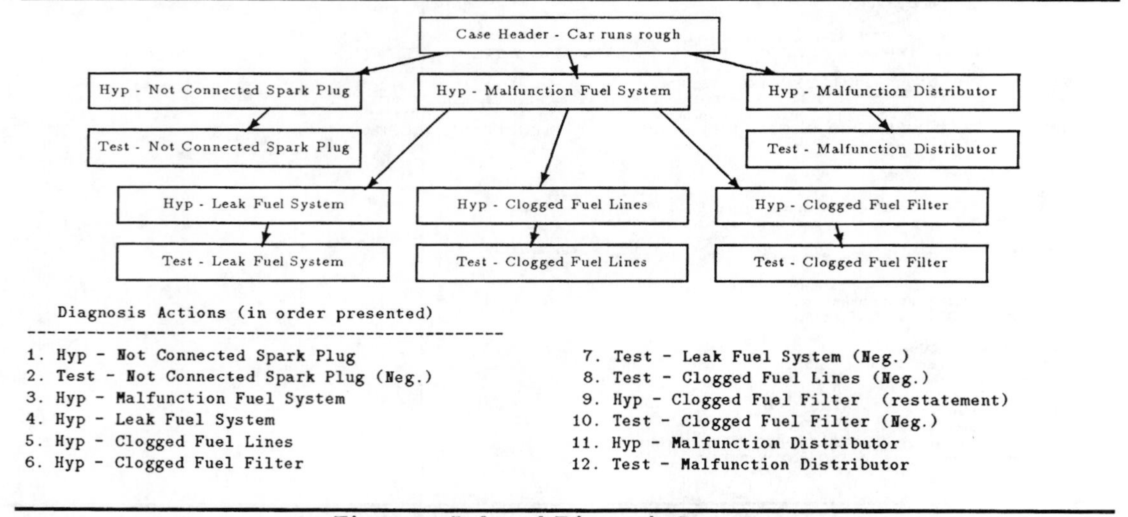

Figure 4: Inferred Diagnosis Structure.

[1987] did not diagnose hierarchically, but the other students, even the one with just six months more experience, did. The ability to diagnose hierarchically requires knowledge of the hierarchy involved. A system cannot rely on a given pattern of actions from the instructor, but must actually explain or understand what is going on. Figure 4 demonstrates this with an example diagnosis sequence. The top part of Figure 4 shows the structure of the instructor's actions which are shown in the bottom part of Figure 4.

Note that a test does not necessarily follow the hypothesis it relates to. Another complication is that there are at least two different reasons that a hypothesis can directly follow another hypothesis - it is a refinement as with the *'fuel system leak'* hypothesis following *'malfunction fuel system'*, or it is another possibility at the same level, such as with the *'clogged fuel lines'* hypothesis directly following the *'leak fuel system'* hypothesis. Also note that there is no 'syntactic' cue that the *'clogged fuel filter'* hypothesis is a refinement of the *'malfunction fuel system'* hypothesis and that the *'malfunction distributor'* hypothesis is not.

Knowledge is necessary to understand the hierarchy being used. Causal knowledge and structural relationships from the model are both useful for this process. A hypothesis can go under a previous hypothesis in the hierarchy if it causes the previous hypothesis, if the component involved is part of the previous component, or if the predicate is more refined.

Chi et al [in press] noted that one type of explanation is relating an action to another action. This process is one way of doing that. It is basically a linking of an action to the action that it follows from, which may *not* be the most recent previous action. The heuristics we use are geared for diagnosis. They were drawn from task analysis of Lancaster and Kolodner's [1987] protocols. They are the set that were necessary to establish the relationships between actions that we saw in the instructor's examples. We don't have any indication whether human students use heuristics such as these to recognize the relationships. Further analysis is required in order to come up with heuristics that would prove useful across domain types, such as for design or planning.

A partial list of heuristics used by our system to explain the instructor's actions in terms of hierarchical diagnosis is shown in Figure 5. The default expectation is that a hypothesis or test will be related to what immediately preceded it. However, as has been noted, this isn't always the case, and the third, fourth, and fifth heuristics are controls on that. The new action must actually

---

1. Try to put new hypothesis under most recent previous hypothesis or test.
2. Try to put new test under most recent previous hypothesis.
3. New hypothesis can go under a previous hypothesis if
   - its component is below the previous hypothesis's component in partonomy,
   - if the component is the same and the new predicate is more specific,
   - if the new hypothesis could cause the previous hypothesized fault
4. New hypothesis can go under a previous test if
   - the test showed results indicating abnormal function and
   - the hypothesis is more refined than the test result (component is below the test's component in partonomy or if the component is the same and the predicate is more specific, or if the hypothesis could cause the test result)
5. New test can go under a previous hypothesis if
   - the tested component is the same or below the hypothesis's component in partonomy and the test predicate is the same or more refined than the predicate in the hypothesis,
   - no component in the test is higher than any component in the hypothesis in partonomy
   - or if the tested clause could be a result of the hypothesis")
6. Don't add anything directly under a hypothesis that has already been tested
7. Don't add anything under a test whose results indicated normal function, this should be followed by backtracking
8. Don't add a new test directly under a hypothesis that already has subhypotheses

---

Figure 5: Heuristics for inferring the structure of a diagnosis.

be related to the previous one, by being more specific or causally related. For example, in Figure 4, the hypothesis *'leak fuel system'* is more specific than the hypothesis *'malfunction fuel system'* because the predicate is more specific and the involved component is the same. The hypothesis *'clogged fuel lines'* is more specific than the hypothesis *'malfunction fuel system'* because fuel lines is below fuel system in the partonomy in memory. However the hypothesis *'malfunction distributor'* did not qualify on either count so it had to go in a different place. The third way to satisfy heuristic 3 is for the later hypothesis to be causally related to the previous hypothesis. The necessity of this is shown by an example. If the hypothesis *'clogged spark plug gap'* follows the hypothesis *'no spark from spark plug'* it would not be placed beneath it because 'clogged' is a different predicate than 'no spark', and isn't more refined. This could easily be a different problem. However, causal knowledge allows linking the one to the other so that the system knows, as a person would, that *'clogged spark plug gap'* is a refinement of the hypothesis *'no spark from spark plug'*.

If the action cannot go after the most recent action then the system must search for its proper place. Many of the other heuristics are limitations on this process, either avoiding potential incorrect placements, or cutting off search that will prove to be unfruitful.

For example, Heuristic 7 allows cutting off search when the instructor would be backtracking. If in Figure 4 the *malfunction fuel system* hypothesis had been followed by a test that showed normal function for the fuel system, then future hypotheses from the instructor should involve other hypotheses that aren't refinements of a fuel system malfunction, and the system can avoid wasted effort by not trying to see if they fit under that hypothesis.

Once the structure of the observed diagnosis has been determined, the case can be stored in memory for use in future problem solving and explanation. The case is stored in pieces so that the particular pieces can be accessed as necessary, and so the representation is flexible enough to handle diagnosis that doesn't have a set pattern of hypotheses and tests. There are pieces for each instance of each goal pursued in the episode. That is, for each hypothesis made, for each test of a hypothesis, for each interpretation of a test, for each fix attempted, there will be a piece. These pieces are linked together to preserve the structure of the case, as inferred in this step. This allows a future diagnosis using the current case to follow the links as long as the findings are the same. The diagnostician following such a hierarchically organized case will diagnose hierarchically rather than haphazardly like a novice. The case pieces, once correctly linked, are stored beneath general knowledge in the model for the car, under related components.

ADJUSTING THE SALIENCE OF FEATURES

Another important explanation type is adjusting the saliency of features for future case retrieval. It may not seem like adjusting the saliency of features is really explanation. However, when two or more hypotheses are both correct hypotheses, in that they can both cause the observed symptom, causal EBL-like explanations do not provide a way of distinguishing between them. The instructor chooses one of the hypotheses to pursue first. The student predicts a particular hypothesis will be pursued first. If the student's prediction is made based on case based reasoning, then the hypothesis predicted first depends on the matching function. Retrieval of previous cases involves searching for a case or generalization piece which served the goal currently being pursued. The retrieved case piece is selected from the candidate pieces based on a comparison of the feature values of the current problem solving context with the feature values of the problem solving context at the time of the previous case pieces. So adjusting the matching function by adjusting the importance of features in the problem solving context will lead to the prediction being correct in the future. This is an implicit way of explaining the choice between the hypotheses without having reason to say that one is more likely than the other. The intuition is that such weighting of competitive hypotheses in diagnosis is generally inductive, the mechanic doesn't know for a fact that x fails more often than y, statistics aren't readily available or used, nor can such preference be explained deductively. The weighting is inductive from experience, and from instruction. There is no evidence of this type of explanation in Lancaster and Kolodner's and Chi et al's observations. However, it isn't the sort of thing that would be amenable to study through protocols.

The method of adjusting the saliency of features is fairly simple. It is based on the idea of making

```
Goal - G-GENERATE-HYPOTHESIS
Piece retrieved - (CASE-HYP-CHOKE-THERM 14.280001)   Hypothesis - (MALFUNCTION CHOKE-THERMOSTAT)
Piece Expert's with hypothesis = (LOW IDLE-SPEED) - (GEN-HYP-ENGINE-STALLS 11.6)
```

Feature	Student's piece	Piece matching Instructor	Feature Importance
CAR-TYPE	Partial match	No Match	less important
CAR-OWNER	Match	No Match	less important
COMPLAINT	Match	Match	no change
FREQUENCY	Partial match	No Match	less important
HOW-LONG	Match	Partial match	less important
OTHER-SYMPT	Match	Match	no change
RULED-IN	Partial match	Match	more important
RULED-OUT	Partial match	Match	more important
TESTS-DONE-N-RESULTS	Partial match	Match	more important
FIXES-DONE	Partial match	Match	more important
CURRENT-HYPOTH	Match (none)	Match (none)	no change
PARTICIPANTS	Partial match	No Match	less important
LOCATION	Match	Match	no change
WHEN	Partial match	No Match	less important

Figure 6: Example Blame Assignment.

features that match when the problem solver is successful more important, and features that match when the problem solver is unsuccessful less important. Since the salience of various features varies depending on the goal being pursued by the problem solver, separate measures of feature importance are maintained for different goals. When the student predicts the same action the instructor makes, the student has been successful. The features of the current problem solving context that matched the features in the previous case are made slightly more important. When the student predicts a different action than the instructor, presumably the student has been unsuccessful. The blame assignment is best made by retrieving another case piece in which the instructor's action was the one done. Figure 6 shows how the blame assignment is done on an example incorrect prediction of a hypothesis. Those features of the current context that more closely match the context of the newly retrieved case piece than the context of the originally retrieved case piece will be made more important. Those features of the current context that more closely match the context of the originally retrieved case piece than the context of the 'correct' piece are made less important. Thus instruction with examples helps deal with the feature saliency problem, by giving feedback on the correctness of case retrieval, allowing comparison of the matching features.

This will lead to the correct piece being retrieved in the same situation in the future. A combination of instruction, case retrieval, and induction has been used to improve the performance of the CBR part of diagnosis.

CAUSAL EXPLANATION OF ACTIONS

Causal explanations of actions enable filling gaps in the causal domain knowledge through the basic LBUE methods described in Redmond and Martin [1988]. These were an extension of explanation-based learning (EBL) [DeJong 1983; DeJong and Mooney 1986; Mitchell, Kellar, and Kedar-Cabelli 1986], to allow learning without a complete and consistent domain model. An example will illustrate the ideas. An instructor may present the student with a malfunctioning car in which the engine cranks but does not start. She may suggest a hypothesis that the distributor cap is cracked. A complete causal explanation would be:

```
(cracked distributor-cap)       causes
   (contains distributor-cap moisture)    causes
      (low (input spark-plug electricity))   causes
         (not (ignite spark-plug))            causes
            (not (combustion cylinder))          causes
               (not (start engine))
```

If the student can complete the explanation, she can learn that a cracked distributor cap causes the symptom of the engine cranking but not starting. If the student was missing some knowledge, it is possible that the knowledge could be inferred as plausible. For example, if the student was missing the fact that moisture in the distributor cap can cause less electricity to reach the spark plug, she may still be able to infer that fact based on the partial explanation having been given by the trusted expert, in conjunction with the partial explanation formed by the student and general knowledge possessed by the student about water's effect on electricity.

In addition to enabling filling gaps in the causal domain knowledge, trying to causally explain actions can make causal explanations available as indices to the new case containing the action. Hammond and Hurwitz [1988], and Barletta and Mark [1988] both use this approach, which hasn't yet been implemented in the current system.

CONCLUSION

Explanation of solved example problems is an effective way of learning. A system has been constructed that uses EBL-like deduction, induction, and retrieval of previous cases in creating explanations, improving future diagnoses and future explanations of observed problem solving. The use of multiple types of explanation of examples follows the lead of the studies by Lancaster and Kolodner [1987, 1988] and Chi et al [in press]. Their observations suggest further types of explanation that could be exploited in making our system a better student. The exploitation of instruction turns out to be a powerful way of learning, and integrates several learning techniques.

ACKNOWLEDGEMENTS

This research was supported by the Army Research Institute for the Behavioral and Social Sciences under Contract No. MDA-903-86-C-173. The author wishes to thank Janet Kolodner for her advice and guidance, and Joel Martin, Louise Penberthy, and Chris Hale for helpful comments on earlier versions of the paper.

REFERENCES

Barletta, R. & Mark, W. (1988). Explanation-based indexing of cases. In *Proceedings of a Workshop on Case-Based Reasoning.*

Chi, M., Bassok, M., Lewis, M., Reimann, P., & Glaser, R. (in press). Self-explanations: how students study and use examples to solve problems. *Cognitive Science, in press.*

DeJong, G. & Mooney, R. (1986). Explanation based learning: an alternative view. *Machine Learning, 1*, 145–176.

DeJong, G. (1983). Acquiring schemata through understanding and generalized plans. In *Proceedings of the Eighth International Joint Conference on Artificial Intelligence.*

Hammond, K. J. & Hurwitz, N. (1988). Extracting diagnostic features from explanations. In *Proceedings of a Workshop on Case-Based Reasoning.*

Kolodner, J. & Simpson., R. Jr. (1984). Experience and problem solving: a framework. In *Proceedings of the Sixth Annual Conference of the Cognitive Science Society.*

Lancaster, J. & Kolodner, J. (1987). Problem solving in a natural task as a function of experience. In *Proceedings of the Ninth Annual Conference of the Cognitive Science Society.*

Lancaster, J. & Kolodner, J. (1988). Varieties of learning from problem solving experience. In *Proceedings of the Tenth Annual Conference of the Cognitive Science Society.*

LeFevre, J. & Dixon, P. (1986). Do written instructions need examples?. *Cognition and Instruction, 3*, 1–30.

Martin, J. & Redmond, M. (1988). The use of explanations for completing and correcting causal models. In *Proceedings of the Tenth Annual Conference of the Cognitive Science Society.*

Mitchell, T. M., Kellar, R. M., & Kedar-Cabelli, S. T. (1986). Explanation based learning: an unifying view. *Machine Learning, 1*, 47–80.

Reder, L., Charney, D., & Morgan, K. (1986). The role of elaborations in learning a skill from an instructional text. *Memory and Cognition, 14*, 64–78.

Redmond, M. & Martin, J. (1988). Learning by understanding explanations. In *Proceedings of the 26th Annual Conference of the Southeast Region ACM.*

SELECTING THE BEST CASE FOR A CASE-BASED REASONER*

Janet L. Kolodner
School of Information and Computer Science
Georgia Institute of Technology

Abstract

The most important support process a case-based reasoner needs is a memory for cases. Among its functions, the memory for cases must be able to select out the most appropriate cases for the case-based reasoner to use at any time. In this paper, we present the selection processes implemented in PARADYME, a case memory designed to work alongside a case-based reasoner. PARADYME has a two-step retrieval process. In the first step, it retrieves the set of partial matches from the memory. In the second, it selects out a small set of "best" matches. PARADYME chooses "best" cases using a set of six preference heuristics: goal-directed preference, salience, specificity, frequency, recency, and ease of adaptation. PARADYME is novel in two ways. Its use of preferences for choosing a best case means that its principles act as *selectors* rather than restrictors. And its emphasis in choosing best cases is on *usefulness* rather than similarity.

Introduction

A host is planning a meal for a set of people who include, among others, several people who eat no meat or poultry, one of whom is also allergic to milk products, several meat-and-potatoes men, and her friend Anne. Since it is tomato season, she wants to use tomatoes as a major ingredient in the meal. As she is planning the meal, she remembers the following:

> I once served tomato tart (made from mozzerella cheese, tomatoes, dijon mustard, basil, and pepper, all in a pie crust) as the main dish during the summer when I had vegetarians come for dinner. It was delicious and easy to make. But I can't serve that to Elana (the one allergic to milk).
>
> I have adapted recipes for Elana before by substituting tofu products for cheese. I could do that, but I don't know how good the tomato tart will taste that way.

She decides not to serve tomato tart and continues planning. Since it is summer, she decides that grilled fish would be a good main course. But now she remembers something else:

> Last time I tried to serve Anne grilled fish, she wouldn't eat it. I had to put hotdogs on the grill at the last minute.

Considering this, she decides that fish as the main dish would be inappropriate. Having already ruled out meat and poultry as main dishes, she is in a quandry, since it seems that no single main dish will satisfy all the guests. At this point, she comes up with a solution.

> I've had this problem before. ... In that case, what I did was to provide a

*This research was supported in part by NSF under grant No. IST-8608362, and in part by DARPA under contract no. F49620-88-C-0058, monitored by AFOSR. Initial work on this project was begun while the author was on sabbatical at Thinking Machines, Inc., Cambridge, Mass. Thanks to Thinking Machines for providing machine and programming support for the project. Programming was done by Robert Thau.

> choice of main dishes with side dishes that matched all of them. In fact, I usually do that whenever I serve buffet style.

The hypothetical host is employing case-based reasoning (cf., Hammond, 1986, Kolodner, et al., 1985) to plan a meal. In case-based reasoning, a reasoner remembers previous situations similar to the current one and solves a new problem by adapting the solutions to those situations to meet the needs of the new one. In this case, the host is remembering meals she has planned previously to help her generate a plan for her new meal. Some are particular meals (e.g., the tomato-tart meal, the time Anne came for dinner, the last time she served a group of picky eaters), while some are generalized or composite ones, i.e., they've been used over and over with only the variables changed each time (e.g., serving buffet style). The meals she remembers are used to suggest means of solving the new problem (e.g., to suggest a main dish, to suggest serving buffet style, to suggest a means of dealing with all the picky eaters easily), to suggest means of adapting a solution that doesn't quite fit (e.g., substitute a tofu product for cheese), and to warn of possible failures (e.g., Anne won't eat fish).

The most important support process a case-based reasoner needs is a memory for cases. The memory must make cases accessible when retrieval cues are provided to it and it must incorporate new cases into its structures as they are experienced, in the process maintaining accessibility of the items already in the memory. It must be able to handle cases in all of their complexity, and it must be able to manage thousands of cases in its memory. But most importantly, it must be able to select out the most appropriate cases for the case-based reasoner to use at any time.

There are three major ways researchers in the case-based reasoning community are addressing the selection problem. Some people are addressing it by trying to determine how to best choose indexes (e.g., Barletta & Mark, 1988, Hammond, 1986, Kolodner, 1983, Owens, 1988, Schank, 1982) so that only the best cases will be retrieved from the memory. Indexes are used to restrict traversal of memory, and only those cases whose indexed features match the retrieval probe are recalled. One problem with this is that one cannot predict every important feature of an event at the time it happens. Thus, this method is too restrictive. Another problem with this method is that it does not insure that only a small number of cases will be recalled, since many cases might be indexed the same way. While it has worked fine in several implementations, the memories have either been so small that selection was not a problem (as in, e.g., CHEF (Hammond, 1986), MEDIATOR (Simpson, 1985)), or they have had as their goal to recall as much as they could (as in CYRUS (Kolodner, 1983)), where again selection is not a problem.

A second selection method is to filter the problem description before probing memory so that only those features of the problem description relevant to the reasoner's current goal are part of the memory probe (as in, e.g., CHEF (Hammond, 1986)). The problem with this is that some process outside of memory has to choose which features of the problem are the salient ones. It makes more sense to have salience judged in the context of cases already in the memory. Considering the example above, it is a coincidence of circumstances that makes the fact that Anne is a guest an important part of the problem description. That is, the experience already in memory is what tells us that that feature is an important one. We cannot expect an outside process to always know which features or combinations of features are relevant to solving a new problem. It is exactly this task that we want memory to help with.

Other researchers propose filtering methods that are used after retrieval (e.g., Koton, 1988, Riesbeck, 1988, Stanfill, 1987, Rissland & Ashley, 1988). The methods all tend to be special purpose, however, and each has restrictions that keep it from being general. Koton's method, for example, depends on a causal model being available. Rissland's method is specific to adversarial situations. Stanfill's depends on the memory having large numbers of cases in it in quantities representative of the problem's domain so that an accurate evaluation function can always be computed based entirely on memory's contents.

And Riesbeck's depends on a static (pre-computed) evaluation function, and thus can't make use of context to decide on a best case.

In the remainder of this paper, we discuss the selection processes used in PARADYME (Kolodner, 1988, Kolodner & Thau, 1988), a case memory designed to be able to select out a small set of best cases from a large case base. PARADYME is designed to work alongside a problem solver. Its cases come from JULIA (Hinrichs, 1988, Kolodner, 1987a,b, Shinn, 1988), a case-based problem solver that plans meals. The problem solver has certain goals to achieve in the context of some problem and a partial solution. The problem, the partial solution, and the goals of the problem solver form the probe to PARADYME's memory (Kolodner, 1988, Kolodner & Thau, 1988).

Upon being probed, PARADYME's first task is to retrieve partial matches from its memory based on the problem description and the partial solution. For the problem described in the introduction, this step would retrieve all meals with vegetarians in attendance, all meals with people allergic to milk products, all meals with meat-and-potatoes men as guests, all meals with Anne as a guest, all meals with tomatoes used as a major ingredient, all summer meals, and all combinations of the above. If the host is someone who entertains or cooks a lot, then clearly, this step will result in retrieval of a lot of cases.

PARADYME's next step, the one we concentrate on in the rest of this paper, is to select out the "best" of those cases. While PARADYME's selection method is based on many of the same principles guiding other case memories, it differs from others in several ways. First, what has been built into previous case memories as restrictors is built into PARADYME as preference heuristics of *selectors*. Thus, PARADYME does not get hurt by the inability to predict every important part of a case at the time it happens. PARADYME prefers cases whose salient features (indexes) match the probe but if no cases with indexed features match, it will recall a case with other matching features. Thus, even if memory update procedures had not indexed the meal where a dish was adapted for Elana by features present in this case, it could still be recalled if no indexed case were found.

PARADYME uses the reasoner's goals similarly. Rather than using reasoning goals to select out a portion of a problem to use as a probe, PARADYME sends the whole problem as a probe and lets previous experience (i.e,. memory) be the guide to which features are the important ones. This way, for example, memory can determine that Anne being a guest is a salient feature at a particular point in the problem solving rather than having the problem solver choose out "guests" as salient features every time an evaluation is done.

Second, PARADYME's emphasis when ranking cases is on usefulness. Using this criterion for ranking means that PARADYME takes the reasoner's goals into account in selecting out a "best" case. Rather than choosing a most similar case, it chooses the most similar of those cases that are first judged most useful. When the hypothetical reasoner above recalls another case where she adapted a recipe with milk for Elana, for example, it is recalled because it predicts how to achieve the goal of adapting a dairy recipe for a non-milk eater. There may be other cases in the memory that are more similar to the situation (perhaps many of the guests match), but this one is most useful for achieving the current goal. Similarly when the case where choice was provided is recalled. There may have been many cases that were more similar than this one, but this one is most useful to the goal of dealing with unsatisfiable food constraints.

Preference Heuristics

PARADYME's selection procedure is based on a set of *preference heuristics*.[1] These heuristics are applied to the set of partially-matching cases to choose a small set of "best" cases. PARADYME uses six different types of preference for this task.

- Goal-Directed Preference

[1] See Rissland & Ashley (1988) for a discussion of why numerical weighting schemes won't work.

- Salient-Feature Preference
- Specificity Preference
- Frequency Preference
- Recency Preference
- Ease-of-Adaptation Preference

The first preference, *goal-directed preference* is based on the principle of utility. That is, since the memory is working in conjunction with a reasoner that has goals, it makes sense to prefer those cases that can help in achieving the problem solver's goals. Thus, when the problem solver is trying to come up with a main dish, those cases that match on main dish constraints will be preferred over others. When it is trying to evaluate the goodness of a solution, those cases that predict success or failure under similar circumstances are preferred. We state this heuristic as follows:

> **Goal-Directed Preference:** Prefer cases that can help address the reasoner's current reasoning goal, and of these, prefer those that share more constraints over those that share fewer.

The second preference heuristic, *salient-feature preference*, is based on the principle that we should use experience to tell us which features of a new situation are the ones to focus on. If memory has done a good job of recording its experiences, they can be used to tell us which features of previous events led to the choice of particular solutions or solution methods and which features of previous events were responsible for success or failure in those cases. These features are the *salient features* of previous cases, and in indexed memories, they form the indexes. When salient features of previous cases exist in a new situation, they can be used to suggest solutions and predict outcomes for the new case. The case where Anne didn't eat fish, for example, has a salient feature set that predicts failure and includes the following facts: Anne was a guest, fish was served, preparation style of the fish was grilled. When all of these features are present in a probe, we can predict that Anne won't eat. PARADYME prefers cases that share full sets of salient features with the new problem over other cases whose full salient feature sets are not in the probe. We state this preference as follows:

> **Salient-Feature Preference:** Prefer cases that match on salient features over those that match on other features, and prefer those that match on a larger subset of salient features over those matching on a smaller subset.

The third preference heuristic is based on the principle that a more specific match can be more predictive than a less specific match. Thus, all other things being equal, cases that match more specifically are preferred over less specific matches. PARADYME has several ways to judge specificity. First, according to PARADYME's definition of specificity, a case is more specific than another if the features that match in the less specific case are a proper subset of the features that match in the more specific case. Thus, a probe is more specifically matched by a case that matches all of its features than one that matches only a subset. Second, a case matches more specifically than one of its ancestors in memory's generalization hierarchy. For example, a particular Italian meal is more specific than a generic Italian meal. Third, a case matches more specifically if the probe matches features in more of its parts. The specificity preference follows:

> **Specificity Preference:** Prefer cases that match more specifically over less specific matches.

The fourth and fifth heuristics are based on two principles psychologists have discovered – that items that are referenced more frequently are more likely to be recalled than other similar items and that items that have been referenced more recently are more likely to be recalled than other similar items (all else being equal). This gives rise to two preference heuristics:

> **Frequency Preference:** Prefer cases that have been accessed more

frequently over less frequently-accessed cases.

Recency Preference: Prefer cases that have been accessed more recently over less recently-accessed cases.

A sixth preference heuristic is also based on the principle of utility, and is specific to case-based reasoning. Some adaptations of previous solutions are easier to make than others. This heuristic says to prefer cases whose solutions are easier to adapt than those whose solutions are harder to adapt.

Ease-of-Adaptation Preference: Cases that match on features that are known to be hard to fix should be preferred over those that match on easy-to-fix features.

Application of Preference Heuristics

The application of preference heuristics is complicated. Each preference heuristic attempts to select out a set of better matches. When a heuristic does this, that set is sent on to the next heuristic for pruning. When no subset of cases is better than the rest using some heuristic, however, the entire set it was selecting from is selected. In this way, the preferences act as *selectors* rather than restrictors. We prefer to recall a case that can address the reasoner's current goal but we don't require it. We prefer to recall a case that matches on salient features, but if there are none, the preference heuristics allow recall of a case that matches on a random set of features.

The heuristics are also ordered. Goal-directed preference is applied first, then salience, then specificity, and then frequency and recency. This way, the set of cases that can be used to achieve the reasoner's current goal is selected out first, then any that match on a full set of salient features (of the right kind) are selected from those, the most specific of those are chosen (if some are more specific than others), and then the more frequently or recently recalled cases are selected from those.

There are also other ways the preference heuristics could be applied. For example, some other order might work better. Or, it may be better to run all the preferences on the whole set of partial matches and then to prefer those cases that were selected by more of the preferences. Our current research is focussing on exactly this problem.

Support Processes

While PARADYME chooses best cases by applying its preference heuristics at retrieval time, there are other parts of PARADYME that contribute to making the preference heuristics work. PARADYME has five parts:

1. a hierarchical organization of knowledge and cases
2. a parallel memory retrieval process that chooses out all partially-matching cases from the memory
3. a set of preference heuristics that choose the best matching case from the partial matches activated in step 2
4. a set of transformation rules that transform and elaborate a retrieval probe to get a better "best match" than is possible from the original set of cues
5. a memory update process that marks cases with their salient features and creates generalizations as called for

The hierarchical organization (1) provides a way of determining which partially matching memory structures are more specific than others and gives a way for the retrieval process to determine which partial matches are in the right ballpark. The memory retrieval process (2) chooses the set of cases to focus on in choosing a best match. The transformation rules (4) allow better matches to be found than could be done with only the initial probe. And memory update processes (5) annotate cases with salient feature sets that tell selection processes under what circumstances the case is likely to be relevant. As we stated previously, salient feature sets are similar in function to indexes found in indexed memories. Since they are so important in allowing the preference heuristics to function, we continue by discussing the types of salient feature sets (indexes) PARADYME assumes its cases will have.

Salient-Feature Sets

We have found three kinds of salient-feature sets (indexes) useful for problem solving. The first contain features that predict the applicability of some method for achieving a goal (*goal-achievement predictor sets*). Second are those that predict the success or failure of a solution (*solution-evaluation predictor sets*). Third are those that describe unusual outcomes (*outcome-achievement descriptor sets*).

Goal-Achievement Predictor Sets are generally conjunctions of goals, constraints on these goals, and problem and environmental features that predict the method or solution for achieving the goal or goal set. If the features of a goal-achievement set are all present in a new situation, and if the problem solver's current goal matches the goal achieved by the salient feature set, then the method of reaching the goal or the solution to the goal can be predicted from the previous case. Cases that match on the basis of goal-achievement predictors are most helpful during problem solving when the problem solver knows what goals it is trying to achieve and knows the environment in which it needs to achieve those goals.

These sets of features may include one or several goals. They include one if the solution that was chosen for that goal did not involve other goals. They include several if solutions to several goals were integrated. Constraints and descriptors on these goals are also included, as are features of the world or features of the problem that determined which of several possible solutions or solution methods was chosen. If all of the features in one of these conjunctive feature sets is designated in a retrieval probe, the solution or solution method used in the previous case can be predicted.

Solution-Evaluation Predictor Sets are conjunctions of features *predicting* unusual outcomes – in general, failures, unexpected successes, and unexpected side effects. If the features of a solution-evaluation prediction set are all present in a new situation, the unexpected result from the previous case can be predicted in the new case. Cases that match on the basis of solution-evaluation sets are most helpful when a reasoner has proposed a solution and needs to evaluate it.

Outcome-Achievement Descriptor Sets are conjunctions of features *describing* unusual outcomes. If the features of an outcome-achievement set are all present in a new situation, the previous case that is recalled can be used to help explain why the unusual outcome arose. In addition, if these features are all present in a new situation and the reasoner is attempting to figure out how to achieve such an outcome, the method by which it was achieved previously can be suggested by the recalled case. These are thus useful in two situations: when the reasoner is trying to explain an anomolous situation and when the reasoner knows the shape of a solution but not how to achieve it.

Any particular case may have several salient feature sets associated with it. For example, it could have one for each goal that was achieved in some unusual way in the course of reasoning about the case. It might also have several associated with outcome and several associated with solution evaluation. When attempting to choose best cases, preference heuristics prefer those cases that have one or more salient feature sets of the right kinds that are fully matched by the new situation. That is, if the reasoner is attempting to evaluate the potential for success of a plan, it prefers cases with fully matching solution-evaluation feature sets. If it is trying to achieve a goal, it prefers cases with fully matching goal-achievement feature sets whose goals match its current goal. If it attempting to explain an anomolous situation, or if it is attempting to find out how to achieve a state of affairs, it prefers cases with fully matching outcome-achievement feature sets.

Discussion

Best cases are chosen in PARADYME by taking into account which features or combinations of features have been found to be most important in the past, and the goodness of fit of a previous case is judged in the context of other possible matches. Preference heuristics select best matches based on what has been relevant in solving previous problems, what the case-based reasoner's current goals are, and the relative specificity of partially-matching cases. This allows the importance of features to be judged in context, where context is provided by the retrieval probe along with the items that are retrieved by partial matching.

While PARADYME's selection method is based on many of the same principles guiding case selection in other case memories, its selection method differs in two ways. First, what has been built into previous case memories as restrictors is built into PARADYME as preference heuristics or *selectors*. Salient feature sets, for example, are equivalent to what others in the case-based reasoning community call *indexes*. That is, they are the features that have been useful previously in making decisions or have been responsible previously for reasoning successes and failures. When salient features from a previous case match features of a new case, they allow predictions or suggestions to be made for the new situation based on the old case. This is the basis of case-based reasoning. Salient feature sets, however, are used differently than indexes have been used. Indexed memories use indexes as restrictors – cases are recalled only when salient features from a previous case match features of the new case. PARADYME's memory, on the other hand, prefers cases that match on salient features over those with no salient features matching, but it also allows recall based on features that were not singled out as salient at memory update time if no cases matching on salient features can be found in memory.

Similarly, PARADYME uses the goals of the reasoner as selectors rather than restrictors. While previous case-based reasoners (e.g., CHEF) used the reasoner's current goal to extract out features from the problem statement to probe memory with, PARADYME sends all the information it has about a situation to memory along with the reasoner's current goals. The preference heuristics use those goals to choose a set of *useful* partially-matching cases. The major advantage to using the reasoner's goal as a selector rather than a restrictor is that it provides a way to let experience (previous cases) designate which features of the new situation are most relevant to consider in achieving a goal.

The second difference between PARADYME and other case memories is in the emphasis on finding a *most useful* set of cases rather than a *most similar* set. Choosing a most similar case means focussing on the correspondences between features of two cases. In aiming to choose a most useful case, on the other hand, we give much attention to what the reasoner needs to do with the case. Correspondences are certainly important (salient-feature preference focusses on these), but they are not sufficient. It only makes sense to focus on the relative goodness of correspondences after we know that the reasoner's goals are being attended to. PARADYME has two preference heuristics that address usefulness: goal-directed preference and ease-of-adaptation preference. Goal-directed preference says that cases that can be used to address the reasoner's current goal should be preferred over others. Ease-of-adaptation is more specifically aimed at the reasoner's method of achieving its current goal – if it is to use case-based reasoning, and two cases are equally good matches based on other criteria, it should prefer cases that require less work to adapt.

Bibliography

1. Barletta, R. (1988). Explanation-Based Indexing of Cases. *Proceedings of the DARPA Workshop on Case-Based Reasoning.*

2. Hammond, K. J. (1986). *Case-Based Planning: An integrated theory of planning, learning, and memory.* Ph.D. Thesis. Dept. of Computer Science. Yale University.

3. Hinrichs, T. (1988). Towards an architecture for open world problem solving. *Proceedings of the DARPA Workshop on Case-Based Reasoning.*

4. Kolodner, J. L. (1983). Reconstructive Memory: A Computer Model. *Cognitive Science*, vol. 7.

5. Kolodner, J. L. (1987a). Extending problem solver capabilities through case-based inference. *Proceedings of the 1987 International Machine Learning Workshop.*

6. Kolodner, J. L. (1987b). Capitalizing on failure through case-based inference. *Proceedings of the 1987 Conference of the Cognitive Science Society.*

7. Kolodner, J. L. (1988). Retrieving Events from a Case Memory: A Parallel Implementation. *Proceedings of the DARPA Case-Based Reasoning Workshop.* Morgan-Kaufmann, San Mateo, CA.

8. Kolodner, J. L., Simpson, R. L., & Sycara, E. (1985). A Process Model of Case-Based Reasoning in Problem Solving. *Proceedings of IJCAI-85.*

9. Kolodner, J. L. & Thau, R. (1988). *Design and Implementation of a Case Memory.* Technical Report No. GIT-ICS-88/34. School of Information and Compute Science. Georgia Institute of Technology, Atlanta, GA.

10. Koton, P. (1988). Reasoning about evidence in causal explanations. *Proceedings of the DARPA Workshop on Case-Based Reasoning.*

11. Owens, C. (1988). Domain-Independent Prototype Cases for Planning. *Proceedings of the DARPA Workshop on Case-Based Reasoning.*

12. Riesbeck, C. (1988). An Interface for Case-Based Knowledge Acquisition. *Proceedings of the DARPA Workshop on Case-Based Reasoning*

13. Rissland, E. & Ashley, K. (1988). Weighting on weighting. *Proceedings of AAAI-88.*

14. Schank, R. C. (1982) *Dynamic Memory.* Cambridge: Cambridge University Press.

15. Shinn, H. (1988). Abstractional Analogy: A Model of Analogical Reasoning. *Proceedings of the DARPA Workshop on Case-Based Reasoning.*

16. Simpson, R. L. (1985). *A Computer Model of Case-Based Reasoning in Problem Solving.* Ph.D. Thesis. Technical Report No. GIT-ICS/85/18. School of Information and Computer Science. Georgia Inst. of Technology. Atlanta, GA.

17. Stanfill, C. (1987). Memory-Based Reasoning Applied to English Pronunciation. *Proceedings of AAAI-87.*

Integrating Feature Extraction and Memory Search

Christopher Owens
Department of Computer Science
Yale University

Reasoning from prior experience depends upon having a large memory of prior cases and a system for retrieving them when they are relevant. Often, relevance means similarity to the current situation on the basis of abstract or thematic features other than the features used to initially describe the current situation. To retrieve cases relevant to some new situation, a system must be able to describe the new situation in abstract terms and use that description as a search key or as a means to judge the appropriateness of prior cases. Typically, the abstract description process has been considered as separate from the memory search process. This paper presents a scheme for integrating the feature extraction and memory search processes and argues in favor of such an approach on methodological and efficiency grounds. It presents a program that exploits parallelism to control some of the high processing costs associated with feature extraction and memory search.

RETRIEVAL AND ABSTRACT FEATURES

Recent work has suggested that a good approach to planning and problem–solving situations is for a system to get reminded of specific prior experiences and to reason based upon the similarities and differences between that prior experience and the current problem. For example, case-based reasoners such as those described by [Simpson, 85], [Hammond, 86], [Sycara, 87], [Kolodner, 87] and [Ashley and Rissland, 87] and analogical reasoners such as those described by [Carbonell and Veloso, 88], [Winston, 80] and elsewhere fundamentally rely upon a large and richly-indexed memory of experiences coupled with some mechanism for recalling the right memory at the right time.

For analogical reasoning or case-based reasoning systems to work well, they must be able to retrieve memories of prior experiences that bear some interesting similarity to a given new problem or situation. The key here is *interesting* similarity: recalling a prior case only helps a reasoner to the degree to which that prior case shares some important functional or causal characteristics with the current problem. If, for example, a shop scheduler is trying to expedite the production of a particular part by having two machines work on it at the same time, prior cases in which it successfully or unsuccessfully tried to speed up production might be useful, as might prior cases in which it tried to use those two machines together. But prior cases involving the manufacture of class 7B flanges at 3:30 on Tuesday afternoons while it was 78 degrees in the shop and while machine 4 was working on a type 2C bracket assembly, although they have all these facts in common with the current situation, are likely to shed little light on the current problem. Although the similarities between those cases and the current one are numerous, they simply don't bear upon the problem that the scheduler is trying to solve.

How to characterize

The problem is describing or characterizing the current problem. Once a system is able to describe the situation presented above, for example, as "trying to speed up production by scheduling multiple agents to work on the same job at the same time," it might be reminded of some cases where this plan worked and some where it did not, perhaps because two machines were trying to perform incompatible tasks, or perhaps because they got in each others' way. Analyzing the differences between these past cases and the current situation might indicate whether or not the plan was a good idea; it might also suggest additional planning steps that might be necessary to anticipate and avoid failures. The machines' actions might be coordinated, for example, to prevent some bad interaction.

But how can a system derive that kind of description? Not only was this characterization of the situation not present in the original or "perceptual" description, but it is also impossible to derive from any boolean combination or weighting of raw perceptual features. If the features available to the shop scheduler consisted of a set of readings from instruments and sensors around the shop plus a list of what machine was working on what part, no weighting or boolean combination of these features would get us the remindings we wanted in the prior example. "Machine 4 and Machine 8 both working on **the same** part" is a description that cannot be so derived. "Two machines working on the same part" even more so.

So an effective case retriever must not only face the problem of choosing which features of a given situation description are relevant retrieval cues in the context of this situation, it also must extract or derive some abstract features that are not initially present in that description, so that those abstract features can be used as search keys or as part of similarity metrics. The task of extracting those features, or of characterizing the current situation, is an inseparable part of the task of memory search and should be so considered theoretically. Memory is not just the process of starting from some description of the input and using it to search. A theory of memory must include a theory of how that description is derived.

EXTRACTION AND SEARCH

Much work in AI memory has either explicitly or implicitly separated the task of deriving abstract descriptions from the task of actually searching memory for objects that match those abstract descriptions, and have focused on the latter. For example, much progress has been made in the memory-based reasoning paradigm (see [Stanfill and Waltz, 88]). Connectionist approaches, too, are very good at deciding how to weight features to measure case similarity, but they do not deal with the problem of how raw data gets turned into sets of features in the first place, nor do they deal with how new features can be learned. Some systems are built on the assumption that input cases come already described in the same representational language as was used to describe the cases already in memory, so that syntactic means can be used to measure similarity. This has been a necessary assumption to allow work to proceed on the mechanics of memory organization and search, but it begs a question that full-fledged memory-based systems will have to face: How are features extracted from raw input?

Given that mechanisms are available to do retrieval and matching based on weighted vectors of features, it is tempting to say that some kind of parsing or feature extraction process should be run over the data to extract the abstract features and weight them, and that then the original and derived features should subsequently be used as input to the retrieval process. But this approach is problematic for several reasons.

Complexity of "parsing"

One problem with this approach is that "parsing" or abstract feature extraction, can be arbitrarily complex when attempted bottom-up. Although features like "multiple machines working on the same part" as described above are quickly and easily calculable from input, others may be much less so. There may be an arbitrarily large number or abstract features that one might potentially want to derive from input, any of them potentially arbitrarily costly to infer. Since the feature extraction process does not know what is in memory and how memory is organized and searched, it might expend inferential cost on extracting features from the input that do not turn out to be particularly useful indices. It is clear that we don't want to extract all possible abstract features before searching memory, we just want to get some reasonable set of them.

Unfortunately, deciding what constitutes a reasonable set of abstract features from a particular episode requires having an abstract thematic understanding of that episode, which is the very problem we were trying to solve in the first place. There is a methodological circularity to this approach. What process can provide this abstract thematic understanding? One that relies on retrieving relevant cases?

Features not static

A second problem is that the set of abstract features that one might need to extract is not static, but depends upon the set of cases in memory. The features that one needs are the ones that describe the similarities and differences between the various cases in memory. As the set of cases changes, so must the set of abstract features. When new cases are added to memory, separate steps must be performed to select indexing features for discriminating among those new objects and to develop procedures for extracting those features from input. When a new indexing feature is learned, all objects in memory must be reexamined to determine whether or not they embody that feature; those that do must be appropriately re-indexed.

Expressing retrieval goals

A third important design consideration for case memories is that there is no one correct or closest match in memory to a given new experience. What constitutes a good match depends upon the goals of the system processing the new event. Different retrieval goals will yield different remindings, and it is important that a retrieval scheme be able to take into account the system's retrieval goals.

An example of this can be found in the discussion of the SWALE case-based explainer system ([Schank, 86], [Kass and Owens, 88], [Leake, 88]). One of the examples the system was called upon to explain was the death of Swale, a three-year-old race horse who died mysteriously, one week after winning the prestigious Belmont Stakes race.

What constitutes a satisfactory explanation of this kind of example depends upon the goals of the explainer. Therefore, the kind of reminding (and therefore the abstract description of Swale's death) that is appropriate depends on the goals of the explainer as well. An insurance examiner, for example, might be reminded of the case of a valuable painting that mysteriously disappeared a year earlier, in what turned out to be a fake burglary staged by the owner to collect the insurance money. A veterinarian might be reminded of the cow that mysteriously died the previous week and begin investigation to see if the medical causes were the same. A racing examiner might be reminded of other cases of one competitor trying to disable another and might suspect the owners of Swale's competitors. A gambler might be reminded of other examples of an odds-on favorite suddenly being disabled or otherwise removed from competition. Each of these individuals will retrieve different remindings from memory because each has described Swale's death in different terms. Each description is equally correct, but each leads to a different path of explanatory reasoning.

It is difficult to account for these differences in retrieval with a system that separates feature extraction from the rest of memory. It is unreasonable to assume that veterinarians, insurance adjusters and gamblers have totally different processes for extracting features from situations. It is possible that the differences could be accounted for by some process that maps retrieval goals to predictive features, as discussed by [Stepp and Michalski, 86] or [Seifert, 88]. This could be used to weight the importance of features depending upon how relevant they were to the current set of retrieval goals. But this approach leaves unanswered the question of how retrieval goals and predictive features are linked together.

A more satisfying explanation of the differences in how the individuals above explained the same event is that abstract feature extraction is driven by the case libraries of each of these individuals. The veterinarian has a large case library of animal diseases and consequently describe the event in terms of features that can discriminate among these cases. Likewise an insurance examiner is discriminating among a second, different library of cases, and a gambler among a third. Each of these individuals extracts, from the story, the features necessary to discriminate among the cases in his own memory. Each individual can be using the same kind of mechanism to extract abstract features from concrete descriptions of situations, but that mechanism is being driven by a different case library in each case, and so results in a different set of features being extracted, a different case retrieved, and a different explanation generated.

INTEGRATING EXTRACTION WITH RETRIEVAL

Some of these issues can be addressed by integrating feature extraction and case retrieval as much as possible. Instead of trying to extract all possible abstract features from input and then using that set of features as a retrieval cue, a system can allow feature extraction and memory search to proceed incrementally. Each time a new feature is extracted from the input it changes the pool of candidate cases that might apply to the current situation; each time the pool of candidates changes it suggests different features that should be extracted from input to try to discriminate among the candidates.

Playing "20 questions"

The model for this approach is that, rather than the front-end or feature extraction portion of the system telling memory what the input case looks like and then memory coming up with a match, memory is now playing a game of "20 questions" with the feature extraction process, asking for features as it needs them to discriminate among its known cases. Since feature extraction is expensive, memory is trying to ask as few "questions" as possible; seeking maximum payoff for its inferential cost with each question. The issue to resolve is how memory should decide what question to ask next.

The simplest and least interesting way to play "20 questions" is via a discrimination tree. the tree is balanced, the program can choose the correct match from among n cases by asking about log(n) features. But the problem with using this approach as a model for case retrieval is that a discrimination tree is a static object. It must be set up at the time the system is built, and, although it can be modified by adding cases and new discriminating features, it is computationally expensive to reorganize. Reorganizing a tree dynamically for each query is prohibitively expensive, so taking into account changeable items like retrieval goals is difficult. Furthermore, a tree-based retrieval algorithm will have difficulty if it asks the feature extraction process for a particular feature and receives the answer "I don't know" or "That's too expensive to calculate." What an integrated approach to feature extraction and memory search needs is a more flexible and dynamic way of playing "20 questions".

The object is to ask about the feature that offers the most information content for the least inferential cost, subject to the current retrieval goals of the system. Part of this problem is difficult: there is no good way of calculating *a priori* the difficulty of inferring any given feature. The best one can do is to remember how difficult it has been in the past to determine the presence or absence of that feature and use that cost as an estimate. Barring any other information, one can make the erroneous but necessary simplifying assumption that all abstract features are equally difficult to extract.

Fortunately, the likely utility of a feature as a retrieval cue is more easily estimable. The simplest basis is that of information content. A feature that is present in or absent from all of a given set of candidates is not worth extracting from new input, because it does not narrow down the space of candidate matches. On the other hand, a feature that is present in about half of the candidate cases is worth examining because knowing whether or not it is present in the new input case cuts the pool of remaining candidate matches in half. Accordingly, an important part of an incremental retrieval algorithm is a scheme for suggesting, given a set of cases, features that, if known to be present or absent in the input case, would discriminate among them. These are the features that the system should try to extract from input. Each time a feature is extracted it can be used to change the members of the current candidate set of cases; each time the set of candidate cases changes it would suggest a new set of discriminating features.

Parallel implementation

The ANON program is an attempt to integrate feature extraction and memory search. It plays the role of a memory in service of an overarching case-based planning or explanation system. Its behavior is to suggest features to an (external) feature extraction process, and, based upon whether each suggested feature is found to be present, absent or too expensive to infer, to continually narrow a set of candidate cases until either it finds either one case or a group of cases that do not differ in their causal implications a propos the current problem. Its case library is a set of abstract knowledge structures characterizing stereotypical plan failure situations. These cases correspond to common advice-giving proverbs like *too many cooks spoil the broth.* (See [Dyer, 82] for a discussion of the relationship of proverbs to stereotypical situations.)

ANON's memory contains about 1000 of these proverbial cases. In a full planning system they would be represented in much more causal detail than has been done to date, but the purpose of this system is to explore retrieval strategies in a large case library. A form for deeper causal representation for these proverbial knowledge structures is similar to the Explanation Patterns (XPs) described by [Schank, 86] or [Kass and Owens, 88].

Each case is represented on one processor of a Connection Machine parallel processor as is each known indexing feature. The system operates in two alternating modes: retrieval and feature suggestion.

Retrieval mode consists of moving from a set of features to a set of cases that embody those features. This is done by instructing the desired features to broadcast to the cases that embody them, the cases can then be ordered according to how many of the desired features they embody. The mechanism is in place here to assign weights to the features based on any of the criteria discussed above; the program currently assumes equal weights. This kind of retrieval is discussed in more detail by [Stanfill and Kahle, 86].

Feature suggestion mode is the more important mode; it is the means whereby the system picks the next feature to try to extract from input. The key to being able to suggest features is to be able to examine any group of cases and to suggest a feature that will discriminate among them. This can be done with any two cases just by comparing the features that participate in their causal structure. If the cases suggest different causal conclusions then there must be a feature in their causal structure that discriminates between them.

With larger groups of cases that cannot be compared individually with each other, the parallel implementation approximates this feature suggestion behavior by means of calculating *representativeness*. To find out how representative a given feature is of the currently active candidate pool, each processor corresponding to a currently active candidate case is instructed to send a message to each processor corresponding to a feature that is represented in that case. Features can thus be ordered on the basis of how well each represents the common qualities of all the cases in the candidate pool.

Features that are highly representative or not at all representative of a given pool are not likely to be good discriminators: they are not worth extracting from the new input case because they cannot be used to reduce the number of candidates in the pool. Features that are representative of about half the candidates in a pool, on the other hand, are very good discriminators. These are the features that the system suggests trying to infer next.

Of course simply counting the number of cases that each feature would index is only the crudest possible use of this calculation strategy. Just as features can be weighted in retrieval mode, cases can be weighted in feature suggestion mode. Representativeness does not have to be determined on the basis of numerical case counts; it can be determined on the basis of weighted case counts. The algorithm can be used to select features that divide the pool of cases not in half, but in half on a weight–adjusted basis. The source of these weights can be, for example, based upon features correlated with the retrieval goals discussed previously.

Features of this algorithm

Since this approach uses the contents of cases for organizing memory and requires no separate indexing knowledge, it makes it easy for the system to accept new cases. Since the cases themselves suggest the indexing features that would discriminate between themselves and other cases in memory, the new cases are included in the next memory retrieval cycle without the need to perform any explicit reorganization or re-indexing.

Adding new indexing knowledge to existing cases, on the other hand, is slightly more complicated. When the retrieval process encounters two cases that cannot be discriminated from each other, that indicates that one or both of the cases are not represented in enough detail. Currently the system is only able to indicate cases that need their degree of detail enhanced; it is not able to add detail to a case representation. The intention is to add detail whenever the system is unable to discriminate between two cases in memory; the mechanism for doing so is to build a causal explanation of the difference between the cases and use the features that participate in that explanation as new discriminating features.

CONCLUSIONS

No matter what kind of architecture one uses to accomplish the actual details of memory search, one must make a strong commitment to the idea of abstract features. The cases of which one wants to be reminded are often those that share abstract, rather than concrete or surface-level similarity to the current problem situation. Often these abstract features cannot be calculated by boolean combination or weightings of the concrete perceptual features and must therefore be derived from complicated and difficult-to-calculate relationships between perceptual features.

But, just because one is committed to the idea of abstract features does not mean that implementations must have a feature extraction or parsing process separate from the memory search process. There is no reason why all possible abstract features must be extracted from the input before the search of memory can begin. In fact, the approach of extracting a vector of abstract features and then using that whole vector as a search key is too costly in terms of processing resources. Instead, a more incremental approach that lets the contents of memory determine what features need to be extracted from input makes much better utilization of a system's inferencing power. This approach controls the complexity of inference, expresses retrieval goals as a function of the cases already in memory, and has desirable properties with regard to the reorganization of memory to take into account new experiences and new indexing features.

Obviously this approach does not solve the problem of how to recognize any given feature in input; that is still an open question. What it does accomplish, however, is to show how a system can have a great many abstract and difficult-to-infer features as part of its indexing vocabulary without having to identify the presence or absence of each one of them every time it processes a new piece of input.

Acknowledgements

This work was supported in part by the Defense Advanced Research Projects Agency, monitored by the Office of Naval Research under contract N00014-85-K-0108 and by the Air Force Office of

Scientific Research under contracts AFOSR-85-0343, AFOSR-89-0100 and F49620-88-C-0058. Larry Birnbaum and Alex Kass provided helpful comments on this material.

References

[Ashley and Rissland, 87] K. Ashley and E. Rissland. Compare and contrast, a test of expertise. In *Proceedings of the Sixth Annual National Conference on Artificial Intelligence*, pages 273–284, Palo Alto, 1987. AAAI, Morgan Kaufmann, Inc.

[Carbonell and Veloso, 88] J. Carbonell and M. Veloso. Integrating derivational analogy into a general problem solving architecture. In J. Kolodner, editor, *Proceedings of a Workshop on Case-Based Reasoning*, pages 104–124, Palo Alto, 1988. Defense Advanced Research Projects Agency, Morgan Kaufmann, Inc.

[Dyer, 82] M. Dyer. In-depth understanding: A computer model of integrated processing for narrative comprehension. Technical Report 219, Yale University Department of Computer Science, May 1982.

[Hammond, 86] K. Hammond. *Case-based Planning: An Integrated Theory of Planning, Learning and Memory*. PhD thesis, Yale University, 1986. Technical Report 488.

[Kass and Owens, 88] A. Kass and C. Owens. Learning new explanations by incremental adaptation. In *Proceedings of the 1988 AAAI Spring Symposium on Explanation-Based Learning*. AAAI, 1988.

[Kolodner, 87] J. Kolodner. Extending problem solver capabilities through case-based inference. In *Proceedings of the Fourth International Workshop on Machine Learning*, pages 167–178, Los Altos, CA, June 1987. University of California, Irvine, Morgan Kaufman Publishers, Inc.

[Leake, 88] D. B. Leake. Using explainer needs to judge operationality. In *Proceedings of the 1988 AAAI Spring Symposium on Explanation-based Learning*. AAAI, 1988.

[Schank, 86] R. Schank. *Explanation Patterns: Understanding Mechanically and Creatively*. Lawrence Erlbaum Associates, Hillsdale, NJ, 1986.

[Seifert, 88] C. Seifert. A retrieval model for case-based memory. In E. Rissland and J. King, editors, *Proceedings of a Case-Based Reasoning Workshop*, pages 120–125. AAAI, 1988.

[Simpson, 85] R. Simpson. *A Computer Model of Case-based Reasoning in Problem-solving: An Investigation in the Domain of Dispute Mediation*. PhD thesis, School of Information and Computer Science, Georgia Institute of Technology, 1985.

[Stanfill and Kahle, 86] C. Stanfill and B. Kahle. Parallel free-text search on the connection machine system. *Communications of the ACM*, 29(12):1213–1228, December 1986.

[Stanfill and Waltz, 88] C. Stanfill and D. Waltz. The memory-based reasoning paradigm. In J. Kolodner, editor, *Proceedings of a Workshop on Case-Based Reasoning*, pages 414–424, Palo Alto, 1988. Defense Advanced Research Projects Agency, Morgan Kaufmann, Inc.

[Stepp and Michalski, 86] R. E. Stepp, III and R. S. Michalski. Conceptual clustering: Inventing goal-oriented classifications of structured objects. In R. S. Michalski, J. G. Carbonell, and T. M. Mitchell, editors, *Machine Learning, Volume II*, chapter 17, pages 471–498. Morgan Kauffmann, Los Altos, CA, 1986.

[Sycara, 87] E. P. Sycara. *Resolving Adversarial Conflicts: An Approach Integrating Case-based and Analytic Methods*. PhD thesis, School of Information and Computer Science, Georgia Institute of Technology, 1987.

[Winston, 80] P. Winston. Learning and reasoning by analogy. *Communications of the ACM*, 23(12):689–703, 1980.

The function of examples in learning a second language from an instructional text

Carol E. Moon and Steven L. Lytinen
Artificial Intelligence Laboratory
The University of Michigan
Ann Arbor, MI 48109

Abstract

This paper addresses the role that examples play in instructional learning. We discuss several roles that examples can serve when they complement an instruction. We provide functional evidence for some of these roles, arguing why instructions and examples are both necessary for efficient learning. We present a system that learns from instructions which are enhanced by examples. The system, ANT (Acquisition using Native-language Transfer), learns a second language by reading instructions about grammatical rules of the second language as well as examples which use these rules. Finally, we argue for the functional utility of examples in instructional learning on more general grounds, showing how such a strategy can be applicable to other domains besides second language learning.

1 Introduction

People learn a great deal of information by being told it. Furthermore, they can readily assimilate this information with what they already know, allowing them to use it to improve their performance in tasks such as problem-solving or planning. For example, if you are learning calculus, and I teach you about a new integration technique, such as integration by parts, then if all goes well you will be able to use that rule to help in your performance of solving integrals.

However, learning from instructions is not quite that simple. If we look at most instructional textbooks, we find that often instructions about a new rule are accompanied by examples of how that rule can be used. A typical calculus book presents integration by parts by first stating the rule in a succinct manner, and then presenting several example problems, including a step-by-step description of how to solve them using integration by parts.

This paper will address the role of examples in instructions. Why are they necessary? At first glance, they seem superfluous. Don't the instructions provide the learner with all the information that is needed? For integration by parts, doesn't the formula alone say it all?

We will argue that in order to apply new information to some task, often the learner needs other information, which is not easily conveyed through instructions. In particular, the learner needs to know how this new information connects up with what he already knows. This is just one role that examples can play in instructions: they can provide the learner with an "experience" that will help to delineate the role of the new information relative to information which is already known.

We are building a program which learns from instructions augmented with examples. The program, called ANT (Acquisition using Native-language Transfer), operates in the domain of second language learning. This domain is a good one for studying the role of examples in instructions. Second language learners seem to "transfer" their knowledge of their native language over to the second language, modifying rules according to the differences between languages (Gass, 1980; Lado, 1957; Selinker, 1983). As a result, incorporating new rules into existing linguistic knowledge is a major part of second language learning. As we will see, our program uses the examples that accompany instructions to determine which English rule(s) need to be modified for German.

ANT begins with a knowledge base of grammar rules and lexical entries for English, which enable it to understand English descriptions of grammar rules. The program also develops a knowledge base of rules for German. Initially, the program assumes that all of its knowledge for English will apply to German. In this way, it expects to be told about differences between the two languages so that it can modify its German rules accordingly. ANT receives input which we have taken from an introductory German textbook. The input consists of instructions about German grammar rules, as well as examples of German sentences that illustrate these rules. Here is a typical input to the system:

> In German, verbs come at the end of relative clauses.
> Example: Der Ameisenbär, der die Amiese fraß, ißt Kaviar auch.
> (The aardvark who ate the ants eats caviar, too.)

ANT modifies its knowledge base of grammar rules for German according to the instructions and examples, and can then understand German sentences which it has not seen previously that use the new construction. In this paper, we will show how ANT utilizes the information in the examples to clarify the meaning of the instructions.

2 The roles of instructions and examples

Examples can function in several distinct ways when they are used to complement instructions. In this section we will discuss several of these roles, and the psychological evidence that exists for many of them. In the next section, we will show how examples serve analagous roles in our computer model.

2.1 Examples

Retrieval cues

Examples can provide additional retrieval cues for the information in an instruction (Reder,Charney, and Morgan, 1986). For example, a learner may forget the original instruction when he is trying to formulate a relative clause. But the learner may be able to remember the example and hence the lesson of the instruction by remembering the example about the aardvark and caviar.

Overcoming abstraction

Often, a learner needs an example which is less abstract than the instruction. Abstraction can be difficult especially when the learner is unfamiliar or inexperienced with the domain (Reder, *et al.*, 1986). For example, if a student is not particularly knowledgeable about grammar rules explicitly, a rule like the relative clause one above will perhaps be too abstract for the student to remember. In other words, his lack of command of grammar rules may inhibit the incorporation of this knowledge into his knowledge about using language. When such a student is given an example which serves as an instance of the application of the rule, he may more easily see both what is meant by a relative clause and which verb is moved. The example can invoke his rules about clauses and illustrate how his original notion of a relative clause must be changed.

The student probably knows many examples of relative clauses without necessarily having a command of the grammatical terminology. In this way, examples avoid the abstraction of the instruction, allowing the learner to build his own generalization after several examples.

Reasoning by analogy

Related to the situation of the student above is the idea that when an instruction is too abstract, examples may allow a learner to solve the next problem (i.e., understand or formulate a subsequent sentence) by analogy. Analogy has been shown to be an important problem solving and skill acquisition method, especially when the learner has little domain knowledge, like in the situation above where the hypothetical student's lack of explicit grammar knowledge (Pirolli and Anderson, 1985).

Modifying prior knowledge

Examples can also be used as a way to discover what existing knowledge must be modified according to the instruction. How is the instruction related to previous knowledge about the domain? In which contexts should the new instruction be used? Examples can show the system how the instruction is applied and in which contexts it should apply (Reder *et al.*, 1986; Stein and Bransford, 1979). Instructions alone usually do not provide this information. How examples perform this role in ANT will be shown in the next section.

Filling in details

Finally, examples can instantiate details not made explicit in the instruction (Reder *et al.*, 1986). Suppose the system was given the following instruction:

> In German, to express 'to like' the verb 'haben' is used with the adverb 'gern.'

Much information that the system would need to build an appropriate rule for this construction would be missing. Where does the object of 'like' (or 'haben') go? What is the relative ordering of 'haben' and 'gern'? Subsequent examples would allow the system to deduce that the noun phrase that is the object comes between 'haben' and 'gern' and that 'haben' precedes 'gern.' ANT utilizes this function of examples to a great extent. Introductory language textbooks seem to rely on this as well, providing the student with rather brief instructions that are supplemented by a series of examples, from which the student must learn the complete details of such a construction.

2.2 Why do we need instructions?

Given the roles of examples discussed above, one might be led to believe that instructions play little or no role in the learning process. Perhaps the learner completely ignores instructions, paying attention only to the examples which accompany them. However, even given the above roles for examples, instructions still can have important roles to play:

Focus

Instructions give the learner clues about what features of the examples are important. If the learner were given no instruction, how would he decide which features of the example to focus on? In our relative clause example, he could just as easily notice the agreement in case and gender between the noun and the determiner as a feature to be learned as he could the different word order in the clause. The instruction thus can make the significant processing of the example more efficient.

Expectations

In ANT, examples play a role in changing the system's expectation of a relative clause. Because ANT assumes that any rules it knows about English apply to German unless it learns otherwise, it tries to use its grammatical and semantic rules to parse the German examples. But certainly in the relative clause example, the German example will not be successfully parsed using the English rules because the constraints on word order in the grammar would not match the constraints determined by the word order in the example. ANT uses the instruction to alter its expectations. It determines that the instruction is focusing on word order in relative clauses. When ANT subsequently parses the German examples using relative clauses, it relaxes word order constraints, thus allowing the parser to build a parse tree and representation of the example. This process will be explained in more detail later.

3 An example of ANT's learning

We have seen many possible roles for examples and instructions to play in the learning process. Let us now turn to ANT, and see how these roles come into play in our computer model. We will see that the roles are essential to the learning process, providing good functional explanations that complement the psychological evidence discussed in the previous section.

All linguistic knowledge in ANT is represented using a unification-style grammar (Shieber, 1986)[1]. In this approach, word order information, as well as information about the functional relations between words, is explicitly and declaratively represented. This is important for the system's task, because it must be able to manipulate various components of English rules in order to form new German rules. Another key feature of this approach is that the structure of grammar rules used by ANT is the same as the structure ANT produces in parsing. (for details, see Lytinen and Moon, 1988). As we will see, this allows ANT to extract new rules from its understanding of examples that it is presented.

Let us now consider the entire process which takes place when ANT learns a new rule. The example we will discuss is our relative clause example:

> In German, verbs come at the end of relative clauses.
> Example: Der Ameisenbär, der die Amiese fraß, ißt Kaviar auch.
> (The aardvark who ate the ants eats caviar, too.)

The representation which ANT produces when it reads the instruction is shown below:

[1] Part of the information in unification rules is analagous to the phrase structure information which is often encoded in context-free grammars. For the sake of simplicity, we will use the context-free notation in this paper, even though ANT uses the unification-style versions of these rules.

Order:

Location : RelClause (**RELC**)
Constituent : Verb (**V**)
Position : last

As ANT processes an instruction, it determines what kind of instruction it is. Does the instruction refer to word order, or does it refer to grammatical features, like case, gender, or number? For the relative clause instruction, ANT categorizes it as a **REORDER** instruction, for it is an instruction about changing word order. After producing the representation above, ANT needs to use what it knows about English relative clauses in order to incorporate this new information. This is because the instruction does not completely describe German relative clauses; it just describes the difference between German and English relative clauses. ANT must retrieve its English relative clause rules, as well as rules about subconstituents of relative clauses, and modify some (or all) of them. As we will see, this is a rather difficult task.

The main problem is that the instruction alone does not tell us which rules to modify. It can cue the system to find rules labeled **RELC** (i.e., rules about relative clauses). But if the surface grammar (embedded within unification rules) of our relative clause rules in English are something like **RELC → RELPRON VP**, the relative clause rules are not the ones which need modification. Rather, it is the rules about verb phrases (as they occur in relative clauses) which must be modified, since they are the ones which ultimately specify where the verb will occur in the relative clause. If we simply tried to incorporate the new information into our English clause rule, we would arrive at an incorrect result. Our surface grammar might end up with a rule like this: **RELC → RELPRON VP V**. This rule would mean that German relative clauses had two verbs, one inside the **VP**, and the other one at the end of the clause.

One possible strategy for finding out which rule should be modified is to expand all of the clause rule's subconstituents, searching the grammar for rules which refer to a **V**. However, this approach could lead to a very extensive search, since in general the constituent which we are trying to find could be nested arbitrarily deep in the grammar. In the worst case, the system would end up inspecting its entire grammar, searching for the constituent in question. In addition, there is no guarantee that the system will find the correct constituent. A verb can be derived from many different places in the grammar. How can we insure that the correct occurrence will be the one that is found in the search?

This is where the processing of an example comes into play. Instead of performing this search, ANT parses the German example, using its English grammar rules. As we will see, the German example forces the system to use the English grammar rule which must be modified. In particular, the clause and verb phrase rules that need to be altered will be used. In this way, the example brings the rules to be altered to the attention of the learning mechanism. As a result, the potentially exhaustive search for relevant rules is avoided.

In order to process the German example, ANT must relax some of the constraints in its English grammar rules. Otherwise, the parse would fail, because the German example does not conform to the grammar of English. In particular, ordering constraints on constituents are relaxed. ANT knows to do this because it has classified the input instruction as a **REORDER**ing rule. Since this instruction is about relative clauses, all constituent-ordering constraints are dropped for subconstituents of the category **RELC**. The relevant rules are the following[2]:

$$\text{RELC} \rightarrow \text{RELPRON VP} \qquad (1)$$
$$\text{VP} \rightarrow \text{V NP} \qquad (2)$$

These rules encode word order information in English that a relative clause consists of a relative pronoun followed by a verb phrase (i.e., a verb and a noun phrase).

When the system tries to apply these rules, the order of the right-hand side constituents is instantiated by the word order of the input examples. Relaxing constraints allows ordering information for constituents to be derived from the examples, not from higher rules in the grammar. In general, the instruction focuses the system on a feature like case, word order, or word choice. Then constraints from the English rules are relaxed so that the information from the example can take precedence and determine the actual correct values for those features in the German rules.

Once the example is parsed, the correct rule for German relative clauses is embedded within the final structure. As we mentioned earlier, this is because the structure of grammar rules used by ANT is the same as the structure ANT produces in parsing. ANT extracts the rule from this structure, once again using the fact that the rule it is learning is a **REORDER**ing rule to extract the constituent ordering information from within the relative clause to replace those constraints in the original English rules. It turns out that the order requirements which change are within rule 2 above. Namely, the order of the constituents **V** and **NP** must be reversed. But ANT cannot simply rewrite the rule this way, since rule 2 is not just used within relative clauses. Modifications should only be local to relative clauses, so ANT generates a new category, called **VP1**, as a subconstituent of German relative clauses, in which the **V** is the final constituent. The resulting rules would be the following:

$$\text{RELC} \rightarrow \text{RELPRON VP1} \qquad (3)$$
$$\text{VP1} \rightarrow \text{NP V} \qquad (4)$$

4 Conclusion

We have discussed many possible roles that examples and instructions can play in learning. Several of these roles turn out to be essential to the learning process used in ANT. First, we have seen why instructions alone do not provide ANT with enough information to learn a new grammar rule. Without the examples, the system would not know which of its existing rules need to be altered. In other words, ANT cannot readily access its previous relevant knowledge unless it is given examples. In addition, the instruction may also omit details (like the exact ordering of constituents) which are necessary to learn the new rule. Without examples, the rule-inferring process could be prohibitively expensive.

We have also seen that the learning process would be much less efficient without the information provided in the instructions. Although given enough examples, it may very well be possible to

[2] These are the relevant rules for the example we are considering. Other relative clause rules would be modified by other examples.

induce the correct grammar rules for a language (see Berwick, 1985), the process would be much slower without the instructions to guide it. They serve as a high-level guide to focus the ANT's attention on the correct item or feature to be learned.

In the relative clause example, the fact that our instruction states that the rule is about relative clauses allows the system to immediately generalize the German example to all **VP**s which appear in relative clauses. Without this knowledge, the system would not be able to determine from a single example just how general the new **VP** rule should be.

The information provided in the instruction can be thought of as analagous to domain knowledge in explanation-based learning methods (DeJong and Mooney, 1986; Mitchell, Keller, and Kedar-Cabelli, 1986). Domain knowledge allows these systems to generalize to the appropriate level from only one example. Without the domain knowledge, these systems would have to use similarity-based learning techniques, examining several examples before reaching the same generalization. In much the same way, without instructions, ANT would not be able to determine how general its new grammar rule should be without looking for similarities over many examples.

Instructions provide ANT with other essential information. By using the instruction to focus on particular features of the example, ANT can avoid considering all features in the example as being the possible topic to be learned. It can more efficiently process the significant features of the example. ANT also uses expectations derived from the instructions to parse examples by relaxing some constraints in its parsing rules. The relaxed constraints allow information from the example, like word order, to determine the ordering of constituents in the grammar instead of having the grammar dictate the correct ordering.

Our proposed roles for instructions and examples in second language learning should apply to many other learning tasks. In fact, the interaction between instructions and examples that we have outlined ought to be very similar in any learning task in which existing knowledge must be modified for the task being learned. In such tasks, determining which existing rule(s) are affected by the newly presented knowledge could result in a very large search of the existing rule base, unless an example is provided which leads the learner to the affected rule(s). Likewise, similar problems of knowing what features of the example to focus on, inferring details, etc., would be encountered by the learner. This seems to include a very broad range of learning tasks. Examples include the learning of a new card game, in which rules might be expressed as modifications of rules from a card game which the learner already knows; or perhaps learning a new piece of software, such as an editor, in which the learner might rely on knowledge of other similar software that he already knows about.

The interplay between instructions and examples surely is more complex than we have described here. Each type of input could potentially play many other roles in the learning process. These roles may vary, depending on the sort of knowledge being learned, as well as the content of the instructions and examples. The various possiblities of interaction between instructions and examples remain a topic for extensive further research.

References

Berwick, R. (1985). *The Acquisition of Syntactic Knowledge.* MIT Press, Cambridge, MA.

DeJong, G., and Mooney, R. (1986). Explanation-based learning: An alternative view." *Machine Learning 1*, Kluwer Academic Publishers, 1986, Boston, MA, pp. 145-176.

Gass, S. (1980) An investigation of syntactic transfer in adult second language learners." in Scarcella, R., and Krashen, S. (eds.), *Research in Second Language Acquisition*, Newbury House Publishing, Rowley, MA.

Lado, R. (1957). *Linguistics Across Cultures.* University of Michigan Press, Ann Arbor, MI.

Lytinen, S., and Moon, C. (1988). Learning a second language. In *Proceedings of the Seventh National Conference on Artificial Intelligence*, St. Paul, MN, pp. 222-227.

Mitchell, T., Keller R., Kedar-Cabelli, S. (1986) Explanation- based generalization: A unifying view. *Machine Learning 1*, Kluwer Academic Publishers, Boston, MA, pp. 47-80.

Mostow, J. (1983). Operationalizing advice: A problem-solving model. In *Proceedings of the International Machine Learning Workshop*, University of Illinois, June 1983.

Pirolli, P., Anderson, J. (1985) The role of learning from examples in the acquisition of programming skills. in *Canadian Journal of Psychology 39*(2), pp. 240-272.

Reder, L., Charney, D., Morgan, K. (1986) The role of elaborations in learning a skill from an instructional text. in *Memory and Cognition 14*(1), pp. 64-78.

Selinker, L. (1983). Language transfer. in Selinker, L., and Gass, S. (eds.), *Language Transfer and Language Learning*, Newbury House Publishing, Rowley, MA.

Shieber, S. (1986). *An Introduction to Unification-based Styles of Grammar.* CSLI, Palo Alto, CA.

Stein, B., Bransford, J. (1979) Constraints on effective elaboration: Effects of precision and subject generation. in *Journal of Verbal Learning and Verbal Behavior 18*, pp. 769-777.

Token Frequency and Phonological Predictability in a Pattern Association Network: Implications for Child Language Acquisition

Virginia Marchman
Department of Psychology
University of California, San Diego

Kim Plunkett
Institute of Psychology
University of Aarhus, Denmark

ABSTRACT

The degree to which the behavior of PDP models of pattern associations (Rumelhart & McClelland, 1986; 1987) approximates children's acquisition of inflectional morphology has recently been highlighted in discussions of the applicability of PDP to the study of human cognition and language (Pinker & Mehler, 1988). In this paper, we attempt to eliminate many of the limitations of the R&M model, adopting an empirical approach to the analysis of learning (hit rate and error type) in two sets of simulations in which vocabulary structure (token frequency) and the presence of phonological subregularities are manipulated. A 3-layer back propagation network is used to implement a pattern association task with strings that are analogous to four types of present and past tense English verbs. We overview resulting "competitions" when strings are randomly assigned to verb classes, in particular, the conditions under which different overgeneralization errors (both "pure" and "blended") are produced. In a second set of simulations, identical type and token frequencies are used, but strings are assigned to the identity and vowel change classes on the basis of phonological shape of the stem. Phonological cues are exploited by the system leading to overall improved performance. However, overgeneralizations continue to be observed in similar conditions. Token frequency works together with phonological subregularities to determine patterns of learning, including the conditions under which "rule-like" behavior will and will not emerge. The results are discussed with reference to behavioral data on children's acquisition of the English past tense.

INTRODUCTION

Most current perspectives in child language acquisition frame language learning and production in terms of symbolic and categorically defined principles or *rules* (Chomsky, 1980; Pinker, 1984; see Derwing & Skousen, 1989). Systems of rules are seen as the indispensable format within which to explain how the language learner achieves a linguistic system that is abstract enough to produce grammatical utterances, but at the same time will allow her to go "beyond the data" and create novel combinations (e.g., Berko, 1958). The goals of the acquisitionist are to outline when children can be said to master the rules that represent linguistic structure and to uncover the mechanisms by which that organization is achieved.

In the past tense in English, irregular or "strong" verbs are not seen to form their past tenses through a suffixation rule (e.g., "add -ed"), but are "exceptions." The majority of the irregular verb stems can be grouped into three general categories (see Bybee & Slobin, 1982; Pinker & Prince, 1988 for more detailed classifications): (a) *identity mapping* (or no marking - doing nothing to the stem, e.g., hit —> hit); (b) *vowel change* (transforming the vowel, e.g., come —> came; (c) *arbitrary* (there is no obvious structural relationship between the present and past tense form, e.g., go —> went). Children will sometimes *overgeneralize* the regular rule and produce erroneous forms such as "goed" in which the regular "-ed" ending cooccurs with irregular stems (e.g., Bybee & Slobin, 1982). Of course, children eventually learn to produce both regular and irregular past tense forms correctly. The apparent regression and subsequent improvement in children's abilities suggests a stage-like *reorganization* of the child's rule system (Bowerman, 1982) and is an oft-cited example of "U-shaped" development. These phenomena are seen as among the most persuasive pieces of behavioral evidence that language learning involves achieving a system in which general rules and their exceptions must come to peacefully *coexist*.

Recently, Rumelhart & McClelland (1986, 1987) set out to capture several of the "facts" of the acquisition of the English past tense (i.e., that the "-ed" suffix is often overgeneralized to irregular verbs and that learning proceeds along a "U-shaped" course) using a 2-layer perceptron network. Their goal was to suggest how a model of language acquisition might be able to avoid rule-based mechanisms and discrete symbols, yet still capture what children "do" at various points in acquisition. The ability of networks of this sort to "behave" as children do is intended to challenge the view that acquisition is *necessarily* a process of organizing and reorganizing explicitly represented rules and their exceptions. Models such as this one characteristically utilize distributed representations and focus on elaborating the microstructure or sub-symbolic nature of cognition and language (Smolensky, 1988). These claims have undergone considerable scrutiny and have been met with resistance in some circles (e.g., Pinker & Mehler, 1988). Several have questioned the details of the R&M past tense simulation, nominating it as the 'test case' for evaluating the extent to which connectionism can offer a substantive *alternative* approach to understanding the nature of linguistic and cognitive systems (Fodor & Pylyshyn, 1988).

Clearly, the R&M model is limited by several of its assumptions about the structure of the input within which language learning takes place. First, children do not hear present and past tense forms side-by-side in the input in the absence of semantic or communicative information. Nor do children receive an explicit "teacher" signal as feedback. In addition, Pinker & Prince (1988) point out that the network's production of overgeneralizations coincided directly with the introduction of a greater number of regular verbs into the learning set. Learnability considerations undermine the results of a model that introduces *discontinuity* into the input, i.e., the "learner" is exposed to only a subset of the available linguistic data early in learning. Further, exemplars (i.e., tokens) of particular verbs were presented with equal frequency to R&M's system. It is highly unlikely that children hear each verb token with equal frequency (Bever, in press). Finally, Pinker & Prince criticize the R&M model for not incorporating higher-order representations such as "word," "root," "regular verb" and "irregular verb" that allow system-internal differentiations between two classes of verbs and two learning mechanisms (rote and rule). Certain aspects of the past tense system in English are conducive to the mechanisms embodied in PDP models, i.e. the abstraction of family resemblance clusters of phonological similarity between and among verbs in the *irregular classes*. However, this mechanism is neither necessary nor appropriate for capturing the "default" nature (or form independence) of verbs in the *regular class*. The operation of the regular rule is assumed to involve higher-level representations that are manipulated regardless of lower-level phonological stem representations. R&M's failure to incorporate symbolic constructs that capture the phonological differences between regular and irregular verbs is interpreted as a significant and fatal shortcoming of the approach.

In this paper, we extend the R&M work by exploring learning in two sets of simulations that are required to master mappings that are analogous to present and past tense forms in English. However, unlike the R&M work, our simulations do not use Wickelfeature representations, and back propagation is employed in a three-layer network. We adopt an empirical, comparative approach in systematically varying token frequency and the presence/absence of phonological subregularities in the input set. At no point are discontinuities introduced into the input set in any simulation.

METHOD

All simulations use an artificial language consisting of randomly generated, possible English CVC, VCC and CCV strings. (See Plunkett & Marchman (1989) for a complete description of the vocabulary and phonological representation used). Each consonant and vowel is represented by a pattern of features distributed across 6 units, reflecting phonological contrasts such as voiced/unvoiced, front/middle/back, etc. The representation of the suffix (2 units) is not phonological, but 3 "allomorphs" are possible depending on the voicing of the final consonant of the stem (analogous to, for example, /-t/ following voiceless stop). Twenty units are used to encode each present and past tense form, and thus, the model is restricted to processing fixed length strings. Eleven English-like vowel change transformations are used (e.g., /i/ —> /A/, ring —> rang). Each vowel can be transformed to one, two or three possible new vowels in the output.

All networks must learn four types of mapping. Thus, the network, like the child, must learn to deal with several different classes of transformations simultaneously. In the *Parent* simulations, the network is at a slight disadvantage compared to the child in that strings are assigned to the different classes *randomly* (except that assignment to vowel change class is conditional upon possession of a vowel which can undergo a legal transformation). Here, no more phonological similarity exists between the members of a given class than between members of different classes. In the *Phonological* simulations, we partially mimic subregularities which characterize the vowel change and identity verbs in English, by assigning verbs to classes on the bases of stem final CV sequences.

The members of the 4 classes are assembled from a "language" of 700 legal strings. For each simulation, total vocabulary size (500 unique strings) and number of unique strings in each class (type frequency) is held constant: ARBITRARY: 2 types; REGULAR: 410 types; IDENTITY: 20 types; VOWEL CHANGE: 65 types. The number of repetitions of a unique string (token frequency) is manipulated across simulation so that the network experiences some items more frequently than others within a given sweep through the data. The token frequencies used in both the *Parent* and the *Phone* simulations are listed in Table 1. All simulations used 20 input, 20 output, and 20 hidden units, and were run on the "rlearn" simulator (Center for Research in Language, UCSD) using a back propagation learning algorithm. Performance is assessed in terms of the percentage of correct outputs for each verb class. For incorrect outputs, we compute the closest phonological representation in order to estimate the actual "verbal" output of the network, and generate categories of error types (Tables 2 and 3).

RESULTS AND DISCUSSION

Previous results from several series of simulations using this architecture and vocabulary (Plunkett & Marchman, 1989) revealed that both type (class size) and token frequency of a class determine rate of learning and final level of performance within that class. These parameters also influence the degree to which characteristics of one class of mappings will be adopted by the network when forming the past tense forms of verbs in other classes. In general, variations in token frequency were found to have a *greater* effect on performance than type frequency. However, effects can be observed in many directions depending on which strategy is dominant in that simulation. Dominance of a particular strategy is determined by the relative type and token frequencies of the competing classes, in interaction with the global characteristics of the total mapping function that the network is required to perform. A noteworthy characteristic of these networks is their inability to map a large number of arbitrary stems simultaneously.

These "network facts" are informative for understanding children's acquisition of language in only a limited sense -- for our purposes, to the degree that the particular input configuration used accurately represents input to children. It is extremely difficult to determine the exact frequency of English verbs to which children are exposed and/or that children find salient in processing. As a first approximation, we use a single type frequency configuration representing the relative class sizes of English, and vary token frequency parametrically across simulation.

Parent Simulations

Manipulations of token frequency in the *parent* simulations influence the performance of a given class and the extent to which overgeneralization errors were observed. The percent of items correctly output in each simulation are provided in Table 1. When type frequency (class size) of an irregular class is small, increasing its token frequency results in a high level of performance without any deleterious effects on the dominant form of mapping (e.g., suffixation). However, if type frequency is relatively large and backed up by a high token frequency, then the performance on the dominant form of mapping deteriorates dramatically. For example, successful learning of the arbitrary mappings only occurs when class size is small yet each exemplar is presented to the system fairly frequently (i.e., token frequency is greater than 20). Because of the initial biases of these networks to perform identity mapping, performance on the arbitraries is poor unless these type/token constraints are met. Interestingly, once the number of exemplars is sufficient for mastery in the arbitrary class, performance is generally unaffected by manipulations of token frequency for the other types of mappings in the network.

When natural languages incorporate arbitrary forms, they are generally highly frequent and constitute a relatively small class of items. For the child acquiring language, these typological characteristics undoubtedly contribute to the early learning of these forms. However, children will often later overgeneralize the regular mappings to the arbitrary class (*go* —> *goed*), but eventually return to using the correct form. We also observe this effect in many of the *parent* simulations. However, unlike the R&M simulation, this behavior cannot result from a discontinuity in the vocabulary to which the network is exposed. In these networks, overgeneralizations on arbitrary mappings arise from the need to satisfy a variety of constraints *within the framework of a single mechanism.* The network is forced to reorganize its weight matrix to meet the requirements of the dominant form of mapping. Once this is achieved, however, the network reestablishes correct performance so that arbitrary forms may peacefully co-exist with stems from the other classes.

In addition, we observe that the regular and vowel change mappings frequently compete with each other for network resources in such a manner that neither class can be completely mastered simultaneously. Competition effects result in the production of complex patterns of overgeneralization errors. (See distribution of error types in Table 2). Vowel change overgeneralizations to the regular class can occur at the same time as suffixation overgeneralizations occur to the identity class. Blended errors are also observed (i.e., the application of two mapping regularities in a single form). In studies of children's acquisition of the past tense in English, irregular sub-regularities sometimes give rise to their own patterns of overgeneralization, albeit less frequently than the standard "add -ed" overgeneralization (Bybee & Slobin, 1982; Marchman, 1988). That is, children will sometimes "overgeneralize" a vowel change or identity mapping to a regular or irregular stem, producing errors such as ***pick* —> *pack***, or combining mapping types to produce blended responses, such as ***ated*** (Kuczaj, 1977). But, because irregular forms are not formed using a "default" rule, errors of this type are generally thought to result via ***analogy*** to the phonological shape of individual stems (Pinker & Prince, 1988; MacWhinney, 1987). In the ***parent*** simulations, none of the overgeneralization errors, of both the standard and irregular variety, can be attributed to the phonological structure of the input set given that verbs were randomly assigned to classes. However, none of the simulations succeeded in reaching "adult-like competence" in all classes simultaneously. The next set of simulations, the ***phones***, explores whether the addition of phonological predictability into the input set will enable these networks to master the past tense.

Phonological Simulations

English irregular verbs possess phonological properties that can be said to characterize the class, however, they are nevertheless insufficient to reliably predict class membership, i.e., both regular and identity stems end with a dental consonant. As discussed by Pinker & Prince (1988), the lack of phonological similarity within the regular class is crucial to the hypothesis that different mechanisms of past tense formation operate on irregular and regular verbs. The regular rule is applied generally, without reference to the properties of the stem; whereas, irregular transformations take this phonological information into account in the production of a past tense form.

In the ***phone*** simulations, we impose the following constraints on class assignment: (a) All identity stems must end in a dental, and (b) All vowel change stems are restricted to eleven possible VC stem final sequences. We also ensure that the regular class contains stems possible irregular stems, e.g., some regulars end in a dental. Two questions are relevant: (1) Do the additional constraints aid in the identification of class membership and lead to improved performance? (2) Do patterns of competition and overgeneralization occur when phonological sub-regularities are available to the network that are similar to those when such information is not available? The *phone* simulations repeat the type and token frequencies of the corresponding *parent* simulations (see Table 1), and represent a second approximation to the task facing the young child learning the relationship between the present and past tense forms of English verbs.

In general, all phonological simulations exhibit a higher level of performance, across mapping types, compared to the *parent* simulations, except for the arbitrary mappings in a few simulations (See Table 1). However, note that the regulars perform minimally better under the *phone* condition. The greatest improvement tends to occur when the token frequency of the *vowel change* class is relatively high (simulations 5, 17, 18 and 27). Since there are no differences between conditions other than the sub-regularities in the identities and vowel changes, we can attribute the lower performance of the regulars in the *parent* condition to the absence of these subregularities. In the *phones*, the phonological subregularities conspire to protect the regulars from interference, despite the facts that (a) the regular class contains stems that resemble the vowel change and identity classes (similar vowel and final consonant), and (b) there are no explicit features marking the regular stems as "regular."

Table 3 presents the distribution of error types in the *phone* simulations. In general, these networks treat regulars which end in a dental as identities, however, many "dental final" regulars are mapped correctly and other regular stems are mapped as vowel changes or blended. Regular stems that conform to the characteristics of the vowel change class are often mapped as vowel changes, though again not all regular stems with vowel change characteristics are incorrectly mapped. There was a clear-cut advantage for the identity mappings in the *phones*. The network makes use of the phonological sub-regularities, however, it is also not indiscriminate in its categorization of verbs into classes on that basis (although they are a source of error). In several of the *phone* simulations, the identity class achieves optimal performance. However, *en route*, the mapping undergoes several reorganizations in which some identity stems are alternately treated as regular and vowel change stems *after* having been mapped correctly (see Plunkett & Marchman, 1989, for a discussion of "U-shaped" learning in these networks). Finally, there was a moderate advantage for vowel change mappings in the *Phone* condition, particularly apparent in simulations 17, 19 and 27. In simulations 17 and 27, both the vowel change class and the identity class have relatively large token frequencies. In the *parent* condition, the lack of phonological sub-regularities permits identity mapping to "spill over" into the vowel change class. However, in the *phone* condition, the regularity in the identity class restricts the application of identity mapping to items that possess these characteristics and hence reduces the level of interference with the vowel change class.

The provision of phonological constraints on class membership enables the competition effects between classes to diminish, improving overall performance in the *phones*. Nevertheless, *patterns* of learning are observed that are similar to those in the *parent* simulations even though many errors do bear the stamp of the phonological structure of the input set. The predominant error types for both sets of simulations are similar: Regulars, the most common error is identity mapping; Identities, the most common error is suffixation; Vowel changes, suffixation, identity mapping and blending, in that order. Similarly, blending errors in the identity class are absent in both the *parent* and *phone* simulations.

Clearly, the *phone* simulations map input stems in light of the phonological information concerning class membership. These networks seem to increasingly resemble a rule-governed, categorical system as the constraints on the network (represented here as *external* pattern constraints rather than *internal* architectural constraints) are tightened. The constraining effect of the phonological sub-regularities is particularly apparent in those simulations which otherwise give rise to substantial competition effects (compare *phones* 5, 17, 18 and 27 to those in the *parent* set). Phonological sub-regularities can, thus, serve to both ***support and constrain*** the observed frequency effects, both factors working together toward successful performance across all classes. Just as these networks can partition the arbitrary mappings so that they appear immune to various parameter manipulations, the introduction of phonological sub-regularities results in a system which is increasingly impervious to token manipulations of the input vocabulary. Frequency effects do not disappear, but instead are modulated by the internal structure of the sets of items that the network is required to process across learning.

CONCLUSIONS

This paper explored the "acquisition" of the English past tense by a 3 layer back-propagation network. Token frequency and phonological regularities crucially affect how well the network solved the problem, as well as the degree to which it "overgeneralized" identity markings and vowel changes in addition to making the standard suffixation error. In some simulations, it may be useful to describe performance (both correct and erroneous) as the result of a general strategy or "rule." However, within any given simulation, overgeneralization errors were rarely restricted to a single type and each verb class was susceptible to a relatively idiosyncratic set of error types. While the production of errors has been the focus here, several networks were indeed able to successfully "memorize" arbitrary forms at the same time that they were overgeneralizing regularities in the other three classes. Yet, the mechanism guiding this memorization was the "same" as that guiding the rule-like overgeneralization behavior.

The degree to which these results are analogous to the acquisition patterns of children is not as yet totally clear. Some analyses suggest that children's production repertoires reflect a variety of competing strategies which determine both correct and incorrect performance (Derwing & Baker, 1986; Marchman, 1988). Children, like these networks, are not likely to be exclusively suffix generalizers, or identity mappers, but will produce several different types of errors in generating past tense forms throughout acquisition. Rule-based models explicate this phenomenon via the competition between two (or more) discrete and explicitly represented hypotheses which, at various points in development, undergo changes in how and when they are likely to apply (see Pinker & Prince, 1988). In these networks, probabilistic differences between individual mapping strategies are a by-product of the learning process. Output fluctuations are the result of the implicit encoding of similarity relationships between the input stems in the weight matrix of the network. High token frequencies tended to "localize" the zones of interference of mapping types while high type frequencies tend to extend them. In addition, errors such as *ated* or *stooded* which blend two potential regularities in a single form were also observed. However, "blends" were relatively rare overall and predominated only in the vowel change class. Identity stems virtually never underwent blending. The introduction of phonological sub-regularities further restricted the occurrence of blending errors. These types of errors are also produced by children, yet they are much less frequent than the standard overgeneralization of "add -ed," and are likely to occur later in development. Further analysis is required to outline the developmental priority of "pure" over "blended" overgeneralizations in these networks.

Within certain limits, these networks sometimes behaved as if they were doing what we know children do when acquiring a morphological system. Classic patterns of overgeneralization were elicited (*without* introducing continuities into the learning set) by manipulating token frequency in networks in which phonological information *was and was not* available to define class membership. Clearly, our representation of the input conditions is far from adequate, and semantic information *must* play a role in the disambiguation of certain present tense/past tense mappings. However, the degree to which these systems behave in ways that are reminiscent of phenomena of acquisition reinforces the assumption that there is much to be gained from careful study of the nature and structure of input in the problem of language acquisition.

ACKNOWLEDGEMENTS

A more detailed description of this research is provided in Plunkett and Marchman (1989). The research was supported in part by grants from Center for Neurodevelopmental Studies at UCSD (NIH PHS NS22343), the Danish Humanities Research Council, and the Danish Technical Research committee. The authors sincerely thank the members of the Center for Research in Language and the PDP Natural Language Processing Discussion group at UCSD.

Table 1. Token frequencies and percent of items correctly produced after 50 sweeps.

SIM	ARBITRARY Token Freq.	ARBITRARY Par	ARBITRARY Phone	REGULAR Token Freq.	REGULAR Par	REGULAR Phone	IDENTITY Token Freq.	IDENTITY Par	IDENTITY Phone	VOWEL CHANGE Token Freq.	VOWEL CHANGE Par	VOWEL CHANGE Phone
1	1	0	0	1	96	94	1	15	50	1	0	3
2	5	0	0	1	92	89	1	10	40	1	5	1
3	10	100	0	1	96	93	1	0	65	1	0	0
4	15	50	100	1	96	90	1	15	40	1	3	1
5	15	50	100	1	50	69	1	20	35	5	82	88
6	20	100	100	1	93	92	1	5	60	1	0	6
7	40	100	100	1	90	92	1	15	65	1	3	6
8	145	100	100	1	87	90	1	10	60	1	3	10
9	15	50	100	1	77	76	1	40	40	2	22	31
10	15	100	50	1	84	88	5	75	95	1	6	13
11	15	100	50	1	82	86	14	100	100	1	6	6
16	15	100	50	1	74	83	16	100	100	1	6	4
17	15	50	50	1	65	71	5	70	100	3	28	62
18	20	100	100	1	59	67	1	30	40	5	72	88
19	20	100	50	1	82	79	1	25	35	2	18	44
20	20	100	100	1	88	87	5	80	100	1	5	7
21	20	100	100	1	82	88	14	100	100	1	2	4
26	20	100	50	1	76	83	16	100	100	1	3	7
27	20	100	100	1	60	73	5	70	100	3	37	57
Mean	--	79	68	--	80	83	--	46	70	--	16	23

(Column group heading: TYPE OF MAPPING)

Table 2: Distribution of Error Types in Parent Simulations

SIM	REGULAR Inap Suf	REGULAR Iden	REGULAR Inap Vow-S	REGULAR Blend	REGULAR Vow Chan	IDENTITY Suf	IDENTITY Inap Suf	IDENTITY Vow Chan	IDENTITY Inap Vow	VOWEL CHANGE Suf	VOWEL CHANGE Iden	VOWEL CHANGE Inap Vow-S	VOWEL CHANGE Inap Suf	VOWEL CHANGE Blend	VOWEL CHANGE Inap Vow
Par1	19	50	19	12		82	18			54	8	18	3	8	3
Par2	59	28		3		94		6		48	16	11	8	11	3
Par3	31	13	31	6		85	15			60	6	20	11	3	
Par4	27	20	27	13		74	21			63	10	14	3	8	2
Par5	18	61	17	2	12	63	6	6		55				18	9
Par6	41	11	30	4		95	5			63	9	13	2	8	5
Par7	50	28	11			82	18			51	10	25	3	5	2
Par8	58	25	6			100				48	10	22	6	6	
Par9	20	30	18	16	2	92		8		20	24	4	2	14	27
Par10	37	55	3	2		80	20			41	20	14	3	11	6
Par11	38	53	4							27	29	13	11	4	9
Par16	35	56	4	1						36	41	3	8	8	2
Par17	22	45	11	6	6	17	83			7	20	20		20	27
Par18	15	28	25	8	4	71			7		19			50	13
Par19	18	46	8	9		89	6	5		48	16	10	65	13	3
Par20	27	51	4	7		75	25			52	19	12	7	3	7
Par21	43	35	10	4						36	34	9	5	6	5
Par26	42	52	3		2					42	35	3	5	3	6
Par27	20	53	9	3	3	67	33			11	14	19		11	46
Mean	33	39	13	6	5	78	23	6	7	42	19	13	9	11	10
sd(σ)	13	15	9	4	3	19	20	1	0	16	10	6	15	10	12

(Column group heading: TYPE OF MAPPING; each mapping subdivided by ERROR TYPE)

Table 3: Distribution of Error Types in the Phone Simulations.

SIM	TYPE OF MAPPING														
	REGULAR					IDENTITY				VOWEL CHANGE					
	ERROR TYPE					ERROR TYPE				ERROR TYPE					
	Inap Suf	Iden	Inap Vow-S	Blend	Vow Chan	Suf	Inap Suf	Vow Chan	Inap Vow	Suf	Iden	Inap Vow-S	Inap Suf	Blend	Inap Vow
Phone1	27	50	9	9			100			33	14	12	9	20	3
Phone2	28	61	4	7		100				28	22	2	9	18	6
Phone3	11	44	15	7		100				30	18	12	6	14	6
Phone4	35	51	8	3		92			8	39	15	14	3	17	4
Phone5	13	33	17	6	8	33	8	17	25					33	50
Phone6	23	57	7	3		87			13	35	8	11	11	20	9
Phone7	13	59	13	6		100				34	25	11	8	8	9
Phone8	11	53	26	5		86	14			42	12	7	3	15	13
Phone9	32	46	8	4	2	92				9	27		7	24	24
Phone10	4	83	2	2		100				22	10	12	14	14	19
Phone11	7	54	15	7						15	18	14	12	23	8
Phone16	21	56	15	2						21	11	9	9	26	10
Phone17	16	45	16	6	4						18		5	23	45
Phone18	10	34	14	11	13	50		10	30		50		33	17	
Phone19	20	34	14	4	5	85	15			14	17	3	3	14	39
Phone20	11	70	4	4	6					48	16	6	3	19	3
Phone21	8	71	4	6	8					34	25	9	5	17	5
Phone26	13	81	3	1						29	32	5	15	5	8
Phone27	14	46	13	3	9					4	29	11		25	14
Mean	**16**	**54**	**11**	**5**	**7**	**84**	**34**	**14**	**19**	**27**	**20**	**9**	**9**	**19**	**15**
sd(σ)	**9**	**14**	**6**	**3**	**3**	**22**	**44**	**5**	**10**	**12**	**10**	**4**	**7**	**6**	**15**

The error categories presented in Tables 2 and 3 are to be interpreted as follows:

Regular Errors

Inap Suf The Stem is suffixized but with the wrong suffix.

Iden The stem is treated as an identity stem.

Inap Vow-S The stem is appropriately suffixized but undergoes an illegal vowel transformation.

Blend The stem is appropriately suffixized but undergoes a legal transformation.

Vow Chan The stem is treated as though it were a vowel change stem.

Identity Errors

Suf The stem is treated as a regular stem.

Inap Suf The stem is treated as a regular stem but inappropriately suffixized.

Vow Chan The stem is treated as though it were a vowel change stem.

Inap Vow The vowel change transformation is inappropriate though may or may not be "illegal".

Vowel Change Errors

Suf The stem is treated as a regular stem.

Iden The stem is treated as an identity stem.

Inap Vow-S The stem is transformed as though it were a vowel change but the vowel change is "illegal". The stem is appropriately suffixized.

Inap Suf The stem is treated as though it were a regular but inappropriately suffixized.

Blend The stem undergoes a legal vowel change but is also appropriately suffixized.

Inap Vow The vowel change transformation is inappropriate though may or may not be "illegal".

REFERENCES

Berko, J. (1958). The child's learning of English morphology. *Word, 14,* 150-177.

Bever, T. G. (in press). The demons and the beast -- Modular and nodular kinds of knowledge. To appear in C. Georgopoulos & R. Ishihara (Eds.), *Interdisciplinary approaches to language: Essays in honor of S-Y. Kuroda.* Kluwer: Dordrecht.

Borer, H. & Wexler, K. (1987). The maturation of syntax. In T. Roeper and E. Williams (Eds.), *Parameter Setting.* Dordrecht, Holland: Reidel.

Bowerman, M. (1982). Reorganizational process in lexical and syntactic development. In E. Wanner & L. Gleitman (Eds.) *Language Acquisition: The State of the Art.* Cambridge: Cambridge University Press.

Bybee, J. & Slobin, D. I. (1982). Rules and schemas in the development and use of the English past tense. *Language, 58,* 265-289.

Chomsky, N. (1980). Rules and Representations. *Behavior and Brain Sciences, 3,* 1-61.

Derwing, B. L. & Baker, W. J. (1986). Assessing morphological development. In P. Fletcher & M. Garman (Eds.), *Language acquisition: Studies in first language development.* Second edition. Cambridge: Cambridge University Press.

Derwing, B. L., & Skousen, R. (1989). Real-time morphology: Symbolic rules or analogical networks. Proceedings of the 15th Annual meeting of the Berkeley Linguistics Society, Berkeley, CA. February.

Fodor, J. & Pylyshyn, Z. (1988). Connectionism and cognitive architecture: A critical analysis. *Cognition, 28,* 3-71.

Kuczaj, S. (1977). The acquisition of regular and irregular past tense verbs. *Journal of Verbal Learning and Verbal Behavior, 16,* 589-600.

MacWhinney, B. (1987). The competition model. In B. MacWhinney (Ed.), *Mechanisms of language acquisition.* Hillsdale, N.J.: Erlbaum.

Marchman, V. (1984). Learning not to overgeneralize. *Papers and reports on child language development, 24,* 69-74.

Marchman, V. (1988). Rules and regularities in the acquisition of the English past tense. *Center for Research on Language Newsletter, 2(4),* April, 1988.

Pinker, S. (1984). *Language learnability and language development.* Cambridge, MA: Harvard University Press.

Pinker, S. & Mehler, J. (Eds.) (1988). *Connections and Symbols.* Cambridge, MA: MIT Press.

Pinker, S. & Prince, A. (1988). On Language and Connectionism: Analysis of a parallel distributed processing model of language acquisition. *Cognition, 28,* 59-108.

Plunkett, K., & Marchman, V. (1989). Pattern association in a back propagation network: Implications for Child Language Acquisition. Technical Report #8902. Center for Research in Language, University of California, San Diego.

Rumelhart, D. E. & McClelland, J.L. (1986). On learning the past tense of English verbs. In D.E. Rumelhart & J.L. McClelland & the PDP Research Group, *Parallel distributed processing: Explorations in the microstructure of cognition. Volume 2.* Cambridge, MA: Bradford Books.

Rumelhart, D. E. & McClelland, J. L. (1987). Learning the past tenses of English verbs: Implicit rules or parallel distributed processing. In B. MacWhinney (Ed.), *Mechanisms of Language Acquisition.* Hillsdale, N.J.: Erlbaum.

Smolensky, P. (1988). The constituent structure of connectionist mental states: A reply to Fodor & Pylshyn. Technical Report, Department of Computer Science, University of Colorado, Boulder, CO.

Towards a Connectionist Phonology: The "Many Maps" Approach to Sequence Manipulation

David S. Touretzky

School of Computer Science
Carnegie Mellon University
Pittsburgh, PA 15213

Abstract: Lakoff's new theory of cognitive phonology appears to be free of the rule ordering constraints that make generative rules computationally awkward. It uses a multilevel representation for utterances, to which multiple rules may apply in parallel. This paper presents the first implementation of Lakoff's proposal, based on a novel "many maps" architecture. The architecture may also explain certain constraints on phonological rules that are not adequately accounted for by more abstract models.

Linguists established long ago the value of describing phonological processes in terms of formal symbolic rules, but they have steadfastly refrained from speculating about the nature of representations in speakers' heads. Rumelhart and McClelland (1986) argue against the neuropsychological reality of rules. Pinker and Prince (1988) offer persuasive counterarguments. The current reaction against rule-based accounts of low-level cognitive phenomena, phonology in particular, is no doubt strengthened by the computational awkwardness of classical generative phonological rules. Constraints on their order of application force the rules to act sequentially and, in some cases, cyclically. In contrast, Rumelhart and McClelland's PDP model of the phonology of English past tense formation maps input patterns to output patterns directly, in one parallel step. It is, despite its weaknesses, computationally sleek.

In 1988 George Lakoff published a new theory of "cognitive phonology" in which parallel rules apply everywhere simultaneously (Lakoff, 1988a, 1988b). Cognitive phonology is therefore free of the cycles and rule ordering constraints that mar earlier, generative theories. Lakoff described his theory as founded on connectionist principles, but did not specify how it should be implemented. The solution is non-obvious, because cognitive phonology relies on a multi-level mapping representation in which insertions, deletions, and mutations all take place at once.

This paper presents the first working implementation of Lakoff's theory. It uses a novel "many maps" architecture to manipulate sequences of phonemes at multiple levels, and to support abstractions such as the "vowel tier" required by some rules. I will begin by reviewing Lakoff's analysis of a Mohawk problem posed in (Halle & Clements, 1983), and then show how the "many maps" model implements Lakoff's solution. Finally I address the question of why one would want to have rules in a connectionist model. I will argue that the simplicity and highly constrained nature of phonology may be a consequence of humans' using a sequence manipulation architecture similar to the one described here.

Six Rules for Mohawk Speakers

Halle and Clements give six generative rules for deriving the Mohawk word /yɔ́krege?/. ("I will push it") from its underlying form /ye + Λ̃k + hrek + ?/. (It may aid understanding to look at Lakoff's solution first; see Figure 1.) We will consider four of these rules here:

Epenthesis: ∅ --> e / C _ ? #
Stress: V --> [+stress] / _ C_0 V C_0 #
Vowel omission: V --> ∅ / _ + V
Intervocalic voicing: C --> [+voice] / V _ V

The epenthesis rule inserts /e/ between a consonant (/k/ in this example) and a word-final glottal stop /?/. The stress rule assigns stress to the penultimate vowel in a word. Notice that in the example /Λ̄/ is penultimate in underlying form but antepenultimate at the surface, due to epenthesis. Thus, the stress assignment rule must be applied prior to epenthesis in order to stress the correct vowel. The intervocalic voicing rule voices a consonant if it appears between two vowels; it changes /eke/ to /ege/. But the second /e/ was inserted by epenthesis; therefore intervocalic voicing must not be applied until after epenthesis. The vowel omission rule deletes the leftmost /e/ in the underlying form, since it precedes another vowel. Evidence from other Mohawk words shows that vowel omission applies before stress assignment. (If it didn't, the rules could perhaps assign stress to a vowel and then delete it, leaving no vowel stressed.)

In the classical account these four rules are totally ordered: vowel omission precedes stress assignment, which precedes epenthesis, which precedes intervocalic voicing. Each of these rewrite rules modifies the "current" derivation, producing a new one. When all the rules have applied, what's left is the surface form of the word.

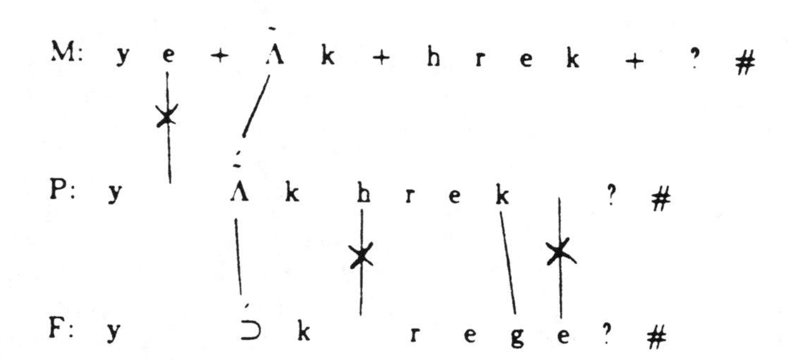

Figure 1: Lakoff's cognitive phonology derivation of the Mohawk word "I will push it."

Lakoff's analysis replaces the sequential rewrite rules with mapping constraints that all apply in parallel. There are three levels of representation: M (morphemic), P (phonemic), and F (phonetic). Sequences at M level are by default simply copied to P level. But M-P constraints can alter the mapping, causing changes in the P-level representation. Intra-level constraints may also affect the representation at P level. The combined effect of M-P and P-level constraints can be seen in the middle line of Figure 1: the first /e/ has been deleted and the penultimate vowel has been stressed. A second mapping takes P-level representations to F-level representations via a combination of P-F and F constraints. At F level we see that the epenthetic /e/ has been inserted and, consequently, the /k/ has been voiced.

Lakoff's solution elegantly answers a number of phonological questions which, unfortunately, we cannot afford to raise here. Elegance aside, though, its implementation in connectionist hardware is problematic. The major problems that arise are: how to efficiently implement insertion, deletion, and mutation operations when several occur in parallel; how associations between corresponding segments at different levels can be maintained, since levels may have varying numbers of elements; and how rules can apply everywhere at once in the input buffer. The "many maps" architecture provides solutions to these problems.

How to Build a Map

As a prelude to discussing the full "many maps" implementation I will describe the workings of a single map. Figure 2 shows the P-level map in the context of the Mohawk example. The input to this map comes from two buffers: M-level and P-deriv (P derivation). The output is the P-level representation of the utterance. The M-level buffer, which is read-only, contains the underlying form of the utterance. Segments are shifted into the buffer from the right, and discarded when they reach the left edge. M-level segments are by default mapped to identical segments at P-level. However, each M-level segment has a slot in P-deriv for describing changes that can be made to it if some rule requests. Three types of changes are supported: mutation, deletion, and insertion. Deletion of an M-level segment means blocking its appearance at P-level. Mutation maps the segment to a segment with slightly different features at P-level. Insertion causes a new segment to appear at P-level to the right of the M-level segment. (Insertion to the left could also be supported, but was omitted to simplify the simulation.) In the figure, the M-level /e/ is marked in P-deriv for deletion, and the /ʌ̃/ is to be mutated by adding stress. Thus the M-level sequence /yeʌ̃k/ appears as /yʌ̃́k/ at P-level.

The upper-diagonal matrix in the figure represents an array of connectionist mapping units. When one of these units is active (shown by a segment appearing inside it), the segment in that input column is copied to the corresponding output row. At the same time, any mutations to the segment that were requested in P-deriv are made.

The units in the mapping matrix are subject to lateral inhibition. At most one unit can be on in each row and each column. The inhibition is asymmetric, so that when choosing which row an input segment should map to, the model prefers to fill higher rows first. In addition, when choosing which segment should appear in a row, the model prefers to select the rightmost segment available. This ensures that the ordering of M-level segments is preserved at P-level, and that the P-level representation always appears right-justified in the buffer with no gaps where M-level segments are deleted, and no collisions where new segments are inserted.

Consider first the fate of the M-level /k/. The active square in the first row of the matrix shows that this segment is mapped to the rightmost position in the P-level buffer. Since this unit is fully active, no other unit can come on in that row or in that column. The /ʌ̃/ is mapped to the second row; simultaneously it is stressed, as specified in the mutation part of P-deriv. The /e/ is marked for deletion in P-deriv. Deletion is accomplished by inhibiting all the units in that column of the matrix, thereby preventing the segment from mapping to any row of P level. Thus the /y/, which is the fourth M-level segment counting from the right, appears as the third segment at P-level. The M-P mapping is computed in parallel (in fact, in constant time), independent of the number of segments in the buffer or the number of insertions and deletions to be performed.

Note that M-level segments are positioned over every other mapping column. The intervening columns are reserved for insertions. If an insertion is specified in P-deriv, the segment to be inserted will be mapped to the next available row, just as an M-level segment would be.

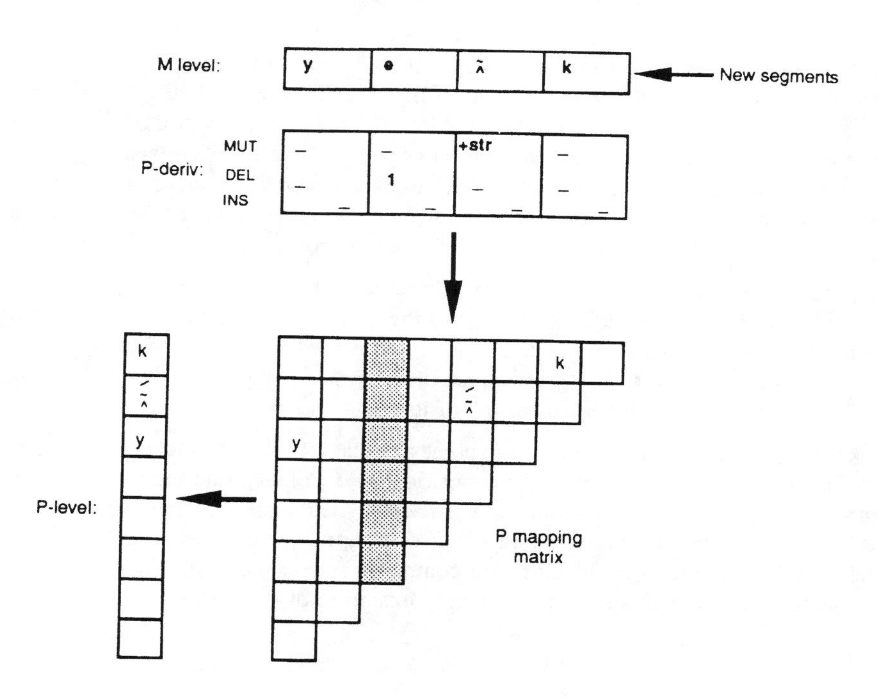

Figure 2: The map that derives P-level representations.

How Rules Work

One of the strengths of cognitive phonology is that rules may locate their environments at one level and their actions at another. Thus the application of an M-P rule does not affect the environments of other M-P rules. It does, however, affect the environments of P and P-F rules.

M-P rules are implemented by connectionist units that take their inputs from the M-level buffer and have output connections to P-deriv. After a new segment is shifted into M-level, M-P rules may cause some P-deriv units to change state, thereby recording a change the rules wish to make in the mapping. P-deriv units maintain their states indefinitely unless disturbed by rule units, thereby serving as a memory of accumulated changes. Each time P-deriv is modified by some M-P rule, the mapping matrix re-derives the P-level representation from the M-level and P-deriv buffers. When the M-level buffer is shifted left to accomodate the next incoming segment, the contents of P-deriv are also shifted left to maintain registration with the M level.

Pure P-level rules are trickier to implement than M-P rules, because they take their inputs from the *output* of the mapper. For example, suppose a purely P-level rule wanted to devoice the /y/ in Figure 2. This segment appears at position three at P level, but it is in position four at M level due to the deletion of a preceding segment. In order for P-level rules to record their changes in the correct P-deriv segment, they must invert the M-P mapping to align their changes with the M-level segments. The circuitry for this is straightforward. The state of the mapping matrix used to produce the current P-level representation provides the necessary information to invert the map.

Since P rules apply to their own outputs, they can feed each other, and there is even a possibility of long rule chains. Here is a simple example. In this implementation of Lakoff's Mohawk solution, epenthesis and intervocalic voicing are both implemented as F-level rules. Even though the rules are unordered, the former feeds the latter, so they will have to fire sequentially. The existence of rule chains appears to prevent the sort of parallel processing that cognitive phonology strives for. However, chunking can be used to automatically collapse a chain of intra-level rules into one complex rule, and thus regain the parallelism. This has been demonstrated for abstract phonological rules in (Touretzky, 1989).

Rules cannot be tied to fixed buffer positions because of feeding relationships. Suppose the intervocalic voicing rule were aligned with the right edge of the buffer, i.e., it looked at the rightmost three segments. When it saw /eke/ it would produce /ege/. But if the buffer initially holds /ek?/, epenthesis will produce /eke?/, and so the first appearance of the /eke/ fragment will not be aligned with the right edge of the buffer. It will be "downstream" of its standard position.

To make rules position-independent, we hypothesize that all rules are independently motivated and hence can be learned in standard (right-aligned) position by a primary rule module. Secondary rule modules are introduced at successive positions downstream. Their input and output connections are forced by link equality constraints to mimic the behavior of the primary module. All the rule modules operate in parallel, and their requests for changes are combined and recorded in P-deriv. In this way we achieve position-independence without having to supply examples of every rule firing in every position.

The "Many Maps" Architecture

At a minimum, cognitive phonology requires two maps: one for P-level representations and one for F-level. The F-level map is similar to the P-level discussed above, except it takes input from three buffers: M-level, P-deriv, and F-deriv. F-level representations are derived directly from M-level by merging the P-deriv and F-deriv changes at the input to the F mapping matrix. In the case of conflict, F-deriv changes are given priority. See Figure 3. This approach allows the model's multiple maps to operate independently instead of increasing the latency with each new level of representation. (This idea is due to Gillette Elvgren.)

Two types of rules influence the contents of F level. P-F rules have their environments at P and their actions at F; their actions are recorded in F-deriv by first inverting the mapping specified by the P matrix to align them properly with M-level segments. (The M-level segments and P-deriv and F-deriv changes are all kept in strict registration.) Since F-level rules have their environment at F, their actions are recorded in F-deriv by inverting the mapping specified by the F matrix. Figure 4 shows the relationships between the various rule types.

In Mohawk, the stress rule is most easily implemented by placing its environment at yet another level: a P-level vowel tier containing only vowels and word boundary markers. This allows the stress rule to look for the pattern VV# in the vowel tier and stress the penultimate vowel. (This solution was suggested by Deirdre Wheeler. Other evidence for an independent vowel tier is cited in (Goldsmith, 1989).) The map that extracts the P vowel tier takes inputs from the same M-level and P-deriv buffers as the regular P-level map, but only vowels appear in its output; consonants are left unmapped. The P vowel tier map operates completely in parallel with the regular P-level map.

We have successfully applied the "many maps" architecture to additional examples Lakoff chose from Slovak, Gidabal, and Lardil. Other languages will require other specialized maps. We expect, though,

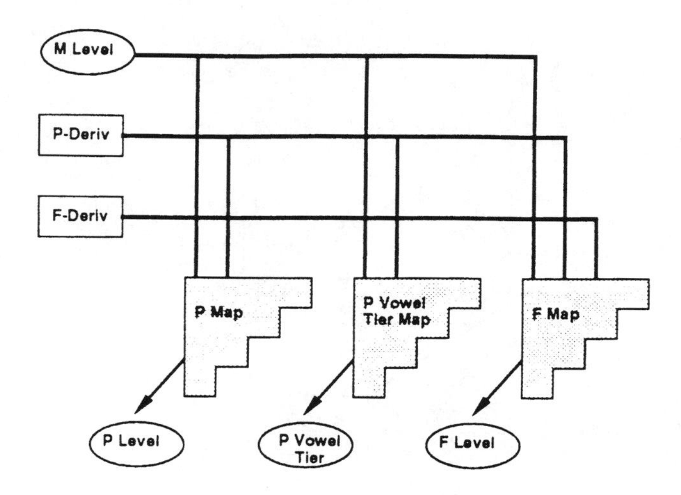

Figure 3: Inputs and outputs of the P-level, F-level, and P-vowel-tier maps. All maps operate independently, and in parallel.

that these can all be built from similar hardware. Perhaps language learners are born with a collection of such maps at their disposal, which are then trained to extract whatever features are salient in the linguistic environment.

Discussion

Phonology continues to be a rich and promising domain for connectionist investigations of language. It is simpler and less plagued by the special cases and exceptions that complicate syntax and morphology, so there is a better chance of finding a complete solution. Another advantage of phonology is its quasi-linear structure, which facilitates experimentation with parallel distributed processing techniques. The PDP approach isn't currently as well suited to manipulating hierarchical structures such as syntactic trees.[1]

The present model is not without limitations. It deals only with segmental phonology; no attempt is made to include morphology. (In contrast, the Rumelhart and McClelland verb learning model combines morphological and phonological processing in a single layer of weights.) Also, currently the model does not represent syllable structure. Certain types of phonological rules therefore cannot be expressed. This is an area where further work is in order.

The mapping architecture does not permit more than one segment to be inserted between segments adjacent at the previous level. Morphology sometimes requires multi-segment insertions, but it appears that phonology does not. If this observation holds true, it is a significant constraint on phonological machinery. The model provides an achitectural explanation for it, unlike more abstract phonological models which ignore implementation issues. Finally, the mapping matrix does not support metathesis (switching of segments) as a primitive operation. Considering the controversial and still unresolved status of metathesis in linguistic theory, we are in no rush to add it.

[1]However, Touretzky (1986), Hinton (1988), and Pollack (1988) offer some hope for handling hierarchical structures.

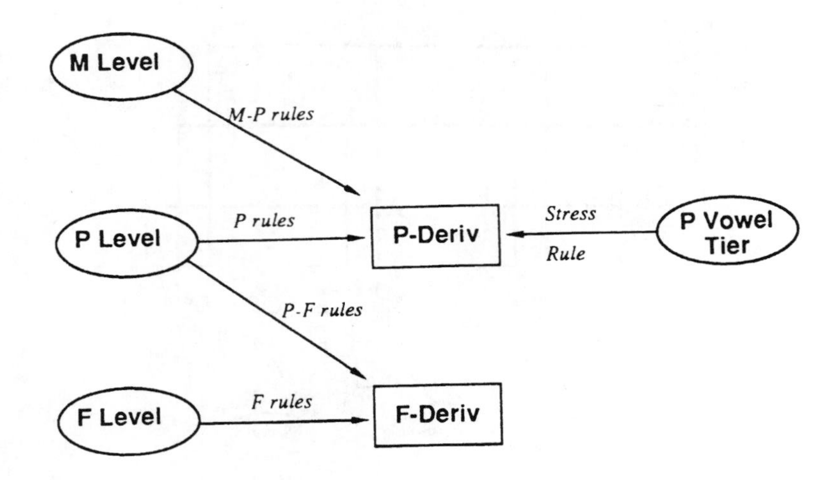

Figure 4: The different types of cognitive phonology rules that relate representations at various levels.

The "many maps" model might be improved by switching to an autosegmental representation with separate phonemic, skeletal, and tonal tiers, as in (Goldsmith, 1989). In fact, the original inspiration for the mapping matrix came from wondering how inter-tier association lines in autosegmental phonology could be represented in a connectionist network. A mapping matrix representation seems particularly appropriate for inter-tier rules, such as the tone-shift rules Goldsmith describes in various Bantu languages.

On the Reality of Rules

Why should human phonology be so regular and tightly constrained? It is amazing that this level of language can be described by classical generative rules which affect only a single segment each. This mode of description is effective, but it remains computationally inelegant. On the other hand, as Pinker and Prince point out, a connectionist architecture that directly maps input sequences to output sequences can perform outlandish transformations never seen in human language, such as reversing all the phonemes of a word.

There appear to be more modest sorts of transforms that are absent from the human repertoire. For example, no language methathesizes non-adjacent segments. Consonants are never changed to vowels, and vice versa. And harmony and assimilation phenomena always spread features from one edge of a cluster to the other, never from the interior outward. To be successful, a connectionist theory of phonology should motivate these constraints by providing computational explanations for them.

We can begin to account for constraints on phonology by adopting a universal, genetically-specified sequence manipulation machine that, like the "many maps" model, operates in parallel but can perform only a limited set of transformations. The function of linguistic rules is to operate this machine — to "press the right buttons at the right times." A speaker's linguistic knowledge does not directly modify sound sequences as in the Rumelhart and McClelland model; it modifies sequences only indirectly, by controlling this built-in machinery.

An input representation plus a discrete set of symbol manipulation primitives defines a *rule system*. If such a system underlies human phonology, then even if speakers do not have symbolic rule representations in their heads, they truly do use rules, as opposed to merely saying their behavior can be described by rules. Classical phonology concerns itself with the regularities of this rule system. Connectionist phonology attempts to ground the system in the design of the sequence manipulation machine, for it is from there that the rule system emerges.

Acknowledgements

I am most grateful to George Lakoff for sharing his work on cognitive phonology with me, and for taking the time to answer so many questions. I also thank Deirdre Wheeler for stimulating conversations, and for the linguistic guidance she has provided during our weekly meetings. Gillette Elvgren programmed the Mohawk simulation, and has made valuable refinements to the mapping architecture.

This work was sponsored by a contract from Hughes Research Laboratories, by National Science Foundation grant EET-8716324, and by the Office of Naval Research under contract number N00014-86-K-0678.

References

Goldsmith, J. (1989) *Autosegmental and Metrical Phonology: A New Synthesis*. Basil Blackwell.

Halle, M., & Clements, G. N. (1983) *Problem Book in Phonology*. MIT Press.

Hinton, G. E. (1988) Representing part-whole hierarchies in connectionist networks. *Proceedings of the Tenth Annual Conference of the Cognitive Science Society*, pp. 48-54.

Lakoff, G. (1988a) A suggestion for a linguistics with connectionist foundations. In D. Touretzky, G. Hinton, and T. Sejnowski (eds.), *Proceedings of the 1988 Connectionist Models Summer School*. Morgan Kaufmann Publishers.

Lakoff, G. (1988b) Cognitive phonology. Manuscript draft; presented at the LSA annual meeting.

Pinker, S., & Prince, A. (1988) On language and connectionism: analysis of a parallel distributed processing model of language acquisition. In S. Pinker & J. Mehler (eds.), *Connections and Symbols*. MIT Press.

Pollack, J. (1988) Recursive auto-associative memory: devising compositional distributed represesnations. *Proceedings of the Tenth Annual Conference of the Cognitive Science Society*, pp. 33-39

Rumelhart, D. E., & McClelland, J. L. (1986) On learning the past tenses of English verbs. In J. L. McClelland & D. E. Rumelhart (eds.), *Parallel Distributed Processing: Explorations in the Microstructure of Cognition*. MIT Press.

Touretzky, D. S. (1986) BoltzCONS: reconciling connectionism with the recursive nature of stacks and trees. *Proceedings of the Eighth Annual Conference of the Cognitive Science Society*, pp. 522-530.

Touretzky, D. S. (1989) Chunking in a connectionist network. *Proceedings of the Eleventh Annual Conference of the Cognitive Science Society*. Lawrence Erlbaum Associates.

A Connectionist Model of Form-related Priming Effects

Robert R. Peterson, Gary S. Dell, Padraig G. O'Seaghdha
University of Rochester

Abstract

In contrast to the results of many previous studies, Colombo (1986) has demonstrated that form-related priming is sometimes inhibitory. Colombo proposed that inhibition reflects the suppression of lexical items orthographically related to the prime. We suggest, however, that form-related inhibition arises as a result of competition between discrepant prime-target phonemes. During the phonological encoding of the target word, active phonemes from the prime might be mistakenly selected, causing a delay in responding. We present a connectionist model that implements this account, and simulates the empirical data. The model is supported by the results of an experiment that distinguishes between the lexical suppression and phonological competition views.

INTRODUCTION

It has often been demonstrated that the processing of a word can be facilitated by the prior presentation of a formally related word. For example, Meyer, Schvaneveldt, and Ruddy (1974) found shorter lexical decision latencies to words following phonologically and orthographically similar primes (e.g., BRIBE-TRIBE) than to targets following unrelated primes (e.g., FENCE-TRIBE). Recently, however, Colombo (1986) has demonstrated that form-related primes can inhibit responses to high frequency targets. The present paper focusses on the inhibition found by Colombo and her theoretical explanation for the effect. We will suggest an alternative explanation for the inhibition, and will present a connectionist model that accounts for the Colombo data.

The Colombo View: Word-level Inhibition

Colombo suggested that when a prime word is presented, it raises the activation level of a set of letter detectors, and subsequently activates a set of word nodes that are at least partially consistent with those letters. This process results in heightened activation for words orthographically consistent with the prime, and therefore facilitates the recognition of those words. To explain the inhibition found for high frequency targets, Colombo assumes that orthographically similar lexical items inhibit one another, but that this inhibition occurs only for nodes that are highly activated. That is, Colombo argues that lexical nodes have an *inhibition threshold*, and become susceptible to inhibitory influences only when their total activation surpasses this threshold level. Since high frequency words have relatively high resting levels of activation, they quickly surpass their inhibition thresholds. Low frequency words, however, start at such a low level of activation that they never reach their inhibition thresholds. Overall, then, low frequency words receive primarily letter-to-word facilitation, while high frequency words receive initial facilitation followed by word-to-word suppression.

An Alternative View: Phonological Competition

We agree with Colombo's claim that facilitation can arise as a result of activation spreading to lexical nodes that share letters with the prime. We disagree, however, with her explanation of form-related inhibition. While Colombo assumes that inhibition occurs at the lexical level, we argue that it arises at the phonological level instead, resulting from competition between discrepant phonemes of the prime and target. According to our view, it is difficult to respond to the word MAN following the prime FAN, not because the lexical item MAN is inhibited, but rather because the phoneme M in MAN must compete with the already activated F of FAN. Since the presentation of the word MAN will tend to activate the lexical node FAN (due to the shared letters), the F phoneme will be initially quite active, creating the possibility that the F rather than the M phoneme will be selected during the phonological encoding of MAN.

If inhibition is indeed caused by competition at a phonological level, why should the effect appear only with high frequency targets? This effect is likely due to the fact that high frequency words are recognized very quickly. This rapidity in recognition has two consequences, both of which accentuate inhibition. The first consequence is that a high frequency target is likely to get little facilitation from orthographic overlap with the prime, since the baseline recognition rate for the target is already so quick. Therefore, if an inhibitory process exists, it will not be washed out by concurrent facilitative processes.

A fast recognition rate also means that phonological encoding will occur more quickly for high than for low frequency words. Thus, for high frequency targets, selection of the target's component phonemes will occur when the prime's phonemes might still be active, thereby increasing the probability that a phoneme from the prime will be mistakenly selected. Recovering from such an error is likely to be time-consuming, and therefore will lead to an overall inhibition effect. In contrast, the selection problem will be less troublesome for low frequency words, since these words are recognized fairly slowly, allowing activation of the prime's phonemes to decay before selection of the target's phonemes occurs.

We make the following specific assumptions regarding phoneme selection. Retrieval of a lexical item makes available information pertaining to the general phonological form of the word. This information might be represented as an abstract frame which specifies the number, type, and order of the phonemes in the word, as well as the word's syllabic structure and stress pattern (Brown & McNeill, 1966; Dell, 1988; Stemberger, in press). The frame can be thought of as containing slots for each of its phonemes, with the slots being filled by selecting from among activated phonological nodes. For example, retrieval of the word MAN might activate a CVC frame, which specifies that three phonemes are to be retrieved: an initial consonant, a medial vowel, and a final consonant. In our model, high frequency words make their frames available more quickly than do low frequency words, and thus attempt to link phonemes to the frames at an earlier point in processing.

Thus, on our view, there are two qualitatively different effects that a prime word has on an orthographically and phonologically similar target word. First, there is facilitation at the lexical level, due to the activation of words sharing letters with the prime. Second, there is confusion at the phonological level over the incompatible phonemes of the prime and target. This confusion is only problematic, however, if an attempt is made to select the target's phonemes while the prime's phonemes are highly activated. Form-related priming can be seen, therefore, as facilitating lexical retrieval, but potentially interfering with the specification of a word's complete phonological form. We have implemented these ideas within a connectionist framework, and the remainder of this paper is a presentation of our model.

THE PHONOLOGICAL COMPETITION MODEL

Components of the Model

The model is made up of three distinct levels of representation: *letters*, *words*, and *phonemes* (see Figure 1). A node at the letter level corresponds to a given letter in a specific word position. The model has been constructed to process 3-letter words only, so there are three nodes for each letter. Likewise, each node at the phoneme level stands for a given phoneme in a particular word position. All of the words in the model are made up of three phonemes, so a given phoneme is represented three times, once for each word position. For both phoneme and letter nodes, the resting level of activation was set at 0.

A node at the word level corresponds to a single word. In the implementation described here, the model was provided with six words: *CAT*, *CAP*, *CAD*, *PEG*, *PEN*, and *PEZ*. The words *CAT* and *PEG* served as related and unrelated prime words, respectively. *CAP* and *CAD* were the critical target items, with *CAP* serving a high frequency target and *CAD* as a low frequency target. The lexical items *PEN* and *PEZ* were included so that related and unrelated primes would have equivalent lexical neighborhoods. *PEN*, like *CAP*, is a high frequency word, and *PEZ*, like *CAD* is a low frequency word. The resting levels were set at 0 for high frequency words, and -50 for low frequency words. The primes (*CAT* and *PEG*) were given an intermediate resting level of -25.[1]

[1]Our assignment of frequency levels to each of the six words does not necessarily correspond to those words' actual frequencies in the language. Our purpose was simply to create high and low frequency lexical nodes that share letters and phonemes. The particular words that we chose to use can best be thought of as convenient labels for these nodes, and hence the actual characteristics of these words in the language is largely irrelevant to our endeavors.

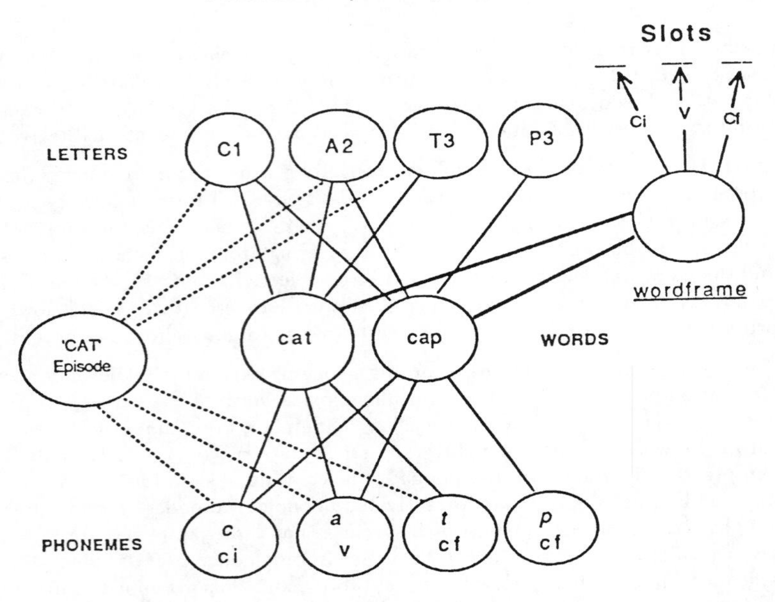

FIGURE 1. Structure of the Model

Connections

There are both excitatory and inhibitory connections in the model. All connections are between nodes at adjacent levels. Word nodes have excitatory connections to their corresponding letter and phoneme nodes (weight = .03). Letter nodes have excitatory connections to words that contain them (weight = .03), and inhibitory connections to other words (weight = .04). Phoneme nodes have excitatory connections to their corresponding words (weight = .03), but no inhibitory connections.

Activation Function

The activation level of a node, at any particular time, is determined by three factors: the node's activation level at the previous timestep, activation received from other nodes during the current timestep, and activation lost during the current timestep due to decay.

The activation received from other nodes is determined according to Equation 1:

$$n_i(t) = \sum_j \alpha_{ij} e_j(t) - \sum_k \gamma_{ik} i_k(t) \tag{1}$$

where $n_i(t)$ is the current input to a node, $e_j(t)$ is the activation of an excitatory neighbor of the node, and $i_k(t)$ is the activation of an inhibitory neighbor of the node. α_{ij} and γ_{ik} are weight constants for excitatory and inhibitory links, respectively.

The amount of decay during a timestep is given in Equation 2:

$$d_i(t) = \Theta_i(a_i(t) - r_i) \tag{2}$$

where $d_i(t)$ is the amount of decay for the node, Θ_i is a constant decay rate (.09 in the present model), $a_i(t)$ is the node's current level of activation, and r_i is the node's resting level of activation. Thus, the amount of decay is proportional to a node's activation relative to its resting level.

The activation of a node at time $t + \Delta t$ is equal, then, to the activation of the node at time t plus the input from other nodes at time t, minus the node's decay. This is expressed mathematically in

Equation 3.

$$a_i(t + \Delta t) = a_i(t) + n_i(t) - d_i(t) \tag{3}$$

There are two important qualifications to Equation 3. First, activation can never go below a node's resting level. Second, we set a maximum level of activation (300) for all the nodes. The output of a node is equal to its activation level if that level is positive. If the node's potential is less than 0, however, the node sends no output.

Episodic Node

In the model, there is an episodic node which operates slightly differently than the rest of the nodes discussed above. The episodic node resides at the lexical level, has a resting level of 0, and has a decay rate of 1.0. During the course of a priming trial, the episodic node establishes connections with the letter and phoneme nodes of the prime, and thereby establishes an episodic memory of the processing of that prime. The actual functioning of the episodic node is described more fully in the next section.

How the Model Works

The model is intended to simulate a priming paradigm, in which a prime word is presented for a certain amount of time and is immediately followed by the presentation of a target word. Prime presentation is simulated by setting the activation level of each of the prime's letter nodes to 300 (their maximum activation). The model is then run for 20 timesteps. The activation of the prime's letter nodes remains fixed at a value of 300 for the entire 20 steps. During these steps, activation spreads throughout the model (from letters to words, from words to both phonemes and letters, and from phonemes to words). The word node corresponding to the prime gets highly activated, primarily due to inputs from its three letter nodes. Orthographically similar words also become active, although to a much lesser extent. These nodes receive excitatory input from the two consistent letter nodes, but receive inhibitory input from the inconsistent third letter.

Following the presentation of the prime, links are created from the prime's letter nodes to the episodic node (weight = .10), and from the episodic node to the prime's phoneme nodes (weight = .015). The episodic node, therefore, is a generic node that is recruited by the model to bind together patterns of activation at the letter and phonological levels. This bound configuration constitutes the model's episodic memory of the prime.

Following the establishment of the episodic links, the presentation of the target is simulated by setting the target's letter nodes to the maximum value of 300. The activation levels of all other letter nodes are set to 0. The model is then run until the target's lexical node reaches its maximum level of activation. Activation spreads through the model in the manner described above for the processing of the prime, with the exception that there are now episodic links active in the model. If the target shares letters with the prime, it will tend to activate the episodic node, which in turn will send activation to the prime's phonemes. Thus, the presentation of an orthographically related target word in effect *reminds* the model of its recent experience with the prime, and causes it to re-create the corresponding phonological representation.

Making Responses

In an actual priming experiment, a subject would be required to make some response to the target. We estimated the model's response time based on Equation 4:

$$RT = \beta l_i + \psi(1 - p(R_i, t)) + \kappa \tag{4}$$

The term βl_i is a measure of lexical access time, with l_i being the number of timesteps required for the target's lexical node to reach its maximum potential and β being a constant specifying the duration of one timestep (5 msec). The component $\psi(1 - p(R_i, t))$ is an estimate of the processing time that is incurred when there is an incorrect selection of the target's critical phoneme. The critical phoneme is the one that is unique to the target, in related prime-target pairs. For example, in the prime-target pair, *CAT-CAD*, the *D* in *CAD* is critical. The probability of correctly selecting the critical phoneme ($p(R_i, t)$ in Equation 4) depends on its activation relative to the activation levels of other phonemes at the same word position. This probability was determined in the same way as in McClelland and Rumelhart (1981), except that it was based on the activation at a single timestep (i.e., the step at which the target's lexical node reached threshold), rather than being based on a running average of a node's activation over time. The probability, then, that an incorrect phoneme is selected is given by $(1 - p(R_i, t))$. The amount of time that is associated with an incorrect selection is given by the constant ψ (set to 150 msec). Finally, κ is a constant (set to 450 msec) which reflects the time required for all of the processing not explicitly represented in the model (e.g., encoding of the stimulus letters, establishment of a motor code for the response, response execution, etc.).

By including the second component in Equation 4, we are assuming that the response to a target word is sensitive to the ease with which the target's phonological form is derived. It is important, therefore, to specify how and when the selection of the target's phonemes occurs. As noted in the introduction, we are assuming that the activation and retrieval of a lexical item makes available an abstract phonological frame that guides the selection process. Although the present model does not contain phonological frames per se, we nevertheless capture the functional effect of these frames by making the selection of phonemes dependent upon the target's lexical node reaching its maximum level of activation.

In the model, there are two important factors that influence the strength of the target's phonemes relative to competing phonemes. The first is how soon phonemes are selected. The earlier the selection process is initiated, the greater the chance that an *incorrect* phoneme is selected. This effect occurs because the prime's phonemes are highly active when the target is first presented, and it takes some time for their activation to decay. A second factor influencing phoneme selection is the relationship between the prime and target. Orthographically and phonologically related prime-target pairs result in greater selection errors than unrelated pairs. This effect occurs because the processing of the related target tends to activate not only the target's lexical node, but also the episodic node and the prime's lexical node. These latter two nodes send activation to the prime's phonemes, thus decreasing the likelihood that the target's critical phoneme will be selected.

Simulations

Relatedness x Frequency Interaction

Colombo (1986) found slower lexical decision latencies to high frequency targets preceded by orthographically and phonologically related primes, relative to unrelated controls. For low frequency targets, on the other hand, the priming effect was facilitatory. We successfully simulated the Colombo results with our model. However, the inhibition effect in our model is not due to direct inhibition of lexical nodes, as proposed by Colombo. Rather the inhibition arises as a result of incorrectly selecting the phonemes of the prime during the processing of the target. This inhibition effect interacts with target frequency in the following way. With high frequency words, the selection process occurs soon after target presentation, when the prime's phonemes are still active. Low frequency words select later, when the activation of the prime's phonemes has subsided. Thus, there is less competition during the selection process for the low frequency targets.

In the simulation, the model was presented with either a high or a low frequency target word (*CAP* or *CAD*, respectively) preceded by either a related or unrelated prime (*CAT* or *PEG*). Figure 2 shows the results of the simulation. The probability of correctly selecting the target's critical phoneme is plotted as a function of the number of timesteps following the target's presentation. In this figure, the four Frequency x Relatedness conditions are plotted separately. The endpoint of each line reflects the timestep at which the target's lexical node reached its maximum activation and phoneme selection occurred.

Several aspects of this figure require comment. First, across timesteps, unrelated targets have a higher probability of correctly selecting their critical phoneme than do related targets. This effect occurs because, on related trials, the target tends to reactivate the prime's phonemes, thus increasing the likelihood of selecting a phoneme from the prime rather than the target. On an unrelated trial, there

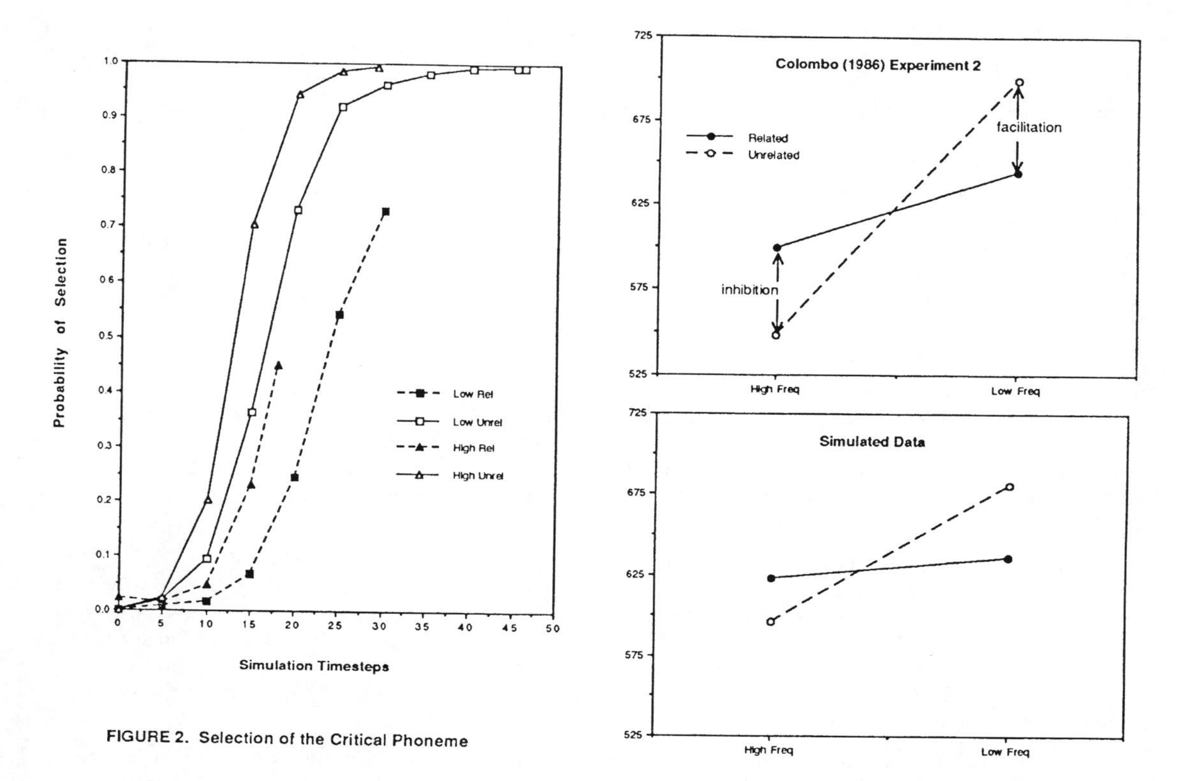

FIGURE 2. Selection of the Critical Phoneme

FIGURE 3. Simulation of Relatedness x Frequency Effect

is no overlap in letters between the prime and target, hence the prime's lexical node is inhibited by each of the target's letter nodes. With no lexical support, the activation of the prime's phonemes quickly decays, thereby increasing the probability of correctly selecting the target's critical phoneme.

A second effect shown in the figure is that high frequency targets, at a given timestep, have a higher probability of correct selection than do low frequency targets (this can be seen most clearly by comparing high and low frequency targets within a given level of relatedness). This frequency effect occurs because high frequency words have higher resting levels of activation than do low frequency words and hence activate their component phonemes more quickly.

Of primary interest in this figure, however, is the probability of correct phoneme selection *at the timestep when selection actually occurs* (i.e., the endpoint of each line). At these points, high frequency words have an overall *lower* probability of correct selection than do low frequency words, and this frequency effect interacts with relatedness. For unrelated targets, there is no difference in selection probability for low and high frequency targets (both have reached a ceiling probability of over 99% when selection occurs). For related targets, on the other hand, there is a large advantage for low frequency words (76% probability for the low frequency target, and 45% for the high frequency target). This difference is due to the fact that the high frequency word node reaches its maximum activation more quickly, thereby not giving its critical phoneme enough time to become sufficiently activated.

The response times for each of the four conditions were calculated using Equation 4. The results are presented in Figure 3, along with the results from the Colombo (1986) study. As can be seen, the model's fit to the data is quite good. In both the simulation and Colombo's experiment, there is facilitation for low frequency targets and inhibiton for high frequency targets. Thus, the model accounts for the Colombo data without positing inhibition among lexical candidates.

Varying Episodic Strength

Inhibition occurs in our model as a result of difficulty in forming a phonological representation of the target word. This difficulty arises because the target word tends to activate both the prime's lexical node and the episodic node. By incorporating the episodic node, we are proposing that inhibition depends on the formation of an episodic trace of the prime. We would predict, therefore, that the strength of this trace should influence the size of the inhibition effect. For example, if the prime is presented so briefly that no episodic representation is formed, it follows from our model that inhibition should be substantially reduced. Consistent with this prediction, Forster (1987) has demonstrated that, with subliminal prime presentation, form-related targets are facilitated (see also Humphreys, Evett, & Taylor, 1982).

In order to quantify the relationship between the strength of the episodic trace and phonological priming, we ran a further series of simulations varying the strength of the letter-to-episode connections in the model. We varied the weight of these connections from 0 to .15 (recall that we used a weight of .10 in the previous run of the model). By performing this manipulation, we are changing the extent to which the model is influenced by memories of the prime. A small weight on the letter-to-episode link implies that the model is able to ignore, in a sense, its prior experience with the prime. A large weight suggests that there is a strong tendency to re-create the prime during the processing of the related target.

Except for varying the letter-to-episode connection strength, the model was run as before. Figure 4 shows the results of these simulations. With very weak, or nonexistent episodic traces (specifically weights .025 and 0) there was actually a small facilitation effect for the high frequency target, and a large facilitation effect for the low frequency target. With increases in episodic strength, the high frequency target began to show inhibition, while the low frequency target showed decreasing levels of facilitation. With an episodic weight of .150 (the largest weight used) there was virtually no facilitation for the low frequency target, and a large inhibitory effect for the high frequency target.

There are three different experiments whose data are described reasonably well by these simulations (see Figure 4). The first is the Colombo experiment presented in Figure 3, whose data our simulation captures nicely using a letter-to-episodic weight of .10. It is not surprising that our model does well with the Colombo study, since the model was constructed in large part to reproduce her results. However, in addition to Colombo's results, the model also captures the results of two recent experiments by Lupker and Williams (1987). In one experiment, Lupker and Williams attempted to replicate Colombo,

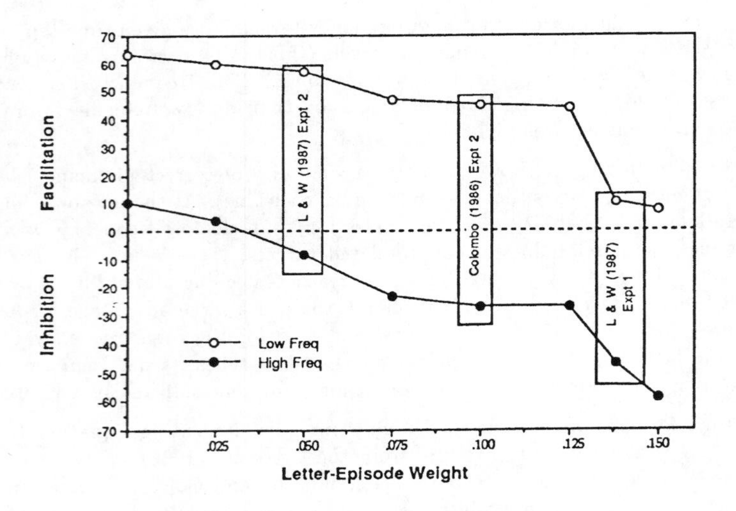

FIGURE 4. Effect of Episodic Strength on Priming

using English rather than Italian materials. They replicated the inhibition effect for high frequency targets, but did not find a significant facilitation effect for low frequency targets. Our model shows a similar pattern of priming with a letter-to-episode weight of .138. In a second experiment, Lupker and Williams used the same materials, but had subjects make lexical decisions to both the prime and the target (in their first experiment, and in Colombo's experiment, subjects made a response to the target only). In this second experiment, there was facilitation for low frequency targets, but only a small (and nonsignificant) inhibition effect for high frequency targets. This pattern of results occurs in our simulations with a weight of about .05.

While the data from the two Lupker and Williams studies and the Colombo experiment may at first appear to be quite disparate, they actually are quite compatible when viewed within the context of Figure 4. According to the analysis provided here, the three experiments differ in terms of vulnerability to episodic interference. Unfortunately, it is difficult to pinpoint the specific aspects of the experiments that might have resulted in these episodic differences. It seems likely, however, that the interference effect might be sensitive to very subtle details within the experimental environment. For example, if the instructions given to the subject at the beginning of the experiment strongly emphasized paying attention to the prime, interference might be more substantial than if the instructions merely informed the subject that a prime word would be presented. Further, the results of Lupker and Williams' second experiment suggest that making an overt response to the prime might significantly modify the nature of the episodic representation of that prime. This modified representation might lead to less confusion during target processing, thus diminishing the interference effect.

CONCLUSIONS

We have presented a model in which there are two distinct loci of form-related priming. Facilitation arises as a result of the activation of orthographically related neighbors during the processing of the prime. On the other hand, inhibition arises during the selection of the target's constituent phonemes, if the prime's phonemes are mistakenly retrieved. Our model is clearly different from that of Colombo, who proposes that both facilitation and inhibition are lexical-level effects. One way to experimentally test our model against Colombo's view is to compare prime-target pairs that are nonhomographic homophones (e.g., *HARE-HAIR*) with pairs that are nonhomophones (e.g., *HATE-HAIR*). Because the primes and targets are orthographically related neighbors in both cases, Colombo would predict a similar pattern of priming for the two types of items. We have conducted this experiment and found inhibition for nonhomophonic items, but facilitation for homophones. This outcome provides strong support for our model: In the absence of phonological competition, orthographically similar words engender facilitation.

REFERENCES

Brown, R., & McNeill, D. (1966). The "Tip of the Tongue" phenomenon. *Journal of Verbal Learning and Verbal Behavior, 5*, 325-337.

Colombo, L. (1986). Activation and inhibition with orthographically similar words. *Journal of Experimental Psychology: Human Perception and Performance, 12*, 226-234.

Dell, G. S. (1988). The retrieval of phonological forms in production: Tests of predictions from a connectionist model. *Journal of Memory and Language, 27*, 124-142.

Forster, K. I., Davis, C., Schoknecht, C., & Carter, R. (1987). Masked priming with graphemically related forms: Repetition or partial activation? *Quarterly Journal of Experimental Psychology, 39A*, 211-251.

Humphreys, G. W., Evett, L. J., & Taylor, D. E. (1982). Automatic phonological priming in visual word recognition. *Memory & Cognition, 10*, 576-590.

Lupker, S. L., & Williams, B. A. (1987). *When do rhyming primes inhibit target processing?* Paper presented at the annual meeting of the Psychonomic Society, Seattle, Washington.

Meyer, D. E., Schvaneveldt, R. W., & Ruddy, M. G. (1974). Functions of graphemic and phonemic codes in visual word-recognition. *Memory & Cognition, 2*, 309-321.

Stemberger, J. P. (in press). Wordshape errors in language production. *Cognition*.

ACKNOWLEDGEMENTS

This research was supported by NIH Grant NS25502, awarded to Gary Dell. Correspondence should be sent to Robert R. Peterson, Psychology Department, University of Rochester, River Campus, Rochester, New York 14627. [Electronic mail: bobp@prodigal.psych.rochester.edu]

Figurative adjective-noun interpretation in a structured connectionist network

Susan Hollbach Weber
Computer Science Department, University of Rochester
hollbach@cs.rochester.edu

Abstract

Non-literal use of an adjective, whether signalled by a category error or by a value expectation violation, invokes the connotations or immediate inferences associated with that adjective in various noun contexts. Immediate inferences reflect the structure of stored knowledge, as they are available too quickly and effortlessly to involve any complex form of information retrieval. Specifically, they suggest the use of the spreading activation model of semantic memory. The relation between the inferences invoked by the adjective and salient features of the noun employed in the figurative usage are exploited by the DIFICIL connectionist inferencing system to interpret the meaning of an unfamiliar adjective-noun phrase.

The interpretation of figurative adjective-noun combinations can be modelled by exploiting the connotations that arise from the adjective's literal usages. In the phrase 'agressive diamond', for example, the high-intensity connotations associated with the adjective maps into large size in diamonds. These immediate inferences must reflect the structure of stored knowledge, as they are available too quickly and effortlessly to involve any complex form of information retrieval. Specifically, they suggest the use of the spreading activation model of semantic memory. The argument is that the patterns of immediate inferences reflect the structure of connections in the underlying spreading activation model, implemented here as a structured connectionist network.

Once the need for a figurative interpretation has been detected, the immediate inferences associated with the adjective are activated in parallel, with a view to later establishing the mapping from a source property of the adjective to a target property of the noun. Once these connotations have been catalogued and incorporated into an adjective's meaning as extended word senses, it is simply a matter of lookup. Of interest here, however, are the methods of arriving at these extended senses, assuming that each word has an unique denotation.

The interpretation of figurative adjective-noun combinations is undertaken in the context of the connectionist inferencing system known as DIFICIL, for Direct Inferences and Figurative Interpretation in a Connectionist Implementation of Language understanding [Weber, 1989b]. The cognitive model underlying the system is described in detail in [Weber, 1989a]. Briefly, categories are represented as structured collections of properties with their attendant values. Functional property values are used to establish coherent groupings of property values, known as *aspects* of the category. For example, the functional property *ripeness* generates two aspects within the *apple* category: unripe apples are green, hard and sour, while ripe apples are red, crisp and sweet. Increased activation of any member of the coalition results in increased activation for the entire aspect. Furthermore, one aspect can inhibit another if incompatible, or stimulate it if logically dependant upon it.

The organization of these aspects depends on the structural characteristics of the properties involved. Properties can permit multiple or concurrently held property values (eg. a cookie tastes at once salt and sweet) or, if the values are mutually exclusive, they can be ordered (eg. hot, warm, cool, cold) or unordered (eg. shape) [Aarts and Calbert, 1979;
Kittay, 1987]. Orthogonal to this is the fact that properties and their attendant values can be classified into three groups: perceptual, constitutive and functional. Perceptual properties are those pertaining to the senses, eg. colour, scent, taste or texture. Constitutive properties are in some sense the definitional properties of a category, often expressed in terms of genetics, compositional makeup and the like. Functional properties relate to an object's usefulness by humans, eg. tameness, edibility or state of repair. Functional properties play a special role in category representation, supplying the various perspectives from which the category can be viewed. For example, the *unripe* property provides the focus of relevance for the *sour* and *green* property values of apples.

This functional aspect model of conceptual representation has been implemented as a structured connectionist network [Feldman and Ballard, 1982] on the Rochester Connectionist Simulator [Goddard *et al.*, 1988], resulting in the DIFICIL inferencing system. The content of a knowledge base is specified with statements in a high level input language. There are six statements in the language. The *subcat* statement sets up the property inheritance or subcategorization hierarchy, and the *abstracts* statement defines the property abstraction hierarchy. The *mutex* and *invokes* statements specify the relations of mutual incompatibility and reinforcement that pertain between aspects. The *hasslot* statement establishes the properties and values belonging to a category, with syntactic variants for perceptual, constitutive and functional properties, and optional scalar positioning parameters. The *aspect* statement creates the conceptual aspects fundamental to the model. For example, the three statements

hasPslot (diamond: cut; marquise (pointy), diamond-cut (round))

hasPslot (diamond: size; large (+), medium (0), small (−))

aspect (diamond: diamond-cut [default]; small, brilliant)

would create the connectionist structures depicted in Figure 1. Categories appear as hexagons, properties as squares, values as circles, positional designators (more on these later, in the section on value mapping) as diamonds, and control nodes as rectangles. The small triangles represent the binder nodes establishing the concept–property–value triplets specified in the *hasslot* statements. The larger triangles are two/three binders [Shastri, 1985], requiring that two of their three inputs be active before firing. The pentagonal *inertial binder* labelled *hub* in the figure controls the spread of activation through the aspect; once activated, it tends to stay on even in the face of active inhibition.

In literal adjective-noun interpretation the DIFICIL system is designed to draw all available *direct inferences* pertaining to the input phrase. *Immediate inferences* are the direct inferences available at the level of the category under consideration. They are performed quickly, in a few hundred milliseconds, and without conscious thought. In DIFICIL, immediate inferences are defined to be the property values available through activation spreading from a category level aspectual hub. For example, the knowledge that diamonds are by default small and brilliant is an immediate inference. *Mediated*

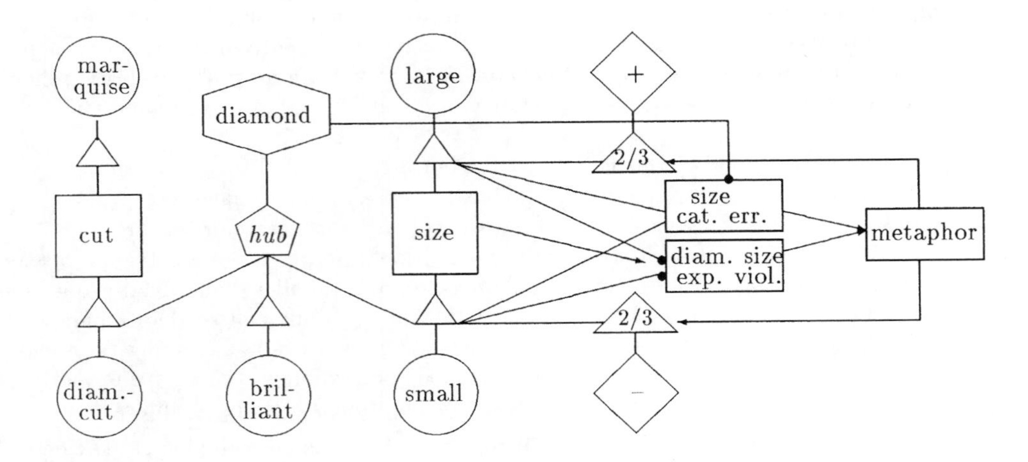

Figure 1: The *diamond-cut* aspect of diamonds, along with the semantic anomaly detection and scalar positioning mechanisms of the *size* property.

inferences are the second form of direct inference, where knowledge about a more abstract category is used to supply the information necessary to understand the discourse. Mediated inferences take somewhat longer to obtain than immediate inferences, as they require chaining up the subcategorization hierarchy created by *subcat* statements. For example, if one knew that all gemstones are expensive and that a diamond is a gemstone, the inference that diamonds are expensive is a mediated inference.

Direct inferences form the fundamental mode of operation of the system. Not only are they the primary mechanism for interpreting literal adjective-noun combinations, but the information encoded as immediate inferences is crucial to the successful interpretation of the figurative adjectival modification of a noun. Before considering how this might work, however, the prior question of distinguishing between literal and figuative usages is dealt with.

Detecting figures of speech

Figurative usage can be signalled in any number of ways, from subtle contextual cues and knowledge of conventional usage to blatant semantic anomaly. For example, the phrase 'cold woman' is ambiguous as to whether body temperature or emotional responsiveness is being referred to, an ambiguity that cannot be resolved without sentential context. On the other hand, the fact that a stare cannot literally be said to have temperature means that the phrase 'cold stare' constitutes a *category error*, a form of semantic anomaly in which a predicate is used in conjunction with a term it does not span [Keil, 1979] (recall that it is assumed throughout that each word has an unique denotation; in the case of 'cold', this would be temperature). The phrase 'cold steam' exemplifies a second form of semantic anomaly, since although steam has the property *temperature*, the only permissible value of this property is *hot*. Thus 'cold steam' constitutes an *expectation violation*, since the named property value is an unusual or impossible choice for the property of the noun. Finally, there are idiomatic phrases, like 'cold shoulder', whose obvious literal interpretation is never considered (by native speakers of the language), since the figurative meaning is so well established.

The mechanisms for detecting the need for a figurative interpretation currently implemented in DIFICIL are limited to category error and expectation violation detection.[1] Category errors are detected on a property by property basis. A detection node, labelled *size cat. err.* in Figure 1, is created for each new property named in a *hasslot* statement. This node receives excitation from the property–value binders and inhibition from the category, so if a property value should be activated while the category is inactive, a semantic anomaly will be reported as required. Expectation violations are detected at the level of the category–property conjunction. The detection node receives inhibition from the property–value binders, and excitation from the property, so if any property value not possessed by the category is named, an expectation violation results. Both forms of semantic anomaly, when detected, transmit their activation to the global *metaphor* control node. When all possible immediate and mediated inferences have been drawn, if there is still an anomaly being reported, the *metaphor* node is activated, signalling a network-wide change of state, from literal interpretive mechanisms to figurative.

Adjective connotations

The connotations of an adjective arise from its associations within its literally allowable noun contexts. The connotations considered by DIFICIL for the purposes of figurative interpretation are the immediate inferences arising from the modification of an arbitrary noun by the given adjective. For any category known to the system, if the adjective names a property value that participates in an aspect of that category, then it will trigger a characteristic set of immediate inferences, as activation spreads from the named value to the aspectual hub and from there propagates to all related property values.

The set of all values activated in this manner form the interpretive base for understanding a figurative usage. The most straightforward interpretations arise when a property value of the target category is made available through an immediate inference associated with another category. For example, suppose it was 'known' to the system that agressive people are also large in size; then the unfamiliar figure of speech 'agressive diamond' would be interpreted as denoting a large diamond.

However, it is the indirect methods of arriving at a plausible interpretation that form the focus of this work. For example, as agressivity in people is ranked high on the intensity scale for agression, the phrase 'agressive diamond' may refer to a large diamond, since size is a salient property of diamonds and large is the high-ranking value on the intensity scale for size. On the other hand, it could be cut in a pointy shape (known as a marquise cut), since the tools of agression (weapons) tend to have pointy shapes. There are doubtless other possibilities, increasingly far-fetched, but the notion of entertaining competing interpretations in parallel is fundamental to the chosen model of spreading activation; only after the novelty of the figure has worn off, and its most likely interpretation catalogued,

[1]This of course does not preclude the possibility of eventually exploiting contextual cues or idiom recognition, if available; thanks to Jim Hendler for pointing this out.

will there be a single correct answer to the interpretation question. When considering novel figurative usages, all possibilities must be explored.

This is accomplished by two interlocking interpretive processes, one to establish all property-to-property mappings, the other to set up the value-to-value correspondences within related properties.

Property mapping

In order to establish a semantic correspondence between the property named by the adjective (eg. 'agressive' names human agression) and properties of the noun (eg, size and shape of diamonds), a property abstraction hierarchy relates all the properties in the knowledge base. As soon as the need for a figurative interpretation has been recognized, activation is permitted to spread throughout the abstraction hierarchy from the property named by the adjective. Activation will eventually spread to every property in the knowledge base, so in some sense the hierarchical arrangement is unnecessary: one could simply stimulate all properties in parallel, and achieve the same end result. But with the hierarchical spread of activation the timing delays between the various meaning hypotheses reflect their plausibility: later suggestions are increasingly implausible, as the semantic distance between the properties increases.

Value mapping

The real interpretive work is done at the level of the value-to-value mappings. There are two methods used to establish semantic correspondences: immediate inferences and scalar position conjunction.

Immediate inferences involve the notion of mutually excitatory functionally related property values. Of interest to the figurative interpretation process are the conceptual aspects participated in by the property value named by the adjective. As conceptual aspects remain inactive until enabled by the excitation of their category, it is necessary to briefly stimulate all category nodes in the network in order to establish all the connotations of the figuratively used adjective. This excitatory signal decays rapidly, however, and soon (within 10 time steps) actually inhibits all the categories previously excited. Those categories possessing an aspect in which the adjective's value participates will receive positive feedback activation sufficient to overcome this inhibitory signal for long enough to establish any further semantic mappings that may exist between properties of the aspect and properties in the noun concept.

The second mechanism for establishing semantic correspondences is *scalar position conjunction*. It turns out that most property values are scalar in nature, that is, the allowable values for a given property can be strictly ranked with respect to each other, from least to greatest [Kittay, 1987]. One example of this behaviour is the *temperature* property, whose values range from freezing through cold, cool, warm, hot and finally to boiling/burning/blistering etc. There will generally be two values that typify the positive and negative extremes (eg. hot and cold) with a third value typifying the neutral setting.

The scalar nature of a property is established with optional parameters to the *hasslot* statement, specifying the *scalar position designator* of the value. Property scales are defined implicitly by choice of position designators: for example, the *intensity* scale may have the positional designators *ipos*, short for *i*ntensity:*pos*itive (previously referred to

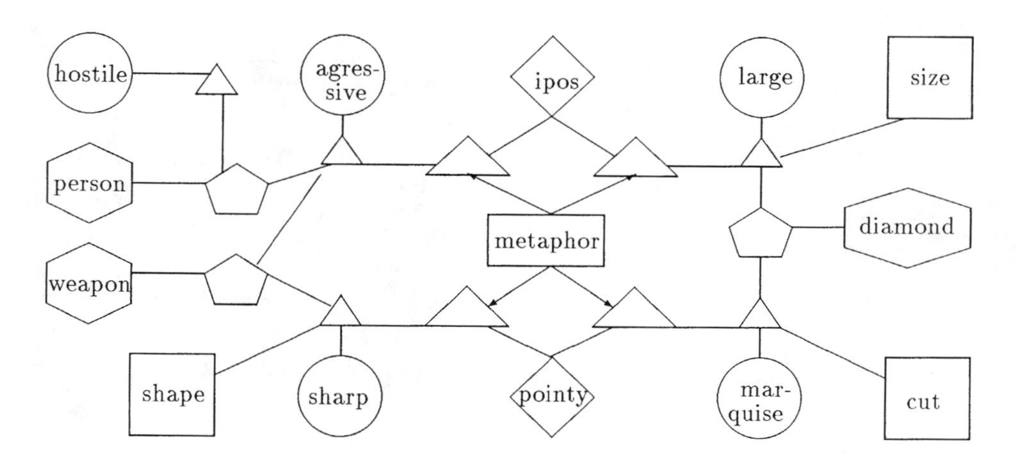

Figure 2: Schematic of the connectionist structures involved in the interpretation of the phrase 'agressive diamond'.

with the symbol '+'), *ineutral* (0), and *ineg* (−), so the relative sizes of diamonds, say, is correctly expressed by

hasPslot (diamond: size; large (ipos), medium (ineutral), small (ineg))

Unranked but mutually exclusive properties are handled in the same way, as there is no attempt to actually impose the scalar ordering implied by the choice of designators, so diamond shape, for example, could be captured with the following statement:

hasPslot (diamond: shape; marquise (pointy), pear-shape (pear-shape), ...)

Terms appearing in different semantic positions in a statement are distinguished, so the first occurrence of 'pear-shape' is taken to be a property value, while the second refers to the positional designator of the same name.

In order to interpret the phrase 'agressive diamond', it is necessary to access all the connotations of the adjective 'agressive'. This is done by briefly stimulating all the categories in the knowledge base, followed almost immediately by an increasingly inhibitory signal. Immediate inferences result for all categories with 'agressive' as a property value, as these categories receive feedback activatation sufficient to defeat the inhibitory input for long enough to establish the aspects, if any, participated in by the value. Suppose the only two such categories are weapons and people:

aspect (people: threat [non-default]; hostile, agressive);

aspect (weapons: sharp [default]; agressive).

The transmission of activation from these aspects to property values of diamonds is mediated by the scalar position designators, as depicted in Figure 2. If it has been established that sharp weapons are classified as *pointy* on the shape scale and that large size is *ipos* on the intensity scale, then it will eventually be decided that agressive diamonds are not only large but also of marquise cut.

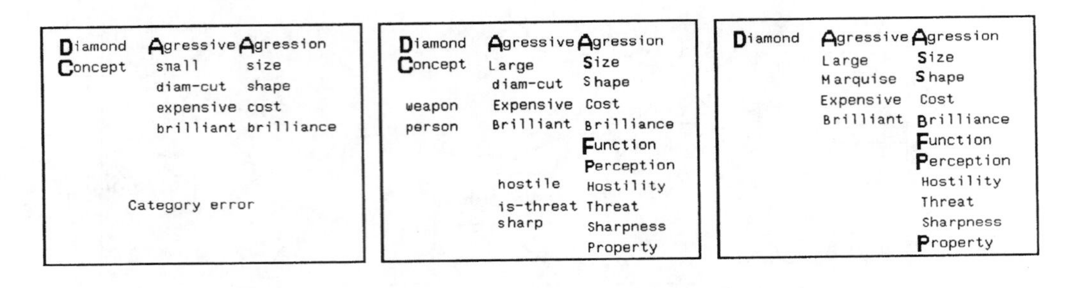

Figure 3: Time lapse shots of system output on the target phrase 'agressive diamond'.

System performance

Figure 3 shows three time-lapse pictures of the output of DIFICIL running the agressive diamond example. The graphics interface to the Rochester Connectionist Simulator permits creating icons to represent the activation levels of individual network units. The icons here take the shape of letters of the alphabet, where the first letter in the word represented by the unit is the one iconified. The icons range from a large capital letter, for significant activation, to a lower case letter, for marginal activation. Words appear in columns according to their semantics: categories on the left, property values in the middle and properties on the right. The leftmost panel shows the state of the network after about 20 simulation steps: a category error has been detected, due to the presence of the adjective 'agressive' in the absence of such nouns as 'person' or 'weapon' that would permit a literal reading. Note the marginal activation on the default property values of diamonds. Even in the face of a semantic anomaly, these default conclusions are primed for possible future reference.

The middle panel shows the state of affairs some 15 time steps later: all the categories in the knowledge base have been briefly stimulated and are now receiving gradually increasing inhibition. The two categories related to 'agressive' are able to overcome this inhibition longer than unrelated categories, due to the positive feedback from the property value. Activation is spreading rapidly through the property abstraction hierarchy, as evidenced by the long list of properties in the right hand column. The central column shows that the two aspects containing the value 'agressive' have been established: an agressive person is hostile and threatening, and an agressive weapon is sharp. Note too that the default diamond properties *expensive* and *brilliant* have been boosted in activation, while the default size *small* is easily defeated in favor of *large*, as indicated by the intensity scale conjunction of *expensive, brilliant* and *large* with *agressive.* No (non-default) conclusions have yet been drawn as to the diamond's shape.

In the leftmost panel, the final figurative interpretation is available, after a total of 40 simulation steps. All concepts but the target *diamond* have been inhibited, shutting down all value–property pairs not directly associated with the target category. Conversely, all properties in the knowledge base are active to varying degrees due to the spread of activation through the abstraction hierarchy, but as properties are incidental to their values, this is unimportant. The relevant values appear in the central column: note that it has been established that since agressive weapons are sharp, and sharp weapons are classified as pointy on the shape scale, as are marquise-cut diamonds, the diamonds in question must be marquise-cut.

Summary

The notion that a property value occupies a scalar position on any number of classification scales associated with the property is exploited in DIFICIL to interpret figurative adjective-noun combinations. The need for a figurative interpretation can be signalled by various forms of semantic anomaly, including category error and expectation violation. When this happens, activation spreads to the immediate inferences associated with the adjective in a wide variety of noun contexts. All scalar positioning conjunctions between property values thus activated and property values of the target noun mediate the transmission of activation to the relevant properties of the noun.

Acknowledgements

Thanks to Jerry Feldman for comments on a draft. This work was supported by ONR research contract no. N00014-82-K-0193 and U.S. Army Communication-Electronics Command Grant no. DAAB 10-87-K-022.

References

[Aarts and Calbert, 1979] Jan M. G. Aarts and Joseph P. Calbert, *Metaphor and Non-Metaphor: The Semantics of Adjective-Noun Combinations*, Max Niemeyer Verlag, 1979.

[Feldman and Ballard, 1982] Jerome A. Feldman and Dana H. Ballard, "Connectionist Models and Their Properties," *Cognitive Science*, 6:205–254, 1982.

[Goddard *et al.*, 1988] Nigel Goddard, Kenton Lynne, and Toby Mintz, "The Rochester Connectionist Simulator User Manual," Technical Report 233, Computer Science Department, University of Rochester, March 1988.

[Keil, 1979] Frank C. Keil, *Semantic and Conceptual Development An Ontological Perspective*, Harvard University Press, Cambridge, Mass., 1979.

[Kittay, 1987] Eva Feder Kittay, *Metaphor: its Cognitive Force and Linguistic Structure*, Clarendon Press, 1987.

[Shastri, 1985] Lokendra Shastri, "Evidential Reasoning in Semantic Networks: A Formal Theory and its Parallel Implementation," Technical Report 166, Computer Science Deparment, University of Rochester, September 1985.

[Weber, 1989a] Susan Hollbach Weber, "Modelling semantic flexibility with a structured connectionist implementatation of functional category organization," submitted to the IEEE Conference on Neural Information Processing Systems (NIPS), May 1989.

[Weber, 1989b] Susan Hollbach Weber, "A Structured Connectionist Approach to Direct Inferences and Figurative Adjective-Noun Combinations," Technical Report 289, PhD. thesis, Department of Computer Science, University of Rochester, May 1989.

Anomalous Conditional Judgments and Ramsey's Thought Experiment

John M. Miyamoto
Department of Psychology
University of Washington

James W. Lundell
Hewlett-Packard

Shihfen Tu
Department of Psychology
University of Washington

The Stalnaker/Lewis semantics for counterfactual conditionals is based on a thought experiment proposed by Frank Ramsey. We show that intuitive judgments of the truth of counterfactuals violate predictions derived from the Stalnaker/Lewis semantics. The pattern of violations suggests that the process of counterfactual reasoning follows a different pattern from the process implicit in Ramsey's thought experiment.

A counterfactual conditional is a statement of the form, "If P were true, then Q would be true", where P is a proposition that is known to be false, and Q is another proposition. For example, "If Richard Nixon had not resigned from the presidency, he would have been impeached", is a counterfactual conditional. The English philosopher, Frank Ramsey, proposed an influential heuristic analysis of conditional statements which was meant to apply to counterfactuals as well as other forms of conditionals.

> In general we can say with Mill that 'If *p*, then *q*' means that *q* is inferrible from *p*, that is, of course, from *p* together with certain facts and laws not stated but in some way indicated by the context. (Ramsey, 1931, p.248).

Stalnaker interpreted Ramsey's approach as a sequence of inferential steps applied to a knowledge base: To evaluate the truth of a counterfactual conditional,

> First, add the antecedent (hypothetically) to your stock of beliefs; second, make whatever adjustments are required to maintain consistency (without modifying the hypothetical belief in the antecedent); finally, consider whether or not the consequent is then true. (Stalnaker, 1968).

We will say that a counterfactual conditional is evaluated by a *Ramsey thought experiment* if the cognitive process by which it is evaluated proceeds through the steps described in the Stalnaker quotation. The heuristic model of the Ramsey thought experiment has been central to investigations of counterfactuals from the diverse standpoints of analytical philosophy (Goodman, 1947, 1965), intensional logic (Stalnaker, 1968, 1984; Lewis, 1973), cognitive psychology (Johnson-Laird, 1986; Rips & Marcus, 1979), and artificial intelligence (Ginsberg, 1986).

It is the thesis of this paper that the cognitive processes underlying intuitive counterfactual reasoning are quite different from the Ramsey thought experiment. We will argue that a counterfactual is evaluated by mentally constructing two alternatives, one alternative in which the antecedent and consequent are both true, and a second in which the antecedent is true and the consequent is false; a counterfactual appears to be true to the extent that the first alternative is more plausible than the second. Our arguments are based on the results of psychological experiments. We first describe a theory of counterfactuals due to Stalnaker (1968, 1984) and Lewis (1973), and derive testable relations among counterfactuals from this theory. These relations are also implied by other theories that elaborate the heuristic of the Ramsey thought experiment. We report the results of an experiment testing whether intuitive counterfactual judgments exhibit the predicted relations. To anticipate our results, intuitive counterfactual judgments violated predictions derived from the Stalnaker/Lewis analysis.

THE STALNAKER/LEWIS THEORY OF COUNTERFACTUAL SEMANTICS

The Stalnaker/Lewis theory is developed within the framework of possible worlds semantics (Kripke, 1963; Lewis, 1973; Montague, 1974). Possible worlds are abstract entities relative to which propositions have truth values. The truth values of propositions can differ from one possible world to the next. The actual state of the world is treated as one world in the set of possible worlds. Let R denote the actual world, and let α and β denote other possible worlds. The Stalnaker/Lewis theory postulates the existence of a measure of similarity, S, between the actual world and other possible worlds[1]; let $S(\alpha, R) > S(\beta, R)$ indicate that α is more similar to the actual world than β. For example, a world in which Richard Nixon did not resign and he remained under political attack is more like the actual world than a world in which he did not resign and the political attacks spontaneously ceased.

We say that α is a P-world if the proposition P is true in α. According to Stalnaker and Lewis, for any P, there exists a set τ_P that satisfies two conditions:

(a) τ_P is a set of P-worlds, i.e., P is true in every world in τ_P,

(b) Every P-world in τ_P is more similar to R than any P-world not in τ_P. In other words, $S(\alpha, R) > S(\beta, R)$ whenever $\alpha \in \tau_P$, $\beta \notin \tau_P$, and α and β are P-worlds.

If α is a world in τ_P, we will say that α is a maximally similar P-world. Stalnaker (1968, 1984) maintained that for any P, there is a unique most similar world in which P is true, i.e., τ_P always contains a single possible world. Lewis (1973) proposed that there might be several different worlds in which P is true, all of which are similar to R to the same maximum degree. We will follow Lewis in postulating that τ_P may contain more than one world.

Let $P \rightarrow Q$ denote the statement, "If P were true, Q would be true." According to Stalnaker/Lewis, $P \rightarrow Q$ is true if and only if either

C1. There is no world in which P is true, or

C2. Q is true in every world in τ_P.

Clause C1 covers the trivial case where P is logically false, e.g., "If 2 + 2 = 3, the national debt would be eliminated" is true because 2 + 2 = 3 is false in every world. Clause C2 captures the primary intuition behind the Stalnaker/Lewis theory. To decide whether $P \rightarrow Q$ is true, we should consider the P-worlds that are most similar to R, and ask whether Q is true in all such worlds. For example, was Richard Nixon impeached in all maximally similar worlds in which

---

1 S is assumed to be an ordinal measure of similarity defined on all pairs of worlds and not merely on pairs of the form (α, R). We will not need these more general relations here.

he did not resign? If so, we can assert that Richard Nixon would have been impeached if he had not resigned.

IMPLICATIONS OF THE STALNAKER/LEWIS THEORY

Let X AND Y denote the truth functional conjunction of X and Y, and let X OR Y denote the truth functional disjunction of X and Y. The Stalnaker/Lewis theory implies the following:

Proposition 1: For any A, X and Y, if A $\rightarrow$ X AND Y is true, then A $\rightarrow$ X and A $\rightarrow$ Y are true.

Proposition 2: For any A, X and Y, if A $\rightarrow$ X is true, then A $\rightarrow$ X OR Y is true, and if A $\rightarrow$ Y is true, then A $\rightarrow$ X OR Y is true.

Proposition 3: For any A, X and Y, if A $\rightarrow$ X AND Y is true, then A AND X $\rightarrow$ Y and A AND Y $\rightarrow$ X are true.

Propositions 1 - 3 are obviously true by clause C1 if A is false in all possible worlds. Therefore we will only consider cases where A is true in at least some possible worlds. To prove proposition 1, suppose that A $\rightarrow$ X AND Y is true. Then X AND Y is true in every world in τ_A; hence, X is true in every world in τ_A, and Y is true in every world in τ_A. Therefore A $\rightarrow$ X and A $\rightarrow$ Y are both true. To prove proposition 2, suppose that A $\rightarrow$ X is true. Then X is true in every world in τ_A. Hence X OR Y is true in every world in τ_A, so A $\rightarrow$ X OR Y is true. To prove proposition 3, suppose that A $\rightarrow$ X AND Y is true. Then X AND Y is true in every world in τ_A. But A is true in every world in τ_A by definition of τ_A, and X is true in every world in τ_A because X AND Y is true in every world in τ_A. Therefore A AND X is true in every world in τ_A. Thus $\tau_{A \text{ AND } X}$ must equal τ_A for if not, A AND X would be true at worlds that are more similar to R than the worlds in τ_A, contradicting that τ_A contains the maximally similar A-worlds. Hence Y is true at every world in $\tau_{A \text{ AND } X}$ (= τ_A). Hence A AND X $\rightarrow$ Y is true by clause C2 of the Stalnaker/Lewis theory.

EXPERIMENTAL TEST OF PROPOSITIONS 1, 2 AND 3

Our general procedure is to present subjects with a background story followed by a series of counterfactual statements. Subjects are asked to rate the statements for "how true or false they seem to be". The critical statements have the forms, A $\rightarrow$ X, A $\rightarrow$ Y, A $\rightarrow$ X AND Y, A $\rightarrow$ X OR Y, and A AND X $\rightarrow$ Y. We assume that if one counterfactual is implied by a second counterfactual, the former counterfactual should receive the higher rating, for any evidence or argument that supports the latter counterfactual must also support the former. The response patterns predicted by propositions 1 - 3 are summarized in Table 1.

Miyamoto and Dibble (1986) tested propositions 1 and 2, and found violations of both propositions. The violations were analogous to conjunction and disjunction fallacies previously observed in subjective probability judgment (Morier & Borgida, 1984; Tversky & Kahneman, 1983). Propositions X and Y were chosen such that X would have been a representative outcome and Y an unrepresentative outcome relative to a background story and a counterfactual antecedent A. Statistically reliable violations of proposition 1 and 2 were found in the degree of truth ratings; A $\rightarrow$ X was rated higher than A $\rightarrow$ X OR Y, and A $\rightarrow$ X AND Y was rated higher than A $\rightarrow$ Y. The present study extends these findings in three ways. First, we test proposition 3 as well as replicating the tests of propositions 1 and 2. Second, we introduce a minor procedural

TABLE 1

Predicted Relations in Rated Truth

Proposition 1 *Conjunction Test*	A → X A → Y	≥ ≥	A → X AND Y A → X AND Y
Proposition 2 *Disjunction Test*	A → X A → Y	≤ ≤	A → X OR Y A → X OR Y
Proposition 3 *Conditionalization Test*	A AND X → Y A AND Y → X	≥ ≥	A → X AND Y A → X AND Y

alteration that controls against an alternative explanation to be described below. Third, and most important, whereas Miyamoto and Dibble (1986) noticed only that violations of propositions 1 and 2 contradict the Stalnaker/Lewis theory, we emphasize that violations of propositions 1 - 3 are inconsistent with the serial inferential process of the Ramsey thought experiment. Thus we are able to identify the information processing implications of these results.

EXPERIMENTAL METHOD

Subjects read a background story concerning a couple, the Conley's, and their decision whether to vacation in New York City or the Canadian Rockies. For brevity, we will omit the story, but the main points are as follows. The Conley's eventually decided to vacation in the Rockies. From their discussion of the New York option, however, it is clear that they were very interested in visiting art museums, lukewarm with respect to attending the opera, very interested in hearing live jazz, and not interested in taking walks in Central Park. Two sets of counterfactual statements were constructed to test propositions 1 - 3. These sets were:

Set 1

A → X: If the Conley's had vacationed in New York, they would have visited art museums.

A → Y: If the Conley's had vacationed in New York, they would have attended the opera.

A → X AND Y: If the Conley's had vacationed in New York, they would have visited art museums, and they would have attended the opera.

A → X OR Y: If the Conley's had vacationed in New York, they would have visited art museums, or they would have attended the opera, or both.

A AND X → Y: If the Conley's had vacationed in New York and visited art museums, they would also have attended the opera.

Set 2

A → X: If the Conley's had vacationed in New York, they would have heard outstanding live jazz.

A → Y: If the Conley's had vacationed in New York, they would have gone for late evening walks in Central Park.

A → X AND Y: If the Conley's had vacationed in New York, they would have heard outstanding live jazz, and gone for late evening walks in Central Park.

A → X OR Y: If the Conley's had vacationed in New York, they would have heard outstanding live jazz, or gone for late evening walks in Central Park, or both.

A AND X → Y: If the Conley's had vacationed in New York and had heard outstanding live jazz, they would have gone for late evening walks in Central Park.

TABLE 2

	Median Rating	
	Set 1	Set 2
A → X	26.0	24.0
A → Y	3.0	15.0
A → X AND Y	11.0	19.0
A → X OR Y	18.0	21.0
A AND X → Y	5.0	15.0

TABLE 3

Percentage of times the row rating exceeded the column rating;
* indicates $p < .05$, two-tailed sign test; ** indicates $p < .01$, two-tailed sign test.

Set 1	A → Y	A → X AND Y	A → X OR Y	A AND X → Y
A → X	97% **	96% **	90% **	97% **
A → Y		12% **	5% **	38%
A → X AND Y			30% **	91% **
A → X OR Y				97% **
Set 2	**A → Y**	**A → X AND Y**	**A → X OR Y**	**A AND X → Y**
A → X	90% **	88% **	72% **	92% **
A → Y		30% **	14% **	61%
A → X AND Y			20% **	80% **
A → X OR Y				90% **

Each subject read the background story and rated the statements for "how true or false they seem based on the information in the preceding story and whatever else you know about the world." The 10 statements in sets 1 and 2 were mixed with 15 additional counterfactual statements concerning related topics. Four random orderings of the statements were used in the experiment; subjects were randomly assigned to one of the four orderings. Ratings were made by placing a mark on a horizontal line that was labeled "Absolutely true" at one end, and "Absolutely false" at the other end. Intermediate positions on the line indicated intermediate degrees of truth. Responses were coded on a scale from 1 (= absolutely false) to 30 (= absolutely true).

RESULTS AND DISCUSSION

Subjects were 70 University of Washington undergraduates (mean age = 20.3, SD age = 3.16). None of the subjects had had a course in logic. There were no important differences between subjects receiving the different orderings of the statements, so results will be pooled across the orderings.

Table 2 lists the median ratings for the five statements in sets 1 and 2, and Table 3 lists the results of sign tests for differences between pairs of statements. For both sets of statements, the conjunction tests yielded violations of proposition 1. The A → Y statement received significantly lower ratings than the A → X AND Y statement ($p < .01$). For both sets of statements, the disjunction tests yielded violations of proposition 2. The A → X statement received significantly higher ratings than the A → X OR Y statement. Finally, for both sets of statements, the conditionalization tests yielded violations of proposition 3. The A → X AND Y statements received significantly higher ratings than the A AND X → Y statement ($p < .01$).

The conjunction and disjunction tests replicate the findings of Miyamoto and Dibble (1986), but also contribute a useful extension of their findings. Whereas the disjunctive statements in Miyamoto and Dibble (1986) did not explicitly indicate whether the disjunction was inclusive or exclusive, the disjunctive statements in the present study tested whether X or Y "or both" would have occurred if A had occurred. If "OR" is regarded as an exclusive disjunction, the finding that A → X is rated higher than A → X OR Y is consistent with the Stalnaker/Lewis theory. Thus, Miyamoto and Dibble (1986) was open to the criticism that the purported violations of proposition 2 were spurious because some subjects may have interpreted the disjunctive statements as exclusive disjunctions. The present study is not open to this objection. It might also be objected that subjects may interpret the A → Y statement as A → Y BUT NOT X because A → Y is perceived as contrasting with A → X AND Y. This objection has already been raised with respect to conjunction fallacies in probability judgment (Marcus & Zajonc, 1985; Pennington, 1984). We have explored this issue in additional experiments which cannot be reported here because of space limitations. To give the gist of our rejoinder, however, we examined the conjunction test in a between-subjects experiment where different subjects rated A → X, A → Y, and A → X AND Y. In such an experiment, one finds that A → X AND Y is still rated higher than A → Y. A between-subjects design eliminates the possibility that subjects contrast A → Y with A → X AND Y because different subjects rate the two statements. We have also presented subjects with statements that have the forms A → X, A → Y, A → X AND Y, and A → Y BUT NOT X. We find that the ratings of A → Y are generally higher than the ratings of A → Y BUT NOT X.

CONCLUSIONS

It is clear that intuitive counterfactual reasoning violates the conjunction, disjunction and conditionalization tests. We will refer to these violations as anomalous counterfactual judgments. What are the implications of these anomalies? First, we should recognize that the Stalnaker/Lewis theory was proposed as a normative theory of counterfactual inference, rather than as a descriptive theory of naive counterfactual judgment (Lewis, 1973; Stalnaker, 1968, 1984). Our results do not undermine the normative status of the Stalnaker/Lewis theory. Second, although we derived propositions 1 - 3 from the Stalnaker/Lewis theory, we believe they are consequences of most theories of counterfactual inference that are based on the Ramsey thought experiment. This is especially clear for propositions 1 and 2. If X AND Y is inferrible from the antecedent A and other contextually relevant beliefs, then surely X alone must be inferrible from A and these beliefs. Similarly, if X is inferrible from A and other contextually relevant beliefs, then surely X OR Y is inferrible from A and these beliefs. Thus propositions 1 and 2 are consequences of the inferential structure of Ramsey's thought experiment, rather than any peculiar feature of the Stalnaker/Lewis theory. Proposition 3 is also plausible within a Ramsey thought experiment, for if X AND Y is inferrible from A together with other contextually relevant beliefs, then X is inferrible from A together with these beliefs, and Y is inferrible from A and X and these other beliefs. Therefore Y is inferrible from A AND X together with other contextually relevant beliefs. Thus proposition 3 also follows from the inferential structure of Ramsey's thought experiment. Of course, the present argument is not rigorous, for the initial statement of the Ramsey thought experiment was heuristic rather than formal and precise.

The essential problem with the Ramsey thought experiment, as we see it, is that *a Ramsey thought experiment derives the consequences of a counterfactual antecedent without regard to the consequent of the specific counterfactual that is being evaluated.* Thus, counterfactuals that have identical antecedents undergo identical processing up to the point at which one tests whether the consequents are true in the belief structure derived from the antecedent and current belief. The existence of anomalous counterfactual judgments demonstrates that intuitive counterfactual inference does not proceed serially through the three steps of a Ramsey thought experiment.

We propose to analyze intuitive counterfactual inference along different lines from the Ramsey thought experiment. Suppose one is evaluating the truth of $A \rightarrow X$. We propose that the inference proceeds through five stages.

1. Add A and X to the current set of beliefs.
2. Construct the most plausible mental model in which A and X are both true. We assume that there is a subjective measure, $\mathcal{P}[A, X]$, that represents the subjective plausibility of this mental model.
3. Return to the initial belief state, and add A and NOT-X to these beliefs.
4. Construct the most plausible mental model in which A and NOT-X are both true. Let $\mathcal{P}[A, \text{NOT-}X]$ denote the subjective plausibility of this mental model.
5. Evaluate the relative plausibility of these two models, i.e., base the judgment of the truth of $A \rightarrow X$ on the ratio, $\mathcal{P}[A, X]/\mathcal{P}[A, \text{NOT-}X]$.

We will refer to the procedure defined by steps 1 - 5 as the Relative Plausibility model.

Space limitations prevent us from fully discussing how the Relative Plausibility model accounts for anomalous conditional judgments, but the general line of argument will be sketched here. To derive the anomalous conjunctive anomalies, assume that the plausibility, $\mathcal{P}[A, X]$, is a function of the similarity between a mental model in which A and X are true and a mental model of the present situation. As Tversky (1977) has shown, it is possible to increase the similarity of an instance by increasing the number of features it shares with a target. Thus, if X is a representative consequence and Y is an unrepresentative consequence of A, we should have that $\mathcal{P}[A, X \text{ AND } Y] > \mathcal{P}[A, Y]$. Furthermore, NOT-X is an unrepresentative consequence and NOT-Y is a representative consequence of A; hence, $\mathcal{P}[A, \text{NOT}(X \text{ AND } Y)] \leq \mathcal{P}[A, \text{NOT-}Y]$. Thus, $\mathcal{P}[A, X \text{ AND } Y]/\mathcal{P}[A, \text{NOT}(X \text{ AND } Y)] > \mathcal{P}[A, Y]/\mathcal{P}[A, \text{NOT-}Y]$. By step 5 of the Relative Plausibility model, $A \rightarrow X \text{ AND } Y$ should be rated as more true than $A \rightarrow Y$. The derivation of disjunctive anomalies is similar. The anomalous conditionalizations (Proposition 3) can be derived as follows. The relative plausibility of $A \rightarrow X \text{ AND } Y$ and $A \text{ AND } X \rightarrow Y$ is determined by the ratios, $\mathcal{P}[A, X \text{ AND } Y]/\mathcal{P}[A, \text{NOT}(X \text{ AND } Y)]$ and $\mathcal{P}[A \text{ AND } X, Y]/\mathcal{P}[A \text{ AND } X, \text{NOT-}Y]$. Assuming that $\mathcal{P}[A, X \text{ AND } Y] = \mathcal{P}[A \text{ AND } X, Y]$, the relative plaubility of $A \rightarrow X \text{ AND } Y$ and $A \text{ AND } X \rightarrow Y$ is determined by $1/\mathcal{P}[A, \text{NOT}(X \text{ AND } Y)]$ and $1/\mathcal{P}[A \text{ AND } X, \text{NOT-}Y]$. But $\mathcal{P}[A, \text{NOT}(X \text{ AND } Y)] <$

$\mathcal{P}$[A AND X, NOT-Y] because A and X are a plausible combination. Therefore A → X AND Y should be rated more true than A AND X → Y.

The Relative Plausibility model differs from the Ramsey thought experiment in that the content of the consequent influences the mental models that are constructed in the course of evaluating a counterfactual. The Relative Plausibility model accounts for anomalous conditional judgments by restructuring the cognitive process that is postulated to underly counterfactual inference, and by adopting aspects of Tversky's similarity model in the evaluation of the plausibility of mental models.

Acknowledgments: We would like to thank Tony Greenwald for commenting on an earlier draft of this work, and Jane Goodman and Elizabeth Loftus for useful discussions of counterfactual reasoning.

REFERENCES

Ginsberg, M. L. (1986). Counterfactuals. Artificial Intelligence, 30, 35-79.

Goodman, N. (1947). The problem of counterfactual conditionals. Journal of Philosophy, 44, 113-128. Reprinted in Goodman (1965).

Goodman, N. (1965). Fact, fiction, and forecast. Second edition by Bobbs-Merrill, Indianapolis.

Johnson-Laird, P. N. (1986). Conditionals and mental models. In E. C. Traugott, A. ter Meulen, J. S. Reilly, & C. A. Ferguson (Eds.), On conditionals. Cambridge, UK: Cambridge University Press.

Kripke, S. (1963). Semantical analysis of modal logics, I. Zeitschrift fur mathematische Logik und Grundlagen der Mathematik, 9, 67-96.

Lewis, D. K. (1973). Counterfactuals. Cambridge, MA: Harvard University Press.

Marcus, H., & Zajonc, R. (1985). The cognitive perspective in social psychology. In G. Lindzey & E. Aronson (Eds.), Handbook of social psychology (3rd ed.). Reading, MA: Addison-Wesley.

Miyamoto, J. M., & Dibble, E. (1986). Counterfactual conditionals and the conjunction fallacy. Proceedings of the Eighth Annual Conference of the Cognitive Science Society.

Montague, R. (1974). Formal philosopy: Selected papers of Richard Montague. Edited with an introduction by R. H. Thomason. New Haven: Yale University Press.

Morier, D. M., & Borgida, E. (1984). The conjunction fallacy: A task specific phenomenon? Personality and Social Psychology Bulletin, 10, 243-252.

Pennington, N. (1984). Technical note on conjunctive explanations. Center for Decision Research, Graduate School of Business, The University of Chicago.

Ramsey, F. P. (1931) The foundations of mathematics and other logical essays. London: Kegan Paul, Trench, Trubner & Co.

Rips, L. J., & Marcus, S. L. (1979). Suppositions and the analysis of conditional sentences. In M. A. Just & P. A. Carpenter (Eds.), Cognitive processes in comprehension. Hillsdale, NJ: Erlbaum, 185-220.

Stalnaker, R. C. (1968). A theory of conditionals. In N. Rescher (Ed.), Studies in logical theory. Oxford: Blackwell, ApQ Monograph No. 2. Reprinted in E. Sosa, Causation and conditionals. Oxford: Oxford University Press, 1975.

Stalnaker, R. C. (1984). Inquiry. Cambridge, MA: MIT Press.

Tversky, A. (1977). Features of similarity. Psychological Review, 84, 327-352.

Tversky, A., & Kahneman, D. (1983). Extensional versus intuitive reasoning: The conjunction fallacy in probability judgment. Psychological Review, 90, 293-315.

Competition for Evidential Support

Gilbert Harman

Department of Philosophy, Princeton University

Abstract

In order to accept a hypothesis on the grounds that it is the best explanation of the evidence, one must know what other hypotheses compete for evidential support with the first hypothesis. But the principles for determining when hypotheses compete are obscure and represent a currently unsolved problem for this form of inference. Competing hypotheses need not contradict each other. A defender of inference to the best explanation as a distinctive form of inference will not want to identify competing hypotheses with hypotheses that are jointly highly improbable. Relying on probabilities to solve this problem would be to put the cart before the horse, since the idea behind taking inference to the best explanation to be a distinctive form of inference is that we use inference to the best explanation to determine probabilities, not the reverse Furthermore, it does not work to rely on a failure by the "hypothesis generator" to generate anything but competing hypotheses, because that just pushes the problem over to the hypothesis generator. Anyway, noncompeting hypotheses often have to be considered and therefore have to be generated Whether there is competition between two hypotheses seems to depend at least in part with whether one might be used to "fill out" the other without leading to a major change in the explanation. But it remains unclear how to distinguish "filling out" an explanation from changing it.

Keywords: explanation, inference, hypothesis, competition

The problem

Inference to the best explanation occurs when one infers the best of competing explanations of the evidence. This raises several issues. One concerns the criteria by which one out of several competing explanations is selected as the "best" of that group. Various suggestions might be made about this (Thagard, 1978, forthcoming; Harman, 1986, Harman et al., 1987, Harman et al., 1988) and I won't try to say anything about it here. Instead, I want to call attention to a different issue, namely, what makes it true that certain possible explanations are in competition for the support of that evidence?

Not all possible explanations compete in this sense Suppose Dan the detective is investigating Albert's cause of death. The evidence consists of various features of the body, the color of the skin, bruises here and there, discolorations, and also certain aspects of the surroundings, broken glass, a piece of string, and so forth Consider the following hypotheses:

(1) Albert died because he was strangled
(2) Albert died because he was poisoned

(3) Albert died because his heart stopped beating
(4) Albert died because of lack of oxygen going to his brain

Normally, under these circumstances, Dan would suppose that the strangling hypothesis competes with the poisoning hypothesis. In other words, the evidence will normally support the poisoning hypothesis only if that hypothesis provides a better explanation of the evidence (in accordance with whatever the relevant criteria are) than the strangling hypothesis does.

But normally the poisoning hypothesis will *not* compete with the heart stopping hypothesis or the lack of oxygen hypothesis. It is just not true that Dan can accept the poisoning hypothesis only if it provides a better explanation of the evidence than the heart stopping hypothesis. Dan may not know just how the poisoning might work, but in the absence of further information Dan might suppose that the heart stopping hypothesis may very well be quite compatible with the poisoning hypothesis and indeed that both might be part of a fuller explanation of the death. Therefore, Dan can envision accepting the poisoning hypothesis as the best explanation of the evidence without supposing that the poisoning hypothesis offers a better explanation than the heart stopping hypothesis.

In general, some possible explanations of the data compete in the relevant sense and some do not. The question is how to determine for any given hypothesis what its competitors are with respect to specified evidence. Such a determination is necessary before a hypothesis can be accepted as providing the best of competing explanations of the evidence.

The question of how to determine competitors raises related problems in psychology, in artificial intelligence, and in philosophy. For psychology, there is the question, "What leads people to treat possible explanations as competing?" In an artificial intelligence system using inference to the best explanation, there is the question, "How is it to be determined what to take as competing hypotheses?" For philosophy, the problem concerns which hypotheses one is "justified" in taking to be competitors for purposes of inference to be best explanation. In the philosophy of science, one question concerns what scientists actually do about this and a related question concerns what they "ought" to do about it.

In part the question concerns what hypotheses should be "generated" in considering what inference to make. But the question also arises when someone else suggests a further possible explanation that one has not or would not normally generate oneself. Sometimes one accepts (or "ought" to accept) the further suggestion as a competitor, sometimes not.

Competition as Contradiction

One natural suggestion might be that hypotheses compete if they contradict each other, given background assumptions and the evidence. This suggestion would account for many cases For example, Kepler's hypothesis that the planets revolve around the sun in elliptical orbits competes with the hypothesis that the planets revolve around the sun in circular orbits. Here the competing hypotheses contradict each other, on the assumption that a circle does not count as an ellipse with coinciding foci.

But in many other cases competing hypotheses do not have to contradict each other. One possible hypothesis about Albert's death is that he was strangled. Another is that he was poisoned. These hypotheses compete for support from Dan's evidence, but they are not inconsistent, since Albert may have been both strangled and poisoned.

It might be objected that the hypotheses are not just (a) that Albert was poisoned and (b) that he was strangled but (a) that he died because he was poisoned and (b) that he died because he was strangled. But (a) and (b) don't contradict each other. Both might be correct. It might be that Albert's death was the overdetermined result of both causes: Sam poisoned Albert and then, just to make sure, Sam strangled him too. Either the poisoning or the strangling would have led to death at exactly the same moment. The death is equally the result of both causes! Alternatively, it could have happened that Sam's poisoning of Albert caused the death by causing someone else to strangle Albert, or vice versa! There are many possibilities of this sort, enough to show that the hypotheses of death by poisoning and death by strangulation are not literally inconsistent given the evidence and background information.

Green and grue

If the evidence is that all examined emeralds are green, one possible hypothesis is that this is so because all emeralds are green. A competing hypothesis is that all emeralds are "grue," that is, green if examined before the year 2000 and otherwise blue (Goodman, 1965). But the hypothesis that all emeralds are green does not contradict the hypothesis that all emeralds are grue, since both hypotheses would be true if all emeralds were examined before the year 2000.

Goodman's solution is to say we "assume" or "posit" conflict between these hypotheses by postulating that there are emeralds that will not be examined before 2000 (Ullian & Goodman, 1976). But the hypotheses would seem to compete in the relevant sense even in the absence of such a postulate. For if we accept one of these hypotheses as the best account of the data, e.g., "All emeralds are green," then there is no need to look any farther. The data need no further explanation of the sort that might be provided by "All emeralds are grue."

Appealing to Probability

Thagard (forthcoming) notes that in the debate over dinosaur extinction, scientists take the following two hypotheses to compete: (1) Dinosaurs became extinct because of a meteorite collision. (2) Dinosaurs became extinct because the sea level fell. These hypotheses do not contradict each other and could both be true. What is it that leads scientists to treat these hypotheses but not others as competing?

Why can't we be content with a theory of inference to the best explanation that has no principled account of when hypotheses are to be treated as competitors? Why not simply rely on scientists' judgments about when hypotheses compete? Answer: because there ought to be some account of where those judgments come from. To refuse to give a principled answer to this question is not very different from simply relying on scientific judgments about whether the evidence supports a given conclusion. If we want to give a principled account of when evidence supports a given conclusion, we need to be able to give a principled account of when hypotheses are in competition for support from particular evidence.

Thagard (forthcoming) speculates that scientists may treat (1) and (2) as competing hypotheses because (a) there are no explanatory relations between them and (b) their conjunction is unlikely. There are two parts to this suggestion, (a) and (b), which I would like to consider separately in reverse order.

Consider the suggestion that possible explanations of the evidence conflict if their conjunction is unlikely. In what way "unlikely"? If what is meant is that their conjunction is *a priori* unlikely without considering the evidence in this particular case, then almost any conjunction of hypotheses will be unlikely and almost any two hypotheses must be treated as conflicting, which is contrary to ordinary practice. On the other hand, if we are to take the evidence into account and consider the probabilities of the conjunction of the two hypotheses given that evidence, then we must ask where these probabilities come from. The thought behind the idea that there is such a thing as inference to the best explanation is that our probability judgments depend on our judgments about the relative merits of competing explanations: the standards of inference to the best explanation influence judgments of probabilities rather than the other way round. If probabilities could be determined without reference to such explanatory considerations, we would not need inference to the best explanation. But then we cannot use probabilities to decide when hypotheses compete, since we have to know what hypotheses compete in order to reach a judgment about probabilities. Thagard (forthcoming) makes a similar point in discussing Pearl's (1986, 1987) work on belief networks.

Generate Only Competitors?

One way to try to circumvent the difficulty of finding a principled account of competition in an artificial intelligence reasoning program that uses inference to the best explanation is to see to it that the program never generates anything but competitors of the hypothesis being considered. But how is this to be accomplished? The usual method is to put ad hoc restrictions on the hypotheses to be considered. But can this be done in a principled and non ad hoc way? Furthermore, what happens when a hypothesis is suggested to the system from outside, a hypothesis that is not thought up by the system itself? How does it decide whether that hypothesis is in competition with the other hypotheses being considered.

Further consideration indicates that trying to restrict what hypotheses are generated is not going to work. Recall Detective Dan who is trying to determine the cause of Albert's death. It is quite likely that explanations like heart stopping and no oxygen to the brain will be *considered* by Dan. The hypotheses will be "generated," they just won't be generated *as* competitors of poisoning or strangling. But how are they distinguished from hypotheses that are generated as competitors of the poisoning and strangling hypotheses?

Explanatory Relations among Hypotheses

Thagard's other suggestion about competition was that scientists treat the meteorite collision hypothesis and the falling seal level hypothesis as competing hypotheses with respect to the extinction of Dinosaurs because "there are no explanatory relations between them ..." This is more promising, although there are difficulties in making the suggestion precise.

Consider again Arthur's death. The hypothesis that he died because he was poisoned does not conflict with the hypothesis that he died because his heart stopped beating The lack of conflict does not have to depend on the definite belief that there in an explanatory relation between these two hypotheses. Dan may have no idea how the poison works. He does not have to have a positive belief that poison works by stopping the heart, for example. The point is rather that he supposes that if the evidence is explained by the poisoning, it is *possible* that further explanatory work might be done by the heart stopping. He envisions that the explanation of Albert's death by poisoning might be filled in with a further account of how the poisoning led to the death, where that further explanation might involve Albert's dying because his heart stopped beating.

That is not what Dan is envisioning in the poisoning and strangling case. He does not expect the poisoning to have been caused by the strangling, or vice versa: although that is possible!

But now there seems to be a dilemma. If we say that hypotheses that might explain the evidence compete if and only if it is *not possible* for the one explanation to be filled out by using the second, then we have to say that poisoning and strangling do not compete! If we say that it is not "expected" that the one hypothesis will be filled out by using the second, then this is rarely "positively expected". If the reference to what is "expected" is a way of appealing to probability, we are back with the problem that appeal to inference to the best explanation is supposed to account of judgments of probability rather than vice versa.

Maybe the answer is this: Although Dan can imagine that someone's poisoning Albert may have caused Albert's death by leading someone else to strangle Albert, that is a different explanation from what Dan envisions when he hypothesizes that Albert died because he was poisoned. Perhaps two hypotheses compete if the use of either to "fill in" the explanation provided by the other would yield a "different explanation" from what one is envisioning.

This raises the question of what the difference is between "filling out" an explanation, e.g. as when Dan explains how the poisoning caused Albert's death by causing Albert's heart to stop beating, and "yielding a different explanation from what was originally envisioned," e.g. as when Dan decides that the poisoning caused Albert's death by leading someone else to strangle Albert.

And how is this sort of difference something that can be used on the spot by a human being or scientist or artificial intelligence system to determine what the competitors of a given hypothesis are for the support of certain evidence the hypothesis might explain?

The preparation of this paper was supported in part by a research grant to Princeton University from the James S McDonnell Foundation.

Bibliography

Goodman, N. (1965). *Fact, Fiction, and Forecast*, 2nd edition. Indianapolis: Bobbs, Merrill.

Harman, G. (1986) *Change in View: Principles of Reasoning*. Cambridge, Massachusetts; M.I.T./Bradford Books.

Harman, G., Bienkowski, M. A., Salem, K., & Pratt, I (1987) "Measuring change and coherence in evaluating potential change in view." *Ninth Annual Conference of the Cognitive Science Society*. Hillsdale, N.J.: Erlbaum, 203-209.

Harman, G., Ranney, M., Salem, K., Döring, F., Epstein, J. & Jaworska, A. (1988). "A theory of simplicity." *Tenth Annual Conference of the Cognitive Science Society*. Hillsdale, N.J.: Erlbaum, 111-117.

Pearl, J. (1986) "Fusion, propagation, and structuring in belief networks," *Artificial Intelligence* 29: 241-288.

Pearl, J. (1987) "Distributed revision of composite beliefs," *Artificial Intelligence*, 33: 173-215.

Thagard, P. (19787). "The best explanation: criteria for theory choice." *Journal of Philosophy* 75: 76-92.

Thagard, P. (forthcoming). "Explanatory coherence." *Behavioral and Brain Sciences*.

Ullian, J. & Goodman, N. (1976). "Projectibility unscathed." *Journal of Philosophy* 73: 527-531.

Managing Uncertainty in Rule-based Reasoning

Thomas R. Shultz, Philip David Zelazo, and Daniel J. Engelberg
Department of Psychology
McGill University

ABSTRACT

There are two major problems associated with propagation of uncertainty in the rule-based modeling of human reasoning. One concerns how the possibly uncertain evidence in a rule's antecedents affects the rule's conclusion. The other concerns the issue of combining evidence across rules having the same conclusion. Two experiments were conducted in which psychological data were compared with a variety of mathematical models for managing uncertainty. Results of an experiment on the first problem suggested that the certainty of the antecedents in a production rule can be summarized by the maximum of disjunctively connected antecedents and the minimum of conjunctively connected antecedents (*maximin* summarizing), and that the maximum certainty of the rule's conclusion can be scaled down by multiplication with the results of that summary (*multiplication* scaling). A second experiment suggested that the second problem can be solved with Heckerman's modified certainty factor model which sums the certainties contributed by each of two rules and divides by 1 plus their product.

INTRODUCTION

Rule-based systems have proven to be among the most successful techniques for the computational modeling of human reasoning. They are able to model human procedural knowledge in a convenient, homogeneous, modular fashion that is consistent with a great deal of psychological evidence. Some of the newer production systems have the capacity to learn or modify their own rules (Klahr, Langley, & Neches, 1987). Many of the artificially intelligent expert systems are also built on a rule-based architecture (Buchanan & Shortliffe, 1984).

Curiously, several of the rule-based expert systems, but very few of the rule-based human simulations, employ techniques for representing and propagating uncertainty. Although it is widely acknowledged that much of human knowledge is uncertain, it is in the field of artificial intelligence that the debate about how to represent and manage uncertainty in rule-based reasoning has been focused (Kanal & Lemmer, 1986; Hink & Woods, 1987).

The problem of uncertainty in rule-based architectures can be broken into two sub-problems. One concerns how the possibly uncertain evidence in a rule's antecedents affects the rule's conclusion. Consider the general case of a production rule with *i* antecedents and *j* conclusions.

IF antecedent_1
antecedent_2
:
antecedent_i
THEN conclusion_1 (maxcf_1)
:
conclusion_j (maxcf_j)

Antecedents and conclusions would typically be represented as propositions, perhaps using a predicate-argument structure. Each of the rule's *j* conclusions would typically be qualified by a numerically represented maximum certainty factor (*maxcf*). If the evidence contained in the rule's antecedents is believed with perfect certainty, then each conclusion_j would be drawn with its maxcf_j. However, in the general case, the evidence in each of the rule's antecedents would be believed with varying degrees of certainty. How should the uncertainty of antecedent evidence be summarized? And how should this summarized antecedent certainty affect the maxcf of each conclusion? Slightly complicating the first question is the fact that the antecedents could be connected either conjunctively or disjunctively. With conjunctive connectives, all of the antecedents must hold in order for the rule to fire. For disjunctive connectives, satisfaction of only a single antecedent could enable the rule to fire.

The other uncertainty sub-problem in rule-based systems concerns the issue of combining evidence across different rules with the same conclusion. Imagine that particular conclusions exist in more than one rule. As rules fire, their conclusions come to be believed with varying degrees of certainty, as outlined above. How should these uncertainties be combined in cases where a previously fired rule has overlapping conclusions with a newly fired rule? This is not a problem in deterministic production systems that do not handle uncertainty since they typically avoid drawing the same conclusion more than once. However, it is a problem in any production system that attempts to propagate uncertainty as its rules fire.

Solution of these two sub-problems is critical for rule-based efforts to model human cognition. Algorithms implementing a solution to each sub-problem are typically invoked every time a rule fires. If these algorithms lack psychological validity, simulation errors will tend to accumulate and be compounded as rules fire.

EXPERIMENT 1: PROPAGATING UNCERTAINTY WITHIN A SINGLE RULE

The purpose of this experiment was to test several different plausible models for combining antecedent uncertainties to create a summary antecedent cf and two models for scaling down the conclusion's maxcf by the summary antecedent cf.

The summary antecedent cf could be computed as the (a) *minimum* of the antecedent cfs, (b) *maximum* of the antecedent cfs, (c) *product* of the antecedent cfs, (d) *sum* of the antecedent cfs *minus* the *overlap* among them, (e) *mean* of the antecedent cfs, or (f) *median* of the antecedent cfs. The first four models derive from insights or assumptions in probability calculus. The last two models represent guesses about what ordinary humans might do. The *minimum* and *product* models would be most appropriate for conjunctively connected antecedents; the *maximum* and *sum-overlap* models for disjunctively connected antecedents.

Barclay and Beach (1972) reported psychological support for the *product* model with conjunctive connectives and for the *sum-overlap* model with disjunctive connectives. Wyer (1976) also found support for the *sum-overlap* model with disjunctive connectives. But with conjunctive connectives, Wyer reported that an averaging together of the results of the *product* and *mean* models was most successful in accounting for his data.

Two hybrid models for summarizing antecedent uncertainty were also tested. The *maximin* model is a combination of the *maximum* and *minimum* models. It uses the maximum of disjunctively connected antecedent cfs and the minimum of conjunctively connected antecedent cfs. *Maximin* is easy to compute and sensitive to the distinction between conjunctive and disjunctive connections. It makes some sense to use the minimum of conjunctively connected antecedent cfs since all of the antecedents need to be satisfied in order for the rule to fire. The weakest link in this evidential chain is that condition with the smallest cf. Similarly, it makes sense to use the maximum of disjunctively connected antecedent cfs since satisfaction of any one of them can qualify the rule for firing. The strongest of this evidential set is the antecedent with the highest cf. The other hybrid model, here termed the *probabilistic* model, combines the *product* and *sum-overlap* models. It computes the product of conjunctively connected antecedents and the sum-overlap of disjunctively connected antecedents.

Scaling down the maxcf in the conclusion by the summary antecedent cf could be done by *multiplication*, or averaging (*mean*). Multiplication is commonly used for scaling in production systems (Shortliffe, 1976; van Melle, Scott, Bennett, & Peairs, 1981). Averaging would be mathematically unsophisticated, but is still a possibility for ordinary humans faced with the task of combining two numerical estimates (Wyer, 1976).

Method

Our subjects learned a rule in which antecedent cfs were assigned and then were asked first about the certainty of the rule's antecedents being satisfied, and second about the certainty of the rule's conclusion. The first set of ratings were correlated with those generated by each of the 8 summarization models above. Then the second set of ratings was correlated with those generated by the two scaling models combined with the best of the summarization models and with the subject's own summarization rating.

A sample item was:

If event A, **or** event B, **or** event C happens, then event D is **highly** certain to happen.
Event A is **highly** certain to happen.
Event B is **moderately** certain to happen.
Event C **slightly** certain to happen.

With this item, subjects were asked to rate the certainty of their belief that one or more of events A, B, and C will happen, and that event D will happen. Across the items, there was systematic variation in the connective (conjunctive or disjunctive), the certainty of both antecedents and conclusions, and the sign of the conclusion (positive or negative) so as to permit a robust test of the models. For conjunctive connectives, subjects were asked to rate the certainty that events A, B, and C will all happen. Additional items were presented at the end of each questionnaire in order to calibrate the subject's use of the certainty descriptors employed in the previous rule items.

Results

Because different subjects may interpret the certainty expressions differently, responses to the calibration questions were used to establish where on the rating scale each subject viewed the adjectives completely-, highly-, moderately-, and slightly certain, and uncertain. These calibrated values were then used to generate model predictions for each subject. Responses to the rule items were converted to cfs.

The first major problem for the results is to identify the best model for summarizing the uncertainty of the antecedent evidence. Predictions for the eight above models on each of the rule items were generated using each subject's calibrated scores. Then the predicted ratings for each of the eight models were correlated with the subject's actual ratings.

The resulting correlation coefficients were subjected to an analysis of variance. The mean correlation coefficients for the various models in descending order were *maximin* .728, *probabilistic* .706, *maximum* .322, *sum-overlap* .319, *mean* .288, *median* .276, *product* .170, and *minimum* .129. The two hybrid models that distinguished conjunctive from disjunctive connectives (*maximin* and *probabilistic*) performed significantly better than any of the other models.

Visual examination of the predicted ratings for these two best models indicated that the *probabilistic* model generated ratings that were too extreme for most subjects. To test this systematically, the variances of the predictions of the *maximin* and *probabilistic* models and those of the subject's actual ratings were subjected to an analysis of variance in which the sole factor was the source of the variances. The mean variances were *probabilistic* .166, *maximin* .091, and *actual* .073. Each of these was significantly different from the other, but the *actual* variances were much more closely approximated by the *maximin* model than by the *probabilistic* model.

Visual examination of the data also suggested that there were substantial differences between subjects in the size but not the pattern of correlations with models. Analysis of variance of the model correlations, with subject as the repeated-measures independent factor, yielded a main effect for subject. Mean correlations for subjects ranged from .04 to .64. The model correlations were also converted to ranks within each subject, and analyzed for concordance, revealing considerable agreement among subjects in the pattern of their correlations with models.

The next major task for the Results was to determine the best model for scaling down the certainty of the conclusion by the summarized antecedent certainty. The summarized antecedent certainties were computed for the two best summarizing models: *maximin* and *probabilistic*. The subject's actual summarized ratings were also used, and this was termed the *pure* model since it permitted a purer test of the scaling model, uncontaminated by the summarizing model. Predicted certainties of the rule's final conclusions were generated for each of these summarized sources by both the *multiplication* and *mean* scaling models. Then each of these six model based predictions was correlated with the subject's actual certainty conclusions across the rule items.

The resulting correlation coefficients were subjected to an analysis of variance in which the repeated measures were summarizing model (*maximin, probabilistic*, and *pure*), and scaling model (*multiplication* and *mean*). The mean correlation coefficients for models using the superior multiplication scaling were .702 *pure*, .634 *maximin*, and .626 *probabilistic*.

Discussion

The results of this experiment clearly suggest that the best way to summarize antecedent evidence is by taking the maximum of disjunctively connected antecedent certainties and the minimum of conjunctively connected antecedent certainties (the *maximin* model). The *probabilistic* model also correlated well with subject data, but the fact that the *maximin* model predicted the absolute values of the subject ratings so much better recommends this model over the *probabilistic* model. *Maximin* also has the advantage of being easy for subjects to compute regardless of the number of rule antecedents. The better of the two tested scaling methods was *multiplication*. Thus, a good technique for propagating uncertainty within a production rule would summarize the uncertainty of the antecedent evidence using *maximin*, and then scale down the maxcf in the conclusion by multiplying the maxcf by the result of *maximin*.

EXPERIMENT 2: COMBINING UNCERTAINTY ACROSS RULES WITH THE SAME CONCLUSION

The problem of combining evidence across rules with the same conclusion has been the focus of a good deal of research in artificial intelligence. A major distinction among the various approaches is between those that use numeric vs. non-numeric approaches. Non-numeric approaches (e.g., P. R. Cohen, 1985; Kuipers, Moskowitz, & Kassirer, 1988) have not yet successfully dealt with the issue of combining conflicting evidence. Numeric approaches use techniques such as certainty factors, Bayes' theorem, fuzzy logic (Zadeh, 1979), and Dempster-Shafer theory. The Bayesian and fuzzy logic approaches have the difficulty of requiring knowledge that people rarely possess. The Dempster-Shafer technique bears some similarities to certainty factors (Gordon & Shortliffe, 1984), which is the method emphasized here.

The certainty factor approach derives from the MYCIN (Shortliffe, 1976) and EMYCIN (van Melle et al., 1981) programs. In the simplest case, where both rules support the same conclusion, the certainty factor approach specifies that a prior cf (cf_p) is updated (cf_u) by new evidence (cf_n) by adding the new evidence to old after first scaling down the new evidence by the amount it could benefit the old evidence

$$cf_u = cf_p + [cf_n * (1 - cf_p)] \tag{1}$$

The scaling down serves to keep the revised cf within the bounds -1 to +1. Interestingly, this reduces to the sum of the two cfs minus their product

$$cf_u = cf_p + cf_n - (cf_p * cf_n) \quad (2)$$

Note that (2) is simply the *sum-overlap* rule for combining probabilities with no assumptions about their correlation . (1) and (2) apply only when both cfs are positive. Where both cfs are negative, one takes the negative of (2) with negated cf arguments

$$cf_u = cf_p + cf_n + (cf_p * cf_n) \quad (3)$$

Taken together, (2) and (3) describe the certainty factor approach to combining confirming evidence. For disconfirming evidence, that is, when only one of the cfs is negative, the function becomes

$$cf_u = (cf_p + cf_n) / (1 - \min(|cf_p|, |cf_n|)) \quad (4)$$

The rationale for the unusual divisor in this third case is that a single new piece of disconfirming evidence should not be allowed to overpower the accumulated evidence produced by possibly a large number of rules (Buchanan & Shortliffe, 1984). The cf approach described in (2) - (4) shall be referred to here as the *classic cf* approach.

Heckerman (1986) demonstrated that there is an unlimited number of probabilistic interpretations of cfs, all of which are monotonic transformations of the likelihood ratio. In addition to the standard cf formulation, revealed in (2) - (4), Heckerman proposed an alternate, simplified version

$$cf_u = (cf_p + cf_n) / [1 + (cf_p * cf_n)] \quad (5)$$

Heckerman showed that both (5) and (2) - (4) are valid probabilistic interpretations of cfs, under the assumptions that the evidence provided by the rules is conditionally independent and that the rule base forms a tree structure. The consequences of violating these two assumptions are unknown. Grosof (1986) showed that (5) is equivalent to a special case of Dempster-Shafer theory. The cf approach in (5) shall here be referred to as the *modified cf* approach.

The *classic* and *modified cf* approaches were contrasted with three mathematically unsophisticated models that we thought ordinary reasoners might employ. The unsophisticated models computed the *mean, maximum,* or *minimum* of the two certainties.

Method

Subjects learned two production rules with the same conclusion, were given antecedent cfs for the two rules, and were then asked to indicate how strongly they believed the conclusion proposition. Subject data were correlated with those generated by the five combining models. In a partial replication of the results of Experiment 1, the maxcf of each rule could be scaled by the antecedent certainty using either *multiplication* or averaging (*mean*). These two scaling models were crossed with the five combining models to produce 10 tested models.

A sample item was:

> Events A and B are independent sources of evidence for event C.
> If event A happens, then event C is **moderately** certain to happen.
> If event B happens, then event C is **moderately** certain **not** to happen.
> Event A is **highly** certain to happen.
> Event B is **slightly** certain to happen.

Subjects were asked to combine this evidence to rate the certainty of their belief that event C will happen. As in Experiment 1, there was systematic variation in the certainty of antecedents and the positivity-negativity of the conclusions so as to permit a robust test of the models. The last few items of each questionnaire were used to calibrate the subject's use of the certainty descriptors.

Results

Predictions were generated for each of the 10 models using each subject's calibrated scores. These predictions were then correlated with the actual certainty conclusions given by each subject. Correlations were subjected to analysis of variance. The mean correlation coefficients were significantly higher for *multiplication* scaling than for *mean* scaling for every combining model except the *maximum* model. Description of differences among the combining models will be limited to those using the superior *multiplication* scaling. The *mean* (.835), *classic cf* (.858), and *modified cf* (.848) combining models yielded significantly higher correlations than did the *maximum* (.694) and *minimum* (.723) combining models, but did not differ from each other.

In order to draw a clearer distinction between the two cf and the mean combining models, their absolute predictions were contrasted with the actual absolute certainty scores. The insight that led to this comparison was that the cf techniques always raise the updated cf, and the *mean* technique always lowers the updated cf, relative to the higher of two original cfs. Thus, the cf combining models produce higher absolute predictions than does the *mean* combining model. An analysis of variance of these absolute predicted and actual scores was undertaken in which the sole within subjects factor was source of the absolute scores. The mean absolute scores were .378 *actual*, .362 *classic cf* model, .380 *modified cf* model, and .189 *mean* model. The *actual* and cf models scores did not differ significantly from each other, but did significantly exceed those generated by the *mean* model.

As in Experiment 1, individual differences were confined to the size rather than to the pattern of correlations with models. Analysis of variance of the model correlations, with subject as the repeated-measures independent factor, yielded a main effect for subject. Mean correlations for subjects ranged from .49 to .86. The model correlations were also converted to ranks within each subject and analyzed for concordance, verifying that there was considerable agreement among subjects in the pattern of their correlations with models.

Discussion

Confirming the results of the previous experiment, the present data indicated strong support for scaling the maxcf in a conclusion by multiplication with the antecedent cf, as opposed to taking the mean of the two values. The main result of this experiment was the finding that the two cf models were the most effective in combining certainties across two production rules. The principal way in which the cf models were superior to the *mean* model was in matching the absolute values of subjects' certainty ratings. Since the two cf models are both monotonic transformations of the same likelihood ratio, it is not surprising that they produce highly similar results. We have a slight preference for the *modified cf* model (5) since it presents a simpler, more unified formula than does the tri-partite *classic cf* model [(2), (3), (4)].

GENERAL DISCUSSION

The results of these two experiments suggest that a modified cf approach produces a good fit to the certainty judgments of ordinary reasoners. Our cf approach summarizes the certainty of antecedent evidence in a production rule by taking the maximum of disjunctively connected antecedents and the minimum of conjunctively connected antecedents (*maximin* model). It scales down the maxcf in the rule's conclusion by multiplying with the summary antecedent cf (*multiplication* model). And it combines certainty evidence across production rules with the same conclusion by dividing the sum of the certainties by 1 plus their product (*modified cf* model).

Previously, the only reported psychological support for a cf approach was provided by the anecdotal testimony of a single expert diagnostician (Shortliffe, 1976). The present data show that the cf approach, when modified to allow for rules with disjunctively connected antecedents, has considerable validity in accounting for the reasoning of ordinary people. The MYCIN (Shortliffe,

1976) and EMYCIN (van Melle et al., 1981) programs that pioneered the use of cfs did not apparently allow disjunctively connected antecedents (except within a conjunct). The assumption was that disjunction could be handled by having multiple rules with the same conclusion. Our approach differs in allowing both disjunctive antecedents within a rule as well as multiple rules with the same conclusion.

The decision about whether to use multiple rules vs. disjunction within a rule can be governed in part by considering the corresponding differences in updating of certainties. Representation of a packet of procedural knowledge in a single rule with disjunctive antecedents specifies that the certainty of the antecedent evidence should be summarized by the maximum of the antecedent cfs. Representation in multiple rules specifies that the updating of certainties across these antecedents should be done using the *modified cf* procedure. The former assumes maximal correlation among the antecedents and implies that cfs of the other antecedents should not increment the maximum cf, whereas the latter assumes conditional independence among the antecedents and implies that cfs from other antecedents (in other rules) may increment the cfs concluded earlier. These considerations can give rule writers, whether cognitive modelers or artificial intelligence programmers, greater expressive power.

Some of the evidence from Experiment 1 suggests that researchers in probabilistic reasoning ought to consider the absolute values predicted by probabilistic models as well as their ability to correlate with human judgments. In particular, the *maximin* model proved superior to the *probabilistic* model in matching absolute values in human data. Use of the *maximin* model could account for the often reported tendency of ordinary reasoners to overestimate the probability of conjunctive events and underestimate the probability of disjunctive events (Barclay & Beach, 1972; Bar-Hillel, 1973; J. Cohen, Chesnick, & Haran, 1972; J. Cohen & Hansell, 1957; Howell, 1972; Slovic, 1969). The minimum will invariably be higher than the product, and the maximum lower than the sum-overlap. Previous explanations of these estimation errors have emphasized the *adjustment and anchoring* heuristic (Hink & Woods, 1987; Tversky and Kahneman, 1974). In that heuristic account, a person might use the certainty of an elementary event as anchor and then insufficiently adjust the certainty for the compound event upward in the case of disjunction and downward in the case of conjunction. But without specifying the degree of adjustment, the adjustment and anchoring model does not generate sufficiently specific predictions to compare with the *maximin* model.

A limitation of the present studies is that they are restricted to reasoning with abstract, de-contextualized material. Future research will be necessary to extend the present findings to more realistic items. As that happens, theoretical ideas about the impact of context on reasoning under uncertainty can be developed and contextual results can be compared to the those generated in the present, abstract situation.

The results of both experiments indicated that there were individual differences in models for managing uncertainty. These differences did not appear to reflect the use of different models by different subjects. On the contrary, subjects showed remarkable agreement in the pattern of their correlations across models. The best models were best for everyone tested. The way that subjects differed from each other was in their tendency to produce moderate or high correlations with the models in general. It is possible that such individual differences in average size of correlations reflect differences in mental ability or motivation. Subjects who fill out questionnaires without much care or who become confused by the items would not be expected to generate data consistent with these sorts of models.

ACKNOWLEDGEMENTS

This research was supported by a grant from the Natural Sciences and Engineering Research Council of Canada. Yoshio Takane provided valuable advice on analyzing individual differences.

REFERENCES

Barclay, S., & Beach, L. R. (1972). Combinatorial properties of personal probabilities. *Organizational Behavior and Human Performance*, **8**, 176-183.

Bar-Hillel, M. (1973). On the subjective probability of compound events. *Organizational Behavior and Human Performance*, **9**, 396-406.

Buchanan, B. G., & Shortliffe, E. H. (Eds.). (1984). *Rule-based expert systems*. Reading, MA: Addison-Wesley.

Cohen, J., Chesnick, E. I., & Haran, D. (1972). A confirmation of the inertial-psi effect in sequential choice and decision. *British Journal of Psychology*, **63**, 41-46.

Cohen, J., & Hansel, C. E. M. (1957). The nature of decisions in gambling. *Acta Psychologica*, **13**, 357-370.

Cohen, P. R. (1985). *Heuristic reasoning about uncertainty: An artificial intelligence approach.* Boston: Pitman.

Gordon, J., & Shortliffe, E. H. (1984). The Dempster-Shafer theory of evidence. In B. G. Buchanan & E. H. Shortliffe (Eds.), *Rule-based expert systems* (pp. 272-292). Reading, MA: Addison-Wesley.

Grosof, B. N. (1986). Evidential confirmation as transformed probability: On the duality of priors and updates. In L. N. Kanal & J. F. Lemmer (Eds.), *Uncertainty in Artificial Intelligence* (pp. 153-166). North-Holland: Elsevier Science Publishers.

Heckerman, D. (1986). Probabilistic Interpretations for MYCIN's certainty factors. In L. N. Kanal & J. F. Lemmer (Eds.), *Uncertainty in Artificial Intelligence* (pp. 167-196). North-Holland: Elsevier Science Publishers.

Hink, R. F., & Woods, D. L. (1987). How humans process uncertain knowledge: An introduction for knowledge engineers. *AI Magazine*, **8**, 41-53.

Howell, W. C. (1972). Compounding uncertainty from internal sources. *Journal of Experimental Psychology*, **95**, 6-13.

Kanal, L. N., & Lemmer, J. F. (Eds.). (1986). *Uncertainty in Artificial Intelligence*. North-Holland: Elsevier Science Publishers.

Klahr, D., Langley, P., & Neches, R. (Eds.). (1987). *Production system models of learning and development*. Cambridge, MA: MIT Press.

Kuipers, B., Moskowitz, A. J., & Kassirer, J. P. (1988). Critical decisions under uncertainty: Representation and structure. *Cognitive Science*, **12**, 177-210.

Shortliffe, E. H. (1976). *Computer-based medical consultations: MYCIN*. North-Holland: Elsevier Science Publishers.

Slovic, P. (1969). Manipulating the attractiveness of a gamble without changing its expected value. *Journal of Experimental Psychology*, **79**, 139-145.

Tversky, A., & Kahneman, D. (1974). Judgment under uncertainty: Heuristics and biases. *Science*, **185**, 1124-1131.

van Melle, W., Scott, A. C., Bennett, J. S., & Peairs, M. A. S. (1981). *The EMYCIN manual.* Unpublished manuscript, Stanford University.

Wyer, R. S., Jr. (1976). An investigation of the relations among probability estimates. *Organizational Behavior and Human Performance*, **15**, 1-18.

Zadeh, L. A. (1979). Approximate reasoning based on fuzzy logic. *Proceedings of the International Joint Conference on Artificial Intelligence*, **6**, 1004-1010.

Explorations in the Contributors to Plausibility

Cynthia L. Loiselle
Paul R. Cohen

Department of Computer and Information Science
University of Massachusetts

ABSTRACT

In previous work, we identified a method for automatically deriving possible rules of plausible inference from a set of relations, and determined that the transitivity of underlying characteristics of the relations was a significant factor in predicting the plausibility of inferences generated from these rules. Recent work by other researchers has also focused on identifying these kinds of characteristics and examining their role in the ability to predict plausibility. We examine these sets of characteristics and conclude that those factors that preserve transitivity provide most of the power of these systems. We then show how inferences can be used to determine the intended semantics, and thus the appropriate set of representational features, of a relation.

INTRODUCTION

One important aspect of research on semantic relations is understanding their behavior in inferences. Studying inferences forces us to examine how we reason with these relations. Of particular interest are common sense or *plausible* inferences, inferences whose rules suggest conclusions that are not guaranteed to be true but are true often enough to be useful. Unlike deductive inference where, given the truth values of the premises, the truth value of the conclusion is determined by the syntax of the inference rule alone, plausible inference requires that we also know something of the semantic content of the inference rule. We have shown that by identifying characteristics of the relations used in inference rules, we can predict the plausibility of their conclusions.

Several recent papers (Cohen & Loiselle, 1988; Huhns & Stephens, 1988; Winston, Chaffin & Herrmann, 1987) have focused on binary relations used in inferences of the form

$$\text{Given} \quad \text{A } R_i \text{ B and B } R_j \text{ C}$$
$$\text{conclude either} \quad \text{A } R_i \text{ C or A } R_j \text{ C.}$$

These efforts analyze relations in terms of more "primitive" elements, which are used to predict the plausibility of these kinds of inferences. This paper will review these results and discuss their contributions, noting especially those factors that seem to provide most of the power behind the ability to predict plausibility. We then examine the role of a relation's interpretation and show that knowing the precise meaning of a relation is crucial to predicting plausibility. We conclude by discussing our current research, which explores how the meaning of a relation, defined to be the assignment of these more primitive elements, can be determined from the behavior of the relation in inferences.

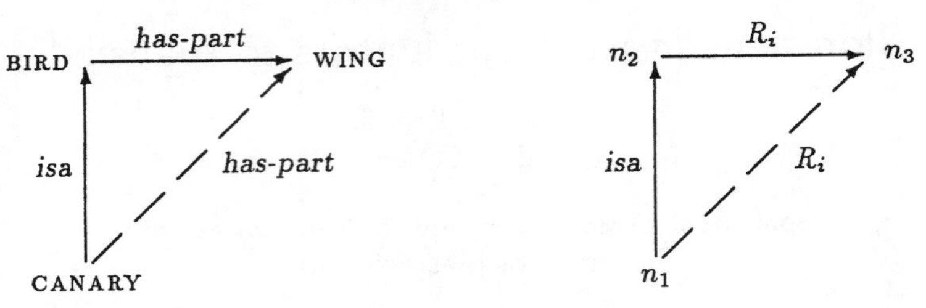

Figure 1: The triangular structure of property inheritance over *isa*

GENERATING RULES OF PLAUSIBLE INFERENCE

Cohen and Loiselle (1988) showed how the structure of property inheritance over *isa*, a common rule of plausible inference, could be generalized to generate other possible plausible inference rules. Figure 1 shows that property inheritance can be drawn as a triangle where the legs represent the known statements (premises) and the hypotenuse represents the conclusion. The left triangle illustrates a specific instantiation of property inheritance: the concept CANARY inherits the property "*has-part* WING" from its superclass BIRD. The right triangle shows the general form of property inheritance over *isa*: if n_1 is related to n_2 by *isa*, and n_2 is related to n_3 by any arbitrary relation R_i, we can infer that n_1 is also related to n_3 by R_i.

Property inheritance requires that the first premise be *isa* and that inheritance occurs only over this *isa* link. By relaxing these requirements we can generate many other possible inference rules with the same triangular structure (Figure 2). Again, the left triangle gives a specific instantiation of one such inference rule while the right triangle shows the corresponding general structure. Since we no longer restrict which link can be "inherited over" we are free to infer either R_i or R_j in the conclusion. So this structure can be used to form two inference rules:

$$n_1\ R_i\ n_2,\ n_2\ R_j\ n_3 \rightarrow n_1\ R_i\ n_3$$
$$n_1\ R_i\ n_2,\ n_2\ R_j\ n_3 \rightarrow n_1\ R_j\ n_3$$

Clearly, although we can use this structure to combine any two relations to yield two possible plausible inference rules, not all the resulting rules will produce plausible conclusions. But if we are able to identify characteristics of these rules that will allow us to predict which rules will produce predominantly plausible conclusions, then this triangular structure is potentially a

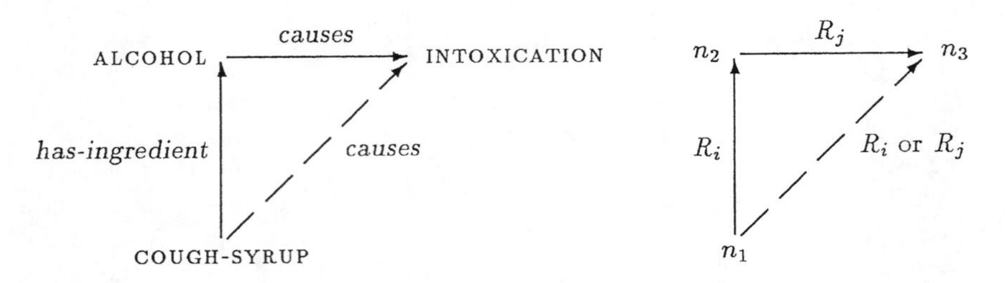

Figure 2: Extending the structure of property inheritance

powerful source of inference rules. The research discussed in the next three sections describes our attempts and those of other researchers to find the characteristics of inference rules that are highly correlated with plausibility.

TRANSITIVITY

Our initial experiments with these kinds of plausible inference rules identified two relation characteristics (Cohen & Loiselle, 1988). We studied a set of nine relations and determined that all had either an underlying sense of hierarchical inclusion, temporal ordering, or both. For example, the relation *component-of* conveys a sense of hierarchical inclusion since a whole includes its parts. Similarly, *caused-by* imposes a temporal order on the concepts it connects. When a relation has more than one interpretation both underlying senses may apply. For example, a mechanism may be either an instrument required prior to pursuing some activity, such as needing a key to unlock a door, or a subprocess subsumed by a superior process, as in respiration being a mechanism of maintaining life; therefore *mechanism-of* admits both a sense of hierarchical inclusion and temporal ordering. These underlying interpretations were used to determine the "deep structure" of the inference rule (Figure 3) where $n_3 \xrightarrow{h} n_2$ indicates that n_3 hierarchically includes n_2 and $n_1 \xrightarrow{t} n_2$ indicates that n_1 precedes n_2.

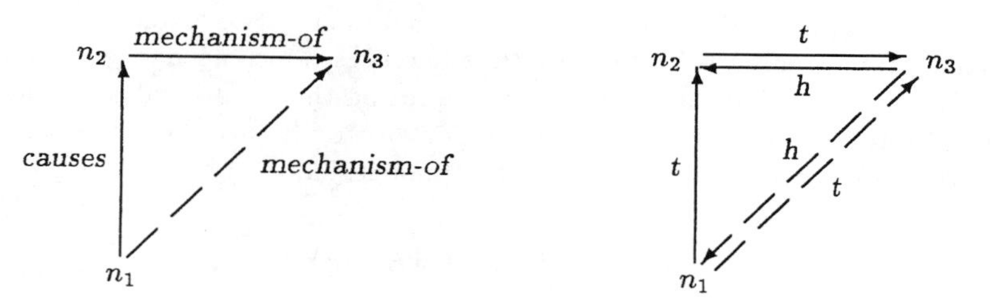

Figure 3: A plausible inference rule and its deep structure

We noted that some of our inference rules' deep structures preserved *transitivity*, that is, the same ordering, either temporal or hierarchical, was maintained between n_1 and n_3 in both the premises and the conclusion. The deep structure in Figure 3 is transitive because the temporal (t) links in both the premises and the conclusion indicate that n_1 comes before n_3. (The premises in intransitive rules do not imply any particular order between n_1 and n_3 nor is any required by the conclusion.) We also identified another characteristic of deep structures called *consistency*. Note that in Figure 3 some of the legs of the triangles are labeled with both temporal and hierarchical links, but only one of these forms a consistent interpretation, that is, we can choose between these two interpretations in such a way that allows us to label all three sides of the triangle with t-links (the consistent interpretation) but not with h-links. When a deep structure has multiple interpretations we use the consistent interpretation to determine transitivity. When no such consistent labeling is possible we call the structure (and its corresponding rule) inconsistent.

Our experiments with human subjects, who collectively viewed over 3000 inferences, showed that transitivity could be used to predict the plausibility of conclusions suggested by these inference rules with a fair degree of accuracy. Transitive rules yielded conclusions that were judged to be plausible in 77.4% of the inferences. For intransitive rules this figure was 38.8% and for rules having no consistent interpretation the results were near chance at 57.3%.[1] Thus with very little information about the specific inferences we are able to make modestly accurate predictions about the plausibility of their conclusions simply by knowing whether or not the rule is transitive.

It may be possible to improve the accuracy of our predictions by including additional information in our analysis. For example, knowing just the deep structure of a rule allows us to determine the rule's transitivity; seeing the transitive deep structure in Figure 3 lets us predict that approximately 77% of the inferences produced by this rule will be judged plausible. Knowledge about the specific relations used in this rule can improve this estimate, however. In this case, our data showed that only 73.6% of the inferences produced by the rule n_1 *causes* n_2, n_2 *mechanism-of* $n_3 \rightarrow n_1$ *mechanism-of* n_3 are judged plausible. If, instead, we knew that our transitive deep structure was derived from the rule n_1 *causes* n_2, n_2 *has-product* $n_3 \rightarrow n_1$ *has-product* n_3 we could predict a higher number of plausible conclusions because 87.9% of the resulting inferences were judged plausible in our experiment. Similarly, knowing the specific concepts that instantiate an inference rule also allows us to make more accurate predictions. The rule n_1 *has-ingredient* n_2, n_2 *causes* $n_3 \rightarrow n_1$ *causes* n_3 shown in Figure 2 seems generally plausible as does the instantiation shown there, but if we substituted AIR for COUGH-SYRUP the conclusion would certainly be judged unacceptable since the concentration of alcohol in air is too low to make us intoxicated.

The above discussion identifies a trade-off. With additional information about the relations in the rules, or the particular nodes used to instantiate the inferences, we could improve the accuracy of our predictions of plausibility. But acquiring and representing this additional information necessarily incurs additional costs. Therefore it is important to identify the amount and kinds of information required to achieve an acceptable level of predictability.

RELATION ELEMENT THEORY

Relation element theory (Chaffin & Herrmann, 1987) provides some of this additional information. By focusing on characteristics of the relations rather than on specific inference rules or instantiations, Chaffin and Herrmann are able to maintain a high degree of generality and incur little additional cost. Relation element theory holds that semantic relations should not be viewed as unitary semantic entities but rather as compositions of a set of simpler relation elements. Originally used to gauge the similarity of two semantic relations, relation element theory can also be used to predict the plausibility of an inference rule's conclusions.

Winston, Chaffin and Herrmann (1987) explore inferences based on the part-whole relation. They first note that although we ordinarily expect this relation to establish a strict partial ordering and thus be transitive many such inferences fail to produce plausible conclusions. For example, given the premises "Simpson's arm is part of Simpson," and "Simpson is part of the Philosophy department," it is not appropriate to conclude that Simpson's arm is part of the Philosophy Department (Winston, Chaffin & Herrmann, 1987). This apparent intransitivity is due to the use of two distinct senses of the relation *part-of* in the premises of the inference. The first statement expresses the relation between a component and the object to which it belongs whereas the

[1] The three classes of rules identified here do not account for all the data. See Cohen and Loiselle (1988) for a complete analysis.

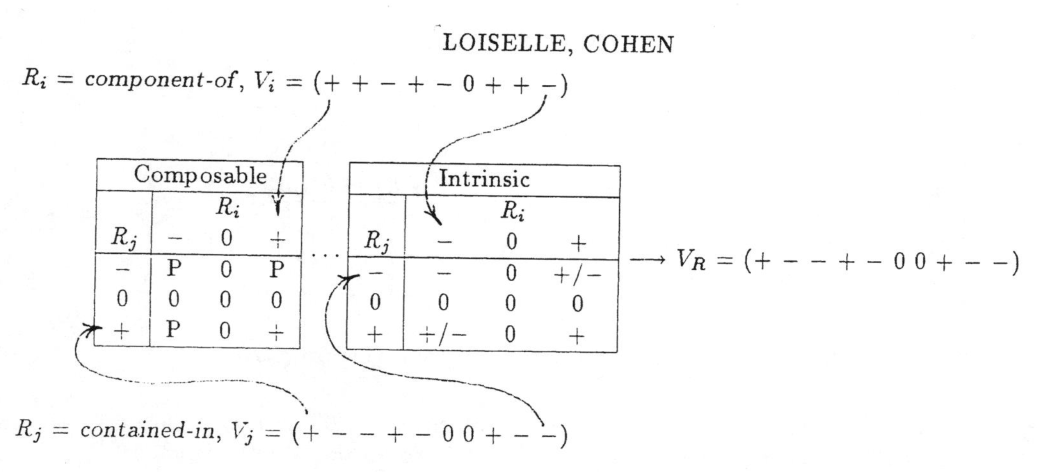

Figure 4: The algebra of extended composition.

second expresses the relation between a collection and one of its members.

The essence of this distinction is captured by relation element theory, which identifies three characteristic properties of the part-whole relation: whether the relation of part to the whole is functional, whether the parts are homeomerous, and whether the part can be, in principle, separated from its whole. According to the theory, all part-whole relations share the common element of *connection* between part and whole, this connection being modified by the values for the elements *functional*, *homeomerous*, and *separable*. Winston, Chaffin and Herrmann identify six kinds of part-whole relations and conclude that an inference is valid only if the same kind of *part-of* occurs in both premises as in the conclusion. This ensures that both the premises and the conclusion will have the identical set of relation elements. It also ensures transitivity.

EXTENDED COMPOSITION

Huhns and Stephens (1988) continue this line of research, identifying ten relation primitives, including several identified in Cohen and Loiselle (1988) and Winston, Chaffin, and Herrmann (1987). Examples of these primitives are composable, which indicates that the "fundamental characteristics" of a relation permits its use in these kinds of inferences; homeomerous, the domain of a relation is "the same kind of thing" as the range; and intrinsic, the relation specifies an intrinsic property of its domain or range. For each relation these primitives are assigned a value of +, meaning the characteristic is present, −, not present, or 0, if the primitive does not apply to the relation. Thus each relation can be represented by a vector of values for these ten primitives. Plausible inference rules are generated by the technique developed in Cohen and Loiselle (1988) and described above. (Huhns and Stephens call this technique "extended composition.") A corresponding algebra uses an operator table for each primitive to determine how the two vectors for R_i and R_j may be combined to yield a result vector for the conclusion (Figure 4). A match of the result vector to either or both of the premise relations' vectors is interpreted to mean the corresponding inference is plausible, provided the domain and range requirements of the relations are also met. For example, in Figure 4, V_R matches V_j so we predict that the inference rule n_1 *component-of* n_2, n_2 *contained-in* n_3 $\rightarrow$ n_1 *contained-in* n_3 will

Structural			
	R_i		
R_j	−	0	+
−	−	0	P
0	0	0	0
+	P	0	+

Temporal			
	R_i		
R_j	−	0	+
−	−	0	P
0	0	0	0
+	P	0	+

Intangible			
	R_i		
R_j	−	0	+
−	−	0	P
0	0	0	0
+	P	0	+

Figure 5: Operator tables for the transitivity-preserving primitives.

produce predominantly plausible conclusions. The results of this composition may be further pruned if the relations have incompatible domains and ranges. For example, although the operator tables may permit the composition of *subfield-of* and *subprocess-of*, the inference will be disallowed because it makes no sense to talk about a subfield of a process.

Huhns and Stephens apply their technique to a set of 21 relations (having a total of 861 possible compositions) to yield a composition matrix of 103 entries where the result vector matches the vector for either R_i or R_j and the corresponding inferred relation also satisfies the domain and range requirements established by the premise relations. That is, their algebra predicts that at least 103 out of 861 inference rules will produce predominantly plausible conclusions. (Since their algebra was designed for correctness instead of completeness, it is possible that some compositions not included the matrix might also produce plausible conclusions.) Huhns and Stephens claim validity for their results based on the plausibility of selected example inferences from the composition matrix.

TRANSITIVITY REVISITED

Three of the primitives in Huhns and Stephens' work indicate an ordering along a single dimension: structural indicates a hierarchical relationship in terms of physical structure, temporal indicates an ordering in time, and intangible indicates a hierarchical relationship in terms of ownership or mental inclusion. Since relations that indicate an ordering along a single dimension can be used transitively, these primitives capture the same kinds of underlying interpretations as our t-links and h-links (Cohen & Loiselle, 1988). Huhns and Stephens' temporal primitive corresponds to our t-link, whereas the structural and intangible primitives distinguish physical from mental inclusion, which are both represented by our h-link. This correspondence is also borne out by the operator tables for these primitives (Figure 5). For these three primitives, the values + and − indicate the direction of this ordering rather than the presence or absence of the characteristic. A value of 0 indicates either that no such ordering exists or that the property does not apply. These tables preserve the ordering of the concepts when both premises have the same value (indicate the same ordering) and prohibit inferences when the premises have incompatible orderings (the value "P" means the inference is prohibited). Thus these operator tables ensure that only those inference rules that preserve transitivity will be generated by the algebra.

Since transitivity alone was shown to predict pretty well the plausibility of inferences in Cohen and Loiselle (1988), we were interested in how much the three transitivity-preserving primitives contributed to the power of Huhns and Stephens' method. To evaluate this, we implemented their algebra and used it to determine the number of matrix entries produced by every subset of three of the ten primitives. Any subset of the original primitives is guaranteed to produce at least the original 103 entries; fewer *additional* entries indicates that a particular subset of primitives comes closer to reproducing Huhns and Stephens' original composition matrix and thus contributes more power to the algebra.

The most powerful set of three primitives, structural, temporal and composable, produced 198 matrix entries. The set of three transitivity-preserving primitives ranked third with 213 entries, tied with the set temporal, intangible and composable. Huhns and Stephens (1988, p. 5) note that the composable primitive is also closely tied to transitivity. They state, "Assignment of values for this property can be guided by consideration of the transitivity of the relation, i.e., if a relation is not transitive (cannot be composed with itself), then it often cannot be composed with any other relation." The remaining set of three of these four primitives, structural, intangible and composable, produced 238 entries, ranking 22nd out of 120. For comparison, the least powerful set of primitives, near, connected and intrinsic, produced 351 entries, while considerations of domain and range incompatibilities alone yielded 444 entries. Based on these rankings we conclude that the transitivity component represented by the primitives structural, temporal, intangible and composable contributes the largest share of the power of Huhns and Stephens' representation and algebra, and that the cost of assigning values to the remaining primitives may often outweigh the slight increase in power they provide.

ONTOLOGY MAINTENANCE: USING INFERENCES TO DETERMINE RELATION SEMANTICS

The work by Winston, Chaffin and Herrmann on the part-whole relation discussed above makes it clear that often what we consider to be a single semantic relation may be used in several different ways with corresponding differences in meaning. Furthermore, it shows that the plausibility of inferences using such a relation cannot be reliably determined unless the intended meaning is known. We cannot say whether the rule n_1 *part-of* n_2, n_2 *part-of* $n_3 \rightarrow n_1$ *part-of* n_3 will produce plausible conclusions unless we know whether both premises use the same type of part-whole relation. While relation element theory, and its extension in Huhns and Stephens' set of relation primitives, gives us a representation for specifying these intended meanings, it doesn't tell us how to determine the correct definition (assignment of primitive values) of a relation. Ontology maintenance offers a solution for this problem.

Ontology maintenance is concerned with assuring that the definitions of relations are correct. "Correct" means that we are able to accurately predict the plausibility of inferences using these relations. Thus, when we add a definition of a new relation to a knowledge base, or modify an existing one, we can check whether the definition is correct by generating inferences we expect to be plausible.

We are currently developing an ontology of semantic relations based on their behavior in inferences. This ontology includes a hierarchy of relations determined by their primitive assignments (Figure 6). Relations inherit primitive values from their parents, therefore their placement in the hierarchy determines the kinds of inferences predicted to be plausible for each relation. Evaluating these inferences thus evaluates the (possibly partial) definition of a relation suggested by its placement in the hierarchy. The following example illustrates how the relation

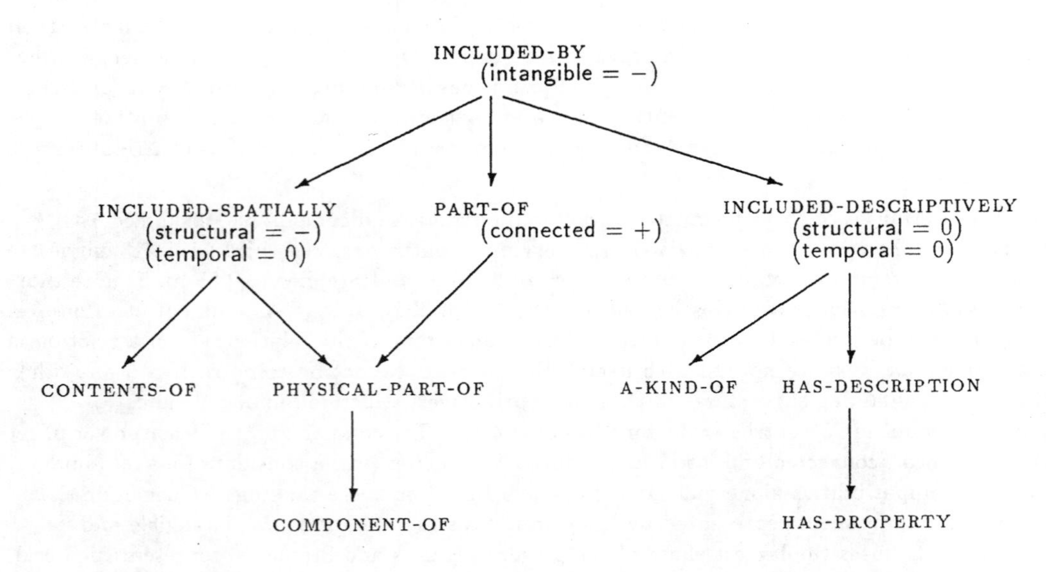

Figure 6: A partial hierarchy of relations with primitive values.

material-of, which indicates the main substance of which an object is made, is placed in the hierarchy, and thus how we determine the correct primitive values for this relation.

At first, we might believe *material-of* to be a kind of *part-of* relation; indeed, Winston, Chaffin and Herrmann (1987) claim that the "stuff-object" relation is a type of part-whole relation. Therefore we begin by placing *material-of* under *physical-part-of* in the relation hierarchy. This results in *material-of* inheriting the primitive assignments structural = −, temporal = 0, intangible = −, and connected = +. We then generate inferences predicted to be plausible. For our experiments these were derived from a knowledge base we are developing to represent common sense information about a house. One such inference is

Given:	WOOD	*material-of*	AXE-HANDLE,	and
	AXE-HANDLE	*component-of*	AXE	
Infer:	WOOD	*material-of*	AXE.	

Immediately we see that to evaluate the inference we must know more precisely the intended meaning of *material-of*. Will we allow it to indicate a substance in any area of an object or do we require it to refer to the entire object? If we had intended the former then this would seem a reasonable inference, but since we intended the latter the inference is unacceptable, and therefore, the value for at least one of these primitives must be incorrect.

Examining the hierarchy, again we decide that perhaps a material is more like a property of an object than it is part of an object. This suggests placing *has-material* (the inverse of *material-of*) under *has-description* in the relation hierarchy. Now *has-material* inherits the primitive values structural = 0, temporal = 0, and intangible = − and we generate inferences like

Given:	BOARD	*has-material*	WOOD,	and
	WOOD	*has-property*	FLAMMABLE	
Infer:	BOARD	*has-property*	FLAMMABLE.	

This time the inference is acceptable, indicating that these primitive values are correct, and we keep *has-material* under *has-description* in the relation hierarchy.

CONCLUSION

Certainly the more information we have about an inference, the better we will be able to judge the plausibility of its conclusion. But for tasks that do not require a high degree of accuracy in such judgments we may realize a savings by placing ourselves relatively low on the information/accuracy trade-off. The cost of assigning values to many different primitives for a large number of relations may cause us to want to limit the set of primitives used. Therefore, it is important to examine the sources of power in our representations. The results presented here suggest that primitives that represent different kinds of transitivity contribute most of the power in predicting plausibility.

Our ability to predict the plausibility of inferences is determined by our ability to define relations correctly. Our research in ontology maintenance explores how we can verify a relation's definition by examining inferences we expect to be plausible.

ACKNOWLEDGMENTS

This research is funded by the Office of Naval Research, under a University Research Initiative Grant, Contract #N00014-86-K-0764. We are indebted to Dave Hart for his comments on drafts of this paper.

REFERENCES

Chaffin, R. and Herrmann, D. (1987) Relation element theory: A new account of the representation and processing of semantic relations. In *Memory and Learning: The Ebbinghaus Centennial Conference*, ed. D. Gorfein and R. Hoffman, 221–245. Hillsdale, NJ:Lawrence Erlbaum Associates.

Cohen, P. R. and Loiselle, C. (1988) Beyond ISA: Structures for plausible inference in semantic networks. In *Proceedings of the Seventh National Conference on Artificial Intelligence*. St. Paul, MN.

Huhns, M. and Stephens, L. (1988) Extended Composition of Relations. Technical Report ACA-AI-376-88, Microelectronics and Computer Technology Corporation, Austin, TX.

Winston, M., Chaffin, R., and Herrmann, D. (1987) A taxonomy of part-whole relations. *Cognitive Science* 11(4):417–442.

A Theory of the Aspectual Progressive

Michael J. Almeida
Department of Computer Science
The Pennsylvania State University

Abstract

The progressive construction in English has an unusually wide range of uses. In this paper, I propose a new theory of what is probably the most important use of the progressive - the *aspectual progressive*. It is the aspectual progressive which is being contrasted with the simple, i.e., nonprogressive, construction in the nonhabitual interpretation of such pairs of sentences as *John was running at three o'clock* versus *John ran at three o'clock*. The proposed theory is based on a particular analysis of the conceptualizations of events and situations commonly called the *aspectual classes*, and is able to account for the temporal properties of the progressive, for the "imperfective paradox" problem, and for the range of applicability of the aspectual progressive.

INTRODUCTION

The progressive construction in English has an unusually wide range of uses. In this paper, I will propose a new theory of what is probably the most important use of the progressive - the *aspectual progressive*. It is the aspectual progressive which is being contrasted with the simple, i.e., nonprogressive, construction in the nonhabitual interpretation of such pairs of sentences as *John was running at three o'clock* versus *John ran at three o'clock*, and *Mary was speaking when I entered the room* versus *Mary spoke when I entered the room.*

In the first part of this paper, I present a survey and analysis of the conceptualizations of events and situations commonly called the *aspectual classes*. The precise explication of the (primarily temporal) properties of these different situation types forms a necessary background to my analysis of the progressive. In the second part of this paper, I describe and critique some previously proposed theories of the progressive, paying particular attention to the well-known theory of Vlach (1981). I then propose a new theory of the aspectual progressive which is able to account for the temporal properties of the progressive, for the full "imperfective paradox" problem, and for the range of applicability of the aspectual progressive.

THE ASPECTUAL CLASSES

The temporal properties of the aspectual classes play a central role in our use and understanding of natural language time expressions. The most familiar of these conceptualizations - achievements, accomplishments, activities, and states - come from the work of Vendler (1967). Following what has become standard practice, I will use *situation* as a cover term for instances of all of these various classes.

The analysis of the aspectual classes presented in this section is based on three fundamental distinctions. The first is that situations in general can be divided into three major classes depending on the nature of the intervals of time at which they can hold or occur: *point-situations*, which can only hold/occur at instantaneous points of time; *point-interval-situations*, which can hold/occur at both instantaneous and noninstantaneous intervals of time; and *interval-situations*, which can only hold/occur at noninstantaneous intervals of time. The second distinction is between situations which are *homogeneous* in overall structure, i.e., the parts are of the same nature as the whole, and those which are *heterogeneous*, i.e., consisting of distinct stages, phases, or subsituations. The third distinction is the contrast between *dynamic situations* and *nondynamic (stative) situations*, where the former class is further divided into *processes* and *nonprocesses*. In the following three subsections, I will discuss first the point-situations, then the point-interval-situations, and then finally the most complex of these major classes: the interval-situations.

Point-Situations

Point-situations can only occur at isolated points of time. The point-situations are Vendler's (1967) achievements, some examples of which are *dying* and *reaching the top*. Since achievements can only occur at points of time, they can be further specified by point-adverbials such as *at 5:00*, and they cannot directly take adverbials of duration. Achievements are dynamic situations, but, being instantaneous, they are not processes nor are they homogeneous or heterogeneous. Many achievements are also preceded by a durative process which leads to, or results in, that achievement. (This process will be discussed in a later section.)

Point-Interval-Situations

Point-interval-situations can hold or occur at both points and nonpoint intervals of time. Therefore, they can take both point-adverbials and adverbials of duration. The point-interval-situations are (most) states and all progressives. All such situations are homogeneous. Two examples of states/progressives holding for nonpoint intervals are: states - *John was out of the house from 3:00 to 4:00/for an hour*; progressives (disregarding the "intentionality" reading) - *John was playing the piano from 3:00 to 4:00/for an hour (yesterday).* (By the "intentionality" reading, I mean the sense which allows us to say *John was playing the piano for an hour, but he was interrupted so he only played for half an hour.*) Also, examples such as *John played the sonata while/when Mary was sleeping* require that the progressive hold for an interval.

A state/progressive in combination with a point-adverbial is generally taken to refer to a moment strictly during, i.e., not an end-point of, some nonpoint interval over which the state/progressive also holds (e.g., Bennett and Partee, 1972). But, there are three apparent difficulties with this analysis. The first is that there seem to be some types of potentially instantaneous states/progressives; that is, they can hold at isolated instants. Here is a typical example: imagine that the temperature is rising continuously over an interval of time which includes 4:00 pm, and that at exactly 4:00 pm the temperature is exactly 90 degrees. It would then seem that the stative sentence *The temperature is 90 degrees* is true within the relevant interval only at the point of time 4:00 pm. Similar examples can be constructed for progressives. However, this instantaneousness is more apparent than real in that such states/progressives can only occur where there is a nonpoint interval of time over which some value is changing smoothly and continuously. I believe that some notion of limits (as in the differential calculus) would reintroduce the notion of a noninstantaneous interval as a fundamental component of the representation of states/progressives. A truly isolated instantaneous state/progressive doesn't seem possible, since in what sense could it be said to exist?

The second problem concerns Vlach's (1981) discussion of examples such as Dowty's *John was watching television when he fell asleep,* which seem to refer to a moment just after the interval occupied by the state/progressive. However, Moens and Steedman's (1988) analysis of *when* solves this problem perfectly: the problem has to do with the meaning of *when.*

The third problem arises with culminations such as *John fell asleep at 4:00 pm.* In ordinary usage, this statement seems to imply that *John was asleep at 4:00 pm* even though 4:00 pm is only the start-time of the state of John's being asleep. Although this case could be characterized as an inceptive use of the state/progressive, I see no reason to separate this use from the more standard interior-point one.

In summary, states/progressives have as one of their properties the ability to hold at each of the points of time which are during an interval over all of which the state/progressive holds. Further, although the point selected by a point-adverbial is ordinarily strictly during, i.e., not an end-point of, the interval, this is for pragmatic reasons and is not strictly required.

Both Vlach (1981) and Dowty (1986) consider progressives to actually be statives; and as near as I can tell, states and progressives have exactly the same temporal properties. However, Passonneau (1988) makes the point that lexical statives cannot be modified by rate adverbials, e.g., *quickly, slowly,* while many progressives can (i.e., they are dynamic). This seems to be a good reason for keeping the two classes at least partially separate. What the two classes do have in common, i.e., their temporal properties, makes them both members of the same super-class: the point-interval-situations.

Interval-Situations

The interval-situations are those that can only hold or occur at noninstantaneous intervals of time. There are a number of different situation types in this category; both homogeneous and heterogeneous, and both statives and dynamic situations. I will use the term *process* to cover all durative dynamic situations (that is, all dynamic situations except achievements), although this is a broader use of the term than is usual. This will allow me to distinguish within the broad class of processes between heterogeneous and homogeneous processes, and between interval and point-interval processes. In this section, I will distinguish between and discuss the following types of interval-situations: accomplishments, activities, homogeneous accomplishment processes, achievement processes (both heterogeneous and homogeneous), interval states, and temporally measured situations.

Accomplishments
Vendler's (1967) *accomplishments* are one type of heterogeneous process. Some standard examples of accomplishments are *playing a sonata* and *building a bridge*. These situations clearly require a noninstantaneous interval of time and have distinct stages and subprocesses. In fact, all heterogeneous situations are interval-situations.

Activities
Vendler's (1967) *activities*, such as *running, playing the piano,* and *reading*, are one type of homogeneous process. Vlach (1981) gives the following analysis of the activity *running*: "suppose Mary starts running at instant 2:00 and continues running until 3:00, when she stops. Then tenseless *Mary run* is true at every instant between 2:00 and 3:00" (p.276). I believe that this analysis is incorrect, that in fact the simple form of activity sentences can only be true at non-point intervals. There are two arguments in favor of this analysis. One (used by Taylor, 1977) is that since running is a process, of necessity it can only occur over non-zero-length intervals; an instantaneous running-event simply makes no sense. Of course, the progressive *Mary was running* can be true at a point, but this point must always be during an actual interval of running. I'm not sure that this argument successfully differentiates activities from states, however.

A different sort of argument in favor of this analysis involves the interactions of different types of situations when they are conjoined by *while*. In the standard analysis of *while*, e.g., Bennett & Partee (1972), the event of the main clause is represented as simply being *during* the event of the subordinate clause; that is, *e1 while e2* would be represented as *during(e1, e2)*. But, as I showed in (Almeida, 1987), this analysis is not adequate. Consider the following two sentences:
(a) We all waited while the riders changed horses and cut off again down the incline to the starting point.
(b) He paced while the girl used the telephone.

In each of these examples, it seems that the main event, i.e., the event of the main clause, is understood as not occurring merely *during* the time occupied by the subordinate event(s) but as actually extending over the entire interval occupied by these events. But, if the effect of *while* is to cause the main event to fill up the time occupied by the subordinate event, then what happens when the main event is an achievement? This case is illustrated by the following examples:
(c) Mary telephoned me while I was reading.
(d) The messenger arrived while I was playing the piano.
In each of these sentences, the event of the main clause is an achievement, that is, a point-situation, and the event of the subordinate clause is a progressive activity, that is, a point-interval-situation. These sentences seem to have the traditional interpretation. Now, notice the effect we get if we change the subordinate events of these examples from progressives to simple activities:
(c') ? Mary telephoned me while I read.
(d') ? The messenger arrived while I played the piano.
The change in effect is subtle but definite: the main events are being awkwardly stretched to fit the passage of time implied by the subordinate clauses. One explanation for this effect is that the simple-form activities of the subordinate clauses must occupy noninstantaneous intervals of time and the point-situations are being forced to fill these intervals. This doesn't happen with examples (c) and (d), because in these cases the subordinate events have the ability to hold at points.

There still remains the problem of the interaction of simple-form activities with point-adverbials, e.g., *Mary ran at 2:30*. In Vlach's analysis of this example, "*Mary run* is true at 2:30, but *Mary ran at 2:30* is false, or at least an odd way to say what is usually expressed by *Mary was running at 2:30*. *Mary ran at 2:30* is more likely to mean that Mary started to run at 2:30" (Vlach, 1981, p.276). However, under the analysis that the simple form of activities can only be true at intervals, to say that *Mary ran at 2:30* means instead that Mary ran for an interval whose *initial-point* was 2:30; and in general, the meaning of *A V-ed at T o'clock* is that there is an interval of A's V-ing whose initial-point is T o'clock. In addition, there is an implicature (but only an implicature) that T o'clock is the initial-point of the entire event. Therefore, under this analysis, what is odd in the current example with saying *Mary ran at 2:30* is not that it is an odd (or false) way to say *Mary was running at 2:30*, but rather that it is odd, in this relatively neutral context, to want to talk about the initial-point of a subinterval of Mary's running given that this interval is only an internal portion of the complete running-event. However, it is not difficult to construct a context in which we might want to do just that. Imagine that Mary is on an exercise program in which she must run for half an hour every day at

2:30. Then we could truthfully report that on the day described above, *Mary ran (for half an hour) at 2:30*, as she was supposed to.

On the assumption that the speech time is a point of time, the interval nature of simple-form activities provides a neat explanation for why we do not use *John runs* to indicate that John is currently engaged in running. Under ordinary circumstances, only point-interval-situations can be used in the present tense, so that, for instance, we can use *John runs* in its habitual sense because habituals are always point-interval-situations. An interesting question is why don't we use present-tense achievements like *John leaves*? The answer seems to be purely pragmatic: in order to use the present tense, the situation we wish to describe must hold at the exact moment of speech, and it is very improbable for a point-situation to occur at exactly the moment we describe it.

Homogeneous Accomplishment Processes

One of the most important points that I wish to make in this paper is that all accomplishments have a related activity-like process that can be derived from them. This seems to be what is involved in, for example, *John played the sonata for 5 minutes*. Although accomplishments themselves are heterogeneous processes, this derived process is homogeneous. One argument for this comes from examples like *John played the sonata for 25 minutes*. The point of this example is that it is completely vague as to how many times the sonata was played: maybe only a portion of it was played, or it was played exactly once, or twice, or it was played one and a third times, etc. These possiblities rule out an analysis in which such sentences are interpreted as involving only a portion of the complete accomplishment process, since such an analysis would not allow the possibility of repetition. Instead, what we seem to need is a function which, when applied to a heterogeneous process, abstracts away its structure, its stages, etc., to produce a homogeneous process which is indifferent to such notions as completion. I will call this function *hm-int-proc*. What this function does is take as its single argument a heterogeneous interval-process and return as its value the corresponding homogeneous interval-process.

An alternative analysis of *John played the sonata for 25 minutes* would be to say that it is ambiguous between a portion-of reading and an iterative reading. Even if this analysis could account for the different possible interpretations of this sentence (which I doubt), it misses the point. This sentence is vague (with respect to completion and repetition anyway), not ambiguous. Of course, given sufficient world knowledge concerning the lengths of various sonatas, one could possibly infer from this sentence that the particular sonata involved must have been played repeatedly (or not), but this is merely an additional inference.

Not all expressions involving what I will call *homogeneous accomplishment processes* sound as natural as the above example. For instance, *We built the bridge for an hour* sounds somewhat awkward. This contrast seems to depend on the nature of the accomplishment involved; for instance, accomplishments which involve a "performance object" (Dowty, 1979), such as *playing a sonata* or *reciting a poem*, work very well in this construction, while accomplishments which result in an actual product, such as *building a bridge* or *painting a picture*, are more awkward. I do not believe that this means that there is no homogeneous bridge-building process, however; rather, in such cases speakers simply tend to use activity expressions like *working on the bridge* instead. This idea that heterogeneous interval-processes have related homogeneous interval-processes will play a central role in my analysis of the progressive.

Achievement Processes

As I mentioned earlier, many achievements can have a preceding process which leads to that achievement. (I call the function which takes an achievement as an argument and produces this preceding process *process-to*.) This process is like an accomplishment in that it is heterogeneous, with definite stages and subprocesses. Also like accomplishments, the duration of this process can be given using an *in*-adverbial. These heterogeneous achievement processes also have related homogeneous, activity-like processes, which are produced using the function *hm-int-proc*. It can, however, be difficult to refer directly to this homogeneous process. For instance, *John died for an hour* seems to say that John was dead for an hour; that is, it refers to the consequent state of dying rather than to the homogeneous process of dying. However, by using rate adverbials, we can refer to a stretch of the homogeneous process, as in, for example, the first clause of: *For an hour John died slowly, then his condition rapidly deteriorated.*

Interval Statives

So far, all of the interval-situations I have discussed have been processes. However, Dowty (1979) discusses a class of apparently stative predicates which can occur in the progressive, for example, one sense each of *sit, stand, lie,* and *perch.* Dowty notes that it is odd that these predicates should not give sentences that can be true at a single moment (according to his theory of the progressive they cannot), since they are nondynamic. One explanation of these examples, discussed by Dowty, is based upon the following observation:

> suppose that a book is being slide (sic) across a series of carefully juxtaposed tables of absolutely equal height. If I am standing in front of one of these tables in the middle of the series, it seems that I can truthfully utter *The book is on this table* at any time that the book is wholly over the surface of the table in question ... But if my intuitions serve me correctly, I cannot truthfully say *The book is lying (sitting, ...) on this table* at any time at all as long as the book is in motion. If this distinction is a real one (and the judgement is admittedly subtle), then the truth conditions of these verbs do require that the object of which they are predicated remain stationary in over-all position for more than one moment, hence they could plausibly be supposed to be true only at intervals, not moments. (pp.176-177)

Dowty therefore calls these states, *interval states.* If we take the two properties (1) taking the progressive and (2) being nondynamic as the defining properties of interval statives, then certain other problematic predicates, such as *remain, stay, wait, sleep,* and *rest* may also be included in this class.

Measured Situations

The durations of homogeneous situations can be given using *for*-adverbials. Such temporally measured situations as *John was sick for a week* or *John ran for an hour* are analogous to spatial examples such as *John ran a mile.* As such, they are heterogeneous interval-situations. For instance, *John ran for an hour* is not true for any of its proper subintervals; further, such measured situations can take *in*-adverbials, e.g., *John ran for an hour in an hour,* although such examples are unusual. The representation of temporally measured situations is based on the function *for*, which takes two arguments: a homogeneous situation (either interval or point-interval) and a duration, and which has as its value a temporally measured situation.

THE ASPECTUAL PROGRESSIVE

In this paper, I am concerned with the analysis of the aspectual progressive only. There are several other types of progressive in English, one of which is the "metaphysical" progressive discussed in Goldsmith & Woisetschlaeger (1982). The contrast between simple/progressive that they discuss marks a distinction that they call the "structural/phenomenal" distinction. An example is the contrast between *John walks to school* and *John is walking to school (these days).* It is important to notice that this distinction applies only to point-interval-situations such as habituals and generics, and there is no aspectual contrast involved.

The Viewpoint Approach to the Progressive

Probably the standard approach to the analysis of the aspectual progressive is to see it not as a situation type itself, but instead as a configuration of an instance of a more basic situation type and a particular type of "viewpoint" into that situation. This is the approach taken in Comrie (1976), for instance. Comrie distinguishes between two major aspects: (1) the *perfective* aspect, which "looks at the situation from outside, without necessarily distinguishing any of the internal structure of the situation," (p.4) and (2) the *imperfective* aspect, which "looks at the situation from inside" (p.4). In English, the progressive is one of the major indicators of imperfective aspect.

There are two versions of this "viewpoint" approach. In the most common version, the viewpoint consists always of an instantaneous point of time (e.g., Almeida (1987), Bennett & Partee (1972), Nakhimovsky (1988), and Passonneau (1988)). This version has the serious problem that, as we have seen, the progressive can also be true at nonpoint intervals of time. Therefore, some additional mechanism would be required to make this version work in general.

The other version of this approach was developed by Taylor (1977) and has been adapted by Dowty (1979, 1986). (Dowty's adaptation consists of the addition of possible worlds notions to handle the "imperfective paradox.") In Taylor's version, "[Prog ϕ] (i.e., the progressive form of ϕ) is true at I iff there is an interval I' properly containing I such that ϕ is true at I' " (Dowty, 1986, p.44). In other words, the viewpoint can be any proper subinterval and is not restricted to just points. Although this version avoids the limitations of the first, it too has some problems: (1) It doesn't in any way distinguish between a progressive holding for a nonpoint interval and the corresponding simple form when it holds at a proper nonpoint subinterval of the complete situation, which as we have seen can occur. (2) It isn't obvious that the progressive can be restricted to only proper subintervals of the complete situation; for example, if *John played the sonata in ten minutes*, then it seems true that both *John played the sonata for ten minutes* and *John was playing the sonata for ten minutes*. While these arguments do not conclusively show that a viewpoint analysis is impossible, they do illustrate some of the problems that such an approach would have to overcome.

Vlach's Approach to the Progressive

In contrast to the above theories, Vlach's (1981) approach to the progressive does not depend on the use of a "viewpoint". Vlach notes that one of the historical antecedents of the progressive were stative constructions such as *John was at hunting*, where *hunting* is a gerundive nominal naming a process or activity, and the preposition *at* has an interpretation something like *engaged in* or *in the process of*. Vlach suggests that the notion *in the process of* is common to the meaning of all progressives. For Vlach, the changing of a process sentence into a stative is central to the meaning of the progressive, and so he introduces an operator *Stat* which does this. Vlach also makes use of an operator *Proc* such that if ϕ is a sentence of the form NP VP, then Proc[ϕ] denotes the process of NP's VP-ing. That is, Proc[ϕ] denotes the process of ϕ-ing.

Given these two operators, Vlach defines the progressive as follows: "Prog[ϕ] if and only if Stat[Proc[ϕ] goes on]" (p.287). It then remains to specify when "Proc[ϕ] goes on" for the different possible types of ϕ. For activities, because they are already processes, this definition reduces to "Prog[ϕ] if and only if Stat[ϕ]". For accomplishments, Proc[ϕ] is "that process that leads to the truth of ϕ, and such that if ϕ is to become true at I, then P starts at the beginning of I and ends at the end of I" (p.288). For some achievements, such as *die*, Proc[ϕ] is "the process that characteristically leads to the truth of ϕ" (p.290), while for other types of achievements, Proc[ϕ] is "the vaguely defined last part of the process that leads to the accomplishment of which ϕ reports the completion" (p.289).

Problems with Vlach's Proposal and a New Formulation of the Progressive

Given my earlier discussion of the aspectual classes, it is clear that Vlach's notion of the process of an accomplishment is the same as my notion of the heterogeneous process that constitutes an accomplishment, and Vlach's notion of the process that leads to an achievement is essentially the same as what I characterized as the heterogeneous process that leads to an achievement. Thus, with both accomplishments and achievements, Vlach's Proc[ϕ] is a heterogeneous process. This means that Vlach's *Stat* operator applies in some cases to homogeneous processes (e.g., activities) and in other cases to heterogeneous processes (e.g., accomplishments and achievement-processes).

In my discussion of heterogeneous processes, I suggested that for every heterogeneous process there is a corresponding homogeneous interval-process that can be derived from it. Therefore, it is possible to unify the interpretation of *Stat* by having it apply solely to homogeneous interval-processes. But, besides the unification of the interpretation of *Stat*, there is a more compelling reason why we might want *Stat* to apply only to homogeneous interval-processes. This reason comes from the "imperfective paradox". As is well-known, progressive sentences such as *John was walking to the store* do not always entail the corresponding simple form sentences. Any representation of the progressive must be able to account for this. But, this problem is not limited to progressive sentences. As I discussed previously, some simple form sentences, such as *John walked to the store for five minutes*, also do not always allow the inference to *John walked to the store* in its "completed" sense. Since we must solve a version of the "imperfective paradox" even with some simple form sentences, it seems reasonable to use the same solution for the problem with progressives as well.

The solution to the simple-form version of the "imperfective paradox" is to make use of the homogeneous interval-process derived from the corresponding heterogeneous interval-process. In other words, to use the function *hm-int-proc*. My solution to the general "imperfective paradox" problem is the same. That is, all progressives should be based on homogeneous interval-situations. This proposal is in contrast to Vlach's theory where the progressives of heterogeneous processes are based directly upon those heterogeneous processes. My proposal has the interesting result that the progressive actually has nothing directly to do with the "imperfective paradox", instead it merely inherits the problem from the homogeneous processes upon which the progressive is based.

Another problem with Vlach's proposal is that there are some progressives which are not based on processes at all, instead they are based on states.

As I discussed earlier, there is a class of interval states, such as *sitting* and *standing*, which can occur in the progressive. Thus, while the notion of *in the process of*, when applied to homogeneous processes, is adequate to account for all progressive processes, it is not sufficiently general to account for all progressives. Interval states are, of course, already states so they do not need to be stativized. However, what they do require is to be converted from situations that hold only at nonpoint intervals of time to situations that can hold at both points and intervals of time, or in other words, to point-interval-situations. Therefore, I propose to replace Vlach's *Stat* operator with the function *pt-int-sit*, which takes as its single argument a homogeneous interval-situation (process or state) and has as its value the corresponding homogeneous point-interval-situation. By defining this function such that it returns a point-interval-situation rather than a point-interval-state, we get the correct temporal properties, while leaving open the exact nature of the relationship between progressives and point-interval-states.

A final difficulty is caused by the existence of temporally measured interval states, such as *John stood in the corner for an hour*. Such measured situations are heterogeneous interval-situations, and they can be progressivized, as in *John was standing in the corner for an hour*. But, of course, measured interval-states are not processes and so the function *hm-int-proc* cannot apply to them. Therefore, I define a new function *hm-int-sit* which is simply a generalisation of *hm-int-proc*. *Hm-int-sit* takes as its argument a heterogeneous interval-situation (process or state) and has as its value the corresponding homogeneous interval-situation.

As an example of the application of these functions, consider the sentence *John was running for an hour*. This sentence is ambiguous between two readings which can be represented as follows (the *time* predicate asserts that a situation of the type named by the first argument holds or occurs at the interval or point of time named by the second argument):
(i) time(for(pt-int-sit(run(john)),one-hour),t1), and
(ii) time(pt-int-sit(hm-int-sit(for(run(john) ,one-hour))),t2).

The first reading is that there was an hour of *John's running*. This reading is strongly favored in the sentence *For an hour, John was running*. The second reading is that there was some period (not necessarily an hour) of *John's running for an hour*. I call the second reading the "intentionality" reading because in such cases there is often a pragmatic implication that the agent has the actual intention of performing the action for a certain period of time. It should be noticed that reading (i) entails reading (ii), but, because of the "imperfective paradox", reading (ii) does not entail reading (i).

Although it is not as obvious, there is also an analogous simple-form version of this ambiguity. For example, *John ran for an hour* is ambiguous between the two readings:
(i) time(for(run(john),one-hour),t3), and
(ii) time(hm-int-sit(for(run(john),one-hour)),t4).
In the simple-form case, reading (i) seems to be strongly preferred, and again, reading (i) entails reading (ii), but not vice versa.

It should be noted that there is an important restriction on the range of application of *hm-int-sit*. It does not apply to heterogeneous interval-situations which are themselves based on point-interval-situations. An example of such a heterogeneous situation would be a measured progressive, such as reading (i) of *John was running for an hour*. Another example would be a measured point-interval-state such as *John was busy for a week*. Among other things, this restriction disallows progressives of measured point-interval-situations.

Relationships Among Situation Types

The following rules express the relationships among the different types of situations.

1. ∀(s,t) . subtype(s,heterogeneous-situation) & ¬has-underlying-pt-int-sit(s) & time(s,t) → time(hm-int-sit(s),t)

This rule expresses the conditions under which it is permissible to apply *hm-int-sit*, that is, the conditions under which a heterogeneous situation has a corresponding homogeneous interval-situation. Naturally, because of the general "imperfective paradox" problem, the implication does not hold in the other direction. The second conjunct disallows the application of the function to heterogeneous situations based on point-interval-situations, as discussed above.

2. ∀(s,t) . subtype(s,interval-situation) & subtype(s,homogeneous-situation) & time(s,t) <—> time(pt-int-sit(s),t) & greater-than(dur(t),0)

In one direction, this rule states that all homogeneous interval-situations have a corresponding point-interval-situation, i.e., a progressive form. In the other direction, the rule states that any progressive situation type that holds for some non-point interval of time has a corresponding homogeneous interval-situation that also holds for that interval. Thus we have *John played the piano* for some period of time iff *John was playing the piano* for that period of time.

3. ∀(s,t) . subtype(s,homogeneous-situation) & time(s,t) & greater-than(dur(t),0) <—> time(for(s,dur(t)),t)

In one direction, this rule states that if a homogeneous situation holds for some nonpoint interval of time, then the corresponding measured situation also holds for that interval. In the other direction, this rule states that if a measured situation holds for some interval, then the underlying homogeneous situation also holds for that interval. For example, *John ran for an hour* holds for some interval (of the proper duration) iff *John ran* holds for the same interval.

4. ∀(s,t,d) . time(hm-int-sit(for(s,d)),t) → time(s,t)

Because of the "imperfective paradox", *time(hm-int-sit(for(s,d)),t)* does not entail *time(for(s,d),t)*, but, because measured situations are based upon homogeneous situations, it does entail *time(s,t)*.

SUMMARY

In this paper, I have described an approach to the analysis of the aspectual classes. Based upon this analysis, I have proposed and argued for an approach to the analysis and representation of the aspectual progressive based on two ideas: (1) a function *pt-int-sit* which takes a homogeneous interval-situation as its argument and has as its value the corresponding point-interval-situation, and (2) a function *hm-int-sit* which takes a heterogeneous interval-situation as its argument and has as its value the corresponding homogeneous interval-situation. The first function is needed to account for the temporal properties of progressives, that is, for the aspectual effect of the progressive. The second function is needed to handle the "imperfective paradox" problem with progressives, and is, in addition, independently motivated by the need to account for the meanings of certain simple form sentences, such as *John played the sonata for twenty-five minutes*. Finally, the proposed theory is able to account for the range of applicability of the aspectual progressive.

REFERENCES

Almeida M.J. (1987) Reasoning about the temporal structure of narratives, TR87-10, Computer Science Department, SUNY at Buffalo, Buffalo, NY.

Bennett M., & Partee B. (1972) *Toward the logic of tense and aspect in English*, System Development Corporation, Santa Monica, CA.

Comrie B. (1976) *Aspect*, Cambridge University Press.

Dowty D.R. (1979) *Word Meaning and Montague Grammar*, D. Reidel Publishing Co.

Dowty D.R. (1986) The effects of aspectual class on the temporal structure of discourse: semantics or pragmatics?, *Linguistics & Philosophy*, Vol.9, pp.37-61.

Goldsmith J., & Woisetschlaeger E. (1982) The logic of the English progressive, *Linguistic Inquiry*, Vol.13, No.1, pp.79-89.

Moens M., & Steedman M. (1988) Temporal ontology and temporal reference, *Computational Linguistics*, Vol.14, No.2, pp.15-28.

Nakhimovsky A. (1988) Aspect, aspectual class and the temporal structure of narrative, *Computational Linguistics*, Vol.14, No.2, pp.29-43.

Passonneau R.J. (1988) A computational model of the semantics of tense and aspect, *Computational Linguistics*, Vol.14, No.2, pp.44-60.

Taylor B. (1977) Tense and continuity, *Linguistics & Philosophy*, Vol.1, pp.199-220.

Vendler Z. (1967) *Linguistics in Philosophy*, Cornell University Press.

Vlach F. (1981) The semantics of the progressive, In P.J. Tedeschi & A. Zaenen (eds.), *Tense and Aspect*, Vol. 14 of *Syntax and Semantics*, Academic Press, pp.271-292.

Default Values in Verb Frames: Cognitive Biases for Learning Verb Meanings

Douglas A. Behrend

University of Michigan

ABSTRACT

Two experiments investigated children's and adults' initial mapping of verb meanings. In Experiment 1, subjects were asked to use a newly learned verb to label events in which the instrument, action, or result was different from the events used to teach the verbs. All subjects showed a bias to interpret the result as the most important component of the novel verbs' meanings, and this bias increased with age. In Experiment 2, either the instrument, action, or result of events was varied during training to test subjects' ability to override their default biases. When results were varied in training, 5-year-olds and adults, but not 3-year-olds, were more likely to use the novel verb to label an event in which the result was changed again. When results were varied in training, all subjects were less likely to use the novel verb to label an event in which the action was changed. These findings suggest that there is a default rule hierarchy for learning novel verbs, and that both default rules and the ability to override these rules when presented with conflicting information about the meaning of a verb are still developing during preschool.

INTRODUCTION

Children's learning of word meanings is best characterized as a rapid, "fast-mapping" (e.g. Heibeck & Markman, 1987) process that is directed at least in part by children's constrained hypotheses about what novel words mean. When learning nouns, for example, children assume that a novel noun is a label for an entire object (Markman & Hutchinson, 1984), rather than any of the many other logical interpretations that could be given to that word (e.g. Quine, 1960). Little, however, is known about children's initial mapping of verb meanings. Verbs differ substantially from nouns in their semantic structure and organization (e.g. Graesser, Hopkinson, & Schmid, 1987; Huttenlocher & Lui, 1979), and given that the learning of verb meanings has been strongly implicated in the acquisition of grammar (e.g. Pinker, 1984), understanding how children acquire verb meanings is an important empirical question with major theoretical implications. This paper examines what children assume a novel verb means upon their first exposures to that verb.

The theoretical framework used in this paper assumes that verb meanings are represented in an event schema such as a script (Schank & Abelson, 1976), or verb frame (Minsky, 1981). A verb frame has a number of placeholders, or "slots", which contain information that is carried in the verb's meaning. An important property of these slots is that they can be filled by a number of values, one or more of which may be more likely to occur or weighted most strongly in the representation. The slots in verb frames correspond to the components of events which can be represented in a verb's meaning. Though there are many different types of information about events that can be represented in verb frames, only three types of information expressed in verb meanings are examined in this paper: 1) the physical action performed by an agent in an event, 2) the result of the event, and 3) an instrument used by an agent in an event. These three components were selected because many of the active verbs in natural language explicitly label one of these aspects of events: there are action verbs ("pound", "squeeze"), result verbs ("break", "clean"), and instrument verbs ("hammer", "mop"). Naturalistic studies have shown that these three kinds of active, transitive verbs account for over 70% of the verbs in preschooler's lexicons (Behrend, 1986). When studying the fast-mapping of verb meanings, we are interested in the *default values* for the slots in verb frames. Default values represent the learner's expectations about what component(s) of an event is most likely to be important in the meaning of a novel verb before anything is learned about the meaning of that verb. Thus, default values guide verb learning by directing the learner to those aspects of events that are most likely to be represented in verb meanings. Two questions are addressed in the current research. What are children's default assumptions about the meanings of novel verbs? Are children able to override these assumptions when presented with information that conflicts with their default values?

These questions are addressed using an original experimental paradigm in which subjects are taught novel verbs and then are asked if they are willing to use those verbs to label events in which the instrument, action, or result is different from the events on which the verbs were trained. It was reasoned that subjects should be less willing to use the newly learned verb to label events in which the component that was changed was one that the subject assumed was an important part of the new verb's meaning.

EXPERIMENT 1

Method

Ten 3-year-olds, 5-year-olds, and adults were subjects. There was an equal number of males and females in each group.

The stimuli were six sets of videotaped events each matched with a novel verb (rem, stipe, pint, chiff, bock, tizz). Each event depicted a person performing a novel action with an unfamiliar instrument to produce a clear and novel result. For each verb, there were three identical training events followed by four test events. One of the test events was identical to the training events. In the other three test events, either the instrument, action, or result was different from the training events (the test change). These events followed the training events for each verb in a random order. Before the first training event, the subject was told, "Watch this person, she is *remming*." Before the other two training events, the experimenter said, "Let's watch her do that again. Look, she's *remming* again." After the last training event, the subject was told, "O.K. Now I want you to tell me if she is *remming* this time or is she is doing something else." The test event was shown, and the experimenter asked, "Was she *remming* that time or was she doing something else?" After the last test event for a verb was shown, the training for the next verb began.

TABLE 1: NUMBER OF TIMES NOVEL VERB IS ACCEPTED AS A LABEL FOR TEST EVENTS IN EXPERIMENT 1 (maximum value = 6)

	Age			
Test Change	Three	Five	Adult	Overall
Instrument	3.6	3.5	5.2	4.1
Action	2.8	2.3	2.9	2.7
Result	1.9	0.3	0.6	0.9
Mean	2.8	2.0	2.9	2.6

Results and Discussion

The key dependent variable was the number of times subjects accepted the novel verb as a label for the test events. Subjects always used the novel verb for the test event identical to the training events, so those data were eliminated from the analysis. The remaining data were analyzed with a 3 (Age) x 3 (Test Change) ANOVA, with the latter factor treated as a within-subject factor. Table 1 summarizes the data. Note that lower values in the table represent stronger effects (i.e. subjects were less willing to accept the novel verb). A significant main effect for test change, $F(2,54) = 61.1$, $p<.001$, showed that result test changes had the strongest negative effect on subjects' acceptance of the novel verb, followed by action, and then instrument changes (all pairwise differences significant by Newman-Keuls test, $p<.05$). There was also an age x test change interaction, $F(4,54) = 2.75$, $p<.05$, which showed that 1) instrument changes were less important to adults than to children and 2) result changes were less important to 3-year-olds than to the older subjects. Still, the 3-year-olds, like older subjects, were most strongly affected by result changes and least strongly affected by instrument changes.

The findings from this experiment suggest that when learning a novel verb that labels a transitive event, children and adults have a default assumption that the result of an event is the most important component in that verb's meaning. It also appears, however, that this default assumption is still developing during the preschool years: 3-year-olds were more willing than 5-year-olds or adults to accept the novel verb as a label for the result change test event. As this assumption will frequently be wrong, it is important to know how easily subjects can change their default mappings when information about a verb's meaning conflicts with their default assumptions. In Experiment 1, all of the training events used to teach a given verb were identical, and thus no conflicting information about a verb's meaning was presented. Experiment 2 examines how children and adults deal with variable information about the meaning of a novel verb by introducing systematic variations into the training events.

EXPERIMENT 2

Method

Twelve 3-year-olds, 5-year-olds, and adults were subjects. There were eight boys and four girls in each group of preschoolers, and an equal number of adult males and females.

The stimuli were again six sets of videotaped events similar to those used in Experiment 1, each matched with a novel verb. The stimuli and procedure were identical to those used in Experiment 1, with the following exceptions. In each set of training events for this study, two of the three components (instrument, action, result) of the events remained constant while the other component was varied in each event (the training variation). Thus, for two verbs, the instrument varied in training; for two, the action varied; and for two, the result varied. These training events were followed by four test events, in random order. One test event was identical to the first training event for that verb, and there was one each in which the instrument, action, or result was different from any training event.

Results and Discussion

The data were analyzed with a 3 (Age) x 3 (Training Variation) x 3 (Test Change) ANOVA with the last two factors treated as within-subject factors. Table 2 summarizes the data. Again, lower values in this table represent stronger effects. The significant main effect for test change, $F(2,66) = 54.3$, $p<.001$, showed, as in Experiment 1, that result changes had the strongest negative effect on subjects' acceptance of the novel verb, followed by action, and instrument changes (all pairwise differences significant by Newman-Keuls test, $p<.05$). One clear effect of the variations in training was that the subjects accepted the novel verb as a label for the test events more frequently than subjects in Experiment 1 (M=3.5 vs. M=2.6, $p<.01$).

It was expected that if subjects were sensitive to the variations in the training events, then they would be more willing to accept the novel verb for a test event in which the component that was changed was also the component that was varied in the training for that verb. For example, subjects should be more willing to accept the novel verb as a label for the action change test events when the action was varied in the training events than when the action was not varied. This prediction, and analagous predictions for the instrument and result test changes, were tested with a set of orthogonal planned comparisons based on the overall ANOVA.

Figure 1 displays both a set of idealized predictions (Figures 1A, 1B, and 1C) and the actual data (Figures 1D, 1E, and 1F) from the study. As expected, there was a significant interaction between training variation and test change, $F(4,132) = 24.7$, $p<.001$. Figure 1D shows that the predicted effect was not observed for instrument test changes, primarily because

TABLE 2: NUMBER OF TIMES NOVEL VERB IS ACCEPTED AS A LABEL FOR TEST EVENTS IN EXPERIMENT 2 (maximum value = 6)

	Age			
Test Change	Three	Five	Adult	Overall
Instrument	4.6	5.3	5.3	5.1
Action	3.3	2.6	3.3	3.1
Result	2.8	2.1	2.3	2.4
Mean	3.5	3.3	3.6	3.5

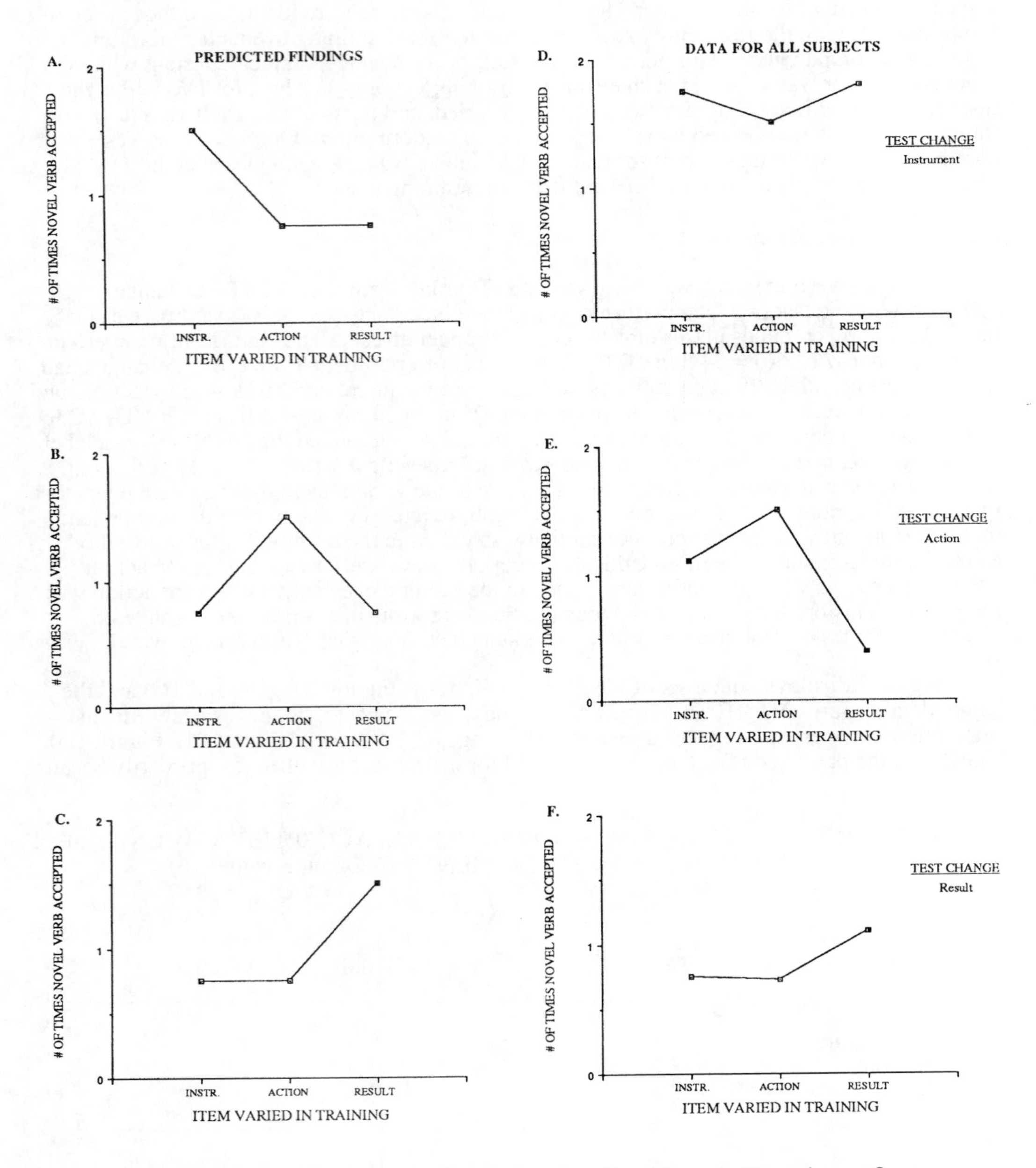

FIGURE 1: Predicted and actual data for all subjects in Experiment 2.

instrument changes did not affect use of the novel verb in the first place. However, the predicted effects for the action and result test changes were observed. Figure 1E shows that the novel verb was more likely to be accepted for action change test events when actions varied in the training events, $F(1,35) = 61.2$, $p<.01$, and Figure 1F shows that the novel verb was more likely to be accepted for the result change test events when results varied in the training events, $F(1,35) = 7.17$, $p<.01$.

There was also a 3-way interaction between age, training variation, and test change $F(8,132) = 2.78$, $p<.01$. This interaction reflects the finding that while the groups did not differ in how they were affected by the instrument and action training variations, varying the result in training had differential effects on the three age groups. While both the 5-year-olds, $F(1,11) = 4.96$, $p<.05$, and the adults, $F(1,11) = 8.43$, $p<.05$, were more likely to accept the novel verb for a result change test event when the result was varied in training, there was no such effect for the 3-year-olds.

One other finding is worthy of attention. Returning to Figure 1E, it can be seen that when results were manipulated in training, *action* changes had a profound negative effect across age groups on subjects' willingness to use the novel verb. This finding suggests that when the results of events were varied and, thus, were reduced in importance in a verb's meaning, subjects abandoned the default assumption that results are most important, and switched to action as the component most likely to be central to the novel verb's meaning.

GENERAL DISCUSSION

The findings from these studies suggest that there is a default assumption that the result is the most important component of a novel verb's meaning (i.e., the novel verb is a result verb). This bias also appears to become stronger during preschool. Actions are assumed to be less important than results, and instruments are rarely assumed to be important to novel verb meanings. In addition, Experiment 2 demonstrated what occurs when default assumptions are in conflict with the input that is received about a verb's meaning. When the result of an event was varied in training, adults and 5-year-olds, as predicted, more frequently accepted the novel verb as a label for an event in which the result was changed again. 3-year-olds, though, were apparently unable to override their default assumption. Also, when results were varied in training, subjects rarely accepted the novel verb for the *action* change test event. This finding suggests that there may be a hierarchy among the slots in verb concepts. When results are decreased in importance in a verb's meaning, learners next hypothesize that action, instead, is the key to the meaning of a novel verb. This account invokes a mechanism similar to a default rule hierarchy that has been proposed to account for various types of animal, human, and machine learning (e.g. Holland, Holyoak, Nisbett, & Thagard, 1986; Jackendoff, 1983) and which demands consideration as the mechanism responsible for this finding of the present research.

The interpretations of the findings of the current studies must be made with some caution. Clearly, more information than just that pertaining to instruments, actions, and results is incorporated in verb frames. For example, causal, temporal, and syntactic information, as well as information dealing with the intentionality of an action must also be represented. Indeed, the strong and increasing bias towards results in the present studies may reflect an increase in children's understanding of intentions and the planfulness of actions, and not a specific verb learning bias. However, given that the verbs studied here account for over two-thirds of the verbs in preschoolers' lexicons, some basis for generalizing these findings is warranted.

To conclude, it appears that the default assumptions that guide the fast-mapping of verb meanings are still changing in the preschool years, and that there may be important, hierarchical relationships between default values in different slots in verb concepts. Additional research with younger children and a wider range of verbs will help to clarify the exact nature of the sources of these changes and the mechanisms involved in the initial mapping of verb meanings.

REFERENCES

Behrend, D.A. (1986). The role of instruments, actions, and results in children's naming of simple events: Experimental and naturalistic data. Unpublished doctoral dissertation.

Graesser, A.C., Hopkinson, D., & Schmid, C. (1987). Differences in interconcept organization between nouns and verbs. *Journal of Memory and Language*, **26**, 242-253.

Heibeck, T.H., & Markman, E.M. (1987). Word learning in children: an examination of fast mapping. *Child Development*, **58**, 1021-1034.

Holland, J.H., Holyoak, K.J., Nisbett, R.E., & Thagard, P.R. (1986). *Induction*. Cambridge, MA: MIT Press.

Huttenlocher, J., & Lui, F. (1979). The semantic organization of some simple nouns and verbs. *Journal of Verbal Learning and Verbal Behavior*, **18**, 141-162.

Jackendoff, R. (1983). *Semantics and cognition*. Cambridge, MA: MIT Press.

Markman, E.M., & Hutchinson, J. (1984). Children's sensitivity to constraints on word meaning: taxonomic vs. thematic relations. *Cognitive Psychology*, **20**, 1-27.

Minsky, M. (1981). A framework for representing knowledge. In J.R. Haugeland (Ed.), *Mind design*. Cambridge, MA: MIT Press.

Pinker, S. (1984). *Language learnability and language development*. Cambridge, MA: Harvard University Press.

Quine, W.V.O. (1960). *Word and object*. Cambridge, MA: MIT Press.

Schank, R.C., & Abelson, R. (1976). *Scripts, plans, goals, and understanding*. Hillsdale, NJ: Erlbaum.

Generating Temporal Expressions in Natural Language

David R. Forster
Department of Computer and Information Science
University of Massachusetts

Abstract

We explore the problem of generating natural language temporal expressions and show that it is amenable to solution by the application of hierarchical constraint propagation. Constraints derived either directly or indirectly (via transformations) from client data are propagated over the hierarchical structure provided by syntactic templates and are required to be consistent at any given node. Multiple sources of constraints must be used to achieve lexical selection of a single item.

INTRODUCTION

Consider an application program which schedules meetings on a calendar. Typically, such a program would need to produce sentences such as "*You will meet John Smith at 2:00 on Tuesday to discuss widgets.*" and "*You won't need to see Smith again today. You already saw him at ten [today].*" No generator, past or present, would be able to deal with all aspects of the generation of these sentences, because a complete model of tense and temporal adverbials is lacking. Linguistic models lack a connection to time units (e.g., minutes, hours, days) and common-sense knowledge in general, and also lack an acceptable mechanism for co-ordinating the processing of tense and temporal adverbials.

We will examine here a theory for the semantics of time units and temporal relations in natural language, and a companion method for processing this type of semantic information. The theory and method are being implemented as part of the semantic component for a text generation system (Forster, 1989). To reduce the work to a manageable level while retaining an interesting and useful body of data, we will concentrate on prepositional phrases serving as temporal adverbials (TPPs), in particular those using the prepositions *in*, *at*, and *on*.

Conventionally, *at* is used to refer to points in time or to intervals which may be treated as points, *on* is used to refer to days or (together with a specific day) to major parts of days, and *in* is used otherwise (Quirk et al., 1985:526-555). Most models for the semantics of these prepositional

This work was supported in part by the Air Force Systems Command, Rome Air Development Center, Griffiss AFB, New York, 13441 under contract No. F30602-85-C-0008. This contract supports the Northeast Artificial Intelligence Consortium (NAIC).

phrases depend on precedence or on containment relations, with no further detail attempted.[1]

There are several problems with the conventional analysis of TPPs. First, it is too vague; for example, no rules are given governing which intervals may be treated as points and which may not. Second, it is both too powerful and too weak — witness examples (1–5) below. Third, it doesn't even touch on the interactions of TPPs with other mechanisms for expressing temporal relations, like those exhibited by examples (6–8) below.[2] Fourth, it does not link the objects being described with the descriptions in any useful way.[3]

1. *?at coffee break*
2. **at Canada Day/Independence Day*
3. **at summer*
4. *on the following evening/morning*
5. *#at 9 in January*
6. *#I saw him tomorrow.*
7. *#At ten I had seen him at ten.*
8. *?It will last [forever] at ten.*

We must draw on our common-sense knowledge of how these events differ to explain these observations. By examining differences between events which figure in examples of acceptable and unacceptable text, we should be able to determine the common-sense knowledge required to correctly generate temporal expressions.

A COHERENT TREATMENT OF TIME

The problems with generating TPPs may be summarised as follows:

1. Certain temporal units require the use of specific prepositions. Where variations on these units are allowed (e.g. *Christmas* vs. *Christmas Day*), the prepositions allowed for the variant usually differ from those allowed for the "root" form.

2. The agreement of tense and temporal adverbials must be ensured in some way.

3. Time intervals can sometimes be treated as points in time.

4. Prepositional phrases detailing different levels of time units describing the same event may be combined, but levels may not be skipped, unless they are clear from context (cf. example (5) above).

The solution I propose has four parts:

[1]**Precedence** simply means that one time is before another, i.e. one precedes another. **Containment** simply refers to the time of a particular event being in the set of times contained by another time or event.

[2]In (6), the tense indicates that $T_s > T_e$, whereas the adverbial indicates that $T_s < T_e$. In (7), the aspect indicates $T_e < T_r$, whereas the adverbial indicates that $T_e = T_r$. In (8), the verb "*last*" asserts that some state holds for a period of time, whereas the adverbial indicates that the state holds only for an instant. Several other forms of interaction are also known.

[3]By this I mean that nothing is specified about the mapping from application program data to linguistic data or about acquiring the data from the application program or even about what sort of data is required. Insofar as the conventional analysis is purely linguistic, performing this mapping may be judged to be beyond the scope of the analysis. For our purposes, however, this link must also be established.

1. Associate constraints with each word and phrase describing how the word or phrase can be used and what it refers to (e.g., "*at*" used to pick out a point in time, "*Tuesday*" referring to a one day long interval).
2. Base the constraints on common-sense knowledge.
3. Allow the constraints to propagate in the syntax tree for the sentence.
4. Require constraints that meet at a node to be consistent.

In addition to this, the client (the program requesting the generation of text) must be required to make some of the decisions which can be expressed in non-linguistic terms, and to bundle some of its information (e.g., the level of detail it requires for a description). If insufficient information is available in the initial generation request made by the client, then it should be possible to query the client about its needs or preferences.[4]

This solution remedies the problems with generation by

1. forcing the use of the correct prepositions and the agreement of tense and temporal adverbials by propagating constraints and enforcing constraint satisfaction
2. enabling the use of variations in phrasing, and enabling the treatment of intervals as points, by basing the constraints on the additional common-sense attributes of described objects.

The solution remedies weaknesses of the current theoretical model by

1. modelling interactions explicitly
2. defining links between client objects (representing real-world objects) and linguistic objects
3. attending to detail to a degree not practicable for a theoretical system, but required for the implementation of a processing model

Time and Common-Sense Knowledge

In light of the data, it is obvious that the choice of a preposition must be in accord with the nature of the temporal datum being described, and equally obvious that more than just the 'size' of that datum, or precedence and containment relations with other data are important. At least the following attributes appear necessary:

Regularity with which an event occurs: breakfast is such a regular event it may be considered to be a useful reference point, thus allowing its treatment as a point in "*at breakfast.*"

[4]It could be argued that the client should include all the information it wants expressed in the initial generation request, since queries made later merely represent a delay in collecting needed information. This argument ignores the fact that the mechanism for bundling the information may well assume things about either the surface structure or the deep structure of sentences, and therefore force the client to have knowledge of language.

Significance of the event: Christmas is such an important event in both the church and secular calendars that we treat it as a point, allowing "*at Christmas.*"

Duration of an interval: the duration of a weekend has the same order of magnitude as a day, thus possibly allowing its treatment as a day in *on weekends.*

Perception of time units: days have clearly defined boundaries, determined by a natural external source (the rising and setting of the sun), thus allowing us to conceive of them as somehow fixed or solid, and by extension, as things "on" which events can in some sense be "put," in analogy to spatial perception.

Granularity of time units:[5] the use of adverbs, such as *just*, is clearly a sign that there is an interval within which events are considered to be recent. Granularity is the size of this interval. Further research may show that a more complex notion, allowing different classes of recency, is required.[6]

Hierarchical Constraint Propagation

Stefik (1981) outlines a method for planning based on constraint satisfaction in a hierarchy, where a rough hierarchical plan is refined by using constraints to determine valid variable values in plan steps, and to reason out further constraints, which are propagated throughout the hierarchy of the plan. Stefik notes that constraint propagation is useful only when the problem involves loosely coupled subsystems. Natural language generation is an ideal candidate for a solution of this kind. The selection process for one word or phrase is loosely coupled with the selection of others. Realisations for words and phrases are selected on the basis of satisfied constraints. The constraints are provided by word meanings or transformations on inherited constraints. The hierarchy is provided by the syntactic structure of the sentence.

Figure 1 shows an example of hierarchical constraint propagation, concentrating on temporal expressions. Let us examine in turn the generation of each temporal expression. "*At*" produces the constraint (time-nature :point), which is propagated to the containing PP at (C) in the figure. "*Nine*" provides the information ((time-nature :point) (time #<TIME see>)), which is propagated to the same PP at (D). The generation of "*at nine*" proceeds by satisfying the point requirement of *at* with the point nature of the hour *nine*. "*On the seventeenth*" is generated similarly (F&G),

[5]This is distinct from Hobbs' (1985) use of the term granularity.

[6]Three such classes which suggest themselves are: remote, recent, and immediate, corresponding to sentences like:

1. "*Bill left a long time ago.*"
2. "*John left today.*"
3. "*Tom just left.*"

It is not clear whether the size of objects in one class is a function of the size of an object in another class, or whether the sizes are unrelated. If these sentences were spoken in this order in close succession, we could imagine a situation in which the departure in (1) was a few hours prior to the time of speech, and the departure in (3) was just seconds prior. Thus, we could have the following correspondences: immediate: $\Delta t \leq minutes$, recent: $\Delta t \leq hours$, and remote: $\Delta t > hours$. By the same token, we could imagine a situation in which the departure in (1) was many years prior to the time of speech, while at the same time maintaining that in (3) was just seconds prior. The given correspondences would remain the same, except for remote being $\Delta t > years$.

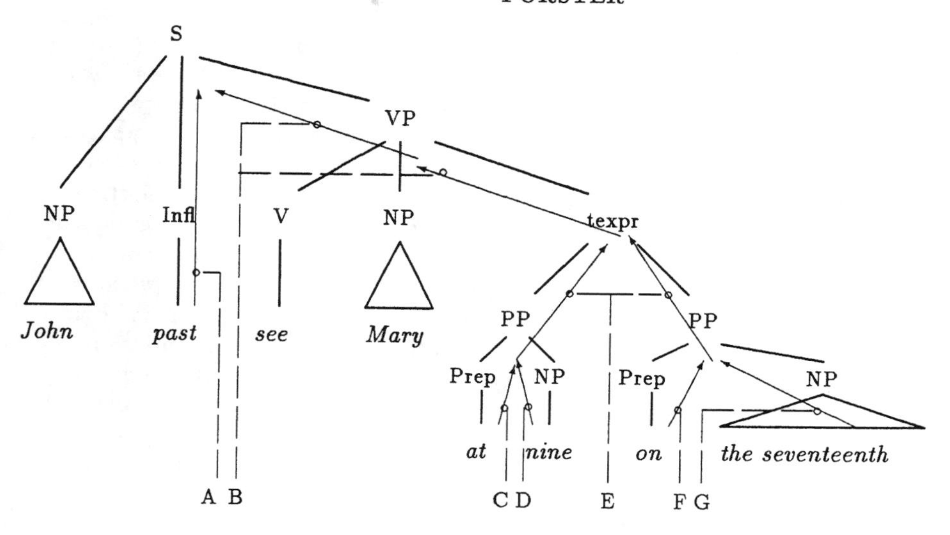

Figure 1: Hierarchical constraint propagation and temporal expressions

with the constraint from *on* being `(time-nature :day-interval)` and the information from *the seventeenth* being `((time-nature :day-interval) (time #<TIME see>))`.[7] Of the information collected at each of these two nodes, only `(time #<TIME see>)` is propagated up to 'texpr' (E). These constraints are combined and propagated ultimately to the S-node (B), to be combined with the constraint derived from the tense to be used (A).

This technique can be extended to the curious phrases examined in section 1. *At* could be modified to allow a holiday season (as opposed to a 'climatic' season, such as summer) as well as a point in time. If the client identifies the time it has provided as "*Christmas*", and also declares it to be a holiday season, then the phrase "*at Christmas*" may be produced, as required by the observations.

IMPLEMENTATION

The overall system includes a client program (currently a calendar scheduling program), a semantic component (GNOMON), and a syntactic component (MUMBLE (McDonald, 1983)). GNOMON uses hierarchical constraint propagation to choose applicable realisations and lexical items based on constraints derived from the realisations themselves and from context. The hierarchy mirrors the syntax tree, with sets of possible realisations at each node. A possible realisation provides information about the syntactic form to be used to realise a particular phrase, the constraints on its use, and the effect the form will have on context. The syntactic form is represented (recursively) by a form consisting of directives for the syntactic component and zero or more uninstantiated forms.

[7]The time referenced here is some client structure representing the time of the 'seeing' event, i.e. nine o'clock on the seventeenth. We refer to it here as TIME see to avoid confusion.

Four operations on the hierarchy and its members are defined: An uninstantiated form in the syntactic form of a possible realisation may be **expanded** by finding possible realisations for it. Constraints may be **propagated** to other parts of the realisation tree, possibly after the application of some reasoning. A set of possible realisations may be **narrowed** by the application of constraints, possibly resulting in the instantiation of one of them. Finally, a set of possible realisations may be **filtered**, drawing on non-linguistic criteria (e.g., brevity) for the selection.[8] GNOMON begins by selecting a top-level underspecified form for realisation and creating a queue containing it alone. GNOMON then processes the entries in the queue, passing on the final syntactic form to the syntactic component and recording the effects on global context when the queue is empty. The exact action to be taken when processing a queue entry depends on advice from a set of higher level constraints. These constraints are intended to reflect conventions in speech which lie outside of semantics and syntax, such as Gricean maxims. Though the actual constraints to be used are in a state of flux, we can assume for the time being that they include:

1. uninstantiated forms are instantiated whenever only one realization is known for it
2. constraints are propagated whenever they are introduced at a node[9]
3. possible realizations found to be inconsistent with already established constraints are automatically filtered out
4. possible realizations are always filtered to prefer anaphoric references, if present
5. the leftmost unexpanded node is selected for expansion.

Processing ends when no forms needing expansion remain. The form is then given to the syntactic component for processing, after which the effects on global context are recorded.

RELATED WORK

Matthiessen (1984) is an excellent survey of work on the use of tense to express the temporal relations underlying an utterance. Pustejovsky (1987) presents a novel theory of aspect which allows the internal event structure of a verb to be modelled. Many linguists (Prior, 1967; Reichenbach, 1947; Montague, 1974; Bennett & Partee, 1978; Dowty, 1979; Johnson, 1981) have suggested models for tense. Not all of them considered the interaction of their model with temporal adverbials. All gloss over some details of the representation. One of the more complete works is that of Dowty (1979), which presents a framework and definitions for a substantial fragment of English, and which discusses temporal adverbials and interactions with tense in some detail.

Hierarchical constraint propagation is related to functional unification grammar (Kay, 1984; Shieber, 1986) but uses constraints instead of features, and consistency checks instead of

[8]Note that filtering is not intended as a stopgap for short-comings of the grammar or the constraint propagation mechanism, but rather as a model of extra-linguistic influences on lexical choice. For example, it may be invoked when the speaker is pressed for time.

[9]More correctly, constraints are propagated whenever they are found to be common to all possible realizations attached to a node.

unification, resulting in general and powerful framework. GNOMON should attain significantly improved computational complexity through judicious use of its filtering capabilities.

CONCLUSIONS

We have explored the problem of generating temporal expressions and shown that it is amenable to solution by the application of hierarchical constraint propagation. Constraints derived either directly or indirectly (via transformations) from client data are propagated over the hierarchical structure provided by syntactic templates and are required to be consistent at every node. Multiple sources of constraints must be used to achieve lexical selection of a single item. Operations on the structure are controlled by higher-order constraints.

This approach allows the proper handling of the temporal prepositional phrases by the application of common-sense knowledge and in particular the simultaneous specification of tense and multiple temporal adverbials. Furthermore, it allows the modelling of non-linguistic interactions within the grammar, a closer integration of common-sense data with 'meaning,' and a better understanding of the interface and underlying knowledge needed by client programs to take advantage of natural language generation programs.

Further work will involve extending the grammar to deal with a wider range of temporal expressions and the application of common-sense knowledge to other types of expressions.

ACKNOWLEDGEMENTS

Thanks are due to James Pustejovsky, Emmon Bach, Victor Lesser, Beverly Woolf, Robin Popplestone, Penni Sibun, and Scott Anderson and the NLG discussion group at UMass who have offered many useful comments on the work.

REFERENCES

Bennett, M., & Partee, B. H. (1978) *Toward the Logic of Tense and Aspect in English,* Indiana University Linguistics Club, Bloomington, Indiana.

Dowty, D. (1979) *Word Meaning and Montague Grammar*, Reidel.

Forster, D. R. (1989) *Time and Natural Language Generation,* Technical Report 89-01, Department of Computer and Information Sciences, University of Massachusetts, Amherst.

Grosz, B., Sparck Jones, K. & Webber, B. L. (eds.) (1986) *Readings in Natural Language Processing,* Kaufmann.

Hobbs, J. R. (1985) *Granularity,* IJCAI-85, 1985, pp. 432-435.

Johnson, M. R. (1981) *A Unified Theory of Tense and Aspect*, in Tedeschi, P., & Zaenen A. (eds.) Tense and Aspect, Syntax and Semantics, v. 14, Academic Press, pp. 145-176.

Kay, M. (1984) *Functional Unification Grammar: A Formalism for Machine Translation*, COLING 84, pp. 75-78.

Matthiessen, C. (1984) *Choosing Tense in English*, ISI/RR-84-143.

McDonald, D. D. (1983) *Description Directed Control*, Computers and Mathematics 9(1), 1983, pp. 111-130, also in Grosz, Sparck Jones & Webber (eds.), 1986, pp. 519-537.

Montague, R. (1974) *The Proper Treatment of Quantification in Ordinary English*, in Thomason (ed.), Formal Philosophy, Yale, pp. 247-270.

Prior, A. N. (1967) *Past, Present, and Future*, Oxford University Press.

Pustejovsky, J. (1987) *An Event Structure for Lexical Semantics*, TR Brandeis University Computer Science Department.

Quirk, R., Greenbaum, S., Leech, G., & Svartvik, J. (1985) *A Comprehensive Grammar of the English Language*, Longman.

Reichenbach, H. (1947) *Elements of Symbolic Logic*, Macmillan, republished by Dover, 1980.

Shieber, S. M. (1986) *An Introduction to Unification-Based Approaches to Grammar*, CSLI Lecture Notes Number 4.

Stefik, M. (1981) *Planning with Constraints (MOLGEN: Part 1)*, AI 16(2), pp. 111-140.

The Role of Abstraction in Place Vocabularies

Paul Nielsen*
Artificial Intelligence Program
General Electric, Corporate Research and Development

ABSTRACT

Understanding mechanical behavior is an important part of both commonsense and expert reasoning which involves extensive spatial knowledge. A key problem in qualitative spatial reasoning is finding the right level of detail to support differing needs of reasoning methods. For example, analysis of failures may involve describing every surface imperfection; but, to gain an initial understanding of device behavior, one needs to eliminate extraneous information.

People seem very good at varying their level of resolution to meet the needs of the activity being described, but in machine understanding this has proven to be a dilemma. In order to understand an artifact one needs to impose some level of abstraction, yet to obtain a sufficient level of abstraction, without omitting critical details, one needs to understand the artifact. Our solution simplifies descriptions of mechanical devices using quantitative information about qualitatively significant regions. Configuration space representation of the kinematic pairs of a mechanism serves as the underlying metric diagram to answer questions concerning contact between the components and provide the foundation for construction of a purely symbolic device description, the place vocabulary. We explore the effect of abstracting the configuration space on condensation of the place vocabulary, showing how it makes qualitative reasoning about complex mechanisms, such as the mechanical clock, tractable. Examples shown are based on an implementation.

INTRODUCTION

The goal of qualitative mechanics is to produce a symbolic theory of analysis for complex, rigid body devices. We base this theory on first principles to allow explanations of the behavior both of common mechanisms such as gear trains, pistons, and ratchets, as well as of mechanisms which contain unusual devices such as mutilated gears and clock escapements. These explanations may be used to predict the behavior of an unknown mechanism, determine the suitability of a given device for a task, diagnose mechanical failures, and critically analyze new mechanisms.

The context of this work is a generative model of mechanical analysis which determines behavior from a geometric description of the components and a dynamic description of external forces affecting the mechanism. Specifically, we take drawings of rigid objects, determine how they will interact, partition these interactions into equivalent behaviors, combine these behaviors for all components

 This paper describes research done at the University of Illinois. Support for this work was through the Office of Naval Research, contract No. N00014-85-K-0225.

in the mechanism, propagate external forces acting on the system, and produce an envisionment showing possible changes in motion and position throughout the mechanism (Nielsen, 1988).

This paper focuses on the qualitative and geometric knowledge required when partitioning equivalent behaviors. We investigate ways to reduce combinatorial explosion when combining the pairwise interactions of components throughout an entire mechanism.

OVERVIEW

This paper begins with a brief history of work done in qualitative kinematics and the ideas necessary to understand this work. The examples provide an introduction to the type of reasoning qualitative mechanics can accomplish. The section "Building the place vocabulary" discusses our theory of place distinction. Following that we discuss the abstraction of these distinctions in order to allow analysis of larger mechanisms which is the core of this work. Finally we discuss future work and conclusions.

BACKGROUND

When inspecting a power train, observing gears gives one some general expectations of their behavior; however, explaining why gears bind requires a focus on the individual parts and more sophisticated observations of their interactions. A purely qualitative description would not benefit from additional observation, but by allowing new metric information to modify our symbolic representation we can construct a new qualitative description which depicts the conditions for the gear to jam. Conversely, if we considered every possible way the gears could jam and bind, we would be overwhelmed and never understand the overall mechanism.

Much of the previous research in symbolic approaches to kinematics (Davis, 1986; de Kleer, 1975; Laughton, 1985; Pu & Badler, 1988; Stanfill, 1985) relied on shape recognition or a priori knowledge of kinematic pairs (the parts of the mechanism which may come into contact). This knowledge would require an enormously large part library, restrict analysis of new designs, and allow only one level of analysis.

One way to simplify analysis of mechanisms is to abstract the shapes of the original components. For example, Gelsey (Gelsey, 1987; 1988) represents gears without teeth. The problem with those approaches is they presuppose the importance of surface features to the device's behavior. Such presupposition cannot be done in general. Removing the teeth from a scape wheel (figure 1A) makes analysis of its behavior impossible.

Order of magnitude reasoning methods (Raiman, 1986; Mavrovouniotis & Stephanopolous, 1987) have proven elusive in the analysis of mechanical devices because the size of a component has no relation to its relative significance. A surface with a small hole would have negligible effect on the motion of most objects across its surface, but in conjunction with an object which has an appropriately sized, spring loaded pin these components create a fundamentally significant behavior, latching.

Faltings, 1987a, demonstrated (based on the results of Reuleaux, 1876) the limitation of reasoning about shape information independently and indicated the need for analysis to proceed at the level of the kinematic pair. We show a generative approach to qualitative kinematics which uses information about the pairwise interactions of the components to determine the significance of a

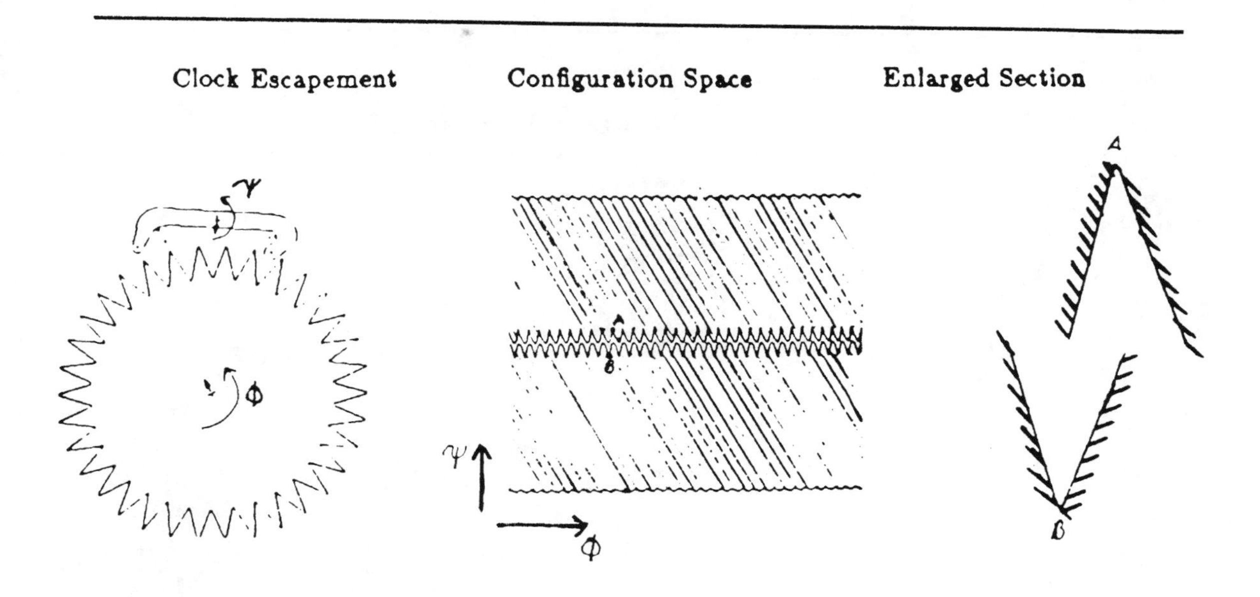

Figure 1: Clock escapement and corresponding configuration space

feature to mechanism behavior. This may be used to construct a library of common mechanisms, to enable reasoning about unforeseen variations, and to facilitate reasoning at varying levels of detail.

BUILDING THE PLACE VOCABULARY

Our initial kinematic analysis consists of a transformation of the kinematic pairs into their *configuration space* (introduced in Lozano-Perez & Wesley, 1979 and developed for mechanisms by Faltings, 1987b). A configuration space is the result of plotting overlapping (blocked) and non-overlapping (free) configurations for each allowable motion of each object. Unconstrained objects have six degrees of freedom, three translational and three rotational motions, and so a configuration space for two unconstrained objects would require six dimensions to describe every combination of positioning. However, components of mechanisms, by definition, are relatively constrained, and "single degree of freedom mechanisms are the forms used most frequently (Erdman & Sandor, 1984)," so each kinematic pair needs only a two dimensional representation to describe all possible interaction.

Figures 1 and 2 show some kinematic pairs and their configuration space representations. Lines parallel to the axes represent a pure rotation of a single object counterclockwise from 0 to 2π. Shaded regions indicate blocked configurations where the objects would overlap, and unshaded regions represent free configurations where the two objects do not touch. The curves between the free and blocked regions represent configurations where the objects are in contact.

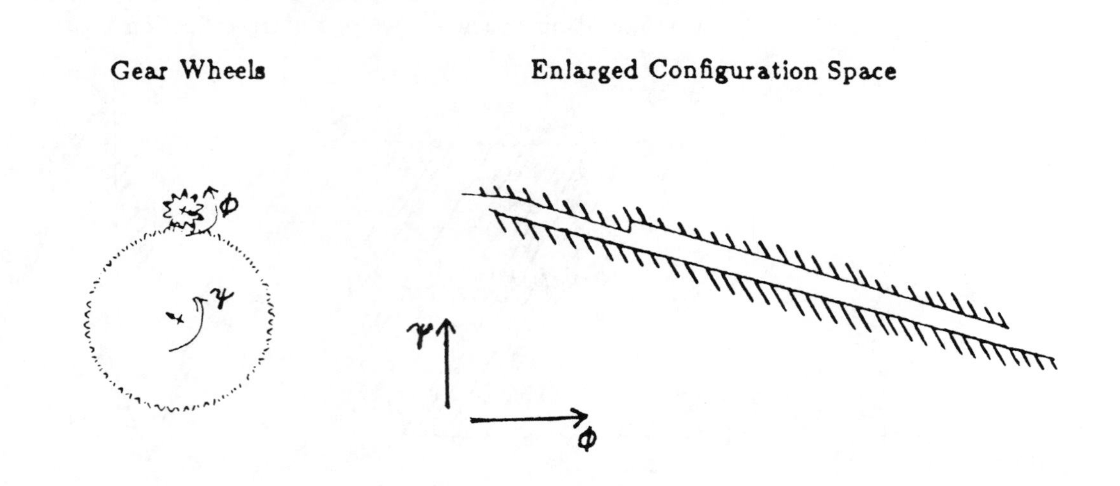

Figure 2: Gear wheels and corresponding configuration space

Because a complete spatial analysis of each point would take infinitely long, the space of consideration must be partitioned; but an unintelligent approach to place abstraction will either require a huge number of cells or lose relevant information. Our approach uses the concept of a place vocabulary[1] (introduced in Forbus, 1981). A *place* is a connected region of space in which all points share relevant properties, and a ***place vocabulary*** is the set of all places covering the space of interest. The metric diagram allows us to determine which places are adjacent and predict the configuration which results when one or more objects move.

For example, as long as one is walking along a wall the expectation is that it will not impede your progress, but upon reaching a corner the direction of travel must cease or change. Despite the size of the wall it may be represented with a single place, and even though the corner is a very small region, it is represented as a distinct place. In mechanism the shape of the surfaces of the objects in contact affect their possible behaviors, and the next possible contacts define the behavioral predictions of objects. So our place vocabulary will consist of regions where the contact is equivalent (in some sense) and non-contact (free) regions which are divided according to the next contact they can transition to.

We group places in the place vocabulary according to four types distinguished by allowable motion and contact. These are constraint segments, joins, free space divisions, and full faces. The properties of each type are discussed below.

Constraint segments (CSEGs) form the boundaries between free and blocked regions in configuration space. They represent arrangements where the objects make contact. A CSEGS prevents

[1] Joskowicz (Joskowicz & Addanki, 1988) uses a similar concept, but refers to it as a *region diagram*.

motion into the open half plane centered on its reverse surface normal.

Joins are the points where surfaces meet. In previous work in qualitative kinematics the analysis of points was largely overlooked. (The exception being Shoham, 1985, which treats only points.) Analysis at a point is only slightly more complex than along a smooth constant curve, but including points in the analysis roughly doubles the size of the place vocabulary.

Joins will have qualitatively different behaviors depending on whether the adjacent surfaces are concave or convex. We call a join an *concave* if the surface normal of the segment on one side of the join lies in the same open half plane as the surface normal of the segment on the opposite side; and *convex* otherwise. The motions prevented by an concave join are the union of the set of motions prevented by each of the adjacent segments, while the motions prevented by a convex join are the intersection of the set of motions prevented by each of the adjacent segments.

Some interesting kinematic pairs, such as clock escapements, do not stay in contact and may produce intermittent motions. Even more common kinematic pairs need to have some play between the parts to reduce friction. Free space divisions (FSDs) partition regions of open space to provide behavioral distinctions when the objects are not in contact.

The number and form of the FSDs affect the complexity of the resultant place vocabulary. The minimum FSDs should distinguish where the shape of the contact changes, since this corresponds to a qualitative change in the behavior of the mechanism, and should divide the open region according to the allowable motions of each individual object. Since each object only has one allowable motion, these divisions are lines.

The open areas of space bounded by CSEGs, FSDs, and joins are called *full faces*. They impose no restrictions on the motion of the object, but by adjacency they answer they question, "If this motion continues, what will happen next?"

One way to characterize the configuration of an entire mechanism would be to calculate the configuration space resulting from each possible motion of each of the components. Yet, even if each component only contributed one degree of freedom, and hence one dimension to this space, even simple mechanisms would produce enormously complex spaces. Further mechanical engineers do not seem to think of the entire mechanism at once as this method would suggest. Instead we use a vector, consisting of one place from each place vocabulary of each kinematic pair, to characterize all possible configurations of the overall mechanism (the *place vector*). As we see in the next section, combining all possible locations of all parts still results in an enormous number of possible place vectors. The solution is to ignore some of these combinations without loosing sight of "significant" behaviors.

ABSTRACTING THE PLACE VOCABULARY

The full place vocabulary for the clock escapement given in figure 1 consists of over 1300 places. This by itself is not an unwieldy number of distinct locations to consider in constructing a detailed analysis of this pair. But combining that information with 6000 to 60,000 places for each gear pair makes analysis of an entire clock become intractable before motion analysis is even considered. Information about periodically recurring patterns[2] reduces the number of places to 96 for the escapement and 16 for a typical gear. But since our clock has 6 gear pairs, its entire place vocabulary after this optimization would consist of about 1,600,000,000 places.

[2]Faltings handles recurring surface patterns by recording repetitive surfaces and performing the configuration space transformation only once for all of these surfaces. (Faltings, 1987b for details.)

To produce a detailed analysis we would like to preserve information about how a qualitatively unique surface on the original part interacts with each surface on its opposite pair. For example, at one level of detail we may be interested in knowing what behavior the fore face of a gear tooth has on the top of the opposite gear tooth. But when reasoning about long kinematic chains we cannot possibly keep track of where each surface comes into play. At the most detailed level CSEG's may be distinguished by a labeling of the object's surfaces which gave rise to them. Alternatively, the most abstract distinction of CSEG's is by the orientation of their surface normals because this orientation restricts the possible motions of the objects and determines the direction of forces transmitted by contact. Adjacent CSEG's with qualitatively equivalent surface normals may be represented by a single place in the place vocabulary.

This abstraction collapses all adjacent surfaces with qualitatively equivalent surface normals into one functionally equivalent surface which reduces the number of places on a gear to 12 and on the escapement to 80 and reduces the overall place vocabulary to about 240,000,000 places.

By reducing the resolution (enlarging the grain size) of the configuration space, interactions between small irregularities on surfaces may be ignored. For example, the gear depicted in Figure 2 has certain interactions between the surfaces which prevent it from turning in the "up left" direction for a small interval. If this interval is below some ϵ it may be ignored at the risk of loss of accuracy. Doing this reduces the number of places on a gear to 3 and the number of places on the escapement to 50. The total number of places is now 36,450.

When resolution is reduced, the gap between parts also becomes less apparent. If the gap size between two parts is less than some ϵ a new place is created which is bounded on two sides. Conceptually this approach eliminates the play between the two parts and collapses three distinct places into one. Only free space may be eliminated this way and not blocked space since that would alter the mechanisms behavior. It is important that any reduction in the number of places collapses many adjacent regions into one rather than eliminating a region since doing otherwise may eliminate a previously possible transition.

These abstractions allow us, when considering gear behaviors, to reduce the number of places to one. (The escapement remains 50, which is the total size of our place vocabulary.) The practical effect of this is that arbitrarily long gear chains contribute no more to the complexity of the mechanism than does a single gear pair. This corresponds to the intuitive notion of a gear as producing a single constant behavior and validates other qualitative analysis rules such as "A and B form a parallel gear pair if their only possible motion are two coordinated rotations(Joskowicz, 1987)." However, our result was obtained from a first principles, geometric analysis. No "knowledge engineering" for specific parts or chains of parts was required.

CONCLUSIONS

We have demonstrated a method of abstracting geometric information to reduce the complexity of symbolic information in mechanism analysis. The advantages of this approach include the ability to construct an analysis of entire mechanisms, rather than of components. While previously the combinatorics of the problem have been prohibitive, we have produced a complete envisionment of a mechanical clock using a total of 234 qualitative states accounting for variations in motion and position.

A more detailed analysis of a mechanism might look at the way a subcomponent participates in the overall behavior of the mechanism, then look at a more detailed analysis of that subcomponent to provide further insight into the behavior of the mechanism. For example, the gear pair depicted will turn freely only in one direction. If we construct an approximate description of the gears turning freely, we should then reinvestigate the behavior of the gear in the overall mechanism to determine if it violates this unidirectional constraint.

In the future we would like to be able to perform analysis from courser sketches of mechanical components rather than from actual components. Slight irregularities could be removed by the simplification techniques discussed here, and barely occluded regions may provide clues to designer's intent. If a region is only slightly blocked, it may in fact have been intended as free.

ACKNOWLEDGMENTS

I want to thank Ken Forbus for his guidance and for the place vocabulary concept. Thanks to Boi Faltings for the work in configuration space and our initial theory of place. Special thanks to John Collins, Brian Falkenhainer, Dennis DeCoste, Gordon Skorstad, and everyone in the Qualitative Reasoning Group.

REFERENCES

Davis, E. (1986) *A Logical Framework for Solid Object Physics.* Technical Report TR No. 245, New York University, Computer Science Department.

de Kleer, J. (1975) *Qualitative and Quantitative Knowledge in Classical Mechanics.* Technical Report TR-352, Artificial Intelligence Laboratory, Massachusetts Institute of Technology, Cambridge, MA.

Erdman, A. & Sandor, G. (1984) *Mechanism Design: Analysis and Synthesis.* Volume 1, Prentice-Hall, Inc., Englewood Cliffs, NJ.

Faltings, B. (1987) Qualitative kinematics in mechanisms. In *Proceedings of IJCAI 87*, International Joint conference on Artificial Intelligence, Milan, Italy.

Faltings, B. (1987) *Qualitative Place Vocabularies for Mechanisms in Configuration Space.* Technical Report UIUCDCS-R-87-1360, University of Illinois.

Forbus, K. (1981) *A Study of Qualitative and Geometric Knowledge in Reasoning about Motion.* Technical Report TR-615, Artificial Intelligence Laboratory, Massachusetts Institute of Technology, Cambridge, MA.

Gelsey, A. (1987) Automated reasoning about machine geometry and kinematics. In *Third IEEE Conference on Artificial Intelligence Applications.*

Gelsey, A. (1988) *Spatial Reasoning about Mechanisms.* Technical Report YALEU/DCS/RR-641, Yale University.

Joskowicz, L. & Addanki, S. (1988) From kinematics to shape: an approach to innovative design. In *Proceedings National Conference on Artificial Intelligence*, American Association of Artificial Intelligence.

Joskowicz, L. (1987) *A Framework for the Kinematic Analysis of Mechanical Devices.* Technical Report TR No. 313, New York University.

Laughton, S. (1985) *Explanation of Mechanical Systems Through Qualitative Simulation.* Technical Report AITR85-19, University of Texas at Austin.

Lozano-Perez, T. & Wesley, M. (1979) An algorithm for planning collision-free paths among polyhedral obstacles. *Communications of the ACM*, **22**:(560 – 570).

Mavrovouniotis, M. & Stephanopolous, G. (1987) Reasoning with orders of magnitude and approximate relations. In *Proceedings National Conference on Artificial Intelligence*, American Association of Artificial Intelligence.

Nielsen, P. (1988) *A Qualitative Approach to Rigid Body Mechanics.* Technical Report UIUCDCS-R-88-1469, University of Illinois.

Pu, P. & Badler, N. (1988) *Behavior Propagation Simulation of Intermittent-Mechanical Systems.* Technical Report, University of Pensylvania.

Raiman, O. (1986) Order of magnitude reasoning. In *Proceedings National Conference on Artificial Intelligence*, American Association of Artificial Intelligence.

Reuleaux, F. (1876) *The Kinematics of Machinery, Outlines of a Theory of Machines.* Macmillan and Co., London, Translated and Edited by Alex B. W. Kennedy, C.E.

Shoham, Y. (1985) Naive kinematics: One aspect of shape. In *Proceedings of the IJCAI 85*, pages (436 – 442), International Joint Conference on Artificial Intelligence.

Stanfill, C. (1985) MACK, a program which deduces the behavior of machines from their forms. *SIGART Newsletter*, **93**:(12 – 16).

Cognitive Efficiency Considerations for Good Graphic Design

Stephen Casner
University of Pittsburgh

Jill H. Larkin
Carnegie Mellon University

ABSTRACT

Larkin and Simon's (1987) analysis of how graphical representations support task performance is applied to designing graphical displays that streamline information-processing tasks. Theoretically this streamlining is done by designing external data structures that (a) allow users to substitute less effortful visual operators for more effortful logical operators, and (b) reduce search for needed information. A design program called BOZ is used to produce four alternative displays of airline schedule information to support a task of making airline reservations. We postulate several procedures that use visual operators to perform the task using the different graphics. The number of times each operator is executed provides one measure of task difficulty (for a procedure and graphic). A second measure is the difficulty of executing each operator. Seven subjects performed the airline reservation task using each of the four graphics. Response times for the different graphics differ by a factor of two, which is statistically highly significant. Detailed data analyses suggest that these differences arise through substitution of visual operators for logical ones and through the use of visual cues that help reduce search. These analyses provide quantitative estimates of the time saved through operator substitutions.

INTRODUCTION

Empirical studies of graphics find little support for any general superiority of graphical representations. Instead, graphic displays seem to vary in usefulness depending on the task involved. Twenty-nine studies (Jarvenpaa and Dickson,1988) found graphics to be more useful than tabular presentations for some tasks, but less useful for others. These results are consistent with the theoretical analysis of Larkin and Simon (1987) that a display (graphic or otherwise) is a data structure. Its utility depends on the nature of the task it supports and the nature of the procedures employed by the human implementer to perform the task. When procedures and data structures match well, there is better cognitive efficiency than when they do not.

Larkin and Simon (1987) suggest that the following forms of cognitive efficiency are offered by good graphical displays.

Substituting Visual Operators: Graphical displays often allow users to substitute less demanding visual operators in place of more complex logical operators. Visual operators (e.g., distance and color comparisons, spatial coincidence judgements) can often give users the same information as more complex non-visual operators. This advantage arises when a display represents explicitly information that is only implicit (or computable) in an alternate representation.

Reducing Search: Effective graphical displays often arrange information so as to reduce the number of items the user must look at in order to find something useful, or they group into one location information required to draw a particular inference. Graphical techniques like shading and spatial arrangement can help guide the eye to relevant information or past irrelevant information.

This paper describes BOZ, a computer-implemented algorithm for designing graphical displays (Casner, 1989). BOZ (described in the second section) systematically exploits the hypothesized advantages of graphical displays, substituting visual operators for logical ones, and constraining the grouping of related information. BOZ analyzes a formal description of the operators required to execute a task and searches a catalog of visual operators to find visual operators that can serve as substitutes for the logical operators. BOZ then proposes graphic displays that support performance of these operators. A single task description typically gives rise to many graphic displays, each supporting different substitutions of visual for logical operators. The next section describes four alternative graphical displays proposed by BOZ to support the task of finding an airline reservation satisfying time and cost constraints. For each of the four graphics, we hypothesize search and information-generation procedures using the different display-supported operators. Simulations of these procedures count the number of times each operator executes for each procedure and graphic. The final section describes an experiment in which participants used the four BOZ-designed graphics. Comparisons of participants' response times with the operator counts support two mechanisms through which these graphics improve cognitive efficiency: (1) substituting visual operators for logical ones, and (2) reducing search by using visual cues to ignore items.

BOZ: DESIGNING EFFECTIVE VISUAL DATA STRUCTURES AND PROCEDURES

A Logical Operator Description Language. BOZ begins with a description of the logical operators (LOPs) required to perform a task. Logical operators are general information-processing activities independent of a particular representation. For example, the following LOP (findLayover) describes finding the layover between two connecting airline flights. It takes two flights as arguments and returns the layover time—the difference between the arrival time of flightA and the departure time flightB.

```
(LOP findLayover (flightA flightB)
    (DIFFERENCE
        (findDeparture flightB) (findArrival flightA)))
```

A Catalog of Visual Operators. BOZ contains a catalog of visual operators that describe information-processing activities that occur within the context of a graphical display. Visual (or perceptual) operators (POPs) include spatial position and coincidence judgements, interval and distance judgements, comparisons of color, shape, size, slope, length, height, width, etc. POPs are encoded using the same formalism as LOPs. For example, the operator for estimating horizontal distance between two graphical objects is:

```
(POP findHorzDistance (objA objB)
    (DIFFERENCE
        (findHorzPos objA) (findHorzPos objB)))
```

Matching Logical to Visual Operators. A matching algorithm considers each logical operator in a task description and searches the catalog of visual operators for substitutes. A visual operator qualifies as a substitute if renaming can map the visual operator into the logical operator. For example, findHorzDistance and findLayover are equivalent because they both compute a difference between two numbers (end times of flights and horizontal locations). Although not discussed here, if no single visual operator matches a LOP, BOZ attempts to match it using two or more visual operators and a set of combination, composition, and repetition rules.

Visually Structuring Related Data. For each proposed substitution of a visual for a logical operator, a data structuring algorithm assesses the information required to perform the operator and tries to ensure that this information is presented in the same spatial locality and in a form that supports easy perceptual performance of that visual operator. For example, if findHorzDistance replaces findLayover, then the data structuring algorithm requires that: (1) all times are encoded along the same axis, allowing a human to substitute estimating horizontal distance between two objects for the logical operator of subtracting their coordinates; and (2) all time information about a flight is encoded using the same graphical object.

EXAMPLE: GRAPHICAL DISPLAYS FOR AIRLINE RESERVATIONS

We used BOZ to design a set of graphical displays to support the following airline reservation task that manipulates information about flights, their origins and destinations, departure and arrival times, and costs.

> Find a pair of connecting flights that travel from Pittsburgh to Mexico City. You are free to choose any intermediate city as long as the layover in that city is no more than four hours. Both flights that you choose must be available. The combined cost of the flights cannot exceed $500.

The task description given to BOZ contained the following logical operators:

findFlight(origin: city1, destination: city2) Sequentially searches a list for a flight with origin and destination equal to city1 and city2. (one of the cities may be left unspecified). Returns the first flight meeting this criterion, together with the name of any unspecified city.

checkAvailability(flight) Returns true if a flight has seats available.

checkLayover(flightA, flightB) Returns true if the layover between two flights is acceptable (non-negative and less than 4 hours).

checkCost(flightA, flightB) Returns true if the cost of the two flights is acceptable (less than $500).

Figure 1 shows four of the displays produced by BOZ from these logical operators. We consider these displays in turn, describing how BOZ created them, and correspondingly their hypothesized advantages to a user.

DISPLAY 1: A CONVENTIONAL AIRLINE SCHEDULE

In substituting visual for logical operators, BOZ can select operators for finding and interpreting text. Therefore, among BOZ's representations is Display 1 (Figure 1), a tabular presentation that supports substituting the following visual operators.

findFlight(origin: city1, destination: city2) searches the rows of the table stopping at a row that has the specified endpoint (s), and returning the flight listed in that row.

readAvailability(flight) returns true if second column reads "ok"; else false

subtractTimes(flight1, flight2) finds departure time in the flight2 row (column 4) and arrival time in the flight1 row (column 5); subtracts arrival time from departure time; returns true if greater than zero and less than 4 hours; else false

addCosts(flight1, flight2) finds cost in flight2 row (column 3) and cost in flight1 row (column 3); adds the two ; returns true if less than $500; else false

We define the following search procedure (rowSearch) using the four operators and considering flights sequentially in the order they appear in the rows of the table. It exploits the row and column indexing of information, the only spatial structure available in Display 1.

```
procedure rowSearch
    repeat
        findFlight(origin: pit; destination: any); returns flight1, city1.
        if  readAvailability(flight1)
            then:   findFlight(origin: city1, destination: mex); returns flight2.
            if      readAvailability(flight2)
                    then:  if  subtractTimes(flight1, flight2)
                               then:  if  addCosts(flight1, flight2) then:
                                          report answer
    until answer found
```

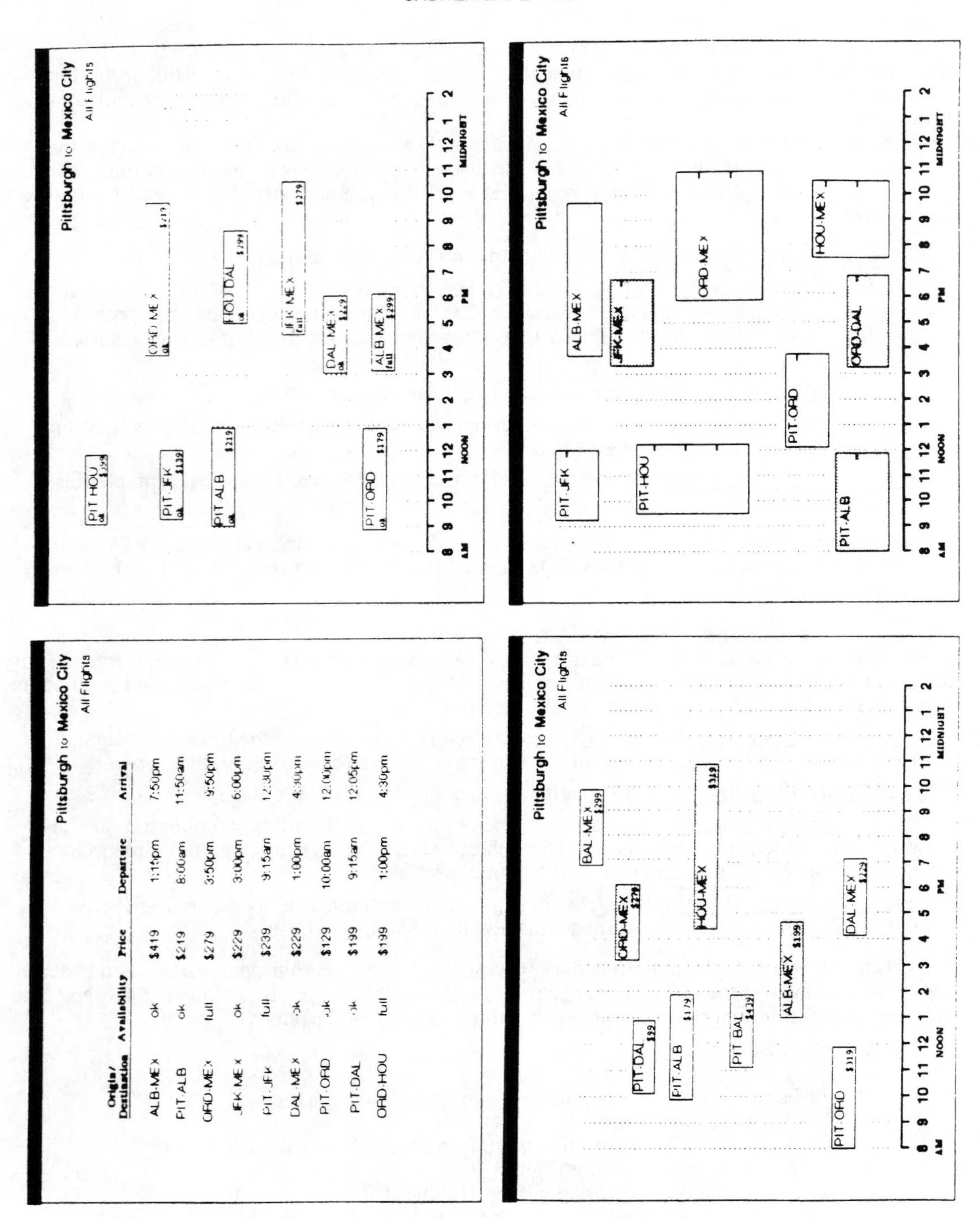

Figure 1: Four BOZ-based displays for the reservation task. (1) A table. (2) Horizontal distance encodes time. (3) Shading encodes availability. (4) Height encodes cost.

DISPLAY 2: HORIZONTAL DISTANCE ENCODES TIMES

Display 2 substitutes the visual findHorzDistance operator for the logical checkLayover operator. If two connecting flights have ends within four units of each other, then the layover is less than four hours. As required by the data structuring algorithm, all times are encoded as horizontal positions, and the two times associated with one flight are encoded by the same graphical object, i.e., a box.

Display 2 also supports two variations of the rowSearch procedure. **rightOfSearch** is the same as rowSearch, but omits consideration of flight boxes that are not to the right of the end of the current flight box. rightOfSearch thus prunes search by eliminating automatically flights leaving before the arrival of flight1. **closeSearch**, users first consider those pairs of flights that not overlapping, but are closest together (have the shortest layovers). closeSearch thus prunes search by considering first flight pairs most likely to meet the layover criterion.

DISPLAY 3: SHADING ENCODES AVAILABILITY

Display 3 adds to display 2 support for the visual judgeShaded operator in place of the checkAvailability operator. Additionally, Display 3 lets users prune any search procedure by skipping all shaded flight boxes. These procedures are indicated by **rowSearchU**, **rightOfSearchU**, and **closeSearchU**, where the final "U" indicates searching only unshaded boxes.

DISPLAY 4: HEIGHT ENCODES COST

Display 4 adds to display 3 support for the visual judgeHeights for the checkCost operator. A user can judge whether the combined heights of two flight boxes is greater than 5 ($500), instead of adding the numerical costs of the two flights. Display 4 also supports pruned search procedures (**cheapSearch** and **cheapSearchU**) in which the user considers first the cheapest (least tall) flight boxes, thereby making it more likely to satisfy the cost constraint early in search.

DISPLAY SUMMARY

Operators. Display 1 (the table) supports only the arithmetic and reading operators listed at the left in Table 1a. Each other display, compared to the previous one supports substitution of one additional visual operator for these read and compute operators. Table 1a lists the operator substitutions and the displays in which each is available.

Search. Table 1b shows the eight search procedures, 4 standard strategies, each with a variant involving skipping shaded boxes indicating filled flights. With each is listed the displays for which it can be applied. The central search procedure is rowSearch, possible for all displays (see Table 1b). Displays 2 - 4 (in which horizontal distance encodes time) allow a user to short-cut rowSearch, when finding a connecting flight, by skipping rows unless the flight box begins to the

Table 1: (a) Operator substitutions. (b) Three search strategy groups.

Table Operators	*Other Display Operators*	**(a)**
subtractTimes	findHorzDistance	2,3,4
readAvailability	checkShaded	3,4
addCosts	judgeHeights	4

(b)	*Standard*	*Ignore unshaded*
rowSearch	1,2,3,4	3,4
rightOfSearch	2,3,4	3,4
closeSearch	2,3,4	3,4
cheapSearch	4	4

right of the initial flight box. This rightOfSearch procedure thus produces a search sequence that is a consistently ordered subset of items considered by rowSearch. These two procedures therefore yield closely related search results. Displays 2-4 also make possible a form of best-first search, by considering first connecting flight boxes with left ends closest to (but right of) the initial flight box. This closeSearch algorithm (compared with rowSearch and its variant rightOfSearch) produces a search sequence with a different ordering of items. Similarly, Display 4, in which box height encodes cost, supports a best-first search with respect to cost (cheapSearch), that yields a search sequence different from that of either rowSearch or closeSearch.

Displays 3 and 4, in which shading encodes availability, support a search variant in which shaded boxes are skipped. Each -SearchU variant produces a consistently ordered subset of the search sequence produced by the corresponding search without use of shading.

To compare search procedures concretely, we used 40 displays, ten instances of each type. A LISP simulation of each search procedure counted the number of search steps for each example. We computed the correlation between the number of search steps for a display for each pair of search strategies. Only pairs within one group in Table 1b had non-negligible correlations. Consider first a procedure and its -U variant in which unshaded boxes are skipped. In the number pair (β, R^2) β is the regression coefficient for the number of search steps with the -U strategy on the number of steps with the non-U strategy. For three of the pairs, these numbers are: rowSearch (.737,.703) rightOfSearch (.502,.646), and closeSearch (.741,.446) [based on 30 cases]. Thus skipping unshaded boxes cuts search consistently for each strategy by amounts from 70% to about 50%. For non -U procedure pairs, non-negligible correlations between number of search steps occurred only for rowSearch and rightOfSearch (β=.66, R^2=.703). The results of this simulation thus verify the grouping of search procedures in Table 1b.

EMPIRICAL TEST OF DESIGN EFFECTIVENESS

METHOD

Participants. Eight employees of the Learning Research and Development Center at the University of Pittsburgh. One participant's data is currently missing from the analysis.

Materials. There were a total of 40 problems, ten instances of each of the four displays. Examples of each of the four displays are shown in Figure 1.

Apparatus. Displays were presented as 9 x 12 inch screen images on a Xerox 1186 computer. Response times were computed using the system clock when the mouse was clicked.

Procedure. Subjects performed the reservations task forty times, ten times using each display. To counterbalance learning and practice, eight orders (one for each participant) of display presentation were used (1234, 2341, 3421, 2341, 4321, 3214, 2143, 1432). At the start of the experiment, all the visual operators were explained. Participants were shown the rowSearch procedure but were told that they could follow any strategy they wished. Their task was to find a flight that satisfied the criteria (not necessarily the flight that minimized any measure). There was one practice trial with each display version. Participants were told not to guess, to work as quickly as possible but not to compromise accuracy, and that they could rest between any two graphics. Time to complete the experiment was typically 40 minutes.

EMPIRICAL PREDICTIONS

Global Efficiency. Each graphic supports the advantages of the previous one, as well as the ones it introduces. Therefore the first prediction is that cognitive efficiency should be linearly ordered as in Figure 1 with the conventional table worst and Display 4 best.

Decrease in operator times. For every combination of display and search procedure, we can count the number of times each operator is executed. If response times are expressed as a function of the number of executions of each operator, a regression analysis yields estimates of the times associated with each operator. If substituting visual operators for reading and computing improves efficiency, then the times associated with the operators (checkAvailability, checkLayover, and checkCost) should be smaller for graphics that support substitution of visual operators.

RESULTS AND DISCUSSION

Global Efficiency

The mean response times for each display (excluding five times differing by more than three standard deviations from the problem mean and the 3 to 6 erroneous responses for each graphic) are: Table: 19.3 (8.4); Horizontal distance encodes times: 10.1 (4.7); Shading encodes availability: 7.2 (2.7); Height encodes cost: 7.4 (2.4)

Graphic version had a highly significant effect on response time ($F(3, 239) = 52.719$, $p < .0001$), and also on the variance of response time ($F(3, 24) = 18.649$, $p < .0001$). Fischer's PLSD for pairwise comparison indicates no significant difference between version 3 and 4 and differences significant at the .05 level between other version pairs for both mean response times and standard errors of the mean. Graphics 3 and 4 produce both the lowest response times and the least variable performance. Graphics 2 and 1 each in turn produce significantly higher response times and greater variability.

The visual operators supported by Displays 2 and 3 thus had the predicted effect on global efficiency. But allowing users to perform judgeHeights (instead of addCosts) produced no observable effect. This should perhaps not surprise us since it is the one visual operator that requires integrating quantitative estimates from two different locations.

Decrease in Operator Times.

Preliminary comparisons of the three procedure groups (rowSearch, closeSearch, and cheapSearch) with the subject response times for each of the four displays suggest that only the rowSearch procedures provide reasonable fits to the data. Thus it seems that, with the practice available, subjects did not adopt the the best-first strategies, but used the rowSearch group shown in Table 1b.

Based on these preliminary results, we used the following process assess the effect of substitution of visual for logical operators: We assumed for each graphic the most efficient rowSearch procedure supported by that graphic, i.e., rowSearch for the table, rightOfSearch for display 2 (with flight boxes), and rightOfSearchU for displays 3 and 4 (with shaded boxes). We considered two alternative operators for assessing layover and cost. The subtractTimes and addCosts operators correspond to subtracting or adding numbers. These operators were assumed for displays that did not support alternative procedures (the table for subtractTimes, and displays 1, 2, and 3 for addCosts). For the remaining displays, we assumed use of the more efficient visual operators findHorzDistance and judgeHeights. We assumed that the time for one search step was the same in all graphics (although the number of such steps varied with the search procedure supported).

Using these assumptions we computed for each of the 40 graphic exemplars the number of search steps and the number of cost and layover computations. A regression of response times on these numbers produced a well-fitting statistical model with $F(4, 238)=73.108$, $p = .0001$, $R^2 = .48$. Removing from the model the counts for either search or checking layovers dramatically reduced the fit. In contrast, removing the counts for checking costs had no effect on the fit. This model yielded the following parameter estimates:

One search step requires 330 ± 35 milliseconds.

The findHorzDistance operator is 2 ± .25 seconds faster than the subtractTimes operator.

The judgeHeights operator is negligibly (100 ± 300 milliseconds) slower than the addCosts operator.

These results are consistent with the global time differences given above. The reduced performance time with successive graphics arises for two reasons. First, attending only to boxes to the right of the current box and to unshaded boxes reduces the number of items that must be searched. Second, substitution of findHorzDistance for subtractTimes produces a substantial saving in time. In contrast judgeHeights, which requires integrating visual information from two separate locations, provides no such advantage. These two effects are sufficient to account for the response time differences between displays 1-3, and for the lack of difference between displays 3 and 4) .

SUMMARY

BOZ is a computer algorithm that starts with the logical operators required to perform a task and designs graphic displays supporting substitution of visual operators for logical ones, and pruning of search through visual cues. In an initial experimental test, four BOZ-designed graphics each included one additional visual operator and corresponding opportunities for pruning search, by using visual cues to ignore certain items or by restructuring search to consider more promising items earlier. Analysis of subjects' response times indicate strongly that two out of these three enhancements dramatically and significantly improved response times to the task. The unhelpful enhancement required integration of information from two separate locations. More detailed analyses suggest that these improvements were due to operator substitution and using visual cues to omit items from search, but not due to restructuring search.

Importantly BOZ is a *synthesis* algorithm. It starts with an abstract task description, and produces a collection of graphics which should, on the basis of information-processing principles, reduce human processing effort for the task. This work is therefore a start on the practically important effort of putting cognitive science to work in practical applications.

REFERENCES

Casner, S. (1989) *A cognitive approach to designing effective graphical illustrations*, Learning Research and Development Technical Report.

Jarvenpaa, S.L. & Dickson, G.W. Graphics and managerial decision making: Research Based Guidelines. *Communications of the ACM*. **31**(*6*) 764-774.

Larkin, J.H. & Simon, H.A. (1987). Why a diagram is (sometimes) worth 10,000 words. *Cognitive Science*, **11**(1), 65-100.

ACKNOWLEDGEMENTS

This work is supported Office of Naval Research, University Research Initiative Contract Number N00014-86-K-0678 and by a grant from the James S. McDonnell Foundation to the second author. William Oliver and Stellan Ohlsson provided helpful comments.

A Process Model of Experience-Based Design

Katia P. Sycara and **D. Navinchandra**
The Robotics Institute, Carnegie Mellon University

ABSTRACT

Human designers use previous designs extensively in the process of producing a new design. When they come up with a partial or complete design, designers perform a mental simulation to verify the design. We present a model for engineering design that integrates case-based reasoning and qualitative simulation. The model involves: (1) setting up the functional requirements, (2) accessing memory to retrieve cases relevant to the requirements, (3) synthesizing pieces of cases into designs, (4) verifying and testing the design, and finally, (5) debugging. This process is applied recursively till the design is complete and bug free. The model integrates different levels of representation and reasoning mechanisms in order to effectively support the design tasks.

INTRODUCTION

Design is the act of devising an artifact which satisfies a useful need, in other words, performs some function. Design is a complex task that challenges human creativity. This is particularly true in our domain of interest: engineering design. Underlying the design task is a core set of principles, rules, laws and techniques which the designer uses for problem solving. His expertise lies in his ability to use these techniques to produce a feasible design. The designer's expertise is a consequence of his experience and training, much of which is based on previous exposure to similar design problems (Pahl & Beitz 84).

Research investigating the role of experience in problem solving domains that involve understanding the behavior of physical devices has primarily focused on diagnosis (e.g., (Lancaster 88)). Engineering design is a domain that involves not only understanding of device behavior so as to recognize and explain faults but also conceiving and synthesizing device components. Previous AI research in engineering design (Mostow & Barley 87) has advocated the hierarchical decomposition of a design and re-use of plan steps that realize the functional specifications of the components. This technique is promising for domains such as software or circuit design because in these domains designs can be characterized as collections of weakly interacting functional modules, each of which implements one of the functional requirements. Good mechanical designs on the other hand are highly integrated, tightly coupled collections of interacting components. Moreover, an artifact (or artifact component) can be used to satisfy more than one function. These observations imply that a problem solver needs to have access to previous cases (or case pieces) as well as previous plans in terms of operators, preconditions and effects. In this paper, we present a model of engineering design that integrates Case-Based reasoning and qualitative reasoning to come up with new designs.

CASE-BASED REASONING AND ENGINEERING DESIGN

Case-Based Reasoning (CBR) is the problem solving paradigm where previous experiences are used to guide problem solving (Kolodner et al. 85, Sycara 87). Cases similar to the current problem are retrieved from memory, the best case is selected from those retrieved and compared to the current problem. The precedent case is adapted to fit the current situation, based on the identified differences between the precedent and the current case. Successful cases are stored so they can be retrieved and re-used in the future. Failed cases are also stored so that they will warn the problem solver of potential difficulties and help recover from failures. If a current case has features similar to a past failure, then the problem solver is warned not to attempt the failed solution. After the problem is solved, the case memory is updated with the new experience. In this way, learning is integrated with problem solving.

For design, case retrieval is done based not just on surface features but also on (a) the qualitative behavior of the device depicted in the case, (b) the causal relations in the explanation of the device's functions, and (c) device topology. To support retrieval, cases need to be represented at several levels ranging from a topological description of the device objects to a linguistic specification of function. At the intervening levels causal explanations of the device behavior and feature relations have to be incorporated. These levels capture the "mechanism", "causality", and "purpose" perspectives used by people to understand physical systems (White 88).

The mechanical design domain has several characteristics that make the problem very complicated and impose a set of requirements on a reasoner.

- During the design process, a designer transforms an abstract functional description for a device into a physical description that satisfies the functional requirements. In this sense, design is a transformation from the functional domain to the physical domain. In order to effect this transformation, a designer needs to reason at different levels of abstraction ranging from the physical to the functional.
- Good mechanical designs are often highly integrated, tightly coupled collections of interacting components with no obvious decomposition of the overall function into subfunctions. Previous cases represent good solutions to these interactions and can be profitably used.
- The initial functional description of the artifact is usually underspecified so that a designer needs to identify information "gaps" during the design process and generate new problem solving subgoals to resolve them.
- A complete design is synthesized from solutions to subproblems that capture desired subfunctions of the artifact. In engineering design, decisions relating to how certain functions are achieved might be taken at a linguistic or qualitative level. Considerable complication arises from the fact that although a design might be verified to be correct at these levels, simulation at the physical level might fail. The problem solver must synthesize snippets at one level of abstraction while making sure the parts will work together in physically correct ways.
- A design needs to be verified to ensure it meets its functional specifications. In engineering design, verifying that the component parts meet their specifications does not guarantee that the design as a whole will meet its specifications. Thus, both partial and complete designs must be verified.

Our process model addresses all the above requirements.

CASE REPRESENTATION

In dealing with physical systems a reasoner needs to retrieve cases based not only on the *physical attributes* of a device but also on its *functional behavior.* The case based problem solver should be able to work at several levels of abstraction ranging from the physical to the functional level. For example, while trying to produce a design to perform a particular function, a functional description may be used to retrieve cases. However, using the case to physically synthesize the design involves extracting appropriate physical features from the case. This requires that the representation be able to capture the relationship between physical form and qualitative function. We now present in some detail the types of representation used in our work.

1. ***Linguistic Description.*** Linguistic representations are best suited for direct indexing based on a matching linguistic cue. Case attributes provide such indices. Features that capture the physical description of the device (object features) need to be included. For example, a simple household water

tap can be indexed in terms of its function, to control water flow; its components, pipe, nozzle, handle, valve and seal; the material out of which it is made, brass; the type of device it is, mechanical; the places where it is intended to be used, kitchen, bathroom, water tank.

2. ***Functional Block-Diagramming.*** Devices can be viewed as black-boxes which take inputs and produce desired outputs. In the physical domain, three types of inputs and outputs have been identified: signals, energy and materials (Pahl & Beitz 84). A characterization of the relationships between the input and the outputs is the device behavior. In our example, the tap takes a material input (water) and outputs the water in response to the signal (open/close). The tap takes the input signal *Sn*, and the input water flow rate of *Qin* and produces the output flow rate of *Qout*. The temperatures of the input and outputs are *Tin* and *Tout*. The tap has the following qualitative relationships: (1) The inflow of water (*Qin*) monotonically increases with the signal *theta*. (2) The inflow is equal to the outflow (*Qin* = *Qout*), (3) Temperature does not change. (4) When *theta* is zero, there is no flow through the tap, and (5) When *theta* is 2π, then the flow is maximum. The device description at this level of detail does not capture the underlying behavior. This is done with the aid of causal explanations represented as acyclic graphs.

3. ***Causal Graphs.*** A causal graph is composed of links and nodes, where the nodes represent device objects and their attributes, while the links represent causal relations among the attributes. For design cases we use an augmented causal graph representation in which causal relations have qualitative equations (Forbus 84, Kuipers 86) associated with them.

4. ***Qualitative states and Configuration Spaces.*** The causal relationships that describe the behavior of an artifact refer to specific artifact components and relate status conditions such as position and size of the components. The next step is to associate the objects and their status directly to the object geometry. In our work, this is done through Qualitative State descriptions. Qualitative states provide a vocabulary for describing the device behavior. Transitions between the states in the vocabulary are expressed in the causal explanation. For example, the tap can take three states that are qualitatively significant: closed, partially open and fully open. These states provide limit cases for qualitative simulation of the causal network.

PROBLEM SOLVING STEPS

This section presents the steps of Case Based Problem Solving for Design. The process is recursively applied as new subgoals are generated during problem solving. Using the multi-level representation presented in section 3, the problem solver can use cases to address new design problems while switching from one representation to another as needed. This section provides details about the problem solving steps of our approach. We illustrate our approach with the aid of an example. The example is about the design of a Hot&Cold water Faucet which allows control of the mix of hot and cold water independently of the rate of flow of the mixture. The problem solving steps are as follows:

1. Development of a Linguistic Description. Surface features of the problem are determined. In design, surface matching has a lot of validity since similar form often embodies similar function. Several studies (Ratterman 87, Faries 88) have found that surface features have a major influence on the possibility of a case-based reminding. Surface matching is tried first. If a failure to get any useful information out of the matched precedents occurs, then structure matching is attempted.

A description of hot-water faucet is: a device which mixes hot and cold water allowing independent control of the temperature and rate of flow of the mixed water. The index attributes are hot, cold, water and flow-control. Contexts of usage are water, bath, kitchen, bar.

2. Describing the required Function. At the simplest level, the desired artifact can be viewed as a black-box which takes certain inputs and produces desired outputs. The function of the black-box is described by qualitative relations explaining how the inputs and outputs are related. This function is provided by the user. It is the system's job to help realize an artifact which will convert the inputs into the desired outputs.

A functional black-box diagram of the faucet is shown in Figure 1. The qualitative functions of the faucet are: (1) A signal *Sm* controls the mix temperature *Tm* monotonically: (*Tm M+ Sm*). (2) The rate of flow of the mix (*Qm*) is controlled by the signal *Sf* monotonically: (*Qm M+ Sf*). Certain constraints have to be satisfied too: (1) When there is no flow, the temperature of the mix is zero, in other words, (*Tm M+ Sm*) does not hold. (2) The temperature of the mix is determined by: *Tm.Qm* = *Th.Qh* + *Tc.Qc*, where *Qm*, *Qh* and *Qc* are the flow rates of the mix, hot and cold streams and the *T*'s are the corresponding temperatures. (3) Mass is conserved through the system: *Qh* + *Qc* = *Qm* .

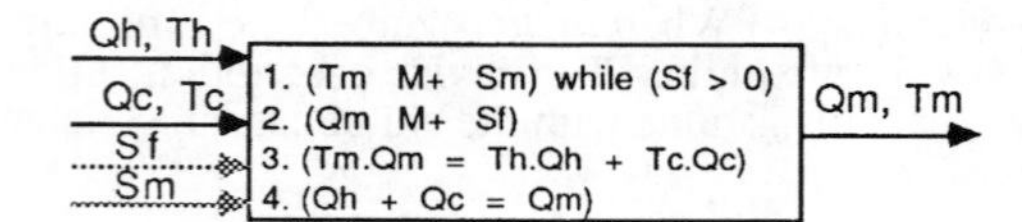

Figure 1: A Qualitative Description of a Faucet

3. Problem Analysis to Identify new Relations. Using the given functional description may not yield relevant cases. It is useful to analyze the given problem in order to generate new relations between inputs and outputs. New relations can be generated by propagating relations using simple combination and propagation rules.

For example, in the faucet problem we are given that the temperature of the mix increases with the mix signal *Sm*. From the equation for calculating the temperature of the mix *Tm* one can qualitatively infer that when there is some flow in the system (*Qm* > 0), then the rate of flow of hot water *Qh* monotonically increases with *Sm* while the rate of flow of cold water decreases. In other words, rate of flow of hot water is inversely proportional to the rate of flow of cold water (*Qh M– Qc*) and the rate of flow of cold water decreases with *Sm*: (*Qc M+ –Sm*) . Other relations which are derived from the given qualitative relations are that the flow of hot water monotonically increases with the signal *Sf* , the same is true for the flow of cold water.

4. Retrieval of Cases. A set of design cases (or case parts) bearing similarity to a given collection of features are accessed and retrieved. Similarity is determined using not only the existing features of the input specification, but also perturbations arising from index generation and reformulation strategies (Sycara & Navinchandra 89) as well as the derived qualitative relations from the above step.

Using the derived relations (*Qc M+ –Sm*) and (*Qh M+ Sm*) the common tap (described in the previous section) is retrieved since it is a water regulator which will change flow in response to a signal. Given that there is only one *Sm*, there has to be some way of splitting the signal into two signals of opposite sense. As it is not known how this function will be realized, it is treated as a new black-box (black-box1) in Figure 2. The figure shows another black-box (black-box2) which takes two flows and merges them. At this point in the problem solving, the system does not have, as yet, any way of controlling the total flow with *Sf*.

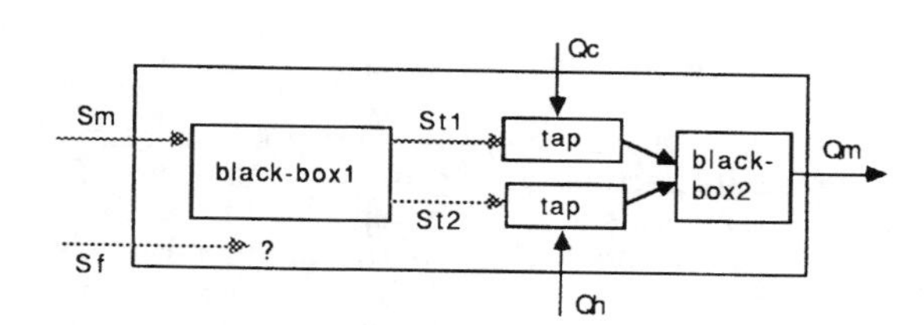

Figure 2: Functional Level Synthesis of the Faucet

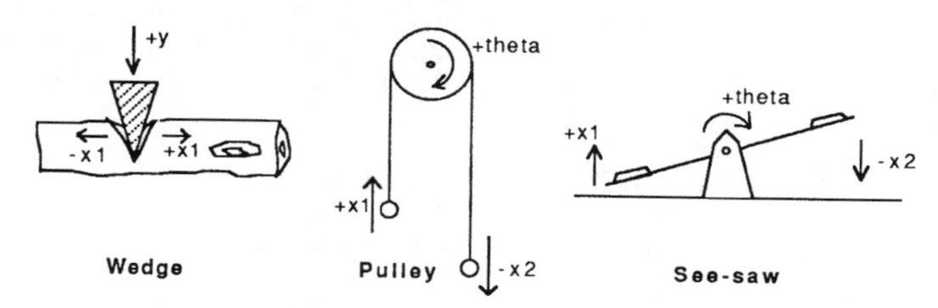

Figure 3: Cases showing one parameter increasing while another decreases

The next step is to find a way of realizing the split of the signal *Sm*. The required function may be used as an index into memory. In this situation, the index would be: "given a signal *Sm* the flow rate of one stream goes up while that of another goes down to maintain a constant total flow rate". For the given case memory, this index is overly specific and thus it fails to retrieve cases. The index is generalized to its corresponding qualitative statement: "given some signal one quantity goes up while another comes down proportionately". Operationally the index is given as:
$(\, Quantity1 \;\; M+ \;\; Signal\,) \wedge (\, Quantity2 \;\; M- \;\; Signal\,)$. This generalization retrieves the cases shown in Figure 3 where one parameter $x1$ increases while another $x2$ decreases given a signal (either of *theta* or *y*).

5. Extraction of relevant "snippets" from cases. A designer may retrieve and adapt not only whole cases but also pieces of cases that might embody appropriate principles useful for the design task. To access a snippet directly, indices based on features appropriate for the snippet are used; to extract a relevant snippet from a retrieved whole case, the subgoals of the problem solver are that are posted at this point are used (Navinchandra 88).

Let us consider the see-saw case retrieved in the last step. Extraction of the appropriate snippet from the see-saw case requires examining the underlying causal structure of the case. The qualitative relations for the see-saw are:

When $d(theta) > 0$: $\quad (x1 \;\; M+ \;\; theta)$ and $(x2 \;\; M- \;\; theta)$,
When $d(theta) < 0$: $\quad (x1 \;\; M- \;\; theta)$ and $(x2 \;\; M+ \;\; theta)$
where: $d(theta) = d(theta)/dt$ (qualitative differential eqn)
$-theta* \leq theta \leq +theta*$ (limits are symmetric)
$0 \leq x1 \leq x^{max}$ and $0 \leq x2 \leq x^{max}$

The angular motion of the see-saw is limited by the ground. Let the limits be $\pm\, theta*$. Correspondingly, the maximum and minimum values of $x1$ and $x2$ are: zero and x^{max}. The algebraic relation among these parameters is: $x^{max} = L Sin(\, theta*\,)$, where L is the length of the see-saw board. Another useful relation is that x^{max} is double the height (h) of the see-saw's fulcrum above the ground: ($x^{max} = 2h$). These algebraic relations are useful in constructing the configuration spaces and for reasoning about parametric adaptation of design snippets. Reasoning about quantitative equations together with qualitative relations is an important part of design process.

6. Snippet Synthesis. Partial designs have to be combined to produce a complete design. This is a difficult problem since undesirable interactions among snippets may occur. Snippet synthesis is done by ensuring that snippet preconditions are satisfied. Each snippet is treated as a small black-box with known inputs and behavior. Snippets are synthesized by attaching their inputs and outputs appropriately. When input types are incompatible, a new subgoal to find a way to convert one output into a compatible input is spawned. Even though each individual snippet has been tested to satisfy required subgoals, the synthesis process may uncover undesirable interactions at "snippet interfaces". These interactions have to be recognized and fixed. Even after the interactions have been fixed, an additional problem may arise. The synthesized solution might not satisfy the original set of specifications, although each solution component satisfies a subspecification. This characteristic is especially true in design. Thus, verification is required after each synthesis step.

Returning to the faucet example, a see-saw has been retrieved (Figure 3) for proportionate up and down motion. The next step is to find cases which will allow translatory motion to control water flow. Using the tap case's current context the cases shown in Figure 4 are retrieved.

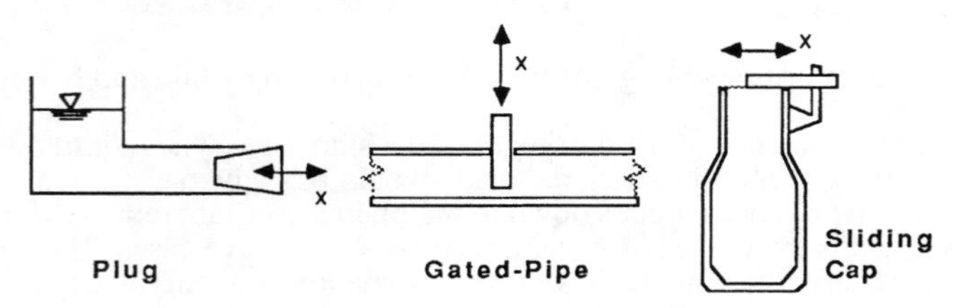

Figure 4: Using translatory motion to control orifice size

Using the causal explanations in the cases, snippets contributing directly to the required functions are retrieved and synthesized. At the qualitative level, the see-saw and the gated-pipe can be synthesized as shown in Figure 2. The see-saw function converts an input mix signal (*Sf*) into two translatory signals *St*1 and *St*2. These two signals are fed into basic "tap"s, one for cold water and the other for hot water. A synthesis of the existing snippets (at the physical level) is done by attaching the signal of one snippet to that of another as dictated by the Functional Level synthesis. An example of a rule that was used is: If the signals are motions, Then their degrees of freedom should match. For example, translation should match translation. The synthesis is shown in Figure 5. The design allows a signal to control the proportion of orifice sizes for the cold and hot water streams.

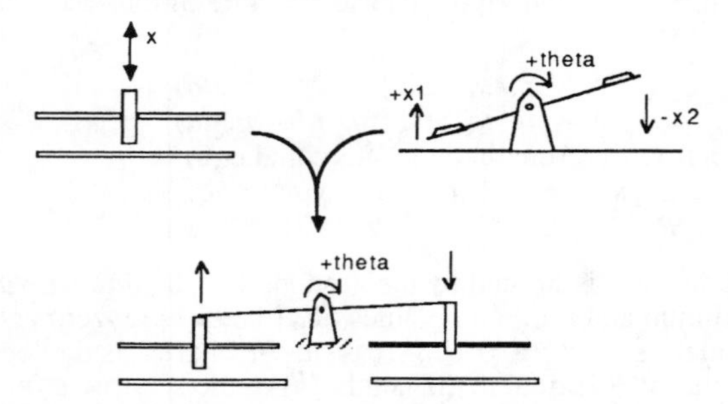

Figure 5: Physical Level Synthesis of the Faucet

7. Verification. During verification adverse interactions could lead to non-conformance of the design to the desired specifications. This is verified through qualitative simulation. If the simulation is correct, and if all the constraints are satisfied, then the design is successful. If not, debugging (next step) is attempted. A qualitative simulation of the tap discovers some "gaps" in the performance. The partial design generated thus far shows how to control the mix of the flows given the signal *Sm* but not how to control the total *Qm* without changing the ratio of hot and cold water. The design is not complete with respect to the signal (*Sf*) which controls the total flow through the tap (*Qm*).

8. Debugging. In debugging designs we have found that relevant cases can be retrieved by using the reasons underlying the bug as cues into memory (Navinchandra 87). Roughly speaking, the idea is to reduce a bug into "sub-bugs" which may relate either directly or analogically to cases in memory. The reasons underlying a given bug are determined by developing a causal explanation for the existence of the bug. Debugging involves a process of asking relevant questions and modifying them based on a causal explanation of the bug. These questions serve as cues into memory (Schank 86). When a bug is found, a corresponding question is posed to the Case Knowledge Base (CKB): "Has this, or some similar, bug been seen before? Is there a known way of repairing it?" If a relevant case is not found, the causal reasons for the bug are used to transform the question. For example, if for a given bug X, related cases are not found, then the debugger goes on to ask "What are the causes of X?", "If it is not known how to eliminate X, can its causes be eliminated?". This questioning process is recursively applied until a relevant case is found.

The process in the faucet design example proceeds as follows: The "gap" found in the verification step needs to be "filled". A way needs to be found to control *Qm* with *Sm* without changing the temperature of the mix. One of the causes of *Qm* is total orifice size (this relation is deduced from the causal graph). Consequently, the following question is generated: "How does one now control total orifice size without changing the ratio of hot and cold water flows?" In terms of constraints, it follows that the ratio: ($St1 / St2 = K$[1]) has to be satisfied, while the signal *Sf* increases the total flow-rate ($St1 + St2$) monotonically. Correspondingly, in the see-saw case, one needs to achieve ($x1 / x2 = constant$) while ($x1 + x2$ $M+$ Sf). From the see-saw equations it is known that $x1 + x2 = x^{max}$. It follows that we need a way of achieving (x^{max} $M+$ Sf). This can be done by working from the see-saw equation: ($x^{max} = 2h$) and finding a way of getting (h $M+$ Sf). This last goal is easily satisfied. As the height (h) is an independent parameter (no other constraints on it), it can be linked directly to the signal: ($h = Sf$).

Finally, by making correspondences between $x1$, $x2$ and $St1$, $St2$, and by recursively applying the process of retrieval, snippet extraction and synthesis, the final conceptual design of the tap can be developed (Figure 6).

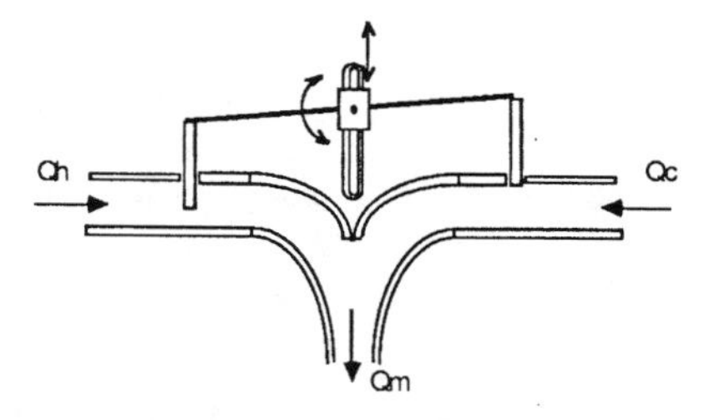

Figure 6: Conceptual Design of a Faucet

[1]A constant

CONCLUDING REMARKS

Problem solving in the domain of Engineering Design imposes a set of requirements on a problem solver: (a) the representation needs to capture and integrate several levels of abstraction from the linguistic to the physical, incorporating linguistic specifications, laws of physics, constraints and tolerances, (b) the problem solver should be able to reason both symbolically and analytically at different problem solving stages and integrate the process and results of its reasoning, (c) verification techniques should be incorporated in the problem solving. To deal with these requirements, we have presented a methodology for design that integrates use of past design cases with qualitative reasoning. Cases are represented at various levels of abstraction, and indices corresponding to these levels allow access to design cases at any of the abstraction levels. Past design cases similar to the current design are used to: focus on the relevant parts of the problem, form the basis for analogical reasoning, avoid past mistakes, and provide guidance in debugging. Qualitative reasoning determines appropriate indices for case retrieval, provides causal explanations of the behavior of an artifact, and forms the basis for verification to check whether the design meets its specifications.

REFERENCES

(Faries 88) Faries, J. M. and Reiser, B.J., ''Access and Use of Previous Solutions in a Problem Solving Situation,'' *Proceedings of the Tenth Annual Conference of the Cognitive Science Society*, The Cognitive Science Society, Montreal, Canada, 1988, pp. 433-439.

(Forbus 84) Forbus, K., ''Qualitative Process Theory,'' *Artificial Intelligence*, Vol. 24, 1984.

(Kolodner et al. 85) Kolodner, J.L., Simpson, R.L., and Sycara-Cyranski, K., ''A Process Model of Case-Based Reasoning in Problem Solving,'' *Proceedings of IJCAI-85*, Los Angeles, CA, 1985, pp. 284-290.

(Kuipers 86) Kuipers, B.J., ''Qualitative Simulation,'' *Aritifial Intelligence*, Vol. 29, 1986, pp. 289-338.

(Lancaster 88) Lancaster, J. and Kolodner, J.L, ''Varieties of Learning from Problem Solving Experience,'' *Proceedings of the Tenth Annual Conference of the Cognitive Science Society*, The Cognitive Science Society, Montreal, Canada, 1988, pp. 447-453.

(Mostow & Barley 87) Mostow, J., M. Barley, ''Automated Reuse of Design Plans,'' *Proceedings of the International Conference on Engineering Design* , February 1987.

(Navinchandra 87) Navinchandra, D., *Exploring for Innovative Designs by Relaxing Criteria and reasoning from Precedent-Based Knowledge,* PhD dissertation, M.I.T., 1987.

(Navinchandra 88) Navinchandra, D., ''Case-Based Reasoning in CYCLOPS, a Design Problem Solver,'' in *Proceedings of the DARPA Workshop on Case-based Reasoning,* Kolodner, J., ed., Morgan Kaufman, 1988, pp. 286-301.

(Pahl & Beitz 84) Pahl, G., W. Beitz, *Engineering Design,* The Design Council, Springer-Verlag, 1984.

(Ratterman 87) Ratterman, M.J., and Gentner, D., ''Analogy and Similarity: Determinants of accessibility and inferential soundness,'' *Proceedings of the Ninth Annual Conference of the Cognitive Science Society*, The Cognitive Science Society, Seattle, Wa., 1987, pp. 23-35.

(Schank 86) Schank, R.C., *Explanation Patterns: Understanding Mechanically and Creatively,* Lawrence Erlbaum Associates, Hillsdale, NJ, 1986.

(Sycara 87) Sycara, K., *Resolving Adversarial Conflicts: An Approach Integrating Case-Based and Analytic Methods,* PhD dissertation, School of Information and Computer Science Georgia Institute of Technology, 1987.

(Sycara & Navinchandra 89) Sycara, K., D. Navinchandra, ''Integrating Case-Based Reasoning and Qualitative Reasoning in Design,'' in *AI in Design,* J. Gero, ed., Computational Mechanics, U.K., 1989.

Cognition in Design Process

Chiu-Shui Chan

Department of Architecture

Carnegie Mellon University

Abstract

The purpose of this research is to study the cognitive process in architectural design problem solving. It also will explore a cognitive structure (model) capable of representing the problem solver's cognitive behavior. The goal plan, schemata, perceptual-test, and generate-and-test are regarded as cognitive mechanisms that evolved in the problem solving process. They were observed in an experiment in which an experienced architectural designer was asked to do a residential design. Results from protocol analysis showed that an invariant cognitive structure could be built upon these cognitive mechanisms to explain the problem solving behavior. This cognitive structure (model) also provides a framework for future simulation.

Introduction

Architectural design problem solving was studied first by psychologists to understand the nature of ill-defined problems (Reitman, 1964, Simon, 1973). Later on, architectural researchers followed the same notion, and studied the cognitive aspects in solving architectural design problems. Among these studies, some used retrospective and introspective methods (Krauss & Myer, 1970, Darke, 1979) while others used protocol analysis (Eastman, 1969, Eastman, 1970, Akin, 1978, Akin, 1986). Each study yielded its own findings. For instance, Eastman explored the operators that caused moves between states in the design process (Eastman, 1970), and Akin used schemata to explain the general design procedure (Akin, 1986). Regardless of the various approaches, they all shared a common observation that cognitive process in design is a cyclic process of generating and testing solutions.

The pioneer studies reviewed provided some understandings about the design process which had not been explored before. However, the cognitive process in design is not fully understood, and it needs more exploration. Simon and Eastman, in particular, declared that ill-defined problems can be broken down into well-defined subproblems (Simon, 1973), and certain processes in ill-defined problems are similar to those used in well-defined ones (Eastman, 1969). Thus, a question arises as to whether those cognitive factors (i.e., knowledge representation, control structure, and generate-and-test) which exist in a well-defined domain, would still remain unchanged in an ill-defined domain, or if there are certain relationships that hold these factors together. It is difficult to find a report that addresses these questions. This research will address those questions and also explore a cognitive model that is capable of simulating the general problem solving behavior.

Fundamentals of Design Problem Solving

The basic concept for exploring design problem solving is similar to that used for well-defined problems. The essential approach is to view the design as if the process occurs in a problem space which consists of immense knowledge states. Since architectural design is unique, its problem space is considered as having three major components. These components are representations existing in the problem states. The first one is a set of design unit hierarchy. The design unit hierarchy is a tree-like structure that arranges design units from larger and more abstract units to more detailed ones.

The set of design units are physical elements of building components either given by the problem task or generated by the designer at any intermediate problem state. For example, a branch of the tree in the hierarchy of a residential design may consist of first floor unit, living room, fireplace, down to the hearth of the fireplace. Each unit is a component of the former one. This hierarchical tree structure explains why design units appear from abstract to detail level as the design progresses, in a top-down fashion.

The second component is a set of design constraints. Design constraints are certain requirements that must be fulfilled in order to design a design unit or a group of design units. The set of design constraints is also given by the problem task or is generated by the designer. For example, these might include information about the owner, site condition, climate condition, specification of design units, and some special design requirements. They are imposed by the problem and thus define the problem space.

The third component is a set of goals in which a designer finds an object that satisfies a set of constraints. These three components plus a set of operators, which are defined as anything that changes the problem states, determine the design problem space. Any change in these components will alter the problem space. From the designer's perspective, it can be explained that at any state in the space, the designer works on a design unit, and applies some knowledge to generate a solution that satisfies certain constraints. And all these actions are under the guidance of a particular goal.

Cognitive Mechanisms

The goals, design constraints, and the design unit hierarchy are retrieved from memory, and are results from the operation of certain factors. These factors, the subject matter of this research, trigger and strategically guide memory retrieval for solving the problem at hand. Since they are the driving forces that move states and produce or even alter cognitive behavior, they are termed cognitive mechanisms in this research. The following descriptions provide a general idea about each of these mechanisms, and they were empirically observed in an experiment that followed.

Schemata

In the domain of design problems, design knowledge is represented by a hierarchical semantic network (Akin, 1978, Akin, 1986). Since a designer must handle design units during the process of design, design units are subjects of the processing of design information. It is appropriate to represent nodes in the semantic network by design units, and design units are grouped by having related architectural functional relationships. A designer must have knowledge of the general components (design units) of a building as well as generic knowledge of what they are and how to design them. Therefore, it is assumed that a set of schemata which contains a large amount of design information is associated with design units in the semantic net. In the network, there is a set of schemata called design constraint schemata which provide declarative knowledge and procedural knowledge about the constraints. For example, climate is a design constraint. The designer must know that the winter breeze from northwest would bring cold into the building (declarative knowledge), and s/he should also know how to use the building mass to block the wind or to reduce the glazing size on the windward surface to minimize the heat lost (procedural knowledge). These pieces of knowledge are stored in the schemata, and a design solution is generated by the application of this knowledge.

Generate and Test

Design problems have the nature of generate-and-test cycles (Eastman, 1969, Akin, 1978, Darke, 1979). Each cycle has two mechanisms: a generator and a tester (Simon, 1973, Akin, 1986). The generator takes some input to generate a solution or solutions. The input is assumed to have three sources: (1) an evocation of schemata from memory that activates information stored in the short-term memory and then applies it; (2) a series of schemata instantiations, in which the generator applies the embedded rules in schemata to generate a solution; (3) a retrieval from memory of a pre-solution model, which the generator either accepts or modifies to generate solutions. After the generator generates a solution, the tester tests against a set of constraints.

Goal Plan

The goal plan is a hierarchical process that controls the sequence of operations. In design problems, designers have a general design method stored in their long-term memory called a general goal plan, which consists of a sequence of general goals to be accomplished. This goal plan is believed to be the key mechanism that converts an ill-defined problem into manageable size.

Perceptual-test

Since design solutions are accumulated from state to state, information presented in external display changes accordingly. A designer must gather information about the problem situation from time to time, and this is done by perception. Researches on perception in problem solving have dealt with the perception of chess positions (DeGroot, 1966, Simon, 1969), or solving the Tower of Hanoi puzzle (Simon, 1975). The perception has been formulated by production systems to describe the function of its mechanisms, and is referred to as perceptual-test (Simon, 1975). The perceptual-test will perceive the problem context and the solution context to determine the appropriate action to be executed next. Hence, it is regarded as the control mechanism in the design process.

Observations

In order to empirically test the existence and the function of these cognitive mechanisms, an experiment was conducted. The subject was a PhD student in architecture. He had eight years of architectural design experience at the time this experiment was conducted. The task was to design a three bedroom dwelling for a single family. Design units included a workshop, living room, dining room, bathroom and two bedrooms for a son and a daughter. The total floor area was limited to 2,200 square feet. The client was a professional architectural perspective draftsman. In order to discern the kind of design knowledge that the subject would retrieve from memory, the design information provided in the instruction was reduced to a minimum. Protocol data were collected for analyses. The methods for coding protocol, classifying episodes, verifying data, and developing problem behavior graph were described in detail in another report (Chan, in press). Results discovered in relating to the cognitive mechanisms were the following.

Constraint Schemata in Design

Constraints in design are of two sorts: global and local ones. Global constraints are applicable to a group of design units. Local constraints are bound to two or fewer design units. In this experiment, the subject retrieved a few global constraints, i.e. light, privacy, accessibility to the road, symmetrical disposition, room dimension, and land slope. These global constraints reflected the following characteristics: (1) they were mostly evoked during the first episode of the protocol data; (2) they were applicable to a group or to all design units; (3) they were able to be used in different tasks.

The subject retrieved 47 local constraints in this protocol, and they appeared only at the two lowest levels in the design unit hierarchy constructed from the data. The sequence of retrieving constraints reflected the following factors. At the early design stage, global constraints are evoked for the purpose of organizing the problem structure. Then, based on the structure developed, a design scenario is formed to guide the later design. As the design progresses, design units are handled from larger units to detailed ones and the associated constraints are retrieved accordingly.

Constraints are retrieved so that embedded knowledge can be applied to generating or testing solutions. An excerpt from the protocol of the subject demonstrates this:

> "Now, somehow, it seems that this (northeast) corner here, seems more private. Because these two edges (west and south) are bound by outside roads. And there is a property on this (north) side and a private property on this (east) side. So, things will be better, if I place things along this (northeastern corner) side."

These protocol statements can be converted into schemata representation as follows.

Schema A: <Site-privacy> (<Building>)
  Rule = If there is a <Private-corner>
    Then put building at <Private-corner>.
Schema B: <Private-corner>
  Rule = If <Private-edge> (<A>) is private
    and <Private-edge> (<B>) is private
    and <A> and <B> are adjacent
    Then the corner formed by A and B is a private corner.
Schema C: <Private-edge> (<X>)
  Rule = If <X> = next-to-a-property
    Then it is private.

A constraint schema as shown in the examples consists of an identifier, a variable, a set of rules, and a value of the variable. For instance, in schema A, the identifier is site-privacy, the variable is the <Building>. The factual knowledge of the private corner in the site is embedded in the left hand side of the production. The procedural knowledge, which is to put the building at the private corner, is at the right hand side. The value of the schema is obtained from evaluating the rules in the schema, as a result, the value is returned to the variable. As in this example, in order to satisfy the privacy constraint, a series of schemata, from A to C, were instantiated to generate the solution. This shows the concept of applying the schemata for solution generation.

Generator and Tester

The generator uses three sources of input. One is to instantiate a series of schemata and to apply a series of rules to generate solutions as described before. The second one is to retrieve pre-solution models from memory and apply these models. A pre-solution model is a design solution generated from experience. Since architectural design deals with graphic representation, design solutions are mainly images, and thus possibly stored in memory by some kind of image code (Chan, 1989). In this experiment, the subject used nine pre-solution models, and seven out of nine were iconic images. For example, in dealing with the porch roof, the subject could quickly retrieve a pitch roof image and draw it. This showed a recognition search method used by the generator. The recognition search involves reducing the problem to a point at which a known procedure or model can be applied to the remaining stages.

Besides recognition search, the generator also used the means-ends analysis method to accommodate a pre-solution model. This occurred when the subject retrieved geometric blocks with central cores (a pre-solution model) to solve the service core problem (the problem that contained the stair case, utility core, and bathroom facilities). But this model did not fit the context because it left no room for a corridor. The subject's strategy was to retrieve seven rules to gradually modify the pre-solution model until he achieved a satisfactory solution. His solution was to put the staircase next to the bathroom and locate them in two rectangular blocks with a corridor running in front. In this example of the means-ends analysis search method, a modified image was the end.

The third input source for the generator is to simply retrieve a constraint schema and apply its rule. This source also apply to the tester, and is regarded as the main characteristic of the generator and tester. The problem behavior graph constructed from protocol data showed that whenever a design solution was generated or tested, at least one design constraint was involved and at least one rule was used. This suggests that the knowledge in constraint schemata is the source for problem solving, and it also explains why design constraints are important in design tasks.

Goal Plan

The protocol of the subject's goal development in this experiment showed some clear distinctions between episodes. In transitions between goals, the new knowledge state did not correlate to the previous one. A new goal was developed and verbalized all of a sudden. This supported an argument that new goals are retrieved from the goal plan in memory. The subject's goal plan looked like this: task understanding, site organization, scenario development, initial space layout, room size arrangement, space generation, first floor layout, second floor layout, elevation, site development, and finally evaluation.

Perceptual-test

The perceptual-test controls the design process and has been observed to have four functions. The first function is to determine whether the current goal has been accomplished. In the protocol, the subject made no statement indicating that he had satisfied a particular goal. The subject simply proceeded from one goal to another. The silent switch suggests that unless a goal is achieved, it is impossible to develop a new one.

The second function is to test the generated solution to perceive the solution path. For example, one of the task requirements was to include a Doric column in the residential design. One of the generated solutions was to locate the Doric column in the center of a room as a single interior element supporting the ceiling. The subject indicated two things: (1) such a form must also match a classical vault, but this usage would change the character of the design; (2) the subject was not keen on doing a historical revival. Therefore, this solution was abandoned. This indicated that the subject perceived a critical problem situation at the time he generated a solution. The critical problem situation refers to the possibility of changing the problem structure or solution path.

The third function is to perceive what is lacking at the present stage and search for a design unit to work on next. Take an excerpt from the protocol for example: "I am trying to see in terms of section what is going to have, and I am trying to see what other things could be attached to this column. One thing is that, you may call it some kind of glazing, in which the column really is a free-standing element, visually." In this example, the subject searched for a new design unit to attach to the column in order to visually make the column a free-standing element. The new design unit he evoked was glazing on the side of the column.

The fourth function is to perceive the problem context and the solution context to determine the next action. Perception of the problem context means understanding the problem structure to determine the goal sequence. For example, the subject perceived the size of the building mass as a small one which would not affect its location on the site, so he decided to develop the site later. And it turned out that the goal of site development appeared at a later stage in the protocol. Perceiving the solution context means seeing the solution path and using it to generate the next solution. For instance, the subject used symmetry as a constraint, which developed while he was arranging the position of a bay window and a Doric column (the Doric column was on the central line of the bay window). This symmetry constraint was again selected later on to solve the living room layout. The subject indicated that "since it (Doric column) is going to be something as striking as an element like that (symmetric character), at least here (in the living room plan) I am trying to keep this (living room) spaces, and try to maintain the same symmetric disposition." This implies that the subject perceived the solution context and selected the next solution which had the best fit. The solution context means that the occurrence of solution B is related to solution A, or that the result of solution A leads to the cause of solution B.

Invariant Structure

Observations based on the protocol data supported hypotheses about the functions of the cognitive mechanisms. Since these mechanisms are major constituents of the system, they control the overall process of design and thus generate a skeleton of an invariant structure.

As shown in Figure 1, this invariant structure represents the cognitive process. It shows that a design task can be broken down by means of the sequence of goals. Goals are generated either from a goal plan that is stored in memory, or from a perceptual-test. The goal plan contains a sequence of goals that the designer must know in order to process the design task, and must achieve in order to get the design problem into the final goal state. In accomplishing a goal, the designer manipulates a set of design units. A package of knowledge about the design unit called a schema, which contains associated design constraints and rules for application, is stored in a knowledge base as a part of the designer's long-term memory. By taking a set of design units and retrieving its associated schemata, design solutions for a particular goal are generated and tested. By repeating the process (taking a goal, activating a design unit, retrieving a set of associated schemata, applying a rule to generate a solution and then testing the solution), the design problem gradually moves toward the final state.

Obviously, the perceptual-test occupies a control position in Figure 1. It is necessary to emphasize the role of the perceptual-test in the system. The perceptual-test serves the following functions:

1. The test of the goal state will guarantee that the system is always in progress and that the process always moves toward a goal. Thus, if the current goal has been achieved, then the

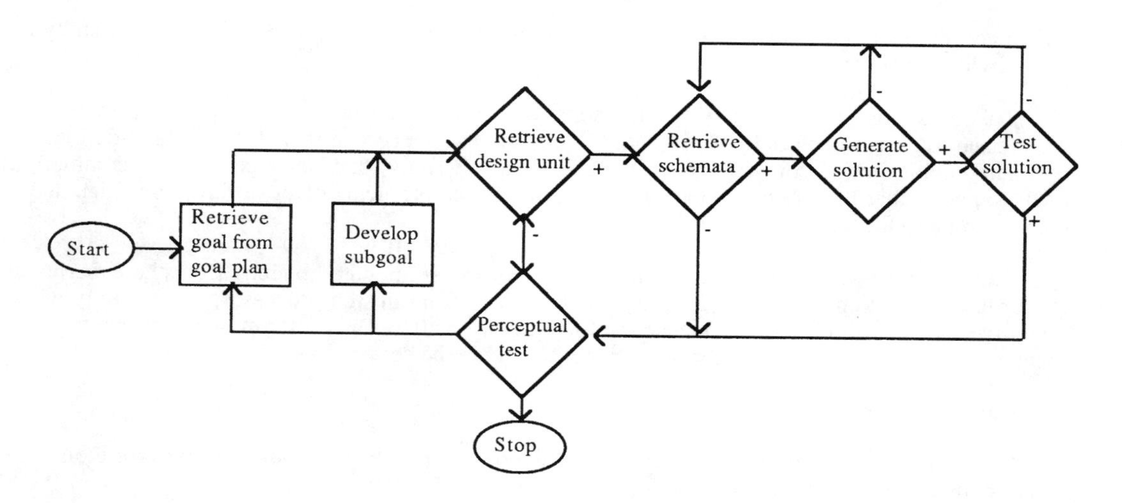

Figure 1: A cognitive model of design process

system will produce the next goal from the goal plan. Otherwise, the perceptual-test will perceive which design unit is the next candidate to continue accomplishing the current goal.

2. The test of global constraints will make sure that the generated solution is optimal. If the generated solution satisfies all the constraints, then the system will proceed to the next design unit under the current goal. Otherwise, a new goal is set up.

3. If a design unit is presented in short-term memory and a set of constraint schemata is evoked, the perceptual-test will recognize that such a design unit must be solved in order to process the next one. Thus, a subgoal is developed to solve the problem being presented.

4. The perceptual-test will perceive what happens at the current state and will determine the appropriate next step.

Conclusion

The cognitive mechanisms are regarded as fundamentals in processing information. Among them, the perceptual-test controls the process, and provides problem solving strategies. A set of production systems to account for the subject's strategy and control structure in this experiment had been explicitly developed and hand simulated elsewhere (Chan, in press). This set of production systems is inferred to be a prototypical template or program stored in the memory, and is instantiated at the time when a problem is encountered. The next step beyond this study is to implement the proposed computer simulation model of this process.

It is further inferred that the cognitive mechanisms studied are essential in solving ill-defined problems. The differences between individual human problem solvers are the *information* stored in the schemata, the *goals* in the goal plan, the *search methods* utilized by generator and tester, and the *control strategies* developed by perceptual-test. These factors can be termed as cognitive variables, which are the operational sources of the cognitive mechanisms and are important clues for studying the individual differences.

This study also provides a systematic approach for studying design processes that are recognized as a part of ill-defined problems. Although it is not certain that all kinds of ill-defined problem solving (music composition, painting, and story writing) have characteristics in common, this study suggests that ill-defined problems rely greatly on the problem solver's prior knowledge and control strategy for tackling problems.

The theory set up in this study is strongly supported by the data obtained from the experiment. Its further application is to study how style is generated from design processes, and to study what cognitive aspects would likely influence the formation of a style. Only after more experiments conducted on more subjects will the accuracy of the model be convincing.

Acknowledgement

The author would like to thank Herbert A. Simon, Omer Akin, and John R. Hayes for their discussions and comments on the theories being set forth in this research.

References

Akin, O. (1978). How do architects design? In J. C. Latombe (Ed.), *Artificial Intelligence and Pattern Recognition in Computer Aided Design*. New York: North-Holland.
Akin, O. (1986). *Psychology of Architectural Design*. London: Pion.
Chan, C. S. (in press), Cognitive Processes in Architectural Design Problem Solving. *Design Studies*.
Chan, C. S. (1989). Mental Image and Internal Representation. Manuscript submitted for publication.
Darke, J. (1979). The primary generator and the design process. *Design Studies*. 1(1), 36-44.
De Groot, A. D. (1969). Perception and memory versus thought: some old ideas and recent findings. In B. Kleinmuntz (Ed.), *Problem Solving*. New York: Wiley.
Eastman, C. M. (1969). Cognitive processes and ill-defined problems: a case study from design. *Proceedings First Joint International Conference on Artificial Intelligence*. Washington, D. C.: Joint International Conference on Artificial Intelligence.
Eastman, C. M. (1970). On the analysis of intuitive design processes. In G. T. Moore (Ed.), *Emerging Methods in Environmental Design and Planning*. Cambridge, MA: M.I.T.Press.
Krauss, R. L., & Myer, J. R. (1970). Design: a case history. In G. T. Moore (Ed.), *Emerging Methods in Environmental Design and Planning*. Cambridge, MA: M.I.T. Press.
Reitman, W. R. (1964). Heuristic decision procedures, open constraints, and the structure of ill-defined problems. In M. W. Shelley, & G. L. Bryan (Eds.), *Human Judgments and Optimality*. New York: Wiley.
Simon, H. A. (1973). The structure of ill-structured problems. *Artificial Intelligence*, 4, 181-201.
Simon, H. A. (1975). The functional equivalence of problem solving skills. *Cognitive Psychology*, 7, 268-288.
Simon, H. A., & Barenfeld, M. (1969). Information processing analysis of perceptual processes in problem solving. *Psychological Review*, 76, 473-483.

Evaluation of Suggestions during Automated Negotiations

Sarit Kraus
Institute for Advanced Computer Studies and
Department of Computer Science
University of Maryland

Eithan Ephrati Daniel Lehmann
Department of Computer Science
The Hebrew University

Abstract

An automated agent that has to act in a multi-agent environment needs the capability to negotiate. In this paper we concentrate on problems that arise while evaluating suggestions during negotiations. We distinguish between different kind of suggestions and present methods and techniques for evaluating them. The suggestions are written using a formal Negotiation Language that we have developed. We show how our approach was successfully implemented in a specific environment: the Diplomacy game. As in other board games, playing Diplomacy involves a certain amount of technical skill but the capacity to negotiate, explain, convince, promise, keep promises or choose not to keep them, is an essential ingredient of good play. Diplomat was evaluated and consistently played better than well experienced players, and in games that were held, many players did not guess which player Diplomat was playing.

INTRODUCTION

Negotiations are part of everyday life. Negotiators try to reach an agreement or arrangement by discussion. Therefore, an automated agent acting in a multi-agent environment needs a capability to negotiate. The need for negotiations arises in an environment where cooperation is beneficial and becomes even more necessary where there also exist conflicts between the agents. Such an environment is common in the real world. Even in distributed cooperative systems, where all agents are designed to achieve the same goal, conflicts between the agents can arise, since every agent makes an effort to perform its mission in a way that may interfere with the other agents' activities. An agent will get even more benefits through negotiations if some or all of the following conditions exist:

1. The cooperation among negotiators requires precise cooperation or division of tasks between the participants.
2. The information the agents have is incomplete and the negotiations enable the agents to gain more information.
3. There are difficult problems to analyze and a single agent is unable to solve its problems alone, but its problem solving power may be multiplied by cooperation and exchange of ideas.
4. There is a multi-agent environment where the other human (or automated) agents have the capability to negotiate and an agent that does not have the capability is at a disadvantage.

In previous work, Rosenschein and Genesereth [Rosenschein & Genesereth, 1985], used certain game-theoretic techniques to model communication and promises in multi agents interaction. There, the process of negotiation was severely restricted (the agents could only make single, simultaneous offers), and it assumes that each agent knows the complete payoff matrix associated with the interaction. Also, for large games involving many agents and outcomes, the kind of environments in which we are interested, the size of a payoff matrix may quickly become intractable.

Davis and Smith [Davis & Smith, 1983] proposed an approach to cooperation using a contract-bid metaphor to model the assignment of tasks to processors. They used negotiation to match idle problem solvers to outstanding tasks as a basis for the transfer of control and as a way of viewing invocation as the matching of knowledge sources to tasks. Sathi, Morton, and Roth, ([Sathi, Morton & Roth 1986]), considered the problem of project management. In their approach the agents negotiate by relaxations so as to achieve a compromise. The constraints and their relaxations are statically known. No attempt is made to influence other agents' relaxation. Sycara [Sycara, 1987] presented a model of negotiation that combines case-based reasoning and optimization of the multi-attribute utilities of the agents. She implemented her ideas in a computer program called the PERSUADER that resolved adversarial conflicts in the domain of labor relations and tested her system using simulations of such domains.

Comparing this to our work, we examine negotiations in a more complex environment where a mediator is not available, where the agents may break their promises, where close cooperation between different agents is needed, and where possible coalitions between other agents must be taken into account. We have implemented our ideas by building a system that negotiates successfully with human partners.

ENVIRONMENTS AND CONCEPTS

Sending a suggestion is the way to propose a plan for acceptance or rejection. Actually, it is the main method used to try to and convince another agent in the environment to perform actions, and it is the way to promise to the other agent, which actions sender will perform. Therefore a negotiator-agent must have the capability to evaluate suggestions and decide whether to accept or reject the suggestions.

Before we get into the details of the evaluation of suggestions, we will briefly describe, the environment and define some concepts that will be used later. In general, the negotiations are performed among a set of agents. Each agent has its own goals and tasks and searches for the best plan to achieve those goals. Each one of the agents negotiates in order to influence the behavior of the other agents' activities, in order to convince them to help him, or, at least, not to interfere with his plans.

We assume that a set $\mathcal{S}$ of strategies is given. The negotiations are performed on the basis of the strategies for common activities of the parties that negotiate. A strategy includes a list of activities, the purpose of each activity, and the expected profit or loss for the agents from those activities. $\mathcal{S}$ may be finite or infinite, but in the environments we are considering, $\mathcal{S}$ is usually infinite (or at least very large).

In order to negotiate effectively, the negotiator-agent must keep and maintain general information about the environment and the current situation. It also has to keep information about the other agents, their personality and their relations and to keep the details of its agreements with the others. We will denote the negotiator-agent knowledge and beliefs base by KBB.

The personality of the human agents influences their behavior while bargaining. Especially, their willingness to take chances must be taken into consideration while evaluating their possible acts ([Bueno de Mesquita, 1981]). Their loyalty has to be considered when deciding whether the other agent will keep a signed agreement. Therefore the negotiator-agent has to try to estimate the personality of the other agents by examining their activities and by exchanging messages with the others. We allow the behavior of the negotiator-agent to be influenced by some "personality" traits such as aggressiveness, willingness to take chances and loyalty, that will be given to it at startup time or during the negotiations, and they will allow the negotiator-agent to change "personality" from time to time.

To make automated negotiations a bit easier, the negotiations need to be performed using a formal language. We have developed a Negotiation Language that includes four kinds of messages: declarations, questions, suggestions and answers ([Kraus, 1988], [Kraus & Lehmann, 1988a]). The building blocks for the messages are simple sentences that are specific to the subject of the negotiations.

Diplomacy

The environment we choose to deal with is a game named Diplomacy, marketed by Avalon Hill Company. Diplomacy is an environment of intense negotiating situation where we could really fit an automated agent against humans without the later knowing. We implemented and tested our ideas by building an automated Diplomacy player called Diplomat (general description in [Kraus, 1988], [Kraus & Lehmann, 1988a], and [Kraus & Lehmann, 1988b]).

Diplomacy is a board game played on a map of Europe during the years just prior to World War I. Each player plays one of seven European powers. The moves of the game are figured as two moves each year: a Spring move and a Fall move, beginning in year 1901. After negotiation, each player privately writes down the orders for all of his units. A unit may be ordered to do only one thing on each season: to hold, move, or to give support. A fleet may be also ordered to convoy another army from one coast to the other. The power that gains control over Europe wins the game. To be a good player one needs some technical skills in moving military units on the board according to the reasonable but complex rules of the game, but above all, one needs the ability to communicate and negotiate with the other players, to make agreements with the others and possibly to decide to break these agreements, since the rules do not bind a player to anything he says. Deciding whom to trust as situations arise is part of the game. Details of the rules of the game can be found in [Rules for Diplomacy, 1984]

Diplomacy satisfies the conditions that increase the need for negotiations that were mentioned in the introduction: it is a repeated game of incomplete information, certain moves require close cooperation between different allied powers (the units of a power may help the moves of another power but they must be explicitly ordered to do so), it is a very complicated game (average of 34^8 possible orders for a season), and the other players negotiate, since experience shows that a power can not last long without taking part in extensive negotiation.

Diplomat is implemented in Ylisp ([Levy & Dimitrovski 1982]) (a dialect of Franz-Lisp) on a Vax 11/785 running Unix, Berkeley 4.3. The current version is the product of three years work by three programmers. It includes over 10,000 lines of Ylisp code.

SUGGESTIONS EVALUATION

One of the main technical problem in evaluating suggestions by a negotiator-agent is the large number of possible suggestions and the fact that different kinds of suggestions need to be evaluated in different ways. In order to be able to solve this problem and to make the negotiations more modular a negotiator-agent can distinguish mainly between two kinds of suggestions: general suggestions and detailed suggestions. A general suggestion discusses the general purpose of the negotiations, as where a detailed suggestion discusses the specific common activities and the ways to achieve those common activities. A general suggestion can include the kind of agreement to be achieved (in Diplomacy, a cooperation or non-aggression

<MESSAGE 1 FROM England TO France> :
I would like to suggest to you a Cooperation Agreement
between England and France against Germany now.
END OF MESSAGE.

Figure 1: Spring 1901: General Suggestion

< MESSAGE 2 FROM Turkey TO Russia > :
I would like you to know the following facts:
Russia seems to be strong, (1)
and Turkey will attack Serbia now, (2)
and Russia will help Turkey's attempt to enter Serbia, (3)
and Russia will move from Warsaw (inland) to Galicia (inland). (4)
END OF MESSAGE.

Figure 2: Spring 1902: Detailed Suggestion

agreement), relations with other agents (in Diplomacy, possible common enemies), or general directions of possible common activities (in Diplomacy, the directions of possible common attacks). For an example see the message in Figure 1 which provides an example of a general suggestion. The detailed suggestions can also be divided as follows:
1. Suggestions concerning general purposes of an agreement (In Diplomacy: spaces on the board to attack, spaces to defend, areas to leave or to enter.)
For example, see sentences (2) and (3) in Figure 2.
2. Suggestions about the specific movements in order to achieve the purposes of 1. (in Diplomacy which unit has to attack or to give support, which fleet can convoy, and which unit has to move in order to cut support). For example, see sentence (4) in Figure 2. We have developed different methods for evaluating different kind of suggestions. The General Suggestion Evaluator (GSE) (see Figure 3) evaluates general suggestions using very fast heuristics, because it is not worthwhile to spend a lot of time searching for good detailed strategies in this step of the negotiations. The principle directing the GSE is that if there is some hope of profiting from the suggested agreement, it is worth continuing the negotiations.

The Detailed Suggestion Evaluator (DSE) (see Figure 3) evaluates detailed suggestions by finding fitted strategies to them. Before sending the suggestion to one of the above modules, we move it through a Pre Analyzer (PA) that will fill in gaps of missing information.

Suppose a negotiator-agent gets a message which includes a detailed suggestion and must decide how to respond. After passing the message through the PA and filling in the gaps, the next step, which is done by the DSE, is to try to evaluate the expected profit (or losses) for the negotiator-agent and its partners from this suggestion. The DSE translates any suggestion into a set of strategies that *fit* the given suggestion, taking into account the current situation and the beliefs of the agent about the other agents and the environment. This translation changes each suggestion received or sent by the negotiator-agent into a unique strategy format, which allows it to be compared with other suggestions or strategies. The translation is done using the Strategies Finder of the negotiator-agent, and the strategy found is used as a basis for further negotiations when needed. The next step is to examine the expected profit from the fitted strategy and compare it with the expected profits from other possible strategies.

A strategy *fits* a suggestion when all the specific activities that are precisely mentioned in the suggestion appear in the strategy and the strategy does not include activities whose negations appear in the suggestion. If general activities are mentioned in the suggestion, the strategy must include at least one order that implements every such general activity. If the parties had agreed upon some details during the previous steps of the negotiations, where messages were exchanged between the parties, and the current suggestion does not contradict those details, then the *fitted* strategy has to fit those details too. So the negotiator-agent assumes that a detail of an agreement is valid until the other party says the opposite or does something that contradicts this assumption. We found out from human negotiators that they make the same assumption, and an automated agent that negotiates with humans should make it, too.

When the set of strategies, $\mathcal{S}$, is finite and small the implementation of the DSE is easy. The agent may check all the strategies and find which of them fit the suggestion. However, in the environments on which we concentrate S is usually too big to be computed and stored, so the negotiator-agent must use heuristic methods to find strategies that fit a suggestion.

CONCLUSION

We have proposed methods for an automated negotiator to evaluate suggestions in a complex environment, where the set of possible strategies is very large, a mediator is not available, the agents may break their promises, close cooperation between different agents is needed and possible coalitions between other agents must be taken into account.

We used our methods to develop the system Diplomat, which plays Diplomacy as one of the players. Diplomat successfully evaluates more than 70% of the suggestions it gets, and answers its partner properly. In the rest of the cases it asks for more details. Also, in its other missions, Diplomat performs well. For example, we examined 63 agreements that were

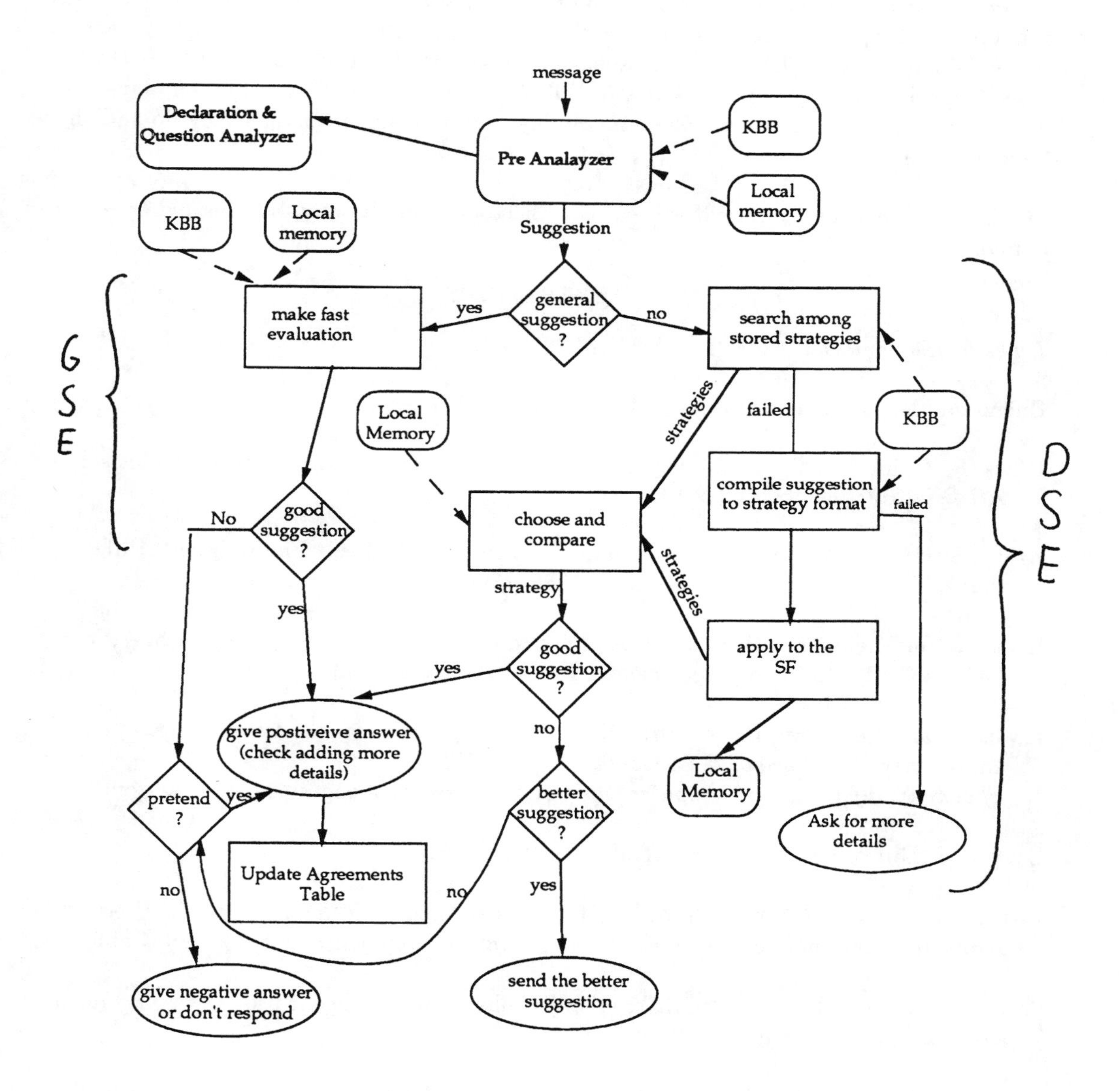

Figure 3: General Description of the Suggestion's Evaluation

signed between Diplomat and another power, and Diplomat predicted successfully the ally's intention to keep an agreement in 92% of all the agreements it had signed. We actually tested Diplomat in 100 Diplomacy seasons and, determined that Diplomat plays better than a well experienced player in a way that is difficult to distinguish from a human player. This is because Diplomat negotiates like human players, break agreements as they do and shows good strategic skills.

Further work will be to extend the used of the tools and the ideas of this paper to other domains.

REFERENCES

Rules for Diplomacy (1984). The Avalon Hill Game co.

Bueno de Mesquita, B. (1981) *The War Trap.* Yale University.

Davis, R. & Smith R.G. (1983) Negotiation as a metaphor for distributed problems solving. *Artificial Intelligence*, 20:63–109.

Kraus, S. (1988), *Planning and Communication in a Multi-Agent Environment.* PhD thesis, Hebrew University, Jerusalem, 1988. (Written largely in Hebrew).

Kraus, S. and Lehmann, D. (1988a), *Automated Negotiator.* Technical Report 88-7, Leibniz Center for Computer Science, Hebrew University, Jerusalem.

Kraus, S. and Lehmann, D. (1988b), Diplomat, an agent in a multi-agent environment: an overview. In *Proc. of the Seventh Annual IEEE Phoenix Conference on Computers and Communications*, pages 434–438, Arizona.

Levy, J. & Dimitrovski, Y. (1982) *The Ylisp 2 Manual.*

Rosenschein J. R. & Genesereth M. R., (1985) Deals among rational agents. In *Proc. of the Ninth International Joint Conference on Artificial Intelligence*, pages 91–99, California.

Sathi, A., Morton, T.E.& Roth, S.F., (1986) Callisto: an intelligent project management system. *The AI Magazine*, 7(5):34–52.

Sycara, K. P. (1987) *Resolving Adversarial Conflicts: An Approach Integrating Case-Based and Analytic Methods.* PhD thesis, School of Information and Computer Science, Georgia Institute of Technology.

Composite Holographic Associative Recall Model (CHARM) and Blended Memories in Eyewitness Testimony

Janet Metcalfe
Department of Psychology
University of California, San Diego.

Abstract

The idea that compositing or blending may occur in human episodic memory stems from two sources: (1) distributed models of human memory, and (2) studies that have focussed on the distortions and mistakes that occur in eyewitness testimony. In this paper, data that have been uncovered within the eyewitness testimony paradigm are simulated by a distributed memory model--CHARM (composite holographic associative recall memory). Studies done by Loftus have been interpreted as indicating that blending does occur; modification of these experiments conducted by McCloskey and Zaragosa have been claimed to refute Loftus' interpretation. It is shown that both of these results are predicted by the composite-trace model.

Introduction

There has been considerable debate about the nature of human memory storage: whether memories are stored discretely or may interact or even blend with one another. Loftus has argued that the fact that subjects who are given misleading information in a realistic, eyewitness testimony situation may be more inaccurate than are subjects not given the misleading information indicates that subsequent information may distort, erase, or combine with earlier information about the target event. McCloskey and Zaragosa suggest that under the appropriate testing conditions, no evidence for distortion, erasure or blending in memory is found.

The situation of primary interest in this debate is exemplified by a number of experiments by McCloskey and Zaragosa (1985). Subjects saw a series of color slides depicting an incident in which a maintenance man enters an office, repairs a chair, finds and steals $20, and then leaves. Embedded in the sequence was a critical slide in which the man picked up a hammer from a tool kit. After viewing the slide sequence, subjects read a narrative in which the misleading information was embedded, in the experimental condition, and in which neutral information was given in the control condition. In the experimental condition, it was suggested to the subjects that the tool the man had picked up was a screwdriver. In the control condition, a generic term-- tool--was used to refer to the detail in question. At time of test, subjects were asked the following question: "The man slid the calculator beneath a ___________ in his tool box".

The test consisted of a two-alternative forced choice procedure. In what will here be designated the "standard" conditions the label of the actually viewed object (in this case the term "hammer") was contrasted with the suggested objects ("screwdriver"). The pervasive finding in this testing procedure was that correct selection of hammer was impaired in the experimental but not in the control condition. McCloskey and Zaragosa modified this testing procedure such that the correct alternative was pitted against another category member ("wrench") but not against the misleading information itself. We will here designate this testing procedure the "Modified" condition. It was found that under these testing conditions, there was no decrement in performance for the term "hammer" in the experimental conditions.

Table 1. The experimental paradigm.

Standard "Loftus" Conditions			
Presentation	Questionaire	Test	Correct
Control			
Man-Hammer	------	Hammer-Screwdriver	72%
Misled			
Man-Hammer	Man-Screwdriver	Hammer-Screwdriver	37%
Modified "McCloskey" Conditions			
Presentation	Questionaire	Test	Correct
Control			
Man-Hammer	------	Hammer-Wrench	75%
Misled			
Man-Hammer	Man-Screwdriver	Hammer-Wrench	72%

On the basis of these findings, summarized in Table 1, McCloskey and Zaragosa argue that there is no loss or distortion of the initially encoded events. Loftus has usually argued for a blending view of memory (rather than for simple loss or erasure, attributable to the misleading information). About this blending or integration view, McCloskey and Zaragosa state:

> "What sorts of data would, then, support or disconfirm the integration claim? Consideration of this question leads quickly to the realization that what is meant by integration is not at all clear. One might suggest that the claim simply asserts that the information from various sources is stored together in memory. Although this answer may be satisfying at an intuitive level, it loses much of its appeal when we ask, What does 'stored together in memory' mean?" (p.15).

In the model, that is outlined below, there is but a single memory trace which consists of the sum of the associations that are entered into it. This composite or superimposed trace is an example of a memory system that produces blended memories. If a cue has been associated with more than one item, that cue will serve to retrieve all of the items with which it has been associated, and they will all be produced together, or in a blend. More explicit computer simulations provide predictions and postdictions about exactly what this composite, or blending model does in the situations outlined above.

Summary of the CHARM model

The model that will be used to investigate the blending predictions under the conditions outlined in McCloskey and Zaragosa's experiment is called the CHARM model (composite holographic associative recall model). The model was not devised specifically to apply to this situation, and has, in fact, been applied with some success to a variety of other classic memory situations, such as paired-associate learning, interference as a function of similarity, encoding specificity effects, concept formation, elaboration effects, recognition failure effects, and others (Metcalfe, in press; Metcalfe-Eich, 1982, 1985). The model is associative in nature, based on the idea that items, represented as distributed patterns of features, or vectors, are associated by the operation of convolution. This operation (denoted *) is given by the following equation, for the mth term of the resulting vector:

$$(F*G) = \sum_{(i,j)\varepsilon S(m)} f_i g_j, \tag{1}$$

where, F and G are the item vectors:

$$(f_1, f_2, f_3, \ldots)\text{and}(g_1, g_2, g_3, \ldots)$$

and

$$S(m) = \left\{ (i,j) \middle| -\frac{n-1}{2} \le i,j \le \frac{n-1}{2}, \text{ and } i+j=m \right\}.$$

The resulting vector is added into a single vector that is the composite memory trace. As each association is added into this vector the values for each element of the vector may change. Thus, the trace is defined as:

$$T=(G*G)+(H*I)+(J*K)+.... \quad \textbf{(2)}$$

The initial item vectors, $F, G, H, I, J,$ and K may bear any similarity relation to one another, and may vary in terms of their initial strength or length. This summation at time of storage is what is meant by blending or storing together in memory.

The operation that allows retrieval from this composite associative trace is called correlation (denoted #) and is defined as:

$$(F\#T)_m = \sum_{(i,j)\varepsilon S(m)} f_i t_j, \quad (3)$$

where

$$S(m) = \left\{ (i,j) \;\middle|\; -\frac{n-1}{2} \leq i,j \leq \frac{n-1}{2}, \text{ and } i-j=m \right\}.$$

The result of retrieval is a single vector. But this vector may be broken down into the components that contribute to it as follows:

$$R=F\#T \quad \text{I}(4)$$

$$=F\#(F*G)+(H*I)+\cdots$$

$$=F\#(F*G)+F\#(H*I)+...$$

$$=S_{FF}G+S_{FG}F+error_{F*G}+S_{FH}I+S_{FI}H+error_{H*I}+\cdots$$

Here, S is a scalar giving the similarity value between F and F, for example, as measured by their dot product. In the case where two items are associated with a single cue, we see that the single vector that is retrieved by this system will contain components of both of the original items. This output from the model can be simulated, and the result can be assessed within the framework of the Loftus-McCloskey forced-choice paradigm, by simply providing the alternative they allowed in the experiment, and letting the model pick the best match to its retrieved output.

Simulations

A number of simulations were conducted on this and related paradigms. Only one series will be reported here.

Method

A lexicon of 90 items was constructed, where each item consisted of 63 features and each feature consisted of a value randomly selected from a truncated Gaussian distribution with an expected value of zero. The items were then normalized so that the self dot products were 1. The first item in the lexicon we will hereinafter assign the name "man"; the second item "hammer"; the 22nd item "screwdriver"; the 32nd item "tool" and the 42nd item "wrench". In the High Similarity conditions, these exemplars were reassigned feature values so that 80% of their features were the same as the prototype item "tool". In the Moderate Similarity conditions, 40% of these features were reassigned values of the prototype. In the unrelated conditions, the items were statistically independent.

Two different traces were formed to depict the experimental and the control conditions of the experiment. The control trace was:

$$T_c=(MAN*HAMMER)+(MAN*TOOL)+5\ \textit{irrelevant convolutions}.$$

The experimental trace was:

$$T_e=(MAN*HAMMER)+(MAN*SCREWDRIVER)+5\ \textit{irrelevant convolutions}.$$

The irrelevant convolutions were included here to indicate that there were other events stored in the trace, and the number is not too important in the present context. (See Metcalfe & Murdock, 1981, for further details on this point).

Retrieval was simulated by correlating the vector for MAN with the composite trace. The retrieved vector that resulted was then compared to HAMMER and SCREWDRIVER, in the standard conditions, or to HAMMER and WRENCH, in the modified conditions. The comparison consisted of taking the dot product of the retrieved vector with that of the lexical item in question. The match that gave the highest value was the winner and was said to be the choice that was made on that particular trial. The entire sequence of simulations was run twice, the first time producing 200 replications or observations per point, and the second time 1000 observations per point.

Results

The pattern of results produced by the simulations is shown in Table 2. As can be seen, in each of the three manipulations of similarity, the model produced the basic pattern shown in McCloskey and Zaragosa's data. In particular, under Standard testing conditions, the misleading information in the Experimental condition resulted in poorer performance than did the neutral information in the Control conditions, whereas when the Modified test situation was simulated, there was no difference between the Control and the Misled conditions.

Conclusions

It is clear that the simple blending model is able to generate data that have been construed as indicating that there are distortions in memory and also data that have been rallied to reject the blending idea. What are the implications for real-world memory? There are some situations in which one might expect blends to occur. One prerequisite in the model for the appearance of evidence for such blends is that there must exist a lexical representation that depicts or at least is very similar to the composite blended entity that is retrieved from memory. Figure 1 shows an example where two objects that are unlike one another are superimposed. But there is no real world object that could correspond to the blend shown in the far right panel. Figure 2 shows a second example that was created in exactly the same way as the first example. However, in this case the items themselves were highly similar to one another, and the blended entity could plausibly be a real-world entity.

Positive blends-- where a composite model will predict a compromise between the presented and suggested items-- are difficult to find. However, Loftus (1977) has

Table 2. Simulation results.

Category Similarity	Test Condition	Information Condition	Percentage Correct	
Unrelated	Standard	Control	68.0	64.2
	(hammer-screwdriver)	Misled	32.5	34.1
	Modified	Control	70.5	64.8
	(hammer-wrench)	Misled	62.0	66.3
Moderate	Standard	Control	58.5	63.1
		Misled	38.0	37.9
	Modified	Control	67.0	63.1
		Misled	65.0	64.7
High	Standard	Control	52.5	55.8
		Misled	37.5	42.0
	Modified	Control	54.5	56.7
		Misled	58.0	57.0

provided one such example in which a car that had in fact been green in a slide sequence was guessed most frequently as having been a blue-green color after misleading blue information about its color was given. In this color-shift experiment, the intermediate colors could and do exist in the real world and so there would be no a priori restriction against the possibility that such a color had occurred. In many other cases, however, there are no real-world objects that comprise a blend. For instance, there is no real world object that consists of a blend between a screwdriver and a hammer. Thus, a literal blend could be ruled out immediately, even if such were retrieved from memory.

Face recognition poses an interesting puzzle, and one that may have practical significance. As Figure 2 illustrates, there may be cases in which the superimposition of two faces could produce a plausible blend. In such a situation even if we were to eliminate from the testing alternative the face that was used as the misleading information the possibility exists that a third face (or actually, in the model, a whole family of intermediate faces) might nevertheless be accepted by the subject as plausible interpretation of the blend that is retrieved from memory. In conclusion, then, the composite model does a good job of predicting the data from both the McCloskey and the Loftus testing conditions. It also makes further predictions that may be of both practical and of theoretical importance.

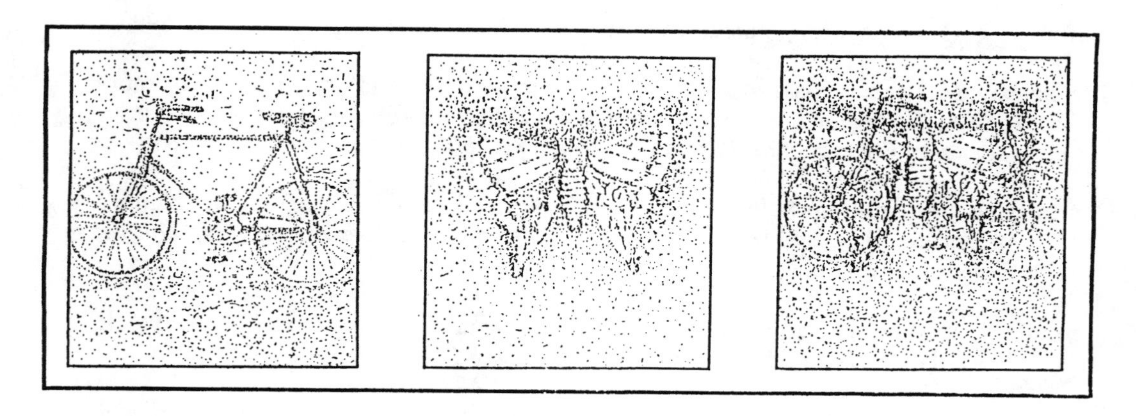

Figure 1. The superposition of two nonintegrable objects that do not yield a positive blend.

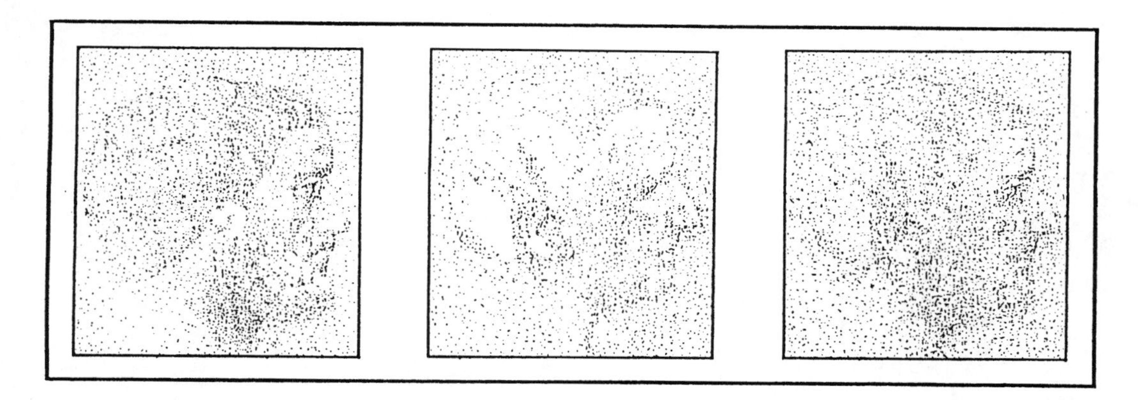

Figure 2. The superpositon of two integrable objects producing a positive blend.

References

Loftus, E. F. (1977). Shifting human color memory. *Memory & Cognition, 5*, 696,699.

McCloskey, M., & Zaragosa, M. (1985). Misleading postevent information and memory for events: Arguments and evidence against the memory impairment hypothesis. *Journal of Experimental Psychology: General, 114*, 3-18.

Metcalfe, J. A composite holographic associative recall model (CHARM) and blended memories in eyewitness testimony. *Journal of Experimental Psychology: General* , in press.

Metcalfe, J. & Murdock, B. B., Jr. (1981) An encoding and retrieval model of free recall. *Journal of Verbal Learning and Verbal Behavior,20*, 161-189.

Metcalfe-Eich, J. (1982). A composite holographic associative recall model. *Psychological Review, 89*, 627-661.

Metcalfe-Eich, J. (1985). Levels of processing, encoding specificity, elaboration, and CHARM. *Psychological Review, 92*, 1-38.

A Two-stage Categorization Model of Family Resemblance Sorting

Woo-Kyoung Ahn and Douglas L. Medin[1]
Department of Psychology
University of Illinois at Champaign-Urbana
Champaign, Il 61820

ABSTRACT

A two-stage model is applied to category construction. The first stage of the model involves looking for a defining feature among exemplars and creating initial categories based on the defining features. In the second stage, overall similarity is calculated to categorize the remaining exemplars that were not classified by the defining feature. For some types of exemplar structures, family resemblance sorting emerges as a product of the two-stage model. A series of experiments was carried out to contrast the two-stage model with Anderson's induction model (Anderson, 1988) and CLUSTER/2 (Michalski & Stepp, 1983). The results showed that the two-stage model is a better predictor of when family resemblance sorting will or will not occur.

INTRODUCTION

Categories in the real world are known to have a family resemblance structure (Rosch & Mervis, 1975). Family resemblance categories are fuzzy categories where the members are generally similar to each other, but where there is no set of defining properties that any and all examples have. Rosch (1975) predicted that when asked to sort examples linked by overall similarity, people would tend to create categories in a way that potential prototypes are at the centers of the categories.

However, Medin, Wattenmaker, and Hampson (1987), in their Experiments 1, 2, and 3, found that people rarely constructed categories based on overall similarity. Instead, subjects typically sorted exemplars on the basis of a single dimension. In one of their experiments, Medin et al. also used trinary-valued dimensions coupled with the requirement that exactly two categories be created, which made subjects unable to create uni-dimensional categories. Under this condition, a few family resemblance sortings were obtained but none of the subjects' descriptions was consistent with a family resemblance explanation. Instead, they simply used a primary dimension plus either a conjunction or a disjunction of features. These results suggest a two-stage model of categorization, in which the first stage involves looking for a defining feature among given exemplars and the second stage involves computing similarity of remaining exemplars to the initially created categories.

Several other alternative models for category construction have also been proposed. For example, Michalski and Stepp (1983) developed CLUSTER/2 which forms a class only if it is describable by a concept from a predefined concept class. Recently several iterative algorithms have been developed by Anderson(1988) and Fisher (1987), which try to maximize the inferential potential of categories. This paper compares these three classes of recent models. The predictions made by each model will be compared with the results obtained in an experiment.

DESCRIPTION OF MODELS

Two-stage Model

The two-stage model is developed to capture people's goal of finding simple structure in the world. The idea is that people may impose more structure than is objectively present. Given that the world is not organized in such a simple manner, people are forced to deal with exceptions. Therefore, two stages seem to be involved in creating categories; In the first stage, the most

[1] The address of both authors will be Department of Psychology, University of Michigan, Perry Building, 330 Packard Rd, Ann Arbor, MI 48104, as of August, 1989.

	D1	D2	D3	D4		D1	D2	D3	D4
E1	0	0	0	0	E6	1	1	1	1
E2	0	0	0	1	E7	1	1	1	0
E3	0	0	1	0	E8	1	1	0	1
E4	0	1	0	0	E9	1	0	1	1
E5	1	0	0	0	E10	0	1	1	1

Figure 1. The structure of Exemplars used in Medin et al's experiment

important dimension is selected as a primary dimension for each category and exemplars are classified along this dimension. In the second stage, the exceptions are classified into initially created categories through various strategies.

A specific version of the two-stage model is developed, in which the model tries to construct two categories from given exemplars. According to this model, subjects will first select the most salient dimension in the exemplars (e.g. size). Then the subjects will divide the exemplars into two groups according to the two extreme values along the selected dimension (e.g. small vs. large). The second stage involves classifying the remaining exemplars which do not have the extreme values (e.g. medium). These exemplars are categorized into either of the two initially created groups depending on their overall similarity to each group. The judgment of the overall similarity involves all the dimensions in the exemplar as in the conventional models.

The two-stage model produces uni-dimensional sorting from the stimuli used in Medin et al's experiment. The structure of the examples used in their experiments was shown in Figure 1. In this figure, D1, D2, D3, and D4 indicate each dimension in the example, 0, 1's indicate different values in the same dimension, and E1, E2,... E10 indicate examples to be categorized.

Given the task demand of creating two categories, the second stage is not even necessary because all the dimensions have only two values and therefore, there cannot be any remaining exemplars after the first stage. No matter which dimension is selected as the most salient one, the model predicts uni-dimensional sorting (e.g. E1, E2, E3, E4, and E10 in one category and the rest in the other when D1 is selected as the most salient dimension).

The two-stage model may seem to be unable to produce family resemblance sorting because the model looks for defining features for each category. However, in some cases, the two-stage model does generate the family resemblance categories as a by-product of the process carried out in the second stage. Shortly we shall see how the model actually produces the family resemblance sorting with concrete examples.

CLUSTER/2

Unlike conventional clustering models, CLUSTER/2 does not use a measure of similarity as a basis for categorization. Instead, it uses a measure based on descriptions of candidate clusterings. The main goal of CLUSTER/2 is to generate categories with a minimum number of attributes used in a description, maximum number of attributes that singly discriminate among all classes, and maximum number of attributes that take different values in different classes. This goal is used as a criterion to judge quality of clustering.

The system goes through several iterations of the following steps. First, the system chooses initial seeds randomly or according to some criterion (e.g. values that are most distant from each other). For each seed, it generates a set of all maximally general descriptions of the seed which do not intersect with the set of remaining seeds. The descriptions are modified according to the clustering quality criterion. New seeds are selected and the entire steps are repeated until there is no improvement in clustering.

One of the most important criteria used in CLUSTER/2 is simplicity of descriptions, which is similar to the first stage of the two-stage model. However, since CLUSTER/2 does not have an additional way of handling exceptions, the system cannot generate family resemblance categories, which cannot be described in simple terms.

Iterative Algorithms

Recently several iterative algorithms of category construction have been developed in which new examples are entered incrementally and classified to the category that maximizes the inferential potential of the resulting partition. As a clustering criterion, Fisher (1987) used category utility developed by Gluck and Corter (1986), which is a product of a base rate of each feature, cue validity, and category validity. For each object, the system calculates category utilities of that object coming from each of existing categories and a category utility of that object coming from a new category. The object is placed into a category which maximizes the category utility.

Similarly, Anderson's iterative algorithm calculates two kinds of probabilities (i.e. the probabilities of a new object coming from old categories, P_k, and the probabilities of the new object coming from a new category, P_o). These two probabilities are operationalized in terms of the equations as follows.

$$P_k = \frac{cn_k}{(1-c)+cn} \prod_{i=1} \frac{C_{ki}+1}{n_k+m_i}$$

$$P_o = \frac{1-c}{(1-c)+cn} \prod_{i=1} \frac{1}{m_i}$$

where n is the number of objects so far, n_k is the number of objects in category K so far, C_{ki} is the number of objects in category so far with the same valued on the ith dimension as the object to be classified, m_i is the number of values on dimension i, and c is a cohesion parameter, which is the probability that any two objects will be in the same category.

This model cannot explain Medin et al's results because it produces family resemblance categories from the examples used in their experiments (i.e. E1, E2, E3, E4, and E5 in one category and the rest in the other category).

TEST OF MODELS

To examine different predictions of each model on concrete examples, three sets of examples (Sets A, B, and C) were developed. The abstract notation of the structure of the examples is shown in Figure 2.

Predictions of the Two-stage Model

For Set A, no matter which dimension was chosen for the most salient dimension, the model categorizes E1, E2, E3, E4, and E5 into one group and the rest into another group. This sorting turns out to be the family resemblance sorting. To illustrate more specifically what the model does, suppose D1 was chosen as the most salient dimension. Then E1, E2, E3, and E4 are classified as one category and E6, E7, E8, and E9 are classified as another category. Then which category E5 and E10 each belong to should be decided. Since E5 has greater overall similarity to E1, E2, E3, and E4 than E6, E7, E8, and E9, it is categorized with the former group. Similarly, E10 is

	Set A				Set B				Set C			
	D1	D2	D3	D4	D1	D2	D3	D4	D1	D2	D3	D4
E1	0	0	0	0	0	0	0	0	0	0	1	0
E2	0	0	0	1	0	0	0	1	0	0	1	1
E3	0	0	1	0	0	0	2	0	0	1	0	0
E4	0	1	0	0	0	1	0	0	1	1	0	0
E5	1	0	0	0	2	0	0	0	1	0	0	1
E6	2	2	2	2	2	2	2	2	1	2	2	1
E7	2	2	2	1	2	2	2	0	2	2	1	2
E8	2	2	1	2	2	2	1	2	2	2	1	1
E9	2	1	2	2	2	0	2	2	2	1	2	2
E10	1	2	2	2	1	2	2	2	1	1	2	2

Figure 2. Three Sets of Exemplars Used to Test Models

Table 1. Predictions of the two-stage model

	Set A	Set B	Set C
Category A	0 0 0 0	0 0 0 0	0 0 1 0
	0 0 0 1	0 0 0 1	0 0 1 1
	0 0 1 0	0 0 2 0	0 1 0 0
	0 1 0 0	0 1 0 0	1 1 0 0
	1 0 0 0		1 0 0 1
Category B	2 2 2 2	2 0 0 0	1 2 2 1
	2 2 2 1	2 2 2 2	2 2 1 2
	2 2 1 2	2 2 2 0	2 2 1 1
	2 1 2 2	2 2 1 2	2 1 2 2
	1 2 2 2	2 0 2 2	1 1 2 2
		1 2 2 2	

categorized with E6, E7, E8, and E9. Therefore, this test of the two-stage model on Set A shows that the model can also generate family-resemblance categories.

For Set B, the model generates uni-dimensional sorting where the defining dimension of a category is the one specified as the most salient dimension. For example, if D1 is selected as the most salient one, then E1, E2, E3, and E4 are grouped together and E5, E6, E7, E8, and E9 are grouped together. In the second stage, E10, the remaining example, is judged to be more similar to E5, E6, E7, E8, and E9 group and is classified into this group, resulting in a uni-dimensional category of E1, E2, E3, and E4 along D1.

For Set C, the model generates the family resemblance categories. For example, if D1 is entered as the most salient dimension, E1, E2, and E3 will be grouped together and E7, E8, and E9 will be grouped together. As in Set A, in the second stage, E4, E5, E6, and E10 are each classified according to overall similarity, resulting in family resemblance sorting.

Table 1 shows the summary of predictions made by the two-stage model.The two categories generated are arbitrarily named Category A and B. The categories generated for Set B are the ones when D1 is selected as the most salient one.

Predictions of CLUSTER/2

For CLUSTER/2, types of dimensions had to be specified. We used the dimensions actually used in the experiment: linear for D1 and D2, and nominal for D3 and D4. The parameters entered were as follows; Mink = 2, Maxk=4, covertype = disjoing, H1=3, H2=2, H3=3, Cbase = 2, probe = 2, NIDspeed= fast, maxheight=99, minsize=4, beta=3.0, LEF = ((sparseness=0.3) (simplicity=0.3)). (See Michalski & Stepp, 1983 for more details on the parameters.) These parameters were used as default values in the current program and we have not yet fully explored the parameter space. With these parameters, CLUSTER/2 generated three clusterings on each set of exemplars, differing in the number of clusters in each clustering. Since the system does not have any preference among those three clusterings, only those clusterings with two clusters were used for comparison with the results obtained in the experiment, in which subjects were asked to categorize the exemplars into two.

Table 2 shows the categorization made by CLUSTER/2 for each set of exemplars. As mentioned earlier, CLUSTER/2 did not generate family resemblance categories from any of the three sets. Instead, all the categories generated are uni-dimensional. If the parameter for the simplicity criteria is lowered, it may produce family resemblance categories but it seems to be against the main idea behind the development of the system (i.e. generating meaningfully describable categories).

Table 2. Predictions of CLUSTER/2

	Set A	Set B	Set C
Category A	0 0 0 0	0 0 0 0	0 0 1 0
	0 0 1 0	0 0 2 0	2 2 1 2
	1 0 0 0	0 1 0 0	0 1 0 0
	0 1 0 0	2 0 0 0	1 1 0 0
	2 2 1 2	2 2 2 2	2 1 2 2
	2 2 2 2	2 2 2 0	1 1 2 2
	2 1 2 2	2 2 1 2	
	1 2 2 2	1 2 2 2	
		2 0 2 2	
Category B	2 2 2 1	0 0 0 1	1 2 2 1
	0 0 0 1		0 0 1 1
			2 2 1 1
			1 0 0 1

Predictions of Anderson's Algorithm

A simulation program of Anderson's iterative algorithm was written in GCLISP. However, the current version of the algorithm has an obvious limitation to be compared to the results of the experiment which will be described in the next section. Since the probabilities are based on matching and mismatching features on the same dimension, the model does not consider the degree of mismatch on continuous dimensions. More specifically, the probability of an object coming from an old category depends on the number of objects in the category so far with the same value on the ith dimension as the object to be classified (C_{ki}). Therefore, for example, in the current algorithm, the difference between 1 cm and 2 cm is same as the difference between 1 cm and 10 cm. Only exact matches can increase the probability.

To extend the model to handle continuous dimensions, the simulation program is written in a way to increase the probability by a certain amount if the two values are similar along a continuous dimension. For example, if there are three values on a continuous dimension (e.g. 3 cm, 4 cm, and 5 cm), the exact match will increase C_{ki} by one, the moderate match (e.g. 3 cm and 4 cm, or 4 cm and 5 cm) will increase it by 0.5, and the extreme mismatch (e.g. 3 cm and 5 cm) will increase it by 0.

Since the algorithm has potential to be order-sensitive, two different presentation orders were tried for each set; one with the lowest variability between two consecutive exemplars (e.g. the order of 0000, 0001, 0010, etc.) and the other with the highest variability (e.g. the order of 0000, 2222, 0001, 2221, etc.). The presentation order affected the categorization of Set B and C, and the two different clusterings are each presented under "with low var" and "with high var" in Table 3.

To compare the predictions with the results obtained in our experiment, the parameter c was adjusted to generate two categories. The range of the value of c which generated the two categories is specified in the last row.

EXPERIMENT

To test which model describes human behavior better, an experiment was conducted where people were asked to construct categories from examples.

Method

Each subject received a set of 10 cards on which examples were drawn. The order of the cards within each set was randomized and one set of cards was given to each subject all at once. Then they were asked to categorize the instances into two groups in a way that seemed natural to them. They were also told that there could be different number of examples in the two groups and that there was no one correct answer.

Table 3. Predictions of Anderson's model

	Set A	Set B with low var	Set B with high var	Set C with low var	Set C with high var
Category A	0 0 0 0 0 0 0 1 0 0 1 0 0 1 0 0 1 0 0 0	0 0 0 0 0 0 0 1 0 0 2 0 0 1 0 0 2 0 0 0 2 0 2 2 2 2 2 0	0 0 0 0 0 0 0 1 0 0 2 0 0 1 0 0 2 0 0 0	0 0 1 0 0 0 1 1 0 1 0 0 1 1 0 0 1 0 0 1 1 2 2 1 1 1 2 2	1 1 2 2 1 0 0 1 2 1 2 2 1 1 0 0 2 2 1 1 0 1 0 0 2 2 1 2 0 0 1 1 0 0 1 0
Category B	2 2 2 2 2 2 2 1 2 2 1 2 2 1 2 2 1 2 2 2	2 2 2 2 2 2 1 2 1 2 2 2	2 2 2 2 2 2 2 0 2 2 1 2 2 0 2 2 1 2 2 2	2 2 1 2 2 2 1 1 2 1 2 2	1 2 2 1
c value	0.3-0.8 for low var 0.3-0.7 for high var	0.3-0.5	0.3-0.7	0.3	0.5-0.6

There were three groups of subjects depending on which set of exemplars they received. We used three sets of exemplars specified in Figure 2. The actual dimensions used were size, number of arms, types of line, and color. Each dimension has three values such as small, medium, and large for the size dimension and green, red, and yellow for the color dimension. Based on these dimensions and values, outline drawings of cartoonlike starfish were developed. A pilot study was also conducted to create roughly equal intervals between two adjacent values on the same dimension and to attempt to equate saliency among dimensions.

Sixty undergraduate students at the University of Illinois participated in the experiment in partial fulfillment of a course requirement for introductory psychology. There were 20 subjects in each condition.

Results and Discussion

For Set A, 55% of the subjects produced family resemblance categories, and 45% of the subjects produced uni-dimensional sorting. For Set B, 100% of the subjects produced uni-dimensional sorting. For Set C, 35% of the subjects produced family-resemblance categories, 55% produced uni-dimensional sorting, and 10% produced other responses. Table 4 summarizes the results from the present experiment and Medin et al's experiments, and the predictions made by each model for comparison. The numbers in parenthesis indicate the percentage of the subjects' sorting predicted by each model. Overall, the two-stage model was the best predictor of the subjects' sorting.

Two-stage model.

Overall, the two-stage model seemed to give the best account of sorting. The two-stage model predicted 55% of the subjects' response on Set A, 100% on Set B and 35% on Set C. The reason why the two-stage model did not predict 45% of the response on Set A and 65% on Set C can be explained in terms of different strategies used in the second stage. At first, it was assumed that people judge overall similarity of exceptions to initially created categories in the second stage. However, subjects could have also classified the remaining examples based on the similarity of the

Table 4. Summary of results and predictions made by each model

	Medin et al.	Set A	Set B	Set C
Subjects	1-D 100%	FR 55% 1-D 45%	FR 0% 1-D 100%	FR 35% 1-D 55% others 10%
Two-stage	1-D (100%)	FR (55%)	1-D (100%)	FR (35%)
CLUSTER/2		1-D along D4 (0%)	1-D along D4 (0%)	1-D along D4 (0%)
Anderson				
with low var	FR (0%)	FR (55%)	other (0 %)	1-D (55%)
with high var	FR (0%)	FR (55%)	FR (0%)	other (0%)

value on the salient dimension to the value on the same dimension in each category created initially. For example, suppose the subjects created small vs. large categories in the first stage and the remaining examples had medium size. Then subjects might compare the similarity of medium to large and the similarity of medium to small. Then they might place the remaining examples in the category with the higher similarity. In this case, uni-dimensional categories were created from Set A and Set C.

To further test this idea, in the follow-up study, we asked subjects to create two categories of equal size. This task presumably prevents subjects from using the strategy that was just described because this strategy creates two unequal sized categories. In this experiment using Set A only, 100% of subjects created family resemblance categories. This result strongly suggests that the uni-dimensional sorting obtained in the current study is due to this strategy difference.

CLUSTER/2.

CLUSTER/2 could not predict any of the family resemblance sorting obtained in this experiment as shown in Table 4. Furthermore, the uni-dimensional categories predicted by the system does not have the same structure as the subjects' uni-dimensional categories. While the system used a nominal dimension (D4) to divide the examples into two, subjects preferred continuous dimensions presumably because they want to use two extreme values to create contrasting categories.

Anderson's model.

Regardless of input ordering, the model correctly predicted family resemblance sorting from Set A, which was 55% of subjects' response. Also, when the low variability ordering was used, the model could predict subjects' uni-dimensional sorting from Set C, which was 55% of subjects' response. However, when the high variability ordering was used, Anderson's model failed to predict any sorting from Set C. Also, the model was not a good predictor for Set B and the set used in Medin et al's experiments, as mentioned earlier.

The predictions of Anderson's model is hard to compare because it is not clear how the effect of different input ordering should be interpreted. Although the subjects received each set of cards all at once, it is possible that the subjects might have selected and classified the examples in the low variability order. Additional assumptions on how subjects handle each example incrementally seem to be necessary. In addition, his model does not seem to be able to explain why all subjects generated family resemblance categories from Set A when asked to create two equal-sized groups as mentioned earlier. The effect of various task demands seems to be outside the boundary conditions for this model.

CONCLUSION

So far, we have shown that the two-stage model predicts the experimental data the best among the three clustering models considered. People seem to like structures with more organization than is present in the examples (i.e. defining features) but then given the demands of the task (assigning all examples to one of two categories), they have to figure out what to do with the examples that do not fit.

In a similar view, Michalski has proposed a two-tiered concept representation (Michalski, in press). In this representation, concepts consist of the first tier, called the Base Concept Representation (i.e. typical properties of a concept in an explicit, comprehensible, and efficient form) and the second tier, called the Inferential Concept Interpretation (i.e. inference rules and metaknowledge that define allowable transformations of the concept under different contexts, and handle special cases and exceptional instances).

Fillmore (1982) and Lakoff (1987) argued that concepts consist of idealized cognitive models with clear boundaries and necessary and sufficient conditions. According to them, the reason why natural concepts have fuzzy boundaries is simply because the background conditions for the idealized model do not exactly fit the real world situations.

In our two-stage model, the first stage represents ideal rather than typical features. Processes associated with the second stage yield categories where these idea or defining features become converted to typical features. In the same way, family resemblance categories may represent a compromise between a preference for highly structured concepts and the necessity of mapping concepts onto real world examples.

Acknowledgement

We thank Brad Whitehall for running CLUSTER/2 to test on the exemplars. This work was supported by NSF grant BNS88-12193 to the second author.

REFERENCES

Anderson, J.R. (1988). The place of cognitive architectures in a rational analysis. Proceedings of the Tenth Annual Conference of the Cognitive Science Society.

Fillmore, C. (1982). Towards a descriptive framework for spatial deixis. In R. Jarvella & W. Klein (Eds.), Speech, place, and action. London: Wiley.

Fiehser, D. (1987). Knowledge acquisition via incremental conceptual clustering, Machine Learning 2, 139-172.

Gluck, M., & Corter, J. (1985). Information, uncertainty, and the utility of categories. Proceedings of the Seventh Annual Conference of the Cognitive Science Society, Irvine, CA. 283-287.

Lakoff, G. (1987). Cognitive models and prototype theory. In U. Neisser (Ed.), Concepts and conceptual development. (pp 63-100). Cambridge, NY: Cambridge University Press,.

Medin, D.L., Wattenmaker, W.D., & Hampson, S.E. (1987). Family resemblance, conceptual cohesiveness, and category construction. Cognitive Psychology, 19, 242-279.

Michalski, R.S. (in press). Two-tiered concept meaning, inferential matching and conceptual cohesiveness. In S. Vosniadou and A. Ortony (Eds.) Similarity and analogy.

Michalski, R.S., & Stepp, R. E. (1983). Learning from observation: Conceptual clustering. In R. S. Michalski, J.G. Carbonnell, & T.M. Mitchell (Eds.) Machine learning: An artificial intelligence approach. Palo Alto, CA: Tioga Publishing.

Rosch, E. (1975). Universals and cultural specifics. In R.Brislin, S.Bochner, & W. Lonner (Eds.) Cross-cultural perspectives on learning. New York: Halsted Press.

Rosch, E., & Mervis, C.B. (1975). Family resemblance: Studies in the internal structure of categories. Cognitive Psychology, 7, 573-605.

Eleventh Annual Conference of the Cognitive Science Society, Ann Arbor, MI. August 16-19, 1989.

A CONFIGURAL-CUE NETWORK MODEL OF ANIMAL AND HUMAN ASSOCIATIVE LEARNING

Mark A. Gluck Gordon H. Bower Michael R. Hee

Department of Psychology
Stanford University

ABSTRACT

We test a configural-cue network model of human classification and recognition learning based on Rescorla & Wagner's (1972) model of classical conditioning. The model extends the stimulus representation assumptions from our earlier one-layer network model (Gluck & Bower, 1988b) to include pair-wise conjunctions of features as unique cues. Like the exemplar context model of Medin & Schaffer (1978), the representational assumptions of the configural-cue network model embody an implicit exponential decay relationship between stimulus similarity and and psychological (Hamming) distance, a relationship which has received substantial independent empirical and theoretical support (Shepard, 1957, 1987). In addition to results from animal learning, the model accounts for several aspects of complex human category learning, including the relationship between category similarity and linear separability in determining classification difficulty (Medin & Schwanenflugel, 1981), the relationship between classification and recognition memory for instances (Hayes-Roth & Hayes-Roth, 1977), and the impact of correlated attributes on classification (Medin, Altom, Edelson, & Freko, 1982).

In earlier papers, we have explored a simple adaptive network as a model of human learning (Gluck & Bower, 1986, 1988a, 1988b; Gluck, Corter, Bower, & Kyleberg, 1988). We have used Rescorla and Wagner's (1972) description of classical conditioning and extended it to human classification learning. The learning rule is the same as the least mean squares (LMS) learning rule for training one-layer networks (proposed by Widrow & Hoff, 1960). The model has been fit to data from experiments on probabilistic classification learning with multiple cues. While this simple model can be applied to only a restricted range of experimental circumstances, it has shown a surprising accuracy in predicting human behavior within that range--people's choice percentages during learning, the relative difficulty of learning various classifications, as well as their responses to generalization tests involving novel combinations of cues.

This paper extends the stimulus representation assumptions used previously. We assume in this "configural-cue" model that pair-wise conjunctions of stimulus features are encoded as unique elements. This configural cue assumption is common in the animal learning literature (e.g., Wagner

---

Correspondence regarding this article should be addressed to: Mark A. Gluck, Department of Psychology, Jordan Hall; Bldg. 420, Stanford University, Stanford, CA 94305; or email to *gluck@psych.stanford.edu*. For their thoughtful comments and advice on this work we are indebted to: James Corter, W. K. Estes, Robert Nosofsky, Jay McClelland, Doug Medin, Misha Pavel, Robert Rescorla, and Allan Wagner. This research was supported by NSF Grant BNS-8618049.

and Rescorla, 1972), and has been used to explain a range of results (e.g., Rescorla, 1972, 1973). This paper shows how this extended model accounts for several aspects of complex category learning by humans.

BACKGROUND

The ingredients of the basic network model are shown in the left side of Figure (1A). Presentation of a stimulus or pattern of cues corresponds to activating one or more of the sensory elements on the left. They send their activations to a single output unit along associative lines which have amplifier weights, the w_i. The weighted inputs are summed at the output node, and this output $\sum_{j=1}^{n} w_j a_j$, is converted into some response measure. In a classical conditioning situation, the inputs are single to-be-conditioned stimuli such as lights and bells that are paired with the unconditional stimulus, such as food for a hungry dog; the output node reflects the animal's expectation of the unconditional stimulus given the cues presented. In a classification experiment involving human adults as subjects, the stimuli might be patterns of, say, medical symptoms displayed by a patient, and the output reflects the degree to which the model expects such a patient to have some target disease (classification) versus alternative diseases.

The network operates in a training environment in which reinforcing feedback (the UCS or the correct classification) is given just after each stimulus pattern. The central axiom of the model is its learning rule, which is that the weights, the w_i's, change on each trial according to Equation 1:

$$\Delta w_i = \beta a_i (\lambda - \sum_{j=1}^{n} w_j a_j) \tag{1}$$

Here, λ is the training signal which might be +1 for the correct category and 0 for an incorrect category. The cue-intensity parameter, a_i is assumed to be 1 if cue i is present on the trial, and 0 if it's not. The learning rate, β, is a parameter (on the order of .01 in most simulations) that determines how much the weights change when the output differs from the training signal, λ.

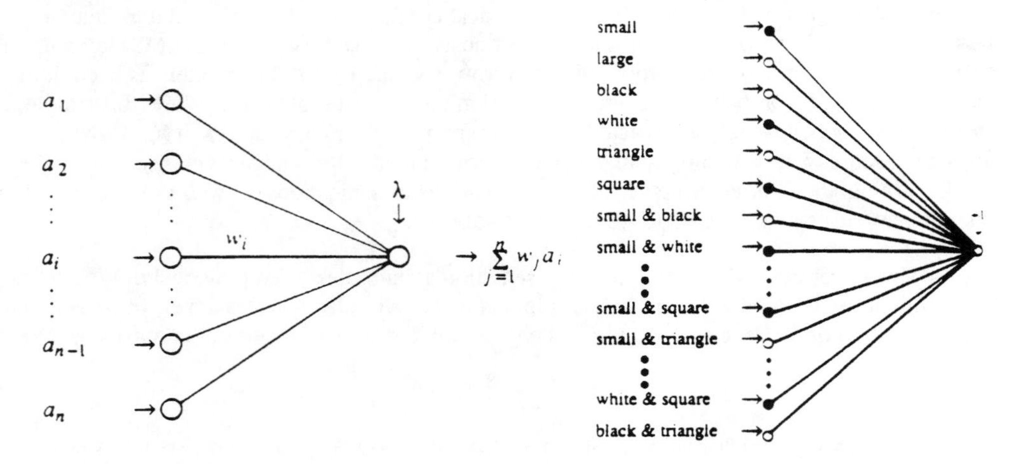

Figure 1. (A) A simple one-layer network which can learn the associations between three cues (CSs) and one outcome (US). (B) A configural-cue network with the cues for a small white square activated.

Equation 1 is variously called the delta rule, the least-mean-square (LMS) rule, or the Rescorla-Wagner conditioning rule (for a discussion, see Gluck & Bower, 1988a). Importantly, it corrects all weights according to the degree of error between the network's current output and what was desired for this pattern. This defines a learning process whereby the weights on the input lines converge to values that reflect the relative correlations of the stimulus features with the feedback signal. In a medical setting, these weights reflect the differential validity of each symptom (cue) for each disease (category). We have applied this baseline model to a variety of classification experiments (see Gluck & Bower, 1986, 1988a, 1988b). In each case, the simplest identifications have been used, viz., presentation of a specific medical symptom (e.g., stomach cramps) corresponded in the model to turning on a specific input node. Thus, a pattern of medical symptoms exhibited by a patient was represented by activation of the corresponding input nodes in the model. These identifications were successful in fitting the data of the early experiments by us and others (Estes et al., in press; MacMillan, 1987; Nosofsky, personal communication).

However, this approach, of theoretically identifying each experimental stimulus cue with a single input node in the model, encounters several difficulties. Most familiarly, one-layer networks with such manifest stimulus identifications are incapable of learning classifications that are not "linearly separable". An example is the exclusive-or (XOR) problem, wherein stimulus patterns (0,0) and (1,1) belong to one category, while patterns (1,0) and (0,1) belong to another. A common approach for solving such non-linear classification problems is to postulate additional, "hidden units" which connect between the input and output units (Parker, 1986; Rumelhart, Hinton, & Williams, 1986). While these multi-layer networks have great power for learning complex discriminations, they are insufficiently constrained to serve yet as testable, psychological models of simple learning. They require large numbers of assumptions regarding their structure (e.g., the basic representation of stimuli and responses, the number and connectivity of hidden units, etc.), their learning rule, and their method for calculating response probabilities.

For such reasons, we preferred initially to explore the viability of a simple extension of the elementary model, one which postulates that conjunctions of elementary stimulus features can serve as "higher-order" features of a stimulus pattern. Thus, given the presentation of an experimental pattern consisting of elementary features BCD, we will assume that this is reflected in activation of input nodes corresponding to the single elements B, C, and D, and the pair-wise conjuncts BC, BD, and CD. As another illustration, Figure 1B shows a network that is learning to classify geometric patterns varying in size, color, and shape: presentation of a "small white square" causes activation of the input nodes blackened in the figure for single and pair-wise cues.

We will assume that such "configural" features obey the same activation and learning rules as do the single features, viz., Eq.1. The inclusion of such configural features as "inputs" now enables the one-layer model to learn the XOR problem as well as other non-linearly separable discriminations.

To include configural cues is hardly a novel move for theories of discrimination learning. Learning theories have traditionally recognized configural learning (Pavlov, 1927; Woodbury, 1943). Wagner and Rescorla (1972, p. 306) explicitly expanded their theory of conditioning to include configural cues; and in a series of studies, Rescorla (1972, 1973) found that configural cues have many of the same associative properties as single cues. In particular, Rescorla found that configural cues can acquire both excitatory and inhibitory associations, that their associative strengths summate with those of single cues to determine behavior, that configural cues can modify the effectiveness of a given reinforcing event, and that their strength can be attenuated by making them irrelevant to the discrimination being trained. Thus, our introduction of configural cues into the one-layer network is supported by a considerable history.

We will impose one arbitrary limitation upon the configural cue model tested in this paper, namely, that only *pair-wise* conjunctions of elementary features will be allowed. An alternative, proposed by Reitman & Bower (1973), Hayes-Roth & Hayes-Roth (1977), and Gluck & Bower (1988a), is to introduce as higher-order features the entire power-set of all subsets of each n-dimensional stimulus presented in the experiment. This power-set model rapidly becomes unwieldy, so we have restricted our explorations to the pair-wise conjunction version of it.

In the following, the predictions of the configural cue model are compared to the data from three representative, critical experiments from the literature on human classification learning. The fit of the configural cue model to the observed data will be compared to the fit of two other models: (1) the single-cue-only model, and (2) an alternate extension of the network model recently proposed by Estes (in press). Estes suggested using as inputs only the single cues and the full patterns, so that presentation of BCD would activate input nodes B, C, D, and (BCD). We will call this the "feature-pattern" model.

LINEAR SEPARABILITY IN CLASSIFICATION LEARNING

We provide three illustrations extending the configural-cue model to account for several aspects of complex human category learning. First, the inability of the simple network model to solve non-linearly-separable classifications has historically been a major reason for introducing configural cues into one's theory. Therefore, we wished to apply the configural-cue model to such a non-linear learning task. An experiment by Medin & Schwanenflugel (1981) provides relevant data. Figure 2 schematizes the 6 stimulus patterns that two groups of college students learned to classify as A's or B's. The two values of the four stimulus dimensions are denoted 1 and 0. To recognize the linear separability of the left-hand classification, note that the number of 1's in Dimensions 1, 3, and 4 equal 2 for the A-stimuli, but is less than 2 for any B stimulus; however, no such linear combination of feature valves will separate the two classes of patterns in the right-hand classification. Note too that the two classifications are perfectly balanced in terms of the average number of shared features among patterns *within* each class (average of 1.33 shared features) and shared features of patterns *across* different classes (average of 1.78). Medin and Schwanenflugel found that their subjects learned this nonlinearly-separable problem more easily than their linearly-separable problem (see Figure 3A). Their model predicted this because it calculates the similarity of two patterns in a nonlinear fashion, so that confusions of a test pattern with memories of two A-patterns with which it shares 1 and 3 features will be much greater than its confusions with two B-patterns with which it shares 2 features each.

We attempted to simulate the Medin & Schwanenflugel results with the network model using three different representations of the stimuli: the single-cue (baseline) model, the pair-wise configural-cue model, and the feature-pattern model. In all the simulations, we used a learning rate of $\beta = 0.01$, one output node, and reinforced the network with $\lambda = +1$ for category A exemplars, and $\lambda = -1$ for category B exemplars. Each network had two cue nodes for each dimension -- one node represented the presence of a cue, the other its complement. The configural-cue network had additional nodes for all pair-wise combinations of feature values.

	Linearly Separable Task		*Non-linearly Separable Task*	
	Exemplar	Dimension 1 2 3 4	Exemplar	Dimension 1 2 3 4
Category A	A1	0 1 1 1	A1	1 1 0 0
	A2	1 1 1 0	A2	0 0 1 1
	A3	1 0 0 1	A3	1 1 1 1
Category B	B1	1 0 0 0	B1	0 0 0 0
	B2	0 0 0 1	B2	0 1 0 1
	B3	0 1 1 0	B3	1 0 1 0

Figure 2. Classification tasks in Medin & Schwanenflugel (1981), Experiment #3.

Figure 3B shows the average mean squared error for each training epoch for the single-cue model. The average MSE for the single-cue model trained on the non-linearly-separable task never reaches zero, meaning that this discrimination is not perfectly learnable by the single-cue model. The pair-wise configural-cue model does, however, predict the correct ordering of the results: it learns the non-linear task faster than the linear one (Figure 3C). Thus, the addition of feature pairs to the input nodes improved the network performance. These theoretical results suggest that the configural-cue model, like Medin & Schaffer's context model, is more sensitive to exemplar similarity (as computed by a non-linear multiplicative similarity rule) than to the linear separability of the patterns in the different categories. As noted by Nosofsky (1984), the multiplicative similarity rule is equivalent to assuming stimulus generalization is an exponential decay function of psychological distance, the latter indexed by the number of featural mismatches. This exponential relationship between similarity and psychological distance has received substantial independent empirical and theoretical support (Shepard, 1957, 1987). That the configural-cue model embodies the same similarity-distance relationship can be seen by computing how the number of overlapping active nodes (similarity) changes as a function of the number of overlapping component cues (distance). If two triplet patterns share one feature (ABC, XYC), they will have only one active node in common and five nodes nonoverlapping; if they share two features (ABC, XBC), they will have three active nodes in common (two component cues and one configural-cue node) and three nonoverlapping nodes; if they share three features in common, they will have six active nodes in common (three component cues and three configural-cue nodes). This implies that the configural-cue network, like the context model, will judge a test pattern to be more similar to a category of two exemplars with which it shares 1 and 3 features (for an average of 3.5 nodes in common), than an alternate category of two exemplars with which it shares 2 features each (for an average of 3 nodes in common).

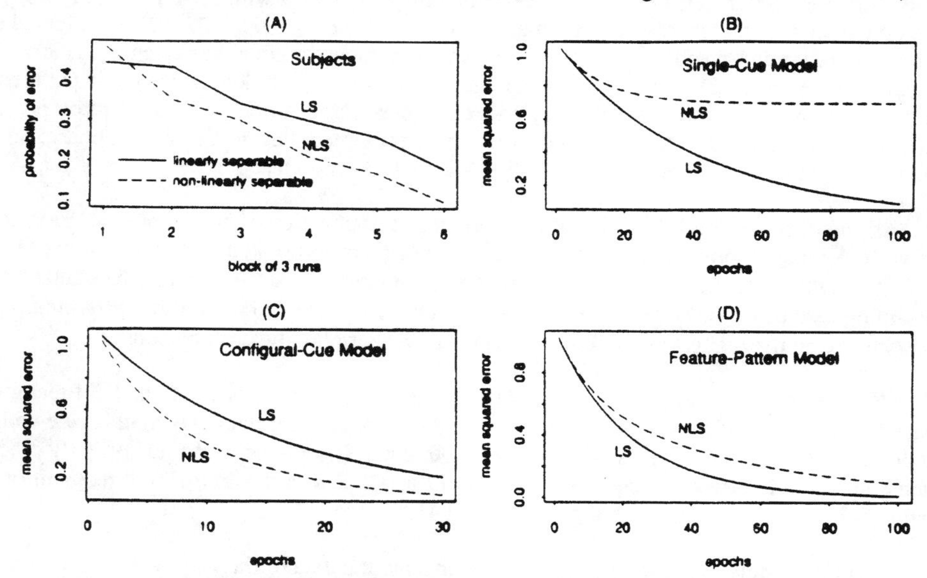

Figure 3. Predicted difficulty of non-linearly versus linearly separable classification tasks in Medin & Schwanenflugel (1981), Experiment #3. LS: linearly separable classification task. NLS: non-linearly separable task. The mean squared error (MSE) represents the absolute difference (squared) between the actual and predicted category classifications averaged over all presentation exemplars. Task difficulty is predicted by the rate at which the model reduces the MSE to zero. (A). The data on percentage errors, showing that the LS problem is more difficult (slower to learn); adapted from Medin & Schwanenflugel (1981). (B). The incorrect predictions of the one-cue network model showing that only the LS task is learnable. (C) The closer predictions of the "pair-wise" configural-cue model showing that the LS category is more difficult (slower to learn). (D). The less accurate predictions of the "feature-pattern" model.

Interestingly, the feature-pattern model which uses only single cue plus full patterns (see Fig. 3D) mispredicts the ordering of the data. Although the addition of nodes representing entire patterns allows the model to learn complex, non-linear discriminations, it expects the non-linearly separable task to be learned more slowly than the linearly-separable one--contrary to fact.

RECOGNITION MEMORY VERSUS CLASSIFICATION

In testing models of category learning, we may examine how the classification of a given test pattern depends on the subjects' remembering specific exemplars that were shown during training. Such "recognition memory" can be tested by asking subjects to judge whether each test pattern is an "old" training instance, or a "new" instance not experienced before. Prototype theories, which assume that people extract only a mean centroid from the training exemplars, expect a strong correlation between the classification and "old" judgments for test exemplars, since both decisions could presumably only be based on the distance of the exemplar from the prototype.

An experiment by Hayes-Roth and Hayes-Roth (1977) examined this issue; they found a surprisingly low correlation between subjects' classifications and their Old (vs. New) judgments over a variety of test patterns. It was of interest to see whether the configural-cue model could duplicate this surprising lack of correlation between classification and recognition memory.

In the Hayes-Roth & Hayes-Roth task, subjects learned to classify into three categories (Club 1, Club 2, or Neither) descriptions of people who varied along three dimensions with four values per dimension (labeled 1-4). The presence of a majority of 1's with no 4's *(e.g., 112,131)* signified membership in club 1, whereas a majority of 2's with no 4's *(e.g., 212, 221)* indicated club 2. An equal number of 1's and 2's with no 4's indicated membership in either category. If any 4's were present, the person belonged to neither category. The 3's were irrelevant. Specific patterns ("persons") were presented with widely varying frequencies. For example, the most prototypical category members *(e.g., 111, 222, 333, 444)* were never presented during the training phase; however, they were shown on subsequent recognition and classification tests.

As noted, Hayes-Roth & Hayes-Roth found that classification of an exemplar correlated poorly with its recognition. For instance, subjects gave the non-presented category prototypes *111* and *222*, the highest classification ratings; in contrast, these prototypes were rarely recognized as "old" training instances. Also, certain exemplars which were presented often during training *(e.g., 112, 121)* received the highest recognition ratings, but weaker classification responses.

Nosofsky (1988) suggested that an exemplar model could predict these results if recognition was based on the summed similarity of that pattern to *all* stored exemplars. Using this rule within his model, Nosofsky fit the Hayes-Roth & Hayes-Roth data. His amended model correctly predicted both the high classification of category prototypes *111* and *222*, along with the high recognition of frequently-presented exemplars (see Figures 4A and 4B).

We fit the single-cue and configural-cue models to the data of the Hayes-Roth and Hayes-Roth experiment. As before, the exemplars were presented in a random order to the network (β = 0.01) for one complete pass through all the exemplars. The network had four input nodes (cue values) for each of the three dimensions (12 total) connected to three output nodes (Club 1, 2 or Neither). The probability of assigning a test pattern to Club 1 vs Club 2 was set equal to the strength of the one output activation divided by the summed strength of the output activations for both clubs (with negative activation values being converted to 0). In contrast, the recognition-memory rating of a test pattern was predicted from the summed activation of all three output nodes (including the Neither node) to that pattern, which is a rule similar to Nosofsky's (1988). Figure 4A illustrates the network model's recognition and classification responses to test patterns (averaged over 10000 simulations),

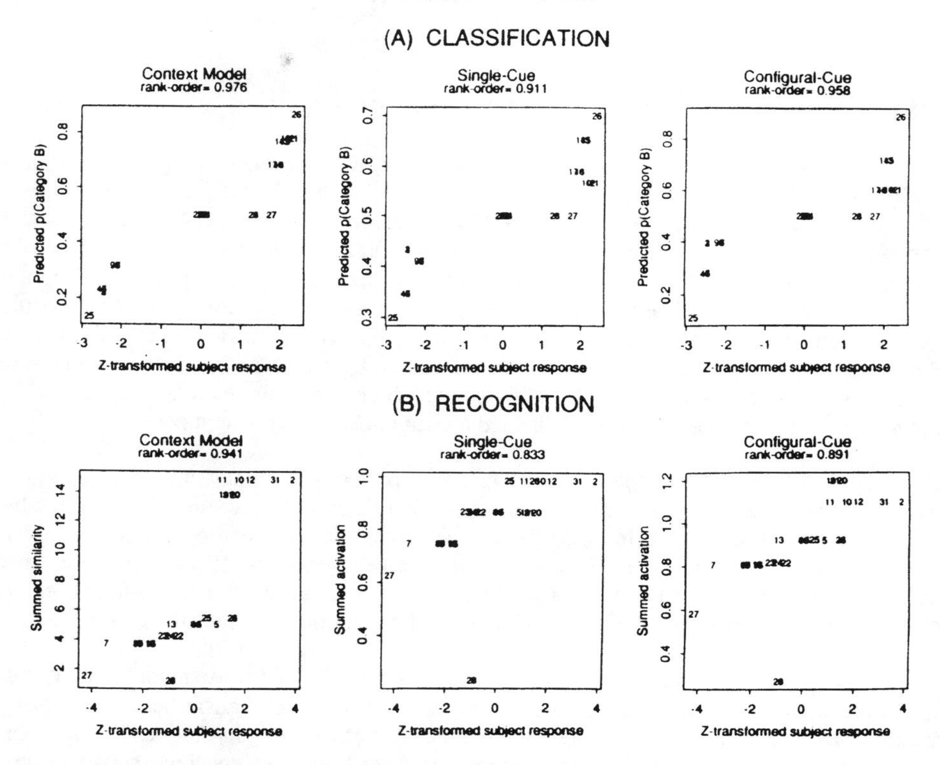

Figure 4. Predicted responses of subjects in the Hayes-Roth & Hayes-Roth (1977) learning task. Predictions of various models are plotted against subject's performance (z-scores) for both the classification (4A) and the recognition (4B) phases of the experiment. The Spearman rank-order correlation between a model's predictions and the subjects' performance is reported. Each number on each plot represents the z-score for classification (4A) or for recognition (4B) for one of the 28 test patterns. (A) Classification ratings for Nosofsky's context model, the single-cue coding model, and the configural-cue network model. (B) Recognition ratings for the three models.

plotted against the observed ratings (transformed z-scores) by subjects. While the single-cue, baseline model correctly predicted subject's classificatory responses (a rank order coefficient of 0.91), it predicted recognition memory less successfully (rank order coefficient of 0.83).

In contrast, the configural cue model was more successful overall. Figure 4 shows its predictions for these data. Predictions of classificatory responses are accurate (rank order correlation = 0.96); importantly, the accuracy of recognition predictions improves over that of the single-cue model (rank order correlation = 0.89). Thus, the configural-cue model accounts for both classification and recognition memory with only a single parameter, viz., the learning rate, β.

Despite this overall success, the configural cue model evidences shortcomings similar to Nosofsky's. Both models, for example, predict a much lower recognition of the "Neither" prototype *444* than was actually obtained. Similarly, both models predict chance classification of the "Neither" (*444*) and the "Unknown" (*333*) prototypes, whereas subjects were biased towards one particular category. Examination of the data reveals no reason for these discrepancies.

Finally, we compared the predictions of Estes' feature-pattern encoding model to the results of the configural-cue network for the Hayes-Roth & Hayes-Roth data. The feature-pattern model's predictions for both sets of data were very similar to those for the pair-wise configural cue model, and yielded no discriminating comparisons.

CORRELATED ATTRIBUTES AND CATEGORY LEARNING

An obvious limitation of the single-cue model is that it is insensitive to the predictive validity of pairs of features. The weights attached to each single cue reflect the associations between it and the several categories, but these cannot capture correlations between cue-combinations and the categories. People, on the other hand, are sensitive to predictive combinations of features. Medin, Altom, Edelson, & Freko (1982) tested subject's use of combinations of symptoms in a simulated medical classification task. Their Experiment #3 put people's classification of patterns according to co-occurring features into opposition to their tendency to classify patterns according to the number of singly representative cues. Subjects first learned to classify patterns of symptoms into a single disease category. Each pattern consisted of five binary dimensions; these are illustrated in Figure 5A where a '1' or a '0' on each dimension indicated a symptom value or its complement.

The fourth and fifth symptom dimensions were perfectly correlated with each other. Also, for any dimension, the total number of '1's across presented patterns exceeded the total number of '0's. Thus, the presence of a '1' in a particular dimension indicated its more typical or characteristic value. The goals of the study were (1) to assess whether people would use the correlation between symptom-dimensions four and five to classify instances, and (2) to see how this information would be combined with information about the typicality of the individual features to determine choice.

Subjects studied the individual cases shown in Figure 5A and subsequently received transfer test pairs containing both new and old patterns (Figure 5B). For each transfer test pair, subjects had to decide which exemplar was more likely to be a member of the category defined by the collection of training instances in Figure 5A . On the critical transfer tests, subjects chose between some exemplar preserving the relationship between the fourth and fifth dimensions versus another exemplar that violated this correlation but had more characteristic features (more '1's).

Because the single-cue model, like all independent cue models, considers each feature separately, it predicts that subjects will select the transfer pattern containing more characteristic attributes as the more likely member of the category. However, the data showed that people preferred the pattern containing the correlated features as more likely to be a member of the category. Thus, even though a test pattern had fewer diagnostic features present, subjects were more likely to say it was a member of the category when the fourth and fifth symptoms preserved the correlation presented during training

(A)

Exemplar	Dimension 1 2 3	4 5
a	0 1 0	**1 1**
b	1 1 0	**1 1**
c	0 0 1	**1 1**
d	1 0 1	**1 1**
e	1 1 1	**1 1**
f	1 1 1	**1 1**
g	1 0 0	**0 0**
h	0 1 1	**0 0**
i	1 1 1	**0 0**

(B)

Exemplar A preserved correlation	network activation		Exemplar B more '1's	network activation
1 1 1 **0 0**	***1.017***	vs.	**1 1 1** 0 1	0.923
0 0 1 **1 1**	***0.992***	vs.	**1 1 1** 0 1	0.923
0 1 0 **1 1**	***0.991***	vs.	**1 1 1** 1 0	0.923
0 0 1 **0 0**	***0.914***	vs.	**0 0 1** 0 1	0.860
1 0 0 **0 0**	***0.981***	vs.	**1 0 0** 1 0	0.887
average	***0.919***		average	0.903

Figure 5. Schematic design of Medin, Altom, Edelson, & Freko (1982), Experiment #3. (A) Training exemplars. A '1' on a particular dimension indicates its more common, or characteristic, value. Dimensions 4 and 5 are perfectly correlated with each other and with the correct category. (B) Transfer choice test pairs. After training, subjects were presented with each choice test pair and asked to choose the exemplar most likely to be a member of the collection described by (A). The choice tests compared exemplars preserving the correlation between dimensions 4 and 5, to those that violated the correlation, but contained more characteristic values (more '1's). In all choice tests the configural model correctly predicts that people will prefer the exemplar preserving the correlation between dimensions 4 and 5 as a more likely member of the category.

Our simulation of this experiment with the configural cue model used all 10 single-cue and all 32 cue pairs as input nodes linked to one output node representing category membership. Since all presented exemplars were members of the category, all presentations were consistently reinforced ($\lambda = +1$). Figure 5B shows that the output activation of the configural-cue model is greater for the exemplar that preserves the correlation between dimensions four and five compared to the activation produced by the exemplar with more characteristic attributes. Because the network's output activation translates into choice probability, the simulation will correctly predict that subjects will prefer those patterns that preserve the correlation in the transfer choice tests. The model expects this result because feature-conjuncts (4 & 5) are perfect predictors of category membership whereas single cues are imperfect predictors; in such cases, the competitive nature of the LMS learning rule implies that a more valid predictive feature (or conjunct) will dominate and beat down the learning of less valid features. This phenomenon, called "overshadowing", is familiar in conditioning studies.

The ability of the configural cue model to predict this configural-cue preference found by Medin et al. is not completely trivial, because the predictions depend on the balance of associative strength to the conjunct cues versus the more characteristic, single cues. Several plausible models do not calculate the balance of these factors appropriately. For instance, we applied to these data Estes' feature-pattern model which has nodes representing the presence of entire patterns as well as single features. Although this is one way to add configural pattern information into the learning process, the outcome was unsuccessful in this case: in four of the five transfer tests, the feature-pattern model expected subjects to prefer that stimulus with the greater number of characteristic features (1's) to the one preserving the correlation of features 4 and 5.

DISCUSSION

We have also applied the configural-cue model to explain and predict the priority of basic levels in category hierarchies, and this is reported elsewhere (Corter, Gluck, & Bower, 1989). The configural-cue model predicts that the basic-level categories of a hierarchy of categories are learned more quickly than other levels, and examples are recognized faster at this level. These results are consistent with much empirical data regarding both natural and artificially-learned categories (Jolicouer, Gluck, & Kosslyn, 1984; Corter, Gluck & Bower, 1988). In Gluck & Bower (1988a), we also applied the configural-cue model to a classic experiment by Shepard, Hovland, & Jenkins (1961) who studied the difficulty subjects had in learning six classifications varying in complexity. The model predicted the same order of difficulty of learning the classification rules as was revealed in the data, except for one slight misordering.

By expanding the representation of stimuli to include pair-wise configurations of features, the network model appears to account for a wider range of learning results from both the animal and human learning literatures. Some of this success can be traced to its using a similarity metric like that of Medin & Shaffer, viz., an implicit exponential decay relationship between stimulus similarity and psychological distance (number of feature mismatches). The configural-cue model has several obvious limitations, including the exponential growth of input nodes with increasing pattern size. Nevertheless, we believe that this model is interesting for four reasons. First, it is simple, understandable, and accounts for a surprisingly wide range of empirical phenomena. Second, it is theoretically parsimonious and uses assumptions for which independent evidence already exists. Third, its successes are instructive in identifying empirical phenomena which can be explained as emergent from the same elementary, associative processes found in lower species. Fourth, explanations of the failures of this model can suggest more sophisticated versions of the network model. Such failures may also indicate performances arising from an entirely different class of learning mechanisms, i.e., the rule-based or symbolic processes which have been well studied by cognitive psychologists.

REFERENCES

Corter, J. E., Gluck, M. A., & Bower, G. H. (1988). Basic levels in hierarchically structured categories Montreal, Canada. In *Proceedings of the Tenth Annual Conference of the Cognitive Science Society, Montreal, Canada.*. Hillsdale, NJ: Lawrence Earlbam Associates.

Corter, J. H., Gluck, M. A., & Bower, G. H. (1989). *Basic levels in hierarchical category structures: An adaptive network interpretation.* Unpublished Manuscript, Stanford University, Stanford, CA 94305..

Estes, W. K., Campbell, J. A., Hatsopoulos, N., & Hurwitz, J. B. (in press). Base-rate effects in category learning: A comparison of parallel network and memory storage-retrieval models. *Journal of Experimental Psychology: Learning, Memory, & Cognition,* .

Gluck, M. A., & Bower, G. H. (1986). Conditioning and categorization: Some common effects of informational variables in animal and human learning. In *Proceedings of the Eighth Annual Conference of the Cognitive Science Society.*. Amherst, Mass..

Gluck, M. A., & Bower, G. H. (1988a). Evaluating an adaptive network model of human learning. *Journal of Memory and Language, 27,* 166-195.

Gluck, M. A., & Bower, G. H. (1988b). From conditioning to category learning: An adaptive network model. *Journal of Experimental Psychology: General, 117*(3), 225-244.

Gluck, M. A., Corter, J. H., Bower, G. H., & Kylberg, R. L. (1988). *Learning of basic levels in hierarchically structured categories.*. Presented at the Annual Conference of the Psychonomic Society, Chicago, IL.

Hayes-Roth, B., & Hayes-Roth, F. (1977). Concept learning and the recognition and classification of exemplars. *Journal of Verbal Learning and Verbal Behavior, 16,* 321-338.

Jolicoeur, P., Gluck, M., & Kosslyn, S. (1984). Pictures and names: Making the connection. *Cognitive Psychology, 16,* 243-275.

MacMillan, J. (1987). *The role of frequency memory in category judgments.* Unpublished doctoral dissertation, Harvard University, Cambridge, MA.

Medin, D. L., Altom, M. W., Edelson, S. M., & Freko, D. (1982). Correlated symptoms and simulated medical classification. *Journal of Experimental Psychology: Learning, Memory, & Cognition, 8,* 37-50.

Medin, D. L., & Schaffer, M. M. (1978). Context theory of classification learning. *Psychological Review, 85,* 207-238.

Medin, D. L., & Schwanenflugel, P. J. (1981). Linear seperability in classification learning. *Journal of Experimental Psychology: Human Learning and Memory, 7,* 355-368.

Nosofsky, R. (1988). Similarity, frequency, and category representation. *Journal of Experimental Psychology: Learning, Memory, and Cognition, 14,* 54-65.

Nosofsky, R. M. (1984). Choice, similarity, and the context theory of classification. *Journal of Experimental Psychology: Learning, Memory and Cognition, 10,* 104-114.

Parker, D. (1986). A comparison of algorithms for neuron-like cells. In *Proceedings of the Neural Networks for Computing Conference.* Snowbird, Utah..

Pavlov, I. (1927). *Conditioned Reflexes.* London: Oxford University Press.

Reitman, J. S., & Bower, G. H. (1973). Storage and later recognition of exemplars of concepts. *Cognitive Psychology, 4,* 194-206.

Rescorla, R. A. (1972). "Configural" conditioning in discrete-trial bar pressing. *Journal of Comparative and Physiological Psychology, 79*(2), 307-317.

Rescorla, R. A. (1973). Evidence for "unique stimulus" account of configural conditioning. *Journal of Comparative and Physiological Psychology, 85*(2), 331-338.

Rescorla, R. A., & Wagner, A. R. (1972). A theory of Pavlovian conditioning: Variations in the effectiveness of reinforcement and non-reinforcement. In A. H. Black, & W. F. Prokasy (Eds.), *Classical conditioning II: Current research and theory.* New York: Appleton-Century-Crofts.

Rumelhart, D. E., Hinton, G. E., & Williams, R. J. (1986). Learning internal representations by error propogation. In D. Rumelhart, & J. McClelland (Eds.), *Parallel distributed processing: Explorations in the microstructure of cognition (Vol. 1: Foundations).* Cambridge, M.A.: MIT Press.

Shepard, R. (1987). Towards a universal law of generalization for psychological science. *Science, 237,* 1317-1323.

Shepard, R. N. (1957). Stimulus and response generalization: A stochastic model relating generalization to distance in psychological space. *Psychometrika, 22,* 325-345.

Shepard, R. N., Hovland, C. I., & Jenkins, H. M. (1961). Learning and memorization of classifications. *Psychological Monographs, 75,* 1-42.

Wagner, A. R., & Rescorla, R. A. (1972). Inhibition in Pavlovian conditioning: Applications of a theory. In R. A. Boakes, & S. Halliday (Eds.), *Inhibition and learning* (pp. 301-36). New York: Academic Press.

Widrow, B., & Hoff, M. E. (1960). Adaptive switching circuits. *Institute of Radio Engineers, Western Electronic Show and Convention, Convention Record, 4,* 96-194.

Woodbury, C. B. (1943). The learning of stimulus patterns by dogs. *Journal of Comparative Psychology, 35,* 29-49.

INDUCTION OF CONTINUOUS STIMULUS-RESPONSE RELATIONS

Kyunghee Koh   David E. Meyer

University of Michigan

ABSTRACT

The present research investigates the mental processes involved in inducing continuous stimulus-response relations. A simple perceptual-motor learning task was used in which subjects learned to produce a continuous variable (response duration) accurately for values chosen from another continuous dimension (stimulus length). Subjects were trained on several "practice" pairs, for which they received feedback about the correct responses. Trials involving practice pairs were intermixed with trials involving "transfer" pairs, for which no feedback was given. The correct responses and stimuli were related by simple mathematical functions: a power (Experiment 1); a logarithmic (Experiment 2); and a linear function with a positive intercept (Experiment 3). Experiment 1 demonstrated that people can learn a power function rapidly and use it to perform as well for transfer pairs as for practice pairs. Experiments 2 and 3 revealed a systematic pattern of bias during early learning, consistent with the hypothesis that people have a predisposition toward inducing a power function. However, the biases decreased in magnitude with practice.

We propose an account for induction of continuous stimulus-response relations called the "adaptive-regression" model. According to it, people are initially biased to induce a power function, but the bias is gradually weakened through experience, so that other stimulus-response relations can be learned with sufficient practice. The present results support the adaptive-regression model.

INTRODUCTION

A major objective in the study of learning is to describe inductive generalization (Holland, Holyoak, Nisbett, & Thagard, 1986). As part of achieving this objective, one must determine how associations between continuous stimulus and response variables that have an indefinitely large set of values are learned. Such learning underlies the development of many physical skills, including reaching, walking, and driving a car, which require accurate mappings of continuous stimulus variables (e.g., distance, size, and velocity) onto continuous response variables (e.g., force and duration). Consequently, interesting questions arise when the acquisition of these skills is viewed as a problem of inducing continuous stimulus-response relations on the basis of specific experiences. For example, how do people use prior experience with specific stimuli and associated responses to select responses to novel stimuli? Are certain types of stimulus-response relations more natural and learnable than others? We report results from three experiments designed to address these and other related questions in the domain of perceptual-motor learning.

EXPERIMENT 1

Overview

Experiment 1 was conducted over 5 sessions. During each session, there was a sequence of 60 trial blocks, in which learning and test trials were interspersed. On the learning trials, we presented subjects with practice stimuli chosen from a continuous stimulus dimension (length). For each practice stimulus, the subjects had to learn to produce a particular response chosen from another continuous response dimension (duration). Their performance was reinforced by giving feedback after each learning trial. The stimuli and associated correct responses were selected so that they were related by an underlying quantitative relation, namely, a power function. Our aim was to study whether subjects would discover and use this rule in making their responses to other transfer stimuli.

To achieve this aim, test trials were intermixed with learning trials. During test trials, the subjects had to produce responses for transfer stimuli whose magnitudes differed from those of the practice stimuli. No feedback about response accuracy was provided for the transfer stimuli. However, it was possible, in principle, for the subjects to produce appropriate responses to the transfer stimuli as well as the practice stimuli, if they successfully induced the underlying relation between the practice stimuli and responses.

Method

Design. Six University of Michigan students participated as subjects. The power function that they had to learn was specified by 12 stimulus-response pairs, as shown in Table 1. These pairs were generated with the equation $D = 257.24\ L^{.33}$, where L and D denote stimulus length (in mm) and response duration (in msec), respectively. Four of the 12 stimulus-response pairs (Pairs 5 through 8) served as transfer pairs, and the remaining 8 served as practice pairs. Each stimulus was presented once per block. The order of stimuli within each block was randomized.

Procedure. At the beginning of each trial, a display containing two vertical bars appeared on a display screen. The two bars were centered on the screen, and were separated by a variable stimulus length. The subjects' task was to produce a response duration that correctly matched the stimulus length, as specified by the underlying stimulus-response relation (i.e., power function). Subjects initiated the response duration by pressing a key and terminated the duration by pressing the same key a second time.

Table 1. The Stimulus-Response Pairs in Experiment 1

Pair	1	2	3	4	5	6	7	8	9	10	11	12
Stimulus Length (mm)	2.5	4.5	6.4	8.0	13.1	18.3	23.4	32.6	41.9	52.4	62.7	75.0
Response Duration (msec)	349	422	475	512	601	671	728	812	882	950	1008	1069

After each practice stimulus-response pair, subjects received feedback regarding the correct response duration for the stimulus length. This was done by presenting two brief beeps, whose onsets were temporally separated by an amount of time that matched the stimulus length, as specified by the stimulus-response relation to be learned. After the beeps, subjects received feedback regarding whether the response duration was longer or shorter than the correct target duration. In addition, a score for the response was shown, indicating how close subject's response duration had come to the correct duration. No feedback was given for transfer stimulus-response pairs.

Rationale

As summarized by the literature on category learning and concept formation, cognitive theories of induction have been proposed in terms of two alternative accounts: *exemplar models* and *abstraction models* (Smith & Medin, 1981). Exemplar models assume that natural and artificial categories (e.g., ANIMALS, VEHICLES, FURNITURE, etc.) are learned by storing specific instances of the categories, and that the production of a categorical response to a new stimulus is based on the similarity between the new stimulus and previously experienced instances. In contrast, abstraction models assume that learning a category entails abstracting a prototype or central tendency of the category, and responses to new stimuli are produced on the basis of distances between these stimuli and the prototype.

Here we are concerned about extending these alternative types of models to characterize the learning of continuous stimulus-response relations. For example, in responding to a transfer stimulus, one possibility is that subjects might produce the response duration associated with whichever practice stimulus best matches the transfer stimulus. This would involve an exemplar-based process, and it could lead to increasingly good performance as the subjects get more and more experience at making responses to the practice stimuli. However, the accuracy of responses to the transfer stimuli would still be less than the accuracy of responses to the practice stimuli, even after many learning trials, because the responses to the practice stimuli are not most appropriate for the transfer stimuli.

Another possibility is that subjects may instead use an abstraction-based process instead; they may actually induce the underlying mathematical function that relates the selected stimulus-response pairs. If so, we would expect equally good performance for the transfer and practice stimuli, because the induced function should work just as well regardless of stimulus type. By examining subjects' performance for each stimulus type, we may therefore distinguish between different models of the learning process.

Results and Discussion

Figure 1 presents log response durations averaged across subjects as a function of log stimulus length for Sessions 1 and 5, respectively. The error bars indicate ±1 standard deviation of individual responses pooled across subjects. The dashed lines represent the power function to be learned. We have plotted it here in terms of log-log coordinates because this makes the chosen function appear as a straight line.

Subjects' responses were close to the required responses even in the first session, indicating that the power function was learned quite rapidly. Furthermore, performance for transfer stimulus-response pairs (closed circles) was as good as that for practice pairs (open circles). The difference between mean biases for the practice and transfer pairs was not significant [$F(1,55) = 1.30$; $p > .05$]. Nor was the difference between standard deviations of responses for the practice and transfer pairs significant [$F(1,55) = .05$].

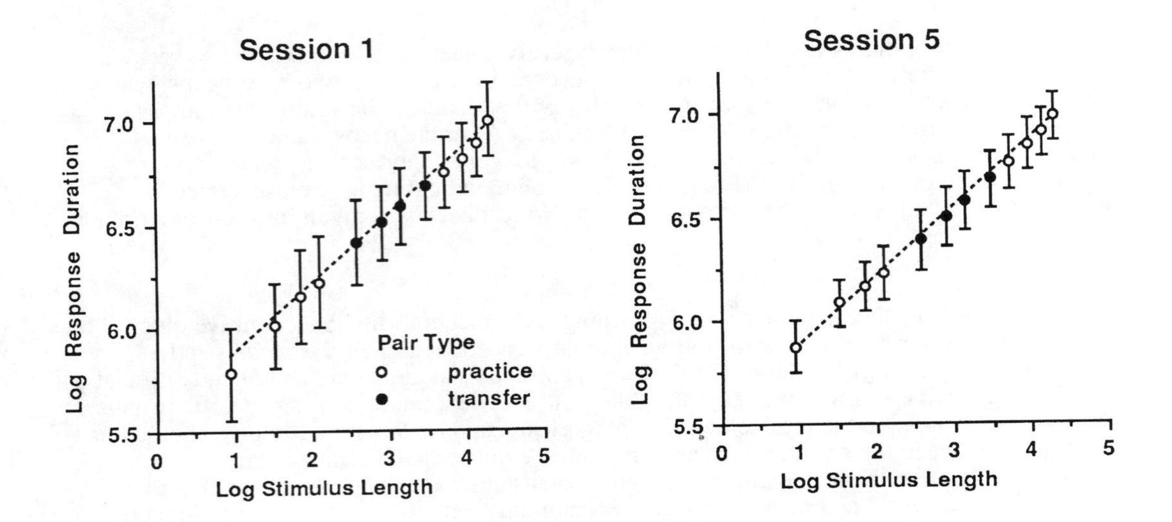

Figure 1. Mean response duration (in $\log_e$ msec) averaged across subjects as a function of stimulus length (in $\log_e$ mm) for the first and last sessions in Experiment 1. The dashed line represents the power function to be learned. The error bars indicate ±1 standard deviation of individual responses pooled across subjects.

Given these results, we have doubts about whether a simple exemplar-based process is the primary mechanism that people use to induce continuous stimulus-response relations. Instead, it seems more likely that such relations are induced through an abstraction-based process as described more fully later (see General Discussion).

EXPERIMENT 2

In subsequent experiments, we have examined whether subjects can accurately induce continuous relations other than the power function used in Experiment 1. Our objective here was to determine how general the abstraction process is. Depending on the nature of the abstraction process, subjects may or may not be able to learn a variety of possible functions.

Method

The basic design and procedure of Experiment 2 were the same as before. However, the underlying relation between the stimulus and response dimensions involved a logarithmic rather than power function. The chosen function was $D = 75 + 223.5 \log_e L$, where D and L denote response duration (in msec) and stimulus length (in mm), respectively. The stimuli were the same as those used in Experiment 1; the range of responses was approximately equal to that of Experiment 1.

Results and Discussion

Log response durations averaged across subjects are plotted in Figure 2 against log stimulus length for Sessions 1 and 5. The dashed curve represents the logarithmic relation to be learned.

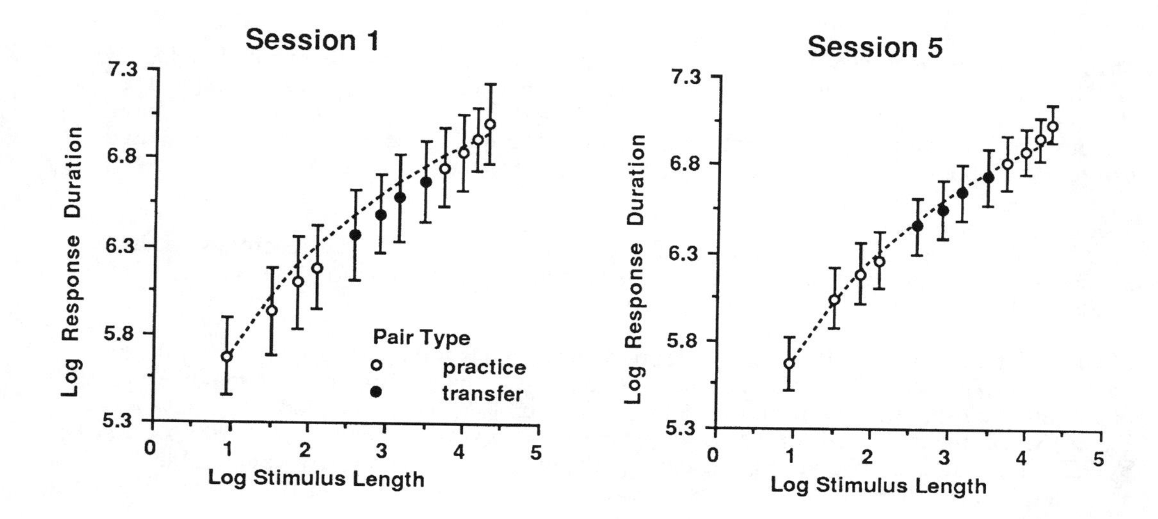

Figure 2. Mean response duration (in $\log_e$ msec) averaged across subjects as a function of stimulus length (in $\log_e$ mm) for the first and last sessions in Experiment 2. The dashed curve represents the logarithmic relation to be learned.

As in Experiment 1, performance for transfer stimulus-response pairs was about as good as that for practice pairs, both in terms of mean bias [$F(1,55) = 3.15$; $p > .05$] and variability [$F(1,55) < 1$]. This provides further evidence of an abstraction-based process. However, unlike in Experiment 1, substantial response biases occurred in Session 1; the observed response durations for the middle stimuli were shorter than required, whereas the observed responses for the short and long stimuli were longer than required. This pattern might result if subjects attempted to fit a power function (which appears linear in log-log coordinates) to the experienced stimulus-response pairs. The magnitude of these biases decreased over sessions [$F(4,20) = 3.03$; $p < .05$], although there still were some residual biases in Session 5.

Overall, it appears that the subjects had an initial bias toward inducing a power stimulus-response relation, but gradually overcame the bias and learned the required logarithmic relation to a relatively close approximation.

EXPERIMENT 3

Experiment 3 was performed to replicate and extend the results of our previous experiments. Here the required stimulus-response relation involved a linear function with a positive intercept. When plotted in log-log coordinates, this function appears curved upward in a mirror image of the logarithmic function used in Experiment 2, which is curved downward. If people indeed have a bias toward inducing power functions, we should observe a systematic pattern of initial bias similar to that found in Experiment 2. Moreover, if people can overcome the bias to learn functional relations other than power ones, then with sufficient practice, they should produce responses according to the present linear function.

Method

The design and procedure of Experiment 3 were identical to those of Experiments 1 and 2, except that the stimuli and responses were related by a linear function with a positive intercept. The stimulus-response relation to be learned here was D = 453.5 + 10.9 L, where D and L denote response duration and stimulus length, respectively. The stimuli were the same as those used before; the responses were approximately equal in range to the previous ones.

Results and Discussion

Figure 3 presents log stimulus length versus log response duration averaged across subjects for Sessions 1 and 5. The dashed curve represents the required linear relation. The results were similar to those of Experiment 2 in all major respects.

Most important, a systematic pattern of response biases, constituting a mirror image of the one obtained in Experiment 2, occurred during Session 1. This pattern supports the hypothesis that people are predisposed toward inducing power functions to relate stimuli and responses. As in Experiment 2, the magnitude of the biases decreased over sessions [$F(4,20) = 11.88$; $p < .0001$]; by Session 5, subjects' responses came close to the required responses. Apparently, the abstraction process used by our subjects is flexible enough to learn various types of relations, even though it is initially biased toward power functions.

GENERAL DISCUSSION

In summary, we have obtained several pieces of evidence suggesting a relatively sophisticated abstraction process for inducing continuous stimulus-response relations. Performance on transfer pairs was as good as performance on practice pairs in all three experiments. Also, subjects' responses revealed certain systematic biases and changes over time that suggest further details about how the abstraction process works.

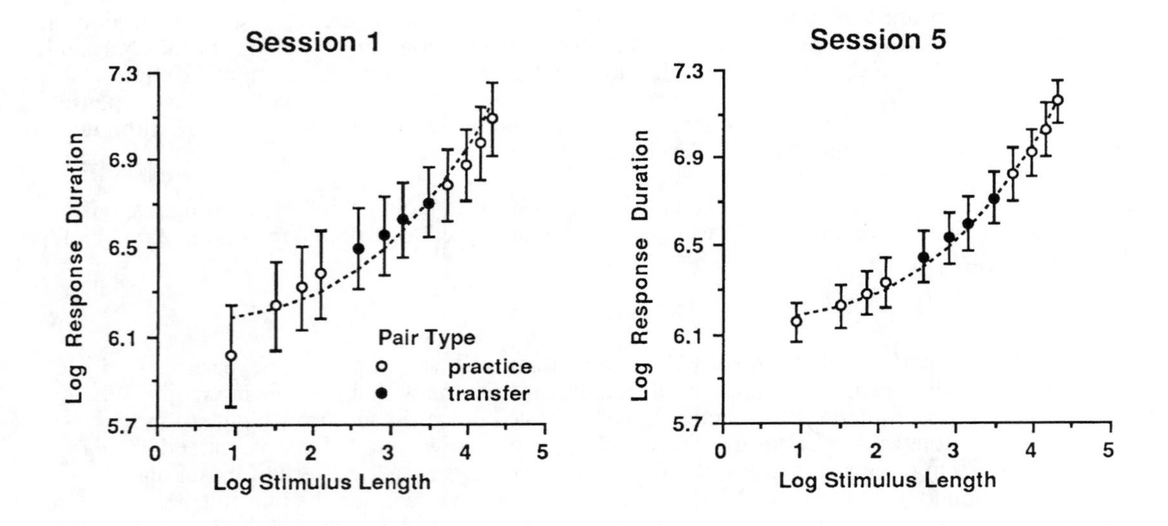

Figure 3. Mean response duration (in $\log_e$ msec) averaged across subjects as a function of stimulus length (in $\log_e$ mm) for the first and last sessions in Experiment 3. The dashed curve represents the linear function to be learned.

A Proposed Model : Adaptive-Regression

To explain our results, we have developed a model of induction called the "adaptive-regression" model that accounts for all major aspects of the obtained data (Koh & Meyer, 1989; Koh, 1989). According to the model, people try to fit a polynomial (e.g., cubic) function to the experienced stimulus-response pairs. The pairs are first transformed logarithmically before being submitted to the fitting algorithm. The algorithm estimates polynomial coefficients so that a weighted combination of 1) the curvature of the fitted function and 2) the summed squared deviations of the fitted function from the experienced stimulus-response pairs is minimized.

Initially, the curvature component of the model has relatively more weight than the squared-deviation component, resulting in a bias toward inducing power functions. This is due to the fact that lines have minimum (i.e., zero) curvature, and that power functions correspond to linear functions in log-log coordinates. As more and more stimulus-response pairs are experienced, however, the squared-deviation component receives relatively more weight, allowing the fitted function to gradually approach the required function.

We have implemented the adaptive-regression model and other models based on exemplar as well as abstraction processes in a computer program; the results clearly favor the adaptive-regression model. The success of this model is illustrated in Figure 4, which presents results from a computer simulation of Experiment 3. The simulated data closely resemble the actually observed data (Figure 3).

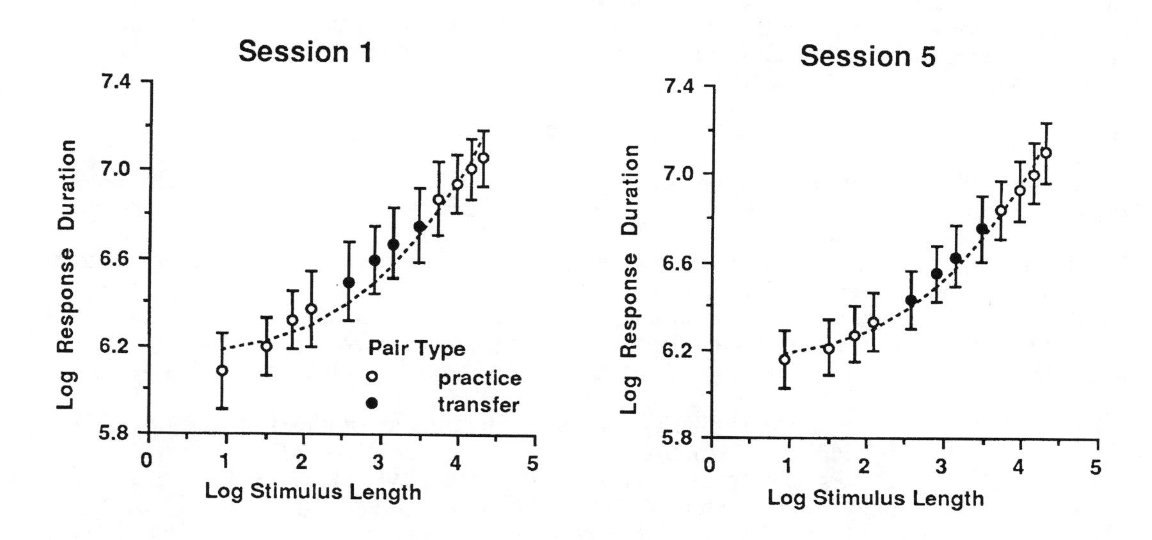

Figure 4. Predictions by the adaptive-regression model for a linear stimulus-response relation used in Experiment 3. Response durations (in $\log_e$ msec) are plotted against stimulus lengths (in $\log_e$ mm).

Relation to Previous Research

The present perceptual-motor learning task is closely related to cross-modality matching tasks for deriving psychophysical functions. Stevens and his colleagues have conducted a series of experiments concerning several sensory modalities, showing that for all of them, matching functions between pairs of modalities come from a family of power functions (Stevens, 1965; Stevens & Marks, 1965). Our results mesh well with Stevens' findings, and together they suggest that people have a natural tendency to establish power relations between pairs of continuous dimensions, and that people learn "natural" relations more readily than others (cf. Shepard, 1981).

Our work is also related to past research on category learning. In recent years, models of category learning based on similarity among perceived and remembered exemplars have received much attention and some empirical support (Estes, 1986; Medin & Shaffer, 1978; Nosofsky, 1984). However, the present results for a perceptual-motor learning task cannot be explained easily by exemplar models. Instead, the results fit quite nicely with the adaptive-regression model, which involves an extensive abstraction process. It would be unappealing to postulate entirely separate inductive mechanisms for category learning and perceptual-motor learning. Developing a unified theory of induction that encompasses both types of learning is therefore an important topic for future research.

AUTHOR NOTE

Support was provided by Grant R01 MH37145 from the National Institute of Mental Health.
Kyunghee Koh is now at the Center for Visual Science, University of Rochester. Correspondence should be sent to: David E. Meyer, Department of Psychology, University of Michigan, 330 Packard Road, Ann Arbor, MI 48104.

REFERENCES

Estes, W. K. (1986). Array models for category learning. *Cognitive Psychology, 18*, 500-549.

Holland, J. H., Holyoak, K. J., Nisbett, R. E., & Thagard, P. R. (1986). *Induction: Processes of inference, learning, and discovery.* Cambridge, MA: MIT Press.

Koh, K. (1989). *Induction of continuous stimulus-response relations.* Unpublished doctoral dissertation, University of Michigan.

Koh, K. & Meyer, D. E. (1989). *Induction of continuous stimulus-response associations for perceptual-motor performance.* Manuscript in preparation, University of Michigan.

Medin, D. L., & Shaffer, M. M. (1978). Context theory of classification learning. *Psychological Review, 85*, 207-238.

Nosofsky, R. M. (1984). Choice, similarity, and the context theory of classification. *Journal of Experimental Psychology: Learning, Memory, and Cognition, 10*, 104-114.

Shepard, R. N. (1981). Psychological relations and psychophysical scales: On the status of "direct" psychophysical measurement. *Journal of Mathematical Psychology, 24,* 21-57.

Smith, E. E., & Medin, D. L. (1981). *Categories and concepts.* Cambridge, MA: Harvard University Press.

Stevens, J. C., & Marks, L. E. (1965). Cross-modality matching of brightness and loudness. *Proceedings of the National Academy of Science, 54*, 407-411.

Stevens, S. S. (1965). Matching functions between loudness and ten other continua. *Perception & Psychophysics, 1*, 5-8.

Structural Evaluation of Analogies: What Counts?

Kenneth D. Forbus
Qualitative Reasoning Group

Dedre Gentner
Psychology Department

Beckman Institute, University of Illinois

Abstract: Judgments of similarity and soundness are important aspects of human analogical processing. This paper explores how these judgments can be modeled using SME, a simulation of Gentner's structure-mapping theory. We focus on structural evaluation, explicating several principles which psychologically plausible algorithms should follow. We introduce the *Specificity Conjecture*, which claims that naturalistic representations include a preponderance of appearance and low-order information. We demonstrate via computational experiments that this conjecture affects how structural evaluation should be performed, including the choice of normalization technique and how the systematicity preference is implemented.

1 Introduction

Judging soundness and structural similarity are important aspects of human analogical processing. While other criteria (such as factual correctness and relevance to current goals) are also important, they cannot replace structural evaluation. For example, neither factual correctness or relevance are enough when an analogy is used to make an argument; the claimed consequences must legitimately follow from the analogy or the argument will be rejected. The importance of structural evaluation is even clearer when one considers the use of analogy to discover new ideas: the learner must have some means of judging the comparison without knowing in advance if its implications are correct or relevant.

We have suggested that human structural evalution of analogies depends largely on the degree to which the analogs share systematic relational structure (i.e., share systems of relations governed by common higher-order relations) [8]. There is psychological evidence supporting this position as a descriptive account [10]. SME[5,6], our simulation of Gentner's structure-mapping theory [7,8], includes a structural evaluator which appears to match psychological data on analogical soundness judgments reasonably well [17]. In this paper we use a combination of theoretical argument and sensitivity analyses to probe more deeply into the issues surrounding structural evaluation.

Section 2 begins with a brief overview of SME and outlines some constraints on psychologically plausible algorithms for structural evaluation. Section 3 summarizes psychological results concerning analogical soundness, and shows how our prior simulation experiment provides a framework for sensitivity analyses. Section 4 proposes that the representations used in AI and cognitive simulation tend to be unrealistically sparse (the *Specificity Conjecture*). The next two sections demonstrate how this conjecture constrains structural evaluation algorithms. Two design dimensions are considered. Section 5 compares alternate normalization strategies (i.e., how evidence is combined). Section 6 compares our original cascade-like technique for implementing the systematicity preference (*trickle-down*) with another technique, *order-scoring*. We conclude that trickle-down with result normalization provides the best fit to human data. We close by considering the broader implications of the Specificity Conjecture.

2 The Structure-Mapping Engine

SME was designed to provide an *accountable* simulation of Gentner's structure-mapping theory. By accountable, we mean that processing choices not explicitly constrained by the theory must be easily changable, so that dependence on alternate choices can be explored. To achieve accountability, SME's input includes two sets of rules which construct and evaluate local matches. By varying these rules SME can be programmed to emulate all the comparisons of structure-mapping, as well other matchers consistent with its assumptions [4]. Here we use this programmability to perform sensitivity analyses to rule out certain processing choices as being unable to account for human data.

Given *base* and *target* descriptions to match, SME produces a set of *Gmaps*, representing the possible interpretations of the comparison. Each Gmap includes a set of correspondences between the items (objects and propositions) in the base and target, the set of ***candidate inferences*** sanctioned by the match (i.e., knowledge about the base conjectured to hold in the target by virtue of the correspondences), and a ***structural evaluation score*** (SES) indicating the "quality" of the match.

SME begins by computing local ***match hypotheses*** (MH's) involving pairs of items from base and target. The construction rules guide this process[1]. At this stage the match is incoherent, in that the set of match hypotheses collectively can contain many-to-one mappings. Local constraints, such as one-to-one mappings and structural consistency (see [6] for details) are enforced next. These constraints rule out match hypotheses which cannot be part of any legal interpretation, and note which pairs of match hypotheses cannot consistently be part of the same interpretation. Gmaps are built by finding the maximal structurally consistent collections of local matches, and using the computed overlap to determine what non-overlapping aspects of the base can be postulated to hold in the target (i.e., the candidate inferences). The structural evalutation score is computed last. First, the evaluation rules are run to provide a score for each match hypothesis. The SES of each Gmap is computed by adding the scores of its match hypotheses.

SME provides a process model for structure-mapping. The goal is to achieve sophisticated results using computationally simple techniques. We believe that combining local match hypotheses into coherent global interpretations is a psychologically plausible aspect of SME [9]. However, not every aspect of SME is equally plausible psychologically. For example, we do not believe people necessarily compute all interpretations, although for experimental purposes we generally have SME compute the complete set of Gmaps to gain more insight into the match. A second limitation is that SME models only the structural component of match quality. Contextual and pragmatic factors can also play a role in match evalution. However, understanding those factors involves simulating larger pieces of the overall processing system, with a subsequent increase in the number of free parameters. By understanding structural evaluation in isolation we hope to tightly constraint that aspect of the system.

Structure-mapping postulates that ***systematicity*** is preferred in structural evaluations [8]; i.e., a Gmap involving a larger connected system of relations, particularly higher-order relations[2], should have a higher SES than one involving a smaller, or disconnected, system of relations. The systematicity constraint is stated at the information processing level (as defined by Marr [14]); additional principles are needed to provide constraint at the algorithm and implementation levels. This paper focuses on the algorithm level, importing only the most general constraints from the prospect of highly parallel, neural-like implementations. Our current ***implementation*** is serial, but that is an accident of technology – the SME algorithm lends itself naturally to a variety of parallel implementations [6][3].

The score associated with a match hypothesis indicates how strongly the correspondence between the base and target items it connects is preferred on structural grounds. We restrict evaluation rules to use only local, structural properties in assigning scores. For example, MH's receive some initial score based on the kinds of items matched (relation, function, or attribute). Under structure-mapping only propositions involving identical relations or attributes match[4], so the same initial score is used for all relations and attributes (i.e., matches involving relations such as CAUSE are given the same score as matches involving relations such as IMPLIES or LEFT-OF). This parameter is called `Same-Predicate`. The parameter `Same-Function` is used for identical

---

[1] Which pairs of items are hypothesized to match and the structural constraints defining consistent global interpretations are fixed by structure-mapping theory.

[2] Structure-mapping defines the *order* of an item in a representation as follows: Objects and constants are order 0. The order of a predicate is one plus the maximum of the order of its arguments. Thus GREATER-THAN(x,y) is first-order if x and y are objects, and CAUSE[GREATER-THAN(x,y), BREAK(x)] is second-order. Examples of higher-order relations include CAUSE and IMPLIES.

[3] We view Holyoak and Thagard's ACME [11] as evidence that SME could be implemented in at least a localist connectionist framework, since there is substantial overlap in the information processing and algorithm levels between SME and ACME.

[4] We assume a decompositional semantics, so that synonyms are translated into some common form (c.f. [1,3]). This allows similarity to be reduced to partial identity. The alternative course of allowing similar predicates to match requires one to define similarity by invoking it.

functions[5]. This part of the structural evaluation can proceed in parallel with match hypothesis construction.

At first glance systematicity might appear to be an inherently global concept, requiring difficult computations to enforce. We implemented it locally via ***trickle-down***, a cascade-like model [12]. In trickle-down, a match hypothesis MH adds its score, scaled by the parameter `Trickle-Down`, to the match hypotheses linking the arguments of the items matched by MH. Thus in a deep system of relations the scores will cascade down, providing high scores for the object correspondences supporting the system (and thus for the system as a whole). This computation, too, can proceed in parallel, taking $\mathcal{O}(log(N))$ for a match hypothesis set of size N [6].

The structural evaluation system thus has three parameters: `Same-Predicate`, `Same-Function`, and `Trickle-Down`[6]. Once the propagation of local scores for all match hypotheses is complete, the SES of an interpretation (Gmap) is computed by summing of the scores of its constituent match hypotheses. In the original version of SME, scores were represented and combined using the Dempster-Shafer formalism [16,2]. We do not normalize Gmap scores, since doing so would only introduce further parameters without theoretical motivations. We also wish to avoid arbitrary assumptions concerning the scaling of human soundness judgments. Consequently, our conclusions will be based completely on ordinal comparisons between scores, never on the actual magnitude of scores themselves.

3 Modeling Soundness Judgments

To perform a sensitivity analysis one must have a standard for comparison. We use the cognitive simulation experiment described in [17], which showed that SME could replicate aspects of human soundness judgments demonstrated empirically [10,15]. In the psychological studies, subjects first read a large set of stories. In a subsequent session, they were shown similar stories and tried to retrieve corresponding original stories (an access measure). Afterwards, subjects were asked to judge the inferential soundness of pairs of stories. What was varied was the kind of similarity between pairs of stories; some cases shared only relational structure (i.e., were analogous), some only shared object similarities (i.e., appearance matches), and some shared both (i.e., were literally similar). Subjects rated literal similarity and analogy pairs as signficantly more sound than appearance matches.

In the original simulation study, five triads of stories were encoded, each consisting of the base story (Base), an analogous story with different surface structure but similar relational structure (AN), and a story with surface similarities but different relational structure (MA). We asked whether SME's structural evaluation system could model these judgments. That is, if we interpret the SES as an indication of the soundness rating a subject would give, then to match the human data the score computed by SME for the Base/AN match should be higher than the score for the Base/MA match. As predicted, SES($Base/AN$) > SES($Base/MA$).

This experiment provides a useful framework for carrying out sensitivity analyses. Suppose we have N triads of stories. For any particular collection of parameters – numerical, symbolic, or algorithmic – we can define the fit with human performance to be the number of triads for which SES($Base/AN$) > SES($Base/MA$). By analyzing how the fit varies we can determine how sensitive the results are to each choice. Figure 1 depicts how this design can be viewed as an experimental apparatus. In the analyses which follow, three triads of stories were used each time. For each manipulation, this ESENSE apparatus was run over a sample of the numerical parameter space to estimate what fraction of the space provides results which fit the psychological data. The desirable outcome is that some portion, but not all, provides such a fit to the human data. If the

[5] Functions are treated differently from predicates, since derived matches between non-identical functions are allowed if the structure above them matches (e.g., `Temperature` to `Pressure`).

[6] The original structural evaluation rules [6] had eight parameters; the reduction to three required some theoretical analysis and about two Symbolics-days of numerical sensitivity analyses. Although our initial use of eight parameters may seem large, it should be noted that simulations often have far more: ACME, for instance, relies on a numerical "similarity score" being available for each pair of predicates, hence the number of parameters is at least as large as the square of the number of predicates in the underlying representation language. Ascertaining the dependence of ACME's performance on its parameters via sensitivity analysis would appear to be a rather formidable task.

Figure 1: ESENSE Experimental setup for sensitivity analyses
The previous simulation experiment can be viewed as an apparatus which, for any particular combination of parameters, representations, and algorithm provides an estimate of fit to psychological data (here, an integer ranging between 0 and 3). Running this apparatus over alternate choices provides insight about how each aspect of the system accounts for the fit.

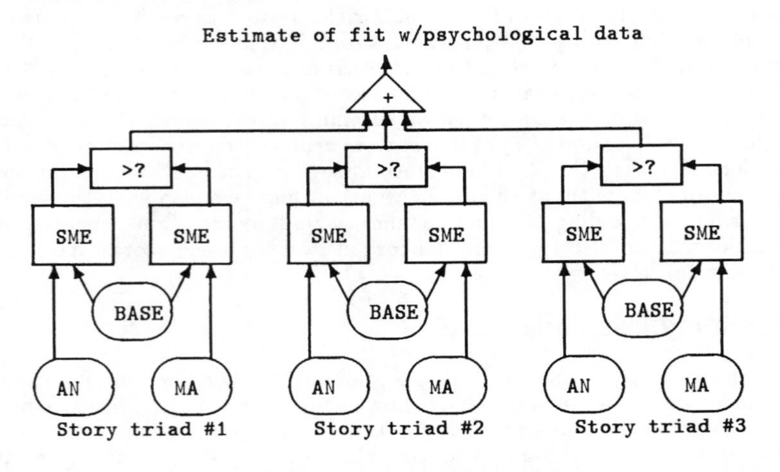

whole space fits, then the parameters are irrelevant. If none of the space fits, then clearly that combination cannot account for human soundness judgments.

4 The Specificity Conjecture

Representational choices are often the most difficult issue in cognitive simulation. Rarely does a theory completely constrain the representational format, and while many choices are logically equivalent, even small changes can yield very different performance for a particular algorithm. Often there is no agreement (and sometimes intense disagreement) on what representations are reasonable. The typical solution is to test programs on a variety of examples to ensure generality. We believe that content variations alone are not always enough. Varying more global representational assumptions, such as the amount of perceptual information, can also be crucial.

The representations used in cognitive simulation tend to have much in common with those used in AI. They focus on the important aspects of what is to be represented, leaving out "irrelevant" information. Consequently they tend to be rather sparse. Such representations are fine if the only purpose is to compute a particular kind of answer (such as how to fix a broken car), and surely some human representations are like that. But is it reasonable to assume that most are? We suspect not. A person solving a problem or reading a story builds an internal representation from a variety of sources. This can include rich visual and auditory information about appearances (possibly including mental imagery) from which the relevant factors must be extracted. In fact, the more realistic the problem-solving scenario, the more irrelevant information there tends to be. While an expert may have an intricate theory of the situation, it is far from clear that the theory, as a percentage of the total number of propositions in the representation, dominates. And a novice faced with the same domain may have no applicable abstract knowledge, and thus can only encode observable properties.

Let us use ***top-heavy*** to refer to descriptions where most of the information is abstract, with very little information about appearances or basic object properties, and ***bottom-heavy*** for descriptions in which appearance information dominates (there may be just as much relational structure as top-heavy descriptions, as long as there is even more appearance information). Based on the observation that we can see far more than we can explain, we make the *Specificity Conjecture:* bottom-heavy descriptions are very common in human memory, perhaps outnumbering top-heavy descriptions. If this conjecture is correct, it is important to test simulations on bottom-heavy descriptions as well as the top-heavy descriptions which have been the favorite of experimenters.

How does the Specificity Conjecture affect structural evaluation of analogy? Structurally, top-heavy descriptions have a preponderance of higher-order relations, while bottom-heavy descriptions have many more attributes and first-order relations (e.g., LEFT-OF, BELOW). Consider the relative number of match hypotheses in the Base/AN and Base/MA comparisons described above. All else being equal, given a top-heavy representation the Base/AN comparison will have more match hypotheses than the Base/MA comparison, since there is more higher-order structure than appearance information. Conversely, in a bottom-heavy representation the Base/MA comparison will have more match hypotheses than the Base/AN comparison, since there is more appearance information to match than higher-order structure. Thus in top-heavy representations $\texttt{SES}(Base/AN) > \texttt{SES}(Base/MA)$ will tend to be true even with uniform MH scores, assuming that the higher-order structures do in fact match. But in bottom-heavy representations the tendency is towards $\texttt{SES}(Base/AN) < \texttt{SES}(Base/MA)$, due to the predominance of appearance information. In this case trickle-down plays a crucial role, to prevent the inferentially important comparison from being "swamped" by the surface comparison. People apparently have the ability to find structural commonalities even when they have bottom-heavy representations[7]. By looking for swamping over a space of numerical parameters and representation choices (i.e., by varying the amount of appearance information), we have a more subtle probe for exploring structural evaluation.

5 Analyzing normalization strategies

Any physically realizable computing scheme must include elements of finite dynamic range, and hence there will always be some normalization scheme which ensures that scores are within that range. The ability of trickle-down to prevent swamping depends in part on the normalization strategy used in computing scores. We can divide such strategies into two broad classes: ***result normalization***, and ***contribution normalization***. Connectionist models tend to use result normalization; a unit's inputs are multiplied by a set of coefficients, added, and then scaled by some non-linear function [13]. Formalisms for probabilistic reasoning tend to use contribution normalization; MYCIN's certainty factors, for instance, scale every contribution to belief in a proposition by the percentage of uncertainty remaining for that belief. Which kind of strategy, when plugged into the ESENSE apparatus, provides a better fit to the data?

To answer this question we set up the following experiment. First, we modified the encoded stories of the original simulation experiment to produce three sets of stories: one consisting of top-heavy descriptions, one consisting of bottom-heavy descriptions (i.e., twice as many match hypotheses for the Base/MA comparison as for the Base/AN comparison) and one "neutral" set, where the number of match hypotheses for the Base/MA and Base/AN comparisons were exactly equal. Then, we implemented a representative algorithm for each type of normalization. For the result normalization case we used the following rule:

$$\texttt{AddMax}: W_{i+1} = Min(1.0, W_i + C_i)$$

where W_i, W_{i+1} are the MH's score before and after the contribution, C_i is the amount contributed, and $W_0 = 0.0$. For the contribution normalization case we used the Dempster/Shafer code from the original SME structural evaluator. We then ran the ESENSE apparatus over every set of stories using each normalization strategy, varying the numerical parameters over a broad range, to see how these choices interacted to affect the fit with human performance.

One complication in setting up the experiment is that these strategies differ in the ranges of parameters they allow. In Dempster/Shafer all parameters must be between zero and one. In

[7]For example, in the experiment described above people gave higher structural evaluations to analogies than to appearance matches. Yet we can infer that they must have stored the stories with a great deal of low-order information, because their memory access was better for appearance matches than for analogical matches.

Table 1: Summary of fit as a function of representation and normalization
This table shows, for each combination of representation type and normalization algorithm, how much of the sampled parameter space can completely account for the data. That is, a value of $X\%$ indicates that given any parameter setting in that fraction of the space, SME's performance will exactly match the original human data. Dempster/Shafer cannot account for the data unless top-heavy representations are assumed.

	Top-heavy	Neutral	Bottom-heavy
Dempster/Shafer	4.1%	0.0%	0.0%
AddMax	75.8%	41.1%	18.1%

AddMax allowing Same-Predicate or Same-Function to be one or greater is equivalent to just counting match hypotheses, so we restrict these to be less than one. Trickle-Down, on the other hand, can be greater than one, since the other parameters could be substantially less than one. (Even if the product is larger than one it makes no difference for AddMax, although it would violate the fundamental assumptions of Dempster/Shafer.) For AddMax we varied the three numerical parameters over the following ranges: Same-Predicate and Same-Function over (0.0, 10^{-4}, 10^{-3}, 0.01, 0.1, 0.3, 0.9) and Trickle-Down over (0.0, 0.5, 1.0, 2.0, 4.0, 8.0, 16.0). For Dempster/Shafer we varied all three parameters (Same-Predicate, Same-Function, and Trickle-Down) over the same set of values: (0.0, 10^{-4}, 10^{-3}, 0.01, 0.1, 0.3, 0.9). The number of samples for each algorithm is thus 7^3, or 343 points. To compute whether or not a point fits requires running each structural evaluator six times for each story set (i.e., to do the Base/AN and Base/MA comparison for each of three story triads in a set). Thus with three story sets 6,174 structural evaulations were required.

Table 1 summarizes the results by showing what percentage of the sampled parameter space yields a perfect fit of the data, as measured by the ESENSE apparatus. Dempster/Shafer clearly allows swamping as the number of attribute matches is increased. Thus it cannot explain the data, unless attention is restricted to top-heavy representations. AddMax, by contrast, can be tuned to fit the data for each type of representation. Can a single setting of parameters suffice? That is, are there subsets of the sample space in which AddMax fits the data for all three types, or are the subsets which fit the data for each type of representation disjoint? Yes, there is a single subset which fits the data. The boundary of this region appears complicated, and the coarseness of our sampling precludes a detailed description of it. However, it is reasonably large, indicating that the algorithm is not overly sensitive to particular choices of parameters. For example, within the ranges Same-Predicate $\in [10^{-3}, 0.01]$, Same-Function $\in [10^{-4}, 0.01]$, and Trickle-Down $\in [4, 16]$, every point fits perfectly. The regions which are clearly outside are interesting: Trickle-Down values of 1.0 or less, values of Same-Predicate of 0.3 or more, and values of Same-Function 0.9 or higher. Intuitively, what seems to be happening is this: Unless Trickle-Down is sufficiently high, not enough score cascades down to overcome the swamping effect of the large number of attribute matches. For the same reason, the "baseline activation" for each MH must be kept small; otherwise the cascade effect will be blocked by normalization.

This experiment suggests an interesting possibility. Since any physical computation scheme incorporates elements of limited dynamic range, for any set of parameters there will be some maximum depth beyond which additional systematicity cannot be distinguished, since the processing elements will have reached their maximum scores. This limit may be so high as to be irrelevant for human representations, or may show up as an "order cutoff" in failing to distinguish one comparison as more sound than another if both are extremely intricate.

6 Trickle-Down versus Order-Scoring

An interesting alternative to trickle-down for implementing systematicity is ***order-scoring***. Consider a large relational structure which is shared by both base and target in some interpretation of an analogy. This structure will have a number of match hypotheses involving relational items of high order. To satisfy structural consistency, the arguments of each such item must themselves have correspondences in the interpretation. Hence its mere presence in the

Table 2: Results of Order Scoring on the story sets
This describes the percentage of the sampled points which perfectly fit the data for the three story sets described above. We repeat the trickle-down AddMax data for easy comparison. Order-scoring fails to account for human data, assuming the Specificity Conjecture holds.

	Top-heavy	Neutral	Bottom-heavy
Order-Scoring	69.1 %	47.2 %	0.0%
Trickle-Down	75.8%	41.1%	18.1%

interpretation indicates the existence of matches "all the way down" to object matches. Order scoring simply scales the score given to each match hypothesis by the order of the items involved, instead of passing scores downward as in trickle-down.

On computational grounds, we find order-scoring less preferable to trickle-down. First, to satisfy our constraints order must itself be computed locally. This is not difficult, if one allows information to propagate "upwards" from match hypotheses between entities (which have order zero) to match hypotheses which include them as arguments, and so on. However, this explicit computation of order seems inelegant, since, to paraphrase [12], it requires "more complex currency" than simply propagating local scores. A second difference is that order-scoring directly signals the existence of higher-order relations, and only indirectly signals the connectivity of a system of relational matches. Trickle-down, on the other hand, directly signals connectivity, leaving order implicit. Intuitively, connectivity seems a better structural reflection of coherence and inferential power than simply the existence of higher-order relations. Thus trickle-down has greater theoretical appeal as a way of deriving a structural evaluation.

But intuitions can be misleading. To see whether order-scoring could account for the data, we implemented a set of evaluation rules using this strategy. The contribution of order was defined by the function $\mathcal{OF}$:

$$\mathcal{OF}\ (MH) = Min(1.0, C \times [1 + Order(MH) \times \texttt{Order-Bias}])$$

where C is either `Same-Predicate` or `Same-Function` as appropriate. We sampled this parameter space in the same way as in the earlier analysis: i.e., `Same-Predicate` and `Same-Function` ranged over (0.0, 10^{-4}, 10^{-3}, 0.01, 0.1, 0.3, 0.9) and `Order-Bias` over (0.0, 0.5, 1.0, 2.0, 4.0, 8.0, 16.0). Table 2 summarizes the results. Clearly, $\mathcal{OF}$ is not a viable candidate for implementing the systematicity preference, since it is swamped on bottom-heavy representations. We suspect that this result will hold for all order-scoring algorithms. Even when `Order-Bias` is high, local normalization prevents the score of any particular MH becoming too high. Trickle-down avoids this limitation by co-opting all the lower-order structure matches under the high-order match, thus providing better resistance to swamping.

7 Discussion

Previous work demonstrated that structural critera are important in judging the relative soundness of analogical comparisons. This paper explores the relationship between the data and simulation in detail, making explicit the principles which constrain the space of algorithms we allow, and using the previous experiments to provide a framework for sensitivity analyses (the ESENSE apparatus) that help provide a deeper account of structural evaluation. In particular, we introduced the Specificity Conjecture, which suggests that in mental representations appearance and other low-order information is likely to dominate. If true, our experiments indicate that (a) normalization of scores for local matches should occur by a result normalization strategy rather than by contribution normalization and (b) trickle-down provides a better implementation of the systematicity preference than order-scoring.

We believe the Specificity Conjecture has important general ramifications for cognitive simulation. The aesthetic for good representations in AI is driven by the desire to solve particular kinds of problems. Since AI workers tend to do more explicit formal representations than workers in other areas of Cognitive Science, their aesthetic tends also to be inherited by other areas, even when it may not be appropriate. There is very little direct evidence about the format and statistical properties of mental representations (i.e., when they tend to be top-heavy versus bottom-heavy). Still, the fact that humans have powerful perceptual systems which deliver a rich assortment of information regardless of whether they know much else about what they are seeing argues for the importance of testing simulations with bottom-heavy representations. Showing that a simulation works in different content areas is now common. This is clearly important, but we now believe that it is not enough. One must explore how well a simulation performs with a range of representations that captures plausible intuitions about what the range of mental representations might be like.

8 Acknowledgements

Brian Falkenhainer provided valuable advice and algorithms for carrying out parts of the sensitivity analyses. This paper benefited from discussions with John Collins, Brian Falkenhainer, Rob Goldstone, Art Markman, Doug Medin, Janice Skorstad, and Ed Smith. This research was supported by the Office of Naval Research, Contract No. N00014-85-K-0559, an NSF Presidential Young Investigator award, and an equipment grant from IBM.

References

[1] Burstein, M. H. (1983). A model of learning by analogical reasoning and debugging. In *Proceedings of the National Conference on Artificial Intelligence*, Washington, D. C.

[2] Falkenhainer, B., Towards a general-purpose belief maintenance system, in: J.F. Lemmer (Ed.), *Uncertainty in Artificial Intelligence, Volume II*, 1987. Also Technical Report, UIUCDCS-R-87-1717, Department of Computer Science, University of Illinois, 1987.

[3] third stage in the analogy process: Verification-Based Analogical Learning, Technical Report UIUCDCS-R-86-1302, Department of Computer Science, University of Illinois, October, 1986. A summary appears in *Proceedings of the Tenth International Joint Conference on Artificial Intelligence*, Milan, Italy, August, 1987.

[4] Falkenhainer, B., The SME user's manual, Technical Report UIUCDCS-R-88-1421, Department of Computer Science, University of Illinois, 1988.

[5] Falkenhainer, B., K.D. Forbus, D. Gentner, The Structure-Mapping Engine, *Proceedings of the Fifth National Conference on Artificial Intelligence*, August, 1986.

[6] Falkenhainer, B., Forbus, K., Gentner, D. The Structure-Mapping Engine: Algorithm and examples *Artificial Intelligence*, to appear, 1989.

[7] Gentner, D., The structure of analogical models in science, BBN Tech. Report No. 4451, Cambridge, MA., Bolt Beranek and Newman Inc., 1980.

[8] Gentner, D., Structure-mapping: A theoretical framework for analogy, *Cognitive Science* **7**(2), 1983.

[9] Gentner, D., Mechanisms of analogical learning. To appear in S. Vosniadou and A. Ortony, (Eds.), *Similarity and analogical reasoning*. Presented in June, 1986.

[10] Gentner, D., & R. Landers, Analogical reminding: A good match is hard to find. In *Proceedings of the International Conference on Systems, Man and Cybernetics*. Tucson, Arizona, 1985.

[11] Holyoak, K. & Thagard, P. Analogical mapping by constraint satisfaction, to appear in *Cognitive Science*.

[12] McClelland, J. L., & Rumelhart, D. E. (1981). An interactive activation model of context effects in letter perception: Part 1. An account of basic findings. *Psychological Review,88*(5), 375-407.

[13] Rumelhart, D. and McClelland, J. *Parallel Distributed Processing, Volumes 1 & 2*, The MIT Press, 1986.

[14] Marr, D. *Vision*, W. H. Freeman and Company, San Francisco, 1982.

[15] Rattermann, M.J., and Gentner, D. Analogy and Similarity: Determinants of accessibility and inferential soundness, *Proceedings of the Cognitive Science Society*, July, 1987.

[16] Shafer, G., *A mathematical theory of evidence*, Princeton University Press, Princeton, New Jersey, 1976.

[17] Skorstad, J., Falkenhainer, B., Gentner, D., Analogical Processing: A simulation and empirical corroboration, in: *Proceedings of the Sixth National Conference on Artificial Intelligence*, Seattle, WA, August, 1987.

Structural Representations of Music Performance

CAROLINE PALMER

PSYCHOLOGY DEPARTMENT, OHIO STATE UNIVERSITY

ABSTRACT

A primary goal of music cognition is to understand mental representations for musical knowledge that allow communication of thoughts and emotions. Theories of musical competence generally model mental representations in terms of structure given in the musical text, and do not model performers' preferential choices of structural content for emphasis. Such choices are an important component of musical interpretation. Two sources of converging evidence are described that support the role of phrases as structures in mental representations for music performance: evidence from expressive timing in skilled performance and from performance breakdowns (errors). The location and amount of expressive timing, and the likelihoods of different error types coincided with musicians' notated interpretations. Evidence from both ideal and non-ideal musical behavior implicate the same structures in representation of musical knowledge, and suggest that individual preferences can explain much variation in music performance.

Introduction

Many theories of music cognition attempt to specify mental representations for musical knowledge; that is, the knowledge that performer, listener, and composer have, that allows communication of thoughts and emotions. The topic of this paper, music performance, provides a rich area in which to study the interaction between representations of musical structure and skilled performance in a naturalistic setting. Mental representations underlying music performance should affect our perception and comprehension of music as well.

Several theories tackle the problem of modelling our musical competence (Cooper & Meyer, 1960; Lerdahl & Jackendoff, 1983; Meyer, 1973). One of the most explicit attempts to formalize musical competence is a recent theory that models experienced listeners' knowledge of Western tonal music (Lerdahl & Jackendoff, 1983). The theory predicts the relative importance of musical events, based on a combination of well-formedness rules that specify the set of possible structural descriptions, and preference rules, that resolve among the competing alternative structures. This theory represents a common approach in music cognition: to model structural aspects in terms of information in the musical text, usually deriving one set of structures per musical excerpt.

This ambitious undertaking has met with some success in predicting effects in music perception (Deliege, 1987; Palmer & Krumhansl, 1987). There are, however, several problems in its application to music performance (shared by all current theories of musical competence): the model is not algorithmic (the particular rules and order in which they are applied are not specified), and it is not clear how preferences resolve among alternative interpretations in many ambiguous musical passages. Of most concern for this paper, the theoretical predictions do not take into account the different expressive variations introduced in different performances of the same musical text. These problems illustrate the tasks faced by any theory of musical competence - how to choose among possible structures composed of different constituents, and how to apply procedures to combine or contrast them in their relative importance.

This paper addresses how the musical structures and processes in a mental representation influence music performance. The specific questions include: how does a musical performance communicate some intended meaning or structural content? How do abstract intentions differentiate one performance from another? What kinds of structures and operations comprise the mapping of abstract musical intentions to sounded performance? I will refer to musical intentions as interpretations. Interpretations are the musicians' modelling of a piece according to their own choices of appropriate musical structure for emphasis, such as melody, phrasing, and dynamics (Apel, 1972). A skilled performer plays not only what is specified in the musical text, but adds much intentional expressiveness that does not appear in the text. Small variations in frequency, timing, intensity, and timbre are thought to govern the assignment of musical meaning to expressive performance (Nakamura, 1987; Palmer, 1989; Shaffer, Clarke, & Todd, 1985; Todd, 1985).

Two sources of evidence are presented that support musical phrases as structures common to mental representations underlying music performance. Phrases are a good candidate for musical structure; they are typically described in music as a unit of meaning, often defined by elements at their boundaries (Cogan & Escot, 1976). Pausing and increasing durations at phrase boundaries in both music (Todd, 1985) and speech (Cooper & Paccia-Cooper, 1980) are assumed to be determined by syntactic and prosodic structure. Algorithms have been developed that predict pausing in speech and music by an amount proportional to the hierarchical level or depth of phrase embedding (Grosjean, Grosjean & Lane, 1979; Todd, 1985). Note that these algorithms predict tempo changes from the information in the text, not by the individual performer's intentions, and thus result in one prediction per musical piece.

I will describe two effects of individual performers' interpretations on mental representations for music performance. The two sources of evidence are: from timing variations in skilled performance (ideal performance) and from performance breakdowns (errors). A set of piano performances were collected, along with the phrasing interpretations of the pianists. All the performances described here were recorded on a computer-monitored Bosendorfer concert grand piano, containing optical sensors and solenoids. This instrument allows precise measurement, recording, and playback of timing and velocity (loudness) parameters of a performance, without affecting the touch or sound of the acoustic instrument.

Expressive Timing in Music Performance

I will first describe a study that addresses the effect of phrasing interpretation on musical performance by comparing each performer's intended structural content with expressive timing variations in the sounded performance. Six professional pianists were asked to perform the same musical piece, a Piano Prelude by Chopin (the musical text was held constant). Afterwards, pianists notated their phrasing interpretations on an unedited musical score. Figure 1a contains a 5-measure excerpt from that piece, with one of the pianist's notated phrasings above the musical score.

A common method for emphasizing phrasing in music performance is to alter the relative timing of events by using rubato (changes in tempo). The experimental goal is to find correspondences between the intended phrasing and the use of rubato. The timing variations in each recorded performance were therefore analyzed relative to each pianists' phrasing interpretation. Shown in Figure 1b are the rubato patterns from one performance, expressed in percent deviation from a mechanically regular performance. The deviations were calculated relative to each pianist's mean tempo or rate; thus, a large positive value indicates slowing down, and a negative value indicates speeding up. The correspondence between amount of rubato and intended phrasing is most evident at phrase boundaries (indicated by gaps in Figure 1b); phrase endings are accompanied by large positive values (indicating slowing down), relative to beginnings of phrases.

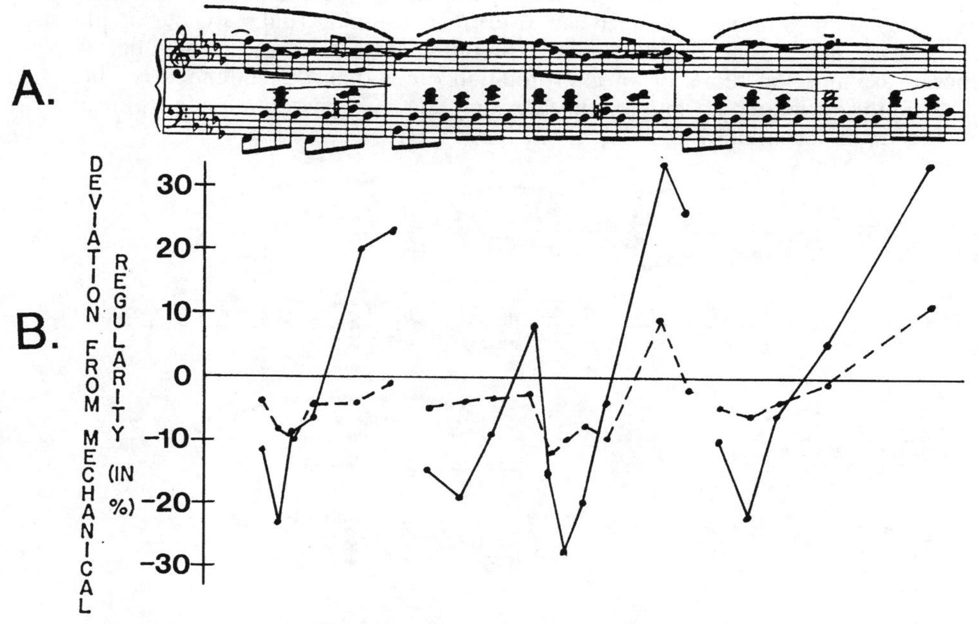

Figure 1. A pianist's performance of the Prelude in D-flat Major by Chopin. a) Notated phrasing of performer. b) Temporal deviations from mechanical regularity of the score.

After performing the musical excerpt, each pianist was asked to play it again, except this time, to play it mechanically, not to add any expressive interpretation to the musical text (the line around zero in Figure 1b reflects a strictly regular performance). The dashed line in Figure 1 reflects the pianist's "mechanical" performance; the relationship between rubato and intended phrasing disappears in the mechanical performance, suggesting that the use of rubato is both voluntary and part of the performer's intention to emphasize phrasing.

I will turn to a study of phrasing in a more ambiguous musical example. Pianists consistently notated the same phrasing for the Chopin excerpt described above. In contrast, they differed often in choice of phrasing for a Brahms Piano Intermezzo, shown in Figure 2 with two phrasing interpretations (notated by different pianists). To study the uniqueness of the mapping from phrasing interpretation to timing variations, one pianist was asked to play the same music twice, with the two different phrasing interpretations. Each performance was analyzed in terms of the different interpretations.

The graphical notation shown in Figure 3 demonstrates the expressive timing variations in the two performances. This nontraditional notation offers the advantage of increased resolution of temporal and intensity (loudness) information. Pitch height is represented on the abscissa, time on the ordinate axis; black denotes loud musical events, white denotes quiet. The two boxes display the first six notes in the melody (in this excerpt, the highest pitches) for each performance. The intended phrasing is marked with lines. The gaps coincident with intended phrase boundaries indicate an increase in expressive timing (pauses occur at phrase boundaries). As shown here, the mapping of interpretation to performance is unique. When a performance is examined in terms of an interpretation other than that intended by the performer, the timing variations no longer coincide; only the performer's intended phrasing characterizes the timing accurately.

Figure 2. Two phrasing interpretations (A and B)
of opening section of Piano Intermezzo, Opus 118 No. 2, by Brahms.

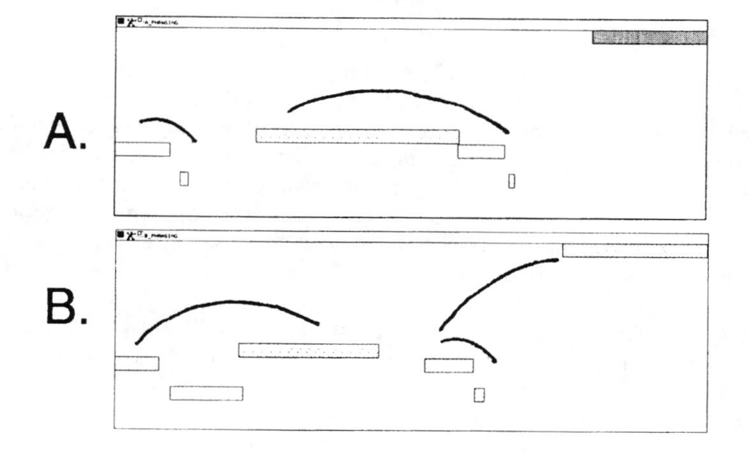

Figure 3. Graphical notation of performances of the two phrasing interpretations (A and B) of opening section from Brahms' Piano Intermezzo.

Thus, the use of rubato to emphasize phrasing accommodates different interpretations of the same music and disappears in the absence of interpretation (as seen in the mechanical performance). These findings support a framework of mental representations for music performance in which expressive timing is directly related to the performers' choice of phrases as constituent structures. However, phrases may serve as constituents at a global level, realized only in performance output; they may be combined from other, more primitive units of representation. A second source of evidence for phrases as basic units of mental representation is described, that argues against this conclusion: evidence from performance breakdowns, or errors.

Performance Errors

Performance breakdowns, or errors resulting in unintended output, are fairly common in many behaviors and often result from conflict among several possible actions, thoughts, or plans. From an analysis of the types and amounts of errors, it is possible to construct a theory that specifies what kinds of structures compete, and what kinds of processes operate on these structures in mental representations for music. If phrases are a basic constituent in mental representations, then performance errors should reflect processes operating on phrase structures. I will describe performance errors and how they coincide with phrasing interpretations. Eight different performances of the same Brahms Piano Intermezzo with ambiguous phrasing structure (shown in Figure 2) are described, including four performances of each phrasing interpretation. The piano performances were recorded on the same computer-monitored musical instrument. Because the computer detects wrong pitches and rhythms, we do not have to rely on a listener's capabilities. This allows us to avoid a problem encountered with speech errors; because errors frequently result from competing items that are similar in class, form, or sound (Dell, 1986; Garrett, 1975), they often go unnoticed by a listener.

Errors in piano performance can involve elements of pitch, duration, or both. I will describe errors restricted to pitch elements, and how they coincide with the constituent structures indicated by each performer's phrasing interpretations. I will concentrate on three error types: deletion errors, perseveration errors, and substitution errors. Deletion errors occur when an intended musical event is dropped or missing in the performance. Perseveration errors occur when an intended musical event is inappropriately repeated at a later time in the performance. Substitution errors occur when an intended musical event is replaced or substituted by an unintended event.

The frequency of occurrence of each error type differed significantly, relative to the performers' intended phrasing. The first error type, deletion errors, was more likely to occur within (71%) than between (29%) phrase boundaries. This finding is similar to phonemic slippage effects in speech, in which a phoneme is deleted more often within a word than at word boundaries. Deletions are found most commonly in various recall tasks for unimportant events, presumably because activation or relative strength of unimportant events is less than that of important events. In this musical context, those events within a phrase appeared to be most susceptible to deletion; this finding coincides with explanations of phrases defined by elements at their boundaries (Cogan & Escot, 1976).

The second error type, perseveration errors, was more likely to occur between (100%), than within (0%), phrase boundaries. Notice that this is in contrast to the frequencies of the deletion errors; both error types are affected by intended phrasing, in alternate ways. Spreading activation models predict that perseveration errors result from the activation or strength of intended elements being lower than that of unintended (perseverating) elements (Dell, 1986). The more strongly activated elements dominate the intended elements. Thus, within phrase boundaries, the intended elements are strong, while between phrases, unintended elements are more likely to intrude.

The third error type, substitution errors, did not coincide with musical phrase locations (they were just as likely to occur within as between phrases). Instead, substitution errors were related to type of unit: chords, or simultaneous note events, were substituted for each other more often (100%) than were elements within chords (0%). This finding suggests that errors are not just a result of attentional biases toward phrase boundaries, because not all error types are affected by positional similarity (that is, similar phrase locations). Instead, substitutions are more likely to involve elements of similar form.

Thus, while the substitution errors reflect processes operating on type of unit or form, the deletion and perseveration errors reflect processes operating on positional information (reflected in frequency of occurrence of errors at similar locations), determined by the performers' phrasing interpretations.

Conclusions

Both the use of expressive timing and the likelihood of various performance errors support the notion of phrases as structures in mental representations for music. The timing measurements from skilled piano performances demonstrated expressive variations coinciding with intended phrase structures (as determined by each performer). The flexibility of expressive timing was emphasized by the accommodation of different phrasing interpretations in the same piece, and by reduction of expressive timing when pianists attempted to play without phrasing interpretation (mechanically). The analysis of performance errors also implicated phrases as units in music representation. Susceptibility to error was directly related to positional information specified by the performers' intended phrasing. These two sources of evidence converge on the same mental structures determined by performers' choices of musical constituents, not by the musical text.

Ideal and non-ideal (errorful) performances may tap different cognitive resources, such as those hypothesized in a distinction between competence and performance. Thus, the evidence from expressive timing may represent "idealized" competence and the evidence from breakdowns "other performance variables". However, both sources of evidence were derived from highly skilled, well-learned performances under natural conditions. And both cases provide evidence that intentions to emphasize structural content directly affect musical behavior. Both the ideal and non-ideal musical behavior implicate the same structures in mental representations underlying music performance.

Instead, differences between well-formedness processes (constraints on mental structures) and preferences (probabilistic influences that choose among the lawful alternatives) may govern the formation of mental representations for music. Much of expressive performance can be explained by the performer's individual preferences, rather than by a generalized set of rules deriving musical structure from a given text. Thus, preference rules may play a larger role in performance than do well-formedness rules (which are already constrained by the composer). This implies that preferences play a larger role in comprehension of (sounded) performances than they do in comprehension of (notated) musical text: the performer's preferences can determine the likelihood with which the listener assigns a particular structural interpretation to a performance, reinforcing the communication of musical thought.

ACKNOWLEDGEMENTS

I would like to thank Mari Jones and Jordan Pollack for their comments, and the members of the Music Cognition Group at the M.I.T. Media Lab, where some of this research was conducted.

REFERENCES

Apel, W. (1972). Harvard dictionary of music (2nd ed.). Cambridge, MA: Harvard Univ. Press.

Cogan, R.D., & Escot, P. (1976). Sonic design: The nature of sound and music. Englewood Cliffs: Prentice-Hall.

Cooper, W.E., & Paccia-Cooper, J. (1980). Syntax and speech. Cambridge, MA: Harvard University Press.

Cooper, G., & Meyer, L.B. (1960). The rhythmic structure of music. Chicago: Chicago University Press.

Dell, G.S. (1986). A spreading-activation theory of retrieval in sentence production. Psychological Review, 93, 281-321.

Deliege, R. (1987). Grouping conditions in listening to music: An approach to Lerdahl & Jackendoff's grouping preference rules. Music Perception, 4, 325-360.

Garrett, M.F. (1975). The analysis of sentence production. In G.H. Bower (Ed), The psychology of learning and motivation (pp. 133-177). NY: Academic Press.

Grosjean, F., Grosjean, L., & Lane H. (1979). The patterns of silence: Performance structures in sentence production. Cognitive Psychology, 11, 58-81.

Lerdahl, F., & Jackendoff, R. (1983). A generative theory of tonal music. Cambridge, MA: MIT Press.

Meyer, L.B. (1973). Explaining music. Berkeley: University of California Press.

Nakamura, T. (1987). The communication of dynamics between musicians and listeners through musical performance. Perception & Psychophysics, 41, 525-553.

Palmer, C. & Krumhansl, C.L. (1987). Temporal and pitch structures in determination of musical phrases. Journal of Experimental Psychology: Human Perception & Performance, 13, 116-126.

Palmer, C. (1989). Mapping musical thought to musical performance. Journal of Experimental Psychology: Human Perception & Performance, 15, 301-315.

Shaffer, L.H., Clarke, E.F., & Todd, N.P. (1985). Metre and rhythm in piano playing. Cognition, 20, 612-77.

Todd, N.P. (1985). A model of expressive timing in tonal music. Music Perception, 3, 33-59.

A Logic for Emotions: a basis for reasoning about commonsense psychological knowledge

Kathryn E. Sanders
Department of Computer Science, Brown University

Abstract

There is a body of commonsense knowledge about human psychology that we all draw upon in everyday life to interpret our own actions and those of the people around us. In this paper, we define a logic in which this knowledge can be expressed. We focus on a cluster of emotions, including approval, disapproval, guilt, and anger, most of which involve some sort of ethical evaluation of the action that triggers them. As a result, we are able to draw on well-studied concepts from deontic logic, such as obligation, prohibition, and permission. We formalize a portion of commonsense psychology and show how a simple problem can be solved using our logic.

1 Introduction

There is a body of commonsense knowledge about human psychology that we all draw upon in everyday life to interpret our own actions and those of the people around us. This knowledge is brought to bear by the reader in interpreting texts involving human actions and reactions.

In this paper, we define a logic in which commonsense knowledge about human psychology can be expressed. We formalize a portion of this knowledge and show how a simple problem can be formulated and solved using this logic. We focus on a cluster of emotions, including approval, disapproval, guilt, and anger, most of which involve some sort of ethical evaluation of the action that triggers them. As a result, we are able to draw on well-studied concepts from deontic logic, such as obligation, prohibition, and permission, in formalizing this knowledge.

In order to handle concrete problems, since emotions do not occur in a vacuum, it is also necessary to formalize some commonsense knowledge about actions and the probable evaluation of those actions by the agents and others. Specifically, we focus on a cluster of actions having to do with ownership and possession of property – giving, lending, selling, and stealing – and the predictable responses to those actions. We demonstrate that our logic is sufficiently expressive to handle a variety of information about human actions and responses, in a way that is substantially more formal than previous work in this area.

In this paper, we focus on the following example:

Jack went to the supermarket. He parked his car in a legal parking place. When he came out, it was gone.

Infer that Jack will be angry.

In Section 2, we describe the logic used in this paper. In Section 3, we outline a proof of the desired inference. In Section 4 we contrast our theory with previous work, and in Section 5 we present our conclusions and discuss future work.

2 The logic

2.1 Syntax

In this paper, we use an extension of the temporal logic developed in [Shoham 1988], modified to incorporate the three modal operators 'want,' 'know,' and 'believe.' We use an S5 axiom set for 'know,' weak S5 for 'believe,' T without veridicality for 'want,' and the inference rules modus ponens and universal instantiation (cf. [Hughes & Cresswell 1968]). Unlike Shoham, we assume that the intervals over which an assertion is interpreted are closed. Shoham deliberately makes no commitment one way or the other; we have found that, for purposes of our proofs, it is useful to make a choice, and in general, closed intervals seem more intuitive.

The syntax of our language is the same as in [Shoham 1988], with the following additions:

1. The symbols in the language include the three modal operators, 'want,' 'know,' and 'believe.'
2. If trm_a and trm_b are temporal terms and ϕ is a modal formula, then TRUE(trm_a, trm_b, ϕ) is a formula.

   The set of *modal formulas* is defined as follows:

   (a) If O is one of the three modal operators, x is a nontemporal term denoting some person, r is an n-ary relation symbol, and $trm_1, ..., trm_n$ are nontemporal terms, then $(O\ x\ (r\ trm_1 ... trm_n))$ is a modal formula.

   (b) If O is one of the three modal operators, x is a nontemporal term denoting some person, and ϕ is a modal formula, then $(O\ x\ \phi)$ is a modal formula.

2.2 Semantics

2.2.1 Informal semantics

Intuitively, the semantics of our language can be understood as follows. We are given a set that includes all of the possible worlds. Possible worlds have a temporal dimension. That is, each possible world is a complete possible history of the world, like a timeline extending infinitely far into the past and the future.

In all the worlds that are knowledge-accessible to an agent x, the propositions that x knows about the past, present, and future all hold. All other propositions vary from world to world. Similarly, in all the worlds that are belief-accessible to x (which may not include the 'real' world, if x has beliefs that are inconsistent with reality) all of x's beliefs hold. Propositions about which x has no particular opinion vary from world to world. Finally, the propositions that x wants to be true are true in all the 'want-accessible' worlds, the propositions x wants to be false are false, and propositions about which x is indifferent vary from world to world.

2.2.2 Formal semantics

Formally, the semantics of our language are as follows:

Let D be a domain of individuals, and let $P \subset D$ be a (nonempty) subset of D consisting of all of the persons in D. Let PW be the set of all possible worlds. With each $x \in P$ we associate three relations on PW, B_x, W_x, and K_x, corresponding to the modal operators 'believe', 'want', and 'know', respectively. Let O represent any one of the three modal operators, and let O_x represent any of the three relations. Each of these relations is serial, i.e., it has the property that from any given world at any time, at least one other world is accessible: $\forall w_i \in PW, \forall t_i(\exists w_j \in PW(O_x\ w_i\ w_j\ t_i))$. An interpretation I is a function that maps the nonlogical symbols in the language to some element of D.

Given these definitions, a sentence ϕ is true in a world $w_i \in PW$ under an interpretation I and a variable assignment VA if and only if one of the following is true:

1. ϕ has the form $trm_1 = trm_2$ and $I(w_i, trm_1) = I(w_i, trm_2)$.
2. ϕ has the form $trm_1 \preceq trm_2$ and $I(w_i, trm_1) \leq I(w_i, trm_2)$.
3. ϕ has the form $\text{TRUE}(trm_a, trm_b, (r\ trm_1 ... trm_n))$ and the relation $I(w_i, I(trm_a), I(trm_b), r)$ holds on $I(w_i, I(trm_a), I(trm_b), trm_1)$ through $I(w_i, I(trm_a), I(trm_b), trm_n)$.
4. ϕ has the form $\text{TRUE}(trm_a, trm_b, \psi)$, where ψ is a modal formula, in the form $\psi = (O\ x\ \zeta)$, O_x is the relation corresponding to O, and $\text{TRUE}(trm_a, trm_b, \zeta)$ holds in all worlds w_j such that $\forall t_i, trm_a \leq t_i \leq trm_b, (O_x\ w_i\ w_j\ t_i))$.
5. ϕ has the form $\phi_1 \wedge \phi_2$, and both ϕ_1 and ϕ_2 are true.
6. ϕ has the form $\neg\phi_1$, and ϕ_1 is false.
7. ϕ has the form $\forall z \phi_1$, and ϕ is true under all variable assignments VA′ that agree with VA everywhere except possibly on z.

2.2.3 Basic concepts

As stated above, we use some key concepts from deontic logic: 'permitted', 'prohibited', and 'obligated' [Wright 1951]. 'Permitted' is a predicate on actions. Thus, the proposition '(permitted rules (do x a))' is true in a given world if and only if the relation corresponding to the symbol 'permitted' holds on the elements corresponding to 'rules' and '(do x a)' in that world, that is, if x is in fact permitted by the body of rules in question (e.g., law or ethics) to perform that action. For example, we might have ¬(permitted Law (do Antigone (bury Polynices))) and ¬(permitted Religion (do Antigone ¬(bury Polynices))). Permission might also be granted by an individual, for example, (permitted Wilma (do Jack (take car))).

'Obligated' and 'prohibited' are defined in terms of 'permitted' in the usual way. An action is prohibited if performing it is not permitted. An action is obligated if *not* performing it is not permitted. Where the source of the rules is religion or ethics, these predicates might be expressed in terms such as 'right' and 'wrong', or 'should' and 'should not.' The more general formulation allows us to express a variety of types of rules and prohibitions using a single set of predicates.

anger $\forall x, t_1 \leq t_2, t_3 \leq t_4, y, a,$
[TRUE(t_1, t_2, (believe x TRUE(t_3, t_4, (occurs (do y a))))) $\wedge$
TRUE(t_1, t_2, (believe x TRUE(t_3, t_4, (obligated Ethics $\neg$(do y a))))) $\wedge$
TRUE(t_1, t_2, (want x TRUE($t_3, t_4, \neg$ (occurs (do y a))))) $\wedge$
TRUE(t_1, t_2, (believe x TRUE(t_3, t_4, (know y TRUE(t_3, t_4, (obligated Ethics $\neg$(do y a)))))))
$\leftrightarrow$
TRUE(t_1, t_2, (angry x y (do y a) t_3 t_4))]

You become angry at someone if you think they did something wrong, you didn't want them to do it, and you think they knew it was wrong.

gratitude $\forall x, a, t_3 \leq t_1 \leq t_2, t_3 \leq t_4 \leq t_2, y \neq x,$
[TRUE(t_1, t_2, (believe x TRUE(t_3, t_4, (occurs (do y a))))) $\wedge$
TRUE(t_1, t_2, (want x TRUE(t_3, t_4, (occurs (do y a))))) $\wedge$
TRUE(t_1, t_2, (believe x TRUE(t_3, t_4, (benefit x (do y a))))) $\wedge$
TRUE(t_1, t_2, (believe x $\neg$ TRUE(t_3, t_4, (conditional (do y a)))))
$\leftrightarrow$
TRUE(t_1, t_2, (grateful x y (do y a) t_3 t_4))]

You are grateful to someone if you think they did something that you wanted them to do that benefited you, and their action was not conditioned on receiving anything in return.

approval $\forall x, y, t_1 \leq t_2, t_3 \leq t_4, a,$
[TRUE(t_1, t_2, (believe x TRUE(t_3, t_4, (occurs (do y a))))) $\wedge$
TRUE(t_1, t_2, (believe x TRUE(t_3, t_4, (obligated Ethics (do y a)))))
$\leftrightarrow$
TRUE(t_1, t_2, (approve x y (do y a) t_3 t_4))]

You approve of someone if you believe that they have done something they should.

disapproval $\forall x, y, t_1 \leq t_2, t_3 \leq t_4, a,$
[TRUE(t_1, t_2, (believe x TRUE(t_3, t_4, (occurs (do y a))))) $\wedge$
TRUE(t_1, t_2, (believe x TRUE(t_3, t_4, (obligated Ethics $\neg$(do y a)))))
$\leftrightarrow$
TRUE(t_1, t_2, (disapprove x y (do y a) t_3 t_4))]

You disapprove of someone if you believe that they have done something they shouldn't.

shame $\forall x, t_1 \leq t_2, t_3 \leq t_4 \leq t_2, a,$
[TRUE(t_1, t_2, (believe x TRUE(t_3, t_4, (occurs (do x a))))) $\wedge$
$\exists y \neq x,$
[TRUE(t_1, t_2, (believe x TRUE(t_1, t_2, (disapprove y x (do x a) t_3 t_4)))) $\wedge$
TRUE(t_1, t_2, (want x TRUE(t_1, t_2, $\neg$(disapprove y x (do x a) t_3 t_4))))]
$\leftrightarrow$
TRUE(t_1, t_2, (ashamed x (do x a) t_3 t_4))]

You feel ashamed if you believe that you have done something that someone else thinks is wrong, you think they know what you've done, and you care what they think.

guilt $\forall x, t_1 \leq t_2, t_3 \leq t_4 \leq t_2, a,$
[TRUE(t_1, t_2, (believe x TRUE(t_3, t_4, (occurs (do x a))))) $\wedge$
TRUE(t_1, t_2, (believe x TRUE(t_3, t_4, (obligated Ethics $\neg$(do x a))))) $\wedge$
TRUE(t_1, t_2, (believe x TRUE(t_3, t_4, (know x TRUE(t_3, t_4, (obligated Ethics $\neg$(do x a)))))))
$\leftrightarrow$
TRUE(t_1, t_2, (guilty x (do x a) t_3 t_4))]

You feel guilty if you believe that you have done something that you think is wrong, and you believe that you knew it was wrong at the time you did it.

Figure 1: Definitions.

Therefore, immediately after Jack parked the car, it was at the parking place. At a certain later time, the car was not at the parking place. Things don't move by themselves. Therefore, someone must have moved it to another place. When things are moved, they are then at the location to which they were moved. Therefore, the car was then at the place to which it was moved.

Jack was at the parking place at a later time when his car was not there. People can't be in two places at once. Therefore, Jack was not at the place where the car was.

Jack owned the car. Jack did not possess the new place where the car was. If you move something out of someone's possession, you have taken it away from them. Therefore, someone took Jack's car between the time he parked it and the later time when it was not in its parking place.

Jack had not given anyone permission to take his car. Therefore, Jack had not given the person who took his car permission to take it. The law permitted Jack to park the car where he did (i.e., it was a legal parking place.) The law doesn't permit anyone to take a car unless it's parked in an illegal location, and then only if that person is an official. Therefore, the law did not permit whoever took Jack's car to do so.

The person who took Jack's car did not own the car. It is wrong (ethically prohibited) to take something that you do not own without the owner's permission. Therefore, it was wrong for the person who took Jack's car to do so.

Jack believes the axioms and can reason. Therefore, Jack believes that someone took his car, and that it was wrong for them to do so. If you own something and you haven't given anyone permission to take it, you don't want anyone to take it. Therefore, Jack didn't want anyone to take his car. Therefore, he was not grateful to the person who took his car.

All agents believe the axioms and can reason. Therefore, whoever took Jack's car knew it was wrong. Jack believes that whoever took his car knew it was wrong. It follows, therefore, that Jack is angry at the person who took his car.

4 Previous Work

Little previous work has been done in this area. Kube encodes a portion of commonsense psychology in [Kube 1985]. That paper is restricted to the ways in which people acquire knowledge and beliefs, however, and explicitly excludes any consideration of agents' emotions or intent.

Dyer attempted to incorporate psychological knowledge in his program BORIS [Dyer 1983]. BORIS's approach is substantially less formal than ours. It processes one basic story using some fairly simple definitions for the emotions involved. According to these definitions, for example, you are happy if you achieve a goal; if one of your goals fails or is suspended, you will be unhappy; and if someone else causes this to happen, you will become angry. In general, these goal-oriented definitions are too broad. For example, if you go to the bank and there is a long line at the teller machine, the people in front of you are causing one of your goals to fail – the goal of obtaining cash quickly. BORIS's definition would sanction the inference that you are angry at all of those people. Our definition would allow this inference only if you believe that their actions are wrong. You might become angry at someone who cut in front of you in line, but not at someone who merely arrived a few minutes before you.

Lehnert uses the concept of 'affect states' in her work on plot units, but makes no attempt to describe complex emotional states in detail. For her purposes, it was only necessary to distinguish between positive events, negative events, and neutral mental states [Lehnert 1982].

There is a substantial psychological literature on the emotions (See, e.g., [Strongman 1987] and works cited therein.) In general, however, this research disregards the kind of commonsense knowledge we are trying to encode. Instead, it focuses on such issues as the possible neurological causes of emotion. Rather than using a commonsense theory as a basis, even when addressing some of the same issues, this work usually takes an independent approach [Harre et al. 1985].

For our purposes, the most interesting of the psychological theories of emotion is the recent work by Ortony, Clore, and Collins [Ortony et al. 1988]. They attempt to characterize the range of possible emotions, rather than the emotional reactions which would be likely to occur in a given culture. They provide a broad framework which is generally consistent with our theory. Like our theory, theirs assumes that emotions are largely caused by people's beliefs about the world. They divide these beliefs into three categories – beliefs about actions, events, and objects – and divide emotions into three basic types, according to the kind of beliefs by which they are triggered. Thus, for example, joy is a positive response to an event, approval is a positive response to an action, and liking is a positive response to an object. All of the emotions considered in this paper would be classified as responses to actions; however, our theory could be extended to handle the other areas as well.

Unlike our theory, Ortony et al.'s work is very informal. Their terminology has no precise semantics. The reader must rely on intuition for the meaning of terms such as 'joy-intensity' and 'fear-potential.' Our theory introduces very few new primitives; most predicates are defined in terms of a small group of well-studied logical concepts. Cain and O'Rorke have begun working on a story-comprehension system based on Ortony et al.'s theory [Cain & O'Rorke 1988]. Because of the breadth of the underlying theory, their system promises to be more general than BORIS; however, like BORIS, this work should be considerably less formal than ours.

5 Conclusions and Future Work

In this paper, we define a logic in which commonsense knowledge about human psychology can be expressed. We demonstrate, by formulating and solving a set of benchmark problems, that our logic is sufficiently expressive to handle a variety of information about human actions and responses, in a way that is substantially more formal than previous work in the area.

Obvious extensions to this work include defining further emotions, such as hope, fear, surprise, and impatience, along with their causes and results. Because our theory is compositional, some extensions fall easily out of the definitions. For example, we could define an emotion that might be labelled 'remorse' – the response when you realize that you have done something wrong, although you didn't know it was wrong at the time – by modifying the definition of guilt only slightly. Other extensions could be obtained by incorporating additional predicates in the theory, perhaps following the directions suggested by [Ortony et al. 1988].

In addition, we would like to integrate this work with a theory of causation. Note that our rules purport to define the 'causes' of states such as anger, gratitude, shame, and guilt. For the purposes of this paper, we have treated the causal inferences as though they were equivalent to logical inference. Technically, however, causation is both stronger and weaker than logical inference (see discussion in [Shoham 1988], pp. 166ff). Ideally, a theory of emotion should incorporate a more precise understanding of causation.

Finally, we would like to explore an issue that is implicit in the definitions of approval and disapproval. Note that these definitions imply a symmetry between approval and disapproval that does not in fact exist. You might disapprove of someone for committing murder (say), but you do not constantly approve of everyone who is refraining from murder. Similarly, you might approve of someone who makes a large donation to charity, while not disapproving of those who do not.

This asymmetry results from a fact which holds for the other emotions as well: typically, we only react to things which we do not take for granted. You do not approve of everyone who fails to commit murder, unless the temptation is particularly severe, because you take that for granted. Similarly, children are not always grateful for the food, clothing, and shelter provided by their parents, because they take these things for granted. We only react to actions that we notice, for one reason or another. Possibly this could be tied in with notions of awareness and implicit/explicit knowledge from epistemic logic [Fagin & Halpern 1985]. Developing a general theory of what kinds of things we take for granted is outside the scope of this paper, but remains an interesting area for future work.

6 Acknowledgements

This research has been supported by NSF grants IRI 8515005 and IRI 8801253. The author gratefully acknowledges the assistance of Leora Morgenstern, Tom Dean, Eugene Charniak, Robert McCartney, and Mary Harper.

References

[Cain & O'Rorke 1988] Cain, Timothy, and Paul O'Rorke. Explanations involving emotions. *Proc. AAAI-88 Workshop on Plan Recognition.*

[Davis 1988] Davis, Ernest. Inferring Ignorance from the Locality of Visual Perception. *AAAI-88.*

[Dyer 1983] Dyer, Michael G. *In-Depth Understanding.* Cambridge, MA: MIT Press (1983).

[Fagin & Halpern 1985] Fagin, Ronald and Joseph Y. Halpern. Belief, Awareness, and Limited Reasoning: Preliminary Report. *IJCAI-85.*

[Harre et al. 1985] Harre, Rom, et al. *Motives and Mechanisms: an introduction to the psychology of action.* London: Methuen (1985).

[Hayes 1985] Hayes, Patrick. Naive Physics I: ontology for liquids. In *Formal Theories of the Commonsense World,* J. Hobbs and R. Moore, edd., Ablex 1985.

[Hughes & Cresswell 1968] Hughes, G.E. and M.J. Cresswell. *An Introduction to Modal Logic.* London: Methuen (1968).

[Kube 1985] Kube, Paul. Cognitive propositional attitudes. In *Commonsense Summer: Final Report.* Stanford University: Center for the Study of Language and Information, Report No. CSLI-85-35 (October 1985).

[Lehnert 1982] Lehnert, Wendy. Plot units: a narrative summarization strategy. In *Strategies for Natural Language Processing,* W. Lehnert and M. Ringle, edd., Hillsdale, NJ: L.E.A. (1982).

[McDermott 1982] McDermott, Drew. A Temporal Logic for Reasoning About Processes and Plans. *Cognitive Science 6:* 101-155 (1982).

[Ortony et al. 1988] Ortony, Andrew, et al. *The Cognitive Structure of Emotions.* Cambridge: Cambridge University Press (1988).

[Sanders 1989] Sanders, Kathryn E. *A Logic for Emotions: a basis for reasoning about commonsense psychological knowledge.* Tech. Rep. 89-23, Brown University Computer Science Dept.

[Shoham 1988] Shoham, Yoav. *Reasoning about Change: Time and Causation from the Standpoint of Artificial Intelligence.* Cambridge, MA: MIT Press (1988).

[Strongman 1987] Strongman, K. T. *The Psychology of Emotion.* Wiley (3d. ed. 1987).

[Wright 1951] Wright, G. H. von. *An Essay in Modal Logic.* North-Holland (1951).

Extracting Visual Information From Text: Using Captions to Label Human Faces in Newspaper Photographs

Rohini K. Srihari and William J. Rapaport

Department of Computer Science
State University of New York at Buffalo
Buffalo, New York 14260 USA

ABSTRACT

There are many situations where linguistic and pictorial data are jointly presented to communicate information. A computer model for synthesising information from the two sources requires an initial interpretation of both the text and the picture followed by consolidation of information. The problem of performing general-purpose vision (without apriori knowledge) would make this a nearly impossible task. However, in some situations, the text describes salient aspects of the picture. In such situations, it is possible to extract visual information from the text, resulting in a relational graph describing the structure of the accompanying picture. This graph can then be used by a computer vision system to guide the interpretation of the picture. This paper discusses an application whereby information obtained from parsing a caption of a newspaper photograph is used to identify human faces in the photograph. Heuristics are described for extracting information from the caption which contributes to the hypothesised structure of the picture. The top-down processing of the image using this information is discussed.

INTRODUCTION

There are many situations where words and pictures are combined to form a communicative unit; examples in the print media include pictures with captions, annotated diagrams, and weather charts. In order for a computer system to synthesise the information from these two diverse sources of information, it is necessary to perform the preliminary operations of natural-language processing of the text and image interpretation of the associated picture. This would result in an initial interpretation of the text and image, following which an attempt at consolidation of the information could be made. Although vision and natural-language processing are challenging tasks, since they are severely under-constrained, natural-language processing can more easily exploit constraints posed by the syntax of the language than vision systems can exploit constraints about the physical world. This fact, combined with the observation that the text often describes salient features of the accompanying picture in joint communicative units, leads to the idea of using the information contained in the text as a guide to interpreting the picture. This paper focuses on a method of extracting visual information from text, which results in a relational graph describing the hypothesised structure of the accompanying picture (in terms of the objects present and their spatial relationships). The relational graph is subsequently used by a vision system to guide the interpretation of the picture. We describe the implementation of a system which labels human faces in a newspaper photograph, based on information obtained from parsing the caption. A common representation, namely a semantic network, is used for the knowledge contained in both the picture and the caption. The theory is general enough to permit construction of a picture when given arbitrary descriptive text (without an accompanying picture).

Newspaper photographs have all the elements required for a true integration of linguistic and visual information. Accompanying captions usually identify objects and provide background information which the photograph alone cannot. Photographs, on the other hand, provide visual detail which the captions do not. Newspaper captions often identify people in a picture through visual detail such as "Tom Jones, wearing sunglasses ...". In order for a computer system to be able to identify Tom Jones, it is necessary to understand the visual implication of the phrase "wearing sunglasses". The face satisfying all the implied visual constraints could then be labeled accordingly.

The idea of integrating natural language and vision has been relatively unexplored. [Abe *et al.*, 1981; Yokota *et al.*, 1984] are two systems which consider the bidirectional flow of control from text to a related picture and vice versa. Several systems have implemented a portion of the task. Generating natural-language descriptions of results obtained from a vision system is considered in [Maddox and Pustejovsky, 1987; Neumann and Novak, 1983]. The reverse process of generating pictures based on natural-language input is considered in [Adorni *et al.*, 1984; Waltz and Boggess, 1979]. [Herskovits, 1986] discusses a theory of encoding and decoding English expressions of location, which focuses on the meaning of prepositional phrases. In the research being presented here, the emphasis is on generating a description of a picture (rather than a picture itself), such that the description can be used by a vision system to actually find the required objects and relationships in an associated picture. [Zernik and Vivier, 1988] attempts a similar task when given locative expressions pertaining to airport scenes.

This paper describes a three-stage process used to identify human faces in newspaper photographs. We consider only those photographs whose captions are factual but sometimes incomplete in their description of the photograph. In the first stage, information pertaining to the story is extracted from the caption, and a structure of the picture in terms of the objects present and spatial relationships between them is predicted. The information contained in this structure would be sufficient for generating a picture representing the meaning of the caption. Using this information to label faces in an existing picture however, entails further processing. The second stage which constitutes the vision component, calls on a procedure to locate human faces in photographs when the number of faces and their approximate sizes are known. Although the second stage locates faces, it does not know whose they are. The last stage establishes a unique correlation between names mentioned in the caption and their corresponding areas in the image. These associations are recorded in a semantic network and enable us to selectively view human faces as well as obtain information about them. Input to the system is a digitized image of a newspaper photograph with a caption, as in Figure 1a. The system returns a labeling of parts of the image corresponding to the faces of the people mentioned in the caption, as in Figure 2a and Figure 2b.

PROCESSING THE CAPTION

The process of interpreting the caption has two main goals. The first is the representation of the factual information contained in the caption. This is explicit information provided by the caption, namely the identification of the people in the photograph and the context under which the photograph was taken. More important for our application, however, is the second goal, the construction of a relational graph representing the expected structure of the picture. The relational graph includes information such as the objects hypothesised to be in the picture, their physical appearance, and spatial relationships between them. This is similar to dynamic schema construction

[Weymouth, 1986]. We use the SNePS knowledge-representation and reasoning system to represent both factual information and the relational graph derived from the caption [Shapiro and Rapaport, 1987]. A common representation facilitates the integration of information from both sources. SNePS is a fully intensional, propositional, semantic-network processing system in which every node represents a unique concept. It can perform node-based and path-based inference [Srihari, 1981], and it also provides a natural-language parsing and generating facility [Shapiro, 1982].

Figure 3 illustrates a small portion of the output of the parser on processing the caption of Figure 1a. It postulates that two humans, namely Diandra (**m12**) and Michael (**m11**), are present in the picture and that Diandra is to the left of Michael (**m41**). We separate factual information obtained from the caption (**m6**) from derived visual information (**m7**). The hypothesised presence of an object in the picture is represented by a node such as (**m30**). This node represents the proposition that an object (whose visual model is represented by **m31**) is present in the picture (whose visual model is **m7**) and that the object is explicitly mentioned in the caption. Node (**m61**) associates the visual model of an object (**m31**) with the node representing the individual mentioned in the caption (in this case, Diandra). For the visual model represented by node **m31**, the model description is contained in the sub-network represented by nodes **m32** and **m34**. The model description of objects reflects configuration details of the object which can be obtained from the caption. Currently, the model description for a human consists of one default configuration containing the single component "face". If the situation arises where some people are standing and others seated, the parser inserts "top-of" relationships to represent the height discrepancies. This information is vital to the face labeling process. We indicate that sofas may be in the picture by using the value "inferred" for the relation "type", as in node (**m42**). At present, we restrict our search for objects to faces only.

Predicting Objects

There are three classes of heuristics used to extract information from the caption: rules that predict the presence of objects, rules that predict spatial relations between objects and rules that predict configurations of objects. Depending on the type of sentence, several rules are used to predict the presence of objects in a picture. We have observed that many captions are of the form "<subject list> <prepositional-phrase list>". A <prepositional-phrase list> is a series of preposition + noun-phrase pairs, as in the caption of Figure 1a. In such sentences, we propose that each of the subjects in <subject list> is present in the picture. A more interesting question is which of the noun phrases in <prepositional-phrase list> are present in the picture. We can judge whether the entire object is present in the picture based on its scale. We carefully avoid predicting objects which are mentioned in the caption but are not present in the picture. In Figure 1a, although we expect to see components of an apartment such as a sofa (Figure 3), we do not expect to see anything pertaining to New York. In many phrases of the form "<subject> <verb-phrase> <direct-object>", the verb-phrase (e.g., wearing, holding, greeting) indicates the presence of the direct object in the picture. The notion of time is very important here. Captions are traditionally in the present tense even though they refer to events in the past. We have observed that any object referred to at a time previous to the current time is not in the picture.

We also stress the importance of correctly predicting the class of an object. A recent photograph in *The Buffalo News* depicted a horse and her trainer. The caption was "Winning Colors being grazed by her trainer, Wayne Lucas, yesterday morning before the running of the Kentucky Derby". A simplistic parser might conclude that the name "Winning Colors" referred to a human, based on the fact that it was a sequence of two capitalized words serving the subject role in a sentence. This would predict the presence of two human faces and thus provide incorrect data to the face-location module. A more sophisticated parser would realise that the object of "grazing" is usually an animal such as a cow or a horse. If the parser had access to information about the Kentucky Derby, it could conclude definitely that "Winning Colors" was a horse. If this information were not known, the vision component of the system would be called on to disambiguate between the possiblities of a horse and cow. The last case illustrates the bi-directional flow of information from the caption to the picture and vice versa.

Predicting Spatial Relations Between Objects

Specifying spatial relations between objects is the principal method of identification. The caption often explicitly specifies the spatial relation, as in "Thomas Walker, left, John Roberts, center ..." thus making the task relatively simple. However, it is not as simple in the case of captions which combine implicit and explicit means of identification. Consider the caption "The All-WNY boys volleyball team surrounds the coach of the year, Frontier's Kevin Starr. Top row, from left, are ..." accompanying a group photograph. The spatial location of the coach must be inferred first through a detailed understanding of the word *surrounds*. The row and column relationships can then be correctly interpeted. Such examples provide are providing a real challenge to both the language-parsing as well as the face-locating stages of our system.

An implicit method of identification frequently used is the ordering of the subjects in the caption to reflect their order in the picture. Our grammar has been designed to assert the spatial relation *left-of* when parsing a list of subjects. This heuristic was used in generating the network of Figure 3. There is frequent departure from the above convention in pictures depicting well-known subjects or in male-female pairs since it is assumed that the reader can disambiguate. Our grammar is designed to raise a flag whenever it encounters such cases, indicating further evidence is required before identification can be made. The labeling procedure uses world knowledge (such as relative heights) to establish a unique correlation between names mentioned in the caption and faces located in the photograph.

Some caption types use detailed information from the picture pertaining to an object in order to uniquely identify that object. For instance, consider the caption "Joseph Crowley, holding the pennant, Thomas Jones ...". The only way to identify Joseph Crowley is first to identify a pennant and then to determine which person in the picture is holding it. Here, identification is not achieved through the constraints posed by spatial relations, but through identification of another object followed by a test for proximity.

Predicting Configurations of Objects

The model description for a class of objects contains a description of a prototype for that class. In the absence of any further information, only the default portions of the model will be instantiated. However, there is often detailed information in the caption pertaining to the specific configuration of an object, which can be represented by instantiating optional components (or configurations) in the model description of the particular object. A simple example of this is the use of words such as "sitting" or "standing" which express different configurations of human body parts. The phrase "shaking hands with" implies a configuration of the arms perpendicular to the body, and the hands of the individuals touching. Consider a caption which refers to a baseball player "diving" for a ball. The use of the word "dive" along with the context of baseball suggest a more horizontal configuration of the body. This information can be valuable if it becomes necessary to detect the entire body (torso, legs etc.), rather than just the face. Jackendoff [Jackendoff, 1987] summarises this idea by saying that many verbs of station and locomotion are used more to express 3D configurations of objects than to express action. Our grammar has been designed to add to or change the default configurations of humans if the text suggests it.

PROCESSING THE PICTURE

Picture processing in this project is the process of using the information in the hypothesised structure to find relevant objects and spatial relationships in the picture. Currently, we only deal with human faces. Since the caption often gives us spatial constraints on the location of objects, it is frequently sufficient to use crude object-detection modules. In this application, we use a face-locator module which generates candidates for faces. It is often the case that spatial constraints alone are sufficient for eliminating false candidates.

Using caption information and heuristics from photojournalism [Arnold, 1969], the possible range of face sizes appearing in a newspaper photograph can be narrowed. From the caption, we are able to determine the number of faces and some weak bounds on the size of faces. These constitute parameters to the face-location module, which works in three stages: feature selection, feature detection, and grouping. We have selected as features the two arcs corresponding to the hair-line and the chin-line, and the two lines corresponding to the sides of the face. These features seem to be robust, since they are not greatly affected by factors such as scale, viewing position, or resolution. Furthermore, they are relatively easy to detect. A first-level Hough transform detects the arcs and collinear edge-elements in the image. A line-finder then uses back-projection from the accumulator array to the original image to extract line segments. The curves and line segments are grouped together by a modified Hough transform to generate candidate regions for locations of faces [Govindaraju *et al.*, 1989].

For each image area hypothesised to be a face, this module returns the coordinates of a bounding rectangle for that area. This facilitates the representation of image data in the semantic network. Figure 1b illustrates the performance of the face-locator on the image shown in Figure 1a.

REFINING CANDIDATES AND LABELING FACES

This section describes how faces can be labeled by using the spatial information contained in the caption and heuristics obtained from photojournalism. In general, the location procedure generates more candidates than required (Figure 1b). We have already shown how linguistic heuristics can be used to derive spatial constraints from the caption when they are not explicitly given. These constraints are applied to the candidates generated by the face-locator in an attempt to first reduce the number of candidates and eventually produce a unique labeling of faces (Figures 2a and 2b).

Because a large number of candidates are generated by the face-locator, spatial constraints alone cannot produce a unique binding between candidates and people mentioned in the caption. We employ additional refinement rules to reduce the number of possibilities. Some of these update the confidence of a candidate pair satisfying a spatial relation, while others update the confidence of the candidate itself. An example of the former is a rule which decreases the confidence of a pair of candidates satisfying a *left-of* or *right-of* relationship where there is a significant vertical difference between the two candidates (in captions where no height discrepancy is indicated). Examples of the second type of rule include one which uses intrinsic image features to update the confidence of a candidate and another which favours centrally located (in the image) candidates.

Identification rules currently operate on pairs of candidates. They contain world knowledge such as "Reagan is taller than Carter" and allow us to further reduce the candidate set. After all the rules have been applied, we employ a procedure which selects the globally best binding based on the confidences of pairs as well as confidence of the candidates comprising the pair. Labeling information is represented in the semantic network by asserting nodes which associate concepts of people with the corresponding areas in the image. In cases where the system cannot uniquely identify faces, all possible candidates for each person appearing in the caption are recorded.

SUMMARY

Our system for understanding newspaper pictures with captions consists of a three-stage process whereby the caption is first parsed with the goal of predicting the structure of the picture. The second stage uses information from the first stage in a top-down processing of the image. The final stage, labeling, is the process of matching pictures of objects with the words representing them in the caption.

The next step in this research is generating visual models for expressions containing certain verb phrases which have a similar visual implication to everyone (e.g. wearing hat, shaking hands). Such phrases are frequently used in captions to identify people in the photograph.

This work was supported by National Science Foundation grants IRI-8613361 and IRI-8610517.

References

[Abe *et al.*, 1981] N. Abe, I. Soga, and S. Tsuji. A Plot Understanding System on Reference to Both Image and Language. In *Proceedings of IJCAI-81*, pages 77–84, 1981.

[Adorni *et al.*, 1984] Giovanni Adorni, Mauro Di Manzo, and Fausto Giunchiglia. Natural Language Driven Image Generation. In *Proceedings of COLING-84*, pages 495–500, 1984.

[Arnold, 1969] Edmund C. Arnold. *Modern Newspaper Design.* Harper and Row, New York, 1969.

[Govindaraju *et al.*, 1989] Venu Govindaraju, David B. Sher, Rohini K. Srihari, and Sargur N. Srihari. Locating Human Faces in Newspaper Photographs. In *Proceedings of CVPR*, 1989.

[Herskovits, 1986] Annette Herskovits. *Language and spatial cognition.* Cambridge University Press, 1986.

[Jackendoff, 1987] Ray Jackendoff. On Beyond Zebra: The Relation of Linguistic and Visual Information. *Cognition*, 26(2):89–114, 1987.

[Maddox and Pustejovsky, 1987] Anthony B. Maddox and James Pustejovsky. Linguistic Descriptions of Visual Event Perceptions. In *Proceedings of the 9th Annual Cognitive Science Society Conference*, pages 442–454, Seattle, 1987.

[Neumann and Novak, 1983] B. Neumann and H. Novak. Event Models for Recognition and Natural Language Description of Events in Real-World Image Sequences. In *Proceedings of IJCAI-83*, pages 724–726, 1983.

[Shapiro, 1982] Stuart C. Shapiro. Generalized Augmented Transition Network Grammars For Generation From Semantic Networks. *American Journal of Computational Linguistics*, 8(2):12–25, 1982.

[Shapiro and Rapaport, 1987] Stuart C. Shapiro and William J. Rapaport. SNePS Considered as a Fully Intensional Propositional Semantic Network. In Nick Cercone and Gordon McCalla, editors, *The Knowledge Frontier: Essays in the Representation of Knowledge*, pages 262–315, Springer-Verlag, New York, 1987.

[Srihari, 1981] Rohini K. Srihari. *Combining Path-based and Node-based Reasoning in SNePS.* Technical Report 183, SUNY at Buffalo, 1981.

[Waltz and Boggess, 1979] David L. Waltz and L. Boggess. Visual Analog Representation for Natural Language Understanding. In *Proceedings of IJCAI-79*, pages 926–934, 1979.

[Weymouth, 1986] T.E. Weymouth. *Using Object Descriptions in a Schema Network for Machine Vision*. PhD thesis, University of Masschussetts at Amherst, 1986.

[Yokota *et al.*, 1984] Masao Yokota, Rin-ichiro Taniguchi, and Eiji Kawaguchi. Language-Picture Question-Answering Through Common Semantic Representation and its Application to the World of Weather Report. In Leonard Bolc, editor, *Natural Language Communication with Pictorial Information Systems*, Springer-Verlag, 1984.

[Zernik and Vivier, 1988] Uri Zernik and Barbara J. Vivier. How Near Is Too Far? Talking about Visual Images. In *Proceedings of the Tenth Annual Conference of the Cognitive Science Society*, pages 202–208, Lawrence Erlbaum Associates, 1988.

(a)

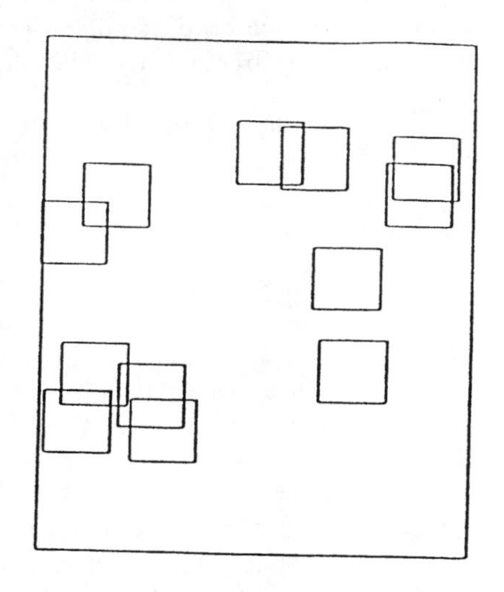

(b)

Figure 1: *(a) a newspaper photograph with caption "Diandra and Michael Douglas at their New York apartment (b) candidates generated by the face-locator module*

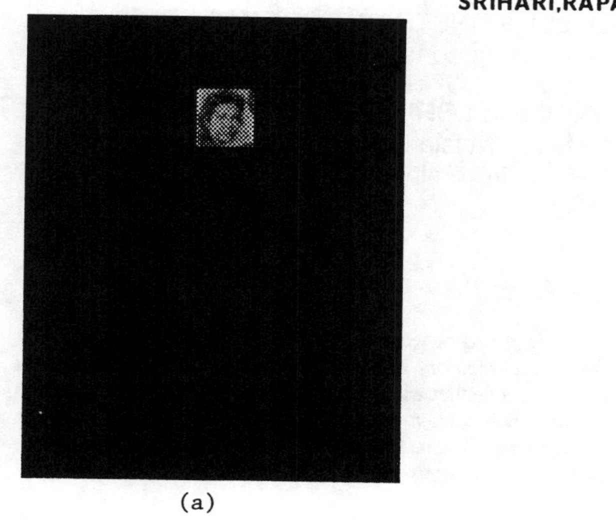

(a)

(b)

Figure 2: *(a) output of system when asked to display Diandra (b) output of system when asked to display Michael*

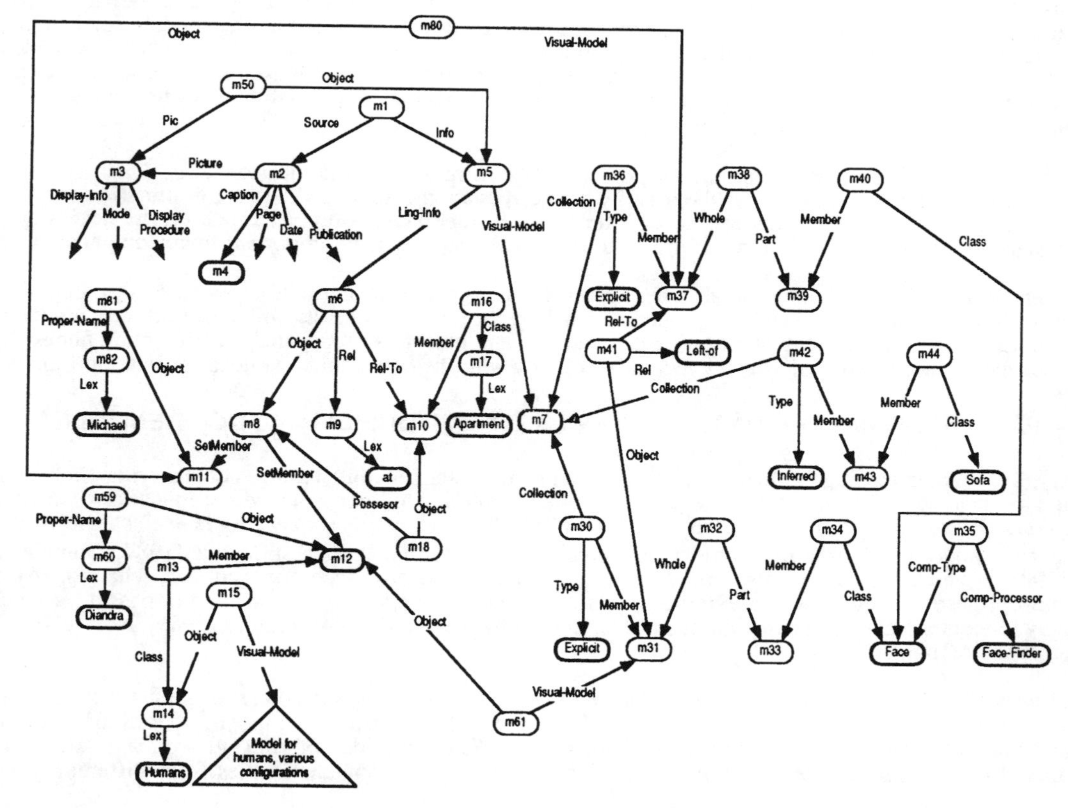

Figure 3: *partial output of the parser on caption of Figure 1a*

HEAD-DRIVEN MASSIVELY-PARALLEL CONSTRAINT PROPAGATION:
Head-features and subcategorization as interacting constraints in associative memory

HIDETO TOMABECHI and LORI LEVIN
Center for Machine Translation
Carnegie Mellon University

ABSTRACT

We will describe a model of natural language understanding based on Head-driven Massively-parallel Constraint Propagation (HMCP). This model contains a massively parallel memory network in which syntactic head-features are propagated along with other information concerning the nodes that triggered the propagation. The propagated head features eventually collide with subcategorization lists which contain constraints on subcategorized arguments. These mechanisms handle linguistic phenomena such as case, agreement, complement order, and control which are fundamental to linguistic analysis but have not been captured in previous marker-passing models.

INTRODUCTION

This paper describes a theory of Head-driven Massively-parallel Constraint Propagation (HMCP). The main motivation for our proposal is the inadequacy of traditional marker-passing models for handling syntactic phenomena such as word order, agreement, case marking, control, and unbounded dependencies. The HMCP paradigm diverges from traditional massively-parallel marker-passing schemes (and connectionist models for that matter), in that the model explicitly allows for syntactic and semantic constraints to be propagated in structured-markers.[1]

In the HMCP paradigm, markers that are propagated contain: 1) syntactic head-features which constrain the combination of constituents, 2) the identity of the activation source, and 3) cost information which is relevant to ambiguity resolution and other inferences. In this paper, we concentrate on the necessity of propagating syntactic *head* feature information to properly capture some important linguistic phenomena.

Under the HMCP model, conceptual nodes representing argument-taking predicates carry subcategorization features which specify syntactic properties (such as case) of constituents which can fill their argument positions. Syntactic information such as case, number, and person is propagated up from noun phrases in a package of 'head features' which eventually collides with the constraints in subcategorization frames.

FAILURE OF MARKER-PASSING MODELS TO CAPTURE SYNTACTIC PHENOMENA

In typical marker-passing (and connectionist) based natural language processing models, syntactic knowledge is handled in either of two ways: 1) a linear ordering of concepts with sequential prediction markers (Riesbeck&Martin[1985], Tomabechi[1987]) which we call a *concept sequence* scheme in this paper[2] 2) nodes configured in a context-free manner (Waltz&Pollack[1985], Bookman[1987], Sumida, *et al*[1988]), which we call a *categorial tree* scheme (i.e., the localist type connectionist scheme). Also, some of these schemes require external modules to handle syntax, using the marker-passing scheme solely for contextual inferences (Charniak[1983/1986], Granger, *et al*[1984], Hendler[1986], Norvig[1987], Tomabechi&Tomita[1988]).

In Riesbeck[1986], the *concept sequence* [*actor* PTRANS-word *dest*] is a template for inputs such as *John flew-to Paris.* This scheme has the advantage of being able to capture the temporal ordering of concepts in an utterance regardless of their levels of abstraction. Thus, the idea of *concept sequence* allows for a model of *phrasal lexicon* (Becker[1975]) which is extended to contain entities from different levels

[1]The HMCP algorithm is described in Tomabechi&Tomita[ms].

[2]There are also schemes to use trained networks for sequential activations (e.g., Servan-Schreiber, *et al*[1988]). Discussions of *concept sequence* schemes should apply to such schemes as well.

of abstraction in the same phrasal lexicon[3]. For example, in the above sentence, the abstract concept *actor* which may be linked to specific scriptal knowledge is coexisting with a more surface specific entity, PTRANS-word. On the other hand, this extended notion of *phrasal lexicon* is all the syntax these models have. Precisely because these models abandoned the notion of syntactic category (and other syntactic features), any generalizations that are captured as interactions between different syntactic categories are either lost or redundantly specified by each *concept sequence*. The *cateogrial tree* scheme is in essence similar to the *concept sequence* scheme in terms of the expressivity of the context-free rules, except that the notion of grammatical categories is introduced and semantic features are represented through separate links.

In general, there are three problems with current traditional marker-passing models: (1) they do not adequately represent syntactic information such as syntactic category, case, number, and verb form. (2) They do not have a notion equivalent to the *head of a phrase* (Jackenoff[1977]) which is subcategorized for the syntactic features of its complements. (3) Interactions are strictly local. Because each sequence is independent, there is no way for an element of a concept sequence to see inside another element of the same sequence. For example, the concept sequence [*PERSON *MTRANS-word that *ACTION] used in recognizing *Sue said that Mary ran* will be activated by any instance of *MTRANS-word and any instance of *ACTION. There is no way to ensure that if the *MTRANS-word is *say*, the set of entities that caused the activation of *ACTION must contain a finite verb. (Unless we create many new concepts such as *fINITE-FORM-RUNNING-ACTION-TAKING-NOMINATIVE-SUBJECT, in which case we will lose generalizations.) The same holds with the *categorial tree* scheme because the contents of embedded nodes are (by the definition of context-free tree) invisible to the external nodes.

The rest of this section lists some syntactic phenomena which have not been addressed in traditional marker passing models.

SUBCATEGORIZING FOR HEAD FEATURES OF COMPLEMENTS

(1)

a. I believe John studies at CMU.

b.*I believe John study at CMU.

c.*I believe John studying at CMU.

The contrast between (1)a, (1)b, and (1)c, is that *believe* is subcategorized for an embedded clause whose head verb takes finite form but base form or present participle form. Correct treatment of grammaticality in these examples requires the non-local operation of passing up head features from *study* to *believe*. As we have already described, traditional concept sequence schemes do not adequately handle non-local interactions and do not have a method for passing up head features of embedded verbs so that they can be constrained by a higher verb.[4]

AGREEMENT OF ANAPHORS AND CONTROL

The following sentences from Pollard[ms] involve additional non-local interactions in *control* and *agreement.*

(2)

a. He tried/seemed to wash himself/*herself.

b. He promised her to wash himself/*herself.

c. She persuaded him to wash himself/*herself.

d. She believed him to be washing himself/*herself.

e. She appealed to him to wash himself/*herself.

[3]See Hovy[1988] for the use of such a scheme in generating a natural language.

[4]Some recent connectionist research (such as Elman[1988] and Servan-Schreiber, *et al*[1988]) has shown some promising results in training simple recurrent networks to develop expectations to capture grammatical category, and to develop some expectations about concepts and words in embedded sentences. However, they have yet to capture the complexity of grammatical constraints in natural language.

Correct assignment of meaning (and grammaticality judgements) is not possible in traditional marker passing schemes because: (1) There is no way to specify generalizations about behavior of groups of syntactic (categorial) nodes such as, Governing Category in GB, Chomsky[1981]. In traditional marker passing schemes, the pronominals and anaphors in the embedded clauses would probably be bound to any contextually salient entity as long their semantic content agrees (i.e., *MALE-PERSON, etc.). (2) There is no way for the main verb to determine anything about the subject of its complement (for example, that it is controlled by the main clause subject) because the concept sequence containing the main verb cannot see inside the concept sequence corresponding to the controlled clause.

WORD ORDER CONSTRAINTS BASED ON OBLIQUENESS

In English, the order of a verb's arguments is partly determined by their relative obliqueness; less oblique complements precede more oblique phrasal complements. (Pollard&Sag[1987]) In the examples in (3) the constraint is that "adverb phrase is the most oblique sister of the post-verbal complements, and hence must follow them all" (Pollard&Sag). Concept sequences can specify the well formed orderings (3)a and (3)b by writing surface-specific concept sequences for the possible combinations, but because they do not represent grammatical functions or a hierarchy of obliqueness of arguments, they will miss the generalization about complement order.

(3)

a. He looked up the number quickly.

b. He looked the number up quickly.

c.*He looked the number quickly up.

d.*He looked quickly up the number.

e.*He looked quickly the number up.

f.*He looked up quickly the number.

WORD ORDER CONSTRAINTS BASED ON THE POSITION OF THE HEAD

Since traditional marker-passing schemes do not have a notion of syntactic head, they cannot capture generalizations about the ordering of complements with respect to the head. (e.g., that the head is always final or that the head is always initial). Japanese allows free ordering of the complements of a verb, but the verb has to come after all of its complements. However, without a notion of head, the only way to specify head-final word order in Japanese is to write surface-specific concept sequences for all possible orders of complements all of which have the head at the end, but this fails to capture generalizations about free complement order in Japanese.

The problems we have identified in this section are inherently problematical in parsing natural language input and are fatal in generating grammatical sentences.

HEAD-DRIVEN MASSIVELY-PARALLEL CONSTRAINT PROPAGATION (HMCP) PARADIGM

CONSTRAINT PROPAGATION

The underlying philosophy of our model is that words (or some smaller linguistic unit) in the input string trigger the propagation of structured markers through a network. The markers carry information about the source of the activation, including many syntactic features. Concepts that represent heads of phrases contain bundles of syntactic features which constrain their complements. When activations of complements collide with activations of heads, the syntactic features of the complement and head are unified. Using propagated constraints and features in this way, it is possible for a head to constrain syntactic properties of its complements such as syntactic category, case, agreement features and whether they can be expletive. It is also possible to specify principles of word order based on obliqueness and the head initial/final distinction. Because most of the features that are propagated and constrained are labeled as *head-features* in linguistic theory (such as GPSG (Gazdar, *et al*[1985]), and HPSG), our model is named Head-driven Massively-parallel Constraint Propagation (HMCP) model.

THE NOTION OF HEAD

The *lexical head* of a phrase is a word which determines many of the syntactic properties of the phrase as a whole (Jackendoff[1977], Pollard&Sag[1987]). Thus the lexical head of a verb phrase or sentence is a verb, the lexical head of a prepositional phrase is a preposition, and so on. The features of the head, determine what syntactic environments the phrase can occur in. For example, a clause headed by a finite verb can occur as a complement of the verb *believe*, but verb phrases headed by present participles cannot occur in this environment. In the HMCP model, we are currently adopting head-features similar to those postulated in the HPSG framework. These include major category, case features, verb forms (tensed, finite, base, and participle forms), noun forms (expletive and normal), and many others. We also include agreement features which are not treated as syntactic head features in some syntactic theories.

These head-features are propagated upward from the lexical head (i.e., the node that is a head and that was activated by the input) and are carried as constraints on future marker collisions and further spreading activation.

THE NOTION OF SUBCATEGORIZATION

Lexical items are organized into subcategories depending on the number and kind of other nodes that they combine with in oder to recognize (or generate) a sentence. Subcategorization is different from the notion of *concept sequence* in that it is independent of the surface order of constituents. In our system, as in HPSG, the subcategorization list reflects the obliqueness order of the grammatical functions that are subcategorized for. It is also a list of constraints that need to be satisfied by nodes that fill argument positions in order to make recognition (and generation) complete. These constraints are most likely to be syntactic head-features that are propagated by lexical activations; however, there may also be semantic constraints on the fillers of argument positions. *Concept sequences*, on the other hand, represent only linear order of concepts and fail to capture syntactic constraints (i.e., head-features) that need to be satisfied in order to complete the subcategorization. Thus, the notion of subcategorization and *concept sequence* should not be confused.

LAYERED NETWORK

FOUR LAYERS OF NETWORK

Under the HMCP model, the network has different layers (not to be confused with the hidden layers in neural-net frameworks) that are independent of the semantic-net based abstraction hierarchy. Currently the layers are 1) the Static Layer (SL) 2) the Potential-activation Layer (PL), 3) the Active-Layer (AL) and 4) the Decaying-Layer (DL). The SL and AL are perhaps analogous to short-term memory (STM) and long-term memory (LTM) in the traditional psychology literature. The layers represent groups of nodes which are differentiated by the level (and time) of activation.

The SL is the layer which nodes belong to by default before the first utterance in the discourse. It is an associative network of memory with nodes corresponding to memory structures that represent entities at different levels of abstraction from phonemic nodes to discourse level nodes.

The PL contains nodes that are potential candidates for filling slots in subcategorization lists.

The AL contains nodes that are activated by words in the current sentence using a standard upward activation scheme (e.g., DMA) and that meet the subcategorization constraint check. At the end of the sentence, the AL will be the nodes that correspond to the elements of all the accepted subcategorization lists. Syntactic constraints such as complement order constraints and parameter-based discourse constraints (such as CENTER and PIVOT constraints (Tomabechi[ms])) apply at this layer. Discourse functions such as *Forward-looking Center (Cf)* (Grosz, *et al*[1986]) and *potential foci* (Sidner[1983]) are also defined at AL.

The DL is simply the AL of the preceding utterance. The levels of activation of nodes in DL decay with time and the nodes will eventually return to SL. The least oblique element of the immediately preceding utterance in this layer corresponds to *Backward-looking Center (Cb)* (Grosz, *et al*) and *discourse focus* (Sidner[1983]).

HMCP CONSTRAINT PROPAGATION

The following three things are propagated from lexically activated nodes: 1) head-features attached to the node, 2) identity of the instance node that is associated with the current lexical activation (i.e., which specific instance should be associated or created with the current lexical activation) and 3) the specific cost (weight) associated with the given lexical activation. The last two are discussed in detail in Tomabechi, *et al*[1989] and Kitano, *et al*[1989] and therefore, will not be discussed in this paper.

EXAMINATION OF THE MODEL WITH A CONTROL CONSTRUCTION

We will describe the HMCP parsing model by walking through the parse of *John tried to give Mary the book*. The equi verb *try* specifies that the entity associated with its subject be shared with that of the unexpressed subject of its VP complement. In other words, *try* specifies that it subcategorizes for a complement which is itself unsaturated and there is a dependency between the embedding subject and the embedded subject. This phenomenon is known as *control*.

Before parsing the sentence, all nodes that potentially satisfy an element of a subcategorization list are put into the Potential-activation Layer (PL). In this example, nodes corresponding to *try* and *give* contain subcategorization lists as the value of the subcat feature. In the node corresponding to *try*, NP[NOM] in the subcategorization list is coindexed with *PERSON in the *trier* role, so *PERSON is added to the PL. *ACTION, *OBJECT, and all other concepts coindexed with subcategorized positions are concurrently added to the PL (massive parallelism). All other nodes in the network are in the Static Layer (SL).

We will be using a network of semantic memory similar to the ones described in the DMA and associative memory literature following the tradition of semantic networks since Quillian[1968,1969] using structured memory nodes (such as Mops, Schank[1982]). For example, the lexical concepts representing the verbs *give* and *tried* are encoded in the network as below:

```
(lex-node *GIVE
 (is-a (*ACTION))
 (phonology </g/ /i/ /v/>)
 (syn-head-feature ((MAJ V) (VFORM BSE) (AUX MINUS)))
 (giver (*PERSON 1))
 (receiver (*PERSON 2))
 (given (*OBJECT 3))
 (subcat <(NP[NOM] 1), (NP[ACC] 2), (NP[ACC] 3)>))

(lex-node *TRY
 (is-a (*ACTION))
 (phonology </t/ /r/ /a/ /i/ /d/>)
 (syn-head-feature ((MAJ V) (VFORM FIN) (AUX MINUS)))
 (trier (*PERSON 1))
 (circumstance (*ACTION 2))
 (subcat <(NP[NOM] 1), ((((MAJ V)
                           (VFORM INF))
                          subcat<(NP 1)>)
                         2)>))
```

The list (NP[NOM] 1) in the subcat feature is a short-hand for (((MAJ N) (CASE NOM)) 1).

The first word *John* activates the node *JOHN and the activation is propagated upward in the abstraction hierarchy along with the head features. When the activation reaches a node in the PL, in this case *PERSON, the head features carried in the activation are checked against the constraints on the position that it fills in a subcategorization list. In this example, the activation triggered by *John* carries the head feature NP[NOM], which is checked against and satisfies the NP[NOM] constraint on the *trier* role. When the constraints on a node in the PL are met, it moves to the AL. In this case, *PERSON moves to the AL. If the constraints are not met, the node moves back to SL.

The constraints on *PERSON are checked concurrently for every other verb and every other role that can be filled with *PERSON. In each parallelly spawned[5] (forked) environment for each concurrently recognized subcategorization, *PERSON is either moved to AL or SL. Thus the processing is massively parallel in nature.

The next word, *tried*, activates the node *TRY, which is subcategorized for NP[NOM] coindexed with *PERSON. In the environment (for the evaluation that was spawned) where *PERSON was trying to get into the *trier* role of *TRY, NP[NOM] is removed from the subcategorization list and the parse continues looking for the other subcategorized argument of *try*. In parallel environments where *PERSON was trying to fill roles for other verbs, nothing happens.

Recognition of *to give Mary the book* continues in a similar manner. *Mary* fills the *receiver* role and *the book* fills the *given* role and (NP[ACC] 2) and (NP[ACC] 3) are removed from the subcategorization list. When items are removed from a subcategorization list, the new subcategorization list and the head features are propagated upward. In this case, *GIVE propagates a subcategorization list of one element, NP[NOM], and the head features of *give*, ((MAJ V) (VFORM bse) (AUX minus)). The concept *ACTION in the PL receives this activation, which satisfies the constraints on the *circumstance* role of *TRY. *TRY specifies that the NP[NOM] which fills the *trier* role is coindexed with the NP[NOM] inside the VP which fills the *circumstance* role. This now indicates that *John* fills the *giver* role in *GIVE. This way, the phenomenon known as control is handled in the HMCP model.

CONCLUSION

It has been accepted in the linguistic and psychological communities that syntactic constraints play an important role in many types of linguistic phenomena. Yet it is our claim that in the current marker-passing and connectionist based natural language schemes, very little has been accounted for in terms of syntactic constraints and the interactions of syntax, semantics and pragmatics. Methods that have been employed for capturing syntactic phenomena have been mostly ad hoc. For example, in the traditional marker passing schemes, the notion of *concept sequence* has been accepted as a central method of capturing English word-order. However, it has been observed that English word order is best described in terms of the obliqueness order of grammatical functions. In *categorial tree* schemes, the nodes were simply organized in a context-free manner and constraints based upon the internal features of the embedded nodes, which are vital in handling phenomena such as control, have not been captured (similarly with the *concept sequence* schemes).

The HMCP model attempts to model interactions among various syntactic features as well as between syntax, semantics and pragmatics in a principled manner. We have seen that HMCP handles case, agreement, and control based upon subcategorization and head-feature propagation. The method of handling subcategorization in HMCP (not presented here for reasons of space) allows for capturing generalizations based on categories and syntactic-features of complements. Therefore, our analysis does not suffer from the adhocness associated with the traditional marker-passing schemes. The layered network based on activation status allows for complement order constraints based on obliqueness, head-initial/head-final distinctions, and discourse-parameter based constraints to be applied at the AL only and thus, the number of parallel constraint applications are controlled to be minimum.

[5]Our algorithm requires a pure parallelism (such as supported by Multilisp (Halstead, *et al*[1986])) in that in order to evaluate two things in parallel (i.e., consideration of two concurrently recognized subcategorizations by two different verbs requiring NP[NOM] filling *person), a new task is spawned to evaluate one of them. The environment of the spawned task must be exactly the same environment as was in effect when the spawn occurred. This means we have massively-parallel worlds (environments) representing each subcategorization check.

The HMCP model is massively-parallel in nature and evaluations are spawned (provided with independent environments) for each subcategorization that is active. HMCP is based upon a massively-parallel structure-passing (MSP) algorithm which presupposes a neural-network that is capable of passing around some amount of information. (One such neural-net architecture, Frequency Modulation Neural Network (FMNN) and its phenomenological plausibility are described in Tomabechi&Kitano[1989]). Currently the MSP algorithm is supported on MULTILISP which is a true parallel Lisp developed at MIT (Halstead, *et al*[1986]) which runs on MACH (Rashid, *et al*[1987]) at CMU.

ACKNOWLEDGEMENTS

The authors would like to thank Jaime Carbonell, Masaru Tomita, Hiroaki Kitano, Hitoshi Iida and Carl Pollard for their assistance in various aspects of work reported in this paper. Thanks are also due to the members of the Center for Machine Translation for fruitful discussions.

References

[1] Becker, J.D. (1975) 'The phrasal lexicon'. In *Theoretical Issues in Natural Language Processing.*

[2] Bookman, L.A. (1987) 'A Microfeature Based Scheme for Modelling Semantics'. In *Proceedings of the IJCAI-87.*

[3] Charniak, E. (1983) 'Passing Markers: A theory of Contextual Influence in Language Comprehension'. *Cognitive Science* 7.

[4] Charniak, E. (1986) 'A neat theory of marker passing'. In *Proceedings of the AAAI-86.*

[5] Chomsky, N. (1981) *Lectures on Government and Binding*, Foris.

[6] Elman, J. (1988) Finding structure in time. CRL TR-8801. Center for Research in Language, University of California, San Diego.

[7] Gazdar, G., Pullum, G., and Sag, I. (1985) *Generalized Phrase Structure Grammar.* Harvard University Press.

[8] Granger, R. and Eiselt, K. (1984) 'The parallel organization of lexical, syntactic, and pragmatic inference processes' In *Proceedings of the First Annual Workshop on Theoretical Issues in Conceptual Information Processing.*

[9] Grosz, B, Joshi, K, and Weinstein, S. (1986) Towards a computational theory of discourse interpretation. Preliminary draft.

[10] Halstead, R., Loaiza, J., and Ma, M. (1986) *The Multilisp Manual.* Massachusetts Institute of Technology.

[11] Hendler, J. (1986) *Integrating Marker-Passing and Problem Solving: A Spreading Activation Approach to Improved Choice in Planning.* Department of Computer Science, University of Maryland.

[12] Hovy, E. (1988) *Generating Natural Language Under Pragmatic Constraints.* Lawrence Erlbaum Associates.

[13] Jackendoff, R. (1977) *X-bar Syntax: A study of Phrase Structure.* MIT Press.

[14] Kitano, H., Tomabechi, H and Levin. L., (1989) 'Ambiguity Resolution in ΦDMTRANS'. In *Proceedings of the fourth Conference of the European Chapter of the Association for Computational Linguistics.*

[15] Norvig, P. (1987) 'Inference in Text Understanding'. In *Proceedings of the AAAI-87.*

[16] Pollard, C. and Sag, I. (1987) *An Information-based Syntax and Semantics*, Volume I. CSLI.

[17] Quillian, M.R. (1968) 'Semantic Memory'. In *Semantic Information Processing*, ed. Minsky, M. MIT Press.

[18] Quillian, M.R. (1969) *The teachable language comprehender.* BBN Scientific Report 10.

[19] Rashid, R., A. Tevanian, M. Younge, D. Youge, R. Baron, D. Black, W. Bolosky and J. Chew (1987) 'Machine-Independent Virtual Memory Management for Paged Uniprocessor and Multiprocessor Architectures'. CMU-CS-87-140. Carnegie Mellon University.

[20] Riesbeck, C. (1986) 'From Conceptual Analyzer to Direct Memory Access Parsing: An Overview'. In *Advances in Cognitive Science 1*, ed. Sharkey, N. Ellis Horwood Ltd.

[21] Riesbeck, C. and Martin, C. (1985) *Direct Memory Access Parsing*. Yale University Report 354.

[22] Schank, R. (1982) *Dynamic Memory: A theory of learning in computers and people*. Cambridge University Press.

[23] Servan-Schreiber, D., Cleeremans, A., and McClelland, J. (1988) 'Encoding sequential structure in simple recurrent networks'. CMU-CS-88-183, Carnegie Mellon University.

[24] Sidner, C. (1983) Focusing in the comprehension of definite anaphora. In M. Brady and R. Berwick, ed., *Computational Models of Discourse*, MIT Press.

[25] Sumida, R., Dyer, M. and Flowers, M., (1988) 'Integrating Marker passing and Connectionism for Handling Conceptual and Structural Ambiguities'. In *Proceedings of the Tenth Annual Conference of the Cognitive Science Society*.

[26] Tomabechi, H. (1987) 'Direct Memory Access Translation'. In *Proceedings of the IJCAI-87*.

[27] Tomabechi, H. and Tomita, M. (1988) 'The Integration of Unification-based Syntax/Semantics and Memory-based Pragmatics for Real-Time Understanding of Noisy Continuous Speech Input'. In *Proceedings of the AAAI-88*.

[28] Tomabechi, H. and Tomita, M. Manuscript. 'Massively Parallel Constraint Propagation: Parsing with Unification-based Grammar'. Center for Machine Translation, Carnegie Mellon University.

[29] Tomabechi, H., and Kitano, H. (1989) 'Beyond PDP: the Frequency Modulation Neural Network Architecture'. In *Proceedings of the IJCAI-89*.

[30] Tomabechi, H., Kitano, H., Mitamura, T., Levin, L., Tomita, M. (1989) *Direct Memory Access Speech-to-Speech Translation: A Theory of Simultaneous Interpretation*. CMU-CMT-89-111, Carnegie Mellon University.

[31] Waltz, D. L. and Pollack, J. B., (1985) 'Massively Parallel Parsing: A Strongly Interactive Model of Natural Language Interpretation.' *Cognitive Science* 9(1).

Virtual Memories and Massive Generalization in Connectionist Combinatorial Learning

Olivier Brousse and Paul Smolensky

Department of Computer Science &
Institute of Cognitive Science
University of Colorado at Boulder
Boulder, CO 80309-0430
olivier@boulder.colorado.edu
smolensky@boulder.colorado.edu

Abstract

We report a series of experiments on connectionist learning that addresses a particularly pressing set of objections to the plausibility of connectionist learning as a model of human learning. Connectionist models have typically suffered from rather severe problems of inadequate generalization (where generalizations are significantly fewer than training inputs) and interference of newly learned items with previously learned items. Taking a cue from the domains in which human learning dramatically overcomes such problems, we see that indeed connectionist learning can escape these problems in *combinatorially structured domains*. In the simple combinatorial domain of letter sequences, we find that a basic connectionist learning model trained on 50 6-letter sequences can correctly generalize to about 10,000 novel sequences. We also discover that the model exhibits over 1,000,000 *virtual memories*: new items which, although not correctly generalized, can be learned in a few presentations while leaving performance on the previously learned items intact. We conclude that connectionist learning is not as harmful to the empiricist position as previously reported experiments might suggest.

1. Introduction

Two important capabilities of human learning that connectionist models have until now seemingly failed to share are these: Acquiring competence from a small set of examples, as children do when they learn their native language by being exposed to only a very small fraction of what they are ultimately competent with, and fast learning of new items with no interference, as when we learn new fact from a single presentation. More specifically, connectionism has until now suffered from the following two problems:

> *The connectionist generalization problem:* Generalizations are few, and do not outnumber training examples. Current models suggests that in order to obtain correct performance on a target set of inputs, a network needs to be trained on a sizable fraction (between 25% and 75%) of the learning set. (While the amount of information that is available during training is still an open issue in the ongoing debate between empiricists and nativists, it would be hard to find *anyone* even remotely comfortable with the idea that children are exposed to 25%-75% of their ultimate competence).
>
> *The connectionist interference problem:* New items to be learned are in current practice intermingled with all the previously trained inputs and subjected again to the lengthy and rather laborious training algorithm. Several experiments have shown that if a network successfully trained on one set of items is then trained on another, the network will unlearn the first set. In McCloskey & Cohen (1988), this is referred as "catastrophic interference."

There is no doubt that connectionism would fail in its claim to be a plausible model for human learning if catastrophic interference and weak generalization were invariably prevailing in all domains. We have hypothesized, however, that connectionist networks will not suffer from the two problems mentioned above in *combinatorial domains*. In this paper we will further define this hypothesis, and report on a series of experiments supporting it.

2. Hypothesis

Taking a cue from the domains in which human learning dramatically overcomes the problems of slow and interferential learning, like language and facts, we have hypothesized that connectionist models will not suffer from the generalization and interference problems in *combinatorial domains.* More specifically, we hypothesize that in such domains, we will see:

Massive generalization: To learn a set of inputs, only a fraction of the set will need to be trained upon.

Fast, interference-free learning: Once a network has learned a subset of inputs, to learn a new input which shares in the structure of previously trained inputs, the new input will only need to be presented a few times and there will be no interference with the previously trained inputs although they are not be trained again.

We will take a domain to be combinatorial if the elements in the domain are constructed by combining smaller elements, and if the correct processing of larger elements can be generalized from correct processing of smaller elements of which they are composed, taking due consideration of the means of composition.

3. Experiments

To test our hypothesis, we have chosen one of the simplest combinatorial domains possible: Cartesian products of sets. X_i are sets, for $i = 1, \dots, n$, and our combinatorial domain is

$$X = X_1 \times X_2 \times \cdots \times X_n = \{(x_1, x_2, \dots, x_n) \,/\, x_i \in X_i\}$$

X is the domain consisting of sequences of n elements, the ith element in each sequence being some member of X_i. In our experiments, all X_i have the same number of elements. We train an auto-associative network on a randomly selected subset of the chosen domain, and then test and train for correct association each of the remaining items of the domain, one by one. The auto-associative network, associating each item with itself, can be interpreted as a graded *recognizer* of whether an input shares in the regularities of the training set.

In our connectionist experiments, each element of each set was represented in the network as some pattern of activities. It is these patterns, of course, that matter, and not whatever name we find convenient to give to the elements. In this paper we will use letters as convenient labels for these elements. As a further convenience we will use the same set of labels for each set X_i in the Cartesian product, but again this is of no consequence. (In particular the network is not charged in any way with discovering that we like to use the same letter to label an element in X_1 and an element in X_2.) Thus if $n = 4$, a typical element of X could be written (A, B, A, C) or, more simply, as the string ABAC. We call the number of elements in X_i A, the alphabet size.

Architecture and training technique

The connectionist learning technique we used is a standard one: auto-association using back-propagation learning.

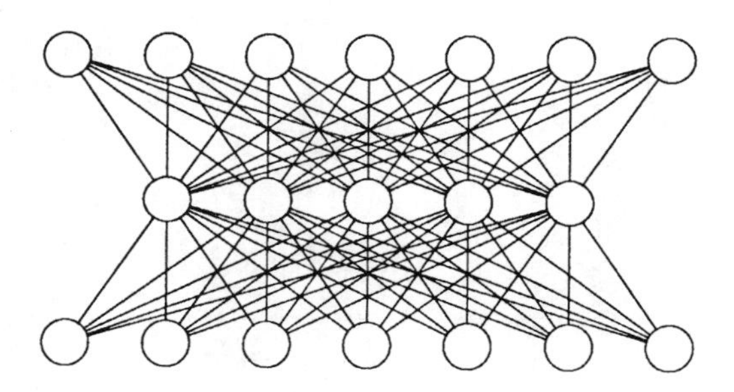

Figure 1: Architecture of the networks used in these experiments

The network is a three-layer feed-forward network in which the input layer and output layer have N units and the hidden layer has H units. The architecture is shown in Figure 1. Each training input (one of the elements of X) is represented as a pattern of activity on the N input units according to a mapping described below. The target output on the N output units is identical to the input pattern: the network must associate each element of X with itself. The network was trained with standard back-propagation, the units of the network being semi-linear units as in Rumelhart, Hinton and Williams (1986).

Representation

Each of the n elements in X were coded using tensor product representation as defined in Smolensky (1987). Random binary vectors were generated to represent each $x_i \in X_i$ (fillers) while the associated roles were a vector representing the set X_i it belonged to. In all the experiments we will report on, the role vectors were simply the vectors of null activities with the exception of the ith coordinate of X_i which had activity 1. The representations were thus semi-local, as defined in Smolensky (1987), and amounted to a simple concatenation of the representations of the x_i's. Thus, in the case $n = 3$, if the random binary vectors of activities representing $x_1 \in X_1$, $x_2 \in X_2$ and $x_3 \in X_3$ were (1, 0, 1, 1, 0), (0, 0, 1, 0, 0) and (1, 1, 1, 0, 0), respectively, then the vector of activities representing (x_1, x_2, x_3) was simply (1, 0, 1, 1, 0, 0, 0, 1, 0, 0, 1, 1, 1, 0, 0) = (1, 0, 1, 1, 0) * (1, 0, 0) + (0, 0, 1, 0, 0) * (0, 1, 0) + (1, 1, 1, 0, 0) * (0, 0, 1), where * denotes the tensor product operation.

Performance measures

Our basic measure of the network's performance on a particular input was the number of output units that were "correct": within a certain error criterion ε of the correct value. In all experiments reported in this paper, we used $\varepsilon = 0.4$. For each experiment, the network was initialized with a random set of small weights, and the back-propagation algorithm was applied to each pattern of the training set, in a random order, weight updates being performed after each pattern presentation. Application of the learning algorithm to the training set was repeated until all inputs were correctly associated according to the performance measure mentioned above. The reader can refer to the appendix for further information on the training procedure and the values of the experimental parameters. In many experiments the "control group" against which performance was tested was the set of all possible inputs with activities in $\{0, 1\}$. We called patterns belonging to this set "random bit patterns".

4. Results

4.1. Regularity detection: English 4-letter words

We report here on early experiments designed to test the basic assumption that a feed-forward auto-associator is capable of learning through back-propagation to recognize whether an unfamiliar sequence shares in the combinatorial regularities characterizing some domain.

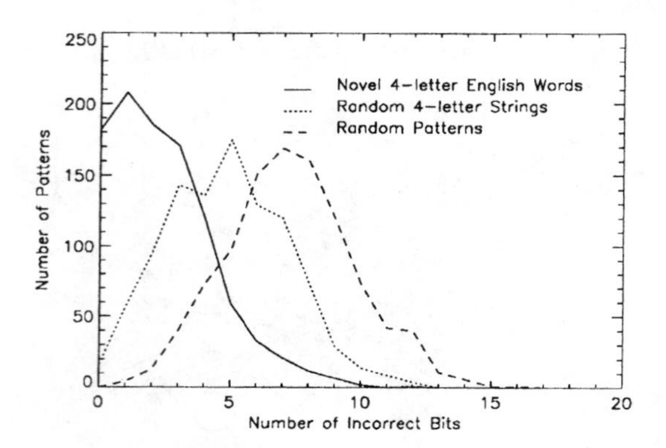

Figure 2: Generalizations; Network trained on 100 English 4-letter words. The network generalizes best on novel English words, then on 4-letter strings, then on random bit patterns.

We took the domain X to be a set of 1100 4-letter English words, and trained a network (here and henceforth, a back-propagation feed-forward auto-associator) on 100 randomly selected such words. We then tested its generalization ability on the 1000 remaining untrained words, on 1000 randomly selected 4-letter strings, and 1000 random bit patterns. If the network can recognize the degree to which new patterns share in the regularities with the training set, it should generalize best with English words, then 4-letter strings, then random-bit patterns. This is confirmed experimentally in Figure 2, where 87% English words have less that 5 incorrect bits, versus 45% for random strings and 22% for random bit patterns.

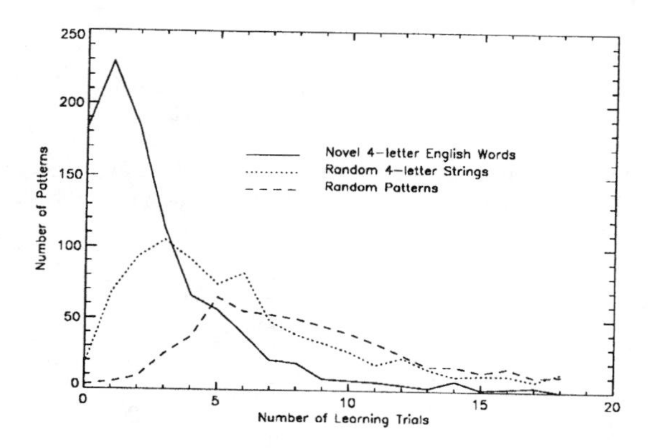

Figure 3: Number of weight updates to learn a new input, after training on 100 4-letter English words. The network learns novel English words the fastest, then 4-letter strings, then random bit patterns.

Not only do new inputs that share in the regularities of the training set produce fewer erroneous output bits, but they are also easier to learn, as shown in Figure 3.

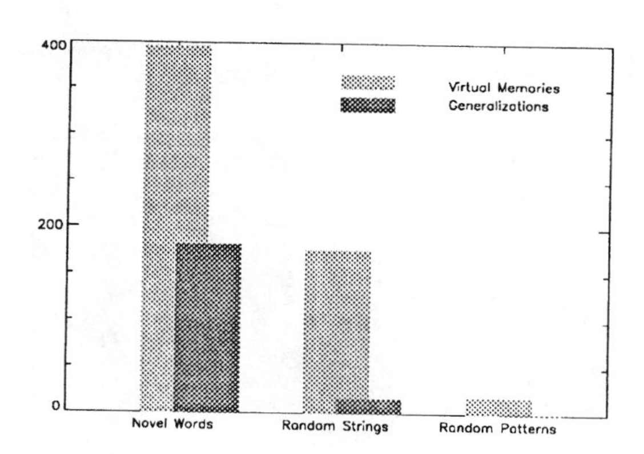

Figure 4: The number of generalizations and virtual memories for the network trained on 100 English 4-letter words.

In the following experiments we will summarize information on generalization and ease of learning of a new input by reporting just the number of generalizations (the number of novel patterns with zero incorrect bits) and the number of *virtual memories*. We define a virtual memory to be a novel input which can be trained to criterion while *leaving performance on the training set error-free*. Figure 4 shows both the generalizations and virtual memories for 1000 untrained words, 1000 randomly selected 4-letter strings, and 1000 random bit patterns. (For computational time reasons, we restricted the number of learning trials when testing for a virtual memory to 5. All our results concerning their number are thus lower bounds only: The use of lower learning rates and/or larger number of trials could yield higher numbers. We will henceforth mean virtual memories that can be learned in less than 5 trials when we refer to virtual memories.) We observe that the number of generalizations and virtual memories is the biggest for the set of English words, then for the set of random 4-letter strings. For the random selection of 1000 random bit patterns, there were simply no generalizations.

4.2. Learning in the Cartesian product domain

In this section we describe the results of our main experiments, addressing learning in Cartesian product domains $X = X_1 \times X_2 \times \cdots \times X_n$ for various values of n and sets X_i.

Generalization: The number of generalizations in networks trained on 50 inputs in the case $A = \|X_i\| = 26$ and $n = 2,3, ..., 6$ is shown in Figure 5, in a semi-logarithmic plot. For the cases $n = 2$ and $n = 3$, it was possible to test the entire set of untrained inputs;

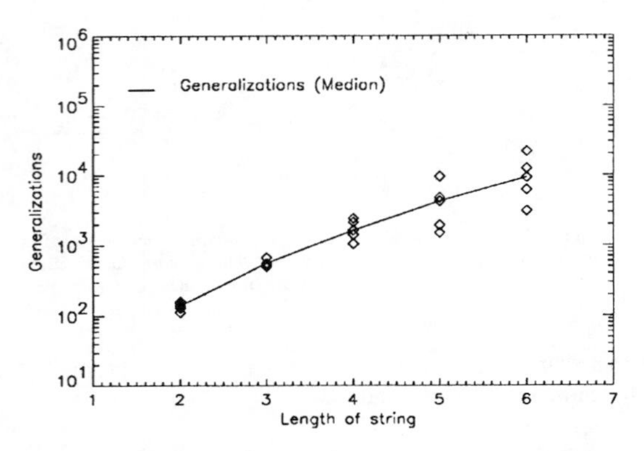

Figure 5: The number of generalizations for networks trained on sets of size 50, with $A = 26$, as n varies from 2 to 6.

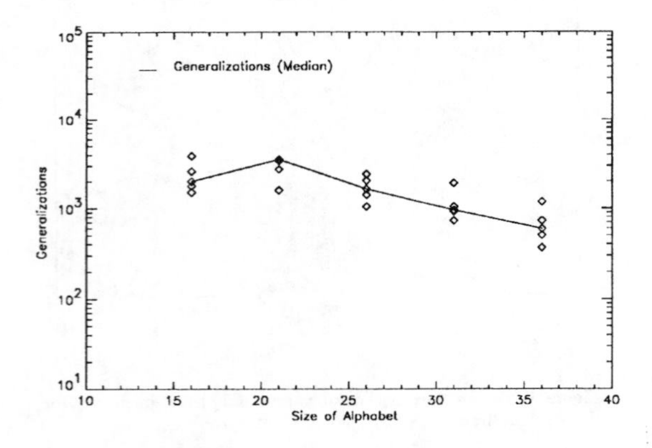

Figure 6: The number of generalizations for networks trained on sets of sizes 50, with $n = 4$, and $A = 16, 21, 26, 31, 36$.

The number of generalizations for these two cases is thus exact. For the cases $n = 4, 5, 6$, complete testing was not feasible for computational time reasons. We therefore tested a sample of T randomly-generated inputs (with replacement). The number of generalizations plotted (and later, the number of virtual memories) is thus an estimate, assuming unbiased samples. For each value of the varying parameter (in this case n), we repeated our experiments 5 times (as in all subsequent experiments), each time starting with new random initial weights, a new randomly selected training set, and a new randomly selected testing set of T patterns in the cases $n = 4, 5, 6$. For $n = 4$ and 5, T was 10,000. For $n = 6$, T was 100,000 for generalizations and 10,000 for virtual memories. Figure 5 displays the number of generalizations obtained for each experiment, as well as the median number of generalizations obtained. Figure 6 shows the number of generalizations as the size of X_i's vary.

Virtual memories: Figure 7 shows the number of virtual memories in the case of a network trained on 50 input patterns, for $n = 2, 3, ..., 6$.

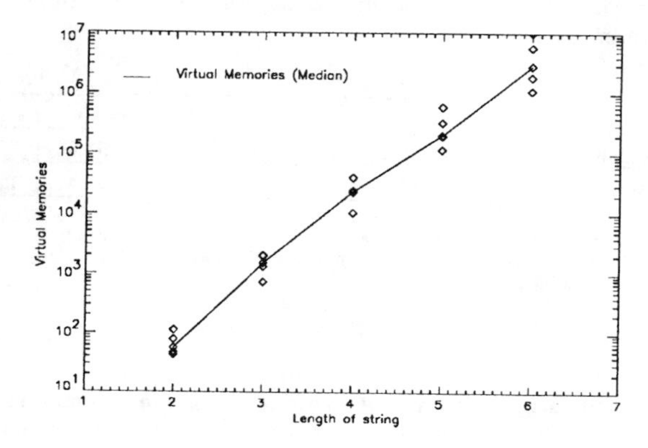

Figure 7: The number of virtual memories for networks trained on sets of size 50, with $A = 26$, as n varies from 2 to 6.

As the combinatorial complexity of the domain increases, we see that large numbers of virtual memories are obtained. For $n = 6$, for instance, we estimate that about 2.8 million virtual memories exist.

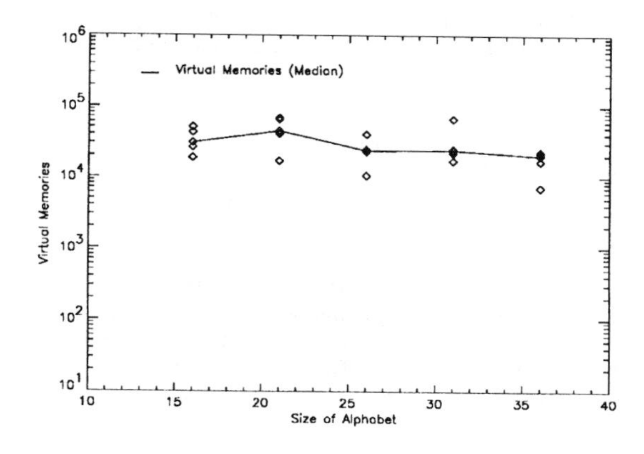

Figure 8: The number of virtual memories for networks trained on sets of sizes 50, with $n = 4$, and $A = 16, 21, 26, 31, 36$.

Figure 8 shows the number of virtual memories for networks trained on sets of size 50, with $n = 4$ and $A = 16, 21, 26, 31, 36$.

Discrimination tests: To see how well our networks were doing at discriminating elements from non-elements of X, we conducted a number of tests using random bit patterns. Although in all our experiments the number of hidden units was always smaller than the number of input and output units, thus preventing the network from computing the identity function, we needed to make sure that it was not computing even an approximation of it. This is confirmed in table 1, where the first row shows the ratio of the number of generalizations in a sample of 10,000 members of X (with $A = 26$ and $n = 4$) to the number of generalizations obtained by testing the same networks with 10,000 random bit patterns. The second row shows the ratios of the number of virtual memories in a sample of 10,000 members of X (with $A = 26$ and $n = 4$) and the number of virtual memories obtained by testing the same networks with 10,000 random bit patterns. We see that the networks generalize poorly for random bit patterns, about 1/35th as well as for elements of X. Similarly, there are about 1/10th as many random bit vectors which are virtual memories as elements of X. Statistical analyses, along with results of additional experiments on discrimination, can be found in Smolensky, Brousse & Mozer (forthcoming).

Experiments	**1**	**2**	**3**	**4**	**5**
Discrimination Ratio for Generalizations	46.99	22.99	51.86	35.22	31.46
Discrimination Ratio for Virtual Memories	6.81	10.40	10.41	12.19	7.26

Table 1: Ratios of generalizations for members of X and random-bit vectors, and ratios of vitual memories for members of X and random-bit vectors.

5. Conclusion

Further experiments and analyses to illucidate these results are in progress, but computational costs are a limiting factor. The data points alone displayed here represent the multiprocessor equivalent of roughly 5,400 hours of Sun3 time. The experiments reported above give optimistic results with respect to the generalization and interference problems for connectionist learning. A fuller discussion of these experiments may be found in Smolensky, Brousse & Mozer, forthcoming. While training a network from scratch may be a lengthy process, we have seen that once a network has acquired some knowledge of the combinatorial domain on which the training is performed, subsequent learning of members of the domain is much easier and less prone to interference than was previously thought. Although we do *not* provide evidence that connectionist induction algorithms are stronger than previously available inductive techniques, we do believe that we have provided evidence that connectionism is more compatible with an empiricist position on human learning than previous results would suggest—at least within combinatorial domains.

Acknowledgments

The authors would like to thank Michael Mozer and Jay McClelland, as well as Gary Bradshaw, Clayton Lewis, Michael Main, and Kelvin Wagner for insightful conversations about this research. Special thanks also to the users of the Encore Multimax machine at the University of Colorado at Boulder for tolerating intensive CPU usage. Computer simulations used a modification of the back propagation simulator of McClelland & Rumelhart (1988).

This work has been supported by NSF grants IRI-8609599 and ECE-8617947 to the second author, by a grant to the second author from the Sloan Foundation's computational neuroscience program, and by the Optical Connectionist Machine Program of the NSF Engineering Research Center for Optoelectronic Computing Systems at the University of Colorado at Boulder.

Appendix: Experimental parameters

In all our experiments, the momentum was 0.9 and the error criterion ε was 0.4 both for training and for testing of virtual memories. The learning rate was 0.01 for training and 0.2 for virtual memory learning, except for $n = 2$ where the training learning rate was 0.005. The vectors representing X_i were random binary vectors of length 8. H, the number of hidden units, was linearly increased as n increased according to $h = 5 \times n$, resulting in a constant compression factor of 8:5 from input to hidden units. Initial weights were generated pseudo-randomly, with equal probability in the interval [-0.5, 0.5]. Patterns in the training set were presented to the network in a random order during an epoch, and weights were updated after each pattern. Because gradient descent suffers from the problem of local minima, some training sets could not be learned in a reasonable time. When that happened we simply started the experiment over. When the error for all inputs of the training sets reached 0, we trained again for 10 epochs to ensure stability. (Since weights are changed after each pattern presentation, a total error of 0 at the end of one epoch does not guarantee that the next will still contain error-free patterns.) All networks were standard three-layer feed-forward back-propagation networks, with bias on all hidden and output units.

The following table shows other relevant parameters. We only show minima and maxima for the number of epochs during training displayed in the rightmost columm. The column labeled "Training set" refers to the number of input patterns in the training sets used.

Figure	Domain X: A	Domain X: n	X: Constraint	Hidden Units	Training Set	Epochs
2	26	4	English	20	100	255
3	26	4	English	20	100	255
4	26	4	English	20	100	555
5	26	Varies	none	Varies ($5n$)	50	119-486
6	Varies	4	none	20	50	164-259
7	26	Varies	none	Varies ($5n$)	50	119-486
8	26	4	none	20	50	164-259

References

McClelland, J.L. & Rumelhart, D.E. (1988). *Explorations in Parallel Distributed Processing: A handbook of models, programs, and exercises.* Cambridge, MA: MIT Press/Bradford Books.

McCloskey, M., & Cohen N.J. (1988). Catastrophic interference in connectionist networks: The sequential learning problem. To appear in G. H. Bower (Ed.), *The Psychology of learning and motivation: Volume 23.*

Rumelhart, D.E., Hinton, G.E., & Williams, R.J. (1986). Learning internal representations by error propagation. In D. E. Rumelhart, J. L. McClelland, & the PDP Research Group, *Parallel distributed processing: Explorations in the microstructure of cognition. Volume 1: Foundations.* Cambridge, MA: MIT Press/Bradford Books.

Smolensky, P., Brousse, O., & Mozer, M. (forthcoming). Exponential growth of generalizations and virtual memories in connectionist combinatorial learning. To be submitted to *Cognitive Science.*

Smolensky, P. (1987). On variable binding and the representation of symbolic structures in connectionist systems. *Technical Report CU–CS–355–87.* Department of Computer Science, University of Colorado at Boulder.

Connectionist Variable-Binding By Optimization

P. Anandan
Computer Science Department, Yale University

Stanley Letovsky
Computer Science Department, Carnegie-Mellon University

Eric Mjolsness
Computer Science Department, Yale University

Abstract

Symbolic AI systems based on logical or frame languages can easily perform inferences that are still beyond the capability of most connectionist networks. This paper presents a strategy for implementing in connectionist networks the basic mechanisms of variable binding, dynamic frame allocation and equality that underlie many of the types of inferences commonly handled by frame systems, including inheritance, subsumption and abductive inference. The paper describes a scheme for translating frame definitions in a simple frame language into objective functions whose minima correspond to partial deductive closures of the legal inferences. The resulting constrained optimization problem can be viewed as a specification for a connectionist network.

1 INTRODUCTION

Connectionist systems are attractive as an approach to computing because they promote such desirable properties as fine-grained parallelism, analog circuitry, fault tolerance, and automatic learning. One of the more potent ideas to have appeared in investigations of these systems, and one which underlies a large fraction of the work in the field, is the use of continuous "objective functions" or "distance metrics". Objective functions can serve as a perspicuous programming language, highly susceptible to analysis, and useful as a specification language for neural networks. This paper uses the objective-function paradigm to address a central limitation of most existing connectionist systems: their inability to perform the kind of inferences that are easy for symbolic AI systems based on logical or frame languages. We present an objective-function-based implementation of the basic mechanisms of variable-binding and dynamic frame allocation that underlie frame based inference. The result is a connectionist frame system with greater expressive and inferential power than previous systems.

Our concern in this paper is with supporting the types of inference that typically occur in frame systems. These include inheritance of properties along type hierarchies; classification of objects within type hierarchies (or *subsumption*[Brachman, 1983]); instantiating frame definitions for particular individuals; and recognizing instances of frames within complex scenes or descriptions. An important variant of this last process is *abductive inference* [Charniak and McDermott, 1987], which involves partial or near-miss recognition of frames. Abductive inference is used to generate possible explanations for observed phenomena in medical diagnosis, language understanding, visual scene interpretation, and other analysis tasks.

In conventional frame systems, the inference processes are built atop a layer of machinery that contains a few simple ingredients. The most important ingredient is variable binding – i.e., the ability to dynamically establish connections between the objects being reasoned about and the frames in the knowledge base. Another ingredient is frame allocation: the ability to dynamically conjure up new frame instances on demand. Much of the difficulty of building symbolic reasoning into connectionist systems arises from the difficulty of implementing these basic underlying mechanisms. The problem is simple: connectionist systems tend to be hard-wired, at least over short timescales. This makes dynamic creation of nodes and links problematic.

The application of frame systems to model-based vision brings forth another set of problems – namely the representation of real-valued numerical parameters that are necessary to describe an instance of a model, and verification of the consistency between the parameters of an object and those of its parts. These checks typically involve coordinate-invariant computations. Doing coordinate transformations and coordinate-invariant recognition has been a difficult problem for connectionist systems (see [Hinton, 1981, Ballard, 1986] for discussion and solutions). Numerical parameters (which can be regarded as real-valued "slots") give rise to additional issues in the design of variable-binding machinery, including the need for ways to compute numeric slot values of frames, and notions of near-miss matching based on numeric differences.

Our approach to modeling frame-style inference involves a translation from a frame notation into real-valued equations whose solutions correspond to extensions of an initial set of axioms by sound or plausible inferences. The intuition underlying this translation scheme is that unification, the backbone of inference, can be viewed as a kind of graph matching on graphs containing variables. Graph matching can in turn be viewed as the minimization of an objective function which reflects the degree of mismatch between the two graphs. One advantage of this translation is that the distance metric representing the structural similarity between the graphs can be easily combined with other distance metrics which express the goodness-of-fit between the data and parametric models associated with specific classes of frames. In fact, there can be an entire database of such model-specific distance metrics.

Our objective functions can be viewed as specifications for connectionist networks. The process of generating a network from such a specification is analogous to compiling, and can be formalized as the application of transformations to the specification. There are usually a number of ways of transforming an objective function into a network [Mjolsness and Garrett, 1989], and the different possible networks may have different efficiency properties, as measured in their use of nodes, connections and time. In this paper we focus on the translation from frames to objective functions, leaving the details of the translation from objective functions to networks for a later paper.

The system described in this paper is an extension of the Frameville system of Mjolsness, Gindi, and Anandan [Mjolsness *et al.*, 1988, Mjolsness *et al.*, 1989]. Our extension involves the representation of equality constraints between slots of a frame or those of its parts, yielding a degree of expressivity comparable to simple symbolic frame systems. This paper focuses solely on the theoretical part of our work – how to represent dynamically varying graph structures (Section 2), the description of the variable binding machinery (Section 3), our method for expressing soundness of inference using numerical constraints (Section 4), and our approach to controlling inference (Section 5). We do not describe any simulations or experimental results here. Preliminary experiments involving simple visual recognition and grouping problems are reported in [Mjolsness *et al.*, 1989]. New experiments involving the current extensions are also under way.

2 DYNAMIC GRAPH STRUCTURES

A key problem in doing symbolic inference in connectionist networks is providing mechanisms to dynamically create concepts and relations between them. In Frameville we divide the world into two parts: a static base of quantified knowledge, called *the model side*, and a dynamic set of ground formulae describing the objects of reasoning, called *the data side*. In an interpretation task, the data side would hold the observations and interpretations, while the model side would hold background knowledge. The model side does not change under our inference processes: dynamic allocation of frames and links occurs on the data side, and in the bindings between the data side and the model side. There are three types of dynamic objects: frame instances, which represent objects in the world, `inst`-links, which connect frame instances on the data side to frame types (or *models*, to borrow a term from model-based vision) on the model side, and `ina`-links, which represent slot-filling relationships between frame instances. In addition, there are three kinds of static links on the model side, called **INA**, **ISA**, and **EQU**. These will be described later.

Each link-type is represented in our system by an array of numbers. For example **inst** links are represented by an $M \times D$ array, where M is the number of models on the model side, and D is the maximum number of frame instances that can be stored in the system at one time. The element α, j of the **inst** array represents an **inst**-link between the model α and frame instance j (denoted $\mathtt{inst}_{\alpha,j}$). If this array element is 1, then there is an **inst**-link between the two; if 0 there is no link. During the optimization process elements can take on real values in the range [0,1]. Numerical constraints in the objective function force these variables to settle on boolean values (section 3), so that when the energy reaches a minimum the state of these arrays describes a graph structure. Similar arrays exist for each of the dynamic link types[1].

If all the potential links leading to a frame instance are zero, then that frame instance effectively does not exist: it is not connected to the graph structure described by the arrays. Conversely, dynamic allocation of frame instances can be achieved by adding a link to a previously unallocated frame instance j. Hence no additional machinery is needed to represent dynamic frame allocation: the dynamic link arrays already imply the power to create new frame instances. The structure of the knowledge base dictates what frames we *could* create – specifically, slot fillers for known frame instances, and new instances whose slots may be filled by known instances. Whether such creation occurs is governed by the inferential control rules described in section 5.

3 FRAME INSTANTIATION

Consider the following frame-style definition of the concept *revenge*, which might occur in a story understander's knowledge base: [Birnbaum, 1986]

```
define revenge
    slots
        gte-1,gte-2: goal-thwarting-event
        aggressor,avenger: actor
    constraints
        thwarter(gte-1) = aggressor
        victim(gte-1)   = avenger
        thwarter(gte-2) = avenger
        victim(gte-2)   = aggressor
```

This definition states that an instance of **revenge** consists of two events of the type **goal-thwarting-event**, and two actors. A **goal-thwarting-event** is a kind of event (presumably defined in another frame definition) where one actor, called the **thwarter**, prevents the realization of a goal held by another actor, called the **victim**. In a **revenge** event, the thwarter of the first goal-thwarting event is the victim of the second, and vice versa. In the above notation, **slotA,slotB:type** means that the fillers of the **slots** must be of the type **type**.

The above definition does several things: it establishes the slots of a frame, it places restrictions on the types of the fillers, and it requires that certain equality constraints hold among the slots, or among the slots of slots. In this paper we will not address slots with multiple fillers (but see [Mjolsness *et al.*, 1989]) or set inclusion relationships between slots, such as *the recipient is a member of the donor's family.* Thus the frame language considered here is not as expressive as possible.

```
                 aggressor
rev127 ---------------------> John16
```

Figure 1: The Usual Graphic View of Role Filling

Applying the definition of **revenge** to an instance of it involves dynamically creating a correspondence between the instance and the **revenge** model. This is the variable-binding problem. Focusing on a single slot of a frame – say, the **aggressor** slot – we will show how to use the machinery of the previous section to bind it to a value. Suppose we want to represent the assertion that **John16** is the aggressor of a particular revenge instance, called **rev127**. The traditional approach would have us create a link of type **aggressor** going from the **rev127** node to the **John16** node (Figure 1). Such a scheme requires

[1] Arrays representing the static link types are compiled into the objective function; they are not variables as far as the optimization process is concerned.

arbitrarily many link types, whereas our machinery for dynamic graph structures requires a fixed, and preferably small number of dynamic link types, since each link-type gives rise to an array in the objective function. One solution to this problem is represent all slot-filling relationships using a single

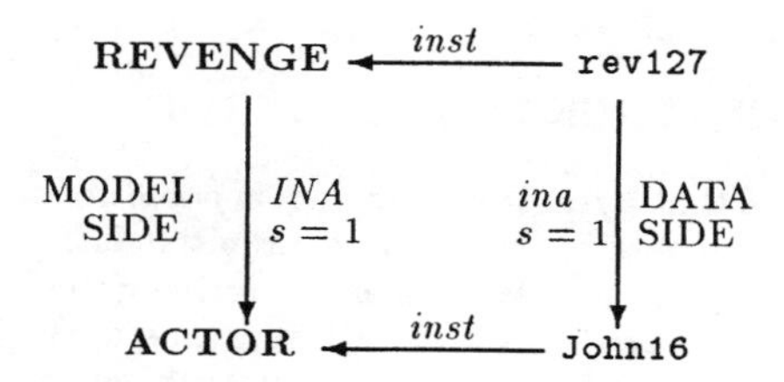

Figure 2: Rectangle Relationship Between **ina** and **inst**.

3-dimensional array called **ina**. The first two dimensions range over the set of dynamically allocatable frame instances, while the third ranges from 1 to S, the maximum number of slots in any frame. Typically S will be a fairly small number, probably between 5 and 10. The slots in each frame are assigned integers in the range [1,S]. $\mathbf{ina}_{i,j,s} = 1$), means that the s'th slot of the i'th frame instance is filled by the j'th frame instance.

In addition to **ina** links on the data side, and **inst** links between the data side and the model side, we have static **INA**, **ISA**, and **EQU** links on the model side. **INA** links express slot filler type restrictions, such as the fact that the **initiator** of a **revenge** must be an **actor**. $\mathbf{INA}_{\alpha,\beta,s} = 1$ means that any object that fills the s'th slot in an object of the model α must be an instance of the model β. **ISA** links on the model side encode class-subclass specializations and allow property inheritance and type subsumption. The **EQU** links will be discussed in the next section. As noted earlier, we also allow real-valued slots (or "analog neurons") $\mathbf{F}_{i,s}, \in [1, S]$ to be associated with each frame instance i. These are described in sections 4 and 5.

We can divide the various constraints incorporated into our objective function into those necessary to ensure the soundness of the inferences made in the network, and those needed for forward chaining and abductive reasoning. As explained in Section 5 such a separation is useful to control the proliferation of possibly correct but irrelevant inferences.

4 SOUNDNESS CONSTRAINTS

Soundness constraints are constraints that force the network to settle on states that describe meaningful frame structures. They are represented in the objective function by numerical equality constraints involving the dynamic variables. Although these constraints may be violated during the optimization process, they must be satisfied when the network reaches a fixedpoint. There is a variety of optimization techniques that can handle such "hard" constraints, some of which have been used in the context of neural networks [Mjolsness *et al.*, 1988].

An important "syntactic" constraint is that there be at most one object (i.e., frame instance) which fills a given slot of any other frame instance. That is, for any given i and s, at most one $\mathbf{ina}_{i,j,s} = 1$. This can be expressed as: [2]

$$\forall\, i, s \quad (1 - \sum_j \mathbf{ina}_{i,j,s}) \sum_j \mathbf{ina}_{i,j,s} = 0 \qquad (1)$$

The meaning of **INA** described in the previous section can be expressed as

$$\begin{aligned} &\forall\, \alpha, \beta, i, j, s \ \text{ s.t. } \mathbf{INA}_{\alpha,\beta,s} \\ &\mathbf{inst}_{\alpha,i}\ \mathbf{ina}_{i,j,s}\ (1 - \mathbf{inst}_{\beta,j}) \ = \ 0 \qquad (2) \end{aligned}$$

This says that if there is an **INA**-link between α and β for slot s, then whenever any i is an instance of α, and the s'th slot of i is j, then j must be an instance of β. The combination of the $(1 - \mathbf{inst}_{\beta,j})$ term on the left hand side, equated to 0 on the right, is an idiom that means the term $\mathbf{inst}_{\beta,j}$ must be 1.

Usually, definitions of frames will also contain equality constraints. For instance, we may require that the same object should fill two different slots of the same frame. Since slot-fillers themselves are frame instances, such equality relations may be nested. For example, the definition of **revenge** given in Section 3 requires that **thwarter(gte-1)**

[2] Each constraint consists of a generative portion and the actual constraint. The generative portion is universally quantified over a set of variables and may contain restrictions on them expressed in terms of model-side links (where for conciseness, we have used **x** and ¬**x** to represent **x** = 1 and **x** = 0 respectively). The constraint may be a hard-constraint of the form $h(\textit{dynamic-links}) = 0$, or a term (soft-constraint) of the form $f(\textit{dynamic-links})$ that is included in the objective function to be minimized.

= **aggressor**. Equality constraints can be expressed as predicate calculus assertion by treating slots as functions of their frames[Charniak, 1988]. They have the following general form:

$$\forall\, i \in \alpha \quad t(s(i)) = u(i)$$

This represents the assertion that the same object (or frame instance) that fills slot t of slot s of any instance i of model α must fill slot u of i as well. We can denote this in terms of an **EQU** matrix as $\mathbf{EQU}_{\alpha,s,t,u} = 1$. Equalities are then expressed by constraints of the form:

$$\begin{aligned}&\forall\, i,j,k,\alpha,\beta,\gamma,s,t,u \text{ s.t.}\\ &\quad \mathbf{INA}_{\alpha,\beta,s} \wedge \mathbf{INA}_{\beta,\gamma,t} \wedge \mathbf{INA}_{\alpha,\gamma,u} \wedge \mathbf{EQU}_{\alpha,s,t,u}\\ &\quad \mathbf{inst}_{\alpha,i}\, \mathbf{ina}_{i,j,s}\, (\mathbf{ina}_{j,k,t} - \mathbf{ina}_{i,k,u}) = 0 \quad (3)\end{aligned}$$

Equality constraints between two sibling slots of a frame instance can also be expressed. Equality constraints between slots that are deeply nested in compositional hierarchies can be transformed into a set of equality constraints none of which involve nesting of depth greater than 2, as in Equation 3 This transformation involves introducing additional "dummy" slots for each of the intervening frames and "copying" the slot of a child frame instance into its parent frame instance. The copy mechanism is itself expressible as an equality constraint.

As noted in Section 2, **ISA** links allow frames to be organized into a specialization hierarchy. Thus $\mathbf{ISA}_{\alpha,\beta} = 1$ means that model β is a specialization of α. A model is allowed to be a specialization of multiple "higher-level" models, so the specialization hierarchy forms a directed acyclic graph. If frame instance i is an instantiation of model α, then it must be an instantiation of exactly one of the specializations of α, unless α is a leaf node in the specialization hierarchy. This is expressed as:

$$\begin{aligned}&\forall\, i,\alpha \ \textbf{s.t.} \ \alpha \textbf{ is not a leaf}\\ &\mathbf{inst}_{\alpha,i} - \sum_{\beta \text{ s.t. } \mathbf{ISA}_{\alpha,\beta}} \mathbf{inst}_{\beta,i} = 0 \quad (4)\end{aligned}$$

This rule implements both inheritance up the type hierarchy, because in **inst** link to model β tends to turn on **inst** links to the **ISA**-parents of β; and subsumption, or discrimination down the type hierarchy, because an **inst** link to α tends to turn on an **inst** link to one of α's **ISA**-children. The constraints associated with the children will rule out inconsistent specializations. More specialized frames must use the same slot-numbering conventions as their parents. In this paper, we do not address the issue of exceptions [Derthick, 1988].

Finally, the requirement that **inst** and **ina** links are boolean-valued can be expressed as:

$$\begin{aligned}\forall\, i,\alpha \quad & \mathbf{inst}_{\alpha,i}\,(1 - \mathbf{inst}_{\alpha,i}) = 0\\ \forall\, i,j,s \quad & \mathbf{ina}_{i,j,s}\,(1 - \mathbf{ina}_{i,j,s}) = 0 \quad (5)\end{aligned}$$

5 INFERENTIAL CONTROL

We suppose that a reasoning problem is posed to a Frameville network by establishing an initial data-side graph structure; array elements describing this graph are "clamped" to a value of 1, so the network must settle into a state which is minimal subject to the restriction that the input is a subgraph of the final graph. The constraints described in the previous section rule out certain types of meaningless network states, but they by no means completely determine the behavior of a network. For instance, if the data only constrain **inst** and **F** variables, a consistent solution is to set all **ina** variables to zero; many variations of this trivial solution are possible. Furthermore, our frame language is rich enough to allow a variety of inferences, which, if applied willy-nilly, will rapidly use up the supply of dynamically allocatable frame instances and links, without necessarily drawing any interesting conclusions. Two particularly "dangerous" types of inference may be termed *recognition* and *slot-filling*.

By *slot-filling* we mean the allocation of new frame instances to fill unfilled slots of existing frames, or using existing instances if they are consistent with the constraints on the slot. For example, if the data says there is a **revenge**, we can create instances for the **initiator**, the **avenger**, the **gte-1** and the **gte-2**, and establish the appropriate relationships between them. This is a legitimate inferential step, since if the **revenge** exists, the slot fillers must exist. Alternatively, we could put an existing instance of the appropriate type – **John17**, say – into the **aggressor** slot. This would be a plausible but not necessary inference. When new instances are created to fill slots, the slot fillers may require their own slots to be filled, leading to an explosion of allocation until the capacity of the network is exhausted.

In Frameville, slot-filling is achieved by minimizing "penalty terms" in the objective function (as opposed to the use of "hard" constraints, which *must* be satisfied). Corresponding to every slot of every frame-definition, we have an additive term in the objective function of the form:

$$\forall\, \alpha, \beta, i, s \text{ s.t. } \mathtt{INA}_{\alpha,\beta,s}$$
$$(\mathtt{inst}_{\alpha,i} - \sum_j \mathtt{ina}_{i,j,s}\ \mathtt{inst}_{\beta,j})^2 \qquad (6)$$

The lowest energy state of the network, which is zero, will be achieved if and only if all the slots of each instance of a frame are properly filled. By themselves, these terms will tend to produce the explosion mentioned above. To counteract this tendency, we add an additional term, called a *parsimony* term, which penalizes the network for the creation of new frames:

$$\sum_i \sum_{\alpha \text{ is a leaf}}^{\alpha \text{ s.t.}} \mathtt{inst}_{\alpha,i} \qquad (7)$$

One consequence of this parsimony term is that the network will prefer using existing frame instances to fill unfilled slots over creating new ones.

Recognition means creating an instance of a frame when we observe a set of frame instances that satisfy the constraints on the frames definition. For example, if we see two goal thwarting events where the thwarters and victims are reversed, we can create a revenge. Pure recognition is not dangerous: it inevitably terminates and is not typically explosive. However, partial recognition, in which the frame definition is partially but not completely satsfied, is a useful variant of pure recognition in a world where the input data is incomplete, and partial recognition tends to be explosive and potentially nonterminating.

Recognition is also achieved by minimization. The terms corresponding to recognition are of the form

$$\forall \alpha, j, \beta \text{ s.t. } \mathtt{INA}_{\alpha,\beta,s}$$
$$(\mathtt{inst}_{\beta,j} - \sum_i \mathtt{ina}_{i,j,s}\ \mathtt{inst}_{\alpha,i})^2 \qquad (8)$$

This rule has the following interpretation. If an instance j of model β is appropriate to fill slot s of frames of type α , then an instance i of α may be created and the appropriate slot-filler binding established. This kind of mechanism is often used to propose hypotheses in abductive inference [Charniak, 1988]. This rule also tends to penalize the occurence of multiple instances of the same frame type having identical fillers for a given slot. In frame systems it is usually desirable to prevent the occurrence of distinct frames having identical fillers in *all* slots. A direct expression of this constraint gives rise to a very high order ($O(S)$) energy function, which is expensive to implement in a network. The recognition term above is a limited attempt to achieve a similar effect.

6 REAL-VALUED PARAMETERS

In addition to the machinery for requiring structural correspondences between data and models, Frameville allows numeric slots constrained by *model-specific* objective function terms whose algebraic form will depend on the models involved. These terms may be idiosyncratic functions of both numerical and frame-valued slots, but for ease of exposition, we restrict our attention to numerical slots here:

$$\forall\, \alpha, \beta, i, j, s \text{ s.t. } \mathtt{INA}_{\alpha,\beta,s}$$
$$\mathtt{inst}_{\alpha,i}\ \mathtt{ina}_{i,j,s}\ \mathtt{inst}_{\beta,j}\ H^{\alpha,s}(\vec{\mathtt{F}}_i, \vec{\mathtt{F}}_j) \qquad (9)$$

where $\vec{\mathtt{F}}_i = (\mathtt{F}_{i1}, \mathtt{F}_{i2}, \ldots)$ represents the vector of numerical parameters of i. This constraint relates the numerical parameters of two frame instances, one a slot-filler of the other. Similar model-specific terms can be used to express relationships between numerical parameters of the fillers of sibling slots of a frame instance. The $H^{\alpha,s}$ functions given above are specific to a model α and may express coordinate system invariant relationships between the parameters of a frame instance and those of its fillers. By doing so, we eliminate the need for explicitly storing the transformation matrices between the coordinate system of an object and those of its parts. If, however, it is useful to explicitly have such a transformation matrix, it can also be represented using numerical slots.

The propagation of constraints among numeric slot values can be expressed either by hard constraints (i.e., by requiring that the expression in Equation 9 be zero) or as penalty terms in the objective function. In the latter case, they affect inferential control in a model-specific way. Our approach also has the advantage that it is not necessary to separate the computation of the numerical parameters of a high-level object from the recognition of the object itself. The optimization process simultaneously determines the object identity and best choice of object parameters to fit the data. When higher-level information is available, top-down propagation of that information is also achieved by the same optimization process. Model-specific constants may also be incorporated into frame-valued slots, thereby biasing the likelihood that particular slots will be filled or that particular types will trigger recognition. Such constants may provide a basis for implementing certainty or probability-like mechanisms.

Each type of penalty term described in this section gets added into the overall objective function, but with possibly different multiplicative coefficients. It is the relative values of these coefficients that determines the competition between parsimony on the one hand and forward-inferencing and abductive "guessing" on the other. Appropriate values of these coefficients may be determined experimentally, or they may be set dynamically by external mechanisms that control the Frameville network.

7 RELATIONSHIP TO OTHER CONNECTIONIST FRAME SYSTEMS

Our approach resembles Derthick's μKLONE system [Derthick, 1988] in several ways, notably in our general method for translating logical assertions into objective functions and numerical constraints, and in our use of a static model-base that is used by a compiler whose output is a network designed for optimization. (Note that this separation of knowledge into "data" and "models" is also present in Shastri's approach [Shastri, 1987].) However, we have introduced a mechanism for variable-binding which greatly increases the expressive and inferential power of the system, and that deals with real-valued parameters and with constraints involving such parameters. In particular, our variable binding mechanism, in combination with the separation of frame types from frame-instances, allows us to have multiple instances of a frame, and to dynamically create new instances and relationships among them. We share with Dolan and Dyer [Dolan and Dyer, 1988] the advantage of being able to perform chains of inferences in parallel, although in both our cases, considerable experimental work needs to be done before a complete evaluation can be made. Our approach differs from that of Dolan and Dyer (as well from that of Touretzky, *et al.* [Touretzky and Geva, 1987]) in some fundamental ways: first our use of objective functions as a specification language allows us to specify the desired properties of the network – namely its fixedpoints – and allows us to perform algebraic fixedpoint-preserving transformations that can lead to efficient networks. Second, the same methodology also allows the modular and incremental design of the system (prior to any algebraic transformations). One more distinction: while in many of these existing systems (including μKLONE) microfeature-based coarse coding mechanisms are used to represent the similarity of concepts, our use of a data-base of model-specific distance metrics $H^{\alpha,s}$, indexed by the `ISA` links, points to a fundamentally new approach to the design of connectionist frame systems.

8 CONCLUSIONS

We have presented a connectionist frame system called Frameville, which can represent dynamically varying graph structures and thereby can inherit some of the representational and reasoning power of symbolic frame systems. In particular, we have described machinery to dynamically instantiate frames and perform variable-binding. All of this has been done within the paradigm of objective function minimization, which is used both as a programming language and a neural-network specification language. Our approach also extends the traditional use of distance metrics by allowing us to systematically integrate constraints involving pointers and real-valued variables into a single objective function, and by allowing us to utilize a data-base of model-specific distance metrics. This work is an extension of previous work described in [Mjolsness *et al.*, 1989], where preliminary experiments are also reported. The present paper has laid out the theoretical ground work necessary to perform new experiments, and we expect that further refinements of our theory will be shaped by these experiments.

ACKNOWLEDGEMENTS

We would like to thank Gene Gindi for his continued collaboration in Frameville research. We would also like to thank Chris Riesbeck for discussions about our work and Denys Duchier for commenting on an earlier draft of this paper. This work was supported in part by AFOSR grant AFOSR-88-0240 and by DARPA grant DAAA15-87-K-00001.

References

[Ballard, 1986] Dana Ballard. Cortical connections and parallel processing: Structure and function. *Behavioral and Brain Sciences*, vol 9:67–120, 1986.

[Birnbaum, 1986] Lawrence Birnbaum. Integrated processing in planning and understanding. Technical Report YALEU/CSD/RR-489, Yale University, 1986. PhD Dissertation.

[Brachman, 1983] Ronald J. Brachman. What is-a is and isn't: An analysis of taxonomic links in semantic networks. *IEEE Computer, Special Issue on Knowledge Representation*, pages 30–36, October 1983.

[Charniak and McDermott, 1987] Eugene Charniak and Drew McDermott. *Introduction to Artificial Intelligence.* Addison Wesley, 1987.

[Charniak, 1988] Eugene Charniak. Motivation analysis, abductive unification, and nonmonotonic equality. *Artificial Intelligence*, 34(3):275–296, 1988.

[Derthick, 1988] Mark Derthick. Mundane reasoning and parallel constraint satisfaction. Technical Report CMU-CS-88-182, Carnegie-Mellon University, September 1988. PhD Dissertation.

[Dolan and Dyer, 1988] Charles P. Dolan and Michael G. Dyer. Parallel retrieval and application of conceptual knowledge. In D. Touretzky, G. Hinton, and T. J. Sejnowski, editors, *Proceedings of the 1988 Connectionist Models Summer School.* Morgan Kaufmann, 1988.

[Hinton, 1981] Geoffrey E. Hinton. Shape representation in parallel systems. In *Proceedings of 7th IJCAI.* IJCAI, 1981.

[Mjolsness and Garrett, 1989] Eric Mjolsness and Charles Garrett. Algebraic transformations of objective functions. Technical Report YALEU/DCS/RR-686, Yale University, March 1989.

[Mjolsness *et al.*, 1988] Eric Mjolsness, Gene Gindi, and P. Anandan. Optimization in model matching and perceptual organization: A first look. Technical Report YALEU/DCS/RR-634, Yale University, June 1988.

[Mjolsness *et al.*, 1989] Eric Mjolsness, Gene Gindi, and P. Anandan. Optimization in model matching and perceptual organization. *Neural Computation*, 1989. to appear.

[Shastri, 1987] Lokendra Shastri. *Semantic Networks: An Evidential Formulation and its Connectionist Realization.* Morgan Kaufmann, 1987.

[Touretzky and Geva, 1987] David S. Touretzky and Shai Geva. A distributed connectionist representation for concept structures. In *Proceedings of the Ninth Annual Conference of the Cognitive Science Society*, pages 155–164. Lawrence Earlbaum Associates, 1987.

Efficient Inference with Multi-Place Predicates and Variables in a Connectionist System

Venkat Ajjanagadde and Lokendra Shastri

Department of Computer and Information Science
University of Pennsylvania

Abstract

The ability to represent structured knowledge and use that knowledge in a systematic way is a very important ingredient of cognition. An often heard criticism of connectionism is that connectionist systems cannot possess that ability. The work reported in this paper demonstrates that a connectionist system can not only represent structured knowledge and display systematic behavior, but can also do so with extreme efficiency. The paper describes a connectionist system that can represent knowledge expressed as *rules* and *facts* involving *multi-place* predicates, and draw *limited*, but *sound*, inferences based on this knowledge. The system is extremely efficient - in fact, optimal, as it draws conclusions in time proportional to the length of the proof. Central to this ability of the system is a solution to the *variable binding* problem. The solution makes use of the notion of a *phased clock* and exploits the time dimension to create and propagate variable bindings.

1 Introduction

McCarthy, in his commentary on Smolensky's paper: On the Proper Treatment of Connectionism[15], asserts that connectionist systems suffer from "the unary or even propositional fixation"; representational power of most connectionist systems is restricted to unary predicates applied to a fixed object. More recently, Fodor and Pylyshyn[10] have made sweeping claims that connectionist systems cannot incorporate systematicity and compositionality. These comments suggest that representing structured knowledge in a connectionist network and using this knowledge in a systematic way is considered difficult, if not impossible. This paper addresses these concerns. It describes a connectionist system that can represent knowledge expressed in terms of *rules* and *facts* involving *multi-place* predicates (i.e., *n-ary relations*) and draw limited but sound inferences based on this knowledge in an extremely efficient manner. The time taken by the system to draw conclusions is proportional to the *length* of the proof, and hence, optimal.

It is observed that the key technical problem that must be solved in order to represent and reason with structured and rule based knowledge is the *variable binding* problem[9, 16]. A solution to this problem using a *multi-phase* clock is proposed. The solution employs the time dimension to maintain and propagate variable bindings during the reasoning process.

The connectionist system for reasoning with rules described in this paper is computationally effective in a strong sense and is consistent with the ability of human agents to draw certain inferences extremely fast - often in a few hundred milliseconds. The proposed system draws inferences in optimal time, i.e., in time proportional to the length of the proof.

2 Related Work

Two major metaphors that have been used for connectionist inference are that of energy minimization and spread of activation.

Ballard and Hayes[2] were the first to develop a connectionist inference system using the energy minimization[11] paradigm. They did not address the problem of variable binding as their system required that all possible bindings be explicitly pre-wired into the network. Explicit pre-wiring is unacceptable as a solution to the variable binding problem as that would correspond to explicitly representing all possible instantiations of the rule. This is not feasible because the number of instantiations may be too many - potentially unbounded. Ballard and Hayes' reasoner has two limitations which are common to all the reasoning systems employing the energy minimization paradigm. First of those limitations is regarding their efficiency. In those reasoners, the inference process is reduced to the problem of finding the lowest energy state of a suitably interconnected network. Such a process may even require not one but several cycles of convergence and it is difficult to place an upper bound on the convergence time of such systems. Even in cases where it is possible to do so, it turns out to be at best polynomial in the size of the knowledge base[5]. Thus, even though systems based on the energy metaphor are massively parallel, they do not meet the efficiency requirement. A second problem with such systems is that they are not always guaranteed to find the prescribed solution because the energy minimization process can get trapped in a local minima.

Touretzky and Hinton[17] have described DCPS, a *distributed* connectionist encoding of a restricted production system. The system uses the energy minimization metaphor for inference. The operation of a production system requires the ability to perform variable bindings, and DCPS exhibits this ability. The restrictions on variable bindings, however, are fairly strong. For example, DCPS only allows one variable in the antecedent. It also assumes that during any cycle there is only one rule with one variable binding that *can* constitute a potential correct match.

Among the other connectionist reasoning systems that employ energy minimization paradigm are the system of Dolan & Smolensky[7] (Dolan & Smolensky's system uses the tensor product based representation proposed in [16]) which is an improvement over Touretzky and Hinton's DCPS, Derthick's system[5] for drawing plausible inferences with respect to a frame based representation language and Dolan and Dyer's system for parallel retrieval and application of conceptual knowledge[6].

In the spreading activation metaphor for reasoning, each piece of information is encoded by a connectionist node and the inferential dependencies between pieces of information are represented by links between the corresponding nodes. Inference reduces to parallel spread of activation in such a network. Shastri's "connectionist realization of semantic networks"[14] follows such an approach. The system solves an interesting class of *inheritance* and *recognition* problems extremely fast - in time proportional to the depth of the conceptual hierarchy. Shastri's system displays the desired level of efficiency as its response is at worst logarithmic in the size of the knowledge base. However, it does not address the problem of variable binding. Although multiple rules participate in a derivation, it is always the case that all variables are bound to the same individual and thus the system can get by without actually solving the variable binding problem.

The suggestion of the usage of time dimension for representing variable bindings appears also in the works of Clossman[4], Fanty[8] and Malsburg[18].

3 Representation and Reasoning

The proposed connectionist system can perform a broad class of deductive inference involving variables and multi-place predicates with extreme efficiency. Specifically, the system can represent knowledge expressed in the form of *rules* and *facts* and determine whether a *query* can be derived as a consequence of the facts and rules encoded in the system. The answers to queries are produced in optimal time: the time taken to draw an inference is only proportional to the *length* of the proof.

The form of rules, facts, and queries is explained below.

Rules in the system are assumed to be sentences of the form
$\forall x_1, ..., x_m \, [P_1(...) \wedge P_2(...) ... \wedge P_n(...) \Rightarrow$
$\forall y_1, ..., y_k \exists z_1, ...z_l \; Q(...)]$
where arguments for P_i's are subsets of $\{x_1, x_2, ...x_m\}$, while the arguments of Q may consist of any number of arguments from among the x_i's and any number of constants besides the universally and existentially quantified arguments introduced in the consequent.

Facts are assumed to be atomic formulas of the form $P(t_1, t_2...t_k)$ where t_i's are either constants or existentially quantified variables.

A query has the same form as a fact: it is an atomic formula whose arguments are either bound to constants or are existentially quantified. The enforcement of the sameness condition on the variables that occur more than once in the antecedents of the rules is limited to those which get bound due to the query.

Some examples of rules, facts, and queries follow:

Rules:

$\forall x, y, z \; give(x,y,z) \Rightarrow owns(y,z)$
$\forall x, y \; owns(x,y) \Rightarrow can\text{-}sell(x,y)$
$\forall x \; omnipresent(x) \Rightarrow \forall y, t \; present(x,y,t)$
$\forall x, y \; born(x,y) \Rightarrow \exists t \; present(x,y,t)$
$\forall x \; triangle(x) \Rightarrow number\text{-}of\text{-}sides(x, 3)$
$\forall x, y \; sibling(x,y) \wedge born\text{-}at\text{-}the\text{-}same\text{-}time(x,y) \Rightarrow twins(x,y)$

Facts:

$give(John, Mary, Book1)$; John gave Mary Book1.
$give(x, Susan, Ball2)$; Someone gave Susan Ball2.
$omnipresent(x)$; There exists someone who is omnipresent.
$triangle(A3)$; A3 is a triangle.
$sibling(Susan, Mary)$; Susan and Mary are siblings.
$born\text{-}at\text{-}the\text{-}same\text{-}time(Susan, Mary)$; Susan and Mary were born at the same time.

Queries:

1. $owns(Mary, Book1)$; Does Mary own Book1?
2. $owns(x,y)$; Does someone own something?
3. $can\text{-}sell(x, Ball2)$; Can someone sell Ball2?
4. $present(x, Northpole, 1/1/89)$; Is someone present at the north pole on 1/1/89?
5. $number\text{-}of\text{-}sides(A3, 4)$; Does A3 have 4 sides?
6. $can\text{-}sell(Mary, Ball2)$; Can Mary sell Ball2?
7. $twins(Susan, Mary)$; Are Susan and Mary twins.?

All queries except 5 and 6 follow from the rules and facts and the system will respond 'yes' to these queries. The system will say 'no' to queries 5 and 6.

3.1 Directed reasoning

The strong efficiency requirement we have imposed on our system entails that it find a solution in a fixed number of passes of spreading activation. Such a convergence behavior ensures that the network can compute a solution in time proportional to the *diameter* of the network which is - in almost all cases - *sublinear* (and often *logarithmic*) in the size of the knowledge base. For the connectionist network to compute solutions in a *single* pass of spreading activation, the inferential dependencies in the knowledge base must be acyclic[13]. The nature of such inferential dependencies can be made explicit by expressing the rule component of the knowledge base in the following graphical manner. Depict each predicate occurring in the rules by a unique node in the graph. Then if there is a rule of the form

$$P_1(\ldots) \wedge P_2(\ldots) \ldots \wedge P_n(\ldots) \Rightarrow Q(\ldots)$$

in the knowledge base, draw directed arcs from the nodes corresponding to P_is to the node corresponding to Q. The requirement that the inferential dependencies of the knowledge base be acyclic amounts to requiring that the directed graph obtained in this manner be acyclic. We will therefore focus on knowledge bases whose *inferential dependency* graph corresponds to a *directed acyclic graph* and henceforth, we will often refer to the rule component of the knowledge base as the PDAG (for Predicate DAG).

In view of the directed nature of inferential dependencies, we refer to the system's inferential ability as *directed reasoning*. Directed reasoning appears to be adequate to capture a broad range of common sense reasoning situations. In particular, it can deal with restricted types of *causal reasoning*, i.e., reasoning about actions and events wherein there is no circular causality (i.e., systems that can be modeled as open loop systems). Terminological reasoning[3], that is, reasoning with definitional knowledge of concepts (terms) is also a case of directed reasoning[1].

4 The Connectionist Encoding

This section discusses the connectionist encoding of rules and facts. During most of our discussions we will be focusing on rules having a single predicate on the antecedent; the extension to rules having more than one predicate on the antecedent is rather simple and will be briefly discussed in a subsequent section. Due to space limitations, we are attempting to provide only a simplified picture of the whole system here and hence, are omitting details such as the soundness and completeness conditions and the details of encoding of rules having constants and existentially quantified variables in the consequent. The full details of the reasoning system can be found in [12].

The whole encoding makes use of only simple phase-sensitive Binary Threshold Units (BTUs). However, for clarity of exposition, we will be making use of two abstract types of nodes, which we call *pred* and *instancer*. The realization of these types of nodes in terms of BTUs is described in [12].

An *n-ary* predicate is represented by a *pred* node (drawn as a rectangular box) and a cluster of *n* *arg* nodes (depicted as diamonds). Thus the ternary predicate *orderhit* is represented by the *pred* node labeled $ORDERHIT$ and the three *arg* nodes - $a1$, $a2$, and $a3$ - drawn next to it (Fig. 1).

Each constant in the domain is represented by a *const* node (an oval shaped node), which is a simple phase sensitive BTU that becomes active in phase i of every clock cycle if it is initially activated in the ith phase of a clock cycle.

A rule is encoded by interconnecting nodes representing the antecedent and consequent predicates. For example, the interconnections corresponding to the rule

$$\forall x, y, z P1(x, y, z) \Rightarrow Q(y, x)$$

are as follows: there will be a link from the *pred* node corresponding to $P1$ to the *pred* node corresponding to Q; there will be links going from the first and second arg nodes of Q to the second and first arg nodes of $P1$ respectively. The links between the arg nodes represent the correspondence between the arguments of the consequent and antecedent predicates of the rule. (Refer to the encoding of the rule $\forall x, y, z(orderhit(x, y, z) \Rightarrow hit(y, z))$ in Fig.1).

A fact is encoded using an *instancer* node (drawn as hexagonal box). An *instancer* node representing a fact concerning an n-ary predicate has n BIND sites. The ith BIND site has links coming from the ith arg node of the corresponding predicate and the *const* node representing the constant bound to the ith argument in the fact represented by the instancer.

5 Inference Process

The inference process, that is, the verification of the truth or falsity of a query, is a controlled spread of activation in the network with no external intervention. The inference process may be thought of as consisting of three stages [1]. In the first stage, the query is posed to the network by external activation of some nodes. During the second stage, a controlled parallel search is carried out to locate all the facts that are relevant to the proof of the query and the *instancer* nodes encoding such relevant facts become active. In the third and final stage the actual proof is constructed. In this stage, activation from the instancers denoting relevant facts flow downwards along the inference paths in the PDAG to produce an answer to the query. The answer corresponds to the resulting activation of the *pred* node that corresponds to the query predicate.

5.1 Posing the query and specifying variable bindings

As said earlier, a query is an atomic formula of the form $P(t_1, ..., t_k)$ where t_is are either constants or existentially quantified variables. Posing the query involves specifying the constant- argument bindings of the query predicate to the network. These bindings of arguments are indicated by using a phased clock. For a given query, each clock cycle of the network consists of a fixed number of phases. If the argument bindings in the query involve p distinct constants, then the clock has p distinct phases[2]. Let $c_1, ..., c_p$ be p distinct constants appearing in the bindings specified in the query. The query will be posed in the following manner:

In the ith phase of the *first* clock cycle, $(1 \leq i \leq p)$, the following nodes will be activated:

- The *const* node corresponding to c_i.
- The *arg* nodes corresponding to the $i_1^{th}, ..., i_j^{th}$ arguments of the query predicate, where $i_1, ..., i_j$ $(j \geq 1)$ are the arguments of the query predicate bound to c_i.

[1] These stages are conceptually distinct, however, during actual processing these stages overlap

[2] In general p can be less than the number of bound arguments in the query because the same constant(s) may be bound to more than one argument.

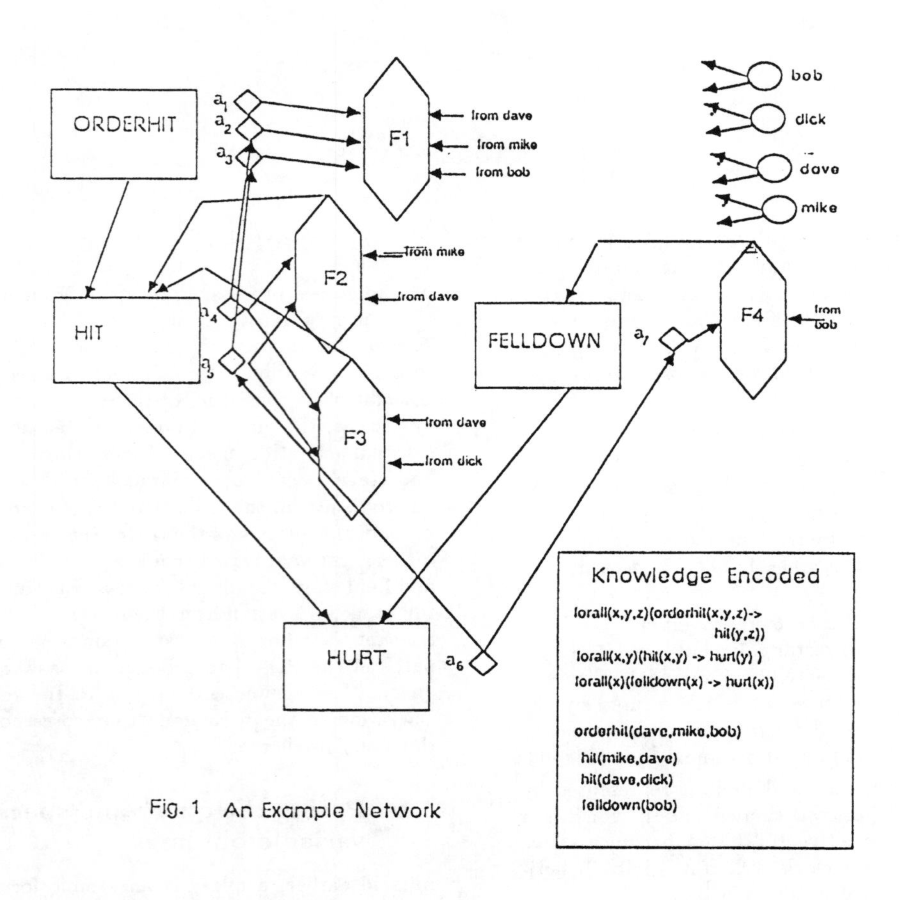

Fig. 1 An Example Network

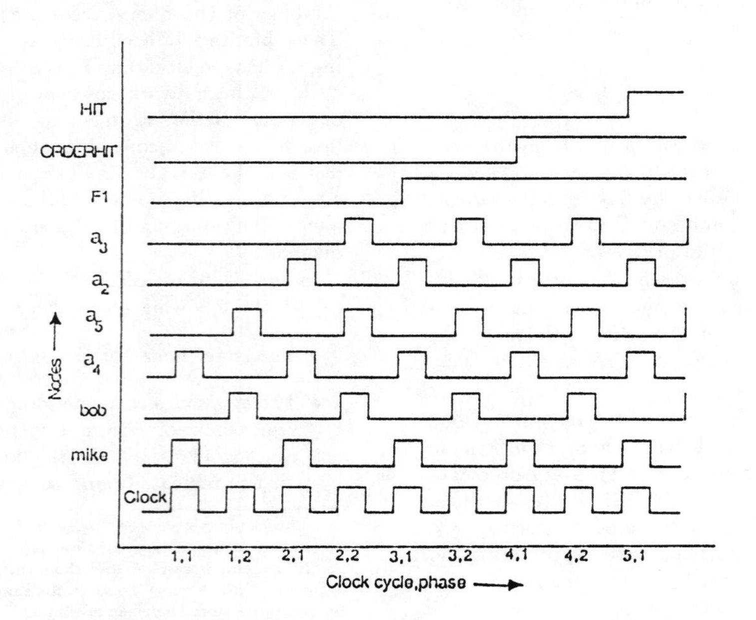

Fig. 2 Activations of different nodes for the query hit(mike,bob)

As stated earlier, *arg* nodes and *const* nodes are phase sensitive and the phases in which they remain active are determined by the clock phases in which they first become active. The simultaneous activation of an *arg* node and a *const* node during a phase represents that the constant denoted by the latter node is bound to the argument denoted by the former node.

5.2 Propagating variable bindings and getting the relevant instancers active

Once the query is posed, the parallel search for the assertions that are relevant to the proof of the query ensues. Relevant assertions can be of two types:

There may exist a fact associated with the query predicate itself whose argument bindings subsume the bindings specified in the query. The query would follow directly from such a fact. For example, the query *hit(dave, dick)* (i.e., "Did Dave hit Dick?") trivially follows from the fact *hit(dave, dick)* (refer to Fig. 1.) [3].

The second possibility is that there exist fact(s) associated with ancestor predicate(s) of the query predicate and whose argument bindings subsume those specified in the query. In this case, the query would follow via a chain of modus ponens. As an example, in Fig.1, the fact *orderhit(dave, mike, bob)* is relevant to the proof of *hit(mike, bob)* this way.

We consider, in turn, how the two types of relevant facts become active during the query process. Consider how the *instancer* node F3 (representing the fact *hit(dave, dick)*) becomes active in response to the query *hit(dave, dick)*. Once this query is posed, the *const* node *dave* and the first *arg* node of *hit* remain active during the first phase of every clock cycle. Similarly, the *const* node *dick* and the second *arg* node of *hit* remains active during the second phase of every clock cycle. The activation from these *arg* and *const* nodes reaches the *instancer* node F3 during the specified phases. An *instancer* node functions as follows:

An *instancer* node becomes active at the end of clock cycle t and remains active throughout cycle $t+1$ if and only if

- During each phase of clock cycle t, *if* it receives activation from an *arg* node, it *also* receives activation from the *const* node bound to this *arg* node.

It follows that as a result of the query *hit(dave, dick)*, the *instancer* F3 will become active at the end of the second clock cycle and remain active thereafter.

To see how relevant *instancer* nodes associated with ancestors of the query predicate become active we shall consider the query *hit(mike, bob)* (refer to Fig. 1). There is no fact associated with *hit* that subsumes the bindings in this query. As a result of the query, the first *arg* node of *hit* (a_4) and the *const* node *mike* will become active in the first phase of every clock cycle. Similarly, the second *arg* node of *hit* (a_5) and the *const* node *bob* will become active during the second phase of every clock cycle. (The clock phases/cycles in which different nodes first become active for the example query being discussed, i.e., *hit(mike, bob)* are indicated in Fig. 2. Note that the *pred* and *instancer* nodes are not phase sensitive).

Activations from the *arg* nodes a_4 and a_5 reach the *arg* nodes a_2 and a_3 of the predicate *orderhit* respectively. As the phase in which an *arg* node becomes active depends on the phase in which it receives activation, the *arg* nodes a_2 and a_3 become active in the first and second phases respectively of every clock cycle. Hence, the second clock cycle onwards, the active *const* and *arg* nodes in the first phase of every clock cycle are: *mike*, a_4 and a_2; and those active in the second phase are: *bob*, a_3 and a_5. Essentially, we have created two new bindings: *mike* has been bound to the second argument of *orderhit* and *bob* has been bound to the third argument of *orderhit*[4]. The *instancer* $F1$ that encodes the fact *orderhit(dave, mike, bob)* will now become active as a result of the activation it receives from the *arg* nodes a_2 and a_3 and the corresponding *const* nodes *mike* and *bob*. The activation from the *instancer* node $F1$ causes the output of the *pred* node *orderhit* to become high. The activation from the *pred* node *orderhit* in turn makes the output of the *pred* node *hit* high - thus resulting in an affirmative answer to the query.

[3] The fact *hit(dave, dick)* also subsumes other queries such as $\exists x hit(x, dick)$, $\exists x hit(dave, x)$, etc., all of which also follow, directly, from this fact.

[4] The newly created bindings of the arguments of *orderhit* can be thought of as encoding the query *orderhit(x, mike, bob)* (i.e., "Did someone order Mike to hit Bob?")!

The above was a brief description of the inference process where the rules encoded in the network had just one predicate as antecedent. In order to encode rules of the form $P_1(...) \wedge P_2(...) \wedge ...P_m(...) \Rightarrow Q(...)$, i.e., rules with conjunctive antecedents, the output of the *pred* nodes $P_1, ..., P_m$ are not connected directly to the *pred* node Q; instead they are connected to a *conjunctive* node, which is in turn linked to the *pred* node Q. The output of the *conjunctive* node is high if and only if it receives activation through all the incoming links. The interconnections between the *arg* nodes of the antecedent predicates and the consequent predicate is similar to that in the case of single-antecedent rules.

6 Conclusion

The work described in this paper has directly addressed a criticism that is often levelled against connectionist systems, namely, that connectionist systems cannot incorporate systematicity and compositionality and hence are unpromising as architectures of cognition. The paper presented a connectionist system that only uses simple phase sensitive binary threshold units to perform a limited class of inferences with rules and facts. The problem of variable binding is central to the connectionist realizations of rule governed symbolic reasoning tasks. The proposed connectionist system employs a phased clock to solve this problem. The design of the system has been verified via simulations.

In the near future we will report an augmented system that can answer *wh*-questions in addition to 'yes/no' questions(i.e., the augmented system is capable of determining the fillers of unbound arguments in the query). We will also show that there exists a direct way of integrating a connectionist semantic network(i.e., an inheritance network) such as the one described in [14] and the rule-based system described here. Such a 'hybrid' system will have more expressive and inferential power but will retain its extreme efficiency.

Acknowledgements
We wish to thank the Knowledge Representation group at the International Computer Science Institute, Berkeley, in particular, Jerry Feldman and Mark Fanty for their helpful comments and suggestions. This work was supported by NSF grants IRI 88-05465, MCS-8219196-CER, MCS-83-05211, DARPA grants N00014-85-K-0018 and N00014-85-K-0807, and ARO grant ARO-DAA29-84-9-0027.

References

[1] Ajjanagadde V., Forthcoming Ph.D. dissertation, University of Pennsylvania.

[2] Ballard, D.H., and Hayes, P.J., Parallel logical inference, Proceedings of the Sixth Annual Conference of the Cognitive Science Society, pp. 114-123., Boulder,Colorado, June.1984.

[3] Brachman, R., Fikes R., and Levesque, H.J. KRYPTON: A Functional Approach to Knowledge Representation. *Readings in Knowledge Representation*, R. Brachman, and H.J. Levesque (eds.) Morgan Kaufman, Los Altos, CA. 1985.

[4] Clossman, Gary., (Personal Communication via John Barnden).

[5] Derthick, M., Mundane reasoning by parallel constraint satisfaction, Ph.D. thesis, CMU-CS-88-182, Carnegie Mellon University, Sept. 1988.

[6] Dolan, C., and Dyer, M., Parallel retrieval and application of conceptual knowledge, Technical Report TR UCLA-AI-88-3, University of California, Los Angeles, Jan. 1988.

[7] Dolan, C., and Smolensky P., Implementing a connectionist production system using tensor products, Technical Report UCLA-AI-88-15, University of California, Los Angeles, CU-CS-411-88 University of Colorado, 1988.

[8] Fanty, M.A., Learning in Structured Connectionist Networks. Ph.D. Dissertation, Computer Science Department, University of Rochester, Rochester, NY. 1988.

[9] Feldman, J.A. Dynamic connections in neural networks, *Bio-Cybernetics*, 46:27-39, 1982.

[10] Fodor J.A. and Pylyshyn Z.W. Connectionism and cognitive architecture: A critical analysis. In *Connections and Symbols* Steven Pinker and Jacques Mehler (eds.) The MIT Press, Cambridge, MA. 1988.

[11] Kirkpatrick, S., C.D.Gelatt, an M.P. Vecchi, Optimization by simulated annealing, *Science* 220, 4598, pp. 671-680, 1983.

[12] Shastri, L., and Ajjanagadde, V., A connectionist system for rule based reasoning with multiplace predicates and variables, Tech. Report MS-CIS-8905, Dept. of Computer Science, Univ. of Pennsylvania, Jan. 1989.

[13] Shastri, L., The Relevance of Connectionism to AI: A representation and reasoning perspective. In *Advances in Connectionist and Neural Computation Theory*, vol. 1., J. Barnden (ed.), Ablex Publishing Company, Norwood, N.J. (To appear). (Also available as a Tech. Report from Computer Science Department, University of Pennsylvania.)

[14] Shastri, L., A connectionist approach to knowledge representation and limited inference, *Cognitive Science*, 12(3), pp. 331-392.

[15] Smolensky, P., Proper treatment of Connectionism, *Behavioral and Brain Sciences*, (1988) 11:1.

[16] Smolensky, P., On variable binding and the representation of symbolic structures in connectionist systems, Technical Report CU-CS-355-87, Department of Computer Science, University of Colorado at Boulder, Feb. 1987.

[17] Touretzky, D. and Hinton, G., A distributed connectionist production system, *Cognitive Science*, 12(3), pp. 423-466.

[18] von der Malsburg, C., Nervous structures with dynamical links, *Berichte der Bunsen-Gelschaft fur Physikakalische Chemie*.

ON THE NATURE OF CHILDREN'S NAIVE KNOWLEDGE

Stella Vosniadou
University of Illinois at Urbana-Champaign, and
Aristotelian University of Thessaloniki/Greece

ABSTRACT

We argue that children construct a naive understanding of the world which gradually becomes modified to conform to adult-scientific views. This naive understanding consists of a number of discrete ontological beliefs, such as that the ground is flat, that things fall down, and that stars are small objects. Children are capable of synthesizing their ontological beliefs to form relatively consistent conceptual structures. However, they also seem to be operating under an epistemological constraint according to which these ontological beliefs represent the true state of affairs about the world. In the process of conceptual change children replace their ontological beliefs with a different explanatory framework.

INTRODUCTION

One of the most interesting results of recent work in cognitive science has been the realization that science-naive individuals have an understanding of the natural world which is based on their interpretation of everyday experience. This naive knowledge is usually quite different from the knowledge expected from the scientifically literate adults in our society. In the process of learning science novices must change their naive knowledge to make it conform to the currently accepted scientific knowledge. This process of conceptual change can be a rather lengthy one to accomplish because naive ideas appear to be robust and difficult to extinguish (e.g., diSessa, 1982; White, 1983).

There is currently a lot of debate about how it is best to characterize the nature of naive knowledge and the mechanisms thereby which it can be modified. Some researchers believe that novices' ideas can be conceptualized as consisting of a coherent and systematic set of ideas which have a status similar to that of a scientific theory (McCloskey, 1983; Wiser & Carey, 1983). Others think that naive physics consists of a fragmented collection of ideas which are loosely connected and do not have the systematicity that one attributes to a scientific theory (e.g., diSessa, 1988).

In addition to its considerable theoretical interest the debate on the nature of naive knowledge has important instructional implications as well. Depending on one's beliefs about the nature of naive knowledge different instructional implications can be drawn. Researchers who view novices as having relatively well organized and internally consistent naive theories think that the process of science learning requires a change in theory similar to the kind of theory change observed in the history of science (Hanson, 1958; Kuhn, 1962; 1970). Although the mechanisms for achieving this kind of theory change are not yet known, most of these researchers believe that it is necessary to confront novice students with enough evidence to make them realize the limitations of their theories and to change them (Anderson, 1977; Collins, 1986; McCloskey, 1983).

On the contrary, researchers who believe in the fragmented nature of naive knowledge think that a one-by-one attack of the knowledge fragments that constitute naive physics is a hopeless task. Some of them suggest that what is needed is to collect and unify these fragments to develop the scientific understanding that a science-naive individual lacks (diSessa, 1988).

In this paper we present an intermediate position based on the results of our investigation of the process of knowledge acquisition in the domain of astronomy (Vosniadou, 1987; Vosniadou & Brewer, 1987; in press; submitted). Crucial to our position is the distinction between global and domain-specific theories. We believe that children start their knowledge acquisition process with a global theory consisting of a set of core concepts and a notion of causality which forms the basis of their ontology and epistemology. This global theory becomes differentiated and restructured into domain-specific theories.

Children's naive understanding of the world is conceptualized as consisting of a set of discrete ontological beliefs which are constructed on the basis of their everyday experience under the constraints of their global theory. Children seem capable of synthesizing these discrete beliefs into larger conceptual units and are sensitive to the internal consistency of these conceptual structures. Ontological beliefs are, however, different from the hypotheses of a domain specific theory in that they are considered by children to represent the true state of affairs about the world and, thus, in no need of being questioned. The emergence of a domain-specific theory requires the replacement of some of the ontological and epistemological beliefs of the global theory with a different explanatory framework.

KNOWLEDGE ACQUISITION IN ASTRONOMY

Everyday experience provides children with enough information to construct an intuitive understanding of many of the phenomena that a theory of observational astronomy accounts for (such as the shape, size, movement and location of the earth, the sun, the moon, and the stars, the day/night cycle, the phases of the moon, etc.). We hypothesized that if children utilize their everyday experience to construct a naive understanding of the physical world, they should believe that the earth is flat and stationary and that it is located in the center of the universe. We also hypothesized that children would think that gravity operates along an up/down gradient and that the day/night cycle is caused by the movement of the sun and the moon rather than by the movement of the earth. Some support for the view that children conceptualize the earth as flat and gravity as operating in an up/down fashion is found in previous research (Nussbaum & Novak, 1976; Nussbaum, 1979; Sneider & Pulos, 1983).

Such a naive understanding of the cosmos is of course very different from currently accepted views. We were interested in finding out whether children do indeed construct such an naive understanding of the world and, if so, how this understanding changes as children are exposed to the Copernican theory.

Methodological Issues

We examined children's knowledge of astronomy using an elaborate questionnaire which was developed after extensive pilot work and which consisted of a total of 207 questions. The children were also asked to make models of the solar objects using play dough and to select from a variety of physical models of the earth, sun, moon and stars. We conducted a series of studies using this questionnaire involving preschool, elementary school, and high school students in the United States (Vosniadou, 1987; Vosniadou & Brewer, submitted), in Samoa (Brewer, Hendrich & Vosniadou, submitted), in India (Samarapungavan & Vosniadou, in preparation), and in Greece (Vosniadou & Brewer, in press).

Children's concepts were identified from their responses not to one but to many questions tapping each concept. Crucial to our methodology was the distinction between *factual* and *generative* questions. Factual questions were designed to test children's exposure to certain theoretically important facts. These were questions like "What is the shape of the earth?", "Does the earth move?" Children could answer these questions either on the basis of their underlying conceptual knowledge or by simply repeating information they had obtained from adults. Generative questions were questions to which children had not been previously exposed and which had the potential of revealing whether the children had assimilated the adult information into their underlying conceptual framework. Consider for example the questions "If one were to walk for many days on a straight line would one ever reach the edge of the earth?"," Does the earth have an edge? ". We assumed that in order to answer these questions children would use their existing conceptual knowledge to form a mental model of the earth. If the children had fully understood the information that the earth is a sphere they should form a mental model of a spherical earth. Based on such a model they should come to the conclusion that the earth does not have an edge and that if someone walked for many days in a straight line one would come back to were one started. On the contrary, if the children had not fully incorporated the information that the earth is a sphere into their underlying conceptual structures they should form a mental model of a flat earth. Based on such a model they should come to the conclusion that the earth has an edge.

Follow-up questions and confrontation questions were also used throughout the interview to try to understand children's concepts. The following is an example of our questioning procedure from the protocol of Renae (grade l).

E: What is the shape of the earth?
C: Round
E: Could you ever reach the edge of the earth?
C: Yes.
E: Could you fall off that edge?
C: No.
E: Why not?
C: Because once you fall off you can't get back on.
E: What if you could get back on, do you think you could fall off then?
C: Yes...and if you took to the edge of the thing, and you had one hand on it, you could fall off easier.

In this protocol we see that Renae starts by saying that the earth is round. Upon further questioning it is, however, revealed that she believes that the earth has an end/edge from which people could potentially fall off, although she is very reluctant to accept this possibility.

Results

Consistency. Children's responses to the individual questions investigating each concept revealed tremendous surface inconsistency. For example, in a study of children's concept of the earth shape (Vosniadou & Brewer, submitted) we found that forty out of sixty children gave responses which did not agree with a consistent use of either a spherical earth concept or a naive concept of a flat earth. Many of these children appeared to have formed an alternative conception regarding the shape of the earth. Here is an example from the protocol of Veronica (grade 3).

E: What is the shape of the earth?
C: Round
E: If you walked for many days in a straight line, where would you end up?
C: Somewhere in the desert.
E. Would you every reach the edge of the earth?
C: No. You would have to have a spaceship if you're going to go to the end of the earth.
E: If there an edge to the earth?
C: No. Only if you go up.
E: Does anyone live here on the bottom of the earth?
C: No because they live in the states up here.
E: But could they live down here?
C: Yes.
E: Why wouldn't they fall off?
C: Because they are inside the earth?
E: What do you mean inside?
C: They don't fall; they have sidewalks, things down like on the bottom.
E: Is the earth round like a ball or round like a thick pancake?
C: Round like a ball.
E: When you say that they live inside the earth, do you mean they live inside the ball?
C: Inside the ball. In the middle of it.

Veronica appears to believe that the earth is round like a ball and that people live deep inside this ball.

Some evidence for the presence of alternative conceptions about the shape of the earth has been provided in previous research on the earth shape and gravity concepts (e.g., Nussbaum & Novak, 1976; Nussbaum, 1979; Sneider & Poulos, 1983). This research has not, however, shown whether children's alternative conceptions about the earth are systematic and are used in a consistent fashion or represent transitory and internally inconsistent problem solving attempts.

In order to determine whether the children were consistent in their use of an alternative conception of the earth we derived from our data and from the previous research in this area as many possible alternative conceptions of the earth as possible. Then, we generated the answers we would expect the children to have given to our individual questions had they made consistent use of that conception. For example, we reasoned that if children believed that the earth is round like a disc, rather than round like a ball, they should think that the earth has an end/edge, that people can fall down from that end/edge, that people live only on top of the earth, and that there is something that supports the earth.

Once the pattern of responses for each alternative earth shape concept was determined we checked children's responses to the relevant questions to see if they agreed with the expected ones. Assigning a concept to a child required no more than one deviation from the expected pattern of responses and only if this deviation occurred in a non-defining item for this category. For example, a child who said that there is an end/edge to the earth could not be assumed to be making consistent use of a spherical earth concept, even in those cases where this response was the child's only deviation from a spherical earth concept response pattern. On the other hand, the response "circle" to the question "What is the shape of the earth?" was considered an acceptable deviation for a child whose responses agreed in all other respects with the spherical earth concept because it could be caused by a linguistic rather than a conceptual confusion (e.g., the child may have used the word "circle" to mean "round").

Using this procedure we were able to determine that the great majority of children in our studies made consistent use of a concept. For example, in the case of the earth shape we were able to determine consistent use of the same concept in 51 out of the 60 children investigated. As is shown in Table 1 most of the children used alternative concepts of the earth which showed a combination naive and scientific views. We have identified three such concepts: The dual earth, the disc earth and the inside-the- sphere concepts. The children who had a dual earth concept believed that there are two earths; a flat one on which people were usually thought to live and a spherical one which was thought to be up in the sky. The children with a disc concept thought that the earth is both flat and round and that it has an end/edge from which people can fall. Finally some children believed that the earth is round like a ball but that people live deep inside this ball. The questionable sphere category included the children who seemed to be making use of a sphere concept but had two or three deviations from the accepted pattern of responses and could not therefore be placed in the sphere category.

Following this procedure we have been able to determine that most children use in a consistent fashion certain concepts of the sun, moon, stars and certain explanations of the day/night cycle. For example, many children believe that the movements of the sun and the moon cause the day/night cycle. Others think that the sun is occluded by clouds or solar objects that move in front of it. One interesting explanation was held by children who knew that the earth rotates around its axis but attributed the day/night cycle to the presence of the moon. These children thought that the moon is fixed in some place in the sky where it is always night; as the earth rotates our part of the earth eventually comes to face the moon and as a result to bring the night.

Table 1
Frequency of Children's Concepts of the Earth's Shape as a Function of Grade

Earth Shape Concepts	Grade 1	Grade 3	Grade 5	TOTAL
1. Sphere	2	8	10	20
2. Questionable Sphere	1	3	6	10
3. Inside-the-Sphere	2	4	4	10
4. Disc	0	1	0	1
5. Dual Earth	7	2	0	9
6. Flat (Rectangle)	1	0	0	1
7. Mixed	7	2	0	9
TOTAL	20	20	20	60

Some children had mixed concepts and for some no consistent concept could be identified. On the whole, however, our results suggested that there was a relatively high degree of internal consistency in children's atomistic concepts about the earth, sun, moon and stars and their explanations of the day/night cycle.

The success in identifying consistent concepts for the great majority of the children in our sample shows that children's conceptual knowledge is not as fragmented as some theorists have argued (e.g., diSessa, 1985; Solomon, 1983), at least at the level of the individual concepts investigated. It appears that children try to synthesize their everyday experience into meaningful and internally consistent conceptual structures.

It could be objected here that some of the alternative conceptions we have identified may not be precompiled but may be constructed by the children on the spot as they are trying to answer our questions. In our view this issue is not critical for our position. Whether precompiled or not the use of relative stable and internally consistent knowledge structures shows that many if not all children are both sensitive to and capable of connecting their knowledge fragments into internally consistent wholes. In that particular respect children's synthetic attempts are not different in kind from scientists' attempts to construct theories.

The robustness of naive conceptions. It appears that one reason why children may construct alternative concepts is because they find it very difficult to give up their naive conceptions. Indeed, all the alternative conceptions of the earth shape we have identified can be seen as attempts to assimilate the scientific concept of a spherical earth to the naive concept of a flat earth. For example, the children with a dual earth concept believe that there are two earths one round and one flat. The children with the disc model interpret round to mean flat. Finally, the children with the inside-the-sphere concept believe that the earth is a sphere but that people live on flat ground inside it. The presence of these alternative concepts shows that naive conceptions are rather robust.

Naive concepts consist of several discrete ontological beliefs. A close examination of the alternative concepts we have identified reveals that these concepts are attempts from the part of the children to synthesize a number of discrete ontological beliefs about the nature of the earth, sun, moon and stars. Let's examine the earth shape concept once more. This concept appears to be composed not only of the belief that the ground is flat but also (among others) of the beliefs that the earth has some kind of an end/edge, that people can fall down from that edge, that there is ground or water underneath the earth, and that people live only on top of the earth.

In forming alternative concepts children change their naive concepts in a way that allows them to retain all or some of their ontological beliefs without contradicting adult teachings. The detailed examination of children's responses reveals that there is a progression of more and more advanced alternative concepts depending on how many ontological beliefs children have given up. For example, the inside-the-sphere view is a more advanced concept than the disc concept. The children who hold the inside-the-sphere concept have given up their ontological belief that the earth is flat, that there is ground all the way down and that the sky is only on top of the earth. These children conceptualize the earth as a sphere suspended in space but still believe that people live on flat ground inside the earth, and that things fall downward rather than toward the center of the earth.

This does not happen only in the case of the earth shape concept. Consider, for example, the children who have constructed an explanation of the day/night cycle according to which the rotation of the earth allows our side of the earth to face the stationary moon. These children have changed their ontological beliefs that the moon moves and the earth does not but have not yet given up on the idea that night is associated with the presence of the moon.

Naive concepts are embedded within global theories. We think that ontological beliefs are constructed by children on the basis of their everyday experience under the constraints of their global theories. Naive concepts are generated by synthesizing these discrete ontological beliefs. In addition, two epistemological constraints appear to further constrain children's concepts: (a) the belief that ontological beliefs represent the true state of affairs about the world, and (b) the belief that adults are usually right. If children did not believe that their ontological beliefs represent the way the world really is there would be no reason to form alternative concepts. They would simply change their beliefs and adopt the adult models. The formation of alternative concepts, especially in cases like the earth shape where the culture provides such massive exposure to the idea that the earth is a sphere, strongly suggests that children are operating under the epistemological constraint that their ontological beliefs are fundamentally true.

The construction of alternative concepts also presupposes the belief that adults are right. If children did not believe that adults are right they would have no difficulty rejecting the adult information and retaining their original naive views. When children construct an alternative concept they try to retain as many of their ontological beliefs as possible without contradicting adult teachings.

In short, the genesis of an alternative concept can be conceptualized in the following way. When children read in a book or hear from an adult that the earth is a sphere they do not want to believe that the adult information is wrong but find it hard to reconcile it with their ontological beliefs. Because children believe that their ontological beliefs represent the true state of affairs about the world they are not likely to question them. Rather, they believe that they have misunderstood what the adults really mean when they say that the earth is round. In trying to interpret the adult information in a way that does not contradict their ontological beliefs children construct alternative concepts or develop unassimilated internally inconsistent concepts.

CONCLUSIONS

Our investigations of the process of knowledge acquisition in the domain of observational astronomy have shown that children start by constructing a naive understanding of the world which is based on their everyday experience. This naive understanding can be decomposed into a number of discrete ontological beliefs such as that the ground is flat, that things fall down when you drop them, that stars are small objects, and that the day/night cycle is caused by the movement of the sun and the moon. Children try to synthesize these ontological beliefs into relatively consistent conceptual structures which are, however, constrained by different epistemological frameworks than those of adult scientists. The process of knowledge acquisition requires the rejection of these ontological and epistemological beliefs and their replacement with a different explanatory framework.

REFERENCES

Anderson, R. C. (1977). The notion of schemata and the educational enterprise: General discussion of the conference. In R. C. Anderson, R. J. Spiro, & W. E. Montague (Eds.), *Schooling and the acquisition of knowledge* (pp. 415-431). Hillsdale, NJ: Erlbaum.

Brewer, W. F., Hendrich, D. J., & Vosniadou, S. (submitted). *Universal and culture-specific aspects of children's cosmological models: Samoan and American data.*

Collins, A. (1986). *A sample dialogue based on a theory of inquiry teaching* (Tech. Rep. No. 367). Urbana: University of Illinois, Center for the Study of Reading.

diSessa, A. (1982). Unlearning aristotelian physics: A study of knowledge based learning. *Cognitive Science, 6,* 37-75.

diSessa, A. (1988). Knowledge in pieces. In G. Forman & P. B. Pufall (Eds.), *Constructivism in the computer age* (pp. 49-70). Hillsdale, NJ: Erlbaum.

Hanson, N. R. (1958). *Experience and the growth of understanding.* London: Routledge and Keagan Paul.

Kuhn, T. S. (1962). *The Copernican Revolution.* Cambridge, MA: Harvard University Press.

Kuhn, T. S. (1970). *The structure of scientific revolutions.* Chicago: University of Chicago Press.

McCloskey, M. (1983). Naive theories of motion. In D. Gentner & A. L. Stevens (Eds.), *Mental models* (pp. 199-324). Hillsdale, NJ: Erlbaum.

Nussbaum, J. (1979). Children's conceptions of the earth as a cosmic body: A cross-age study. *Science Education, 63,* 83-93.

Nussbaum, J., & Novak, J. D. (1976). An assessment of children's concepts of the earth utilizing structural interviews. *Science Education, 60,* 535-550.

Sneider, C., & Poulos, S. (1983). Children's cosmographies: Understanding the earth's shape and gravity. *Science Education, 67,* 205-221.

Vosniadou, S. (1987, April). Children's acquisition and restructuring of science knowledge. In N. Fredericksen (Chair), *Children's procedural knowledge in science.* Symposium conducted at the annual meeting of the American Educational Research Association, Washington, D.C.

Vosniadou, S., & Brewer, W. F. (1987). Theories of knowledge restructuring in development. *Review of Educational Research, 57*(1), 51-67.

Vosniadou, S., & Brewer, W. F. (in press). A cross-cultural investigation of knowledge acquisition in astronomy: Greek and American data. In H. Mandl, E. DeCorte, N. Bennett, & H. C. Friedrich (Eds.), *Learning and instruction: European research in an international context* (Vol. II). Oxford: Pergamon.

Vosniadou, S., & Brewer, W. (submitted). *The concept of the earth's shape: A study of conceptual change in childhood.*

White, B. Y. (1983). Sources of difficulty in understanding Newtonian dynamics. *Cognitive Science, 7,* 41-65.

Wiser, M., & Carey, S. (1983). When heat and temperature were one. In D. Gentner & A. L. Stevens (Eds.), *Mental models* (pp. 267-297). Hillsdale, NJ: Erlbaum.

Comparing Historical and Intuitive Explanations of Motion: Does "Naive Physics" Have a Structure?

Nancy J. Nersessian
Program in History of Science
Princeton University

Lauren B. Resnick
Learning Research and Development Center
University of Pittsburgh

ABSTRACT

Are students' explanations of motion generated by an underlying structure? We address this question by exploring striking parallels between intuitive explanations and those offered by medieval scholastics. Using the historical record, it is possible to reconstruct an inferential structure that generates medieval explanations. We posit a parallel structure for intuitive explanations.

INTRODUCTION

There is an extensive literature that establishes that intuitive explanations of motion differ fundamentally from Newtonian explanations (cf. Caramazza, McCloskey, & Green, 1981; Clement, 1982; Halloun & Hestenes, 1985; McCloskey, 1983; McDermott, 1984; and Viennot, 1979). The literature also shows that students exit physics classes with their intuitive beliefs pretty much intact, even though some of them may have learned to manipulate the mathematical formalism of Newtonian physics. Thus it is clear that our strategies for teaching physics need to be re-evaluated.

Among the prerequisites for developing more successful instructional strategies are the following: First, we need to know, at a deeper level of analysis than exists at present, just what are the intuitive beliefs and concepts, whether these form a structure, and if so, what kind; second, we need to characterize the differences between an intuitive representation of physical phenomena and a scientific representation; and, third, we need to understand the methods through which a scientific representation can be constructed. In this paper we focus on the first prerequisite.

There are substantial data on student predictions and explanations of projectile motion and free fall (cf. Caramazza et al., 1981; Halloun & Hestenes, 1985; McCloskey, 1983; McDermott, 1984; and Viennot, 1979). The interpretation of these data is the subject of some controversy. In particular, researchers disagree over whether there is an underlying structure that generates intuitive explanations. McCloskey (1983) has been the strongest advocate of structure, claiming that these explanations are generated from an intuitive theory of motion, whereas di Sessa (1987) represents the most radical position on the side opposing structure. For him, intuitive knowledge of physical phenomena is piecemeal and fragmented.

Our approach to the question of the nature and structure of the content of "naive physics" is to explore the intriguing parallels between historical pre-Newtonian explanations of motion and those used in our "everyday" modes of thought. Although many researchers have pointed out parallels, most of the literature is vague about their nature and what we can hope to learn from them. We propose that, if there actually is a significant degree of recapitulation of the content of historical pre-scientific representations in intuitive representations, knowledge of the historical structures and of the reasoning processes through which these were replaced by scientific representations will provide a valuable resource for enhancing our understanding of "restructuring" in science learning.

METHOD

In our larger study, we examine medieval explanations of projectile motion and free fall and formulate the beliefs that underlie these explanations (Nersessian & Resnick, 1989). We then reconstruct relevant portions of the medieval inference structure, comprising presuppositions, observations, and beliefs, that generates their explanations. Additionally, we extract the medieval categories and conceptual structure for these domains. This analysis makes use of the extensive record of arguments and discussions by medieval scholars concerning motion (Clagett, 1959).

In a parallel analysis, we take summaries of student protocols found in the literature on "naive physics" and extract what seem to be widespread beliefs underlying intuitive explanations of projectile motion and free fall. As shown in Table 1, these turn out to be quite similar to the medieval beliefs. We thus attempt to construct an inferential structure--comparable to the medieval structure--comprising presuppositions, observations, and beliefs, that could produce their explanations. Finally, we abstract the underlying categories and conceptual structure for these domains. The postulated inferential structure provides a competence model for intuitive reasoning about motion; that is, we claim that, if pushed, students will either generate the structure or agree with it and will generate novel statements consistent with it.

Constructing a belief structure for intuitive explanations is more difficult than for the medieval case. Students have rarely been asked to explicate in detail the assumptions underlying their explanations of projectile motion and free fall, and they have not been probed deeply for the meanings they attach to words they repeatedly use in their explanations, such as energy, force, gravity, momentum. Thus, we have had to make inferences about what they mean and how they could be reasoning. We made the minimal assumptions we thought could be supported by what is reported in the literature. Although our reconstructions of the historical and the intuitive structures are independent, we did use the historical analysis as a guide to abstracting the intuitive categories and presuppositions.

We have been able to construct structures constraining all the medieval beliefs and the intuitive beliefs in Table 1. Since only a small part of the analysis can be presented here, we concentrate on the categories and structures pertaining to the intuitive belief that has most intrigued researchers, IB 3: continuing motion is sustained by a stored force and its medieval correlate, MB3: motion is sustained by impetus.

MEDIEVAL BELIEFS

MB 1: ALL MOTION REQUIRES A CAUSAL EXPLANATION

The medieval categories and presuppositions are in essence Aristotelian. The division between heavenly and earthly motion is central. The motion of heavenly bodies is eternal and presents no problem. All earthly or "local" motion is a process of change that bodies undergo, much like that of an acorn growing into a tree. All changes require a causal explanation; thus all local motion requires a causal explanation. The category of "motion" is opposed to that of "rest," which is the state bodies are in naturally. No explanation is needed for why objects remain at rest.

MB 2: MOTION IS CAUSED BY A MOVER

Things either move by themselves (for example, by falling) or they are moved by an external agent (that pushes, pulls, etc.). Medievals reasoned that, in the latter case, the motive power comes from the agent, and in the former case it must come from something internal to the object. In both cases the motion comes from the activity or power of the source, that is, from what was called a mover.

MB 3: CONTINUING MOTION IS SUSTAINED BY IMPETUS

Two local motions, "violent" (e.g., projectile) and free fall, presented problems for medieval theorists. First, objects in free fall speed up as they fall, and there is no satisfactory explanation in Aristotelian theory as to why this should happen. Second, objects in violent motion do not immediately fall downward when they are detached from their source of motion but continue in motion for a finite duration. Medievals argued that for violent motion to continue some of the power the agent imparts to the body must be stored in it. They called this stored power impetus. Early medievals believed that impetus would dissipate on its own, but in the final versions of the theory, Buridan claimed that impetus would keep a body in motion forever if it were not interfered with. The theory also explained the increasing speed of free fall by postulating that falling bodies acquired impetus from their heaviness.

Figure 1 shows the belief structure of medieval impetus theory. The structure consists of:

1. presuppositions: enclosed in ellipses
2. pervasive observations: enclosed in hexagons
3. beliefs: enclosed in rectangles.

Figure 3 shows the relevant portion of the medieval conceptual structure. The concept map consists of:

1. concept nodes: names enclosed in ellipses
2. links between concepts:
   a. kind links: straight lines, labelled "K"
   b. property links: lines ending in arrows, labelled "Pr"
   c. relation links: lines ending in arrows, labelled "R" or with a particular relation.

INTUITIVE BELIEFS

In explicating these beliefs, it will be useful to give some indication of how they compare with the medieval and the Newtonian beliefs. Additionally, Table 2 compares the intuitive categories with the medieval and the Newtonian categories.

IB 1: ALL MOTION REQUIRES A CAUSAL EXPLANATION

This is perhaps the most fundamental of intuitive beliefs. As in historical pre-inertial thought, "motion," in the intuitive conceptual system, seems to be categorized as a kind change. "Rest" is not a well-developed category in intuitive thinking but does seem to oppose "motion," as in the medieval case. Why something remains at rest does not require explanation. However, the types of explanations students offer of motion indicate that, like other changes, all motions require a causal explanation. This parallels the medieval view and stands in contrast to the Newtonian view that motion is a state and only changes of state (i.e., accelerated motion) require an explanation.

IB 2: MOTION IS CAUSED BY "FORCE"

This, together with IB 3, is the most frequently noted intuitive belief, "motion implies force." What is usually not noted is that "motion" and "force" have meanings quite different from the meanings they have in Newtonian mechanics. For intuitive physics, "motion" is a process, not a state, and "force" is either a causal agent or a property of the object, and not a functional quantity (i.e., a relation between objects). Projectile motion is caused by some external agent ("force"), while for self-propelled motion, the agent can be a "motor" of some sort. The problem case is where motion continues after the object has separated from the agent.

IB 3: CONTINUING MOTION IS SUSTAINED BY A STORED "FORCE"

Students explain motion that continues after detachment by using such words as energy, inertia, impetus, oomph. From their patterns of responses, we hypothesize that all of these terms make reference to an invisible force stored inside moving objects. This stored-up force is a property of the object, imparted to it by the agent. Thus, these words correspond most closely with the medieval notion of "impetus" and not to the modern notions of "energy" and "inertia."

Further, virtually all students claimed that in the absence of an external "force" objects will "run out of steam" and come to rest. This indicates that they expect the stored force to get used up as motion continues. It is unclear whether students believe friction plays a role here, or the force dissipates on its own.

Figure 2 shows the postulated intuitive belief structure. Figure 4 maps the intuitive conceptual structure.

CONCLUSIONS

We have been able to construct an intuitive belief structure, with its associated conceptual structure, that parallels an actual historical structure. The similarities between the intuitive and the medieval categories, conceptual structure, and belief structure are striking. This lends plausibility to our hypothesis that the postulated structure is capable of generating frequent intuitive explanations of certain kinds of motion. We also hypothesize that, given all the pertinent data for a situation, the seemingly inconsistent explanations that students occasionally give will prove to be consistent with the structure. We plan to test these hypotheses by implementing the structure in a computer model and by designing studies to test its empirical consequences.

Our structure provides an alternative to the major proposals in the literature. We agree with di Sessa that intuitive thinking is not developed sufficiently to constitute a theory. However, intuitive thinking about motion can still have a structure in that there is entailment and consistency among the beliefs.

ACKNOWLEDGMENTS

Preparation of this paper was supported in part by the National Science Foundation Scholars Award SES-8821422 to Nersessian and by the Office of Naval Research Grant N00014-84-K-0223 to the Learning Research and Development Center at the University of Pittsburgh. We thank Michael Ranney for his comments.

BIBLIOGRAPHY

Caramazza, A., McCloskey, M., & Green, B. (1981). Naive beliefs in 'sophisticated' subjects: Misconceptions about trajectories of objects. Cognition, 9, 117-123.

Calgett, M. (1959). The science of mechanics in the Middle Ages. Madison: University of Wisconsin Press.

Clement, J. (1982). Students' preconceptions in elementary mechanics. AJP, 50, 66-71.

di Sessa, A. (1987). Toward an epistemology of physics. Unpublished manuscript, Institute of Cognitive Studies, University of California at Berkeley.

Halloun, I. A., & Hestenes, D. (1985). Common sense concepts about motion. AJP, 53, 1056-1065.

McCloskey, M. (1983). Naive theories of motion. In D. Gentner & A. L. Stevens (Eds.), Mental models. Hillsdale, NJ: Erlbaum.

McDermott, L. (1984). An overview on conceptual understanding in physics. Physics Today, 37, 636-649.

Nersessian, N. J., & Resnick, L. B. (1989). Epistemological obstacles to constructing an inertial representation of motion. Unpublished manuscript, Learning Research and Development Center, University of Pittsburgh.

Viennot, L. (1979). Spontaneous reasoning in elementary dynamics. European Journal of Science Education, 1, 205-221.

QUALITATIVE GEOMETRIC REASONING

Robert K. Lindsay

Artificial Intelligence Laboratory
University of Michigan

ABSTRACT

This paper addresses an old and fundamental problem, the role of visual imagery in cognition. While the problem has a long history in philosophy and psychology, it has had less attention explicitly directed toward it in artificial intelligence research on *reasoning* (as opposed to machine vision and graphics). This paper addresses the question of what it means for a cognitive agent to think directly in visual images (*depictions*), and how such abilities might be formalized and accomplished with computer hardware. It is argued that the identification of imagery with non-propositional or with non-digital representations is incorrect; rather, the quality of imagery that gives it a special character is that it employs non-deductive inference, and this may well be achieved by descriptive, digital representations. Furthermore, research on knowledge representation within AI suggests approaches to the classical problems of imagistic thinking. A program is described for translating propositionally stated geometric assertions into diagrammatic representations and employing a constraint-propagating procedure to manipulate the representations, thereby making inferences and testing conjectures.

INTRODUCTION

Much of the imagery debate within psychology still grapples with several puzzles that have been long with us: If knowledge is represented as depictions which must be "observed", how can an endless regress of homunculi within homunculi be avoided? Since imagery lacks the detail and vividness of perception, and is not restricted by actual observation of the world but may be produced "at will" even to represent non-veridical possibilities, how can it be of use in reasoning? Since anything that can be represented can be represented descriptionally to any desired amount of detail, and since descriptions can be dealt with computationally in straightforward ways, why bother with depictional representation at all? Since depictions must be specific, how can they be used to reach general conclusions? The debate between Kosslyn (1980; Kosslyn & Pomerantz, 1977; Kosslyn et al., 1979) and Pylyshyn (1973, 1980, 1981) testifies to the continuing concern these problems cause.

Research in artificial intelligence has illuminated many of the issues that have stimulated cognitive research in general, and its emphasis on explicitly defined computational models offers certain insights and techniques that can apply productively to the imagery problem. For example, since a programmed model requires the specification of the processes that construct and use its representations (in this paper these are called *construction and retrieval processes*), the homunculus problem is addressed and solved with each AI implementation. But the major relevant insight of AI is that, while some sort of general calculus for reasoning may be possible, when one considers the computational complexity and efficiency issues that must be addressed in the construction of a real-time intelligence, it becomes clear that not all in-principle adequate representations are equivalent. Specifically, a representation that captures the geometric properties of space would be able to make inferences (and, as we will propose here, conjectures as well) by constraint satisfaction methods that avoid the combinatorial problems of deductive proof. Such methods, then, are a tool that addresses the frame problem (how knowledge should be updated when some facts change) by letting "the side effects take care of themselves (Haugeland, 1985, page 229)".

Anderson (1978) has argued that it cannot ultimately be decided whether human thinking is imagistic or propositional, since it is always possible to impose an imagistic interpretation on a propositional description, and vice versa. However, two informationally equivalent representations may nonetheless not be computationally equivalent (as pointed out by Larkin and Simon, 1987). Thus specific models can succeed or fail to match empirical facts, exhibit varying amounts of explanatory power, or be computationally and biologically more or less plausible. Theories must be judged not by direct verification of their underlying assumptions, but by the usual standards of empirical test of their predictions of observable behavior and their coherence with other established theory and fact. See Hayes-Roth, 1979. Consequently, this paper is concerned with accounts of the *functional* properties of representations rather than with issues of the nature of the base representation. I believe that imagery is indeed functionally different from logic-based systems, though not because logic is propositional. I have argued elsewhere (Lindsay, 1988) that there is a difference between knowledge representations that support inference by deduction, that is, by the use of a proof procedure such as that of first-order logic, and those that support inference without deduction, such as by heuristic search and/or constraint mechanisms inherent in the representation. In other words, it is not the distinction between propositional and non-propositional representations that is at issue, but the distinction between representations based on a logico-deductive formalism and those that have inherent structure, including but not limited to schema systems. This is an idea that has also been advanced by others in somewhat different terms, including Palmer (1978) and Dretske (1981).

Palmer's analysis is particularly illuminating. He defines a hierarchy of three types of isomorphism between a representation and that which it represents. Physical isomorphisms preserve information by virtue of representing relations that are *identical* to the relations represented. Thus a physical model of a natural terrain preserves the spatial relations of the represented terrain with the very same relations, including for example elevation, but on a different scale. Functional isomorphisms, on the other hand, preserve information by representing relations that have the same algebraic structure as the relations represented. Thus the elevations of a natural terrain may be represented as colors on a map of the terrain, provided the colors are interpreted appropriately (as an ordered set) and mapped so as to preserve the order of the physical elevations of the terrain. Thus physical models are a proper subset of functional models. Palmer introduces a class of isomorphisms between physical and functional, which he calls natural isomorphisms. In a natural isomorphism, the representation of preserved relations need not be by means of *identical* relations, as in physical isomorphism, hence not all natural isomorphisms are physical isomorphisms. On the other hand, not just any algebraically equivalent set of relations qualifies. In a natural isomorphism, the representing constructs have *inherent constraints* (Palmer's term); that is, there is additional structure imposed on the representing objects that limits the ways in which they may relate. If these inherent constraints preserve the relations of the represented world, we have a natural isomorphism.

Palmer identifies natural (including physical) isomorphisms with analog (including pictorial) representations, and functional but non-natural isomorphisms with propositional representations. Propositional representations are thus less restricted, as we normally suppose, because the structure of the representing world is extrinsic to it, that is it may be arbitrarily imposed, say in the form of rules of deduction. However, analog (including pictorial) representations employ representations that have inherent (non-arbitrary, unalterable) structure ('inherent constraints') that allow us to do away with deduction rules. This limits their applicability, but at the same time increases their power by reducing the computational complexity of inference (and easing the frame problem). A similar definition of "analog" was suggested by Dretske. Note that this use does not identify *analog* with *continuous* (non-digital) representations.

The concepts of *simulation* and *constraint satisfaction* which derive from artificial intelligence research provide means to realize these ideas. A program that simulates the behavior of a physical, geometric, or abstract system may serve the role of a natural isomorphism. A cognitive agent or program makes inferences about the external situation by running its model, whose inherent constraints mirror the structural and functional constraints of the situation. With appropriate implementations, the costly search required by proof procedure methods is avoided. The cost of using such representations is a loss of the generality of, say, a logic based system which both permits arbitrary descriptions and provides a proof procedure. A second cost is a loss of generality due to the need for a variety of representations for a variety of problems. This cost may be partially offset by the use of analogy, such as when non-geometric problems are translated into geometric terms.

The essence of this dissolution of the imagery problem is present in many knowledge representation methods that are not overtly depictional. For example, inheritance hierarchies (Touretzky, 1986) exhibit the essence of depictional representation simply because certain inferences (that property P is true of each member of any subset of a class to which P is appropriately attributed) follow "automatically" from the addition of information to the representation. Such inferences are inherent in the construction and use of the representation, without explicitly employing a proof procedure. Hierarchies are, of course, readily and universally represented propositionally.

Inheritance of properties, however, is a limited and specific form of reasoning. Reasoning with visual images is a more general and ubiquitous ability for which *cognitive* (as well as perceptual) mechanisms are presumably already in place in any organism with vision. Visual reasoning can be accomplished with a representation whose construction and retrieval processes embody the inherent geometric and/or physical constraints of space and mechanics. Once this is understood, the research issues no longer turn on whether the representation is propositional or not, nor whether it is analog or digital. The issue is how to represent geometric and physical systems in ways that are *computationally efficient* and can interface appropriately with other forms of knowledge representation. Should the representations look like or be readily translatable into a conventional descriptive format, such as frames, they remain, through the fact of their specialization, basically different in kind from a general, arbitrarily structurable formalism such as predicate calculus. They are "natural isomorphisms", which combine the virtues of a physical model, whose behavior is forced to obey physical laws, with the virtues of an abstract representation, which can be recorded and processed by digital computers or brains.

GEOMETRIC REASONING

The bulk of artificial intelligence research on reasoning has not directly addressed imagistic reasoning in spite of the seeming centrality, along with verbal reasoning, of this mode of thought as suggested by the long-standing interest in psychology, the common introspective impression of the layman, and extensive anecdotal evidence from literature on the history of scientific discovery. The special case of reasoning about two dimensional geometric objects has been addressed both in the cognitive modelling and AI literature, however. Space does not permit discussion and comparison with the present work except to acknowledge related research by Gelernter (1959), Novak (1977), Funt (1977, 1981), Kosslyn (1980), Forbus (1983), Anderson et al. (1985), Larkin & Simon (1987), and Koedinger & Anderson (in press). Some of this research has employed deductive methods augmented by *ad hoc* coding of diagrammatic information, while some of it has employed non-deductive representations more centrally, although for circumscribed tasks. The present work is an attempt to abstract and generalize the insights of these authors.

It is now widely understood that any knowledge representation must specify, in addition to the underlying format of the recorded data, the procedures for adding and recalling information from the store. As noted, I call these *construction processes* and *retrieval processes* respectively; I refer to the passive record as the *representation-proper*. Previous work on models of imagery have employed several representations-proper. None of these is "purely depictional" in any intuitively clear way, but as I have argued, that is not the issue.

Predicate representations: Individual constants are single letters, such as A, B, C, and D. Predicates introduce objects, for example, POINT(A), POINT(B), POINT(C), POINT(D), SEGMENT(POINT(A), POINT(C)), ANGLE(POINT(A), POINT(D), POINT(B)) and QUADRANGLE(POINT(A), POINT(D), POINT(B), POINT(C)). Metric relations may be introduced with the use of a numerical equality predicate '=' and numbers [LENGTH(SEGMENT(B,C)) = 10 and MEASURE(ANGLE(D, A, C)) = 90] or with additional predicates such as RIGHTANGLE(D, A, C). Non ratio-scale positional relations are expressed with predicates such as BELOW(D, C) and LONGER(SEGMENT(A, C), SEGMENT(A, D)). In general, arbitrary descriptions may be constructed including diagrammatically impossible descriptions such as BELOW(D, C) & ABOVE(D, C). Descriptions may also be incomplete and inaccurate.

Schema (Frame) representations: Schemas are structured propositional knowledge that relate several predicates and impose restrictions on variable types. For example, a schema for triangle includes the fact that it is composed of three vertices (which must be point names) and three sides (which must be segments). Point schemas and segment schemas in turn contain information about names, locations, and imposed constraints (such as rigidity of a segment or fixedness of a location); some of this information may be unknown at any given time. For example, a segment could be recorded in a schema with this format:

SEGMENT SCHEMA

NAME	NIL
END1	A
END2	C
SEGMENTPOINTS	({POINT}#61666 {POINT}#63333 . . . .)
MARKING	BLACK
SOURCE PREMISE	INPUT-1: "QUADRANGLE(A, D, B, C)"
LENGTH	10
LENGTHSTATUS	FIXED
BEARING	30
BEARINGSTATUS	ARBITRARY

Coordinate representations: The representation-proper consists of a set of marked points, each of which is assigned numerical x,y coordinates. Some of the marked points may have associated names. Objects exist by virtue of their coordinates satisfying certain defining numerical relations. For example, a segment exists if all of the coordinates "between" (algebraically defined) its endpoints correspond to marked points. The definition of a triangle is more complex. Metric relations are represented implicitly, and are retrieved by computations. For example, the length of a segment is computed by applying the Euclidian distance function to the coordinates of its endpoints. Ordinal metric relations such as "to the right of" are defined by appropriate computations on coordinates.

Pixel Array representations: This representation is similar to Cartesian coordinate representations except that it is digitized: coordinates must be, say, integers or rational decimals of limited precision. Each pixel may be one of a finite number of values to denote a grey level or a color. Pixels are referenced by indices, and relative locations may be determined by arithmetic on indices. In more elaborate pixel array representations, the "grain" of the array may be stratified under program control so that some or all of the representation may be "exploded" or "compressed" to obtain varying levels of detail.

Pixel Network representations: Elements of the representation-proper are interpreted as points each of which is connected to eight neighbors: in the north, northeast, east, southeast, south, southwest, west, and northwest directions. An element may have an associated name and a marking. Objects such as segments are represented implicitly by marking a connected, appropriately straight set of elements. Metric relations such as length are retrieved by determining the cardinality of the set of marked points. Ordinal metric relations are implicit in the topology and must be retrieved or tested by searching of the connections and applying appropriate definitions (e.g., B is right of A if there is a path from A to B that goes through more steps in the three "right" directions (northeast, east, southeast) than in the three "left" directions.

I have implemented a system for the representation of simple geometric elements such as points, lines, and triangles in two-dimensional space. At the heart of the system is a fixed set of construction and retrieval processes. For example, there is a process that constructs a line segment between two given points (a construction process) and a process that determines whether or not two line segments are of the same length (a retrieval process). The representation is a pixel array/network that combines the features of both of these representation types in a single structure, plus a structure of inter-related schemas for geometric objects (point, line segment, triangle, and so forth) present in a depiction. The pixel array is finite in extent, and has a certain inherent grain or minimum resolution both in distance and direction. The distance resolution can be set to coarser values and this will affect the behavior of the construction and retrieval processes; thus the test of segment length checks equality to within the currently operative resolution, and the construction of a line segment will exhibit a corresponding compliance. The frames relate the geometric objects to the pixel array, and record propositionally specified or derived descriptions of the objects, such as that a particular line segment is required to be rigid. Predicate representations are used as input (only). The information thus given to the system is used by the construction processes to build the three components of the representation system, thereby describing a specific instance of that which was described in the predicate input.

Although lines in a depiction have specific lengths and polygons have specific areas, only qualitative judgments about these metric quantities are known to the processes. Thus, a line may be judged longer, shorter, or equal in length to another, but differences in lengths cannot be compared unless a construction can be made (with these processes) that produces new line segments of the appropriate lengths to be compared.

In the human mind, imagery and verbal thought cohabit, interact, and complement one another. Therefore, it is important to see how such interactions could come about. Although the system cannot produce representations through visual perception, it can do so from descriptions provided either externally or by its own higher order goal-driven processes. In addition, the programs illustrate how images can be used both to produce and to test conjectures about what is possible, and thus have the ability to run *Gedanken* experiments in the service of problem solving. This requires the interaction of the representation with the more conventional search methods of AI as discussed later.

QUALITATIVE GEOMETRIC REASONING

Certain inferences are straightforward in the system. For example, if a triangle is constructed with two equal angles, the inference that it has two equal sides can be made by "observation", using the above cited retrieval process; this is an inference but not a deduction. More interesting is the use of the system to produce and test conjectures. This depends on the architecture of higher processes that set appropriate tasks. In my model, all of these problem solving methods work through a set of "visual routines" that employ the construction and retrieval processes. These visual routines manipulate existing depictions by propagating small perturbations of point positions or line lengths. This, in effect, simulates "in the mind's eye" what would happen if real geometric objects were manipulated physically.

These processes are called qualitative geometric reasoning processes, on analogy to work by de Kleer & Brown (1984), Forbus (1984), and others (see Bobrow, 1985) on qualitative physical reasoning methods. In that work, composite physical structures, such as an electronic circuit or a pressure regulating valve, are modelled from an inventory of components, each of which behaves according to equations that relate its inputs and outputs. A program reasons about the composite model by observing its behavior while small qualitative perturbations of physical quantities are propagated through the model, obeying the componential equations. In my model of qualitative geometric reasoning, small perturbations of positions (suggested by the higher processes in service of testing a conjecture or attempting to make a construction in accordance with an externally supplied propositional description) are propagated while obeying the inherent constraints of two-space (as implemented by the construction and retrieval processes) and any arbitrary, externally specified constraints on the depiction (as recorded in the frame structures). Thus the representation determines whether a proposed alteration is possible, and if it is possible, what follows from it.

To illustrate, consider Figure 1, interpreted as a shortest path problem. A representation of the left side of Figure 1 is constructed by the program from descriptive statements about points and lines, including that all line segments are rigid (and hence can be rotated but not stretched or compressed). External "pulls" are imposed on points A and B in the directions indicated by the arrows. This manipulation is external in the sense that it is imposed by the "higher processes" alluded to above, rather than by the geometric representation system itself. A step-wise simulation of the effects of these forces causes a gradual transformation to the representation illustrated to the right. At this configuration, no further motion is possible without violation of the rigidity constraints. This effectively demonstrates that the shortest path from A to B is through D, not C. While proof of this would require relatively little search of path combinations in this simple example, the manipulation provides a number of other inferences at the same time, such as that C remains above D, and the resulting figure is a triangle. On the other hand, while the same computational procedure could in principle handle networks of dozens or hundreds of nodes to compute shortest path, we note that people are unable to do so without the aid of a physical string model or some such external aid. The explanation of this within the terms of the present model comes from the amplification of errors by the qualitative, low resolution representation. Note further that the computations involved in this experiment were time consuming because they were carried out serially, point by point. However, the same computations lend themselves to distributed processing. If each pixel element in the representation had its own associated processor to do the vector calculations, the processes would be more rapid.

TESTING OF GEOMETRIC CONJECTURES

The testing of conjectures requires an exploration of "all possible" alterations of a given type. This involves higher processes that control search, backtracking, and enumeration of possibilities. For example, it is well-known (to us) that two triangles with corresponding sides equal in length must be congruent. A non-deductive "visual proof" of this theorem amounts to showing that at most one triangle can be constructed from three line segments of fixed length. The higher processes set the task of constructing one such triangle. This would prove impossible if the lengths chosen do not satisfy the triangle inequality; otherwise, the construction processes succeed in constructing a triangle. Doing so requires making specific choices for locations of vertices. The motivation of these choices is determined by the higher processes, and these embody important strategic assumptions. In the present case, choices are made to produce depictions of a size appropriate to the current resolution and at locations and orientations that avoid ambiguities and potential interference during subsequent manipulations of the depiction. Once a triangle is constructed, the higher processes construct the second triangle, with sides of the same lengths as those chosen for the first triangle. The triangles of course prove to be congruent. Then to complete the task of conjecture testing, modifications of the second triangle are proposed to "see" if another triangle can be constructed that differs from the first. *Any* proposed modification of the position of a point will force the modification of other positions in order that lengths remain unchanged, and it will be observed that angles thus do not change (the triangle can only rotate or translate rigidly). *Any* is here stressed to emphasize that the higher processes must be able to propose all possible modifications. This is not a trivial matter since it would be foolish to consider all possible triangles that could be marked on the array: it must be possible for the higher processes to recognize equivalence classes of proposed perturbations in order to avoid exhaustive search and yet conclude that a triangle is uniquely determined by three sides. It will be necessary to integrate the depictional representation with a search architecture to enable the model of geometric reasoning to be fully goal-directed.

REFERENCES

Anderson, J. R. (1978) Arguments concerning representations for mental imagery. *Psychological Review*, **85**, 249-277.

Anderson, J. R., Boyle, C. F., and Yost, G. (1985) The geometry tutor. In *Proc. of the International Joint Conference on Artificial Intelligence-85* held in Los Angeles. Los Altos, CA: Morgan-Kaufmann.

Bobrow, D. G. (1985) *Qualitative reasoning about physical systems.* Cambridge, MA: Bradford Books.

de Kleer, J. and Brown, J. S. (1984) A qualitative physics based on confluences. In D. G. Bobrow (Ed.) *Qualitative reasoning about physical systems.* Cambridge, MA: Bradford Books, 7-83.

Dretske, F. I. (1981) *Knowledge and the Flow of Information.* Cambridge, MA: MIT Press.

Forbus, K. (1983) Qualitative reasoning about space and motion. In D. Gentner and A. L. Stevens (Eds.) *Mental Models.* Hillsdale, NJ: Lawrence Erlbaum, 53-73.

Forbus, K. (1984) Qualitative process theory. In D. G. Bobrow (Ed.) *Qualitative reasoning about physical systems.* Cambridge, MA: Bradford Books, 85-168.

Funt, B. V. (1977) Whisper: A problem-solving system utilizing diagrams and a parallel processing retina. *Proc. of the 5th International Joint Conference on Artificial Intelligence, IJCAI-77*, held at MIT, August 1977. Pittsburgh: Carnegie-Mellon University, 459-464.

Funt, B. V. (1981) Multi-processor rotation and comparison of objects. *Proc. of the 7th International Joint Conference on Artificial Intelligence, IJCAI-81*, held at the University of British Columbia, August 1981. Menlo Park: AAAI, 218-220.

Gelernter, H. (1959) Realization of a geometry theorem proving machine. *Proc. International Conference on Information Processing*, pp. 273-282. Paris: UNESCO. Reprinted in E. A. Feigenbaum and J. Feldman, eds. (1963), *Computers and Thought.* New York: McGraw-Hill, 134-152.

Haugeland, J. (1985) *Artificial Intelligence: The Very Idea.* Cambridge, MA: MIT Press.

Hayes-Roth, F. (1979) Distinguishing theories of representation: A critique of Anderson's "Arguments concerning mental imagery". *Psychological Review,* **86**: 376-382.

Koedinger, K. R. and Anderson, J. R. (in press) Abstract planning and perceptual chunks: Elements of expertise in geometry. *Cognitive Science.*

Kosslyn, S. M. (1980) *Images and Mind.* Cambridge, Mass.: Harvard University Press.

Kosslyn, S. M., Pinker, S., Smith, G. E., and Shwartz, S. P. (1979) On the demystification of mental imagery. In Block (1981) *Imagery.* Cambridge, Mass.: MIT Press, 131-150.

Kosslyn, S. M. and Pomerantz, J. R. (1977) Imagery, propositions, and the form of internal representations. *Cognitive Psychology,* **9**:52-76.

Larkin, J. and Simon, H. A. (1987) Why a diagram is (sometimes) worth ten thousand words. *Cognitive Science,* **11**, 65-100.

Novak, G. S. (1977) Representations of knowledge in a program for solving physics problems. *Proc. of the 5th International Joint Conference on Artificial Intelligence, IJCAI-77,* held at the Massachusetts Institute of Technology, August 1977. Menlo Park: AAAI, 286-291.

Lindsay, R. K. (1988) Images and inference. *Cognition,* **29**: 229-250.

Palmer, S. (1978) Aspects of representation. In E. Rosch and B. B. Lloyd (Eds.) *Computing and Categorization.* Hillsdale, NJ: Erlbaum. 259-303.

Pylyshyn, Z. W. (1973) What the mind's eye tells the mind's brain: A critique of mental imagery. *Psychological Bulletin,* **80:** 1-24.

Pylyshyn, Z. W. (1980) Computation and cognition: Issues in the foundations of cognitive science. *The Behavioral and Brain Sciences,* **3**: 111-133.

Pylyshyn, Z. W. (1981) The imagery debate: Analog media versus tacit knowledge. *Psychological Review,* **87**. In Block (1981) *Imagery.* Cambridge, Mass.: MIT Press, 151-206.

Touretzky, D. S. (1986) *The mathematics of inheritance systems.* Los Altos, CA: Morgan-Kaufmann.

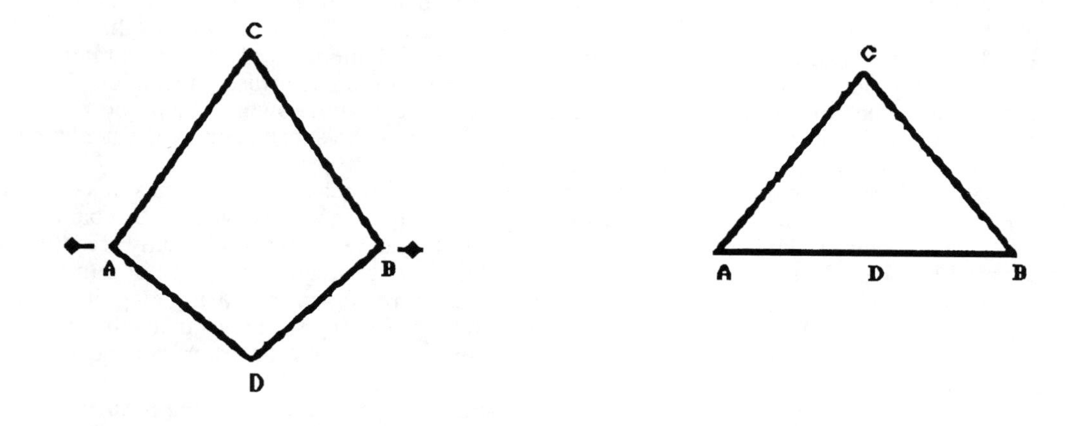

Figure 1
SHORTEST PATH PROBLEM

SCIENTIFIC REASONING STRATEGIES IN A SIMULATED MOLECULAR GENETICS ENVIRONMENT

Kevin Dunbar, Dept of Psychology, McGill University

ABSTRACT

Two studies are reported investigating the strategies that subjects use to revise hypotheses following disconfirmation. Subjects attempted to discover how genes are controlled by conducting experiments in a simulated molecular genetics laboratory. In Study 1, subjects set a goal of finding an experimental result, when this goal was not achieved they adopted one of the three following strategies. (1) Distort the logic of evidence interpretation to fit the current goal. (2) Conduct a parametric analysis of the Experiment space to achieve the goal. (3) Set a new experimental goal of trying to discover the cause of unexpected findings. Only the third group discovered how the genes are controlled. In Study 2, the hypothesis that the subject's experimental goal blocks consideration of alternative hypotheses was investigated. When subjects were allowed to reach their initial goal, they then set a new goal of accounting for unusual findings and discovered the mechanism of control. These results suggest that the goal of the subjects constrains search of both an Hypothesis and an Experiment space. This strategy can produce distortions in reasoning and a failure to generate new hypotheses.

One of the most interesting paradoxes in research on human reasoning is that subjects and scientists alike tend to seek evidence that confirms and ignore evidence that disconfirms their hypotheses, yet both subjects and scientists discover concepts and make scientific progress. While many researchers have argued that these strategies are inappropriate (e.g., Popper, 1959; Wason, 1960; Mynatt, Doherty, & Tweney, 1977), others have argued that when the probability of having one's hypothesis disconfirmed is high, a useful strategy is to seek confirmation. This latter view is based on the premise that disconfirming evidence can be used to guide formation of new hypotheses and generation of new experiments (cf. Dunbar & Klahr, 1989; Klahr & Dunbar, 1988; Klayman & Ha, 1987). While Klayman and Ha have demonstrated that this strategy is statistically appropriate when the predominant experimental outcome is disconfirmation, the cognitive strategies for dealing with disconfirming evidence are unknown. The purpose of the two studies reported here is to investigate hypothesis revision and subsequent experimentation following the disconfirmation of initial hypotheses.

A further goal of this research is to investigate scientific reasoning strategies in a task that more closely resembles real scientific reasoning. As we have argued elsewhere (Dunbar & Klahr, 1989; Klahr & Dunbar, 1988) many of the tasks that have been used to study scientific reasoning involve arbitrary experiments (e.g., pick this card, generate a sequence of numbers), and arbitrary hypotheses (e.g., all cards with one border, numbers of increasing magnitude). While these studies have provided many insights into the reasoning strategies that subjects use, they involve little prior knowledge and the to-be-discovered concept is an arbitrary concatenation of features.

In the studies reported below, a different approach to scientific reasoning is taken: subjects must propose hypotheses and conduct experiments in a real scientific domain -- molecular genetics. Subjects were given the task of discovering the mechanism by which genes are controlled by other genes. This particular problem has been of central concern to molecular biologists for the past forty years, and provides an interesting domain within which to investigate scientific reasoning. Using this task, subjects were given some initial knowledge about the domain and a number of experimental tools that are similar to those used in genetics laboratories. This task makes it possible to investigate the cognitive processes that are involved in scientific reasoning and more particularly the nature of hypothesis revision and experimentation following disconfirmation.

The Molecular Genetics domain. One of the major events in science of this century has been the founding of molecular genetics. The most well-known breakthrough in this field being the discovery of the structure of DNA by Watson and Crick in 1953. This field has had many other discoveries that are at the core of current day theorizing about genetics. One such discovery was the mechanisms by which genes are controlled (Jacob & Monod, 1961). Monod and Jacob discovered that some genes control the functioning of other genes and specified the mechanisms by which this control occurs. Because of the major importance of this finding, Jacob and Monod were awarded the Nobel Prize in 1965.

Monod and Jacob demonstrated that in the bacterium ecoli, there are regulator genes that control the activity of other genes. This mechanism of genetic control is known as the Lac Operon. Ecoli need glucose to live and one of the common sources of glucose for ecoli is lactose. When there is lactose present the ecoli secrete enzymes that break down the lactose into glucose. The ecoli can then use the glucose as an energy source. The ecoli only secrete the enzymes that breakdown the lactose when the lactose is present. When there is no lactose present the enzymes are not secreted. The question that Monod and Jacob investigated was how the ecoli regulates its activity so that it only secretes enzymes when lactose is present. They discovered that the regulator genes inhibit the production of various enzymes until the enzymes are needed. The details of the mechanism are given below in Figure 1.

Simulating molecular genetics in the cognitive laboratory. The work of Monod and Jacob provides an interesting problem that can be transposed to the psychological laboratory and subjects can be given the task of discovering the mechanisms of genetic control. Thus rather than inventing an arbitrary task that embodies certain aspects of science it is possible to give subjects a real scientific problem to work with. In the studies presented below, subjects were taught about genetics and shown how to conduct simulated molecular genetics experiments on the computer, and then were asked to discover how the genes were controlled. The task that the subjects were presented with was to discover the Lac Operon. Note that the purpose of this work is not to simulate the way in which Monod and Jacob discovered the Lac Operon, but to use a task that involves some real scientific concepts and experimentation to address the cognitive components of the scientific discovery process.

Figure 1:
The Lac Operon

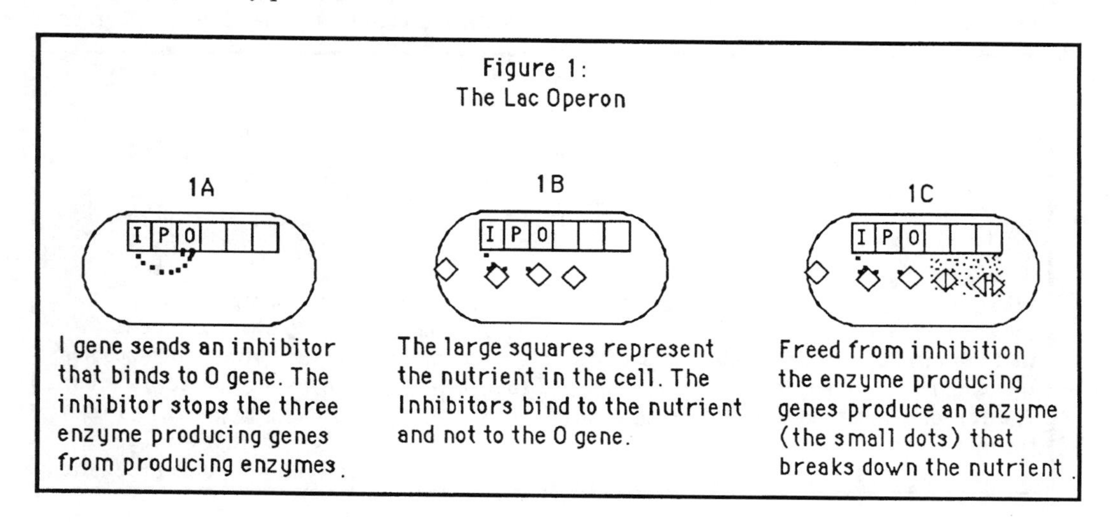

1A
I P O
I gene sends an inhibitor that binds to O gene. The inhibitor stops the three enzyme producing genes from producing enzymes.
1B
I P O
The large squares represent the nutrient in the cell. The Inhibitors bind to the nutrient and not to the O gene.
1C
I P O
Freed from inhibition the enzyme producing genes produce an enzyme (the small dots) that breaks down the nutrient.

Standard Experimental Procedure. Subjects were trained in some of the very elementary concepts of molecular genetics on a MacIntosh II computer. The display was highly interactive: subjects conducted experiments by pulling down menus and selecting various options from the menus. Once the experiment was designed subjects could run the experiment to see what happens. The screen display was similar to that displayed in Figures 1 and 2. However, unlike figure 1, subjects could not see any genes secreting inhibitors and activators, they had to induce this concept from experimental results. Subjects learned that chromosomes consist of genes and that the genes have particular functions. Subjects were told that certain genes control the activities of other genes by switching them on when there is a nutrient present. This is an example of activation -- the controller gene senses that there is a nutrient present and then releases substances that instruct other genes to secrete enzymes that can utilize the nutrient.

Subjects were shown how to conduct simulated experiments that allowed them to determine how the controller genes switch on the other genes. These experiments were conducted using three controller genes A, B, and C that are attached to three enzyme producing genes (see Figure 2A). Subjects were taught a number of standard techniques for discovering the functions of the genes.

The first technique was specifying the amount of nutrient given (zero, 100, 200, 300, 400 and 500 microgrammes). The second technique was using various types of genetic mutations. One type of mutant is haploid. Normal haploid ecoli have the A, B, C, and enzyme producing genes present. Mutant haploid ecoli have either the A, B, or C genes missing. Only one gene can be removed at a time. For example in Figure 2B the A gene is missing. Diploid ecoli have two chromosomes. The normal diploid has the A, B, C, and enzyme producing genes on one chromosome, and has a second chromosome that has the A, B, and C genes on it. In diploid mutants one chromosome may have a gene missing (as in Figure 2C), or both chromosomes may have a gene missing. As can be seen from figure 2, Diploid ecoli can be used to discover the mechanisms of control: if a gene is missing from one chromosome and is present on the other chromosome the ecoli may now work normally. In figure 2 this suggests activation. Other experimental results might suggest inhibition.

The third component of experimentation was monitoring the output of the enzyme. After every experiment the subjects saw a table of results showing whether the ecoli was haploid or diploid, what mutations were made (i.e., what genes were missing), how much nutrient was added, and how much enzyme was produced. This data was displayed in a table that appeared after every experiment. This table also contained the results of all previous experiments. After subjects had learned to use these techniques they were given some problems that demonstrated that they understood the theoretical concepts and experimental techniques that they had learned.

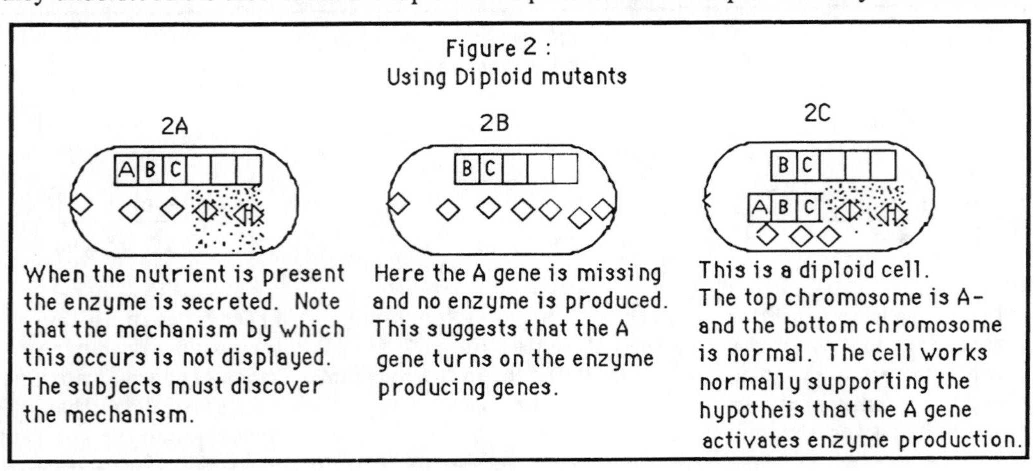

Figure 2 :
Using Diploid mutants

2A: When the nutrient is present the enzyme is secreted. Note that the mechanism by which this occurs is not displayed. The subjects must discover the mechanism.

2B: Here the A gene is missing and no enzyme is produced. This suggests that the A gene turns on the enzyme producing genes.

2C: This is a diploid cell. The top chromosome is A- and the bottom chromosome is normal. The cell works normally supporting the hypotheis that the A gene activates enzyme production.

In the second part of the study, subjects were presented with two findings about a set of genes and were asked to discover how the enzyme producing genes are controlled. The genes was very similar to the learning experience for the A, B, and C genes. In this case, the genes are labelled I, O, and P. The I, O, and P controller genes work very differently from the A, B, and C genes that the subjects had just learned. Here, the I and O genes inhibit the activity of the enzyme producing genes until a nutrient is present (as in Figure 1). Note that in the training phase subjects learned that gene regulation can occur by activation (one gene switches other genes on), but that in the second part of the study the type of genetic regulation to be discovered is very different, the subjects must discover inhibition (genes turn other genes off).

There are 120 possible experiments that can be conducted. Different types of experiments produce different amounts of enzyme given a certain amount of nutrient. For an experiment with normal Ecoli, the amount of enzyme produced is half whatever the amount of nutrient is. Mutants with the I gene missing (designated I- mutants) produce an output of 876, and O- mutants produce an output of 527. The I- and O- mutants produce this amount of enzyme regardless of the amount of nutrient administered. Thus, I- and O- nutrients will produce enzymes even when no nutrient is administered. This is a strong clue for inhibition being involved. In Study 1, the P gene plays no role at all. A mutant with a P gene missing (P-) will produce the same amount of nutrient as the normal ecoli. That is, the P gene plays no role in Study 1. In the real ecoli, and in Study 2, the P gene does play a role.

The to-be-discovered mechanism is very different from the mechanism that subjects learned during training. The mechanism learned during training was activation -- the controller genes turn the enzyme producing genes on. The to-be-discovered mechanism is inhibition -- the controller genes inhibit the enzyme producing genes. It was expected that subjects initial hypotheses would be that the controller genes turn the enzyme producing genes on. Because the genes work by inhibition, subjects initial hypotheses will be disconfirmed and they will have to do a considerable amount of experimentation and hypothesis generation before they discover that the mechanism of genetic control is inhibition.

Research questions. The first set of questions focus on subjects use of disconfirming evidence. It was expected that subjects initial hypotheses would be that either the I, P, or O genes turn on the enzyme producing genes. These initial hypotheses would be disconfirmed after a few experiments. A number of possible strategies could be used at this point. One strategy would be to ignore the disconfirming evidence. This is a common finding when subjects cannot think of alternate hypotheses (cf. Einhorn & Hogarth, 1987; Klahr & Dunbar, 1988). Another strategy would be to use disconfirming evidence to modify the current hypothesis, but stay within the current frame. In this experiment, it would entail switching from one activation hypothesis to another. Again this is an approach that has been mentioned but not well documented (cf. Klahr & Dunbar, 1988). Another strategy would be to focus on the disconfirming evidence and attempt to discover what the cause of the surprising findings is. Many theorists have argued that this is a useful strategy, but there has been little evidence for the use of this strategy (e.g., Kulkarni & Simon, 1988; Einhorn & Hogarth, 1982).

A second set of questions are concerned with the processes that govern the generation of hypotheses and experiments. Klahr and Dunbar (1988) have proposed that scientific reasoning can be described as a search in an Hypothesis and an Experiment space. We identified a number of different strategies for searching both spaces: some subjects mainly searched the hypothesis space, and others switched to searching an experiment space. In the genetics domain, the hypotheses are more complex, and no single result provides enough evidence to confirm an hypothesis. Would the search strategies be similar in a radically different domain?

STUDY 1: DISCOVERING THE MECHANISM OF GENETIC CONTROL

Method

Subjects. Twenty McGill undergraduates were paid to participate in a 2 hour study. All subjects had taken one introductory biology course and none of the subjects knew about gene regulation. Their knowledge of molecular genetics consisted of knowing that DNA and RNA exist and having a vague idea of how this is involved in gene reproduction.

Procedure. The study was carried out in three phases. First, the subjects were taught some basic facts about molecular biology, and were shown how a gene could be switched on by another gene. Second, the subjects were instructed on how to give a verbal protocol (cf. Ericsson & Simon, 1984). The subjects were given a 15 puzzle and were asked to think out loud while they solved the puzzle. Third, subjects were shown a new set of genes that produce a beta enzyme when there is lactose present and no beta enzyme when lactose is not present. They were told that the I, P, and O genes were potential candidates for controlling the beta genes and that their task was to discover how the beta genes are controlled. The subjects were told to state everything that they were thinking while they were performing the task. Subjects were told that they could finish either when they felt that they had discovered how the beta genes were controlled, or when they felt that they could not discover how the beta genes are controlled. If the subjects had not discovered how the genes are controlled within ninety minutes the study was stopped.

RESULTS

Two criteria for success were adopted in analyzing the results of this study. The first criterion was that subjects who determined that the I and O genes inhibit the production of beta were successful. Five subjects were able to determine that the mechanism of gene control was inhibition. The second criterion was that subjects who discovered that the O gene had to be on the same gene as the beta genes, and postulated a mechanism that could account for these findings. Two of the five subjects reached this criterion. Subjects took, on average, 60 minutes to do the task. There was no significant difference in the amount of time it took the subjects who succeeded (criterion 1) and those who did not. Subjects conducted an average of 16 experiments. There was no significant difference in the number of experiments by those who succeeded and those who did not. Of the 16 experiments, 13 were conducted with greater than zero amounts of lactose, and 3 were conducted with zero lactose.

The results of the study will be analyzed in terms of the strategies that subjects used after obtaining disconfirming evidence for their initial hypothesis. As expected, all subjects initially proposed that either the I, O, or P genes, or a combination of these genes turns on the enzyme producing genes. Eighteen of the twenty subjects tried a P-, O-, I- mutants with the same amount of lactose for their first three experiments. Subjects set their initial goal to find the activator gene. To achieve this goal they attempted to discover a situation that when the gene was absent the ecoli would not produce any enzyme. However, this initial goal was not fulfilled. Subjects did not find a situation where there was no output with a gene missing. The subjects discovered that when the I or O genes were missing there was a large output of enzyme, and that when the P gene was missing the ecoli behaved normally.

At this point, subjects adopted three different strategies for dealing with disconfirmation. One group stayed within their Activation frame and distorted the logic of experimentation to maintain their hypothesis. A second group embarked upon a search for a particular experimental result that would demonstrate activation. A third group switched their goal from one of finding activation to attempting to discover the cause of the unexpected findings. These strategies will now be discussed in detail.

Strategy A: Maintain frame By changing Logic of interpretation (N=6). Once these subjects obtained evidence that did not fit in with their initial hypothesis, they maintained the goal of finding an activator gene. However, they changed the logic of evidence interpretation. Their original goal was to discover that when a particular controller gene was missing no enzyme would be produced. Much to their surprise, they discovered that, no matter what gene was missing, there was always an output of enzyme. They also discovered that some mutants resulted in less output than others. They then proposed that if the controller gene is absent then there is little output. They substituted little output for for no output. They argued that the gene that is absent when the least output appears is the controller gene. The P gene -- which has no role whatsoever -- is absent when the least output appears and this group of subjects argued that the P gene is the controller gene. As a way of testing this hypothesis they proposed that if the P gene is present there will be a large output. Using this strategy, these subjects noticed that mutations with the P gene present produce large amounts of enzyme and concluded that the P gene is the controller gene.

It is important to note that the P gene plays no role whatsoever in controlling the genes. The subjects notice that when P is present the most enzyme is produced, and that when it is absent the least amount of enzyme is produced. They conclude that P activates the ecoli to produce a certain amount of enzyme. To reach this conclusion, subjects must ignore the fact that a normal gene only produces small amounts of enzyme and the P gene is present. Also, there are 4 diploid experiments that disprove this hypothesis and all the subjects in this group conducted at least one of these experiments. Subjects in this group all had a constrained search of the experiment space. The subjects did not conduct experiments with zero amounts of lactose. This is because their goal was to discover activation, therefore a zero lactose experiment was regarded as unnecessary.

In summary, the strategy that this group used was one of setting up a goal of discovering an activator gene. All subjects stated that this was their goal. When this goal was not fulfilled, the subjects distorted the logic of evidence interpretation until their goal of discovering the activator gene was fulfilled. The goal of finding activation constrained every stage of the discovery process.

<u>Strategy B: Search Experiment Space (N=7).</u> At the end of the first phase these subjects proposed that the mechanism probably involves some interaction of the genes and they hoped to find a certain combination of mutant genes that will not produce an enzyme when there is lactose present. To achieve the goal of finding this result they parametrically searched for an experiment that would produce this result. These subjects conducted more experiments and also searched different regions of the experiment space. However, they eventually gave up because they could not find an experimental result that fills the goal of discovering an activator gene.

<u>Strategy C: Opportunistic Subgoaling (N=7)</u>. This group initially believed that the controller gene works by activation, however as with the other two groups, they discovered that no matter what type of mutation there was always an output. However, instead of maintaining the goal of finding a gene that will not produce an enzyme when there is lactose present, these subjects set a goal of discovering why such unexpected results occurred. They focused on why there is a large output for I and O mutants, why the output is instantaneous for I- and O- mutants, and why the amount of nutrient administered is irrelevant. They first proposed that the I and O genes control the size of the output. Then, when they realized that the amount is irrelevant, they conducted experiments with zero lactose, and proposed that the I and O genes work by inhibition. Five of the seven subjects in this group discovered inhibition. The other two subjects did not get past the stage of proposing that the I and O genes govern the amount secreted. In sum, this group of subjects made significant progress by setting up new goals rather than maintaining the original goal.

DISCUSSION

The results of this study suggest that the major effect of disconfirmation is to induce subjects to propose minor changes in hypotheses. Despite disconfirmation, subjects maintain their original frame and continue to search for a particular type of experimental result. Maintaining the goal can lead subjects to change the logic of data interpretation to fit in with the current hypothesis. Thus, it appears that the major difficulty that subjects have is of changing their goal from trying to generate a particular finding to one of trying to discover the cause of their unusual findings. The successful subjects abandoned the goal of discovering activation and set up a new goal of trying to account for the set of findings that they obtained. Thus the goal of finding a particular mechanism prevents subjects from discovering alternative mechanisms of genetic control.

If the goal of discovering activation prevents subjects from considering the nature of disconfirming evidence, and constrains search of both the Hypothesis and Experiment spaces, then if this goal is eliminated, the subjects should set a new goal and discover the correct solution. The second study was conducted to test this hypothesis.

STUDY 2: GOALS AND DISCOVERY

The results of Study 1 suggest that the goal of finding supporting evidence for the current hypothesis constrains search of the hypothesis and experiment spaces. To test this idea, the genetic mechanism was changed so that one gene works by activation-- the P gene. The I and the O genes still work by inhibition. The only change from study 1 is that the P gene must be present for the ecoli to secrete an enzyme. If the P gene is absent no enzyme is produced. The subjects now have to discover that the I and O genes work by inhibition, and that the P gene works by activation. Thus, the genes work in a more complex mechanism than in Study 1. One possible outcome of this manipulation would be that once the subjects have discovered the P gene works by activation they will say that they have discovered the genetic mechanism: They have achieved their goal and the task is done. Another possible outcome is that once the subjects have discovered activation, this goal will be popped and a new goal will be set of accounting for the other findings. If this occurs, then many more subjects should discover that the genes work by inhibition than in the Study 1. This finding would suggest that the goals of the subject constrain the scientific discovery process.

Method

Subjects. Twenty subjects participated in the experiment. The subjects were from the same population as those in Study 1.

Procedure. The procedure was identical to that used in Study 1: There were three phases, training, giving protocols, and discovering the mechanism of genetic control. The only difference between this and study 1 was that here the P gene was an activator gene: the P gene must be present for an output to occur.

RESULTS

Subjects took considerably less time than in Study 1. Subjects spent an average of 38 minutes on the task (Study 1: 60 minutes). The mean number of experiments conducted was 15 (Study1: 16 experiments). Nineteen of the 20 subjects discovered that the P gene was an activator gene. Fourteen subjects discovered that the I and O genes work by inhibition (Study 1: 5 subjects). Eleven of the 14 subjects discovered activation before inhibition.

The results of this second study are consistent with the view that the current goal has a large effect on the hypotheses proposed and experiments conducted. When the top level goal of finding an activator gene is achieved, the subjects set themselves a new goal of discovering the cause of the other surprising results. Thus, many more subjects discovered inhibition in Study 2.

GENERAL DISCUSSION

Subjects do make use of disconfirming evidence. They use disconfirmation to generate new hypotheses and experiments. Disconfirming evidence is used to guide search through both the hypothesis and experiment spaces. However, Studies 1 and 2 demonstrate that there are some serious constraints on the search initiated after disconfirmation. The search is constrained by the current goal. The goal can be to find evidence in favor of the current hypothesis, or it can be to explain surprising results. If the goal is to find evidence in favor of the current hypothesis, the goal can have major effects on the reasoning strategies used: Subjects consider few alternate hypotheses, and they distort their analyses of experimental results. This result suggests that some of the findings of faulty uses of logic (e.g., Wason's 2 4 6 task) is due to the goal that the subjects have rather than an inability to reason in a normative manner.

Subjects propose an hypothesis and set up an experimental goal. They then search the experiment space to achieve the goal. When the goal is not achieved they continue to search the Experiment space. Rather than popping back up to the Hypothesis space to formulate new hypotheses, subjects stay at an experimental level. The strategy that they use to formulate new hypotheses depends on setting a new experimental goal: accounting for the unexpected findings. This new goal allows them to generate evidence over which new hypotheses can be induced. It is only then that subjects pop back to the Hypothesis space and propose radically new hypotheses. This suggests that the problem for subjects is not that they are always looking for evidence that confirms their current hypothesis, but that they are engaged in Experiment space search trying to achieve a certain experimental result. Subjects either have to change their experimental goal (as in study 1), or reach their goal before they can consider new hypotheses (as in study2). Thus, it is the goal that subjects have that is the source of confirmation bias, rather than the hypothesis per se.

While the negative side of goals constraining search is apparent, there are also a number of computational advantages to constrained search. In fact, many AI programs constrain search by the current goal (e.g., Turner, 1988). By using the current goal to constrain search, subjects only have to consider a small number of hypotheses, and also conduct a small number of experiments. Thus, the current goal prunes both the hypothesis and experiment spaces, making the problem tractable. Thus, the strategies discovered here may be in general useful, but because of their conservative nature, make it difficult to overthrow current theories.

REFERENCES

Dunbar, K., & Klahr, D. (1989). Developmental differences in Scientific Discovery Strategies. In D. Klahr, & K. Kotovsky (Eds.). *Simon and Cognition: Proceedings of the 21st Carnegie-Mellon Symposium on Cognition* . Erlbaum: Hillsdale, New Jersey.

Einhorn, H.J., & Hogarth, R.M., (1986). Judging probable cause. *Psychological Bulletin* , 99, 3-19.

Ericsson, K.A., & Simon, H. A. (1984). *Protocol Analysis: Verbal Reports as Data* . Cambridge, MA: MIT Press.

Jacob, F., & Monod, J. (1961). Genetic regulatory mechanisms in the synthesis of proteins. *Journal of Molecular Biology*, 3, 318-356.

Klahr, D., & Dunbar, K. (1988). Dual space search during scientific reasoning. *Cognitive Science* . 12, 1-48.

Klayman, J., & Ha, Y. (1987). Confirmation, disconfirmation, and information in hypothesis testing. *Psychological Review*, 94 , 211-228.

Kulkarni, D., & Simon, H.A. (1988). The processes of scientific Discovery: The strategy of experimentation. *Cognitive Science*, 12, 139-176.

Mynatt, C.R., Doherty, M.E., & Tweney, R.D. (1977). Confirmation bias in a simulated research environment: an experimental study of scientific inference. *Quarterly Journal of Experimental Psychology*, 29 , 85-95.

Popper K. R. (1959). *The Logic of Scientific discovery*. Basic Books, New York.

Turner, R. M. (1988). Opportunistic use of Schemata for Medical Diagnosis. In *Proceedings of the tenth annual conference of the Cognitive Science Society*. 160-166.

Wason, P. C. (1960). On the failure to eliminate hypotheses in a conceptual task. *Quarterly Journal of Experimental Psychology*, 12 129-140.

ACKNOWLEDGEMENT

This research was supported by grant number OGP0037356 from the National Sciences and Engineering Council Canada to Kevin Dunbar.

Learning events in the acquisition of three skills

Kurt VanLehn
Departments of Psychology and Computer Science
Carnegie-Mellon University

Abstract

According to current theories of cognitive skill acquisition, new problem solving rules are constructed by proceduralization, production compounding, chunking, syntactic generalization, and a variety of other mechanisms. All these mechanisms are assumed to run rather quickly, so a rule's acquisition should be a matter of a few seconds at most. Such "learning events" might be visible in protocol data. This paper discusses a method for locating the initial use of a rule in protocol data. The method is applied to protocols of subjects learning three tasks: a river crossing puzzle, the Tower of Hanoi, and a topic in college physics. Rules were discovered at the rate of about one every half hour. Most rules required several learning events before they were used consistently, which is not consistent with the one-trial learning predicted by explanation-based learning methods. Some observed patterns of learning events were consistent with a learning mechanism based on syntactic generalization of rules. Although most rules seem to have been acquired at impasses--occasions when the subject does not know what to do next--there were clear cases of rules being learned without visible signs of an impasse, which does not support the popular hypothesis that all learning occurs at impasses.

Introduction

The goal of this research is to see if people's behavior during the initial construction of a rule sheds any light on which of the many contemporary models of rule acquisition is a better characterization of human learning methods. Many theories of cognitive skill acquisition assume that rules are initially formed during events lasting only a few seconds. This is about the same time scale as a protocol line, so such "learning events" might be visible in a protocol. However, it is difficult to locate the exact line of a protocol where a rule is formed. All the existing simulations of cognitive skill acquisition (e.g., Anderson, Farrell & Saurers, 1984; Anzai & Simon, 1979; Klahr, Langley & Neches, 1987; VanLehn, 1983, in press) use multi-line episodes or other units of analysis that are too large for this purpose.

This paper first presents a method for locating protocol lines where rules are acquired, then discusses the results obtained by applying it to protocols from three task domains. Two of the tasks are puzzles: the Tower of Hanoi and a river-crossing puzzle. Although these two studies were intended merely to check that the analytic method works, they nonetheless yielded some interesting findings. In the third study, the task domain is college physics. This simulation is still under construction, so only some preliminary results can be reported. All three tasks are similar in that the subjects are "learning by doing" -- they are solving problems without help from a tutor or an instruction manual. It is an open question whether the results and methods discuss herein extend to other instructional situations.

A method for locating protocol lines where rules are learned

The following two-step method is used to locate lines of the protocol corresponding to the construction of a rule. The first step is to postulate a large set of plausible rules for problem solving in the task domain. The rules can be inferred from analyzing other subjects' protocols, from task analysis, from interviewing subjects, from one's own intuition, from writing a simulation program, or from any other source. Each rule is written with the weakest preconditions possible so that it will be applicable in the widest possible range of situations. The second step is to fit this vocabulary of rules to the given protocol. At almost every cycle of the simulation, there will be many rules that can be applied because the rules have weak preconditions. The user selects one, and the simulation applies it. The user's job is to find a sequence of rule selections that maximizes the fit of the simulation to the protocol. If the protocol can be formally encoded, this step can be automated (VanLehn & Garlick, 1987; Kowalski & VanLehn, 1988). The result is a table which aligns the protocol with rule firings and "missed opportunities"--occasions where a rule could have fired but did not. For instance, in Tables 1 and 4 below, rows correspond to protocol lines and columns correspond to rules. Cells of the table contain a "1" if the rule fired during that line of the protocol, a "0" if it could have fired and did not, and a blank if it was not applicable at that time.

Given such a table, two kinds of analysis are performed. The first is simply to look for patterns in the firings

Table 1: Protocol and simulation of a subject solving a river crossing problem

Cycle	State	Protocol	Rule 1	Rule 2
1	LMSb,_	The boat can hold only 200 pounds? (E: The boat can hold only 200 pounds.) Okay... first... Small and Medium go back (E: Uh-huh.)... go across the river on it.	1	
2	L,MSb	And then, um, ... Oh... Large...	1	
3	"	[3 second pause](E: Yeah, go on... talk out loud.)...and... um... Large... um... [3 second pause] (E: Talk out loud. Tell me everything you're thinking.) But, I can't do it because someone has to sail the boat back.		0
4	"	(E: Ok... That's right. Somebody has to sail the boat back.) Oh! Ok... so... [4 second pause] Small sails the boat back and gets off,		1
5	LSb,M	and lets Large sail the boat back.	1	
6	S,LMb	(E: Um-hmm. And then what happens.) Uh...	1	
7	"	[3 second pause] (E: Talk out loud.) And then Small... Small... can't think of anything... (E: Keep talking.)		0
8	"	So... Medium... sails back.		1
9	MSb,L	And... Medium and Small sail back.	1	
	,LMSb	(E: Keep talking.) And they're all across! (E: Very good!)		

and missed opportunities. Using this kind of analysis, it was discovered that rules are rarely learned completely in one trial. Typically, the initial firing of a rule is followed by one or more missed opportunities, then another firing, a missed opportunity, and so on with an increasing ratio of firings to missed opportunities. Such patterns have theoretical implications. For instance, gradual acquisition is not consistent with the operation of learning methods, such as explanation-based learning (e.g., DeJong & Mooney, 1986), that acquire rules in one trial. In one case, the precise pattern of gradually increasing frequency of usage was predicted by a learning mechanism based on syntactic generalization of the rule.

Although the mere pattern of rule usage has shed some light on learning mechanisms, a second type of analysis has proved to be even more productive. This type of analysis examines the subject's utterances in the vicinity of each learning event. For instance, several authors have claimed that all learning occurs at *impasses* (Laird, Rosenbloom, & Newell, 1986; VanLehn, 1988). An impasse can only be precisely specified relative to a given simulation model, but the rough idea is that the model "doesn't know what to do next." If this idea is taken at face value, and impasse-driven learning is universal, then the subject's protocol at the first use of a rule should show signs of confusion or hesitation because the subject is at an impasse. The analyses presented below show that most initial uses of a rule are, as predicted, accompanied by unusually long pauses or by comments such as "I can't do it," or "It's not that easy." However, several cases were found where there are no such signs of an impasse at all. Thus, the data are consistent with the claim that most but not all rule acquisitions are triggered by impasses.

Study 1: A river crossing puzzle

The protocol analyzed in this initial study was not collected with the intention of studying the rule acquisition process, so it has some methodological flaws. However, it has the expositional advantage of being a very short protocol that nonetheless demonstrates some of the paper's claims.

The subject, a 9-year old girl, was given standard instructions for talk-aloud protocols then asked to solve the following puzzle:

> Three men want to cross a river. They find a boat, but it is a very small boat. It will only hold 200 pounds. The men are named Large, Medium and Small. Large weights 200 pounds, Medium weights 120 pounds, and Small weights 80 pounds. How can they all get across? They might have to make several trips in the boat.

The subject's protocol and an analysis of it appear Table 1. The first column numbers the cycles of rule execution. The second column abbreviates the puzzle's state--the notation "LMSb,_" means that Large, Medium, Small and the boat are on the source bank, and nothing is on the destination bank. The third column contains the subject's protocol. The remaining columns indicate rule firings and missed opportunities. The major rules used in the simulation appear in Table 2. Rule 1 is selected for firing at every opportunity (cycles 1, 2, 5, 6 and 9). The firing of the rule at cycles 2 and 6 causes a subgoal to be generated because the boat is not on the source bank. This assumes a cognitive architecture that automatically translates precondition violations into subgoals. (The simulation was conducted on Teton (VanLehn & Ball, in press), but ACT*, Soar, GPS and many other architectures have this

Table 2: Majors rules used in simulating the solution of the river crossing puzzle

1. If the goal is to move some men from bank X to bank Y, and the boat is on bank X, then load the boat to its maximum capacity, sail it across, and unload it.
2. If the goal is that the boat be on bank X, and the boat is on another bank, Y, and the boat requires someone to sail it, and there are some men on bank Y, then load the boat with a small man, sail it across, and unload it.

property.) The subgoal of getting the boat back to the source bank causes the application of rule 2 at cycles 4 and 8.

Although all applications of rule 1 go smoothly, the first application of rule 2 is preceded by verbal evidence of an impasse. In the last line of cycle 3, the subject says, "But, I can't do it because somebody has to sail the boat back." The subject says she is stuck while at the same time mentioning an operation that could be applied. My interpretation of this line goes as follows. The subject recognizes that the puzzle situation is an idealization of reality, but she is unsure about how much of an idealization it is. In particular, she does not know whether the experimenter intends her to adopt the real-life constraint that most boats require a helmsman. The puzzle instructions do not state this constraint. (Indeed, another subject chose the other interpretation of the instructions, allowed the boat to sail itself back, and answered that it takes only two trips to get all the men across.) On this interpretation, the subject already "has" rule 2, but she does not know whether she is supposed to use it in this puzzle. After the experimenter confirms that this type of boat requires someone to sail it, the subject applies the rule (cycle 4). Although this learning event is arguably not rule acquisition, it is clearly learning of some kind. As will be seen shortly, it shares several properties with cases that are quite clearly rule acquisition events.

The second application of rule 2 is also preceded by signs of an impasse (cycle 7). The subject again claims to be stuck, saying "...can't think of anything...." Apparently, whatever she learned during cycle 3 is not immediately applicable at cycle 7. As will be seen later, this is quite typical--the first firing of a rule is followed by one or more missed opportunities. Several learning mechanisms are consistent with this behavior. For instance, it could be that the rule (or assertion) learned at cycle 3 has such a highly specific precondition that it does not apply at cycle 7, so the learning mechanism must create a generalized version of it. Another possible explanation rests on context effects--when the new rule is stored in memory, it is indexed in part by the context of cycle 3, which is assumed to be so different from the subsequent retrieval context (cycle 7) that retrieval fails. Although protocol data can differentiate such learning mechanisms (see below for an example), this particular case is consistent with a variety of learning mechanisms.

Depending on which learning mechanism one believes in, cycle 8 represents either a second firing of rule 2 or the firing of a new rule that is a generalization of rule 2. As mentioned earlier, this research method uses rules with the weakest preconditions possible, so in the simulation of this protocol, cycle 8 is a second firing of rule 2. However, this is just a methodological device for locating learning events in protocols. It is not intended as a claim about detailed learning mechanisms. I will continue to speak as if general rules were firing intermittently, even though it may be each general rule is actually an evolving collection of specific rules.

In summary, this protocol shows three interesting features. (1) The initial acquisition of the rule did not suffice to make it reliably operational. A second learning event was required (cycle 7). The second learning event took less time than the first (cycle 3). This pattern -- an initial formulation of a rule followed by one or more refinements of it -- occurs in later protocols as well. (2) Both learning events seem to be triggered by an impasse--a point where the subject does not know what to do next. Impasse-driven learning has been touted as a universal method for acquiring rules (VanLehn, 1988; Laird, Rosenbloom, & Newell, 1986). It will be seen later that although it is common for impasses to trigger learning, other types of triggering can also occur. (3) The subject reported neither the rule that was formed nor the processes that constructed it. The existence of the rule can be inferred from her actions, but if it was ever present in her working memory, she chose not to mention it. This too will turn out to be a common feature of learning events.

Study 2: The Tower of Hanoi

This study is a reanalysis of the classic protocol of Anzai and Simon (1979) wherein the subject invents several solution strategies for the five-disk Tower of Hanoi over the course of 90 minutes. During this time she receives no instruction. This corrects a methodological flaw in the first study, where the experimenter's comments seem to have been instrumental in the subject's learning.

Anzai and Simon uncovered the major strategies that the subject acquired and postulated learning mechanisms sufficient to acquire those strategies. They did not attempt a line-by-line comparison of the protocol and the behavior of their model. Using Teton (VanLehn & Ball, in press), we found that additional assumptions were necessary in order to achieve a line-by-line simulation of the protocol. The most important new assumption is that the subject has a strategy that develops around the first ten minutes of the protocol and remains fixed throughout the rest of the protocol. However, this strategy gives ambiguous advice on 25% of the moves, which will be called the *major* moves. On the major moves, the subject's fixed strategy narrows the choices down to two possibilities, but it does not say which one to take. The bulk of the subject's learning consists of a progression of strategies for making these decisions. With this new assumption, a model was formulated that fits the lines of the protocol with high accuracy, exceeding even that found in Newell and Simon (1972). The details can be found in VanLehn (1989).

Table 3 shows the rules used to make the major move decisions. Table 4 shows the analysis of the protocol. Each row of Table 4 is a major move. The first column numbers the major moves, the second column abbreviates the puzzle's state just prior to the move, and the third column abbreviates what the subject said while making the move. The puzzle's pegs are labeled A, B and C, where A is the peg that the disks start on and C is the peg they should end up on. The disks are labeled 1 through 5, with 5 being the largest disk. The notation "125,34,_" means that disks 1, 2 and 5 are on peg A, disks 3 and 4 are on peg B, and peg C is empty. The notation "2B, 1A" means that the subject announced a goal of moving disk 2 to peg B, then announced a movement of disk 1 to peg A. The notation "4pC" indicates a goal of moving a pyramid or group of four disks. Sometimes the subject announces a series of goals, pauses, and announces a different series of goals. This behavior is indicated by placing two rows in the table, one for each series of goals, and placing ditto marks in the first two cells of the second row. Horizontal lines in the table indicate places where the subject reset the puzzle to an initial state. The rightmost six columns of Table 4 show the applicability of rules. As always, a "1" indicates a rule firing, a "0" indicates a missed opportunity, and a blank indicates that the rule was not applicable. A "?" indicates that the rule may or may not have been fired -- the protocol evidence is unclear. The asterisks will be explained in a moment.

Table 3: Abbreviations and descriptions of rules for handling major moves

Initial rules

- *Look* The Anzai and Simon look-ahead search strategy.
- *1 blk* If the goal is to move a disk from one peg to another, and there is a single disk blocking the move, then get the blocking disk to the peg that is not involved in the move.
- *2 blk* If the goal is to move a disk from one peg to another, and the 2-high pyramid (i.e., disks 1 and 2) blocks the move, then get disk 1 to one of the pegs involved in the move (thus freeing disk 2 to move to the peg not involved in the move).

Rules acquired during the protocol

- *4B* Before attempting any of the top level goals, try to get disk 4 to peg B.
- *Dsk* (The Anzai and Simon disk subgoaling strategy.) If the goal is to get a disk from one peg to another, and there are some disks blocking the move, then get the largest blocking disk to the peg that is not involved in the move.
- *Pyr* (The Anzai and Simon pyramid subgoaling strategy.) If the goal is to move a pyramid from a peg to another peg, then get the next smallest pyramid to the peg that is not involved in the move.

Table 4: Rule firings and missed opportunities for the major moves

Move	State	Protocol	Initial rules			Learned rules		
			Look	1blk	2blk	4B	Disk	Pyr.
1	12345, _, _	1B	1			0	0	0
2	45, 3, 12	2B, 1A	1	1	?	0	0	0
3	5, 123, 4	5C, 1A	1			•1•	0	0
4	12345, _, _	1C	1			0	0	0
5	45, 12, 3	4B, 1A	0		1	•1•	0	0
6	5, 4, 123	1B	1				0	0
7	125,34,_	1C	0		1		0	0
8	_, 1234, 5	1A	1				0	0
9	3, 4, 125	1B	0		1		0	0
10	123, _, 45	3C, 1C	0		1		0	0
11	12, _, 345	1B	0	1			0	0
12	1, _, _	1C						
13	12, _, _	1B	0	1			?	
14	123, _, _	3C, 2B, 1C	0		0		•1•	0
15	_, 12, 3	quits	0	1			0	0
16	1234, _, _	3B, 2C, 1B	0		0		1	0
17	4, 3, 12	1A	0		1		0	0
18	_, 123, 4	1C	0		1		0	0
"	"	3B, 2A, 1C	0		0		•1•	0
19	12, _, 34	1B	0	1			0	0
20	12345, _, _	5C, 4B, 3C, 2B, 1C	0		0	0	1	0
21	45, 12, 3	4B, 1A	0		1	1	0	0
"	"	4B, 2C, 1A	0		0	1	•1•	0
22	5, 4, 123	5C, 3B, 2A, 1A	0		1		1	0
23	125,34,_	1C	0		1		0	0
24	_, 1234, 5	4C, 3A, 2B, 1A	0		0		1	0
25	3, 4, 125	1B	0		1		0	0
26	123, _, 45	3C, 2B, 1C	0		0		1	0
27	12, _, 345	1B	0	1			0	0
28	12345, _, _	5C, 4B, 3C, 2B, 1C	0		0	0	1	0
29	45, 12, 3	4B, 1A	0		1	1	0	0
30	5, 4, 123	3pB, 1B	0		0		0	1
31	125,34,_	1C	0		1		0	0
32	_, 1234, 5	4pC,4C,3pA,3A,2C,1A	0		0		1	1
33	3, 4, 125	2pA, 1B	0		0		0	1
34	123, _, 45	3pC, 2pB, 1C	0		0		0	1
35	12, _, 345	2pC, 1B	0	0			0	1

Some interesting findings are visible in the patterns of firings and missed opportunities. As in the river crossing puzzle, it is never the case that a rule is used consistently after it is first acquired. Instead, the usage of a new rule increases gradually. A second observation is that this subject occasionally compares the results of an old rule with those of the rule that supplants it. This can be seen in both cases where the subject re-does the planning of a move (moves 18 and 21). It can also be seen in move 32 where the subject mixes pyramid goals with disk goals. Thus, we do not see a rapid transition from an old rule to a new one, but a gradual transition that is sometimes accompanied by deliberate comparison of the old and new rules.

Obtaining further insight into the character of the rule acquisition process requires examining the protocol in the vicinity of the initial occurrences of the rules (see VanLehn, 1989, or Anzai & Simon, 1979, for the protocol itself). In the river crossing study, there were signs of impasses at both the initial firing of rule 2 and the subsequent firing. In this study, impasses were also present at most of the early rule firings. Asterisks are used in Table 4 to mark rule firings that were accompanied by long pauses and negative comments, such as "It's not that easy" or "I should have moved 5 to C." Impasses were common in the acquisition of both rule 4B and the disk subgoaling rule. However, there seem to have been no impasses involved in the learning of the pyramid subgoaling rule. At the first firing of the rule (move 30), the subject simply started phrasing her goals in terms of pyramid instead of disks. Instead of saying "3 will have to go to B..." as she said at move 22, she said, "I only need move three blocking disks to...B." There seems to have been no impasse here. At 32, the subject said

> I will move the remaining four from B to C... It's just like moving four, isn't it? So... I will have to move 4 from B to C... For that, the three that are on top have to go from B to A... Oh, yeah, 3 goes from B to A! For that, 2 has to go from B to C, for that, 1 has to go from B to A.

Although this segment is long, it contains none of the signs of consternation that mark the other learning events. Instead, the subject seems to have been excitedly comparing the disk rule and the pyramid rule and proving to herself that they generate the same plan. If an impasse is defined to be an occasion when the subject does not know what to do, then this segment is not an impasse, for the subject seems to have two alternatives and believe that both are equally correct. In short, it seems that most rule acquisitions (2 of 3) are triggered by impasses, but rules can sometimes be learned without impasses.

There is a subtle pattern in the acquisition of the disk subgoaling rule. Some of the early firings of the rule are marked by pauses and other signs of impasses, and some are not. Although space does not permit a detailed examination of the data (see VanLehn, 1989), it appears to be the case that the subject's initial formulation of the disk rule is highly specific in that it mentions the particular disks and pegs involved in the major move where it is acquired. Subsequent applications of the rule cause the names of specific pegs and disks to be replaced by variables. This gradual generalization of the rule means that some major moves can be handled by the evolving rule, while others cannot and force the rule to be further generalized. Pauses and other signs of impasses correlate perfectly with the places where generalization is predicted to occur. In particular, if it is assumed that the subject follows the policy of generalizing just enough to get the rule to accommodate the present situation, then it will take four learning events to learn a fully general version of the disk subgoaling rule. All four of these predicted learning events are marked by impasses in the protocol (two occur during move 14, and both are marked by a distinct pause). So it appears that impasse-driven syntactic generalization, which has played an important role in several models of skill acquisition (e.g., VanLehn, 1983, 1986, in press), seems to be behind the acquisition of the disk subgoaling strategy.

A last point to mention is that rules were discovered at a rate of about one every half hour (three were discovered in the 90 minute protocol). This rate seems to hold in the next study as well.

Study 3: College Physics

The protocols for the third study come from a study by Chi, Bassok, Lewis, Reimann and Glaser (in press) of eight students learning college physics from a standard textbook. Chi et al's study used a training format that comes close to the way students learn physics in college, except that the subjects could only refer to a textbook; they could not ask questions of a teacher. The subjects first learned the initial four chapters of a standard college physics textbook to criterion. They then read the fifth chapter, which covers the target subject matter, Newtonian particle dynamics. When they came to the worked examples at the end of the chapter, protocol collection began. Protocols were collected as the students studied 3 examples and worked 19 problems. The examples and the problems present ample opportunities for learning because they address issues that simply are not covered anywhere in the preceding material. For instance, the concept of a "normal force" is first introduced in the context of an example. The students took between 8 and 29 hours to complete the study. The protocols cover the last 3 to 6 hours.

As simulations are currently being constructed for each of the 8 protocols, it is too early to report accurate data on learning events. However, Bernadette Kowalski and I could not resist doing a hand analysis of one protocol. We found clear indications of five rules being acquired. As the protocol lasts 3.5 hours, this is an average of one rule every 40 minutes, which is comparable to the rate found in the Tower of Hanoi study (one rule per 30 minutes). We found some evidence that rules are acquired gradually, but we are reluctant to put a number on it because it is difficult to detect missed opportunities without a simulation. The usual signs of impasses marked the initial firing of 3 of the 5 rules. The other two rules seem to be acquired as the subject reflects on a just-completed solution. As an illustration, the next few paragraphs present one of these rule's acquisition event.

Subject 101 is confused about the difference between weight and mass throughout most of the experiment. (Many other students had the same confusion.) Eventually he discovers that weight is the force due to gravity while he is solving the following problem: "A fireman weighing 160 pounds slides down a vertical pole with an average acceleration of 10 feet per second. What is the average vertical force he exerts on the pole?" The subject reads the problem, then says:

```
6.  Okay.  Um, we'd have to consider...the force of gravity.
7.  Okay.  Let's find out what the force of gravity is exerting
8.  on them and then we can figure out what, what his, what he's
9.  exerting on it.
10. Now, let me remember, weight is equal to, what's force equal
11. to, weight?
12. Force is equal to weight over gravity times acceleration.
```

The subject decides to follow a generic plan, which he has used many times before. The plan is to find the forces acting on the body (the fireman, in this case), sum them, and apply F=ma. He summarizes his intentions in lines 7, 8 and 9. However, the plan's first goal, which is to find the force of gravity acting on the fireman, thwarts him. He does not know that the 160 pound weight *is* the force of gravity on the fireman, so he sets about to calculate the force using the derived law, F=(W/g)a. After fumbling with the units and looking up the appropriate value for the gravitational acceleration, g, he substitutes the freefall acceleration for a and obtains F=(W/g)g=W. At this point, he says:

```
42.  Oh, I'm going to get force is equal to weight divided by
43.  gravity times gravity which is going to be equal to weight.
44.  Right?
45.  Is that right?
46.  Okay.  Um, so I'm going to get 160 pounds.  That's the force.
47.  Yeah.  It kind of makes sense 'cause they, they weight you in
48.  pounds, don't they?
49.  That's force.
50.  Okay.  So, average acceleration, the force he, the gravity is
51.  exerting on him, yeah, yeah, that makes sense, is 160.
```

At line 43, he has the solution to his subgoal. He double checks the math in lines 44 and 45 (probably), and again states the solution in line 46. Although he could simply go on to the next step in his plan, the simplicity of the equation F=W apparently prompts him to reflect on his solution. Thus, a learning event begins around line 47. The subject appears to use a kind of explanation-based reasoning. Although he has just built a proof that F=W for this problem, he adds a second "proof" based on the units of force and weight (both are measured in pounds). This seems to be critical to establishing the generality of the result, which is that weight is the force exerted by gravity on an object. The learning event ends at line 49, and the subject returns to the plan in line 50. However, he indulges in one last check of the result, in line 51, before going on to finish the problem off. The next time he has an opportunity to apply his new rule, he initially fails to retrieve it, but is reminded of it halfway through the problem, and happily applies it. Thereafter, he always uses the new rule whenever it is applicable.

This segment of the protocol illustrates that rule acquisition in a knowledge-rich context has much the same character as it does in the knowledge-lean context of learning to solve a puzzle. For instance, it appears that the acquired rule is not completely learned during the first instance of its use, for the subject nearly misses the opportunity of applying it later. This particular rule does not seem to be acquired at an impasse. Instead, the subject seems to infer it while reflecting on his just-completed solution to a subproblem (line 47). However, other physics rules do seem to be learned at impasses.

Conclusions

Three analyses have been presented showing that the initial uses of problem solving rules can be located in protocol data. This analysis method yielded the following observations about the acquisition of rules:

1. Rules are seldom completely learned in one trial. The initial firing of a rule is often followed by several missed opportunities before the rule comes to be fired at every opportunity.

2. Sometimes, this gradual increase in applicability is consistent with a learning mechanism (VanLehn, 1983, in press) that operates by initially constructing a highly specific rule then generalizing it only when an impasse forces it to.

3. Long pauses, negative comments and other signs of impasses are common at the early firings of rules, but some rules are acquired without any visible signs of an impasse.

4. Sometimes, the subject explicitly compares a new rule to the old rule that it replaces. This indicates that the subject is probably aware of both of them, although none of the subjects in any of these studies explicitly mentions or describes their rules. It also indicates a more-or-less deliberate application of a method for improving one's knowledge.

5. In the context of learning-by-doing, wherein the subject receives no instruction from tutors or manuals, rule acquisition occurs at the rate of about one rule every half hour.

Acknowledgments

I would like to thank Bill Ball and Bernadette Kowalski for their indispensable help with the analysis, and Micki Chi for her thoughtful advice. This research was supported by the Cognitive Sciences Division and the Information Sciences Division of the Office of Naval Research under contracts N00014-86-K-0678 and N00014-88-K-0086.

References

Anderson, J. R., Farrell, R., & Saurers, R. (1984). Learning to program in LISP. *Cognitive Science, 8*, 87-129.

Anzai, Y. & Simon, H.A. (1979). The theory of learning by doing. *Psychological Review, 86*, 124-140.

Chi, M.T.H., Bassok, M., Lewis, M., Reimann, P. & Glaser, R. (in press, 19??). Learning problem solving skills from studying examples. *Cognitive Science*, .

DeJong, G. & Mooney, R. (1986). Explanation-based learning: An alternative view. *Machine Learning, 1*(2), 145-176.

Klahr, D., Langley, P. & Neches, R. (1987). *Production System Models of Learning and Development*. Cambridge, MA: MIT Press.

Kowalski, B. & VanLehn, K. (1988). Inducing subject models from protocol data. In V. Patel (Eds.), *Proceedings of the Tenth Annual Conference of the Cognitive Science Society*. Hillsdale, NJ: Erlbaum.

Laird, J. E., Rosenbloom, P. S., and Newell, A. (1986). Chunking in Soar: The anatomy of a general learning mechanism. *Machine Learning, 1*(1), 11-46.

Newell, A. & Simon, H. A. (1972). *Human Problem Solving*. Englewood Cliffs, NJ: Prentice-Hall.

VanLehn, K. (1983). Human skill acquisition: Theory, model and psychological validation. In *Proceedings of AAAI-83*. Los Altos, CA: Morgan Kaufmann,

VanLehn, K. (1988). Toward a theory of impasse-driven learning. In H. Mandl & A. Lesgold (Ed.), *Learning Issues for Intelligent Tutoring Systems*. New York, NY: Springer Verlag.

VanLehn, K. (1989). *Learning events in the discovery of problem solving strategies* (Tech. Rep. PCG-17). Dept. of Psychology, Carnegie-Mellon University.

VanLehn, K. (in press, 19??). *Mind Bugs: The origins of procedural misconceptions*. Cambridge, MA: MIT Press.

VanLehn, K. & Ball, W. (in press, 19??). Teton: A large-grained architecture for studying learning. In VanLehn, K. (Ed.), *Architectures for Intelligence*. Hillsdale, NJ: Erlbaum.

VanLehn, K. & Garlick, S. (1987). Cirrus: an automated protocol analysis tool. In Langley, P. (Ed.), *Proceedings of the Fourth Machine Learning Workshop*. Los Altos, CA: Morgan-Kaufmann.

Perceptual Chunks in Geometry Problem Solving: A Challenge to Theories of Skill Acquisition

Kenneth R. Koedinger & John R. Anderson
Psychology Department, Carnegie Mellon University

ABSTRACT

In current theories of skill acquisition it is quite common to assume that the input to learning mechanisms is a problem representation based on direct translations of problem instructions or simple inductions from problem solving examples. We call such a problem representation an *execution space* because it is made up of operators corresponding to the external actions agents perform while executing problem solutions. Learning proceeds by modifications and combinations of these execution space operators. We have built a model of geometry expertise based on verbal report evidence which contains operators which can be *described* as modifications (e.g., abstractions) and combinations (e.g., compositions) of execution operators. However, a number of points of evidence lead us to conclude that these operators were *not derived* from execution space operators. In contrast, it appears these operators derive from discoveries about the structure and properties of domain objects, particularly, perceptual properties. We have yet to develop a detailed and integrated theory of this "perceptual chunking", but we present the expert model is a challenge to current theories of skill acquisition.

1. Introduction

The process of skill acquisition is generally described as involving two phases as shown in Figure 1. In the knowledge acquisition phase, the system uses information about the problem domain, e.g., problem descriptions, problem constraints, example solutions, etc., to build some kind of basic problem space[1], essentially, a set of simple condition-action operators that it can use to attempt to solve problems in the domain. In the knowledge tuning phase, the basic problem space is elaborated through problem solving practice so that the system becomes more effective and efficient. The elaborated problem space may incorporate heuristics that control the system's search or may be an abstracted version of the basic problem space in which operators make larger steps allowing for faster solutions.

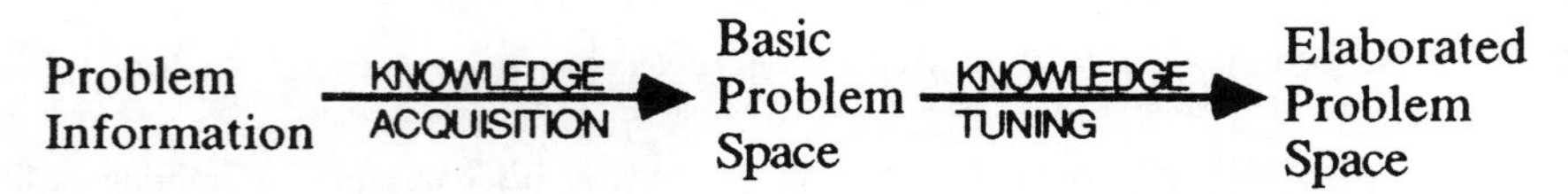

Figure 1. A framework common to many theories of skill acquisition and learning.

The framework in Figure 1 is characteristic of a number of theories of skill acquisition. In ACT* (Anderson, 1983), knowledge acquisition is modelled by a mechanism called proceduralization while knowledge tuning is modelled by composition, generalization, and discrimination. In Soar (Newell, in press), knowledge acquisition has been modelled by a program called TAQ while knowledge tuning is modelled by Soar's chunking mechanism. Other research efforts have focussed on one or the other of these phases. For example, knowledge acquisition has been modelled in the UNDERSTAND program (Hayes and Simon, 1974) which built a problem space from a natural language description, and in a program by Neves (1978) which built a problem space from example solutions. Knowledge tuning has been modelled in terms of macro-operator learning (Korf, 1987) and in terms of problem space abstraction (Sacerdoti, 1974; Unruh, Rosenbloom, and Laird, 1987).

While this framework has certainly proven useful, we argue that it is inadequate for a complete and general theory of skill acquisition. We support this argument with empirical data and a model of expert geometry problem solving which cannot plausibly be learned within this framework. The basic argument is as follows. We have found that geometry experts skip steps in developing proof plans. By

[1]We don't mean to suggest that a system can have only one problem space associated with a domain. Thus, when we refer to a system's problem space for a domain, one can think of it as the collection of all problem spaces for that domain.

itself this behavior is not contrary to the standard framework – it might be explained, for example, by ACT*'s composition or Soar's chunking mechanism. However, a closer look at the details of this step-skipping behavior brings such explanations into question. In particular, we identified a regularity in the kinds of steps experts skip which cannot be easily explained in terms of compositions or chunks of consecutive production or operator applications. We present a schema-based model, called DC, which accounts for this regularity. While DC's schemas could be represented in terms of production rules, it is difficult to imagine how current production rule learning models could produce the organization inherent in these schemas.

2. The Basic Phenomenon: Step-Skipping

We analyzed 12 protocols coming from the concurrent verbal reports (Ericsson and Simon, 1984) of four subjects solving one problem and one subject solving eight problems. Two of the subjects were mathematics graduate students, two were psychology researchers with extensive experience in geometry, and one was a Pittsburgh area high school geometry teacher.

In analyzing these protocols we were surprised to find that the steps subjects took in the process of planning a proof do not correspond with the rules of geometry: the definitions, postulates, and theorems. In contrast, most previous models of geometry theorem proving have worked in a problem space based on these rules (Gelernter, 1963; Goldstein, 1973; Anderson, Boyle, & Yost, 1985). We call this the *execution space* because these rules correspond with the steps that are written down in the final execution of a proof plan. While the the steps subjects wrote down or stated in explaining their final solution correspond with the execution space, they skipped many of these steps in planning a solution.

TABLE 1

A Verbal Protocol for a Subject Solving the Problem in Figure 2.

	Verbalization	Summary
		****** Planning phase ******
B1:	We're given a right angle – this is a right angle,	Reading given: rt $\angle ADB$
B2:	perpendicular on both sides [makes perpendicular markings on diagram];	Inference step 1: $AC \cong BD$
B3:	BD bisects angle ABC [marks angles ABD and CBD]	Reading given: BD bisects $\angle ABC$
B4:	and *we're done*.	Inference step 2: $\triangle ABD \cong \triangle CBD$
		****** Execution phase ******
B5:	We know that this is a reflexive [marks line BD],	In this phase, the subject refines and explains his solution to the experimenter.
B6:	we know that we have congruent triangles; we can determine anything from there in terms of corresponding parts	
B7:	and that's what this [looking at the goal statement for the first time] is going to mean ... that these are congruent [marks segments AD and DC as equal on the diagram].	

Figure 2 shows one of the problems we used and its solution in proof tree format. Table 1 contains the protocol of a subject solving this problem. The subject's verbalizations are shown in the left column of Table 1. The right column contains a summary of the steps the subject mentions. The protocol is divided up into 1) a *planning phase* in which the subject is searching for a solution and 2) an *execution phase* in which he executes the previously outlined solution by reporting it to the experimenter.

This expert had a plan for solving this problem in 13 seconds at the point where he said "we're done". We can describe his planning as follows. In block B1 of the protocol he reads the first given. Next at B2, he makes the inference that the lines AC and BD are perpendicular – "perpendicular on both sides", which follows from the first given. At B3, he reads the second given and then at B4 he says "we're done" which appears to indicate that he has made an inference from the second given which proves the goal. Further inspection of his explanation of the solution, particularly at block B6, makes it clear that this inference was that the two triangles ABD and CBD are congruent.

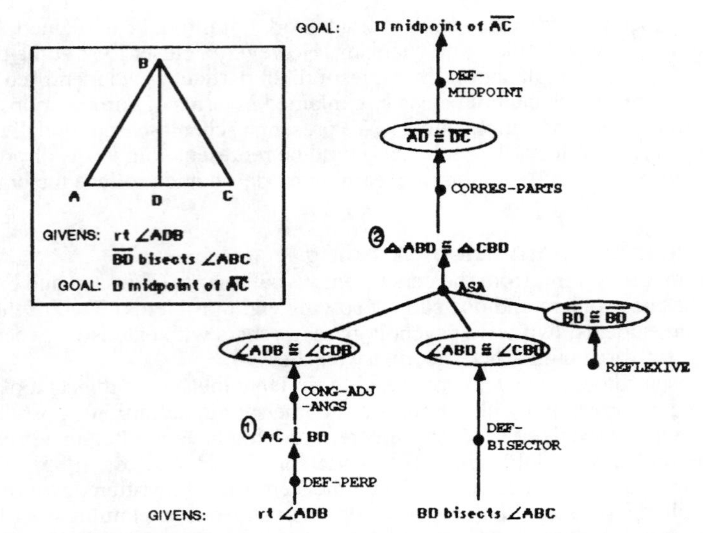

Figure 2. A problem (in the box) and its solution. The numbered steps are ones a subject mentioned during planning (see Table 1), while the circled steps are ones he skipped.

Of the four verbalizations in the planning phase, two indicate his reading and encoding of the given statements and two indicate inferences. In other words, he came up with a solution plan in two steps. In contrast, the final solution to this problem requires seven steps as shown in Figure 2.

The problem solving protocols of all the skilled subjects had this flavor where there were phases of planning where steps were skipped and phases of execution where these steps were filled in. It was clear that subjects were not searching step-by-step in the execution space. Rather, subjects were planning in some other more abstract problem space using knowledge that allows them to focus on the key inferences and ignore the minor inferences. We have characterized the nature of this knowledge in a computer simulation called the diagram configuration model (DC).

3. The Diagram Configuration Model (DC)

The core idea of DC is that the knowledge of skilled geometry problem solvers is organized around certain prototypical geometric figures we call *diagram configurations*. Clustered around each diagram configuration are related geometry facts. We call such clusters of geometry information *diagram configuration schemas*. Two examples are illustrated in Figure 3.

Diagram configuration schemas have four attributes: 1) the configuration, 2) the whole-statement, 3) the part-statements, and 4) the ways-to-prove. The *whole-statement* and *part-statements* attributes of a schema contain statements which refer to the geometric figure stored in the *configuration* attribute. The whole-statement refers to the configuration as a whole, while the part-statements are relationships among segment and angle parts of the configuration. The main action of a diagram configuration schema comes from the *ways-to-prove* attribute. This attribute contains different ways to "prove the schema". Saying a schema is "proven" is a brief way of saying that the whole-statement and all the part-statements of the schema can be proven. Each of the ways-to-prove is a list of part-statements, indicated by their number, which are sufficient to prove the schema. For example, one of the ways-to-prove of the TRIANGLE-CONGRUENCE-SHARED-SIDE schema is {1 2} which indicates that if part-statements 1. XY=XZ and 2. YW =ZW are proven, the schema can be proven.

The essential idea behind diagram configuration schemas is that skilled geometry problem solvers can recognize certain configurations in problem diagrams and they know that if certain statements about a configuration have been proven, *all* the statements about the configuration can be proven. Instead of planning proofs one statement at a time, diagram configuration schemas allow skilled problem solvers to plan multiple proof steps in a single thought.

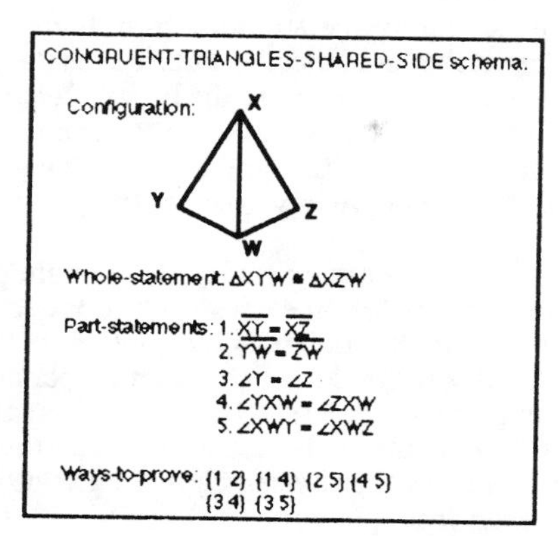

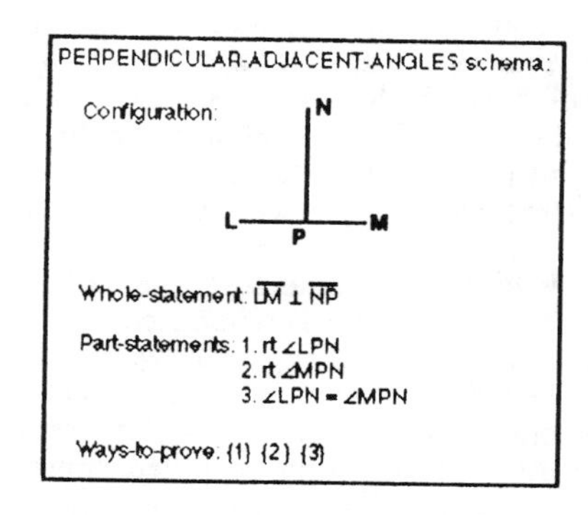

Figure 3. Two diagram configuration schemas.

In Table 1, we saw a skilled subject plan a seven step proof in two steps. We can explain his planning in terms of DC. DC visually parses a problem diagram into instances of the various configurations it knows about. Inside the rounded boxes in Figure 4 are the configurations DC recognizes in the problem diagram in Figure 2. Attached to each configuration are the part-statements which refer to it. Notice that certain part-statements are associated with more than one configuration. For example, ∠ADB ≅ ∠CDB is a part-statement for both the PERPENDICULAR-ADJACENT-ANGLES and TRIANGLE-CONGRUENCE-SHARED-SIDE schemas.

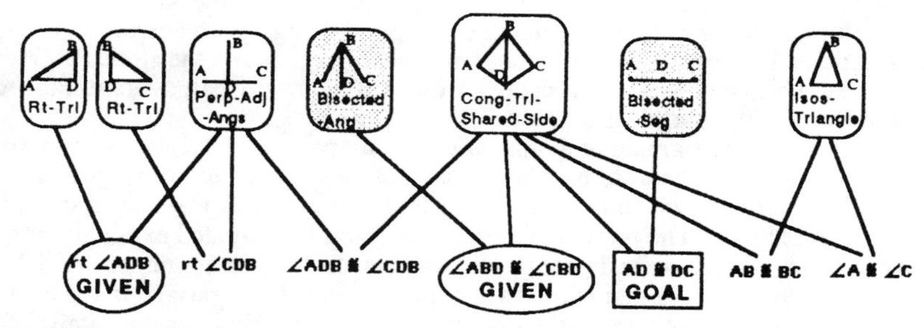

Figure 4. The configurations and associated part-statements that appear in the problem diagram in Figure 2.

At block B1 in Table 1, the subject reads and encodes the first given rt ∠ADB which we have circled in Figure 4. By "encodes" we mean he determines what the statement means. In this case, by encoding the given rt ∠ADB we believe the subject understands this to mean that the measure of ∠ADB is 90 degrees. At block B2, he makes an inference corresponding with proving the PERPENDICULAR-ADJACENT-ANGLES schema. The result of this inference is that he knows the other two part-statements rt ∠CDB and ∠ADB ≅ ∠CDB are true. At block B3, he reads and encodes the second given BD bisects ∠ABC. This statement is the whole-statement for the BISECTED-ANGLE schema and he encodes it by considering the part-statements of this schema as given. This schema has only one part-statement, ∠ABD ≅ ∠CBD, which is marked as given in Figure 4. When the subject reads the goal statement (B7), we claim he encodes it in a similar way, thinking of the corresponding part-statement AD ≅ DC.

Following B3, the subject knows that the four part-statements on the left in Figure 4, rt ∠ADB through ∠ABD ≅ ∠CBD, are true – only the three on the right remain unknown. Two of the known statements, ∠ADB ≅ ∠CDB and ∠ABD ≅ ∠CBD, correspond with the one of the ways-to-prove of the TRIANGLE-CONGRUENCE-SHARED-SIDE schema, namely {4 5}. At B4, the subject makes an inference which we claim corresponds with proving this schema. His explanations at B6 and B7 support this claim. If, in fact, he is proving the TRIANGLE-CONGRUENCE-SHARED-SIDE schema at B4, he should know the three other part-statements AD ≅ DC, AB ≅ BC, and ∠A ≅ ∠C are true. It seems clear that he knows this from B6, "... we have congruent triangles; we can determine anything from there ...." The fact that he first looked at the goal statement at B7 provides further evidence. It indicates that earlier in the protocol, at B4, he had some other way of detecting that he was done with the proof. Assuming his inference at B4 corresponds with proving the TRIANGLE-CONGRUENCE-SHARED-SIDE schema, he knows, at this point, that all the part-statements in all the configurations that appear in the diagram are true. Thus, the use of this schema explains how he knows he can prove any goal statement no matter what it is.

We now turn to a general description of DC. DC has three processing stages: 1) diagram parsing, 2) statement encoding, and 3) schema search. In the computer simulation each stage is done to completion before the next begins, however, we believe that human problem solvers integrate these processes. Our simulation approach allows us to evaluate the contribution of the diagram parsing process makes to limiting search independent of the schema search process. Note that DC is intended as a model of the panning phases of skilled subjects and not the execution phases. A model of the execution phases would involve finding solutions, either by retrieval or by search in the execution space, to the series of trivial one to three step subproblems that result from planning.

3.1. Diagram Parsing and Schema Instantiation. Diagram parsing is the process of looking for configurations in the problem diagram and instantiating the schemas associated with any of the configurations identified. The diagram is input as ordered lists of the points that appear in each line and xy-coordinates for each point. From this representation, DC's diagram parser can directly recognize any occurrence of a *basic configuration.* Basic configurations are recognizable purely from their form, for example, the ADJACENT-SUPPLEMENTARY-ANGLES configuration is recognized when the end of one line meets another line somewhere in the middle. Other configurations are specializations of basic configurations in which some relationships among the parts are constrained. For example, the PERPENDICULAR-ADJACENT-ANGLES configuration is a specialization of the ADJACENT-SUPPLEMENTARY-ANGLES configuration in which the component angles are equal. To recognize these specialized configurations, DC uses appearances in the diagram to estimate the slopes of lines and sizes of segments and angles. This is a heuristic procedure which, in the case of an overspecialized diagram, can result in extra irrelevant, but harmless schemas.

DC's diagram parser also recognizes and associates certain pairs of basic configurations. For example, two basic TRIANGLE configurations can be paired if they appear to be congruent. DC recognizes apparent congruence by checking if the sides of the triangles can be paired so that each pair of sides are the same estimated size. The pairing of congruent triangles is treated explicitly in geometry textbooks, however, other pairings of basic configurations that DC forms are not commonly discussed. These pairings amount to visual ways of cueing certain inferences that are proven in the execution space using algebra. The corresponding schemas allow problem solvers to skip over the details of algebra sub-proofs which are a large source of combinatoric explosion in the execution space (see Koedinger & Anderson, in press). These schemas are called *whole-part congruence* schemas and were also identified and discussed by Greeno (1983).

The final result of diagram parsing is a network of instantiated schemas and part-statements as illustrated in Figure 4. It is interesting to note that although no problem solving search is done in this first stage, in effect, most of the problem solving work is done here. The resulting network is finite, in fact, usually quite small, and is fully instantiated. Searching it is fairly trivial.

3.2. Statement Encoding. Before search is started, the given and goal statements of the problem must be read into the system. Statement encoding corresponds to problem solvers' comprehension of the meaning of given/goal statements. We claim that problem solvers comprehend given/goal statements in terms of part-statements. When a given/goal statement is already a part-statement, DC encodes it directly by appropriately tagging the part-statement as either "known" or "desired". However, there are two other possibilities. First, if the given/goal statement is one of a number of alternative ways of expressing the same part-statement, it is encoded in terms of a single canonical form. For example, measure equality and congruence, as in $m\overline{AB} = m\overline{CD}$ and $\overline{AB} \cong \overline{CD}$, are encoded as the same part-statement. Second, if the given/goal statement is the whole-statement of a schema, it is encoded by appropriately tagging all of the part-statements of that schema as either "known" or "desired". For example, recall DC's encoding of the goal and second given of the problem discussed above and shown in Figure 2.

3.3. Schema Search. The network that results from diagram parsing contains a set of diagram configuration schemas which are possible consequences of the problem givens. In schema search, DC attempts to prove enough of these schemas so that the goal statement is proven in the process. This search amounts to looking for a path through the network that connects the given part-statement(s) with the goal part-statement(s) subject to the ways-to-prove of each schema in the path.

DC is performing a search through the space defined by its diagram configuration schemas. We call this the *diagram configuration space.* Previous models of geometry problem solving performed search in the execution space and required heuristics to guide choices in this large search space (Gelernter, 1963; Goldstein, 1973; Anderson, Boyle, & Yost, 1985). In contrast, the diagram configuration space is small enough that DC can effectively plan proofs without extra heuristics to aid search in this space. DC can perform a brute force forward search of the diagram configuration space by arbitrarily choosing any schema which can be proven at each step in problem solving. DC's default control scheme is slightly more elaborate – see Koedinger and Anderson (in press).

The feasibility of this simple control scheme is demonstrated by a task analysis we did of one of the more difficult problems the subjects solved. The shortest solution to this problem in the execution space is 7 steps and we estimated that a breadth-first search for this solution visits more than a million states. The shortest solution to this problem in the diagram configuration space is 3 steps and a breadth-first search for this solution visits at the most eight states.

4. Evidence for DC: Step-Skipping Regularity

In evaluating DC, it is worthwhile to consider whether the step-skipping behavior of skilled subjects could be explained in terms of an alternative abstract problem space. We consider two possible alternatives both based on modifications of the execution space. First, an abstract space can be created from the execution space by an *abstraction* process where the conditions (if-part) of execution operators are generalized, for example, by dropping a clause which, ideally, refers to some detail which can be temporarily ignored (Sacerdoti, 1974). Such "minor" clauses in the execution operators of geometry are rare – dropping clauses most often results in operators that can propose future states which cannot be proven. Such incorrect plans can cause significant efficiency problems, however, this is not our major criticism of the adequacy of this abstraction method for modelling skilled geometry problem solving. Rather, this method is inconsistent with the observation that the abstract plans of our skilled subjects were always correct. That is, the abstract inferences they made, like the ones in Table 1, never produced unprovable statements. Thus, it appears unlikely that their abstract operators have been learned through a "clause-dropping" type abstraction process.

A second approach to building an abstract problem space is by *composition* of consecutively applicable execution operators. This general approach has received numerous instantiations, e.g., ACT*'s composition (Anderson, 1983), Soar's chunking (Laird, et. al., 1987), Korf's macro-operator learning (Korf, 1987). Although most of these approaches have some stipulations of the appropriate context in which composition can occur, there is little in them that indicates whether or when some pairs of consecutively applicable operators are more likely to be composed than other pairs. Thus, we would not expect any regularity in the kinds of steps that would be skipped in an abstract problem space of composed execution operators. However, such a regularity is exactly what we observed of subjects.

We analyzed the protocols of all our subjects as illustrated in Table 1 and Figure 2. In particular, we divided each protocol into segments corresponding to planning and execution phases and we annotated the protocol with the inference steps subjects verbalized. We made a proof graph of each subject's final solution and then identified each step in this solution the subject mentioned while planning.

Our claim is that the steps taken in planning tend to correspond with diagram configuration schemas. In other words, we predicted that subjects would tend to mention statements which are whole-statements of diagram configuration schemas and tend to skip those statements which are not. For certain schemas, like the algebra-related schemas, which do not have whole-statements, we predicted subjects would only mention one part-statement of the schema, in particular, the one which concludes the inference. As an example, these predictions exactly match the planning behavior of the subject in Table 1. In the eleven other cases, the predictions were not as perfect, however, they tended to be correct. Figure 5 shows the results from all twelve cases. Clearly, there is a regularity in the steps being skipped and DC captures a lot of this regularity. A Chi square test ($X^2(1) = 41.5$) indicates it is unlikely that the model's fit to the data is a chance occurrence ($p < .001$).

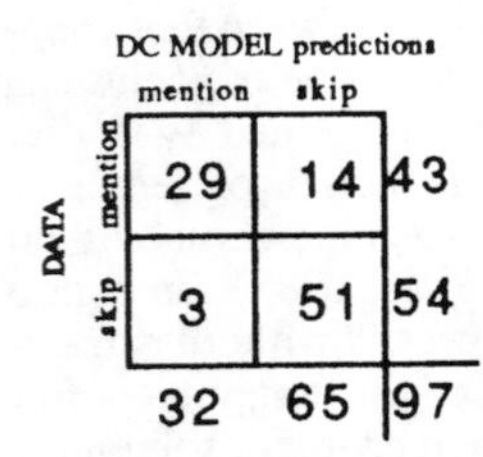

Figure 5. DC's account of the step-skipping behavior.

In addition to the evidence of regularity in step-skipping, we found other evidence in the problem solving protocols inconsistent with an abstract planning model based on compositions of execution operators. In the process of executing an abstract plan, subjects could not always immediately fill in the steps they had skipped during planning. However, if subjects learned abstract planning operators from previously compiled execution operators, the knowledge to fill in the skipped steps should be readily available. Since these execution operators remain necessary to execute proof plans, there is no reason why they would be forgotten.

Finally, there are computational reasons to question the composition-based explanation of step-skipping. On one hand, diagram configuration schemas can be viewed merely as a more compact notation for a set of macro-operators or composed production rules. On the other hand, these schemas indicate a particular organization of macro-operators and this organization may be difficult to achieve in typical composition mechanisms. To illustrate the point, consider the TRIANGLE-CONGRUENCE-SHARED-SIDE schema in Figure 3. This schema can be represented as 6 macro-operators whose left-hand sides correspond to the 6 ways-to-prove of the schema and whose right-hand sides contain 5 actions which correspond with the 5 part-statements of the schema. The collection of such macro-operators for each schema, call it S, is a restricted subset of the space of possible macro-operators. S is restricted in two ways. First, S does not contain any of the possible macro-operators which could make inferences between statements which are whole-statements of schemas, for example, it doesn't contain an operator that could infer perpendicularity directly from triangle congruence in a problem like the one in Figure 2. Second, S does not contain any of the 2, 3, or 4 action macro-operators that would be learned on the way to a 5 action macro-operator like the ones corresponding with the TRIANGLE-CONGRUENCE-SHARED-SIDE schema. To achieve DC's simplicity in search control and match to the human data, a composition mechanism would need to prevent a proliferation of unnecessary macro-operators. It is not clear how this restriction could be implemented in current mechanisms[1].

5. Discussion and Conclusion

We have posed the DC model as a challenge to current theories of skill acquisition characterized by the framework in Figure 1. The problem with this framework is not so much with the mechanisms of knowledge acquisition and knowledge tuning, but rather in the assumed form of the basic problem space which is the interface between them. It is commonly assumed that this basic problem space is made up of operators which correspond to the external actions problem solvers take in solving problems (the execution space) and that the bulk of learning is in terms of this problem space. In contrast, it seems that the human knowledge acquisition system occasionally modifies its problem space for a domain – not by modifying the operators as models of the knowledge tuning already do, but by changing the representation of problem states, for example, by creating new perceptual chunks.

That such changes in the problem state representation occur is supported by other research. In their work on the learning of the Tower of Hanoi puzzle, Anzai and Simon (1979) identified the perceptual chunking of disks into "pyramids" as crucial to learning the advanced pyramid subgoal strategy.

[1]One might consider whether this restriction could be achieved within the Soar architecture by having a hierarchy of problem spaces corresponding with the desired organization. However, this approach begs the question – how would this hierarchy be learned in the first place?

Research on the nature of expertise has identified the possession of perceptual chunks as a special characteristic of expertise in a number of domains (for example, see Chase and Simon, 1973). The role of these perceptual chunks in problem solving has not been well established. The DC model serves as a detailed demonstration of how perceptual chunks can be used in problem solving and, at the same time, as a challenge to current theories of skill acquisition.

A first order challenge is to specify a knowledge acquisition mechanism which is capable of perceptual chunking and of changing the basic problem space representation appropriately. Theories of categorization or Soar's data chunking (Rosenbloom, et. al., 1987) are possible candidate mechanisms. A second order challenge is to specify a knowledge tuning mechanism which can deal with the shifting nature of the basic problem space as it is changed by the acquisition of new chunks. Perhaps meeting this challenge will require rethinking the two phase framework.

REFERENCES

Anderson, J. R. (1983). *The Architecture of Cognition.* Cambridge, MA: Harvard University Press.

Anderson, J. R., Boyle, C. F., & Yost, G. (1985). The geometry tutor. In *Proceedings of the International Joint Conference on Artificial Intelligence-85.* Los Angelos: International Joint Conference on Artificial Intelligence.

Anzai, Y., & Simon, H. A. (1979). The theory of learning by doing. *Psychological Review, 86,* 124-140.

Chase, W. G., & Simon H. A. (1973). The mind's eye in chess. In W. G. Chase (Ed.) *Visual Information Processing.* New York: Academic Press.

Ericsson, K. A., & Simon, H. A. (1984). *Protocol Analysis: Verbal Reports as Data.* Cambridge, MA: The MIT Press.

Gelernter, H. (1963). Realization of a geometry theorem proving machine. In E. A. Feigenbaum & J. Feldman (Eds.), *Computers and Thought.* New York: McGraw-Hill Book Company.

Goldstein, I. (1973). Elementary geometry theorem proving. MIT AI Memo 280.

Greeno, J. G. (1983). Forms of understanding in mathematical problem solving. In S. G. Paris, G. M. Olson, & H. W. Stevenson (Eds.), *Learning and Motivation in the Classroom.* Hillsdale, NJ: Erlbaum.

Hayes, J. R., & Simon, H. A. (1974). Understanding written problem instructions. In L. W. Gregg (ed.), *Knowledge and Cognition.* Potomac, Md.: Erlbaum.

Koedinger, K. R., & Anderson, J. R. (in press). Abstract planning and perceptual chunks: elements of expertise in geometry. *Cognitive Science.*

Korf, R. E. (1987). Macro-operators: A weak method for learning. *Artificial Intelligence, 27,* 35-77.

Neves, D. M. (1978). A computer program that learns algebraic procedures by examining examples and by working test problem in a textbook. In *Proceedings of the 2nd Conference on Computational Studies of Intelligence.* Toronto: Canadian Society for Computational Studies of Intelligence.

Newell, A. (in press). *Unified Theories of Cognition.* Harvard University Press, Cambridge, MA.

Newell, A., & Simon, H. A. (1972). *Human problem solving.* Englewood Cliffs, NJ: Prentice-Hall.

Rosenbloom, P. S., Laird, J. E., & Newell, A. (1987). Knowledge level learning in Soar. In *Proceedings of the Sixth National Conference on Artificial Intelligence,* 499-504.

Sacerdoti, E. D. (1974). Planning in a hierarchy of abstraction spaces. *Artificial Intelligence, 5,* 115-136.

Unruh, A., Rosenbloom, P. S., & Laird, J. E. (1987). Dynamic abstraction problem solving in Soar. In *Proceedings of the AOG/AAAIC Joint Conference,* Dayton, OH.

Empirical Analyses of Self-Explanation and Transfer in Learning to Program

Peter Pirolli and Kate Bielaczyc

School of Education
University of California, Berkeley

ABSTRACT

Building upon recent work on production system models of transfer and analysis-based generalization techniques, we present analyses of three studies of learning to program recursion. In Experiment 1, a production system model was used to identify problem solving that involved previously acquired skills or required novel solutions. A mathematical model based on this analysis accounts for inter-problem transfer. Programming performance was also affected by particular examples presented in instruction. Experiment 2 examined these example effects in finer detail. Using a production system analysis, examples were found to affect the initial error rates, but not the learning rates on cognitive skills. Experiment 3 examined relations between the ways in which people explain examples to themselves and subsequent learning. Results suggest that good learners engage in more metacognition, generate more domain-specific elaborations of examples, make connections between examples and abstract text, and focus on the semantics of programs rather than syntax.

INTRODUCTION

One of the classic debates in psychology has concerned the nature of the transfer of knowledge across situations of potential use (for a useful review see Singley & Anderson, 1989). One school of thought is typified by Thorndike's *theory of identical elements* (1903), which holds that transfer is a function of the stimulus-response elements acquired in one task that can be used in another task. Another school of thought is typified by Gestaltists such as Wertheimer (1945) or Katona (1940) who distinguished between *senseless* and *meaningful* learning. The Gestaltists did not deny that transfer of the kind predicted by the theory of identical elements would occur in situations of senseless learning (Singley & Anderson, 1989). However, the Gestaltists argued that transfer would be qualitatively different and superior in situations of meaningful learning, in which the learner grasped the *inner structural relationships* of the problem or task (Lewis, 1988).

The ultimate goal of the project presented here is to develop a model of the knowledge acquisition and transfer that occurs in a fairly typical lesson on programming. Here we discuss studies that suggest that transfer can be characterized by an updated version of the identical elements theory, but also that learners do differ in ways that they come to understand problems and these understandings have an impact on learning. We suggest that recent work on production system models of transfer (Singley & Anderson, 1989) and of analysis-based generalization (Lewis, 1988) may provide the basis for a model of learning and transfer that integrates the main ideas of identical elements theory and of meaningful learning.

THE LEARNING PARADIGM

Our studies focus on learning a lesson on programming recursive functions, which takes place in a longer sequence of instruction on programming. A typical programming lesson involves reading a text or listening to an instructor on some novel topic and then working through a set of relevant

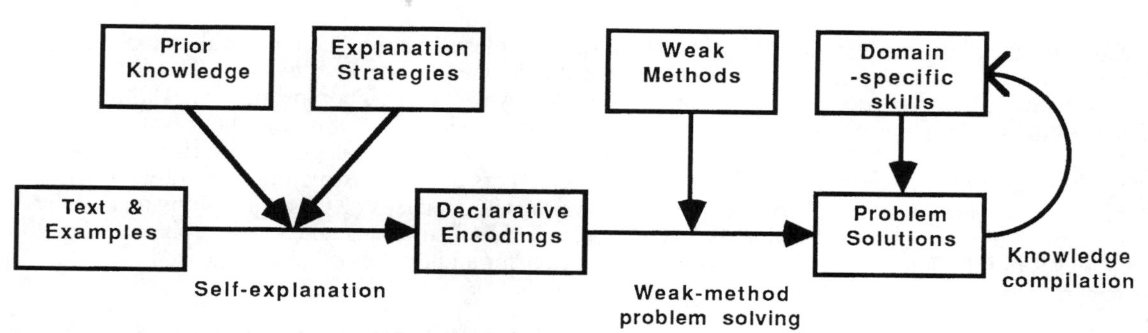

FIGURE 1: THE ANALYSIS OF INSTRUCTION AND ITS TRANSFER TO DOMAIN-SPECIFIC SKILL

exercise problems. Typically, the text or instructor will discuss some illustrative examples to facilitate learning. Figure 1 presents a simplified model of learning in a typical lesson. The boxes in Figure 1 indicate knowledge content and arrows indicate processes. In this learning situation, the learner actively constructs representations of texts and examples based on prior knowledge. This produces a set of example encodings and other relevant facts and principles that are stored as declarative knowledge in the learner's memory. Upon encountering a partially novel problem, the learner will use as much of her existing domain-specific skill as possible. At problem-solving impasses, in which no previously acquired skills are applicable, the learner resorts to weak-method problem solving. These methods operate on the declarative knowledge acquired from texts and examples. *Knowledge compilation mechanisms* (Anderson, 1987) summarize each novel problem-solving experience into new domain-specific skills.

In previous research on the acquisition of skills for programming recursive functions (Pirolli, 1986), we developed production system models of novice skill acquisition in the GRAPES production system language which emulates the skill acquisition components of the ACT* theory (Anderson, 1987). Goals are explicitly represented in GRAPES goal memory. Operators are represented by production rules that implement the basic actions available in programming (e.g., writing out a function name). Programming plans are implemented as productions that achieve goals activated in goal memory.

Such production system analyses can serve as a useful starting point in the analysis of the transfer of cognitive skill. Singley and Anderson (1989) have recently presented an ACT* theory of transfer that is in the spirit of Thorndike's identical elements theory of transfer. In its bare-bones form, the ACT* theory of transfer states that productions are the elements of transfer. Complexity is added to the ACT* analysis of transfer by considering the role of declarative knowledge. New productions are compiled as summarizations of the operation of weak methods, such as analogy, over declarative structures. Studies (Chi, Bassok, Lewis, Reiman, & Glaser, 1987; Pirolli, 1987) suggest that the effectiveness of analogy is related to the richness and content of the representations of example solutions.

Recently, Chi et al. (1987) analyzed the statements made by students learning from a physics text as they explained examples to themselves and solved a set of physics problems. Subjects were divided into groups of good and poor learners based on their problem solving performance. Good learners made significantly more elaborations of presented examples than poor students and showed greater evidence of monitoring their comprehension. In addition, there were qualitative differences in the kinds of elaborations made by good vs. poor learners with good learners showing more explanations and justifications of content relevant to subsequent problem solving.

Computational models that address the analysis of examples and subsequent generalization to novel problem solutions are called analysis-based generalization techniques by Lewis (1988). These models include production system models of analogy (Anderson & Thompson, 1986; Pirolli, 1987) and explanation-based learning methods (DeJong & Mooney, 1986; Mitchell, Kellar, & Kedar-Cabelli, 1986). One deficiency in current analysis-based generalization models is that we know little about the strategies and knowledge that learners use in constructing and using their analyses of examples. In the following studies, we present analyses of the acquisition and transfer of knowledge from instructional texts and examples to novel solutions and across problems. Our analyses build upon production system models of transfer and models of analysis-based generalization.

EXPERIMENT 1: EFFECTS OF EXAMPLES AND INTER-PROBLEM TRANSFER

Subjects (N = 20) in Experiment 1 proceeded through a series of programming lessons in LISP centered around an intelligent tutoring system called the LISP Tutor (Reiser, Anderson, & Farrell, 1985). For each lesson, students read some text introducing some new programming feature or technique and then worked through a set of programming problems with the LISP Tutor. The LISP Tutor instructs using a *model tracing methodology* which involves comparing a student's programming behavior to the behavior of the LISP Tutor's internal *ideal* and *buggy* models. An ideal model is a production system model of the programming skill to be acquired by subjects. A buggy model is a representation of common misconceptions and mistakes made by subjects.

Subjects were divided into groups that received a text on recursion that included either (a) an example program that worked with list inputs (list recursion example), or (b) an example program that worked with integer inputs (number recursion example). After reading their texts on recursion, subjects solved 10 recursion programming problems using the LISP Tutor. Five of these problems worked with list inputs (list problems), and the other five worked with integer inputs (number problems). Subjects were also divided into groups that received either: (a) a *blocked* sequence of problems, in which four number recursion problems were followed by four list recursion problems, with two final problems, or (b) an *intermixed* sequence, in which four number recursion problems occurred as problem trials 1, 3, 5, and 7, and four list recursion problems occurred as problem trials 2, 4, 6, and 8 (with the same final problems as the blocked sequence). For all subjects, the ordering of number recursion problems and list recursion problems was the same (although the two kinds of problems may or may not be intermixed).

Inter-Problem Transfer

Figures 2 and 3 present the mean number of errors per problem across problem trials for the intermixed and blocked sequences. An ANOVA of Sequence by Example by Problem Trial carried out on the errors per problem data revealed a main effect of Problem Trial, $F(9, 144) = 5.74, p < .0001$, but no main effect of Sequence, indicating that the two kinds of sequence did not produce substantially different performance overall. However, as suggested by Figures 2 and 3, there was a significant Sequence by Problem Trial interaction, $F(9, 144) = 84.38, p < .0001$, indicating that performance across problem trials was radically different for the two problem sequences.

According to the ACT* model of transfer of cognitive skill, the data in Figures 2 and 3 should be captured by a production system analysis that takes into account the individual productions used to solve a problem, their strength from prior practice, and the learning of new productions at the appropriate opportunities. We performed a simplified version of this analysis in which production strength was ignored, and all productions were treated as equals (i.e., we ignored variations in learning difficulties and errors rates across different productions). In this simplified model, errors

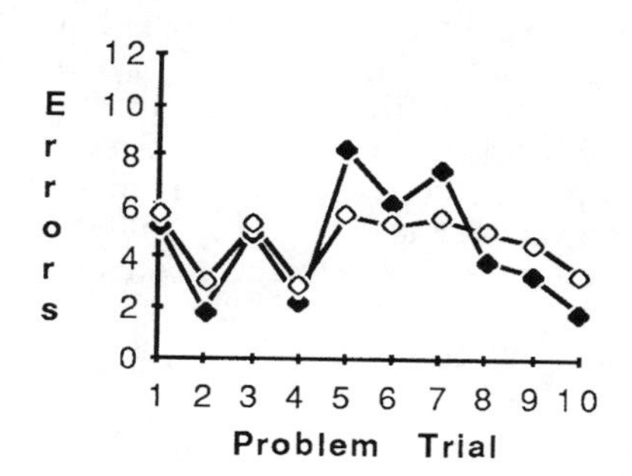

FIGURE 2:
ERRORS PER PROBLEM
FOR THE *BLOCKED* SEQUENCE

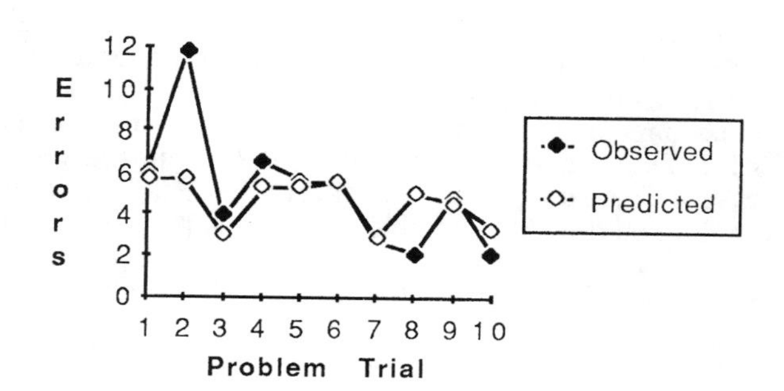

FIGURE 3:
ERRORS PER PROBLEM
FOR THE *INTERMIXED* SEQUENCE

on problem trial, t, are a linear function, $E(t)$ of the number of previously acquired productions, $P_{old}(t)$, that apply in a problem solution on trial t, and the number of novel problem solving steps, $P_{new}(t)$, for which new productions will be acquired. P_{old} and P_{new} were estimated by examining the productions used by the LISP Tutor's ideal models for the minimal program solutions across a sequence of problems. Regression of this linear model to the data in Figures 2 and 3 yields:

$$E(t) = .56\, P_{new}(t) \ + .14\, P_{old}(t) \tag{1}$$

with $R = .51$. Thus a substantial proportion of the variance in Figures 2 and 3 can be captured by a simple characterization of the opportunities for the application of previously acquired productions and the places where new productions will need to be acquired.

Effects of Examples

Figure 4 presents mean errors per problem on list and number recursion problems broken down by the type of example available during instruction. Performance on problems similar to the available example is superior to performance on problems different from the example, and the interaction in Figure 4 is significant, $t(144) = 2.00$, $p < .05$.

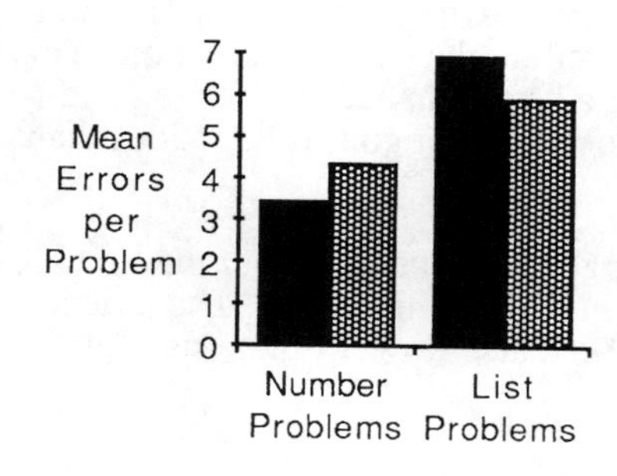

FIGURE 4:
EFFECTS OF EXAMPLES
ON PROBLEM ERRORS

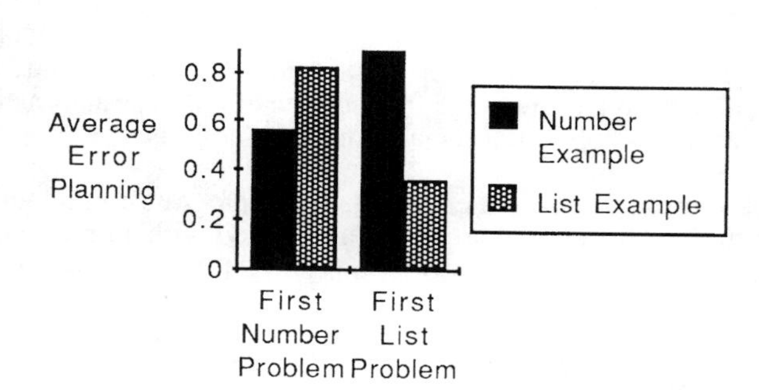

FIGURE 5:
EFFECTS OF EXAMPLES
ON PLANNING THE RECURSIVE CASES

Another measure of the impact of examples can be attained by examining a particular skill that is especially important in the task of programming recursive functions. This is the skill of *planning the recursive cases* of a recursive function. This skill involves characterizing how a function will make a recursive call to itself and use the result of that call to form an output. Figure 5 presents the LISP Tutor's diagnosis of whether or not subjects had determined a correct plan for recursive cases. The data in Figure 5 concern the first list or number problem encountered by subjects and are broken down by the kind of example presented in instruction. Again, subjects make more errors on problems that are different from the presented example. On list problems the effect is significant, Fisher $p = .02$, but on number problems it is only marginal, Fisher $p = .18$.

Summary

The results of Experiment 1 indicate that a production system analyses of the transfer of skill across problems captures a substantial amount of the performance effects as subjects progress through a sequence of problems. Interestingly, there was no effect of differences in problem sequencing as is predicted by a production system model of transfer. The examples used in Experiment 1 had clear effects on both general performance on problems and on specific skills, again in line with the general idea that knowledge is very tied to specific situations. In Experiment 2, we examine the impact of examples on the acquisition of domain-specific skills in further detail.

EXPERIMENT 2: A PRODUCTION SYSTEM ANALYSIS OF EXAMPLE EFFECTS

Subjects in Experiment 2 learned to program recursion in a simplified version of LISP without the aid of the LISP Tutor. In the target lesson on recursion, 19 subjects were presented with a text introducing recursion, and an example program was available on-line on their computer terminals. A set of 16 recursion problems and associated program solutions were created for Experiment 2. Subjects received four of these problems in a training phase, in which they received feedback for errors. The selection of examples and training problems was counterbalanced across subjects.

Example Effects

A production system model was developed in GRAPES that was capable of coding all 16 recursive functions used in Experiment 2. Of the 19 productions in this model, 16 yield some identifiable portion of code. Each attempt at coding a training program by each subject was scored for errors on the code associated with these 16 productions. Further, we identified the productions that would be used by our GRAPES model to code the example presented to each subject. On training problems, we expected subjects to show better performance on these *analogous* productions than on *nonanalogous* productions that are not used by our model in coding the example solution. This expectation is based on the assumption that subjects would have a better chance of inferring and using declarative knowledge from the example in situations involving analogous productions than in situations involving nonanalogous productions.

Figure 6 presents percent error data for analogous and nonanalogous productions over the first six opportunities for coding an action associated with a production in the training phase. The practice curves for both kinds of productions show the usual power law effects. Power functions of the form

$$P(t) = a\, t^{-b} \qquad (2)$$

are fit to the data in Figure 6, where $P(t)$ is the probability of error on trial t, a is the error rate on

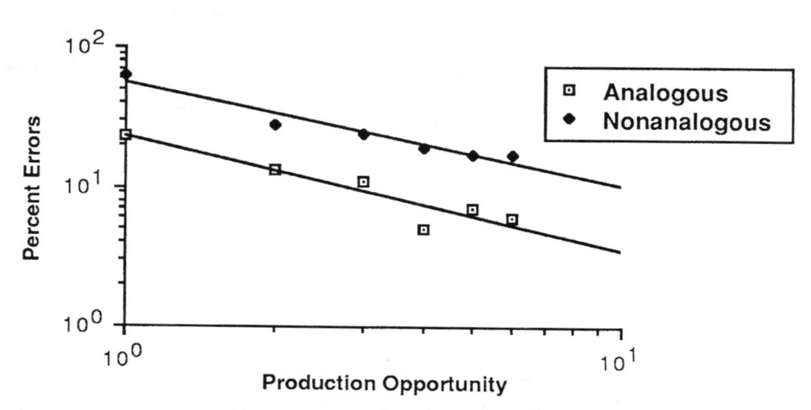

FIGURE 6: ERROR RATES AS AS A FUNCTION OF PRACTICE FOR ANALOGOUS AND NONANALOGOUS PRODUCTIONS

the first trial, and b is a rate parameter. For the analogous productions, $a = .23$ and $b = .80$, with $r = -.93$. For the nonanalogous productions, $a = .55$, $b = .73$, with $r = -.97$. Thus, the major difference, as indicated by differences in a, is in the error rates on the initial trials of analogous and nonanalogous productions. Given that the rate parameters, b, are relatively close for the two kinds of productions, it appears that the available example largely acts as if it were several trials of practice for the analogous productions. Thus, the results of Experiment 2 show that examples have a substantial effect on the first opportunity for acquiring a production but little or no interaction with subsequent improvement due to practice.

EXPERIMENT 3: EFFECTS OF SELF-EXPLANATION OF EXAMPLES

The model outlined in Figure 1 suggests that the manner in which subjects analyze examples will have an impact on subsequent acquisition of skill. Experiment 3 was partly modelled after the research of Chi et al. (1987). Subjects in Experiment 3 ($N = 12$) learned to program recursive functions in LISP using the LISP Tutor. While subjects were reading through their text-based instruction on recursion, we asked subjects to think out loud, and further, we asked subjects to explain all examples to themselves.

Self-explanations

Our first pass in analysis has focused on correlations between the number and kinds of self-explanations made while processing the text instruction (including examples) and subsequent performance in problem solving with the LISP Tutor. Based on the mean error rates per problem using the LISP Tutor, we performed a median split, dividing subjects into groups of good and poor learners. Verbal protocols collected while subjects read texts and examples were segmented into individual statements. Table 1 presents a summary of the mean number of *elaborations* produced by good and poor subjects as they worked through their examples. The elaborations in Table 1 are divided into different kinds. A *monitoring* elaboration refers to statements about the subjects' strategies or state of knowledge. *Activity* elaborations are comments about the instruction or the task. *Domain* elaborations concern statements about programming and recursion. The *other* category refers to incomplete phrases. Good subjects are superior to poor in all but the "other"

TABLE 1
ELABORATIONS OF EXAMPLES MADE BY GOOD AND POOR LEARNERS

	ELABORATIONS			
SUBJECTS	Monitoring	Activity	Domain	Other
Good	19.00	6.00	23.17	.17
Poor	2.50	.50	10.33	.00

category in Table 1 ($p < .05$ by t-tests). That good learners show more evidence of monitoring themselves and the instructional situations suggests higher amounts of metacognition. The greater amounts of domain-specific elaborations made by good learners also suggests that they are producing, in general, more information of potential use in later problem solving contexts.

The domain explanations given by subjects were further categorized into *syntax-oriented* statements or *semantics-oriented* statements. Syntax statements are ones that refer to the syntax of program code, or other surface features of the examples. Semantic statements are ones that provide an abstract interpretation of the process generated by a piece of code, indicate the significance of a program element, or identify the goal or purpose achieved by a piece of code. All six of the good subjects made more semantics-oriented than syntax-oriented elaborations, whereas four of the six poor subjects showed the opposite trend, an interaction significant by sign test, $p < .05$. This focus on the semantics of programming, rather than syntax, suggests that the good learners are indeed grasping the "inner structural relations" of the examples.

Connecting Examples to Text

The text of the instruction used in Experiment 3 was constructed at a fairly abstract level, with no direct references to the examples. We identified statements made while explaining the example that connected portions of the example back to concepts introduced in text. The mean number of such connections for good subjects was 4.33 and for poor subjects was .50, which is a significant difference, $t(10) = 2.18$, $p < .05$. The generation of connections between the examples and abstract information derived from text is the sort of process that would be predicted to be effective by analysis-based generalization methods.

GENERAL DISCUSSION

The results of Experiments 1 and 2 indicate that transfer of knowledge derived from examples to subsequent problem solving and across problem solving tasks can be substantially accounted for by production system analyses of transfer. Our current analyses in Experiment 3 indicate that complexity is added to this analysis by individual differences in the processes used in understanding instructional texts and examples. Our model in Figure 1 suggests that such differences can be attributed to differences in the prior knowledge and explanation strategies used in processing texts and examples. Current models of analysis-based generalization say little about the ways in which example analyses may vary (Lewis, 1988). In future analyses, we expect to focus on identification of process models that characterize the learning strategies of good and poor learners in programming. Although our results suggest that aspects of both the identical elements theory and the theory of meaningful learning are corroborated by our data, we do not see any reason that precludes their integration into a process model of learning and cognition.

REFERENCES

Anderson, J.R. (1987). Skill acquisition: The compilation of weak-method problem solutions. *Psychological Review, 94*, 192-210.

Anderson, J.R. & Thompson, R. (1986). *Use of analogy in a production system architecture.* Unpublished manuscript, Carnegie-Mellon University, Department of Psychology, Pittsburgh, PA.

Chi, M.T.H, Bassok, M., Lewis, M.W., Reiman, P., & Glaser, R. (1987). *Self-explanations: How students study and use examples in learning to solve problems* (Tech. Rep. 9). Pittsburgh, PA: University of Pittsburgh, Learning Research and Development Center.

DeJong, G. & Mooney, R. (1986). Explanation-based learning: An alternative view. *Machine Learning, 1*, 145-176.

Katona, G. (1940). *Organizing and memorizing.* New York: Columbia University Press.

Lewis, C. (1988). Why and how to learn why: Analysis-based generalization of procedures. *Cognitive Science, 12*, 211-256.

Mitchell, T.M., Kellar, R.M., & Kedar-Cabelli, S.T. (1986). Explanation-based generalization: A unifying view. *Machine Learning, 1*, 47-80.

Pirolli, P. (1986). A cognitive model and computer tutor for programming recursion. *Human-Computer Interaction, 2*, 319-355.

Pirolli, P. (1987). A model of purpose-driven analogy and skill acquisition in programming. In *Proceedings of the Cognitive Science Society Conference.*

Reiser, B.J., Anderson, J.R., & Farrell, R. (1985). Dynamic student modelling in an intelligent tutor for LISP programming. In *Proceedings of the Ninth International Joint Conference on Artificial Intelligence*, 8-14, Los Altos, CA: Morgan-Kaufman.

Singley, M.K., & Anderson, J.R. (1989). *Transfer of cognitive skill.* Cambridge, MA: Harvard University Press.

Thorndike, E.L. (1903). *Educational psychology.* New York: Lemke & Buechner.

Wertheimer, M. (1945). *Productive thinking.* New York: Harper and Row.

ACKNOWLEDGEMENTS

This research was supported by a National Academy of Education Fellowship granted to the first author. We would like to thank Beatrice Lauman for her work in running subjects and coding data and David Rockower for implementing the GRAPES models used in Experiment 2.

Action Planning: Producing UNIX Commands

Stephanie M. Doane, Walter Kintsch, Peter Polson

University of Colorado, Boulder

Our goal is to construct a detailed simulation of UNIX user command production based on the construction integration theory of Kintsch, (1988), and building on the action planning model developed by Mannes and Kintsch (1988) and Mannes (1989). The performance we are modeling is that of UNIX users producing legal UNIX commands. Our subjects vary in expertise, and some of the tasks are difficult. But even for the easy tasks, the solutions cannot be precompiled, because familiar elements are put together in a novel fashion. It is presumed that subjects are not recalling fixed scripts from memory. Rather, they are producing action plans for each task.

THEORETICAL BACKGROUND

Subjects are presented with their task through a textual description of the goal. For example "sort the first ten lines of file x alphabetically". We are simulating user understanding of this instruction and the generation of appropriate plans by extending the Mannes and Kintsch (1988) planning model which is based on the discourse comprehension theory of van Dijk and Kintsch (1983), and Kintsch (1988).

Mannes and Kintsch (1988) constructed a simulation of subjects doing routine computing tasks involving a file and mail system. They built their knowledge base from the results of verbal protocols, where subjects verbalized how they would accomplish given tasks (Kintsch and Mannes, 1987). Their model simulated retrieval of relevant knowledge using instructional text as cues, and it showed how this led to the formulation and execution of action plans.

van Dijk and Kintsch (1983) and Kintsch (1988) make the point that comprehension of text that describes a problem to be solved (e.g., an algebra story problem) involves formulating an effective solution plan for that problem, retrieval of relevant factual knowledge, and utilization of appropriate procedural knowledge (knowledge of algebraic and arithmetic operations). In Mannes and Kintsch (1988) this is modeled by retrieving both relevant general knowledge and specific knowledge about files and editing tasks, and then formulating editing action plans. Thus, understanding an editing task means generating a mental representation of the elements of an editing system (e.g., files) and the relationships between those elements, and then using this information to accomplish the task.

Our goal is to determine what knowledge about UNIX the model requires to produce legal UNIX commands. The fundamental assumption underlying the UNIX user interface is that complex commands can be created by concatenating simple commands with the use of advanced features that redirect command input and output (e.g., pipes). We wish to understand what kinds of knowledge are necessary to use these advanced features (e.g., input/output redirection). We are also interested in the actions themselves; part of producing a UNIX command includes making a plan for action, but knowing the specific action (e.g., knowing the command "ls" lists file names) is critical to plan execution. Thus, we are extending the Mannes and Kintsch work to include actions, in a manner analogous to work of Card, Moran and Newell (1983) and Kieras and Polson (1985).

Unlike Mannes and Kintsch, we are starting from a rational analysis of knowledge necessary to perform tasks within the UNIX system, and performance data, rather than from verbal protocols. As such, we have attempted to develop a performance model based on our assumptions about the knowledge of UNIX required to produce legal command syntax.

PERFORMANCE DATA

Doane, Pellegrino, and Klatzky (1989, in press) examined the development of expertise within the UNIX operating system by studying UNIX users with varying levels of experience. A portion of their research measured users' performance in tasks requiring them to produce UNIX commands. Included in their studies were both longitudinal and cross-sectional analyses of the emergence of command production expertise.

In this research we are attempting to model a portion of the production performance measured in the Doane et. al., (in press) research. In the production task, subjects were asked to produce the most efficient (i.e., the least number of keystrokes) legal UNIX command that they could to accomplish a specified task. Tasks ranged in difficulty from individual, frequently used UNIX commands to composite commands that effected several actions that had to be sequenced appropriately using pipes or other input/output redirection symbols. The tasks were designed to assess the impact of two types of knowledge; knowledge of individual commands and knowledge of the processes involved in sequencing those commands properly. Tasks involving more elementary commands were designed to include elements that had to be put together in order to generate a successful composite command.

An example composite task would be "display the first ten alphabetically arranged file names of the current directory". A component single would be "display the file names of the current directory". A multiple would be "display the file names of the current directory", "arrange the contents of file x alphabetically on the screen", and "display the first ten lines of file y". Thus, "single" commands caused just one action, multiple commands caused several independent actions and composite commands caused several actions that had to be sequenced appropriately using pipes and/or redirection symbols. These were equal in length to the multiple commands; thus the essential difference between the two was that composites had dependencies among their components whereas multiples did not.

The production data indicate that UNIX users differ markedly in performance, according to their history of use with the operating system. The striking aspect of these data was that only the experts could successfully produce the composites, even though the intermediates and novices could perform the other tasks that were designed to assess the component knowledge required to successfully generate a composite (e.g., singles). This is somewhat surprising, since the knowledge necessary to perform the composites is taught to intermediates and novices. The novices and intermediates had, on the average, 8 months and 2 years of experience with the system, respectively. And all of the subjects had taken a course which taught about pipes and other redirection symbols, and required their use for course homework. Thus, the less expert groups have the knowledge, but can't use it productively in the sense discussed by Wertheimer. (1982/1945).

To summarize the Doane et al. (in press) data, novice and intermediate UNIX users appear to have knowledge of the elements of the system, they can successfully produce the single and multiple commands that make up a composite. They could not, however, put these elements together using pipes and/or other redirection symbols to produce the composite commands. As previously stated, the symbols that enable input/output redirection are fundamental design features of UNIX, and these features are taught in elementary classes. Doane et al (in press) demonstrate that these features can only be used reliably after extensive experience (e.g.,experts had, on the average, 5 years of experience with UNIX).

RESEARCH GOALS

One of our goals is to understand in detail the kinds of knowledge that are sufficient to make effective use of these advanced features. To simulate expert performance on composites, the model requires more knowledge than is necessary to perform singles and multiples. In addition to knowledge of the basic types of commands and their syntax (the only knowledge required to execute singles and multiples), the model must have knowledge of the ordering of commands in a sequence. For example,to execute the task "display the first ten lines of the alphabetically sorted file x",the model must know that the command that sorts files alphabetically (SORT) should be executed on file x prior to executing the command that will display the first ten lines of the file (HEAD). The model must also know about the specific redirection properties of each command. In the example task above, the model must know that the output of SORT can be redirected to another command, and that the input to HEAD can be redirected from another command.

A possible application of such research is to guide instruction How would you modify instruction to novices to assist their performance? Another application is to guide system design. By modeling performance, we hope to gain some insight into the attributes of UNIX system design that may hinder acquisition of expertise. This may provide some guidance toward designing a system which would provide similar advances facilities without demanding such strenuous knowledge prerequisites.

We are trying to simulate the solution of tasks that cannot be precompiled, because while the elements of some of the tasks may be familiar, and indeed overlearned, they are often put together in novel sequences. That is, we are not dealing with fixed scripts which can be retrieved from memory, but with plans of action that are constructed in the context of a specific task. The construction - integration model is an appropriate model for our goals. It is a comprehension model of problem solving that does not assume a highly structured precompiled knowledge.

THE MODEL

The construction - integration model proposed by Kintsch (1988) contains four main components. The first two components are representations of knowledge; a propositional textbase derived from the instructional text, and an associative long-term memory. The next two components are processes which activate the represented knowledge; an activation process which allows text propositions to activate information in long-term memory, and a final integration process which selects relevant knowledge, and deactivates irrelevant knowledge. These processes are repeated cyclically. When some action is executed, the state of the world is changed to include the result of that action. The model continues processing in cycles until the desired state of the world is achieved (the task is accomplished), or until the system fails. Described below are the elements that together form a simulation of UNIX user's performance. Portions of the description of the model's calculations are a summary of discussion found in Mannes and Kintsch (1988).

Long-term Memory

Eighty-eight propositions were constructed from our rational analysis about the knowledge of UNIX required to execute 29 of the UNIX production tasks from the Doane et al. (in press) experiment. These 29 tasks were made up of different combinations of 9 single commands. There were 9 single tasks, 8 multiple tasks, and 12 composite tasks. (These 29 tasks are a small subset of the tasks used by Doane et al. .) These propositions were used to simulate a portion of the user's long-term memory (LTM) network.

As mentioned above, we are interested in understanding the knowledge required to use the advanced features of UNIX. This knowledge is represented in three main forms in the LTM portion of the knowledge base. First, the LTM contains knowledge of the atomic commands that one can perform (e.g., print a file). Second, it contains knowledge of the redirection properties of these commands required to combine them into composite commands. For example, in order to execute the action LS|LPR, a modeled user must know that the output from LS can be redirected to another command, and that the LPR command will take input from another command. Third, the LTM contains knowledge of the syntax required to produce a command sequence (e.g., knowing that LPR prints a file, and that the pipe symbol redirects input and output).

Interconnections for this network were calculated based on argument overlap, and proposition embedding. Additive connection strengths of .7 were used for each case of argument overlap or embedding. A LISP program computes the interconnection values among all the items in long-term memory, creating a nxn connectivity matrix. The connectivity matrix is intended to approximate an association matrix. We recognize that this relatively simple and objective way of estimating values provides us with crude and fallible measures of association. The next portion of the long-term memory consists of 11 plan elements, 9 of which correspond to the single building-block commands, and 2 of which are plan elements that allow creation of new plans. These latter plan elements are called building plan elements, because they allow the modeled user to build a composite command from the single building-block commands.

Three of the single plan elements, and one of the build plan elements are shown, with their text in abbreviated form in Table 1. There are three components in each plan, a plan name, preconditions, and outcomes. The preconditions are propositions which represent states of the world which must exist for the plan to be executed. The outcomes are propositions which become states of the world if the plan is executed. The plan names are also propositions.

Connection between propositions in the long-term memory net and the plans are based on certain types of propositions which Mannes and Kintsch call REQUESTS and OUTCOMES. Requests are imperative verbs that are used in task descriptions, requesting that the user accomplish a task (e.g., sort a file, print a file). The relationship between these verbs and plans is more precise than that given by argument overlap. Each REQUEST proposition must be associated with a particular plan or set of plans. For example, the REQUEST DISPLAY FILE NAMES DIRECTORY is associated directly with the plan (DISPLAY FILE NAMES DIRECTORY), and with other plans that are considered to be DISPLAY plans (e.g., DISPLAY FIRST-TEN LINES FILE) with a connection value of +1, and with all other plans with a connection value of 0.

Each OUTCOME proposition is associated with a +1 value to the plan that produces this outcome, with a value of -1 to plans which produce an incompatible outcome (e.g., the outcome CREATE FILE X and a plan which DELETES FILE X), and with a value of 0 to plans which produce an irrelevant outcome (e.g., the outcome CREATE FILE X and a plan to DELETE FILE Y). Only final goals are connected in this manner. Plans which need to be executed before the final goal can be executed must be contextually activated through the network activations.

Textbase

A propositional textbase was derived from the text of the problems posed to subjects (e.g., display the file names of the current directory) following the methods outlined in Kintsch (1985). Each textbase proposition activates two other associated propositions in the long-term memory net. The exact computations are described in Mannes and Kintsch (1988). As before, the request

Table 1. List of four plans.

Plan Name	Preconditions	Outcomes
(DISP FL DIR)	(@SYS)(EXIST DIR) (KNOW LS)	(DISP FL DIR)
(SORT FL)	(@SYS) (EXIST FL) (KNOW SORT)	(SORT FL)
(DISP 1ST TEN LINES FL)	(@SYS) (EXIST FL) (KNOW HEAD)	(DISP 1ST TEN FL)
(BUILD PIPE)	(KNOW LS 1ST) (DISP FL DIR) (KNOW SORT 2ND) (SORT FL) (KNOW HEAD 3RD) (DISP 1ST TEN FL) (KNOW REDIRECT HEAD OUTPUT) (KNOW REDIRECT SORT INPUT) (KNOW REDIRECT SORT OUTPUT) (KNOW REDIRECT HEAD INPUT)	(USE PIPE PLAN)

propositions require special treatment. They do not randomly activate associated knowledge, but must be used to retrieve a particular outcome. Specifically, REQUESTS and OUTCOMES are used as a joint retrieval cue to retrieve the outcome of the appropriate request -- which is associated with both retrieval cues, as in Raaijmakers & Shiffrin (1981) and Kintsch and Mannes (1987). In summary, the model now contains the text propositions along with their associates and their outcomes. When the model is trying to accomplish a task, all plans must have the potential of being activated. Thus, to the text propositions we add all 11 plan elements.

A matrix is constructed from this textbase, and the interconnections between items are calculated in the same manner as it was for the long-term memory matrix, with three additional calculations. The first calculation concerns the relationships between outcomes and plans. If all of the outcomes of a plan currently exist in the current world of the model, they inhibit the firing of that plan. For example, if the FILE X is already printed, the plan (SEND FILE X TO THE LINE PRINTER) will be inhibited. The next two calculations concern the relationships between the plans themselves. Expected outcomes of plans are related to each other in the same way as in the long-term memory matrix. That is, plans can activate other plans which produce compatible outcomes, and inhibit plans which produce incompatible outcomes. Finally, plans themselves are interconnected by a causal chaining mechanism. For example, a plan that requires that FILE X exist will activate plans that have the existence of FILE X as an outcome. Thus, Mannes and Kintsch (1988) designed the model so that interconnections among plans represent the user's knowledge about causal relationships within, in this case, the UNIX operating system.

The connectivity matrix of size nxn is obtained for each task description, corresponding to the original m text propositions and to the (n-m) associates, outcomes, and plans that have been added to the text. An initial activation vector with n elements is then constructed, with activation values 1/m for the m original text propositions and 0 for all others. This vector is then repeatedly postmultiplied with the connectivity matrix, with the m values in the vector reset to 1/m and the remainder of the vector renormalized after each multiplication. This multiplication computes the spread of activation among the elements of the vector, with the reset of the m elements trapping the activation value of the in the world propositions such that it prevents weakening of their effects with each iteration. When the change in the activation vector between iterations reaches an arbitrary criterion of .0001, the activation pattern is assumed to reflect the stable state of knowledge formed by the modeled user given the current task.

To summarize, in terms of the van Dijk and Kintsch model (1983), our small textbase activated both irrelevant and relevant knowledge. The model then used an integration process to spread activation to the relevant knowledge, and thus to simulate the modeled user's state of knowledge given the current task.

Plans and Action

The model of the user's state of knowledge results in plans with different levels of activation. Mannes and Kintsch (1988) propose an executive process which examines plan activation values, and picks for execution the plan with the highest level of activation. If the preconditions of that plan are met (the preconditions exist in the world), then the plan is fired. However, if the preconditions are not met, then the executive process goes to the next most highly activated plan, and so on. If the outcome of the executed plan is the expected outcome, then the task is complete. If not, then the outcome of the executed plan is added to the model of in the world knowledge, and the integration process is repeated, resulting in a new pattern of plan activation. The process described above is reiterated until the plan with the expected outcome fires.

THREE EXAMPLES

Table 2 depicts the main results of simulating the component tasks shown in Table 1 in the form of singles, multiples and a composite. The table shows only those plans considered by the executive process, along with their relative activation values. The simulation of the single command to display the file names of the current directory (LS problem) is very simple for the model, as it was for the subjects in Doane et. al. The system finds all of the preconditions are met, and the plan is executed immediately. For the multiple problem (LS, SORT, HEAD), the executive first chooses the LS task, its preconditions are met, and its outcome (the proposition (DISPLAY FILE-NAMES) is added to the in the world knowledge. After a new integration phase, the most activated plan is SORT. The executive chooses to fire the SORT plan, and its outcome (SORT FILE) is added to the knowledge base. Finally, the same process occurs for the plan HEAD, and the task is complete.

The composite problem (to produce LS|SORT|HEAD) is far more complex, since the task requires that the model go thru both a planning phase and a building phase. In the single and multiple tasks, there are no interrelationships between sequences of actions, and the model immediately generates appropriate user actions upon determination of the correct plan. In the case of the composites, we argue that the appropriate plans must be determined, and then sequenced correctly using the interrelationships among the preconditions for the various plans. Following each integration phase, this planning process adds representations of the individual commands and the order in which they should be executed to the in the world knowledge. In our example, the

Table 2. Traces of solutions to example production tasks.

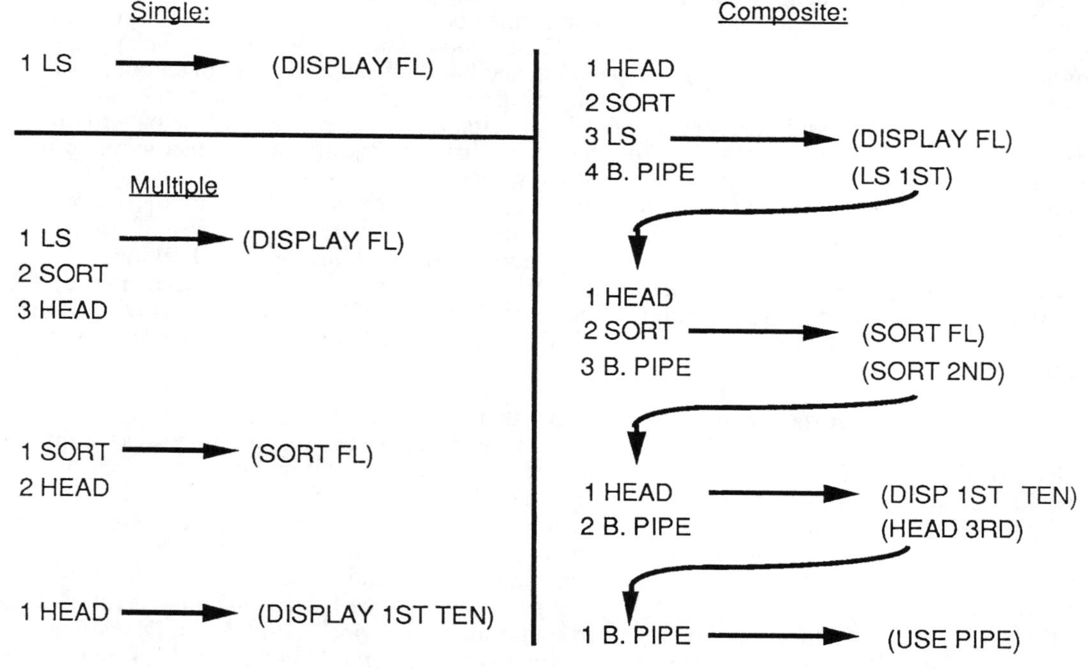

request which is acted on first is LS; the system would like to execute the HEAD plan, but its preconditions have not been met. The preconditions for HEAD in this task require the existence of an alphabetically sorted listing of the file names in the current directory. That is, the (EXIST FL) precondition has been bound to a specific file; the required file contains the alphabetically sorted file names from the current directory. The next most highly activated plan is SORT, but it has the precondition that a display of the file names exist. The (EXIST FL) precondition is now bound to a file containing the file names of the current directory. The only plan with satisfied preconditions is LS. It is fired, and the outcome (DISPLAY FILE-NAMES) is added to the current knowledge base, along with a representation of its order in the task sequence (i.e., that it is first). After the next iteration, the simulation would again like to fire the HEAD plan, but can't. The preconditions for the SORT plan are now met, and it fires, and the outcome (DISPLAY SORTED FILE-NAMES) is added to the knowledge base, as is the information that it is second in the sequence, following LS. On the final planning iteration, the HEAD plan is again the desired plan, its preconditions are now met, the plan is fired, relevant in the world knowledge is added, and the planning phase is complete.

Following the planning phase, these new representations are used by the build pipe plan to create the actual composite command. The model will execute the build pipe plan when its preconditions are met, but the preconditions for the build pipe plan are extensive. In order for the plan to fire, the modeled user must have, for each command, knowledge of the command syntax, knowledge of the command order in the sequence, and knowledge of the command redirection properties. Since we are modeling the expert, the system has all of the prerequisite knowledge, and the build pipe plan fires. The outcome of this plan is the creation of a "use pipe" plan, which is bound to the syntactically correct sequence of commands. When the use pipe plan fires, the task is complete.

While on the surface, the construction of a composite command seems simple, the psychological processes involved appear to be very complex. The creation of a composite command appears to involve the use of complex knowledge in planning and building activities. Our planning phase suggests that it should take longer to begin composing a composite command than to begin composing a single or multiple, especially for the experts. In fact, this is exactly the pattern of response time reported in Doane et. al., (in press). Experts took significantly longer to make an initial keystroke when composing composites than when they were composing less complex commands. This pattern was not found with novices, which suggests that they did not complete a satisfactory planning phase. In addition to the knowledge prerequisites, the planning phase for construction of composites seems to make a large demand on working memory. Previous researchers have suggested (e.g., Anderson & Jeffries, 1985) that novice performance may suffer due to loss of information from working memory. Perhaps one of the reasons that novices don't succeed in constructing composite commands is that planning these tasks create a large working memory load.

WORK IN PROGRESS AND FURTHER DEVELOPMENTS

The ability of the construction - integration model to simulate the production processes for the tasks considered here is encouraging, though our results are not yet definitive. The simulations described above model the ideal expert performing UNIX command production tasks. One of our major goals is to systematically break down the knowledge base in a manner that explains UNIX performance for users at different levels of expertise. That is, we want to determine what aspects of the knowledge base must be deleted to simulate intermediate and novice performance. This will allow us to simulate the nature of UNIX knowledge acquisition, perhaps even on the level of individual differences. The longitudinal data from the studies provide us with an initial starting point for this task. We will need to develop a methodology for comparing the details of model predictions to the empirical data. In our current comparisons, we have noted good correspondence.

Another goal is to analyze the results of these simulations, such that we can make some recommendations about teaching UNIX skills, and about system design. All that we have noted so far is that use of the advanced features of UNIX requires a good amount of knowledge above and beyond knowledge of the command elements themselves

CONCLUSIONS

Though this work is currently incomplete, we are encouraged by our progress. As in Mannes and Kintsch (1988), what has been accomplished is not in itself surprising: we are using a means-end, backward problem solving mechanism similar to mechanisms included in the General Problem Solver. Unlike previous problem solving models, we are using this mechanism in the context of a general theory of discourse comprehension. We are extending the work of Kintsch and Mannes (1988), which adapts this comprehension model to the problem solving domain by representing the domain specific knowledge as plans.

REFERENCES

Card, S. K., Moran, T. P., & Newell, A. (1983). *The psychology of human-computer interaction.* Hillsdale, NJ: Erlbaum.

Doane, S. M., Pellegrino, J. W. and Klatzky, R. L. (1989). Mental Models of UNIX as Revealed by Sorting and Graphing Tasks. *Proceedings of the 22nd Annual Hawaii International Conference on System Sciences*, Kailua, Kona, Hawaii: IEEE Computer Society.

Doane, S. M., Pellegrino, J. W., & Klatzky, R. L. (in press) _Expertise in a computer operating system: Conceptualization and performance. *Human-Computer Interaction.*

Anderson, J. A., & Jeffries, R. (1985). Novice LISP errors: Undetected losses of information from working memory. *Human-Computer Interaction, 1*, 133-161.

Kieras, D. E., and Polson, P. G. (1985). An approach to the formal analysis of user complexity. *International Journal of Man-Machine Studies, 22*, 365-394.

Kintsch, W. (1985). Text processing: A psychological model. In T. A. van Dijk (Ed.), *Handbook of Discourse Analysis*, Vol. 2 (pp. 231-244). London: Academic Press.

Kintsch, W. (1988). The use of knowledge in discourse processing: A construction-integration model. *Psychological Review, 95*, 163-182.

Kintsch, W. & Mannes, S. M. (1987). Generating scripts from memory. In E.vanderMeer & J. Hoffman (Eds.), *Knowledge aided information processing* (pp. 61-80). Amsterdam: North-Holland.

Mannes, S. M. (1989). *Problem-solving as text comprehension: A unitary approach.* Unpublished doctoral dissertation, University of Colorado, Boulder.

Mannes, S. M. & Kintsch, W. (1988). Action planning: Routine computing tasks. *Proceedings of the Tenth Annual Conference of the Cognitive Science Society* (pp. 97-103). Montreal, Quebec, Canada: Erlbaum.

Raaijmakers, J. G. & Shiffrin, R. M. (1981). Search of associative memory. *Psychological Review, 88*, 93-134.

van Dijk, T. A. & Kintsch, W. (1983). *Strategies of discourse comprehension.* New York: Academic Press.

Wertheimer, M. (1982/1945). *Productive thinking.* Chicago, IL: University of Chicago Press.

Lexical processing and the mechanism of context effects in text comprehension

Amanda J.C. Sharkey
and
Noel E. Sharkey

Centre for Connection Science,
University of Exeter.

Two models of context effects on lexical processing are described; (a) the Construction-integration (CI) model (Kintsch, 1988) and (b) the Lexical Distance (LD) model (Sharkey, N.E. in press; 1989). Both can account for some well known effects in the priming and ambiguity literature. However the mechanisms by which they operate differ. The CI model presumes connections between related items in the lexicon. In this model, it is assumed that, during the initial stages of processing, the associates of a word in the lexicon are *always* activated in a context-independent manner. It is postulated that textual priming effects can only occur after this phase of sense activation. Lexical priming effects and textual priming effects are the result of the operation of different processes. In the LD model, on the other hand, there are no associations between items in the lexicon. Words are represented in the lexicon as vectors of microfeatures. Context effects are conceptualised as a measure of network distance from an initial state to a target state. Both lexical priming effects and textual effects exert their influence in the same way; reducing the time taken to move to the target state. An experiment is reported in which textual priming effects are examined in an attempt to test the predictions made by the two models. In this experiment, a facilitatory influence of knowledge-based texts on a lexical decision task was demonstrated, despite short SOAs and the absence of an immediately preceding associatively related word. According to the CI model the SOAs involved were too short to allow anything but associative priming; therefore the results of this experiment favour the LD model. This research clears up a conflict in the literature between two sets of experimental findings (Kintsch & Mross, 1985; Sharkey & Mitchell, 1985). It also illustrates the use of psychological experimentation in allowing a principled choice to be made between two models.

Two kinds of context effects on lexical processing can be identified; lexical priming effects and textual priming effects (Foss, 1982; Kintsch & Mross, 1985; Keenan et al, in press; Sharkey, A.J.C., 1989; Sharkey & Mitchell, 1985). Lexical priming effects stem from the presence of an immediately preceding associatively-related word (e.g if the word NURSE is immediately preceded by the word DOCTOR it will be recognised faster than if it is preceded by a row of Xs). Lexical priming effects, as they occur in word lists have been extensively studied (e.g. Gough et al, 1981; Meyer & Schvaneveldt, 1971). Textual priming effects are those that are due to the relationship of the processed word to the preceding text, rather than the immediately preceding word (e.g the word MENU might be processed faster if it occurred in a story about a restaurant, than in a story about visiting the dentist). These effects have been less extensively studied. In this paper we shall attempt an empirical evaluation of the accounts given of both kinds of context effects in two models; Kintsch's (1988) Construction-Integration (CI) model and Sharkey's Lexical Distance (LD) model (Sharkey, N.E. in press; 1989).

These two models were selected for comparison because, unlike other models of word recognition (i) they are computationally specified, and (ii) they deal with lexical processing in terms of a global view of text comprehension - in both, lexical processing takes place in a model which also accounts for the inferences made at the propositional level. These models are similar in certain other respects; for instance they both posit the existence of a propositional and a lexical level of representation. However, quite different contextual mechanisms are proposed. As will be discussed later, these processing differences have empirically testable consequences.

Lexical priming effects: A major difference between the CI and LD models is whether or not activation is assumed to spread between items in the lexicon. In Kintsch's CI model, words are represented in the lexicon such that there are connections between related items. By means of the mechanism of spreading activation (Meyer & Schvaneveldt, 1971), the level of activation in one unit in the lexicon can affect the level of activation of other units. In Sharkey's LD model there are no connections between related lexical nodes. Instead words have a distributed representation in the lexicon made up of three types of microfeatures: semantic, situational and graphemic. Access to the lexicon is through graphemic microfeature activation; the semantic microfeatures are similar to semantic features such as is-male, has wings etc; and the situational microfeatures provide information about the contextual setting (e.g. the situational microfeatures for NURSE would contain information about hospitals). Each microfeature may be shared by several concepts. For example, DOCTOR is likely to share many situational microfeatures with NURSE because of overlapping job roles, and place of work. Each microfeature has an activation value; therefore a lexical entry can be characterised as a vector of microfeatures. Each vector of microfeatural activations can be identified as a point in n-dimensional space (where n is the number of microfeatures in the lexicon).

Because the nature of the lexical representation assumed by the two models differs, so too does the way in which lexical priming effects are accounted for. In the CI model, lexical priming effects are assumed to be the result of spreading activation in the lexicon: '..right after a word is perceived, it activates its whole associative neighbourhood in a context-independent way with the consequence that strong associates of a word are likely to be represented in working memory and hence will be primed in a lexical decision task..' (Kintsch, 1988 pg 172). Therefore, if the word 'nurse' is presented to the system just after the word 'doctor', its recognition will be speeded.

In the LD model, lexical priming is not the result of spreading activation in the lexicon; rather it reflects a measure of network distance from an initial state to a target state. When a prime word is presented to the system it activates its corresponding set of graphemic microfeatures, and sets the system on a downward descent in the energy function until a stable minimum of microfeature activity has been reached. Finding a stable minimum is the equivalent of locating the lexical entry for the prime word. We refer to this as the *initial* state of the system. Now, it is the relationship of this initial state to the representation of the target word which is responsible for the response time predictions. To make this clear, imagine the representation of the prime and target words as two vectors of microfeature activations in the lexical space $\mathbf{L}^n$. Let these vectors represent the starting state of the system **s** and the required or target state **r**. Then the Euclidean distance between the two points **s** and **r** is given by $\|\mathbf{s} - \mathbf{r}\|^{1/2}$, where length $\|\mathbf{v}\| = (\mathbf{v} \cdot \mathbf{v})^{1/2}$. A major assumption of the model is that the greater the distance from an initial state to a target state, the longer will be the recognition time for a target word. If a target word is related to the prime, it will take less time to process because the two words will share some microfeatures and the system will be closer to the target state than if the target was not related to the prime. Thus both models make the same general predictions about lexical priming effects (although the LD model also accounts for a number of other effects as well such as interactions between context, frequency and stimulus quality).

Textual priming effects: The two models differ in their accounts of textual priming effects. In the LD model, textual priming effects have the same causal factor as lexical priming effects i.e. the time taken to move through n-dimensional lexical space from an initial state (the vector of microfeatures that resulted from the processing of the previous word) to a target state (the vector of microfeatures implied by the word being processed). The difference between textual priming and lexical priming in the LD model is the result of processes occurring in a knowledge-net which is external to the lexicon. This net holds the model's knowledge of the world in the form of a network of massively interconnected propositions. During reading, once a proposition has been constructed, it activates the knowledge net with the result that it relaxes on a stable configuration of situationally related propositions. This stable state is maintained until cues from the text indicate otherwise. These active propositions broadcast activation to the situational microfeatures in the lexicon, holding them constant. This means that incoming words that are related to the knowledge structure will be processed faster, since the activation of the situational microfeatures will ensure that their representations will be closer to the state of the lexical system than the representations of contextually unrelated words; so it will take less time to traverse the intervening distance.

In the CI model, unlike the LD model, it is assumed that textual priming effects result from the operation of a different mechanism from that implicated in lexical priming effects. When a word is encountered in text, in the initial stages of processing, its associates are activated through spreading activation in the lexicon. This activation of associates occurs in a context-independent manner. Textual priming effects exert their influence only as a result of the process of integration in the following phases of sense selection and sense elaboration. The process of construction that results in context-independent activation of concepts at the lexical level is also assumed to operate at the propositional level; when a proposition is constructed, associatively and semantically related propositions are also activated. The result of the construction process is the production of a network expressable as a connectivity matrix. Via the process of integration, activation is then spread through the network until the system stabilises. More specifically, an activation vector representing the activation values of all the nodes in the network is repeatedly postmultiplied with the connectivity matrix. This cycle is repeated until the system stabilises. The end result of this process of integration is that '..positively interconnected items strengthen each other, while unrelated items drop out and inconsistent items become inhibited..' (Kintsch, 1988 pg 171).

Kintsch (1988, pg 164) criticises top-down accounts of lexical processing. He suggests that it is too difficult to '..make a system smart enough so that it will make the right decisions, yet keep it flexible enough so that it will perform well in a variety of situations..'(Kintsch, 1988, pg 164). In other words, a system that expects particular lexical items is unlikely to perform well (a point with which we agree). He seeks to avoid the problem of inflexibility through the use of the combined processes of construction and integration. In his system, the process of construction results in the activation of a number of elements which are selected amongst during the operation of the integration process. The idea is that the correct element is likely to be amongst those that are generated in this haphazard manner. Nonetheless, it is claimed here that even though the LD model admits a top-down influence on the lexicon, it does not suffer from the sort of inflexibility that Kintsch discusses. This is because the system does not expect particular lexical items. Instead, it is predisposed towards the reception of a *class* of lexical items - those which share situational microfeatures with the active knowledge structure.

Kintsch (1988) illustrates his account of textual context effects in terms of the processing of lexically ambiguous words. When an ambiguous word is processed, it activates its associates in a context-independent manner (e.g. the word 'mint' will activate both 'candy' and 'money'). Then the process of integration will result in the selection of one of these alternatives, and the deactivation of the other. This account fits with available data on lexical ambiguity. If the interval between the presentation of the ambiguous word and the subsequent presentation of an associatively related word is short, then even the processing of context-inappropriate associates will be facilitated. However, if the interval is longer then the process of integration will have been called into operation, and only the context-appropriate associates of the ambiguous word will be primed.

This explanation fits much of the available data on lexical ambiguity resolution (e.g Kintsch & Mross, 1985; Seidenberg et al, 1982; Swinney, 1979), although there are some exceptions (Blutner & Sommer, 1988; Glucksberg, Kreuz & Rho, 1986; Tabossi, 1988). An explanation of these findings can also be couched in terms of the LD model, through use of the distance metric as in a related connectionist model by Kawamoto (in press). Kawamoto also discusses the structure of his lexical network in terms of points in energy space. He shows that homophones are close together in the energy landscape and separated by a high energy ridge. Before the system settles on the final meaning of a homophone, the system may move along the ridge between the alternative meanings. Therefore, until the system has stabilised, both sets of microfeatures will be equally available and words sharing either set will be primed. Once the system has stabilised, only words that share microfeatures with the stable configuration will be primed.

In summary, the LD and CI models are fairly equivalent in their ability to account for effects reported in the literature on lexical priming. Where they differ is in their explanations of the effects of textual context on unambiguous words. Sharkey and Mitchell (1985) demonstrated facilitation of lexical decision responses to words related to knowledge-based contexts (e.g MENU in a restaurant context). It is clear how such an effect would be explained in the LD model. As the restaurant story is processed, a related set of propositions would be assembled. These propositions would then hold active in the lexicon the situational microfeatures associated with restaurants. Since the word MENU is associated with restaurants it shares these microfeatures, and therefore it will take less time for the lexical processor to move from its initial state when the word is perceived to the target state which represents its meaning.

It is less clear how such an effect would be explained in the CI model. The CI model is primarily designed to select among alternatives generated when the previous word is processed. Unless, MENU was an associate of the preceding word, it is not clear how its processing would be facilitated. Kintsch is more specific about *when* textual context exerts its influence on lexical processing, than he is about *how* this influence is exerted. He argues that '..if the target word closely follows the priming word, so that the processing of the prime is still in its initial stages ..... context-appropriate inferences that are not associatively related to the priming word are not responded to any faster than unrelated control words..' (Kintsch, 1988 pg 171). On the other hand, if more time is allowed, '..context-appropriate associates are still primed, but inappropriate associates no longer are, whereas context-appropriate inferences now become strongly primed..' (Kintsch, 1988 pg 171).

In the CI model, the interval of time between the target word and the immediately preceding word is crucial in determining the effects that will be obtained. Kintsch (1988) refers to another study (Till, Mross & Kintsch, 1988) which suggests that context-inappropriate associates are not deactivated until 300 milliseconds have passed. In an earlier paper, Kintsch & Mross, (1985) suggest that Sharkey and Mitchell's (1985) facilitation results are due to the self-paced method of presentation they used. Kintsch and Mross's argument is that the self-paced presentation of the sentences in the knowledge-based contexts allowed enough time for evidence of textual context effects to become detectable. When Kintsch and Mross (1985) used an experimenter-paced visual presentation of knowledge-based texts (each word appeared on the screen for 150 milliseconds), they found no clear evidence of any knowledge-based facilitation of lexical decisions. In fact, they failed to find any clear evidence of knowledge-based facilitation, even when they used a self-paced or a delayed presentation of the knowledge-based texts. This finding supports the CI model, but means that there is a discrepancy in the literature between the results obtained by Kintsch and Mross (1985) and those obtained by Sharkey and Mitchell (1985). One reason might be that Sharkey and Mitchell's results were in some way the result of the task they employed. A more likely explanation is that the discrepancy was due to a difference in the materials used. Kintsch and Mross (1985) based their materials on Galambos's (1982) norms. However, unlike the norms used by Sharkey and Mitchell (1985), the Galambos norms were first generated by Galambos, and subsequently rated by subjects. The subject-generated norms of Sharkey and Mitchell may therefore have provided a better reflection of the subjects' knowledge.

In the experiment reported in this paper, an attempt was made to resolve this inconsistency by looking at the effect of textual priming effects using the same task as that employed by Kintsch and Mross (1985), but with materials based on the subject-generated norms of Sharkey and Mitchell (1985). Knowledge-based texts were presented visually on a screen at a rate of one word per 200 milliseconds. This control over the rate of presentation made it possible to test predictions derived from the two models. According to the CI model, at short delays only associates of the preceding word should be primed. Kintsch is very specific about this; following short SOAs, '..the discourse context is actually irrelevant to the priming effect. What matters is merely the associative relation between the prime word and the target word..' (Kintsch, 1988 pg 171). However, in the experiment, care was taken to ensure that the word which preceded the lexical decision target was not associatively related to it. Therefore, according to the CI model, the processing of the target word should not be facilitated. According to the LD model, evidence of priming should be detected under these circumstances. In the LD model, as long as enough time has been allowed to construct propositions on the basis of the text, then words which share situational microfeatures with the text will be facilitated. No delay between the immediately preceding word and the target is needed for this textual facilitation to occur. According to the LD model, lexical priming does not contribute to the process of textual priming. Therefore, the LD model predicts that evidence of facilitation should be obtained in the proposed experiment despite the absence of an immediately preceding associatively related word.

AN EMPIRICAL STUDY OF THE ONSET OF TEXTUAL PRIMING

Texts based on Sharkey and Mitchell's (1985) norms were presented to subjects using a task similar to that employed by Kintsch and Mross (1985) (see Example 1). Lexical decision targets interrupted the text at certain points. A crucial factor in this experiment is that the knowledge-based stories were written so as to ensure that the word that immediately preceded the lexical decision target had not appeared in the subject-generated norms, and was not associatively related to the target. The lexical priming effects that are obtained in word lists have been shown to disappear if even one word intervenes between prime and target (e.g Gough et al, 1981). Therefore, if any facilitation is evident in this experiment it must be the result of the influence of textual context, not associative relations between words.

As stated above, the predictions of the two models about the outcome of this experiment are clear. According to the CI model, priming should not occur. The delay that intervenes between the preceding word and the lexical decision target is too short to implicate anything but context-independent activation of associates, and the word that immediately preceded the lexical decision target was not associatively related to it. In contrast, the LD model predicts the occurrence of priming. According to the LD model, once related propositions have been constructed, (by reading introductory sentences such as those shown in Example 1), the influence of the propositional level will predispose the system towards words which share situational microfeatures with the relevant knowledge structure. Therefore priming should occur despite the relatively short SOAs and the absence of an immediately preceding associatively related word.

Materials and Design: 24 subjects took part in this experiment, and each read 40 stories. Twenty of these stories were knowledge-based passages based on Sharkey and Mitchell's norms (Sharkey & Mitchell, 1985). Twenty were distractor stories (containing a mixture of word and nonword targets). The stories were presented on a computer screen, one word at a time, at a rate of one word every 200 milliseconds. The task was self-paced in one respect; subjects initiated the presentation of each sentence. This ensured that they had time to understand one sentence before moving on to the next.

At certain points in each story, a lexical decision target was presented. Subjects were required to indicate as quickly as possible whether or not this target was a word. Care was taken to ensure that the word that immediately preceded the lexical decision target was not associatively related to it. There were 6 conditions in the experiment (as shown in Example 1 below). The targets were either related or unrelated to the surrounding text and they were presented in one of three sentence positions; in an initial sentence position, at the end of a main clause or at the end of a subordinate clause.

<u>Example 1</u>

Introductory sentences
Toby was going to his little friend Edward's birthday party. Toby's mother took him along to the party. Toby rushed into the room to see everyone else.
Sentences containing related targets
a) The balloon GAMES he grabbed belonged to someone else.
b) He grabbed hold of a balloon GAMES and waved it above his head.
c) Whether he grabbed hold of a balloon GAMES or not he certainly had one in his hand.
Two Fillers: The children were all very excited. Edward was quite red in the face.
Sentences containing unrelated targets
a) The sofa FIRMS was fun to jump on, Toby decided.
b) Toby jumped on the sofa FIRMS and was told off by the adults.
c) Given that Toby jumped on the sofa FIRMS its not surprising he got told off by the adults.
Concluding sentences
He sobered up a little. The adults tried to get the children under control. By the end of the party they were completely shattered.

Results and Discussion: The differences between Unrelated and Related targets were statistically significant for all conditions (see Table 1 below). The magnitude of the differences were as follows:

Initial portion of sentence - MinF(1,61) = 10.33, $p < .005$); End of subordinate clause - $F_1(1,23)$ = 4.97, $p < .036$, $F_2(1,38)$ = 3.56 $p < 0.067$; End of main clause MinF(1,60) = 5.72, $p < .025$. These results clearly favour the LD model over the CI model. The CI model cannot account for textual context effects which occur following short delays. The LD model predicts the occurrence of textual context effects even at short delays and when the immediately preceding word is not associatively related.

Table 1

SENTENCE POSITION

	Within-clause	End-main-clause	End-sub-clause
Related	810.03	851.73	806.94
E%	0.48	0.35	0.0
Unrelated	902.94	910.84	896.72
E%	0.71	0.48	0.83
Neutral baseline (words in isolation) =		723.51	
E%		0.47	

Overall the findings suggest that (a) a difference in materials is likely to have been responsible for the difference in the results obtained by Sharkey and Mitchell (1985) and Kintsch and Mross (1985), and (b) because the word that immediately preceded the target was not related to it, the knowledge-based priming results were not due to the confounding influence of lexical priming from an immediately preceding word. Nonetheless, one way in which an attempt might be made to weaken the current experimental results would be to suggest that the effects obtained were in fact due to the confounding influence of lexical priming from earlier parts of the text (even though an attempt was made to avoid this possibility when writing the materials). Keenan et al (in press) raise the possibility that lexical priming effects in text sustain for longer than they do in word lists. They in fact explicitly suggest that Sharkey and Mitchell's (1985) results might be due to the confounded influence of lexical priming. Keenan et al (in press), and Ratcliff (1987) both argue that it is important to control for the potentially confounding influence of lexical priming. Our argument is that the reverse may also be true, and apparent examples of lexical priming may actually be textual context effects. If subjects are allowed time to interpret a text, how can it be demonstrated that apparent lexical priming effects are really due to context-independent sense activation, and not to the influence of the interpreted text? Foss and Ross (1983) make a similar point when they suggest that apparent instances of lexical priming may be deceiving since, '... the operative relation is that between the semantically interpreted phrase and the next word..' (Foss & Ross, 1983). In any case, two studies reported by Sharkey, A.J.C. (1989) suggest that lexical priming effects are unlikely to have been responsible for the apparent textual priming effects reported above.

In the first of these two experiments, associative prime words were presented in sentence contexts as shown in Example 2.

Example 2
(the ^ sign indicates the various positions at which the target could be presented)

Associative
The boy ^ is sometimes ^ unkind and ^ thoughtless.
The boy unkind and sometimes is ^ thoughtless.
Unrelated
The law ^ is sometimes ^ unkind and ^ uncompromising.
The law unkind and sometimes is ^ uncompromising.
Target: GIRL

Like the experiment reported above, the words in the sentence were presented visually at a rate of one word per 200 milliseconds. The prime words were followed by lexical decision targets that were either related or unrelated to the prime. The lexical decision targets followed the prime words after an interval of either 0,2 or 4 words in sentences, or after an interval of 4 words in a scrambled sentence, as illustrated in Example 2 below.

In this experiment, no evidence of priming was found for associative words, even at the beginning of sentence. That is, there were no statistically significant difference between the Unrelated and Related in any of the sentence positions (F1 and F2 < 1 in all cases except lag 2 where $F_2(1,29) = 1.40$, $p > .24$).

The second experiment was conducted to check that evidence of lexical priming effects could be obtained, under some circumstances, using the same task. Essentially the same experiment was run with the same materials, but the sentences were presented in scrambled form, as shown in Example 3. Scrambled sentences are the equivalent of word lists. The results obtained were those that would be expected when associative primes are presented in word lists. Clear evidence of priming was obtained when there were no intervening words between prime and target ($MinF(1,44) = 6.05$, $p < 0.025$). No priming was obtained when the interval between prime and target was filled with intervening words.

<u>Example 3</u>

Associative
Thoughtless boy ^ unkind the ^ sometimes is ^ and.
Unrelated
Thoughtless law ^ unkind the ^ sometimes is ^ and.
Target: GIRL

These findings add to others in the literature, (e.g. Gough et al, 1981; Meyer & Schvaneveldt, 1971;) by demonstrating that lexical priming effects are less likely to occur in texts than in word lists. Not only do lexical priming effects in normal texts seem not to sustain, they do not even seem to occur. Since the textual priming experiment reported here used the same task and experimental settings it is clear that lexical priming effects could not be responsible for the evidence of facilitation that was obtained.

CONCLUSIONS

The experimental results reported here favour the Lexical Distance model (Sharkey, in press; 1989) as a more accurate account of lexical processing in humans than the Construction-Integration model (Kintsch, 1988). In the textual priming study reported here, evidence of the effect of knowledge-based contexts on lexical processing was obtained even though the targets were not preceded by related words, and the SOAs involved were short. These findings run counter to predictions arising from the CI model. Kintsch (1988) proposes that the effects of knowledge-based contexts will be detected only if an SOA greater than 400 milliseconds is used, and as we have seen this delay is crucial to the operation of the model in its ability to explain effects in the ambiguity literature. In contrast, the LD model accurately predicts the results of the current experiment. Sharkey (in press; 1989) proposes that propositions activate situational microfeatures at the lexical level, thus holding the lexical processor close to the target state of incoming contextually related words until contextual cues indicate a change of context. Potential criticisms of the experiment were allayed by presenting data which demonstrated that in the same task lexical priming effects occurred only in word lists and not in sentences. These findings show that our textual priming results were not due to the confounding influence of lexical priming.

Although the results of the textual priming study favour the LD model over the CI model, it cannot be conclusively stated that textual context exerts an influence on the lexicon prior to lexical access. As argued elsewhere, (Sharkey A.J.C., 1989), current techniques do not permit an unassailable demonstration of non-modularity in language processing. It is possible that the results reported here could be accounted for in some other incarnation of a modular system. However, as yet such a system has not been developed in sufficient computational detail to allow the derivation of precise empirically testable predictions. It is therefore concluded that the minimal top down account offered by the LD model fits the data better than its alternatives.

REFERENCES

Blutner, R. & Sommer, R. (1988) Sentence processing and lexical access: The influence of the focus identifying task. *Journal of Memory and Language*, 27, 359-367.

Foss, D.J. (1982) A discourse on semantic priming. *Cognitive Psychology*, 14, 590-607.

Foss, D.J. & Ross, J.R. (1983) Great expectations: Context effects during sentence processing. In G.B. Flores d'Arcais & R.J. Jarvella (Eds) *The process of language understanding*. New York: John Wiley.

Galambos, J.A. (1982) Normative studies of six characteristics of our knowledge of common activities. Cognitive Science Tech. Rep. 14, Yale University

Glucksberg, S., Kreutz, R.J., & Rho, S. (1986) Context can constrain lexical access: Implications for models of language comprehension. *Journal of Experimental Psychology: Learning, Memory and Cognition*, 3, 323-333.

Gough, P.B., Alford, J.A. & Holley-Wilcox, P. (1981) Words and Contexts. In O.J.L. Tzeng & H. Singer (Eds) *Perception of print: Reading research in experimental psychology*. Hillsdale, NJ: Erlbaum

Kawamoto, A.H. (in press) Distributed representations of ambiguous words and their resolution in a connectionist network. In S.L. Small, G. W. Cottrell, and M.K. Tanenhaus (Eds) *Lexical ambiguity resolution in the comprehension of human language*.

Keenan, J.M., Golding, J.M., Potts, G.R., Jennings, T.M. & Aman, C.J. (in press) Methodological issues in evaluating the occurrence of inferences. In A. Graesser and G.H. Bower, (Eds) *Learning and Motivation, Vol 24*: Academic Press.

Kintsch, W. (1988) The role of knowledge in discourse comprehension: A construction-integration model. *Psychological Review*, 95, 163-182.

Kintsch, W. & Mross, E.F. (1985) Context effects in word identification. *Journal of Memory and Language*, 24, 336-349.

Meyer, D.E. & Schvaneveldt, R.W. (1971) Facilitation in recognising pairs of words: Evidence of a dependence between retrieval operations. *Journal of Experimental Psychology*. 90, 227-35.

Ratcliff, J. (1987) The plausibility effect: Lexical priming or sentential processing? *Memory and Cognition* 15, 6, 482-496.

Seidenberg, M.S., Tanenhaus, M.K., Leiman, J.M. & Bienkowski, M. (1982) Automatic access of the meanings of ambiguous words in context: Some limitations of knowledge-based processing. *Cognitive Psychology*, 14, 489-537.

Sharkey, A.J.C. (1989) Contextual mechanisms of text comprehension. Unpublished PhD dissertation.

Sharkey, N.E. (in press) A connectionist model of text comprehension. To appear in D.Balota, G.B. Flores d'Arcais, and K.Rayner (Eds) Comprehension processes in reading.

Sharkey, N.E. (1989) The Lexical Distance model and word priming. Proceedings of the 11th Annual Conference of the Cognitive Science Society.

Sharkey, N.E. & Mitchell, D.C. (1985) Word recognition in a functional context: The use of scripts in reading. *Journal of Memory and Language*, 24, 253-270.

Swinney, D.A. (1979) Lexical access during sentence comprehension: (Re)consideration of context effects. *Journal of Verbal Learning and Verbal Behavior*, 18, 645-659.

Tabossi, P. (1988) Accessing Lexical Ambiguity in different types of sentential contexts. *Journal of Memory and Language*, 27, 324-340.

Acknowledgements: We would like to thank Economic and Social Research Council (C08250015) and Leverhulme Trust (A/87/153) for supporting this research.

Pragmatic Interpretation and Ambiguity

Charles E. Martin
Yale University

Abstract

An approach to pragmatic interpretation in natural language understanding is described. The approach trades off a full generative natural language capacity for the ability to recognize the flow of familiar (and often complex) arguments.

The theory requires considerable domain-dependent knowledge and specific domain-dependent goals for the understanding system. The process model described, however, is domain-independent with fairly relaxed representational constraints. All processing takes place within a hierarchical episodic memory, allowing expectations to be posted to quite general concepts from multiple sources in parallel.

INTRODUCTION

The Direct Memory Access Parser (Riesbeck and Martin, 1985, Martin, 1989) uses phrases to guide memory search. DMAP tries to recognize specific concepts in memory; new memory structures are added to reflect differences between these concepts and the input.

The DMAP system is an example of a *pragmatic* natural language understander; it understands new texts only in terms of existing memory structures. Interpretation is determined by the character of these existing concepts: at any time, its interpretive goals—and thus the range of target concepts for understanding—are determined by which existing concepts are in the process of being recognized.

The simultaneous strength and weakness of DMAP is its reliance on pre-existing memory structures. The phrases used in parsing are tied to existing concepts; the sequence of elements that make up the phrase constitute the only store of linguistic knowledge in the system. This resembles the familiar "pattern-concept" pairs of phrase-based systems (Arens, 1981). The key difference between past phrasal systems and DMAP is that the *concept* is used to retrieve the *pattern*, rather than the reverse.

Instead of using a pattern to *build* a concept, a predicted concept is used to retrieve patterns which will suffice to *recognize* that concept. The system has expectations about the content of the text in advance of seeing the text itself. The patterns serve as a mechanism to *verify* predictions made by the system. As in traditional phrase-based systems, some pattern elements appearing in the text will differ from their general specification in the pattern, and new concepts are built to reflect these differences.

INTERPRETATION AND AMBIGUITY

At the most general level, natural language understanding systems for semantic interpretation can be thought of as choosing which of several hypotheses best explains the input text. For example, a traditional conceptual analyzer (Riesbeck, 1974) might retrieve a lexically-indexed production containing information to determine which of several competing knowledge structures should be selected as the proper representation for a word. Modern marker-passing schemes such as the WIMP parsers of Charniak (1986) or Norvig's FAUSTUS (1987) take a conceptually similar approach: a marker-passing or spreading activation algorithm identifies candidate hypotheses in the form of explanatory memory structures; the choice between candidates is determined by an evaluation metric of some kind.

The high-level structuring of semantic interpretation into the component parts (1) find candidates and (2) select among them puts a tremendous amount of responsibility on the evaluation metric. In the case of a conceptual analyzer, this is reflected in increasingly larger cond clauses (or mutually antagonistic demons) which seem ad hoc, disassociated from memory, and hard to learn. For marker-passers and their brethren, this is reflected in large numbers of false candidates and a "hit rate" of valid inference which decreases with the size of the memory. These problems are well known.

The general theory behind DMAP is that interpretation is easier given a different breakdown of the problem. First, the understanding system is assumed to have some *expectations* about what the input text will be about. Second, given these expectations, the interpretation problem is cast as *verifying* that these expectations are fulfilled. Hypothesis verification is generally easier than determining hypothesis applicability. This breakdown is the basis for script and frame-based parsers such as SAM (Cullingford, 1978), later extended to include much more of the inferential processes of memory in (Schank, Lebowitz, and Birnbaum, 1980).

This traditional theory of scriptal expectations has well-known limitations. It is unclear what is to occur when more than one script is active at a time; if each has its own lexicon, the problem of choice among alternatives has simply reappeared under a different guise. Second, more than one word sense may match active expectations; at this point the script-based analyzer must simply choose one. See (Birnbaum, 1986) for a fuller critique.

DIRECT MEMORY ACCESS PARSING

The solution advocated to these problems is to recast the theory of scriptal expectations in terms of predicting memory structures and relationships in memory, rather than isolated representational structures. Using a hierarchical episodic memory based on the Memory Organization Packets of (Schank, 1982), the system allows any concept in memory, at any level of generalization, to post expectations to another concept or lexical item. The general DMAP algorithm breaks this process of posting expectations and verifying predictions into two components: directed prediction, and opportunistic recognition.

Directed prediction

1. Predict a concept.
2. Retrieve associated patterns which will recognize that concept.
3. Predict patterns' leading edges (can be concepts or lexical items).

Opportunistic recognition

1. Activate a concept.
2. Find all referenced predictions.
3. Refine to more specific predictions.
4. If the prediction's pattern is complete
   then activate the predicted concept
   else predict the pattern's next element.

The system reads articles about the economy; initial predictions come from high-level memory structures such as "article about interest rates." Specific predicted concepts may use patterns associated with more abstract concepts; as input is recognized, the activated concepts may provide information allowing the predicted concepts to be refined to even more specific concepts in memory. This use of specific memory structures as interpretations for new input is similar to recent techniques of case-based reasoning (see Kolodner, 1988, for a variety approaches).

Patterns are the sole store of pragmatic knowledge in the system. When a target concept is predicted, the patterns supply expectations about what other concepts the system should *attempt* to recognize in order to recognize the target. There are two restrictions on patterns:

1. *(Index patterns)* How expectations are posted must be represented as a linear sequence of lexical items and references to other concepts, and
2. *(Relative reference)* References to other concepts must be expressed in terms of the packaging relationship between the concepts and the source of the expectation.

As a trivial example, the concept MTRANS for communication events is a relatively general concept in its hierarchy, which includes specific instances of communication below it and more general concepts of action above it. The MTRANS concept itself packages (in the usual labelled part-subpart relationship of semantic networks) concepts for the *(actor)* of the action and the *(content)* of the communication. A simple index pattern for this concept would be:

{ *(actor)* **says** *(content)* } ⟶ MTRANS

If MTRANS is predicted, then the index pattern can be applied. To apply the index pattern, the first element of that pattern is examined. If it is a lexical item, then the lexicon is updated with the information that that lexical item refers to that index pattern. If it is a packaging relationship, the concept packaged serves to index the expectation ***directly in the memory structure referred to by that packaging relationship.*** This latter memory structure is "predicted."

The index patterns provide a distributed representation of pragmatic lexical and conceptual knowledge in the system, in the sense that the same elements of a pattern (lexical or referential) may appear in different patterns attached to quite different concepts in memory. For example, "come back to" appears in the phrase { **come back to** *(topic)* } associated with the concept INTERVIEW-TOPIC-INTRODUCTION, and also in the phrase { *(actor)* **come back to** *(plan)* } associated with the concept REPEATED-PLAN. Since there is no central generative definition of "come back to," the priming of these phrases is dependent only upon the expectations in memory. The first concept (and pattern) will be predicted while reading a newspaper interview, while the second will be predicted in explaining the actions of economic actors.

It is arguable that this pragmatic, concept-specific, distributed representation of patterns loses some of the generative capacity of our linguistic knowledge; surely there is some deeply-rooted similarity between these two phrases and their concepts. But the direct indexing of expectations in memory structures is crucial to allowing expectations to be placed on any concept in memory, no matter how specific or general. The existence of an abstraction hierarchy is then exploited by indexing the expectation under all abstractions of the predicted concept. This is "marker passing," but only according to the rigid constraints of the hierarchy and the predicted concept.

Marker Passing[1]

When concepts are recognized, they spread their recognition up the abstraction hierarchy as well. Intersections of expectation and recognition causes further predictions based on the index patterns associated with the expectation. When an index pattern is completed, it results in the recognition of its predicted concept.

Intersections also result in the refinement of the system's predictions. Given a prediction for MTRANS, knowledge that the actor of the communication is Milton Friedman allows the prediction of communication to be refined to specific episodes in memory in which Milton Friedman has had something to say. Once at this specific level, information unique to understanding the kinds of arguments Milton Friedman makes (for example, monetarist arguments) is available to the system. The memory search algorithm therefore acts as a kind of giant script applier, in which concept refinement can cause scriptal expectations to be posted at any level of abstraction or packaging.

Intersections occur in DMAP only as a result of the guided passing of markers, not as a result of blind memory search. Since the index patterns which guide this passing of markers are tied to domain-dependent memory structures, the algorithm as a whole behaves as determined by domain-dependent knowledge even though the algorithm itself is domain-independent.

Prediction Failure

The DMAP system uses the input to supply specific information to confirm or deny the predictions in memory. The refinement of those predictions supplies additional, specific expectations based on the concepts already existing in memory: "Ah, it's Friedman's column in *Newsweek*. He must be talking about the money supply." For the most part, these expectations are satisfied, and the system does quite well with many vague or ambiguous referents: "He's talking about an 'economic nightmare.' He must be referring to the increase in the money supply."

Quite often, however, these expectations are too specific, or just incorrect. For example, Friedman might call for the active application of expansionary money supply—not expected, but possible. Such an input creates an *expectation failure* for DMAP, in which the input did not match the prediction.

Most interesting texts contain expectation failures. DMAP treats them as specific input used to recognize memory structures representing the failure and a possible repair. These failure and repair structures are represented in the same memory format as all other concepts, and operated on by the same *directed prediction* and *opportunistic recognition* algorithms. The difference is that an internal processing distinction—the mismatch of input and prediction—is used as input to the recognition process, instead of an external text. Space prohibits discussing the failure and repair mechanisms further, but see Martin and Riesbeck, 1986, and Martin, 1989 for details.

UNDERSTANDING ECONOMIC ARGUMENTS

This section presents a detailed example of how DMAP runs on the following input text.

[1]Although the theory makes no committment to marker passing, it is a convenient device for explanation. The program is implemented as a marker passer. See (Martin, 1989) for details.

Donald Regan: On a long term basis, interest rates are headed down.

This is part of a very long text handled by the parser. The parser has the problem of connecting the parts of the text to memory. It's domain goals are to determine an explanation for possible future states of the economy; in other words, the program is interested in figuring out what will happen to interest rates. Represented in memory is specific domain knowledge as well as general knowledge about argumentation (Birnbaum, Flowers, and McGuire, 1980).

The example presents successive words as they are seen by the parser. Following each word are the index patterns whose expectations have been satisfied by the reference to the input word. With the index pattern is the associated concept in memory. An asterisk (*) indicates what remains of the pattern to be recognized. When a pattern is complete, the concept is noted as `referenced`, and expectations which it satisfies will follow with their index patterns and associated concepts follow.

Program annotations include:

- `Specialization Failure`, which reports which relationship failed and what new structure was built or used.
- `Refinement Failure`, which reports what new structure was built or used, the source of the failure, and any repairs which were performed.
- `Repair`, which reports new memory structures built to record the repair and what the content of those concepts are.

```
Reading DONALD
    { DONALD * REGAN } = REGAN
Reading REGAN
    { DONALD REGAN * } = REGAN referenced
    { (actor) * (mtrans) (mobject) } = IR-UP-COMMUNICATION
        Specialization Failure: (actor) REGAN
        Built: IR-UP-COMMUNICATION.1
```

This demonstrates the parsing of a simple lexical phrase. Recognition of the index pattern results in the reference of the REGAN concept, which in turn satisfies an expectation from IR-COMMUNICATION. There is no refinement specific to Regan, so a new specialization is built.

```
Reading :
    { : * } = MTRANS referenced
    { (actor) (mtrans) * (mobject) } = IR-UP-COMMUNICATION.1
Reading ON
    { ON * A (horizon) BASIS } = BEHAVIOR
Reading A
    { ON A * (horizon) BASIS } = BEHAVIOR
Reading LONG
    { LONG * TERM } = LONG-RUN
Reading TERM
    { LONG TERM * } = LONG-RUN referenced
    { ON A (horizon) * BASIS } = BEHAVIOR = TRUE-BEHAVIOR
```

This is the normal refinement process; the associated concept for this index pattern was BEHAVIOR, but the reference in the input to a LONG-RUN (horizon) caused refinement of the concept to that of TRUE-BEHAVIOR. (The underlying model of economic reasoning being that the long-term action of an economic quantity reflects its true behavior, rather than its (uncertain) short-term activity.)

It is worth noting here that the concept for "long" was expected because the higher-level index pattern for BEHAVIOR was looking for its horizon relationship. "Long term" was connected to this concept because of the presence of the higher-level expectation.

```
Reading BASIS
    { ON A (horizon) BASIS * } = TRUE-BEHAVIOR referenced
    { (behavior) * (event) } = TRUE-TREND
    { (behavior) * (quantity) (action) } = IR-INCREASE
        Specialization Failure: (behavior) TRUE-BEHAVIOR
        Built: IR-INCREASE.2
Reading RATES
    { RATES * } = RATES referenced
    { (topic) (mention) * } = INTEREST-RATES referenced
    { (behavior) (quantity) * (action) } = IR-INCREASE.2
```

"Interest rates" is the topic of the entire sequence of newspaper texts, and the parser has already represented this from its prior processing. Interest rates are often referred to simply as "rates," and the second index pattern in the immediately preceeding trace captures the connection between the topic concept and its corresponding mention concept. Recognition of this sequence from the mention results in the topic concept being referenced.

```
Reading ARE
    { ARE * HEADED (direction) } = INCREASE
Reading HEADED
    { ARE HEADED * (direction) } = INCREASE
Reading DOWN
    { DOWN * } = DOWN referenced
    { ARE HEADED * (direction) } = INCREASE
        Refinement Failure: (direction) is DOWN not UP
        Using: DECREASE
        Source: IR-INCREASE.2 no repair
```

This is the first refinement failure so far. The expectations from the previous texts have generated an expectation at this level for another argument supporting a future increase in interest rates. The text does not support this interpretation, and so the (already constructed) text-supported interpretation DECREASE is referenced. The parser attempts to *repair* the failure by recovering the source of the expectation. Unfortunately, no repair structures are able to be found from this failed refinement.

```
    { (behavior) (quantity) (action) * } = IR-INCREASE.2
        Refinement Failure: (action) is DECREASE not INCREASE
        Built: IR-DECREASE.3
        Source: IR-UP-COMMUNICATION.1 no repair
```

This index pattern recognizes the argument for a particular economic event. Once again, the prior expectations have failed, but no repair is possible.

It should be stressed that the lack of repairs is a function of the knowledge of the system; in other words, there is no *a priori* reason why sensible repairs for this failure might not be present.

```
{ (behavior) (event) * } = TRUE-TREND
    Specialization Failure: (event) IR-DECREASE.3
    Built: TRUE-TREND.4
```

The TRUE-TREND structure essentially represents the concept mentioned in passing in the annotations following the word "long," above. Regan's argument results in the recognition of this index pattern and the reference of this concept. There is no refinement failure here, but a new specialization must be built.

```
{ (actor) (mtrans) (mobject) * } = IR-UP-COMMUNICATION.1
    Refinement Failure: (mobject) is IR-DECREASE.3 not IR-INCREASE.2
    Built: IR-COMMUNICATION.5
    Source: SUPPORT-IR-UP (argument) found REPAIR:FAILED-SUPPORT
    Repair: ATTACK-POINT
    Built: ATTACK-POINT.6
        (point) IR-INCREASE
        (basis) TRUE-TREND.4
    Built: SUPPORT.8
        (argument) IR-COMMUNICATION.5
    Built: REPAIR.7
        (source) SUPPORT.8
        (expected) IR-INCREASE
        (reference) IR-DECREASE.3
        (repair) ATTACK-POINT.6
```

The failure of the argument communicated by Regan to match the expectations from prior texts finds a suitable repair. This repair, REPAIR:FAILED-SUPPORT, represents knowledge about how to argue: to challenge a point, you may attack it directly. In this case, since the parser is trying to come to a conclusion about the behavior of interest rates, challenging the previous texts' main point may be done by asserting that interest rates will decrease.

The repair is to modify memory to include a new attack structure, which contains packaging relationships to the point attacked and the basis for the attack. Since the TRUE-TREND structure is now part of memory, it is seized upon as a reasonable part of the attack structure. In paraphrase, this new concept represents "interest rates will not increase because decreasing interest rates reflect the true long-term behavior of the quantity."

```
{ (support) (attack) * } = DISPUTED-IR
    Specialization Failure: (attack) ATTACK-POINT.6
    Built: DISPUTED-IR.9
```

The fact that previous texts supported the opinion that interest rates would rise means that the current attack on that opinion indicates that the opinion is disputed. A new specialization must be built to record this interpretation.

Finally, the fact that the system had already come to an internal conclusion about interest rates based on its previous understanding provokes an internal response to the attack. Although the notion that there is concord about the behavior of interest rates is not necessarily the final decision of the system, it prompts index patterns which can be used to discredit the attack to generate expectations looking for some basis for an attack on the attack.

CONCLUSIONS

The point of the DMAP approach is to make interpretation wholly dependent on the expectations in memory. DMAP presents a theory of understanding based on script-frame theory, but updated to our modern concepts of hierarchical memory organization. As implemented, it works on quite large examples in the absence of any specialized domain-dependent control structure; all knowledge is represented in a typical abstraction and packaging hierarchy and linear sequences of index patterns.

Acknowledgements. Thanks to anonymous reviewers for their comments. This work was supported in part by the Defense Advanced Research Projects Agency, monitored by the Office of Naval Research under contract N0014-85-K-0108 and by the Air Force Office of Scientific Research under contract F49620-88-C-0058.

REFERENCES

Arens, Y. (1981) Using Language and Context in the Analysis of Text. In *Proceedings of the Seventh International Joint Conference on Artificial Intelligence*, Vancouver, B.C., Canada.

Birnbaum, L. (1986) *Integrated Processing for Planning and Understanding.* Ph. D. Thesis, Yale University.

Birnbaum, L., Flowers, M., McGuire, R. (1980) Towards an AI model of argumentation. *Proceedings of AAAI-80.*

Charniak, E. (1986) *A neat theory of marker passing. Proceedings of AAAI-86.*

Cullingford, R. (1978) *Script application.* Ph. D. Thesis, Yale University.

Kolodner, J.L. (ed.) (1988) *Proceedings: Case-Based Reasoning Workshop.* Morgan Kaufman.

Martin, C.E., and Riesbeck, C.K. (1986) *Uniform Parsing and Inferencing for Learning. Proceedings of AAAI-86.*

Martin, C.E. (1989) *Direct Memory Access Parsing.* Ph. D. Thesis, Yale University. Forthcoming.

Norvig, P. (1987) *Inference in text understanding. Proceedings of AAAI-87.*

Riesbeck, C.K. (1974) *Conputational Understanding: Analysis of Sentences and Context.* PhD thesis, Stanford University, Stanford, CA.

Riesbeck, C.K., and Martin, C.E. (1985) *Direct Memory Access Parsing.* YALEU/DCS/RR 354, Yale University.

Schank, R.C., Lebowitz, M., and Birnbaum, L. (1980) An integrated understander. *Am. J. Comp. Ling.* **6**.

Schank, R.C. (1982) *Dynamic Memory: A Theory of Learning in Computers and People.* Cambridge University Press.

EXPERTISE AND CONSTRAINTS IN INTERACTIVE SENTENCE PROCESSING

David J. Townsend
Montclair State College

T. Bever
University of Rochester

ABSTRACT

We examined individual variation in the integration of conceptual and linguistic knowledge during discourse processing. Skilled and average processors received sentences that were strongly or weakly supported by context. To reduce the contribution of special processing strategies, the syntactic constructions and topics were highly familiar. The interactions of context with linguistic processing were more constrained by sentential connectives for skilled processors, but less constrained by imposed reading units, which varied from words to incomplete sentences to complete sentences. These results suggest that a characteristic of expertise in discourse processing is an almost continual focus on organizing the results of linguistic processing into a conceptual framework. The results are discussed in terms of an interactive model with autonomous processors, but with shared resources for attending to the products of these processors.

INTRODUCTION

Discourse processing produces a mental model that is based on the sentences of a text and the knowledge they elicit. Integrating a sentence into this mental model is easy when it is strongly supported by preceding context, as in the second text below:

(1) Jones found a wreck by the road. She found nothing suspicious inside the car. She examined the damage outside the car. The windshield was shattered. She noticed that one wheel was damaged and a fender was smashed in. Jones took off the tire.

(2) While driving her car, Jones heard a loud bang and a flapping sound. She stopped the car and set the brake. She took the jack, a wrench, and the spare from the trunk. She loosened the bolts on the wheel. She jacked up the car. Jones took off the tire.

Two components in obtaining a model of text are organizing words into propositional units, and revising the model in light of these meaningful units. However, the fact that we can conceive of discourse processing in this way does not mean that the component processes are computationally distinct. Unfortunately, evidence on the issue of information flow frequently appeals to performance on complex syntactic forms in minimal linguistic contexts (e.g., Crain & Fodor, 1985; Clifton & Frazier, 1986; Tyler & Marslen-Wilson, 1977); this leaves open the possibility that it does not adequately represent normal discourse processing.

A model in which there are constraints on the interactions between conceptual and linguistic processes is as follows:

(a) Several rules for comprehension map linguistic representations onto conceptual representations, autonomously and in parallel. For example, the sequence of linguistic categories noun-verb-noun yields a conceptual unit consisting of agent-action-object. The mapping rules apply only to representations in a particular format: propositional rules apply to syntactic representations, pragmatic to propositional, etc. Representations become available to mapping rules when there are complete representational units. For example, rules that organize a pair of sentences into a temporally-organized model apply when linguistic mapping rules have produced a pair of complete propositions.

(b) Discourse production rules map between levels to generate expectations. These representations interact with those that are formed by comprehension mapping rules when the representations from the two sources are in similar formats.

(c) Several factors influence the allocation of attentional resources to the products of mapping rules. Completion of a linguistic unit shifts attention to the more conceptual outcome of the rule. Sentential connectives may shift attention toward either the linguistic or the conceptual level.

We determined whether these constraints on integration are similar at different levels of discourse processing skill. Expertise in discourse processing may depend largely on the application of conceptual knowledge about the world (e.g., Riesbeck & Schank, 1978). However, expertise may be better conceived as a process of integrating superficial and conceptual levels of representation. If so, expertise is another factor that influences the fluctuations of attention between linguistic and conceptual representations, with highly skilled processors presumably focusing more on the conceptual level.

EXPERIMENT 1

The meanings of connectives such as because and although shift the focus of attention (Townsend, 1983). Because states that two propositions are causally related; it is a cue to organize propositions causally as they are formed. Although, however, denies an expected causal relation; it is a cue to search for information about what aspect of the presumed cause is responsible for this denial. In terms of the interactive model, because shifts attention to a conceptual representation, but although shifts it to a linguistic representation. With no linguistic context, listeners show poorer access to the meaning of an initial clause introduced by although (e.g., Townsend, 1983). Experiments 1 and 2 determined whether contextual supports that provide the expected causal relation facilitate processing an although clause, and whether skilled processors show larger effects of context in reading although clauses, as predicted by the view that they focus more on integrating linguistic information into a coherent conceptual framework.

METHOD

To prepare materials for the four experiments, 24 students at Montclair State College listed 10 events that typically occur in common situations like "changing a flat tire," "finding an abandoned car", and so on (see Bower, Black, & Turner, 1979). These responses were used to construct eight "supportive" stories (e.g., (2)) which included a target event that was mentioned by 90% or more of the subjects, as well as several other events that were frequently mentioned by the subjects. Eight "neutral" stories (e.g., (1)) were constructed which contained the frequently-mentioned target event from the supportive story; none of the subjects mentioned this event in their list of events for the neutral scenario. Target events appeared in the third through sixth sentence in the stories, and position was matched within pairs. Independent ratings confirmed that target events were more essential in supportive stories than in neutral stories, F (1,157) = 66.4, $p < .01$.

Subjects read eight stories one clause at a time on a computer screen. In all four experiments, their goal was to write a two-sentence summary of each story. Target sentences (e.g., "Jones took off the punctured tire") were introduced by because or although. Subjects moved through the stories by pressing a key on the keyboard; each key-press removed the previous clause, displayed the next clause, and recorded the time from the last key-press. Half of the stories presented target sentences in supportive contexts, and half in neutral contexts. Connective was crossed with type of context. Since combinations of the materials variables on items were randomly assigned to subjects, statistical tests treating subjects and items as random variables are identical (Clark, 1973).

The subjects were 32 right-handed undergraduates from Montclair State College and Columbia University. In all four experiments, subjects with Verbal Scholastic Aptitude Test scores from 400 to 520 (mean = 440) were designated "average processors;" those with scores from 540 to 700 (mean = 645) were designated "skilled processors."

TABLE 1

MEAN READING TIMES PER WORD (MSEC) IN TARGET SENTENCES

	Skilled		Average	
	Because	Although	Because	Although
Neutral	301	295	392	339
Supportive	310	278	336	321
Facilitation	-9	17	56	18

RESULTS AND DISCUSSION

Table 1 shows that skilled processors read target sentences faster than average processors, F (1,33) = 5.04, $p < .01$, and reading times were faster in supportive contexts than in neutral contexts, F (1,33) = 4.45, $p < .05$. Average processors showed facilitation with both connectives, F (1,33) = 8.06, $p < .01$, but skilled processors showed facilitation only with although, F (1,33) = 6.25, $p < .05$. Skilled and average processors differ in their sensitivity to connectives that map propositions onto a conceptual model of text.

EXPERIMENT 2

Experiment 2 showed that reading time differences for connectives are associated with strategies for focusing on different levels of representation.

METHOD

Thirty-two subjects listened to recordings of the eight critical stories plus 18 filler stories. A brief tone before the last word of the target clause signalled a test 300 msec later; subjects heard a phrase (e.g., REMOVING A FLAT) and indicated whether the phrase was similar in meaning to any part of the story. The correct answer was always 'yes' for the critical stories. After responding, the subjects heard the rest of the story, then wrote a two-sentence summary. Filler stories balanced for correct answer, contextual supportiveness, and connective.

RESULTS AND DISCUSSION

Response times for trials on which errors occurred (10%) were replaced with the corresponding mean for correct trials. Table 2 shows that skilled processors responded faster than average processors, F (1,33) = 12.2, $p < .01$, and that response times were faster in supportive than in neutral contexts, F (1,33) = 6.24, $p < .01$.

TABLE 2

MEAN TIMES TO JUDGE MEANING SIMILARITY (SEC) IN TARGET SENTENCES

	Skilled		Average	
	Because	Although	Because	Although
Neutral	2.31	2.39	2.55	2.48
Supportive	2.30	2.22	2.33	2.30
Facilitation	.01	.17	.22	.18

Average processors showed facilitation for both connectives, but skilled processors showed facilitation only for although, F (1, 33) = 4.48, $p < .05$. Both connectives and context influence skilled processors' accessibility to meaning, but it is mainly context that influences average processors' accessibility to meaning. Expertise in discourse processing is not simply a matter of applying a large store of conceptual knowledge to the interpretation of sentences.

EXPERIMENT 3

The interactive model predicts that supportive contexts have greater effects at the ends of sentences, but that skilled processors may show effects of supportive contexts within sentences as well.

METHOD

Subjects read stories like (1) and (2) one line at a time on a screen. The target line presented either a complete or an incomplete sentence. As in Experiment 1, a key-press removed the previous line, presented the next line, and recorded the viewing time. There were 32 subjects.

RESULTS AND DISCUSSION

Table 3 shows that reading times were faster for skilled processors, F (1, 30) = 10.2, $p < .01$, and faster for complete sentences than for incomplete sentences, F (1, 30) = 6.1, $p < .01$. Facilitation was greater for complete sentences than for incomplete sentences, F (1, 30) = 4.5, $p < .05$.

Skilled processors showed significant facilitation for incomplete sentences, compared to average processors, F (1, 30) = 3.8, $p < .05$. This suggests that skilled processors use context to inform linguistic processing.

TABLE 3

MEAN READING TIMES PER WORD (MSEC) IN TARGET SENTENCES

	Skilled		Average	
	Incomplete	Complete	Incomplete	Complete
Neutral	313	289	488	456
Supportive	299	247	508	323
Facilitation	14	42	-20	133

EXPERIMENT 4

According to the interactive model, context effects depend partly on the form in which contextual information is represented.

Subjects read texts with active vs. passive forms of the target sentences, either one clause at a time or one word at a time. We expected whole-clause presentation to allow readers to form a more conceptual representation of context, producing facilitation especially for more complex passive constructions: the conceptual representation may 'prime' the subject, verb, and object concepts in the target, but in an unordered conceptual representation. Subjects who read word-by-word, however, must assign a structure to each word in sequence as it appears and build up an ordered, linguistic representation; this should induce readers to generate expectations in a more ordered, linguistic format. Since the normal order of a transitive proposition in English is 'agent, patient', word-by-word presentation should produce contextual facilitation of active sentences, which correspond to the canonical order. Passive sentences, however, should be read SLOWER in supportive contexts because of the mismatch between the ordered prediction and the actual form of the sentence.

METHOD

One group of subjects read the critical stories clause-by-clause on a screen and another read them word-by-word. Each key-press recorded the viewing time for a segment, removed it from the screen, and displayed the next one. Target sentences contained an inanimate logical object and a verb that required an animate logical subject, as in (1)-(2). They were introduced by <u>when</u>. Syntactic form and supportiveness were varied factorially. There were 64 subjects.

TABLE 4

MEAN READING TIMES PER WORD (MSEC) IN TARGET SENTENCES

	Clause Format		Word Format	
	Active	Passive	Active	Passive
Neutral Context	322	436	465	477
Supportive Context	294	316	439	497
Facilitation-Overall	28	120	26	-20
Facilitation-Skilled	40	168	59	24
Facilitation-Average	17	72	-7	-63

RESULTS AND DISCUSSION

Outliers (4.1%) were replaced with a value of 900 msec in the clause format and 1100 msec in the word format. Subjects read actives faster than passives, $F(1, 60) = 10.3$, $p < .01$. They read target sentences faster in supportive contexts than in neutral contexts, $F(1, 60) = 6.8$, $p < .05$, and faster in the clause format than in the word format, $F(1, 60) = 16.6$, $p < .01$.

Table 4 shows that supportive contexts facilitated reading times more for passives in the clause format, $F(1,60) = 9.8$, $p < .01$, but more for actives in the word format, $F(1,60) = 4.9$, $p < .05$. In fact, the numerical effect of supportive contexts on passives in the word format was to INCREASE reading time. For passive sentences in the word format, the slowing effect was 63 msec/word in the initial noun phrase, $F(1,60) = 14.5$, $p < .01$, and 39 msec/word in the final noun phrase, $F(1,60) = 6.4$, $p < .01$; in contrast, the only effect of supportiveness on reading active sentences was a 53 msec/word facilitation in the final noun phrase, $F(1,60) = 7.5$, $p < .01$. Table 4 also shows greater facilitation for skilled than for average processors, $F(1, 60) = 16.9$, $p < .01$. The interaction between syntactic form, supportiveness and format was virtually identical for the two groups of subjects, producing the surprising consequence that in the word format, average processors read passives more slowly in supportive contexts than in neutral contexts.

Discourse supportiveness interacts in different ways with linguistic processing as a function of the size of the imposed reading unit. When subjects read whole clauses, supportiveness facilitates the processing of all sentences, but especially those that are otherwise structurally complex. But when subjects are forced to read one word at a time, supportiveness facilitates only active sentences; most striking about this condition is that supportiveness actually slows down the processing of sentences with non-canonical word order, especially for subjects who normally focus more on linguistic representations. This suggests that both reading format and expertise influence the form in which expectations are represented.

GENERAL DISCUSSION

The observed contextual facilitation of performance on linguistic tasks superficially supports the claim that conceptual knowledge informs linguistic processing. Several findings, however, indicate important constraints on interactive processing: the effects of contextual support depend on the integrative processes that sentential connectives elicit, they are stronger at the boundaries of linguistic units, and they depend on the way in which anticipated events are represented. These results support an interactive model which explains variations in discourse processing skill in terms of emphasis on integrating levels of representation: skilled processors shift attention more frequently between conceptual and linguistic representations. They show greater interactions of contextual information with connectives, but the interactions of context with linguistic processing occur more naturally when information from different sources is represented in similar formats, such as when the reader reaches a linguistic boundary, or when the reading format encourages representations in a particular form.

ACKNOWLEDGEMENTS

This research was supported by grant BNS-8120463 from NSF, Separately Budgeted Research awards and a Princeton Faculty Fellowship from Montclair State College, and a Faculty Fellowship from the Army Research Institute for Behavioral Sciences to the author. Portions of this report were presented at the Human Sentence Processing Conference at the City University of New York and the Practical Aspects of Memory Conference at the University of Swansea.

REFERENCES

Bower, G., Black, J., & Turner, T. (1979). Scripts in memory for text. Cognitive Psychology, 11, 177-220.

Clark, H. (1973). The language-as-a-fixed-effect fallacy: A critique of language statistics in psychological research. Journal of Verbal Learning and Verbal Behavior, 12, 335-359.

Clifton, C. & Frazier, L. (1986). The use of syntactic information in filling gaps. Journal of Psycholinguistic Research, 15, 209-224.

Crain, S. & Fodor, J. (1985). How can grammars help parsers?. In D. Dowty, L. Kartunnen, & A. Zwicky (eds.), Natural Language Parsing. Cambridge University Press, Cambridge.

Riesbeck, C., & Schank, R. (1978). Comprehension by computer: Expectation-based analysis of sentences in context. In W. Levelt & G. Flores d'Arcais (eds.), Studies in the perception of language. New York: Wiley.

Townsend, D. J. (1983). Thematic processing in sentences and texts. Cognition, 13, 223-261.

Tyler, L., & Marslen-Wilson, W. (1977). The on-line effects of semantic context on syntactic processing. Journal of Verbal Learning and Verbal Behavior, 16, 683-692.

Anomaly Detection Strategies For Schema-Based Story Understanding

David B. Leake
Department of Computer Science, Yale University

ABSTRACT

Schema-based story understanding allows systems to process routine stories efficiently. However, a system that blindly applies active schemas may fail to recognize and understand novel events. To deal effectively with novelty, a story understander needs to be able to recognize when new information conflicts with its model of a situation. Thus it needs to be able to do anomaly detection.

Anomaly detection is the process that identifies when new information is inconsistent with current beliefs and expectations. Checking for all possible inconsistencies would be an explosive inference problem: it would require comparing all the ramifications of a new fact to all the ramifications of the facts in memory. We argue that this inference problem can be controlled by selective consistency checking: An initial set of inexpensive tests can be applied to detect potential problems, and more thorough tests used only when a likely problem is found.

We describe a set of stereotype-based *basic believability checks*, designed to identify potential problems with minimal inference, and *fine-grained tests* that can be used to diagnose the problems that basic believability checks detect. These tests are implemented in the story understanding program ACCEPTER.

INTRODUCTION

An important issue in story understanding is how to infer the connections between events. To control inferences, many systems rely on schema-based approaches (*e.g.*, [Schank and Abelson, 1977], [Charniak, 1977], [Cullingford, 1978], [DeJong, 1979], and [Lebowitz, 1980]). As long as an appropriate schema is available, a schema-based system needs only to follow the schema's guidance in order to generate the appropriate inferences.

However, no system dealing with real-world situations can have pre-stored knowledge about every possible eventuality. Even if the system's set of schemas *were* complete, the system would often have to select which schema to apply on the basis of partial information— it still would not be assured of activating the appropriate schema. Yet schema-based systems seldom have any capability to recognize when they've gone astray: they cannot detect contradiction of an active schema.

In order to correct erroneous expectations, systems need to decide whether new information is consistent with active expectations and beliefs. Inconsistencies signal the need to revise beliefs and expectations. Unfortunately, complete consistency checking is unfeasible. The only way to catch every conflict is to compare all the ramifications of new information to all the ramifications of the active knowledge, which would be an explosive inference task. For anomaly detection to be feasible, we need ways to limit the effort expended, even though such limits will necessarily mean that some inconsistencies remain unnoticed.

In this paper I argue for a multi-phase approach to anomaly detection. The first phase checks whether a fact is expected or already known; if so, the fact is accepted. Otherwise, the fact is compared with stereotypes; conflicts are considered anomalous. These comparisons with stereotypes constitute ***basic believability checks***, which are efficient enough to be applied to each input, but are also likely to detect a large proportion of problems. When stereotype conflicts are found, *fine grained* checks are used to decide the severity of the problem, and to characterize the difficulty in more detail.

The following sections discuss a set of basic believability checks, and fine-grained tests that can be applied when the basic checks detect problems. Both sets of checks are implemented in ACCEPTER, a story understanding program that detects anomalous events in stories and evaluates candidate explanations for them ([Leake, 1988a], [Leake, 1988b], [Kass and Leake, 1988]).

ACCEPTER

ACCEPTER is a story understanding program that detects anomalies and evaluates candidate explanations for them. Its domain is incidents of death and destruction; the stories it processes include the premature death of the racehorse Swale, the death of basketball star Len Bias, and the explosion of the space shuttle Challenger.

ACCEPTER understands routine events in terms of expectations given by prestored schemas; its understanding process is loosely modeled on that of SAM [Cullingford, 1978]. However, it supplements that understanding process with the following three-step anomaly detection procedure:

1. **Compare input to expectations and prior beliefs.** If they match, no further checks are needed; conflicts are anomalous.
2. **Do basic believability checks.** These checks are coarse-grained tests that compare aspects of an action against standard patterns. The basic checks identify potential problems, while requiring minimal inference.
3. **If standard patterns are not consistent with an event, use fine-grained tests.** More detailed tests can focus on the aspects of the event that conflicted with the pattern, in order to diagnose the problem further.

The sections below examine phases 2 and 3 of this process. Comparison of facts to expectations is described in [Leake, 1988a].

BASIC BELIEVABILITY CHECKS

The idea underlying ACCEPTER's routine verification level is analogous to the idea of basic level categories [Rosch *et al.*, 1976]: that there is a level at which anomaly detection maximizes the amount of return per unit of effort. I call tests at this level *basic believability checks.* Although finer-grained checks might detect additional anomalies, they give proportionately less return, since they need to check specialized aspects of the situation that are irrelevant to many situations.

In order to detect problems efficiently, ACCEPTER relies on comparisons with stereotyped patterns. Such patterns are usually only viewed as ways to characterize routine objects or situations. (For example, knowledge structures such as *Memory Organization Packets* (MOPs) can organize standard event sequences in memory [Schank, 1982], [Kolodner, 1984].) However, seeing how well inputs agree with stereotypes is also useful for monitoring the expectations guiding understanding. Conflicts with stereotypes suggest that the wrong knowledge structures are being used to understand an event; similarity to stereotypes suggests that the active knowledge structures are reasonable.[1]

Using patterns for anomaly detection raises two questions: *what types of patterns are important to check?* and *how are the relevant patterns accessed and applied?*. We answer these questions in context of basic verification in ACCEPTER.

Which Patterns to Check

ACCEPTER finds potential anomalies by comparing events to four kinds of stereotypes:

Event sequence patterns: ACCEPTER uses MOPs to represent stereotyped expectations for

[1]This is similar to the *representativeness* heuristic discussed in [Kahneman *et al.*, 1982]. People are likely to accept statements of category membership, if observable features of the object match the stereotypes for category members.

the events that occur in a given context. For example, the MOP for dining in a restaurant includes knowledge about the normal sequence of events in a restaurant meal (the customer enters, is seated, orders, eats, etc.), and about the normal temporal separation between these events. Conflicts such as premature events (*e.g.*, being given food without being seated) are anomalous, and may show that the restaurant MOP does not apply. For example, the customer may be picking up a take-out order, rather than eating there.

Normative role-filler types: For each role in its MOPs, ACCEPTER maintains information on the types of objects that usually fill the role. For example, the roles in the restaurant MOP include the diner, the waiter, and the customer's order. Normally, the customer and waiter are both human, and the order is for food. (These types are only normative: the waiter might actually be a robot, or the diner could be a pampered pet.) ACCEPTER checks each role-filler in a new action to see if it is a novel type of filler. If not, an anomaly is noted.

Again, explaining the anomaly may show that the wrong MOP is being applied. For example, if someone enters a fast food restaurant, we normally assume that he'll eat there. But if he buys a pack of cigarettes instead of food, we'll retract our assumption that he entered for a meal.

Class limitations: Objects of a subclass may have features or functional limitations that are unusual, compared to most members of the class to which they belong. For example, if our stereotyped view of expensive sports cars is that they are fast and handle well, but we find that cars of brand X have bad handling, this deficiency makes it anomalous for the car to be used in a situation where handling is very important (such as a prestigious race). Noticing the limitation problem may make us change our expectations. For example, if we expected the car to win because it had a good driver, we might want to change the assumption in view of the car he's using.

Decision patterns: ACCEPTER represents knowledge about the types of actions that an actor favors, and avoids. For example, fraternity members seek out wild parties; athletes in training are supposed to avoid them. If an actor participates in an unusual action— for example, an athlete goes to a party the night before a big game— his behavior is anomalous, and related expectations may need to be changed.

How the Patterns are Organized and Accessed in Memory

ACCEPTER's memory is organized in an abstraction net. For example, abstractions of the MOP for running in a race include athletic competition and exercise; abstractions of racehorse include horses (which have the abstraction of living things) and valuable objects. Patterns are indexed under nodes in this hierarchy.

The scenes of a MOP are stored under the memory node associated with that MOP, as are normative filler types for the MOP's roles. (Both can be inherited from abstractions, if no information is indexed under the specific MOP.) Decision patterns are indexed under actors they involve. When ACCEPTER retrieves patterns to apply, it attempts to retrieve the most specific relevant patterns.

The patterns are applied as follows. Given an action that is hypothesized to fit within a MOP or plan, ACCEPTER matches the action against the packaging structure's expectations, in order to identify problems such as premature events, delayed events, or missing events. Restrictions on role-filler types are retrieved from the MOP or its abstractions, and the system compares hypothesized role-fillers to them. More specifically:

Applying normative-filler information: For each role in the input, ACCEPTER retrieves role-filler patterns for that role. These patterns are stored in memory under the action, indexed by the role. If ACCEPTER fails to find a pattern under the current action, it does a breadth-first search up the hierarchy of abstractions for the action, checking each to see if a relevant pattern is indexed under it.

Applying class limitations: Normative types for a role-filler are also used to guide the search for limitations of particular objects that might interfere with their ability to fill a role. Guiding the search for limitations is important, since any object can have many abstractions, and can have limitations compared to any of its abstractions. To restrict its consideration to features that are relevant in the current context, ACCEPTER only considers limitations of the filler *compared to the normative role-filler.* For example, if a hypothesized car theft is being evaluated, the normative role-filler type for the object of the theft is *valuable object.* Compared to other valuable objects, a brand X sports car might have no limitations, so the theft would have no basic-level problems. However, if a hypothesized automobile race were being checked for anomalies, and *sports cars* were the normative filler type for vehicles involved, a different limitation— that cars of brand X had bad handling, compared to other sports cars— might be retrieved. This limitation would be flagged as something to check with fine-grained tests— would the bad handling make it unable to perform in the race?

Applying decision patterns: For each actor involved in an action, the system tries to retrieve actor decision patterns that are relevant to the actor's involvement. These patterns may be indexed under the actor (*e.g.*, we know that John loves eating at MacDonalds), or under the actor's abstractions (*e.g.*, John is a taxi driver, and we know that taxi drivers often eat at MacDonalds). It is sometimes necessary to abstract both the actor and the action involved: we might know that taxi drivers often eat at fast-food restaurants. These patterns can show that a decision is believable. (When retrieving decision patterns, ACCEPTER does a breadth-first search over abstractions of the actor and action, to try to find the most specific pattern that is relevant to an actor's decision.)

FINE-GRAINED CHECKS

Basic-level checks give little information about the reasons for problems: they simply identify that something is unusual. When ACCEPTER encounters a potential problem, it diagnoses the problem more specifically by applying fine-grained checks. These checks give a more specific problem characterization, which points to specific information that an explanation must address.

ACCEPTER uses three types of fine-grained checks. They are *basic action decomposition*, which evaluates a role-filler's ability to perform in a role, and two motivational checks: *examination of direct effects*, which is used to check whether an action is consistent with actor goals, and *plan choice checks*, which see if the actor's plan choice conflicts with our model of his plan preferences. Thus when an action is unusual for an actor, ACCEPTER checks three things: whether the actor probably could have performed the action, whether the action was consistent with his goals, and whether the action was consistent with his planning style. Although these checks are more expensive to apply than pattern-based checks, the inferencing they involve is still limited.

Basic Action Decomposition

The primary purpose of basic-action decomposition is identifying causal problems that might result from an unusual action, making it even more anomalous. Basic action decomposition takes a composite action, decomposes it into its constituent parts, and checks any restrictions associated with those parts that are relevant to the unusual role-filler.

For example, anyone who participates in jogging is usually human. Either a fish, or a monkey, would violate this stereotype, so a hypothesis that either one was jogging would be anomalous. However, there is a difference in the seriousness of the problem. There's no reason why a monkey couldn't perform the actions of a jogger; basic-action decomposition shows that the only problem would be that a monkey wouldn't have the normal goal of physical fitness that drives joggers. Consequently, an explanation would have to show an alternative goal being served— perhaps the monkey was owned by someone who gave him a banana every time he jogged a quarter mile. Basic action decomposition shows more severe problems for the fish: for example, since it doesn't have legs, it couldn't even perform the actions involved.

In addition to showing the severity of a problem, basic-action decomposition helps focus explanation: if causal problems are found, explanation should focus on how they might have been overcome. For example, we might have the stereotype that people who fly first class are usually businessmen. If a non-businessman flies first class, basic believability checks detect the stereotype conflict. However, the characterization "a non-businessman flying first class" isn't very helpful in finding an explanation. If we look at the detailed requirements for flying first class, we can identify more specific problems, which can then be addressed by an explanation. For example, one specific requirement is paying for an expensive ticket. If we find that the person flying didn't have much money, we can describe the anomaly more specifically as "how could he do something he couldn't afford?" This characterization gives more guidance to the explanation process. For example, by looking for ways he could have recently obtained money, we might find that he'd just won a lottery, or received a substantial raise.

Examination of Direct Effects

Examination of direct effects tests whether the unusual action is consistent with an actor's goals. If an action doesn't fit an actor's usual behavior patterns, we can ask whether the action has bad effects. If so, explanation should show how other goals took precedence over the normal reasons for avoiding the action.

However, we cannot hope to detect all possible bad effects of an action: for any action, there would be infinitely-many effects to check. Nevertheless, simply checking an action's direct effects can give an indication of whether the action undermines the actor's goals. For example, direct effects of buying a car include having possession of the car, and having less money.[2] If we know that someone is avoiding buying a car, and he buys it anyway, we can compare his goals to the direct effects of buying the car. If he's trying to save money for college, we can reformulate the anomaly as spending money, which conflicts with his goal to save money. Our explanation would then focus on the tradeoff between having the car or having savings.

ACCEPTER identifies goal problems by checking actions that conflict with their actor's behavior patterns, to see if the actions' direct effects undermine the actor's goals (either specifically known for the actor, or inherited from abstractions). For example, when the system evaluates the explanation that the racehorse Swale was poisoned by his owner, basic checks show that the poisoning is something his owner would have been expected to avoid, since it's illegal. This prompts ACCEPTER to check the direct effects of the action, to see if they account for the poisoning. The only direct effect it finds is that the owner's property is destroyed, which conflicts with the businessman's theme goal of increasing wealth, so the poisoning is anomalous.

Plan Choice Checks

Plan choice checks compare an unusual plan with the types of plans that are typical for the actor, in order to see if the plan is consistent with his planning patterns. In general, it could be very difficult to decide if a plan matches the planner's planning patterns, simply because it is hard to predict a plan's possible ramifications. However, actors often use standard plans, for which relative advantages and disadvantages are known in ad-

[2] ACCEPTER's characterization of direct effects is quite arbitrary: it considers direct effects to be the effects that are reached by short inference chains (in the current implementation, chains of length 4 or less).

vance.

When we use standard plans, or observe others using them, we gather comparative information about alternative ways of accomplishing a goal. For example, we learn the likely cost of the plan, whether the plan is likely to fail, and how efficient it is compared to plans we have used before. We can use this knowledge to decide between plans. For example, suppose bus service is a cheap but unreliable way to travel, and taxis are more expensive, but more efficient and reliable as well. If we lack money and punctuality is unimportant, we'll choose the bus; otherwise we'll prefer taxis.

Knowledge of plan characteristics also helps us predict the actions of others. If we know the goal orderings of different actors, we can anticipate their priorities, and expect their plans to reflect their priorities— both in the goals for which they plan [Carbonell, 1979], and in the plans that they select for a given goal. For example, an impatient executive puts a low priority on money, but a high priority on saving time. From this, we might expect him to fly on the Concorde when he goes to Europe.

To reason about plan selection, we need to be able to characterize plans along the dimensions that affect people's plan choices. One way to start is to look at stereotypes about priorities, and to translate them into parameters for characterizing plans. For example, the stereotype of a miser directs the choice of the lowest-cost plans possible. To know which plans a miser is likely to pick, we need to have an estimate of their relative monetary costs. People who are impatient give time a high priority; thus relative speed of a plan is important. Cautious people avoid risk; thus risk must be represented also. Once the dimensions are specified, we can represent both general preferences, and those that only apply in particular domains. For example, someone might avoid risk in relationships, but be indifferent to financial risks. The most important differences between plans can be characterized along four basic dimensions:

- **Reliability** of a plan for accomplishing goal.

  Reliability can be either absolute (*e.g.*, this plan always works) or relative to other plans for the goal (*e.g.*, this treatment has only a 50 percent success rate, but it's still the best way we know of to deal with cancer.)

- **Risks** of using the plan.

  This is a characterization of the possible bad side effects of the plan.

- **Cost** compared to other plans for the same goal.

  This can be characterized along standard dimensions, such as those described in [Wilensky, 1978]: time, consumable functional objects (like money), nonconsumable functional objects (like a stove), and abilities.

- **Yield** compared to other plans for the same goal.

  If the effects of a plan can be measured along a scale, yield can be used to compare the effectiveness of the plan. For example, having a paper route and being a lawyer are both plans for making money, but the yield of the paper route is low, while the yield of law is high. Yield could also be balanced against costs, to determine a plan's efficiency.

Table 1 shows how these dimensions can be used to characterize bank robbery and medical school as plans for getting money.

In order to decide if the type of plan is anomalous, ACCEPTER compares the plan's dimensions to the values that the actor usually favors. It determines the plan parameters by retrieving and applying a procedure for generating the plan dimensions of any instantiation of the plan. (The procedure is indexed under the plan, or one of its abstractions, in ACCEPTER'S memory.) A question for future research is how a system might learn the parameters for a plan, based on observation of use of that plan and alternative ones.

A PROGRAM EXAMPLE

The output below is an edited trace of ACCEPTER applying plan choice checks. The sys-

Bank robbery as a plan for A-wealth

Dimension	Value
Reliability	LOW
Risks	HIGH
Cost	LOW
Yield	HIGH

Medical school as a plan for A-wealth

Dimension	Value
Reliability	NORMAL
Risks	LOW
Cost	HIGH
Yield	HIGH

Table 1: Plan choice dimensions of two plans.

tem has previously processed the explosion of the space shuttle Challenger, and is given as input the conjecture that Russia sabotaged it.

Sabotage doesn't fit standard patterns for Russia, so ACCEPTER does fine-grained checks. It finds no problems with basic-action decomposition, and the effect of the plan— harming the U.S.— is consistent with its picture of Russia's goals. To find if the type of plan matches Russia's policies, it checks the plan parameters of sabotage. It determines that sabotage against the U.S. is risky, because of possible retaliation. Since Russia is not especially prone to risky plans, sabotage seems unlikely.

Checking if "RUSSIA'S SABOTAGE" is believable.

Searching for plan dimension generator for RUSSIA'S SABOTAGE.

... No generator stored under SABOTAGE.

Searching for plan dimension generator under abstractions of SABOTAGE.

... Generator found under abstraction VIOLENT-ACTION.

Applying generator to check RISK of RUSSIA'S SABOTAGE. Description of test:

> "Risk of VIOLENT-ACTION depends on comparative PHYSICAL-STRENGTH of actor and victim."
>
> For countries, PHYSICAL-STRENGTH specifies to MILITARY-STRENGTH. Comparing....
>
> RUSSIA inherits HIGH as its MILITARY-STRENGTH, from abstraction INDUSTRIALIZED-COUNTRY.
>
> USA inherits HIGH as its MILITARY-STRENGTH, from abstraction INDUSTRIALIZED-COUNTRY.
>
> ... STRENGTH is the same.

... Risk is HIGH.

Comparing to planning tendencies for RUSSIA.

PLAN-SELECTION problem: "RUSSIA'S SABOTAGE" CONFLICTS-WITH planning tendencies for RUSSIA, due to HIGH RISK.

When ACCEPTER evaluates the explanation that Challenger was sabotaged by Libya, ACCEPTER considers that explanation more likely, because Libya often uses risky plans.

CONCLUSION

In order to maintain an accurate picture of the world, and to be able to learn from novel situations, story understanders need to be able to detect anomalies. Since anomalies could arise at any point in a story, anomaly detection needs to be applied as a routine part of understanding. Consequently, the anomaly detection process must be efficient.

ACCEPTER reduces the cost of anomaly detection by having two levels of tests for how well new information fits prior beliefs. Comparatively inexpensive tests are applied to all inputs. These basic believability checks will not detect all problems, nor will the problems they identify always be significant, but they detect many of the situations that are likely to need explanation. When basic believability checks detect potential problems, fine-grained tests are used to do more careful analysis.

By first comparing an input to specific beliefs in memory and active expectations, and then verifying in terms of the patterns described above, ACCEPTER can often detect potential problems without doing extensive inference. Only when potential problems are detected does it apply more costly checks.

A topic for future research is how verification should change to reflect the importance of certainty in a given situation: the effort expended on verification should depend on an estimate of its value to the system. This might depend on factors such as the potential consequences of missing an anomaly, or the availability of resources needed for verification.

Acknowledgements

This work was supported in part by the Defense Advanced Research Projects Agency, monitored by the Office of Naval Research under contract N0014-85-K-0108 and by the Air Force Office of Scientific Research under contract F49620-88-C-0058.

References

[Carbonell, 1979] J. Carbonell. *Subjective Understanding: Computer Models of Belief Systems.* PhD thesis, Yale University, 1979. Technical Report 150.

[Charniak, 1977] E. Charniak. Ms. malaprop: A language comprehension program. In *Proceedings of the Fifth International Joint Conference on Artificial Intelligence*, Cambridge, Mass., August 1977. IJCAI.

[Cullingford, 1978] R. Cullingford. *Script Application: Computer Understanding of Newspaper Stories.* PhD thesis, Yale University, 1978. Technical Report 116.

[DeJong, 1979] G. DeJong. *Skimming Stories in Real Time: An Experiment in Integrated Understanding.* PhD thesis, Yale University, May 1979. Technical Report 158.

[Kahneman *et al.*, 1982] D. Kahneman, P. Slovic, and A. Tversky. *Judgement under uncertainty: Heuristics and biases.* Cambridge University Press, 1982.

[Kass and Leake, 1988] A. Kass and D. Leake. Case-based reasoning applied to constructing explanations. In J. Kolodner, editor, *Proceedings of the Case-Based Reasoning Workshop*, pages 190–208, Palo Alto, 1988. DARPA, Morgan Kaufmann, Inc.

[Kolodner, 1984] J.L. Kolodner. *Retrieval and Organizational Strategies in Conceptual Memory.* Lawrence Erlbaum Associates, Hillsdale, N.J., 1984.

[Leake, 1988a] D.B. Leake. Evaluating explanations. In *Proceedings of the Seventh National Conference on Artificial Intelligence*, pages 251–255, Minneapolis, MN, August 1988. AAAI, Morgan Kaufman Publishers, Inc.

[Leake, 1988b] D.B. Leake. Using explainer needs to judge operationality. In *Proceedings of the 1988 AAAI Spring Symposium on Explanation-based Learning.* AAAI, 1988.

[Lebowitz, 1980] M. Lebowitz. *Generalization and Memory in an Integrated Understanding System.* PhD thesis, Yale University, October 1980. Technical Report 186.

[Rosch *et al.*, 1976] E. Rosch, C.B. Mervis, W. Gray, D. Johnson, and P. Boyes-Braem. Basic objects in natural categories. *Cognitive Psychology*, 8:382–439, 1976.

[Schank and Abelson, 1977] R.C. Schank and R. Abelson. *Scripts, Plans, Goals and Understanding.* Lawrence Erlbaum Associates, Hillsdale, New Jersey, 1977.

[Schank, 1982] R.C. Schank. *Dynamic Memory: A Theory of Learning in Computers and People.* Cambridge University Press, 1982.

[Wilensky, 1978] R. Wilensky. *Understanding Goal-Based Stories.* PhD thesis, Yale University, 1978. Technical Report 140.

Expectation Verification: A Mechanism for the Generation of Meta Comments

Ingrid Zukerman
Department of Computer Science
Monash University

ABSTRACT

Meta Comments, such as "however," "as I have stated before" and "if you pardon the expression," are pervasive in human discourse. In this paper, we present a predictive mechanism for the generation of Meta Comments based on the tenet that they signal a change in the status of beliefs and expectations a listener is conjectured to possess. In particular, our mechanism anticipates a listener's expectations by activating prescribed inferences on the state of the discourse. It is being implemented in a system called FIGMENT II which generates commentaries on the solution of algebraic equations.

INTRODUCTION

It is generally believed that an important aspect of competent writing involves anticipating and addressing a reader's† beliefs and expectations arising from the presented information. This premise has been applied to a certain extent in natural language parsing (Riesbeck 1982), however, it has been largely ignored in natural language generation systems. Text generation systems implemented to date focus on the generation of utterances which directly reflect a speaker's communicative intent, under the implicit assumption that the only inferences drawn by a listener are those which directly follow from the presented information (Appelt 1982, Swartout 1982, Kukich 1984, McKeown 1985, Paris 1987, Hovy 1987).

In this paper, we consider the generation of a class of Meta Comments (MCs), denoted *Expectation Verification MCs*, which are generated to notify a reader of an impending change in the status of his/her beliefs or expectations due to a forthcoming message. We postulate that these MCs are generated, if, in their absence, the reader is likely to experience affective responses which may inhibit the acquisition of forthcoming information. In particular, we focus on the generation of MCs with respect to the attributes of a message, such as focus, length and style. For instance, if a normally strict math teacher walks into the classroom and starts talking about a movie he saw recently, most students are likely to wonder about this abnormal behaviour, instead of attending to the current discourse. This adverse effect may have been minimized or avoided by means of an MC indicative of a shift from the expected focus, such as "Before we start with equations, I would like to tell you about ... ." (If this behaviour constitutes an extreme departure from the norm, additional rhetorical devices, such as justification or motivation, may be called for.)

In the next section, we consider beliefs and expectations which affect the generation of MCs. We then examine a mechanism for generating MCs and discuss the different types of MCs accounted for by this mechanism.

† The terms writer/speaker and reader/listener are used interchangeably in this paper.

EXPECTATIONS AND BELIEFS

During the knowledge acquisition process, a listener exhibits expectations with respect to various aspects of a message, such as its content, level of difficulty, length and context. A correctly understood message may still inhibit the smooth continuation of the knowledge acquisition process, if either (1) the listener fails to notice its effect on the status of his/her expectations or beliefs, or (2) its effect is noticed, but due to the absence or inadequate use of an MC, the listener loses confidence either in the speaker's ability, as in the classroom scenario discussed above, or in his/her own perception.

The beliefs and expectations which are relevant to the text generation task in general, and the generation of Meta Comments in particular, are those which a speaker conjectures are maintained by a listener. We distinguish between two types of beliefs/expectations based on the type of information they refer to:

i. *Content Beliefs* pertain to a listener's knowledge. In particular, *Content Expectations* usually pertain to the result of an action or a feature of an object, and are largely domain dependent. In a technical domain, common content expectations are for: (1) the existence/absence of a solution, (2) a particular result, and (3) a particular sequence of steps in a solution path.

ii. *Attribute Beliefs* pertain to meta-knowledge, i.e., attributes of an item of knowledge which affect its acquisition, such as (1) Focus, (2) Informational Status (new or previously seen?), (3) Length, (4) Difficulty, (5) Style, (6) Timing, and (7) Orientation with respect to a baseline measure. In general, attribute beliefs are relevant to discourse generation when they become *Attribute Expectations* with respect to a forthcoming message.

The status of an expectation may be *active, inactive* or *confirmed.* An active expectation may be inactivated by its violation or realization. However, when an active expectation for some result requires the existence of a sequence of events or objects which are necessary to produce this result, each of the elements in the sequence has to agree with the expectation. In this case, if the first element in the sequence complies with the expectation, its status is changed to confirmed. This status is maintained until the expectation is either violated or fully realized. The status of a belief may change due to the presentation of contradicting or corroborating information (violation and realization, respectively).

A change in the status of an expectation or a belief may be accomplished *explicitly*, by means of a direct inference from an utterance, or *implicitly*, by means of an indirect inference. In addition, we postulate that people also use some general purpose inference mechanisms to activate implicit attribute expectations. We model these mechanisms by means of *Expectation Activation Demons (EADs).* The following Expectation Activation Demons account for a variety of attribute expectations maintained by a listener.

Inertia reflects one's tendency to expect the continuation of an established behaviour pattern.

Default represents expectations associated with a context. This context may be established by the discourse focus, the social setting and/or the speaker.

Diversity represents an expectation for a forthcoming utterance to be different from a recently presented or known utterance. The level of discourse for which this expectation is active depends on the current context.

The activation of EADs may yield conflicting expectations. However, when more than one demon is applicable to a given situation, the expectation activated by the demon which yields the most specific expectation is accepted. In addition, the activation of conflicting expectations at the same level of specificity indicates that an MC should be generated to resolve the conflict.

GENERATING META COMMENTS

In order to determine the need for MCs, a system must keep track the evolution of a listener's conjectured expectations and beliefs. To this effect, for each message, it must activate direct and indirect inferences which affect a listener's attribute and content beliefs and expectations, and also activate EADs with respect to attribute expectations. Upon discovering that a message causes a change in the status of a belief or an active expectation, one or more MCs which indicate the nature of the change may be proposed. This process supports the generation of the following types of MCs.

i. Expectative — Indicate a violation or realization (confirmation) of an expectation or a belief entertained by the speaker and/or the listener. They range from the implicit [''*However,*'' ''*Indeed*''] to the explicit [''*We were expecting X, but* we got Y,'' ''*As you may have suspected,* the butler did it'']. Expectation Violation MCs are also used to signal a violation of orientation expectations, e.g., ''This is important *but* boring,'' where the first adjective is considered positive in some sense, while the second one is negative. In addition, Expectation Violation MCs in conjunction with Temporal MCs (Halliday & Hasan 1976), signal a violation of timing expectations, e.g., ''Today we shall do X, *but first* let us revise Y.''

ii. Focal — Signal the focus or context of a message [''*Now, about his sister, ... ,*'' ''*By the way*''].

iii. Implementational — Signal the informational status of a message, i.e., whether it contains new information or information to be verified against existing knowledge [''Let us consider a *new* topic,'' ''*As I said before*''].

iv. Estimational — Indicate the length and/or difficulty of a message [''*Here comes the tricky part,*'' ''*The proof is rather long*''].

v. Interpretive — Advise which ''parsing mechanism'' (style) should be used to interpret a message [''*If you pardon the expression*'' — colloquial, ''*Technically speaking*'' — technical].

vi. Affective† — Advise of the affective impact associated with a message [''*Unfortunately*''].

Focal, Implementational, Estimational and Interpretive MCs advise a listener of the value of an attribute, and are generated when this value causes a change in the status of an attribute expectation. Expectative MCs, on the other hand, advertise the type of change which has taken place in the status of a belief or expectation, e.g., violation or realization, without specifying the cause of the change.

The Basic Mechanism

In this section, we present algorithm *Determine-MC* which generates codes representing requirements for MCs with respect to attribute expectations‡. This mechanism is basically domain independent, however, it assumes a hierarchical discourse and domain structure. A domain hierarchy is also used to model a listener's knowledge, where each node contains an *Own Attribute List* and a *Descendant Attribute List.* The Own List contains the values of the length, difficulty, style and timing attributes of a node, and the Descendant List contains the focus, informational status and Own List attributes of an expected successor of this node. *Determine-MC* receives two arguments: a message sequence M and a starting node N, and assumes that the message sequence is compatible with a relevant portion of the hierarchy representing the listener's knowledge base. The activation of the algorithm starts at a

† The term *affects* is used throughout this paper in the sense used in [Dyer 1982], i.e., meaning ''emotions.''

‡ A similar algorithm is used to determine requirements for MCs with respect to content expectations, except that line 6, line 10, and the second disjunct in line 4 are omitted, since they are not applicable to content expectations.

node arrived at by means of default expectations with respect to a given context, and the first message in the sequence corresponds to one of the children of this node.

```
Procedure Determine-MC (M , N)
1    If M is empty Then return nil
2    Create a list called MC-list which is initially set to head(M)
3    For each attribute a_j in N do
4       If { [ head(M) causes a change in the status an expectation for a_j ] or
              [ There are conflicting expectations with respect to a_j ] }
          Then propose an MC-code and add it to MC-list
5       end
6    If { [ MC-list = head(M) ] and [ The information in head(M) was expected ] }
        Then let N' = N   ; omit head(M)
7    Else
8      For each item in MC-list
9         Perform direct and indirect inferences with respect to expectations
10        Activate EADs where applicable
11        end
12     Let N' be the node put in focus by head(M)
13   Append (MC-list, Determine-MC(tail(M), N'))
14   end
```

To determine whether a message causes a change in the status of an expectation (line 4), we first consider the expectations in node N pertaining to the focus and informational status of this message. An active focus expectation in node N points to one of its children, and an expected informational status may be either *new, existing* or *repeated.* These expectations determine the need for a Focal and an Implementational MC, respectively. We now proceed to the node put in focus by the current message, denoted N', in order to ascertain the need for additional MCs. We determine whether a change in the status of an attribute expectation has occurred by taking into consideration the Descendant List of N, the Own List of N', and the information in the message. If N' has no Own List (e.g., it is a new node), or its Own List agrees with the Descendant List of N (e.g., it realizes a focus expectation), then the message attributes are compared against the Descendant List of N. Otherwise, if the value of attribute a_j in N disagrees with the value of a_j in N', then an expectation violation has taken place even prior to considering the corresponding attribute in the message. Once a change in the status of an expectation has been detected, or the presence of conflicting active expectations is ascertained, the system proposes MCs where necessary (see next section). Finally, if all the information in a message is expected and no expectation realization or confirmation MCs were proposed (line 6), the entire message may be omitted. However, in this case, one must ensure that the listener's active expectations are sufficient to overcome the lack of continuity in the hierarchy traversal. (The issues related to this case are currently being investigated.)

Proposing MCs

The procedure which determines the need for MCs caters for three subgoals maintained by a speaker in a knowledge acquisition setting: (1) Transfer knowledge, (2) Enhance his/her own credibility, and (3) Foster a positive attitude in the listener. These subgoals may be violated if, in the absence of an MC, the user is likely not to notice a change in the status of an expectation, or to experience negative affects, such as confusion or loss of confidence in the system. The MCs proposed to prevent these undesirable effects depend on the nature of the change in the status of an expectation or belief (violation, realization or confirmation), the type of the expectation or belief (content or attribute), its explicitness, the level of certainty associated with it, and its affective impact.

A speaker's failure to generate an MC which signals a change in the status of a listener's expectations or beliefs may be interpreted by the listener as an indication that the speaker has either failed to notice this change, or that s/he does not consider this change worth mentioning (it may be either too obvious or too inconsequential). A listener's choice of interpretation and subsequent reaction depend both on his/her opinion regarding his/her knowledge status relative to the speaker's, and on his/her evaluation of the significance of the change in question. For example, consider the text "We factor out x hoping to find a common factor. *However*, we get $x(x+1)+7$," where the second sentence, stating the result of the factoring out operation, violates the explicit content expectation activated by the first sentence. If the Expectation Violation MC is omitted, one of the following events may take place: (1) a novice may not even notice that the expectation for a common factor has been violated, (2) a listener who does not feel confident in the subject matter might notice the expectation violation, but may conclude s/he is probably mistaken, since the speaker hasn't mentioned it, (3) a listener who considers him/herself familiar with the subject may lose respect for a speaker who hasn't mentioned (and hence probably hasn't noticed) the expectation violation, or (4) if both the listener and the speaker are proficient mathematicians, the expectation violation will be accepted without further ado. A similar analysis may be performed for the realization of content expectations. For instance, in the text "This procedure is polynomial. *Indeed*, it is used in many algorithms," the second sentence realizes an implicit expectation resulting from the inference that polynomial procedures are efficient and hence are used often. If the Expectation Realization MC is omitted, an inexperienced listener may completely fail to infer the relationship between the two sentences, a more experienced listener may be troubled by the fact that the speaker has neglected to point out this relationship, and an expert may simply carry on after making the appropriate inferences.

In principle, a similar scenario may take place for attribute expectations, where Focal, Implementational, Estimational and Interpretive MCs are generated to inform a listener of the cause of a change in the status of an expectation or a belief with respect to an attribute. However, since people are generally relatively competent with respect to discourse attributes and believe that most other people are equally competent in this area, case (4) occurs most frequently, obviating the need for Expectative MCs, and cases (1) and (2), on the other hand, are extremely rare. Case (3) may occur only due to the violation of a strong attribute expectation, e.g., "Today we shall do X. *On second thought*, let's do Y" (explicit focus expectation) and "*Contrary to custom*, we shall start with dessert" (implicit focus expectation).

Finally, Expectation Realization MCs are generated in additional cases which are not accounted for by this analysis, namely they directly contribute to the satisfaction of a speaker's subgoals of enhancing his/her credibility and fostering a positive attitude in the listener, by allocating credit to the speaker or the listener, respectively. The former is illustrated by "*As I expected*, Bush won the election," and the latter by "*As you may know*, this is a linear equation." In particular, if the Expectative MC is omitted from the second text, a listener who did possess the belief in question may resent a speaker who is underestimating his/her knowledge.

These arguments are operationalized as follows:

Expectation Violation MCs are generated to signal the violation of (1) beliefs or expectations with respect to the content of a forthcoming message, and (2) strong attribute expectations. ***Expectation Realization MCs*** are generated to indicate the realization or confirmation of (1) expectations or beliefs a listener is likely to entertain both with respect to content and attributes, and (2) weak content expectations or beliefs, where the weakness of a belief or an expectation may stem from its uncertainty or from the inferences which must be performed to activate it.

Focal, Implementational, Estimational and ***Interpretive MCs*** are generated to advertise the violation of attribute expectations, such as changes in the topic of conversation or the difficulty of the problems being considered, the realization of weak attribute expectations, and the resolution of conflicting attribute expectations.

Affective MCs are generated to signal the inactivation or confirmation of content and attribute expectations due to an event which carries an affective impact for the speaker or the listener and is associated with some uncertainty, e.g., "There is a way to solve this problem. *Unfortunately*, it is quite difficult," where the affective impact of an event is obtained from models of the speaker and the listener.

The explicitness of an English referent representing an Expectative MC depends on the number of concurrently active expectations and on the distance (in time and number of messages) between the last reference to an expectation and an inactivating or confirming result, e.g., whereas an implicit Expectative MC is suitable for an expectation currently in context, a more distant expectation may require a more explicit reference, such as "*We were hoping to obtain a product of factors, however,* we got ... ." The lexical choices made for MCs which pertain to discourse related attributes depend on the type of the message in question and on the conditions surrounding its generation. For instance, an Implementational MC indicative of verification would be "revise" or "return" for a topic, and "too" or "again" for an algebraic operation.

We conclude this section with a trace of our mechanism which accounts for the output generated for the partial input in figure 1.

	Input	Output
1	(topic *quadratic*)	*Let us go on with* the topic of quadratic equations.
2	(equation $(x-3)^2-4(x-3)-7=0$) (# alt = 3)	*An equation follows*: $(x-3)^2 - 4(x-3) - 7 = 0$ *There are three ways of solving it.*
3	(alternative 1)	*The first alternative consists of the following operations*:
	{Solutions to the equation}	...

Fig. 1: Partial Input to FIGMENT II and its Corresponding Output†

Since our domain is algebra, the Default demon activates an initial expectation for the focus to be Math → Algebra. Now, the topic of quadratic equations has been discussed in the previous session, causing a Diversity demon to activate an expectation for a new topic, and a Default demon to activate a weak expectation for the continuation of quadratic equations based on length considerations, i.e.,

† At present, the input to FIGMENT II is hand-coded, however work is currently in progress on a complete interface between FIGMENT II and a system which produces human oriented solutions to algebraic equations (Oliver & Zukerman 1988).

one expects to discuss a topic for more than one session. These expectations yield conflicts with respect to the focus and the informational status entries in the Descendant List of the Algebra node, which demand the generation of a Focal MC and a verification Implementational MC, e.g., "Let us continue with the topic of quadratic equations." The Quadratic Equations node is now visited, and any inferred expectations are incorporated into its Own List: a direct inference results in the activation of an explicit timing expectation for this topic to be discussed immediately, and the firing of a Default demon yields an implicit length expectation for this topic to be discussed for a default time period. Since a variety of subtopics of quadratic equations may have been discussed in the previous session, there isn't a strong expectation for any of them. Hence, a Focal MC, such as "Here is an equation" is required. Notice, however, that the type of activity, namely problem solving, does not need to be mentioned, since, in this case, the mere presentation of an equation triggers a strong expectation for problem solving. Since a Default length expectation for one solution alternative is active in the Own List of the node corresponding to the equation and the number of presented solution alternatives violates this expectation, an Estimational MC is required, e.g., "There are three ways of solving this equation." This MC, however, points to all three alternatives, thereby weakening the focus expectation in the Descendant List of the Equation node. Hence, a Focal MC for each alternative is called for.

RELATED RESEARCH

The research reported in this paper builds on the mechanism presented in [Zukerman & Pearl 1986] which generates a subclass of MCs that signal a discrepancy between a given message and "normal" expectations. The current mechanism is able to provide a more uniform account for the generation of a broader class of MCs by dynamically drawing inferences from the state of the discourse to anticipate a listener's expectations. In addition, this mechanism accounts both for the presence and the absence of MCs in situations where the previous mechanism failed to provide a competent explanation.

Taxonomies of a subclass of MCs, namely conjunctive expressions, appear in [Halliday & Hasan 1976], [Longacre 1976] and others. A functional taxonomy encompassing additional Meta Comments appears in [Zukerman & Pearl 1986]. Theoretical work on Interpretive MCs appears in [Sigurd 1986], and several researchers (Cohen 1987, Reichman-Adar 1984, Grosz & Sidner 1985, McCoy & Cheng 1988) have presented mechanisms which view Focal Meta Comments as indicators of non-default traversals of a structure representative of the discourse. Finally, a detailed discussion on expectations can be found in [Ortony & Partridge 1987].

CONCLUSIONS

In this paper, we have introduced a mechanism for the generation of Meta Comments based on the tenet that they signal the inactivation or confirmation of a listener's beliefs and expectations. We have presented a simple knowledge representation scheme which supports this mechanism with respect to attribute and content expectations. To support this mechanism with respect to beliefs, a representation of a listener's beliefs resulting from previous discourse is required (Zukerman & Cheong 1988). In addition, we have introduced the concept of Expectation Activation Demons which emulate human behaviour in the activation of attribute expectations. We have incorporated our model in a text generation facility, demonstrating its use as a tool for the generation of fluent and cogent text.

REFERENCES

Appelt, D. E. (1982), Planning Natural Language Utterances to Satisfy Multiple Goals. Technical Note 259, SRI International, March 1982.

Cohen, R. (1987), Interpreting Clues in Conjunction with Processing Restrictions and Arguments and Discourse. In *AAAI-87 Conference Proceedings*, Seattle, August 1987.

Dyer, M.G. (1982), *In-depth Understanding: A Computer Model of Integrated Processing for Narrative Comprehension.* Doctoral Dissertation, Department of Computer Science, Yale University, New Haven, Connecticut.

Grosz, B.J. & Sidner, C.L. (1985), Discourse Structure and the Proper Treatment of Interruptions. In *IJCAI-85 Conference Proceedings*, Los Angeles, August 1985.

Halliday, M.A.K. & Hasan, R. (1976), *Cohesion in English.* Layman Press, London.

Hovy, E.H. (1987), Pragmatics and Natural Language Generation. Technical Report, Information Sciences Institute, Los Angeles, July 1987.

Kukich, K. (1983), *Knowledge-Based Report Generation: A Knowledge-Engineering Approach to Natural Language Report Generation.* Doctoral Dissertation, The Interdisciplinary Department of Information Science, University of Pittsburgh, Pennsylvania.

Longacre, R.E. (1976), *An Anatomy of Speech Notions*, Peter de Ridder Press, Publications in Tagmemics No. 3.

McCoy, K.F. & Cheng, J. (1988), Focus of Attention: Constraining What Can Be Said Next. *Unpublished Manuscript.*

McKeown, K.R. (1985), Discourse Strategies for Generating Natural Language Text. In *Artificial Intelligence* 27, pp. 1-41.

Oliver, J. & Zukerman, I. (1988), DISSOLVE: A System for the Generation of Human-Oriented Solution to Algebraic Equations. In *Proceedings of AI'88*, Adelaide, November 1988.

Ortony, A. & Partridge, D. (1987), Surprisingness and Expectation Failure: What is the Difference? In *IJCAI-10 Conference Proceedings*, Milan, August 1987.

Paris, C.L. (1987), Combining Discourse Strategies to Generate Descriptions to Users along a Naive/Expert Spectrum. In *IJCAI-10 Conference Proceedings*, Milan, August 1987.

Reichman-Adar, R. (1984), Extended Person-Machine Interface. In *Artificial Intelligence* 22, pp. 157-218.

Riesbeck, C.K. (1982), Realistic Language Comprehension. In *Strategies for Natural Language Processing*, W.G. Lehnert and M.H. Ringle (Eds.), Lawrence Erlbaum Associates.

Sigurd, B. (1986), Meta Comments in Text Generation. In G. Kempen (Ed.), *Natural Language Generation: New Results in Artificial Intelligence, Psychology and Linguistics*, pp. 453-461, Kluwer Academic Publishers.

Swartout, W.R. (1982), XPLAIN: A System for Creating and Explaining Expert Consulting Programs, USC/Information Sciences Institute.

Zukerman, I. (1986), *Computer Generation of Meta-technical Utterances in Tutoring Mathematics.* Doctoral Dissertation, Computer Science Department, University of California, Los Angeles.

Zukerman, I. & Pearl, J. (1986), Comprehension-Driven Generation of Meta-technical Utterances in Math Tutoring. In *AAAI Conference Proceedings*, August 1986.

Zukerman, I. & Cheong, Y.H. (1988), Impairment Invalidation: A Computational Model for the Generation of Rhetorical Devices. In *Proceedings of the International Computer Science Conference '88: Artificial Intelligence, Theory and Applications*, Hong Kong, December 1988.

Toward a Unified Theory of Immediate Reasoning in Soar

Thad A. Polk, Allen Newell, and Richard L. Lewis
School of Computer Science
Carnegie Mellon University

Abstract

Soar is an architecture for general intelligence that has been proposed as a unified theory of human cognition (UTC) (Newell, 1989) and has been shown to be capable of supporting a wide range of intelligent behavior (Laird, Newell & Rosenbloom, 1987; Steier *et al.*, 1987). Polk & Newell (1988) showed that a Soar theory could account for human data in syllogistic reasoning. In this paper, we begin to generalize this theory into a unified theory of immediate reasoning based on Soar and some assumptions about subjects' representation and knowledge. The theory, embodied in a Soar system (IR-Soar), posits three basic problem spaces (**comprehend**, **test-proposition**, and **build-proposition**) that construct annotated models and extract knowledge from them, learn (via chunking) from experience and use an attention mechanism to guide search. Acquiring task specific knowledge is modeled with the **comprehend** space, thus reducing the degrees of freedom available to fit data. The theory explains the qualitative phenomena in four immediate reasoning tasks and accounts for an individual's responses in syllogistic reasoning. It represents a first step toward a unified theory of immediate reasoning and moves Soar another step closer to being a unified theory of all of cognition.

IMMEDIATE REASONING TASKS

An immediate reasoning task involves extracting implicit information from a given situation within a few tens of seconds. The examples addressed here are relational reasoning, categorical syllogisms, the Wason selection task, and conditional reasoning. Typically, they involve testing the validity of a statement about the situation or generating a new statement about it. The situation, and often the task instructions, are novel and require comprehension. Usually, but not invariably, they are presented verbally. All the specific knowledge required to perform the task is available in the situation and the instructions and need not be consistent with other knowledge about the world (hence the task can be about unlikely or imaginary states of affairs).

THE SOAR THEORY OF IMMEDIATE REASONING

The Soar theory of immediate reasoning makes the following assumptions (elaborated below):

1. **Problem spaces.** All tasks, routine or difficult, are formulated as search in problem spaces. Behavior is always occurring in some problem space.
2. **Recognition memory.** All long-term knowledge is held in an associative recognition memory (realized as a production system).
3. **Decision cycle.** All available knowledge about the acceptability and desirability of problem spaces, states, or operators for any role in the current total context is accumulated, and the best choice made within the acceptable alternatives.
4. **Impasse driven subgoals.** Incomplete or conflicting knowledge at a decision cycle produces an

impasse. The architecture creates a subgoal to resolve the impasse. Cascaded impasses create a subgoal hierarchy.

5. **Chunking.** The experience in resolving impasses continually becomes new knowledge in recognition memory, in the form of chunks (constructed productions).
6. **Annotated models.** Problem space states are annotated models whose structure corresponds to that of the situation they represent.
7. **Focus of attention.** Attention can be focused on a small number of model objects. Operators are triggered by objects in the focus. When no operators are triggered, an impasse occurs and attention operators add other objects to the focus. Matching and related objects are added first.
8. **Model manipulation spaces.** Immediate reasoning occurs by heuristic search in model manipulation spaces that support comprehension, proposition construction, and proposition testing.
9. **Distribution of errors.** The main sources of errors are interpretation, carefulness and independent knowledge.

The first five assumptions are part of the Soar architecture. Annotated models and attention embody a discipline that is used for modeling cognition (and may become part of the architecture). The last two assumptions are specific to immediate reasoning.

A Soar system consists of a collection of problem spaces with states and operators. At each step during problem solving, the recognition memory brings all relevant knowledge to bear and the decision cycle determines how to proceed. An impasse arises if the decision cycle is unable to make a unique choice. This leads to the creation of a subgoal to resolve the impasse. Upon resolving the impasse, a chunk that summarizes the relevant problem solving is added to recognition memory, obviating the need for similar problem solving in the future.

The states in problem spaces are represented as *annotated models*. A *model* is a representation that satisfies the *structure correspondence condition*: parts, properties, and relations in the model (model elements) correspond to parts, properties, and relations in the represented situation, without completeness (Johnson-Laird, 1983). By exploiting the correspondence condition, processing of models can be match-like and efficient. The price paid is limited expressibility (e.g., models cannot directly represent disjunction or universal quantification). Arbitrary propositions can be represented, but only indirectly, by building a model of a proposition — a model interpretable as an abstract proposition, rather than a concrete object. Some expressibility can be regained without losing efficiency by attaching *annotations* to model elements. An annotation asserts a variant interpretation for the element to which it is attached, but is local to that element and does not admit unbounded processing (e.g., **optional** means that the model element *may* correspond to an element in the situation, but not necessarily).

Problem space states maintain a *focus of attention* that points to a small set of model objects. An operator is proposed when attention is focused on model objects that match its proposal conditions. When no operators are proposed, an impasse occurs and the system searches for a focus of attention that triggers one. Objects that share properties with a current focus of attention or are linked by a relation to one are tried first (others are implicitly assumed to be less relevant). When attention focuses on an object that triggers an operator, the impasse is resolved and problem solving continues.

Immediate reasoning occurs by heuristic search in *model manipulation spaces* (**comprehend, build-proposition**, and **test-proposition**). These spaces provide the basic capabilities necessary for immediate reasoning tasks, namely, constructing representations and generating and testing conclusions (Johnson-Laird, 1988). We assume that normal adults possess these spaces before they are confronted with these tasks. All of these problem spaces use the attention mechanism described above. **Comprehend** reads language and generates models that correspond to situations. It produces a model both of what is described (a *situation model*) and of the linguistic structure of the utterance itself (an *utterance model*). **Build-proposition** searches the space of possible propositions until it finds a proposition that is consistent with the situation model and that satisfies any added constraints in the goal test (e.g., its subject is "fork"). It works by combining properties and relations of model objects into constructed propositions. If attention is focused on an existing proposition, the attention mechanism biases the problem solving toward using parts of it. As a result, constructed propositions tend to be similar to existing propositions on which attention is focused. **Test-proposition** tests models of propositions against models of situations to see if they are valid. It does so by searching for objects in the situation model that correspond to those described in the proposition, and checking if the proposition is true of them. A proposition is considered true or false only if the situation model explicitly confirms or denies the proposition in question (i.e., there are objects in the situation model that correspond to the subject and object of the proposition that are (not) related in the way specified by the proposition). If a proposition is about an object(s) that does not match anything in the situation model, the proposition is considered irrelevant. If a proposition is about an object(s) that does appear in the situation model, but is neither explicitly confirmed nor denied, the proposition is considered relevant but unknown.

Individual subjects respond quite differently from each other in many immediate reasoning tasks. The theory predicts that these differences arise mainly from four sources: (1) the interpretation of certain words and phrases (e.g., quantifiers, connectives), (2) the care taken during reasoning (e.g., completeness of search, testing candidate solutions), (3) knowledge from sources outside the task (such as familiarity with the subject matter), and (4) the order in which attention is focused on model objects. We propose that most errors arise from interpretation mistakes (failing to consider all of the implicit ramifications of the premises or making unwarranted assumptions), incomplete search for conclusions (including the generation of other models if necessary), and less frequently from the inappropriate use of independent knowledge. This predicts that better subjects will interpret premises more completely and correctly or will search more exhaustively for a conclusion. Immediate reasoning tasks are difficult to the extent that they present opportunities for these errors.

ACQUIRING TASKS FROM INSTRUCTIONS

Immediate reasoning is so intimately involved in acquiring knowledge, both of the situation to be reasoned about and the task to be performed, that a theory of immediate reasoning needs to include a theory of acquisition. A companion paper (Lewis, Newell & Polk, 1989) describes NL-BI-Soar, a Soar system that acquires tasks from simple natural language utterances. NL-BI-Soar provides the **comprehend** problem space for IR-Soar, producing both the situation model and the utterance model. It also comprehends the instructions for these tasks. This leads to the creation of a problem space that is unique to the task, whose operators make use of the pre-existing spaces, **comprehend, test-proposition** and **build-proposition**. It is usual in cognitive theories for this structuring of the task to be posited by the theory — to be, in effect, added degrees of freedom in fitting the theory to the data. In the Soar

Relational Reasoning

Instructions	**Relation** Problem Space
1. Read four premises.	1. Read-input [**comprehend**]
2. Then read a statement.	2. Read-input [**comprehend**]
3. If the statement is "true", say "true".	3. Test-prop [**test-proposition**]
4. Then produce a statement ...	4. Make-conclusion [**build-proposition**]
5. ...that relates the fork to the knife	5. [goal-test]

Categorical Syllogisms

Instructions	**Syllogism** Problem Space
1. Read two premises that share a term.	1. Read-input [**comprehend**]
2. Then produce a statement that follows from the premises.	2. Make-conclusion [**build-proposition**]
3. The statement relates the unique terms of the premises.	3. [goal-test]

Wason Selection Task

Instructions	**Wason** Problem Space
1. Examine four cards that have a number on one side and a letter on the other side.	1. Read-input [**comprehend**]
2. Then read a statement.	2. Read-input [**comprehend**]
3. For each card, does deciding if the statement is true require turning over the card?	3. Test-prop [**test-proposition**]

Conditional Reasoning

Instructions	**Conditional** Problem Space
1. Read two premises.	1. Read-input [**comprehend**]
2. Then read a statement.	2. Read-input [**comprehend**]
3. Then decide if the statement is true.	3. Test-prop [**test-proposition**]
OR	
1. Read two premises.	1. Read-input [**comprehend**]
2. Then produce a statement that follows from the premises.	2. Make-conclusion [**build-proposition**]

Figure 1: **Task instructions and the corresponding problem spaces.**

theory, comprising NL-BI-Soar and IR-Soar jointly, these degrees of freedom no longer exist. The instructions do not specify all details of IR-Soar versions (there are still substantial individual differences among subjects), but do add a major constraint.

Figure 1 lists the English instructions and the corresponding operators for each task. The subspace used to implement each operator is given in brackets next to the operator name. As NL-BI-Soar reads the instructions it builds a model of what they describe (i.e., the required behavior). When the described task is attempted, impasses arise and NL-BI-Soar consults the behavior model to determine how to proceed, leading to the construction of the problem space (see Lewis, Newell, and Polk (1989) for details).

RELATIONAL REASONING

Relational reasoning involves deducing implicit relationships between objects given explicit relationships (e.g., 3-term series problems). Figure 2 illustrates a version similar to that in Johnson-Laird (1988). Given a set of premises (Figure 2, left) that describe a spatial configuration of objects, the task is to answer questions or make conclusions about the described situation (Figure 2, right).

Premises
1. A plate is left of a knife.
2. A fork is left of the plate.
3. A jug is above the knife.
4. The fork is below a cup.

Read this statement and say if it is true:
"The cup is left of the jug"
then
Produce a statement that relates the fork to the knife

Figure 2: **Relational reasoning task (after Johnson-Laird, 1988).**

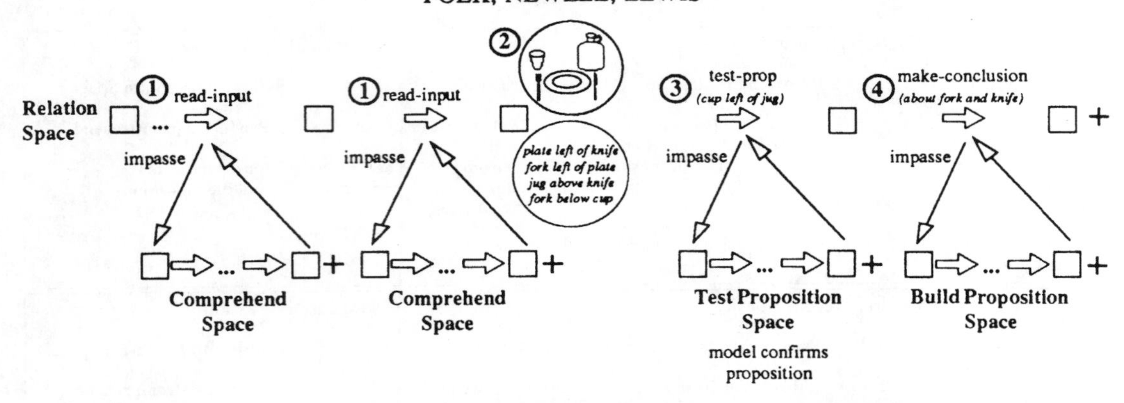

Figure 3: **Behavior of IR-Soar on the relational reasoning task.**

Reading the instructions for this task (Figure 1, top left) leads to a model of the required behavior. The objects in this behavior model are actions that need to be performed for this task. When the task is attempted, NL-BI-Soar consults this behavior model and evokes the operators listed in the figure, instantiating them with the appropriate arguments and goal tests.

Figure 3 illustrates the system's behavior on this task. (1) After acquiring the task from the instructions, the system starts in **relation** and applies read-input, implemented in **comprehend**, to each of the premises describing the situation. (2) This results in an initial model of the situation as well as a model of the premises (the utterance model). (3) The third instruction triggers the test-prop operator for the proposition "The cup is left of the jug". This operator is implemented in **test-proposition**. Since the situation model contains an object with property cup that is related via a left-of relation to an object with property jug, the proposition is considered true. (4) Instructions four and five call for generating a proposition about the fork and knife so make-conclusion is chosen, implemented in **build-proposition**. **Build-proposition**'s initial state is focused on a proposition with subject fork and object knife but no relation. Attending to the proposition's fork leads to focusing on the fork in the situation model (which is left of the situation's knife). This leads to constructing the proposition "A fork is left of a knife".

The theory predicts the same relative difficulty of problems of this type as Johnson-Laird (1988). It predicts that problems that have an unambiguous interpretation (i.e., admit only a single model) will be the easiest since they do not present opportunities for interpretational errors (assumption nine). Further, since a single model cannot represent disjunction (assumption six), realizing that a relation holds in some situations while not in others requires using multiple models in searching for a conclusion. Hence, problems without valid conclusions will be the hardest since they invite incomplete search (assumption nine). Ambiguous problems that support a valid conclusion will be of intermediate difficulty since conclusions based on considering only a single model may be correct. The percentage of correct responses for each of these problem types confirms these predictions (70%, 8%, and 46% correct, respectively). Many relational reasoning studies have focused on response latencies (Huttenlocher, 1968) and we have not yet addressed this data. The emphasis here is on accounting for major phenomena from many different tasks rather than explaining a single task in its entirety. Eventually we

Premise 1 : No archers are bowlers
Premise 2 : Some bowlers are clowns
Conclusion : Some clowns are not archers
(classified as EabIbc Oca)

A : All a are b
I : Some a are b
E : No a are b
O : Some a are not b

#1 ab #2 bc (EabIbc)	#1 ba #2 bc (AbaObc)
#1 ab #2 cb (OabAcb)	#1 ba #2 cb (IbaEcb)

Figure 4: **Syllogism task.**

expect deep coverage in all of them.

CATEGORICAL SYLLOGISMS

Syllogisms are reasoning tasks consisting of two premises and a conclusion (Figure 4, left). Each premise relates two sets of objects (a and b) in one of four ways (Figure 4, middle), and they share a common set (*bowlers*). A conclusion states a relation between the two sets of objects that are not common (the end-terms, *archers* and *clowns*) or that no valid conclusion exists. The three terms **a,b,c** can occur in four different orders, called *figures* (Figure 4, right, examples in parentheses), producing 64 distinct premise pairs.

In addition to the basic model manipulation spaces, the task-specific **syllogism** space is used in syllogistic reasoning. Figure 1 shows the correspondence between this problem space and the instructions. This problem space arises directly from the English instructions via NL-BI-Soar. After acquiring the task from the instructions, the system reads both premises and builds a situation model and a model of each of the premises (the utterance model) via **comprehend**. It then attempts to make a conclusion in the **build-proposition** problem space. The attention mechanism biases the form of the constructed conclusion to be similar to that of existing propositions (the premises) (assumptions seven and eight), leading to both the *atmosphere* and *figural* effects. The system may then test the proposition in **test-proposition** and construct additional models, though we have not found this necessary in modeling subjects in the Johnson-Laird & Bara (1984) data.

Polk & Newell (1988) showed how an earlier version of this theory could account for the main trends in group data. Our coverage with the more general theory is almost identical. We have also modeled the individual responses of a randomly chosen subject (subject 16 from Johnson-Laird & Bara (1984)). This subject was modeled by assuming the following processing errors (assumption nine): (1) *all x are y* implies *all y are x* (interpretation), (2) *no x are y* does *not* imply *no y are x* (interpretation), and (3) if neither premise has an end-term as subject, the search is abandoned (carefulness). The focus of attention was treated as a degree of freedom in fitting the subject. For this subject, we were able to predict 55/64 responses (86%).

THE WASON SELECTION TASK

The Wason selection task involves deciding which of four cards (Figure 5, left) *must* be turned over to decide whether or not a particular rule (Figure 5, right) is true (Wason, 1966). This task has been much studied mainly because very few subjects solve it correctly.

Figure 1 shows the top-level **wason** problem space and its correspondence with the instructions. For

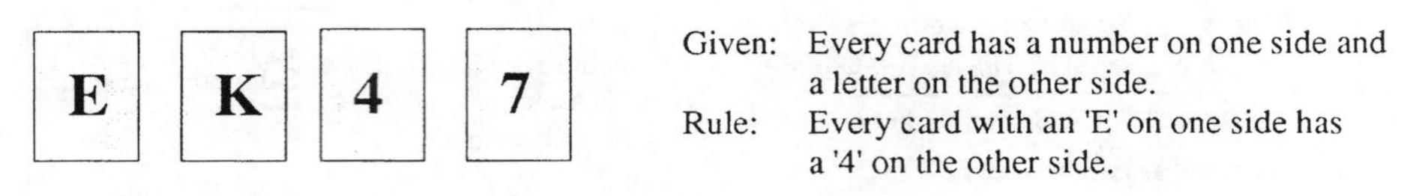

E
K
4
7
Given: Every card has a number on one side and a letter on the other side.
Rule: Every card with an 'E' on one side has a '4' on the other side.

Figure 5: **Wason selection task.**

each of the four cards, this problem space uses the **test-proposition** problem space to try to decide whether it must be turned over. Since the model will not directly answer this question, the system impasses and tries to augment the model. It does so by watching itself decide whether the rule is true while only turning over relevant cards (again using the **test-proposition** problem space). The system will often mistakenly consider cards that do not match the rule to be irrelevant (assumptions seven and eight) and will not select them. The model of deciding whether the rule is true is then inspected to see if the card was in fact turned over, thus resolving the initial impasse of deciding if it must be.

In this task, the cards can be classified into four cases: (1) those that satisfy the antecendent of the rule (the 'E'), (2) those that deny the antecedent of the rule (the 'K'), (3) those that affirm the consequent of the rule (the '4'), and (4) those that deny the consequent of the rule (the '7'). Cards in cases (1) and (4) are the only ones that must be turned over. The theory predicts that, ceteris paribus, cards that do not match the rule will be selected less frequently than those that do (assumptions seven and eight). Evans & Lynch (1973) demonstrated this *matching bias* in an experiment in which they varied the presence of negatives while holding the logical case constant (e.g., they used rules like "Every card with an E on one side does *not* have a '4' on the other side"). In all four logical cases, cards that did not match the rule were selected less frequently than those that did (56% vs. 90%, 6% vs 38%, 19% vs. 54%, and 38% vs. 67%). The standard task is difficult because the correct solution requires overcoming this matching bias to select the '7' (which does not match and hence seems irrelevant) and to reject the '4' (which does match and hence does seem relevant). These mistakes are indeed the two most common made by subjects. A number of other phenomena (e.g., facilitation) arise in variants of this task and the theory has not yet been applied to these.

CONDITIONAL REASONING

Conditional reasoning tasks involve deriving or testing the validity of a conclusion, given a conditional rule and a proposition affirming or denying either the rule's antecedent or consequent (Figure 6).

Figure 1 shows the correspondence between the top-level problem space and the instructions. For this task, the system comprehends the conditional rule and the proposition. It then either constructs a conclusion or tests one that is given, depending on the instructions (using **build-proposition** or **test-proposition**, respectively). In the absence of other knowledge, the system will consider given

Conditional Rule:	If the letter is 'A' then the number is '4'.
Assumed Proposition:	The number is not '4'.
Derive or Test:	The letter is not 'A'.

Figure 6: **Conditional reasoning task.**

conclusions that do not match the conditional to be less relevant (assumptions seven and eight). When constructing conclusions, the system is similarly biased toward conclusions that match (share one or more terms with) the rule (assumptions seven and eight).

Thus, as in the selection task, the theory predicts a matching bias. For conditional reasoning, this implies that conclusions that do not match the conditional will be less frequently constructed and considered relevant than those that do. Evans (1972) showed that when the logical case was factored out, conclusions whose terms did not match the rule were indeed less likely to be constructed than those that share one or both terms (the percentage of subjects constructing conclusions with zero, one, and two shared terms were 39%, 70%, and 86% respectively). Further, when Evans & Newstead (1977) asked subjects to classify conclusions as 'true', 'false', or 'irrelevant', mismatching conclusions were indeed often considered irrelevant.

CONCLUSION

We have presented a theory of human behavior in immediate reasoning tasks based on Soar. The theory uses model manipulation spaces (**comprehend**, **test-proposition**, and **build-proposition**) to construct and extract knowledge from annotated models and is guided by an attention mechanism. Though not reported on here, it includes a theory of learning (chunking). The theory accounts for qualitative phenomena in multiple immediate reasoning tasks and for detailed individual behavior in syllogistic reasoning. This theory is joined by the Soar subtheory for taking instructions in moving Soar to be a unified theory of cognition that deals in depth with a wide range of psychological phenomena.

Acknowledgements

Thanks to Norma Pribadi for making the intricate figures and to Kathy Swedlow for technical editing. Thanks to Erik Altmann and Shirley Tessler for comment and criticism. This work was supported by the Information Sciences Division, Office of Naval Research, under contract N00014-86-K-0678, and by the Kodak and NSF fellowship programs in which Thad Polk and Richard Lewis, respectively, participate. The views expressed in this paper are those of the authors and do not necessarily reflect those of the supporting agencies. Reproduction in whole or in part is permitted for any purpose of the United States government. Approved for public release; distribution unlimited.

References

Evans, J. S. B. (1972). Interpretation and 'matching bias' in a reasoning task. *Quartlerly Journal of Experimental Psychology, 24(2)*, 193–199.

Evans, J. S. B. and Lynch, J. (1973). Matching bias on the selection task. *British Journal of Psychology, 64*, 391–397.

Evans, J. S. B. and Newstead, S. (1977). Language and reasoning: A study of temporal factors. *Cognition, 5(3)*, 265–283.

Huttenlocher, J. (1968). Constructing spatial images: A strategy in reasoning. *Psychological Review, 75(6)*, 550–560.

Johnson-Laird, P. (1988). Reasoning by rule or model? In *Proceedings of the Annual Conference of the Cognitive Science Society*, pages 765–771.

Johnson-Laird, P. and Bara, B. (1984). Syllogistic Inference. *Cognition, 16*, 1–61.

Johnson-Laird, P. N. (1983). *Mental models: Towards a cognitive science of language, inference and consciousness.* Harvard University Press, Cambridge, Massachusetts.

Laird, J. E., Newell, A., and Rosenbloom, P. S. (1987). Soar: An architecture for general intelligence. *Artificial Intelligence, 33(1)*, 1–64.

Lewis, R., Newell, A., and Polk, T. (1989). Toward a Soar Theory of Taking Instructions for Immediate Reasoning Tasks. To appear in the Proceedings of the Annual Conference of the Cognitive Science Society, August, 1989.

Newell, A. (1989). *Unified Theories of Cognition.* Harvard University Press, Cambridge, Massachusetts. In press.

Polk, T. A. and Newell, A. (1988). Modeling human syllogistic reasoning in Soar. In *Proceedings of the Annual Conference of the Cognitive Science Society*, pages 181–187.

Steier, D. M., Laird, J. E., Newell, A., Rosenbloom, P. S., Flynn, R. A., Golding, A., Polk, T. A., Shivers, O. G., Unruh, A., and Yost, G. R. (1987). Varieties of learning in Soar: 1987. In *Proceedings of the Fourth International Workshop on Machine Learning*, pages 300–311.

Wason, P. C. (1966). Reasoning. In Foss, B. M., editor, *New Horizons in Psychology I*, Penguin, Harmondsworth, England.

Toward a Soar Theory of Taking Instructions for Immediate Reasoning Tasks

Richard L. Lewis, Allen Newell, and Thad A. Polk
School of Computer Science
Carnegie Mellon University

Abstract
Soar is a theory of the human cognitive architecture. We present here the Soar theory of taking instructions for *immediate reasoning* tasks, which involve extracting implicit information from simple situations in a few tens of seconds. This theory is realized in a computer system that comprehends simple English instructions and organizes itself to perform a required task. Comprehending instructions produces a *model of future behavior* that is interpretively executed to yield task behavior. Soar thereby acquires task-specific problem spaces that, together with basic reasoning capabilities, model human performance in multiple immediate reasoning tasks. By providing an account of taking instructions, we reduce the *degrees of freedom* available to our theory of immediate reasoning, and also give more support for Soar as a unified theory of cognition.

Soar is a theory of human cognition (Newell, 1989), embodied in a computer system. Soar specifies the cognitive architecture, which is the relatively fixed set of mechanisms that permit goals and knowledge of the task environment to be encoded in memory and brought to bear to produce behavior. Soar is proposed as a unified theory of cognition, and it has been applied to human behavior in a broad spectrum of domains. This paper reports progress in getting Soar to take instructions and organize itself to perform a required task.

There are three important reasons for wanting a theory of instructions. First, taking instructions is a domain of cognitive activity, with interesting phenomena and practical importance. Any unified theory of cognition must ultimately provide such a theory. Second, a major issue for psychology has always been the radical underdetermination of theory by data. Though an issue for all sciences, it is particularly irksome for psychology (and the social sciences) because humans bring massive knowledge to a task and dynamically organize themselves accordingly. Taking instructions to perform tasks is an important instance of such self-organization (e.g., as it takes place in psychological experiments). By specifying how task specific organization arises from instructions, a theory of instruction comprehension would go some way toward removing what can be called *theory degrees of freedom*. Instructions are only one source of knowledge determining behavior, but understanding them could pave the way for dealing with other sources. Third, including both instruction taking and task performance in the same theoretical account provides mutual constraint. This constraint is an instance of the gains to be made from a unified theory of cognition.

In this paper we take some steps toward a theory of instruction taking.[1] The system we present here, NL-Soar, comprehends instructions given in elementary English for *immediate reasoning* tasks, such as the *relational reasoning* task (Johnson-Laird, 1988) shown in Figure 1. This comprehension is part of a system, IR-Soar, that models the way humans perform immediate reasoning (reported in a companion paper (Polk, Newell & Lewis, 1989)). Here we focus on the internal representation of instructions, how

[1]Building on earlier work in (Newell, 1989, Chap. 7; Yost & Newell, 1988).

Instructions

Read four premises. Then read a statement. If the statement is true say "true". Then stop.

Task input

Premises	A plate is left of a knife. A fork is left of the plate. A jug is above the knife. The fork is below a cup.
Statement	The cup is left of the jug.

Figure 1: **Relational reasoning task.**

Soar organizes itself to do the task, and the associated psychological claims. The process of comprehending the language of instructions to create these representations is also part of the total theory, and involves both linguistic and psycholinguistic issues. Although we do not deal with these issues here, NL-Soar does embody a theory of language comprehension (Newell, 1989, Chap. 8). We also do not present direct behavioral evidence for instruction taking. For the moment, the psychological relevance of the instruction taking is that it leads to an organization of IR-Soar that explains how people do immediate reasoning tasks.

There has been relatively little work on the psychology of instruction taking. The most notable was the UNDERSTAND program (Simon & Hayes, 1979), which took instructions for the Tower of Hanoi and constructed a problem space in which to do the task. Our account is consonant with the broad thrust of that work, the main advances being in the plausibility of the processes and representations used, and in the embedding of this in a unified theory. Our account is also consonant with the implications from ACT* (Anderson, 1983): that conversion from declarative to procedural form occurs by an interpretive process that leads to creating chunks of conditional behavior (productions).

We first present the psychological claims of the Soar theory of taking instructions, and in passing review the basic assumptions of the Soar architecture. We then illustrate the theory by tracing the behavior of the system in detail on the relational reasoning task in Figure 1. Finally, we briefly describe how the theory has been applied to two other immediate reasoning tasks.

THE SOAR THEORY OF TAKING INSTRUCTIONS

Soar as a cognitive architecture has been described in several places (Laird, Newell & Rosenbloom, 1987) and we will take its major outlines to be familiar. All tasks are formulated in *problem spaces*; all long term knowledge is held in a *recognition memory* (realized as productions); processing proceeds by a sequence of *decision cycles* that accumulate knowledge about what spaces, states and operators to select; *subgoals* are generated in an attempt to resolve *impasses* that occur when the decision-making knowledge is insufficient or conflicting; and the experience gained in resolving impasses is learned in the form of *chunks* (new productions in recognition memory).

One additional assumption is that states in problem spaces are *annotated models*.[2] Models consist of

[2]This is not yet an architectural assumption for Soar, which only assumes a representation consisting of attributes and values.

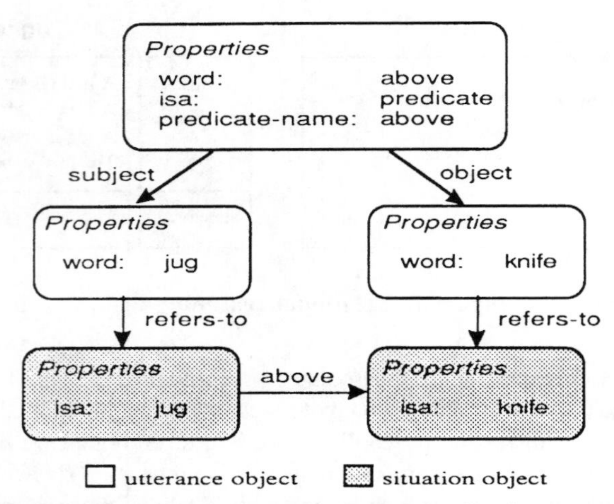

Figure 2: **Utterance and situation models for "A jug is above the knife."**

objects, properties, and relations (model elements) and satisfy the semantic assumption that each element in the representation corresponds to an element in the referent. This assumption may be violated in principled ways by attaching annotations to model elements. An annotation specifies a non-standard interpretation for the single element to which it is attached (e.g., an element annotated **many** corresponds to multiple elements in the referent). There are computational advantages to processing annotated models and there is also evidence that humans use them (Johnson-Laird, 1983; Polk & Newell, 1988). We do not review these considerations, but simply assume annotated models. Beyond these assumptions, the Soar theory of taking instructions embodies the following psychological claims:

1. **Situation model.** The objective of comprehending an utterance is to represent the situation that the utterance is about. To do so, comprehension builds a *model of the situation.*
2. **Utterance model.** As a processing side effect, comprehension produces a *model of the utterance*—a model that reflects the logical form of the utterance, and that can be interpreted as the abstract proposition or description asserted by the utterance.
3. **Behavior model.** If instructions are comprehended, the situation model that comprehension produces is a *model of the subject's future behavior.*
4. **Performance by interpretation.** Task performance proceeds initially by *interpretively executing* the behavior model. During this interpretation process, chunks are learned that directly perform the task.

The theory of comprehension

Comprehension (construction of the situation model) occurs in the **comprehend** problem space by applying a *comprehension operator* to each incoming word (Newell, 1989). These operators iteratively

---

Nevertheless, the current work in Soar on human cognition assumes models (Newell, 1989, Chap. 7; Polk & Newell, 1988).

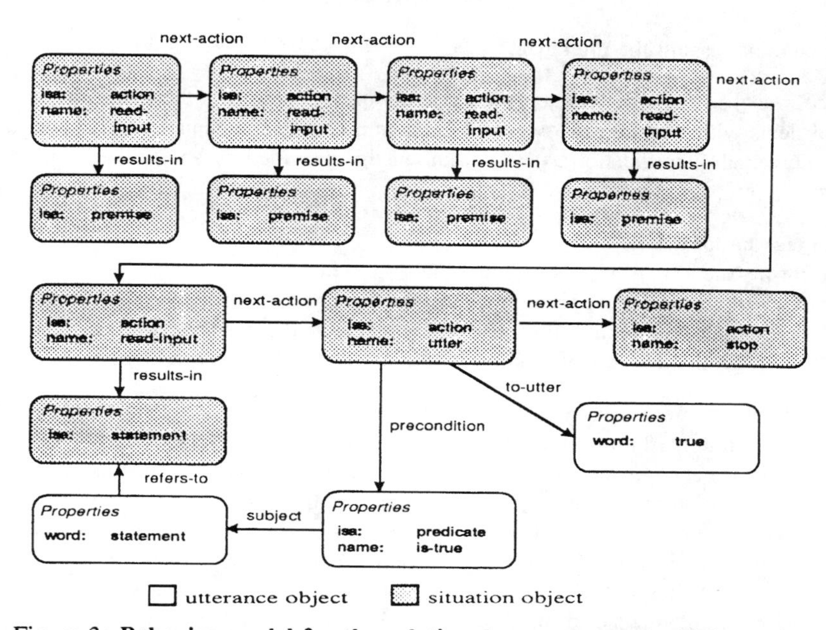

Figure 3: **Behavior model for the relational reasoning task of Figure 1.**

augment and refine the situation model as the utterance is comprehended. Figure 2, bottom, shows a simple situation model produced by **comprehend** for the third premise of Figure 1.

Since all the knowledge that a word contributes to an utterance may not be available at the moment the word is read, the comprehension process must have some means of holding partial comprehension knowledge. In the **comprehend** space, this knowledge is held by *expectation* data structures. Expectations can be syntactic, semantic, or pragmatic. In particular, part of what is delivered by a comprehension operator for a word is knowledge about what is expected to come in the rest of the utterance. Thus, there must be some way of modeling the utterance itself. The utterance model that serves this processing requirement is a structured linguistic form. As comprehension proceeds, it evolves into a model that reflects the underlying logical form of the utterance. In contrast to the situation model, the utterance model is closer to a predicate calculus-like language.

As an example, Figure 2, top, gives the final utterance model for "A jug is above the knife." [3] It is useful to compare the two models in this figure. The objects in the situation model correspond to the jug and knife in the situation, and the relation "above" corresponds to the spatial relation in the situation. In contrast, the objects in the utterance model correspond to linguistic objects that can be interpreted as predicates and arguments. Thus, "above" in the utterance model corresponds to the predicate "above", and the relations correspond to relations between the predicate and its arguments. Since objects in the utterance model originate as words, the language of predicates is as rich as the

[3]The utterance model in this figure is actually somewhat simplified for expository purposes.

natural language expressing the utterance.

The utterance model is not a deliberate product of comprehension; it is the means by which **comprehend** deals with language. However, since some knowledge cannot be encoded in the situation model (e.g., universal quantification), the total knowledge provided by an utterance may reside jointly in both models.

The theory of task performance

Comprehending instructions produces a model that represents future actions to be taken. An element in a behavior model corresponds to an action or an object related to an action (such as the expected input or output). For example, the model in Figure 3, produced by NL-Soar for the task of Figure 1, specifies that the task begins with four acts of reading input, and that each act should yield a premise.

After reading the instructions, the system attempts to perform the task. It is initially unable to proceed, because it lacks operational knowledge of the task in recognition memory (the knowledge is in the static data structures of the behavior model). This leads to interpreting the behavior model. Earlier work with Soar has shown how such processes can yield chunks that directly implement the task and bypass interpretation (Yost & Newell, 1988; Newell, 1989). Currently, this capability is embodied in BI-Soar (behavior-model interpretation), a set of problem spaces that are independent of NL-Soar and IR-Soar. For immediate reasoning tasks, the interpretation of the behavior model gives rise to problem spaces whose operators are implemented in the three basic IR-Soar spaces (**comprehend, test-proposition**, and **build-proposition**). Polk, Newell & Lewis (1989) show that the task spaces so acquired can indeed be used to model human performance.

AN EXAMPLE: RELATIONAL REASONING

We illustrate the theory by tracing through the task of Figure 1. Figure 4 shows the behavior of the system as it comprehends the instructions and attempts to perform the task. The system begins in the **read** problem space (see (1) in Figure 4), and applies a series of comprehend-input operators to read the instructions. Each operator application comprehends one statement, and builds up the behavior model accordingly. (2) The comprehend-input operator is implemented in the **comprehend** space, where a series of comprehension operators fire for each incoming word. These operators actually fire multiple times as expectations build up and are satisfied.

(3) Processing continues until comprehension of the word "begin," which the system takes to mean it should start the task. (4) It deliberately sets the goal of doing the task by selecting the do-new-task operator. (5) Since the knowledge required to perform the task is not directly available in recognition memory, Soar impasses and creates a new problem space (**relation**) to implement the operator.

(6) Once in the **relation** space, Soar impasses again because it has no operators to propose for this new space. Resolving the impasse requires consulting the behavior model for what to do next. (7) This is the function of the **fetch-operator** problem space (a space of BI-Soar), which contains the knowledge required to locate the next action in the behavior model and interpret it as an operator in the task space. (8) In this case, the impasse is resolved by selecting read-input, an instantiation of the comprehend-input operator that will yield a premise (Figure 3). (9) The premise object from the behavior model is set up

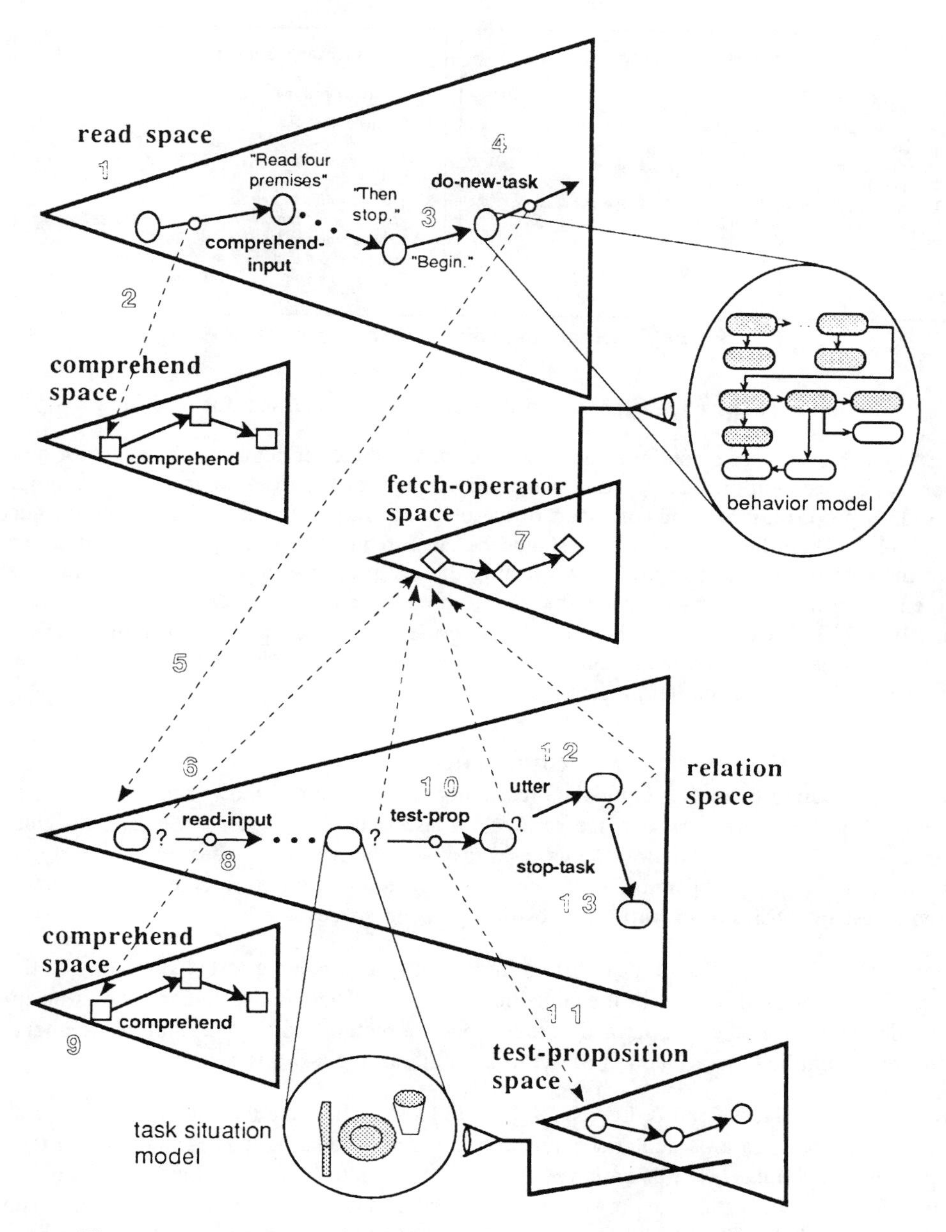

Figure 4: **Acquiring and performing the relational reasoning task.**

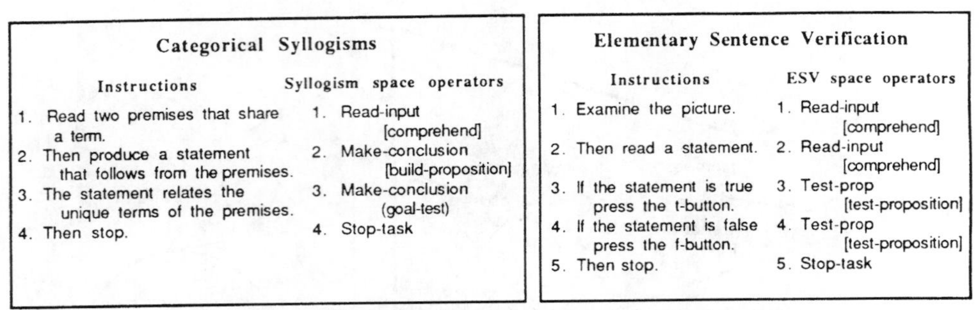

Figure 5: **Other immediate reasoning tasks.**

as an expectation in the **comprehend** space, and thus provides the goal test for read-input.

This *impasse-fetch-apply* cycle continues until Soar arrives at the utter action in the behavior model. This action has a precondition (namely, that the statement just read is true), interpreted as a proposition (Figure 3). This proposition originated as part of the utterance model for one of the comprehended instructions. (10) Determining if this action should be taken requires verifying the proposition, so the impasse in the **relation** space is resolved by selecting the test-prop operator. (11) This operator is implemented in the **test-proposition** space, one of the three basic IR-Soar problem spaces (Polk, Newell & Lewis, 1989). (12) Once the proposition has been verified by consulting the situation model, the **fetch-operator** space selects and instantiates the utter operator in the next fetch cycle. (13) Finally, the stop-task operator is selected and terminates the task.

OTHER TASKS

NL-BI-Soar has acquired two other immediate reasoning tasks. Figure 5 shows the instructions and problem-spaces for the elementary sentence verification task (Clark & Chase, 1972), and the categorical syllogisms task. As in the relational reasoning task, task-specific behavior arises by interpreting the behavior model, and applying operators in the new task space that are implemented in IR-Soar's **comprehend, test-proposition,** or **build-proposition** problem spaces[4].

The elementary sentence verification task differs from relational reasoning in the simplicity of the initial situation, and the form used to present the situation (a picture). The latter difference shows up in the behavior model as a comprehend-input action that expects a picture rather than a linguistic utterance. The difference in simplicity is a function of the task input, not the task instructions.

The syllogisms task (Polk, Newell & Lewis, 1989) is interesting because the subject must utter a conclusion that conforms to a particular specification given in the instructions— namely, that the conclusion relate the *unique terms of the premises*. Soar realizes this as an application of the build-proposition operator instantiated to relate the correct terms. Knowledge in the comprehension operators for the words "unique" and "relate" leads to construction of the appropriate behavior model

---

[4]NL-Soar will deal with the conditional reasoning and Wason tasks, which are the additional examples in (Polk, Newell & Lewis, 1989); as of submission of this paper, the runs are not completed, but no difficulties are expected.

that captures this constraint.

CONCLUSION

We have presented a Soar theory of taking instructions for immediate reasoning tasks. This theory is implemented in two collections of Soar problem spaces, NL-Soar and BI-Soar. NL-Soar uses the **comprehend** problem space to read simple English statements and produce an annotated model of the situation being described. As a side effect of comprehending these statements, **comprehend** produces a model that reflects the logical form of the utterance. When reading task instructions, **comprehend** creates a model of the behavior described by the instructions. By repeatedly consulting this behavior model, BI-Soar can acquire the problem spaces necessary to perform the task.

Besides being interesting in its own right, this theory opens up some interesting possibilities. For one, it begins to significantly alleviate the problem of the underdetermination of theories by data. In a companion paper (Polk, Newell & Lewis, 1989), we have presented a theory of immediate reasoning that depends on the task-specific problem spaces that arise from the instructions given to NL-Soar. The degrees of freedom available to that theory are significantly reduced as a result. Further, the two subtheories of taking instructions and immediate reasoning mutually constrain each other, making both significantly stronger. For instance, it is not an independent assumption of the immediate reasoning theory that both the utterance model and the situation model are available as sources of knowledge to do the task. Similarly, the problem spaces acquired through task instructions must be used to model behavior in immediate reasoning tasks, significantly constraining the theory presented here. Finally, this theory represents another step toward making Soar a unified theory of cognition.

Acknowledgements

Many thanks to Erik Altmann, Norma Pribadi, Kathryn Swedlow, and Shirley Tessler for useful comments and invaluable assistance in preparing the draft and the figures, as well as to Chris Tuck for helping bridge the Pittsburgh-Ann Arbor gap. This work was supported by the Information Sciences Division, Office of Naval Research, under contract N00014-86-K-0678, and by the National Science Foundation and Kodak fellowship programs in which Richard Lewis and Thad Polk, respectively, participate. The views expressed in this paper are those of the authors and do not necessarily reflect those of the supporting agencies. Reproduction in whole or in part is permitted for any purpose of the United States government. Approved for public release; distribution unlimited.

References

Anderson, J. R. (1983). *The Architecture of Cognition.* Harvard University Press, Cambridge, Massachusetts.

Clark, H. and Chase, W. (1972). On the process of comparing sentences against pictures. *Cognitive Psychology, 3*, 472–517.

Johnson-Laird, P. (1988). Reasoning by rule or model? In *Proceedings of the Annual Conference of the Cognitive Science Society*, pages 765–771.

Johnson-Laird, P. N. (1983). *Mental models: Towards a cognitive science of language, inference and consciousness.* Harvard University Press, Cambridge, Massachusetts.

Laird, J. E., Newell, A., and Rosenbloom, P. S. (1987). Soar: An architecture for general intelligence. *Artificial Intelligence, 33(1)*, 1–64.

Newell, A. (1989). *Unified Theories of Cognition.* Harvard University Press, Cambridge, Massachusetts. In press.

Polk, T., Newell, A., and Lewis, R. (1989). Toward a Unified Theory of Immediate Reasoning in Soar. To appear in the Proceedings of the Annual Conference of the Cognitive Science Society, August, 1989.

Polk, T. A. and Newell, A. (1988). Modeling human syllogistic reasoning in Soar. In *Proceedings of the Annual Conference of the Cognitive Science Society*, pages 181–187.

Simon, H. and Hayes, J. (1979). Understanding written problem instructions. In Simon, H., editor, *Models of Thought*, pages 451–476, Yale University Press, New Haven, Conneticut.

Yost, G. R. and Newell, A. (1988). Learning New Tasks in Soar. Unpublished.

Tower-Noticing Triggers Strategy-Change in the Tower of Hanoi: A Soar Model

Dirk Ruiz and Allen Newell

Departments of Psychology and Computer Science
Carnegie Mellon University

People who solve the Tower of Hanoi start out with a guided trial-and-error strategy and later acquire a recursive strategy, the generally most effective strategy. Protocol data shows that noticing and using subtowers in problem-solving differentiates two subjects who acquired the recursive strategy from one who did not. A working Soar model explains Tower of Hanoi strategy-acquisition by first assuming the basic ability to notice and use subtowers, and then charting the process by which this new knowledge is integrated with existing knowledge to produce the recursive strategy. Of particular importance in the integration is learning to see *nested* subtowers and using simple spatial-manipulation reasoning to figure out how to move those subtowers. The model shows a good qualitative fit to the data, providing support for Soar as a unified theory of human cognition.

THE PHENOMENON

How are new problem-solving strategies acquired? In particular, what new information triggers the acquisition process, and how is that information integrated into problem-solving to produce a new strategy? We address this question within the Tower of Hanoi domain. The puzzle (Figure 1) consists of five disks of graded sizes which in the initial state are sitting on one peg (the Source) to form a tower. The object is to move the disks to the Destination peg while moving only one disk at a time from peg to peg and never placing a larger disk on a smaller. Much is already known about this problem. In particular, it has been found that the Tower of Hanoi can be solved with a small number of well-defined, easily detectable strategies and that people tend to learn new strategies while solving it (Simon, 1975; Anzai & Simon, 1979). These characteristics make the problem ideal for studying strategy-acquisition.

Subjects start out solving the Tower of Hanoi using a guided trial-and-error (GTE) strategy and frequently end up using a recursive strategy (Egan & Greeno, 1974; Simon, 1975; Anzai & Simon, 1979; Ruiz, 1988; VanLehn, 1989). The GTE strategy consists of never moving the same disk twice in a row and never returning a disk to the peg from which it most recently came. The recursive strategy consists of setting a goal to move the largest disk that is not yet on the Destination to the Destination, followed by recursively setting subgoals to move blocking disks out of the way. Prior speculations and models of this change have typically relied on three assumptions (Egan & Greeno, 1974; Simon, 1975; Anzai & Simon, 1979). First, search takes place only in the Tower of Hanoi problem-space. Second, prior knowledge of (domain-independent) means-ends analyses (MEA) is necessary either to guide the acquisition of new

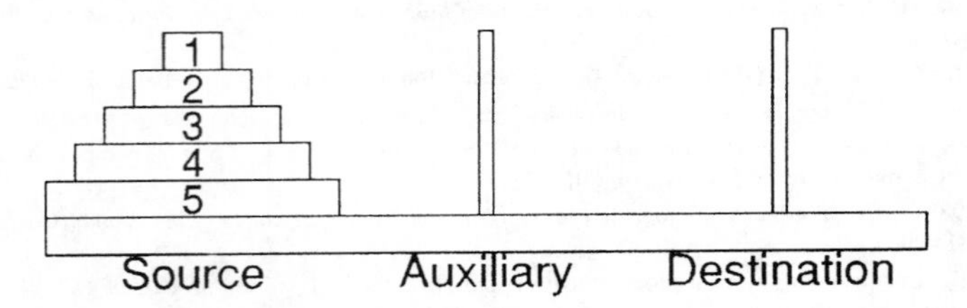

Figure 1: The Five-Disk Tower of Hanoi.

information that will later lead to the development of the recursive strategy, or to directly provide a template for building the recursive strategy. Third, little prior knowledge, drawn from other domains, is assumed. (VanLehn's model sets aside the MEA assumption, but retains the assumptions of a single problem-space and little prior knowledge.) Our theory, a working Soar model (Newell, in press), provides a new explanation of Tower of Hanoi strategy acquisition without having to make these sometimes overly restrictive assumptions.

HUMAN DATA

Our model is based on thinking-aloud protocols taken from three subjects solving the five-disk Tower of Hanoi problem: AS, RN, and PD. AS is Anzai and Simon's well-known (1979) subject, who did the following trials using a physical problem: part of a five-disk, a complete five-disk, a one-disk, a two-disk, a three-disk, a four-disk (these last four problems were experiments initiated by AS), and then two more five-disks. RN and PD were run in our laboratory on an IBM PC; they used special keys to pick up and drop disks. Numbers were printed on the disks to aid identification. They each did five complete trials of the five-disk Tower of Hanoi. Their moves and times were recorded. The following regularities were observed in the protocols:

1. All three subjects initially used the GTE strategy; RN and AS later acquired the recursive strategy. AS acquired it upon starting her three-disk experiment; RN acquired it during his first trial at state _,1234,5 (the Source is blank, Auxiliary has disks 1-4, and 5 is on Destination). While PD was able to solve the Tower of Hanoi, he did not acquire the recursive strategy; he did use lookahead, but that only infrequently (six times).
2. Solving one-disk and two-disk subtowers was trivial for all subjects.
3. Before acquiring the recursive strategy, RN set five subgoals and AS set six. Two of RN's subgoals and three of AS's subgoals were to move a two-disk subtower. In both, the two-disk tower was then planned out and moved. The remaining goals were to move larger towers; they were abandoned in favor of a move generated according to the GTE strategy.
4. Upon or after placing disk 4 on the Destination, all three subjects realized they had made an error and tried to rectify it.
5. Subtowers figured prominently in RN's and AS's pre-recursive problem-solving, but not in PD's pre-lookahead problem-solving. (A subtower is defined as a stack of *k* consecutive-sized disks, with disk 1 as the first disk.) RN mentioned them explicitly in six statements such as "Now I need to move disks one, two, and three [to the] auxiliary." AS did her aforementioned four experiments solving subtowers. PD did mention subtowers five times in his pre-lookahead problem-solving. These mentionings were either vague or were comments on a tower just about to be completed; they never occurred while planning a move.
6. Recursion was displayed suddenly by both AS and RN, within one move.
7. Recursive reasoning occurred when AS and RN were confronted with subtowers (e.g., the state 5,4,123); there was little mention of goals while moving between subtowers.

SOAR

The theory we shall present is a subtheory within Soar. Soar provides the general theoretical constructs (learning, problem-spaces, memory structure, etc) that support and realize our strategy-change explanation. To understand the subtheory, it is necessary to first understand Soar.

Soar is a general cognitive architecture which models the human cognitive architecture (Newell, in press). Soar has an associative, recognition-based long-term memory (LTM), realized by productions, and a working memory to hold intermediate results of computation. As with humans, the *problem-space* (the problem-states and operators that can be used to solve the problem) is the basis of Soar's cognition (Newell, 1980). Given a goal to solve a problem, Soar makes progress by first deciding on a problem-space for that goal, then deciding on a problem-state, and then deciding on an *operator* to apply to that state. The operator is used to create a new state, to which new operators are applied, and so on. Each decision (problem-space, state, and operator) takes place within a *decision-cycle*, during which candidates are first generated via production match from LTM, followed by the selection of the best candidate. The selection is done by collecting desirability information about each candidate from LTM, and then applying a fixed decision procedure to this information. If Soar has conflicting or insufficient information to make a decision, it sets up a subgoal to resolve the *impasse*. By searching in one or more problem-spaces, Soar generates the needed information and resolves the impasse. Impasses can occur within impasses, leading to a subgoal hierarchy. Soar learns from its experience in resolving impasses by determining which working-memory elements were responsible for generating the results that resolved the most recent impasse in the stack. The responsible elements and the generated results become the condition and action, respectively, of a new production, a *chunk*. The chunk will fire when the impasse situation (or any other sufficiently similar situation) occurs in the future. Thus the chunk both avoids impasses and causes transfer of learning. Soar has no pre-built procedures for handling faulty chunks: they must be detected and overriden by deliberate problem-solving.

THE MODEL

The model consists of productions that provide the knowledge Soar needs to use the various problem-spaces. Each problem-space corresponds to a particular cognitive function (e.g., how to generate operators, and how to reason about generated operators). Our description of the model will first be problem-space oriented, with the exception of subtower-noticing, which does not occur in its own problem-space (Figure 2). Then, we will describe the mechanics of the individual models for RN and AS, and finally their general behavior. (PD is not modeled here, but is used simply to supply contrasting data.)

TOH

Tower Of Hanoi moves disks in the real world. TOH is assumed to arise from comprehending the

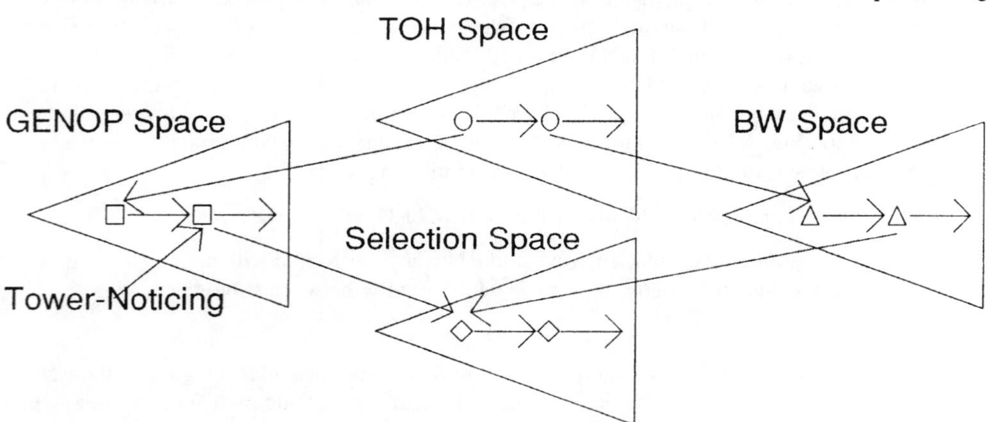

Figure 2: Summary of Problem-Spaces.

problem instructions, which specify how disks may be moved. (Future versions of this model will actually comprehend problem instructions, using the language comprehension system developed by Lewis, Newell & Polk (1989).) TOH translates the physically realizable results of operator generation and reasoning into disk movements. TOH is implemented in Soar with the move-disk operator, which transfers a disk from one peg to another.

GENOP

GENerate OPerator generates move-disk operators for TOH by first choosing a disk to move and then choosing a peg to which to move it. Operator generation is given a separate problem-space because it is a complex cognitive activity, as indicated by the fact that subjects employ several heuristics in generating operators. GENOP uses two heuristics to select disks for movement: do not repetitively move an object, and prefer the largest (non-repetitive) object which can be moved. GENOP employs three heuristics to select pegs: do not block the goal on the first move, do not move an object to the location from which it was last moved, and prefer to move an object to its final location (the Destination peg). Prior to the problem-solver perceiving a stack of consecutive-sized disks as both a unit (a subtower) and as movable, GENOP generates move-disk operators from the tops of the stacks, as they are the only movable disks. This effectively implements the GTE strategy. After a problem-solver has started seeing stacks of disks as movable subtowers, GENOP will generate operators to move the bottom disk of an encountered subtower. This effectively generates the operators needed to begin the recursive strategy. In the Soar model, GENOP has two operators: choose-disk and choose-to-peg. The results of these operators are recorded on the problem-state and then used to form a move-disk operator for TOH.

BW

Blocks World reasons about TOH's unimplementable move-disk operators. BW is so named because it reflects people's ability to do simple spatial-manipulation reasoning, of which blocks-world type problems are a paradigmatic case. This reasoning capability is called into use by the Tower of Hanoi's spatial character. Since spatial-manipulation reasoning is at least able to solve a two-disk problem, BW was built with enough knowledge to do that. BW does three things. First, given an unimplementable move, it determines the *blocking* object using two heuristics: prefer the largest movable object, and prefer the object that blocks the unimplementable move's desired location. Second, BW chooses a peg to which to move the blocking object, using the heuristic that it is best to move the blocking object out of the way of the desired move. Third, BW tries out the assembled move-disk operator. If this results in a new state, then the move-disk operator is implementable and is used to resolve the unimplementable operator's impasse. If no new state is produced, an impasse has occurred and BW is used again to resolve this new impasse. The final result of BW's reasoning is returned to TOH and executed. In the Soar model, BW has one operator for each action: a mark-blocking-disk operator, a mark-receiving-peg operator, and an operator called try-operator. The results of the first two operators are recorded on the state. Try-operator tries out the assembled operator as discussed above. When BW finally reasons out a move, it provides TOH with both the move and the operator it should use next, as determined in the reasoning chain.

Selection

Selection is a default, domain-independent problem-space that collects information about alternatives (usually, operators) and uses that information to choose one of them. The selection-space is derived from people's ability to use heuristics and to make simple choices as a result of applying those heuristics. The selection-space is used when a problem-space encounters an impasse in which it has insufficient information to directly choose between several alternatives. The selection-space applies all relevant heuristics for each alternative separately, and then integrates the results of those heuristics into a single choice, thus resolving the original problem-space's impasse. (The selection-space does not generate heuristics; it only applies them.) The selection-space has one operator: evaluate-object, which evaluates each alternative and records the results of each evaluation on the selection-space's problem-state.

Subtower-Noticing

Subtower-noticing distinguished RN and AS from PD, and thus is postulated to be the crucial variable in discovering the recursive strategy. Subtower-noticing occurs when the subject realizes that a series of consecutive, stacked disks (starting with disk 1) forms a tower, and makes the assumption that this tower might be moved as a unit. The subject's ability to see consecutive disks as a tower is derived from his/her prior knowledge of such things as towers, pyramids and triangles. The impetus to apply this knowledge to the problem comes from the problem name (the TOWER of Hanoi) plus the frequency with which subtowers occur in the problem. For example, in a perfect solution to a 5-disk problem, 12 of the 32 problem-states will have a subtower sitting by itself on a peg. Most important, the subject will, during his/her solution, encounter these subtowers in order of size. For example, s/he may see a two-disk tower followed by a three-disk tower, followed by a four-disk tower. This experience should lead the subject to see the subtowers as being nested, i.e., that a three-disk tower really consists of a two-disk tower sitting on top of disk 3. Seeing subtowers as nested is important because it effectively breaks a subtower down into components about which BW can reason. For, a nested subtower of k disks is really just a two-disk subtower: a (k - 1)-disk subtower sitting on disk k. (Of course, the (k - 1)-disk tower must itself be a two-disk tower for reasoning to proceed.) In Soar, tower-noticing occurs in the GENOP problem-space upon seeing a k-disk subtower sitting by itself on a peg. The noticing (implemented via productions) results in a minor change to the problem-state: the tower's bottom disk is marked as a tower and as movable. A chunk gets built that can then label that tower in any context, including when it is the subtower of another tower. Repeated experience with single subtowers thus gives Soar the ability (i.e., the chunks) to see nested subtowers. Since these chunks allow the use of BW, they (and not the subtower-noticing productions) are directly responsible for the development of the recursive strategy.

Model Mechanics

Two variant models were created, one each for RN and AS. The GENOP, BW, and TOH problem-spaces were the same in the two models. The productions constituting these problem-spaces were integrated into LTM before solving the Tower of Hanoi. The two models differed in three areas. First, RN's model was given the ability to label subtowers as subtowers before it was given the ability to label them as movable, while AS' model was given the two abilities simultaneously. This corresponds to the fact that RN noticed subtowers well before trying to move them, whereas AS noticed and used subtowers at the same time. In both models, the relevant productions were integrated into LTM at the indicated point in the human subjects' problem-solving. Second, AS required several additional productions to model the different initial states in her one-disk through four-disk problems. These were integrated into LTM before the start of each problem. Third, a small set of special-case productions (two for AS and one for RN) modeled instances in which the subjects used reasoning processes outside of the scope of the GENOP, BW, and TOH problem-spaces. In AS' model, one production was used to halt her simulation after placing disk 4 on the Destination in the first trial, mimicking AS' giving up midway on her first trial. Another production mimicked AS' second-trial realization that disk 1 had to go to the Destination on the first move. Finally, one production mimicked RN's violation of the disk non-repetition heuristic at state 5,_,1234. The first of these productions was introduced along with the three problem-spaces; the last two were introduced at the appropriate points in the problem-solving. Effectively, the two models only explained moves that corresponded to a strict use of the recursive and GTE strategies. Learning was always on; the models therefore learned continuously from their experience.

Model Behavior

Upon starting to solve the problem, the models used the TOH problem-space. Since TOH cannot generate operators, it encountered impasses and used GENOP to supply the needed move-disk operators. At this point, the models did not notice subtowers, and therefore generated implementable operators according to the GTE strategy. Upon learning about subtowers, GENOP began generating operators to move (the bottom disks of) subtowers. Since such operators were not directly implementable, impasses resulted and BW was used to reason out how to make progress towards applying the operators. BW tried to generate an operator to move the blocking disk/tower out of the way. If BW produced an implementable move-disk operator, the new operator was used in TOH. If BW produced an unimplementable operator, another impasse resulted and BW was once again used to reason about the new unimplementable operator. This successive use of BW on a single move produced the observed recursion. BW's first implementable result was used to continue progress in TOH. The selection-space was used every time GENOP or BW had to choose between several versions of an operator. The selection-space applied the heuristics discussed above to make the choices. Learning had three major effects on the model's behavior. First, it produced the chunks that noticed nested subtowers. Second, it abbreviated, with time, the amount of processing needed to use both the GTE and recursive strategies. Third, it eventually built chunks that directly generated move-disk operators in TOH, thus bypassing strategic processing.

MODEL AND DATA: THE FIT

Problem-Solving Fit

The models show a good quantitative fit to the subjects' external problem-solving behavior. Moves made by the model corresponded to 77% and 67% of AS's and RN's first-trial moves, respectively. In the remaining trials, the correspondence was almost always 100% with the exception of AS's second trial (94%) and RN's last trial (97%). Unmodeled moves were the result of errors or error-recovery on the subjects' part, both of which deviated from a perfect GTE or recursive sequence; these moves either had no analog in the models, or were mimicked with the special-purpose productions described above. (Both types of moves were counted against the models.) To test the models further, RN's move-times were correlated with the number of decision-cycles that his model required to make the corresponding moves. (Unmodeled moves were not included in this correlation.) The correlations, in order of trials, were r = 0.69, 0.61, 0.85, 0.45 (0.75), and 0.01. The Trial 4 correlation was low because RN remembered the first move and executed it directly, whereas the model reasoned it out; without this outlier, the correlation goes to 0.75. The final correlation was nil (and should be), because both RN and the model had low variance. Move-time data was not reported for AS in Anzai & Simon (1979) so no correlations could be calculated.

The models' problem-solving strategies displayed a good qualitative fit to the subjects'. We simulated a pure form of the GTE and recursive strategies. Therefore, the models showed some differences: their GTE showed no occasional goal-setting and their recursive strategy showed excess goal-setting between subtowers. Within these boundaries, the models' GTE and recursive strategies showed the same type of reasoning and behavior as AS and RN. The protocols might be fit more closely by remembering more of BW's reasoning chain or using the BW problem-space earlier. However, a closer fit would not change the basic result, i.e., that the recursive strategy arises from noticing and using (nested) subtowers in problem-solving.

Strategy-Change Fit

The models closely fit the qualitative aspects of the subjects' strategy-change. AS's and RN's models acquired the recursive strategy at the same point that AS and RN did. RN's model, like RN, acquires the recursive strategy at state _,1234,5; AS's model, like AS, acquires it during its 3-disk experiment. In both cases, the model's acquisition was the result of having correctly mimicked subtower-noticing and use. RN's model had been learning to notice subtowers for the same amount of time that

RN did; upon acquiring the ability to mark labeled towers as movable, the model was immediately able to make use of that information. AS's model had had previous experience with a two-disk tower, and thus saw the three-disk tower as a nested tower (a two-disk tower sitting on disk 3), allowing it to apply BW. Thus, the switch to the recursive strategy is not due to the subtower-noticing productions per se, but to the chunks that allow the models to see the subtowers as nested and to Soar's ability to recursively use problem-spaces. Finally, the models, like RN and AS, acquired the recursive strategy suddenly. This is because the models treat movable objects (disks or subtowers) alike: as soon as subtowers are noticed, they can immediately be reasoned about.

Learning Fit

The learning displayed by the models showed a good qualitative fit to the subjects'. Besides noticing subtowers, the models' learning did two major things: it abbreviated strategic processing and it eventually caused well-learned moves to be executed directly, without the need for any strategic processing. The abbreviation of strategic processing appeared in the protocols as decreased verbalization over trials, as well as corresponding decreases of move-times in RN's protocol. Making well-learned moves directly executable brought the model more in line with the sparse recursive reasoning displayed by the subjects. After the moves between major subtowers had been well-learned, the model, like the subjects, only reasoned out moves when confronted with a subtower.

CONCLUSIONS

Our model has provided a simple answer to the question of Tower of Hanoi strategy-acquisition. It comes about because people notice nested subtowers and use spatial-manipulation reasoning to move them. This latter capability is cast in terms of physical objects in general, and so is able to work with either disks or towers once these have been noted as relevant to the task at hand. In positing this answer, our model has bypassed the need for some of the basic assumptions of previous models and speculations. Our model, like previous models, works by problem-space search. However, our model works in multiple problem-spaces, not one, and thus claims that people (who can use multiple types of reasoning on a single task) do likewise. The claim of multiple problem-spaces is both a specific claim of our model and a general claim of Soar, which processes information in many problem-spaces.

Second, we have reduced the types of information that prior models claimed had to be learned. Like previous models, ours learns continuously from its experience. But, the crucial information that allows the switch to the recursive strategy is noticing (nested) subtowers. This paper has described how this knowledge is incorporated into problem-solving to produce a new strategy; future work will tackle the mechanics of subtower-noticing per se.

Third, our model has eliminated prior knowledge of domain-independent MEA as the cause of strategy-change. While our model certainly behaves according to MEA in the BW problem-space, that MEA is a direct result of domain-specific knowledge, and is not necessarily transferable to non-spatial-manipulation domains. The recursion characteristic of Tower of Hanoi solutions comes about because of Soar's ability to recursively use problem-spaces to resolve impasses. We have therefore set up a strong alternative hypothesis to strategy-adaptation: strategy-building. This claim about MEA is a general Soar claim, as Soar has nothing corresponding to a domain-independent MEA. Rather, Soar's use of weak methods stems from its task knowledge against the background of its use of multiple problem-spaces (Laird & Newell, 1983)

Fourth, our model directly relies on prior knowledge of a specific domain: spatial-manipulation problems. We have therefore taken this task out of the realm of knowledge-lean tasks, and made it more knowledge-intensive, where the knowledge used is knowledge of spatial relationships and operators. In so doing, we have blurred the boundaries of the traditional toy-task category.

Finally, the work done here will generalize to other task domains. The fundamental insight, that strategy-change comes about via noticing aggregate problem features and attempting to operate on them, is certainly empirically verifiable, and therefore amenable to modeling, in other tasks. The GENOP problem-space might be easily extended to other tasks, thus providing a source of models and ideas about people's default strategies. Finally, the BW problem-space might be expanded to include many other spatial-manipulation tasks, and thus might be the starting point for a single Soar theory of puzzle problem-solving.

To conclude, this model derives its explanatory power from being a subtheory of Soar. Soar provides the ability to search in problem-spaces, the learning, and the theory of how knowledge is transmitted between problem-spaces. Our task as theorists has been to carefully specify the knowledge people have about the Tower of Hanoi. What Soar has thus done is not only ease our burden as theorists, but reduce our theoretical degrees of freedom as well. In return, the success of this model supports Soar as a unified theory of human cognition.

ACKNOWLEDGEMENTS

We thank the members of the Soar group and the Carnegie-Mellon Department of Psychology, particularly David Klahr, Kenneth Kotovsky, and Kurt VanLehn for helpful criticism and insights on this work. We offer special thanks to two anonymous reviewers for their helpful comments. This work was supported by the Information Sciences Division, Office of Naval Research, under contract N00014-86-K-0678, and by a Ford Foundation Minority Postdoctoral Fellowship awarded to Dirk Ruiz. The views expressed in this paper are those of the authors and do not necessarily reflect those of the supporting agencies.

REFERENCES

Anzai, Y., & Simon, H. A. (1979). The theory of learning by doing. *Psychological Review, 86(2)*, 124-140.

Egan, D. E., & Greeno, J. G. (1974). Theory of rule induction: Knowledge acquired in concept learning, serial pattern learning, and problem solving. In L. W. Gregg (Ed.), *Knowledge and cognition*, Hillsdale, New Jersey: Lawrence Erlbaum Associates.

Laird, J. & Newell, A. (1983) A universal weak method: Summary of results. In *Proceedings of IJCAI-83*, Los Altos, CA: Kaufman.

Lewis, R., Newell, A. & Polk, T. (1989). *Towards a Soar theory of taking instructions for immediate reasoning tasks.* Manuscript submitted for publication.

Newell, A. (1980). Reasoning, problem solving, and decision processes: The problem space as a fundamental category. In R. Nickerson (Ed.), *Attention and Performance VIII*, Hillsdale, New Jersey: Lawrence Erlbaum Associates.

Newell, A. (in press). *Unified theories of cognition*. Cambridge, MA: Harvard University Press.

Ruiz, D. (1988). Learning and problem-solving: What is learned while solving the Towers of Hanoi (Doctoral dissertation, Stanford University, 1987). *Dissertation Abstracts International, 42*, 3438B.

Simon, H. A. (1975). The functional equivalence of problem-solving skills. *Cognitive Psychology, 7*, 268-288.

VanLehn, K. (1989). *Learning events in the discovery of problem solving strategies.* Manuscript submitted for publication.

LEARNING RELATIVE ATTRIBUTE WEIGHTS FOR INSTANCE-BASED CONCEPT DESCRIPTIONS

David W. Aha Dale M. McNulty
Department of Information & Computer Science
University of California, Irvine, CA 92717 U.S.A.
(714) 856-8779 (714) 631-3021
aha@ics.uci.edu mcnulty@ics.uci.edu

ABSTRACT

Nosofsky recently described an elegant instance-based model (GCM) for concept learning that defined similarity (partly) in terms of a set of attribute weights. He showed that, when given the proper parameter settings, the GCM model closely fit his human subject data on classification performance. However, no algorithm was described for learning the attribute weights. The central thesis of the GCM model is that subjects distribute their attention among attributes to optimize their classification and learning performance. In this paper, we introduce two comprehensive process models based on the GCM. Our first model is simply an extension of the GCM that learns relative attribute weights. The GCM's learning and representational capabilities are limited – concept descriptions are assumed to be disjoint and exhaustive. Therefore, our second model is a further extension that learns a unique set of attribute weights for each concept description. Our empirical evidence indicates that this extension outperforms the simple GCM process model when the domain includes overlapping concept descriptions with conflicting attribute relevancies.

Keywords: concept learning, concept-dependent attribute weights, instance-based concept descriptions, Generalized Context Model, categorization

1. MOTIVATION

Research on supervised learning algorithms and categorization models share the goal of designing an intelligent concept learning model and associated concept description representation. Of course, the concentrations in the two disciplines differ (i.e., computational tractability and psychological plausibility respectively). We believe that these two perspectives are complementary and mutually beneficial. For example, supervised learning strategies can be used to support processing components for models of categorization.

In this paper we introduce two process models for categorization, each of which is an extension of Nosofsky's (1986, 1987) Generalized Context Model (GCM). Nosofsky posited that an attention-focusing process learns the GCM's attribute weights, but no such algorithm was described. Our first model, GCM-SW (**S**ingle set of **W**eights), is a principled process model that learns a single set of attribute weights for the GCM (but not the GCM's scale or concept bias parameters). Our second model, GCM-MW (**M**ultiple sets of **W**eights), combines separate progress described in the machine learning and categorization theory literatures. GCM-MW learns a separate set of attribute weights and concept description for each concept (Aha, 1989) in Nosofsky's GCM.

Nosofsky (1986; 1987) showed that the GCM model closely fit human subject data on several simple concept learning tasks. However, its performance degrades when the concepts being learned require conflicting attribute settings to optimize categorization of their instances. Therefore, our contribution is twofold. First, we describe an algorithm for learning the GCM's attribute weights. Second, we show that, by using separate sets of attribute weights, the process model learns more quickly and accurately during complex concept learning tasks.

GCM-SW and GCM-MW are examples of *instance-based learning* (IBL) algorithms. We introduce the methodology and framework for IBL algorithms in the following section.

2. INSTANCE-BASED LEARNING AND THE PROCESS FRAMEWORK

IBL algorithms process a sequence of *training instances* and output a set of *concept descriptions* whose accuracy can be evaluated by a disjoint set of *test instances.* IBL algorithms process instances incrementally; concept descriptions are updated after each classification attempt. Each instance is represented with a set of n attribute-value pairs. Instances represent unique points in an *instance space*, where each attribute represents one dimension in the space.[1] Concept descriptions are updated after each instance is classified. These descriptions map instances to an interpretation of the instance space called the *psychological space* (Shepard, 1987). *Concepts* are unions of regions in psychological space.

IBL algorithms represent each concept description with a set of instances rather than with abstractions derived from them (i.e., rules, decision trees). The extension of the concept description in the psychological space is made with respect to a similarity function and a classification function. IBL algorithms neither modify nor discard informative instances – they are simply added to a concept description. Therefore, IBL algorithms have low learning (updating) costs and retain the concept-describing information present in specific instances.

IBL algorithms are specified by a framework consisting of three components.

1. First, a *similarity function* computes the continuously-valued *similarity* of a training instance i to an instance in a concept description.
2. Next, a *classification function* inputs the similarity function's results on all concept description instances and yields a probabilistic classification of i for that concept.
3. Finally, a *concept description updater* is used to maintain summary information, such as attribute weight settings. Inputs include i, the similarity results, the classification results, and the concept descriptions. It yields the modified concept descriptions.

These components are sufficient to support the application and acquisition of concept descriptions. This framework specifies a spectrum of IBL models, obtained by varying these components. Our models will be described with respect to this framework.

3. LEARNING THE GCM'S ATTRIBUTE WEIGHTS

This section introduces a process model interpretation of Nosofsky's GCM (1986, 1987). This model is described using the framework introduced in Section 2.

[1] In this paper, we restrict attribute values to be either Boolean, nominal, or continuously-valued.

Table 1: The attribute weight updating algorithm, where the inputs are the current training instance x, current concept description D, and Classguess(x) (the predicted classification of x). Variable λ is the higher relative observed class frequency of x's actual and its predicted class. Variable y is x's most similar neighbor that is also in x's predicted class. Since the instances are normalized, step 3 yields a value in $[0, 1]$.

1. **LET** λ = max(ObservedRelativeFrequency(Class(x)),ObservedRelativeFrequency(Classguess(x)))
2. **LET** $y = \{d \in D | \forall d' \in D$ {Class(d')=Classguess(x) & Similarity(x,d) $\geq$ Similarity(x,d')}}
3. **LET** difference = $|x_a - y_a|$
4. **IF** (x's classification was correctly predicted)
   THEN increment = (1-λ)$\times$(1-difference)
   ELSE increment = (1-λ)$\times$difference
5. total-attribute-weight$_a$ = total-attribute-weight$_a$ + increment
6. total-possible-attribute-weight$_a$ = total-possible-attribute-weight$_a$ + (1-λ)

3.1 GCM-SW: An Interpretation of the Generalized Context Model

Our interpretation of Nosofsky's Generalized Context Model is named *GCM-SW*.

3.1.1 Similarity Function: The distance between instances x and y in an n-dimensional instance space is defined as:[2]

$$\text{Distance}(x, y) = \sqrt{\sum_{a=1,n} \text{Weight}_a (x_a - y_a)^2} \tag{1}$$

Similarity is subsequently defined as:

$$\text{Similarity}(x, y) = e^{-\text{Distance}(x,y)^2} \tag{2}$$

3.1.2 Classification Function: The probability of classifying x in concept c is defined as:[3]

$$\Pr(c|x) = \frac{\sum_{y \in cd(c)} \text{Similarity}(x, y)}{\sum_{c \in C} \sum_{y \in cd(c)} \text{Similarity}(x, y)} \tag{3}$$

where $cd(c)$ is the set of instances in c's concept description and C is the set of concepts to be learned.

3.1.3 Concept Description Updater: All training instances are saved in a single concept description. GCM-SW's attribute weights are defined as follows: (for each attribute a)[4]

$$\text{Weight}_a = max(\frac{\text{total-attribute-weight}_a}{\text{total-possible-attribute-weight}_a} - 0.5, 0). \tag{4}$$

The attribute weights are updated after each training instance x is classified. Its most similar neighbor y in the concept description is used to update the weights, as described in Table 1. The total-attribute-weight is incremented by a fraction of that added to the total-possible-attribute-weight$_a$. The total-attribute-weight's reward is high when it assists

[2]Missing is Nosofsky's *scale parameter*, which reflects overall discriminability in a psychological space (i.e., it increases with increasing domain knowledge). This parameter's effect is an emergent property of GCM-SW's learning behavior.

[3]Missing are Nosofsky's *concept bias parameters*, which involve other topics of attention that we do not address here.

[4]Attribute weight values are defined in the range $[0, 0.5]$ instead of $[0, 1]$ because (1) an irrelevant attribute's total attribute weight is expected to be half its total possible attribute weight and (2) we wanted irrelevant attributes to have 0 weight.

making a correct classification decision and is low otherwise. More specifically, its increment is high when either (1) a correct classification occurs and the instances' attribute values are similar to each other or (2) an incorrect classification occurs and they are dissimilar. Otherwise, the total-attribute-weight's addend is small since the attribute's value did not assist in predicting the correct classification. This algorithm attends to classes with low observed relative frequency in order to overcome highly skewed concept frequency distributions.

Finally, the weights are linearly scaled to sum to 1. This simulates the distribution of resource-limited "attention" across attributes (Nosofsky, 1986; 1987).

The weight-learning algorithm is best explained with an example. For this purpose we will study GCM-SW's ability to learn the concept "Ph.D. student" from instances (people) described with three Boolean attributes ("is enrolled","has M.S. degree", and "is married"). Suppose that GCM-SW has been trained on 4 instances, only one of which was a Ph.D. student (with attribute values <True,True,True>), the resultant total-attribute-weights settings are (0.65,0.65,0.65), and the total-possible-attribute-weights are all 0.75. If the fifth instance is incorrectly classified as a Ph.D. student and has attribute values <False,False,True> (i.e., not enrolled, no M.S., married), then the new total-attribute-weight settings are (0.8,0.8,0.65) and the total-possible-attribute-weights are all 1.0. Finally, if the sixth instance is correctly classified as a Ph.D. student and has attribute values <True,False,False> (i.e., enrolled, no M.S., unmarried), then the new total-attribute-weight settings are (1.6,0.8,0.65) and the new total-possible-attribute-weights are 1.8. This indicates that GCM-SW has learned that the attribute "is enrolled" is more predictive of the Ph.D. class than either "has M.S. degree" or "is married." Good attribute predictors will have higher attribute weights than less relevant attributes.

3.2 The Utility of the GCM-SW Model

The GCM-SW algorithm increases concept learning rate by allowing relevant attributes to have greater influence in similarity calculations and, subsequently, classification decisions. When learning tasks involve concepts with conflicting attribute relevancies, GCM-SW learns concept descriptions more quickly than does the equivalent algorithm that weights all attributes equally. We studied GCM-SW's learning behavior, with and without learning attribute weights, in a domain described by twelve Boolean attributes. Instances were randomly drawn from a uniform distribution of the instance space. Only positive instances had values of 1 for their first attribute. The resulting learning curve (Figure 1) indicates that GCM-SW learns the concept far more quickly when attribute weights are learned.

GCM-SW assigns the same initial weight to each attribute. As training progresses, the relevant attribute's weight increases while the irrelevant attributes' weights decrease. Figure 2 summarizes GCM-SW's weight-learning behavior for this concept learning task.

3.3 A Limitation of the GCM-SW Model

Nosofsky (1986, 1987) did not apply the GCM to complex concept learning tasks. In particular, concepts were assumed to be disjoint. They were also assumed to exhaust the instance space. These simplifications limit the GCM's learning capabilities.

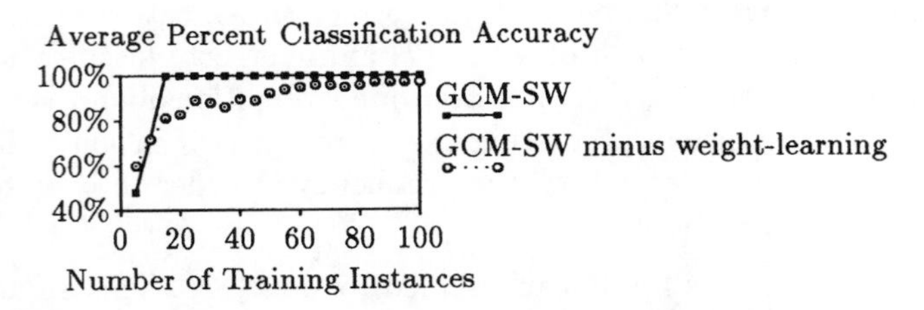

Figure 1: Average percent classification accuracies (over 25 trials) of GCM-SW with and without its attribute weight-learning capability. The rate of learning is increased when attribute weights are learned.

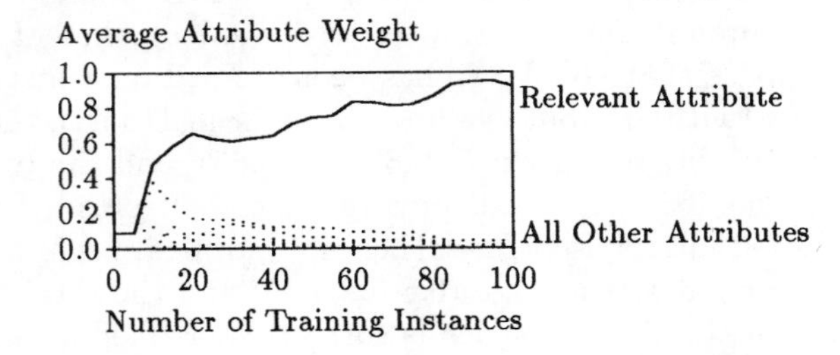

Figure 2: GCM-SW's average (25 trials) attribute weight settings during training. The relevant attribute's weight is quickly distinguished from the irrelevant attributes' weights.

The GCM was designed to model the *attention-optimization hypothesis*, which posits that humans optimize their classification performance by distributing their attention among the given attributes. To satisfy this assumption, the GCM's representation needs to be extended to simultaneously learn overlapping concepts which require conflicting attribute weight settings to optimize classification performance. In Section 4, we present GCM-MW, an extension of the GCM that can learn overlapping, non-exhaustive concept descriptions, where each concept is associated with a unique set of attribute weights. We show that GCM-MW has a faster learning rate than GCM-SW for these concept learning tasks.

4. LEARNING MULTIPLE PSYCHOLOGICAL SPACES

Our extension of the GCM-SW algorithm is *GCM-MW*, which learns a separate set of attribute weights for each concept description being learned. Like GCM-SW, GCM-MW is best described as an instantiation of our instance-based process framework.

4.1 GCM-MW: An Extension of the Generalized Context Model

4.1.1 Similarity Function: GCM-MW's similarity function is concept-dependent, but otherwise identical to that used in GCM-SW. The distance between instances x and y in an n-dimensional instance space with respect to a concept c is defined as:

$$\text{Distance}(c, x, y) = \sqrt{\sum_{a=1,n} \text{Weight}_{c_a}(x_a - y_a)^2} \tag{5}$$

Similarity is subsequently defined as:

$$\text{Similarity}(c, x, y) = e^{-\text{Distance}(c,x,y)^2} \tag{6}$$

Similarity is concept-dependent. For example, we would expect that, for any tiger t and cat c, Similarity($animal, t, c$) is greater than Similarity(pet, t, c).

4.1.2 Classification Function: The probability of classifying x in concept c is:

$$\Pr(c|x) = \frac{\sum_{y \in cd(c)} \text{Similarity}(c, x, y)}{\sum_{c \in C} \sum_{y \in cd(c)} \text{Similarity}(c, x, y)} \tag{7}$$

where $cd(c)$ is the set of instances in c's concept description and C is the set of concepts to be learned. (Note that instances in $cd(c)$ are either positive or negative.)

4.1.3 Concept Description Updater: Finally, weight learning in GCM-MW is the same as in GCM-SW except that *each concept description has a separate set of weights.*

$$\text{Weight}_{c_a} = max(\frac{\text{total-attribute-weight}_{c_a}}{\text{total-possible-attribute-weight}_{c_a}} - 0.5, 0). \tag{8}$$

In our previous example, we saw that being enrolled in a Ph.D. program was highly diagnostic of the Ph.D. class. However, if GCM-SW was simultaneously trying to learn the concept of being married, the attribute weight for "is enrolled" would decrease. Subsequently, this attribute would have less impact on classifying people as Ph.D. students. GCM-MW avoids this conflict by maintaining a separate set of attribute weights and description for each concept being learned.

Updating the attribute weights after each classification continuously changes a concept's similarity function. This notion was originally captured by Salzberg's (1988) exemplar-based system, which inspired our work on weight-learning algorithms. We extended Salzberg's algorithm by (1) removing an ad-hoc parameter that required different settings for each domain, (2) defining how it learns weights for continuously-valued attributes, and (3) extending it to learn attribute weights separately for each concept. Thus, GCM-MW learns similarity functions independently for each concept description. This is an important capability for distinguishing different contexts during classification and other problem solving tasks.

In summary, GCM-MW is an incremental concept learning algorithm that updates its concept descriptions after classifying each training instance and learns the appropriate attribute weight settings *for each concept.* Furthermore, GCM-MW's concept descriptions need not exhaust the instance space nor be disjoint. Finally, since GCM-MW employs a separate interpretation of the instance space for each concept, it can represent independent and overlapping concept descriptions.

4.2 The Utility of the GCM-MW Model

GCM-MW models the attention-optimization hypothesis even when the learned concept descriptions overlap and differ in their attribute weight settings. We applied GCM-SW and GCM-MW to an instance space described by five numeric-valued attributes whose values

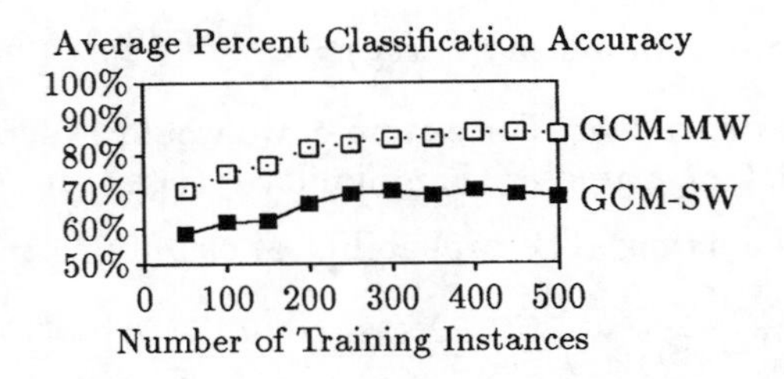

Figure 3: Average learning curves (over 25 trials) on a domain with five overlapping and non-exhaustive concepts. GCM-MW learns more quickly by building independent descriptions for each concept.

range in [0, 100]. This space contains five overlapping and non-exhaustive concepts. Each concept is defined in terms of a single attribute. For each $n \in [1,5]$, the nth concept's instances have values greater than 50 in their n^{th} attribute. Instances are randomly drawn from a uniform distribution over the instance space and can be members of any subset (possibly empty) of the five concepts.

The learning curve in Figure 3 summarizes the applications of these two algorithms to this domain. In summary, GCM-MW learns the concepts' descriptions more quickly because it builds an independent interpretation of the instance space for each concept.[5] In effect, GCM-MW simultaneously learns multiple psychological spaces.

5. SOME LIMITATIONS AND FUTURE WORK

While GCM-MW performs well along a number of dimensions, it has several limitations. First, we have incorrectly defined similarity such that the similarity between two instances cannot increase with additional attribute comparisons, even when the additional attribute values indicate that these instances are similar. We plan to experiment with variants of Tversky's (1977) contrast model, which defines similarity both in terms of attribute value commonalities *and* (directed) differences, in an attempt to solve this problem.

Also, GCM-MW's classification function's behavior in the presence of millions of attributes and/or instances is needlessly expensive. Some control is needed so that similarities are computed only for relevant instances (i.e., those in the concept's description that are most similar to the instance being classified). We plan to explore the role of attention and intelligent indexing schemes in the future (McNulty, 1988).

We plan to demonstrate how IBL models can learn non-normal category distributions. Neumann (1977) presented evidence that people can learn such distributions. Moreover, Fried and Holyoak (1984) argue that only instance-based models can describe non-normal category distributions.

We would also like to determine whether the GCM-SW and GCM-MW models simulate human categorization behavior on complex concept learning tasks. While Nosofsky (1986, 1987) showed that the GCM model can closely fit human subject data on simple tasks, he

[5]Preliminary experiments indicate that GCM-SW's classification accuracy begins to approach GCM-MW's after processing several thousand instances from this domain.

did not describe how it behaves when concept descriptions overlap and have conflicting, optimal attribute-weight settings.

6. SUMMARY

In this paper, we introduced two instance-based process models, GCM-SW and GCM-MW. Both models are based on Nosofsky's (1986, 1987) generalized context model. We introduced a simple algorithm for learning GCM's attribute weights. We have also argued that a separate set of relative attribute weights for each concept description, as used in GCM-MW, is needed to represent and accurately learn complex concept descriptions (i.e., overlapping). GCM-MW can learn independent and overlapping concept descriptions by developing a separate psychological space for each concept to be described.

However, our model has several limitations. For example, similarity should not increase monotonically with fewer numbers of attributes. Also, our instance-based model needlessly computes the similarity of an instance with all previously observed instances for each classification. It should instead compute similarities for only a relevant subset of the instances. We plan to extend our model in these and other directions in the future.

ACKNOWLEDGEMENTS

We would like to thank Dennis Kibler, John Gennari, David Ruby, and our reviewers for their suggestions on earlier drafts of this paper.

REFERENCES

Aha, D. W. (1989). Incremental, Instance-Based Learning of independent and graded concept descriptions. To appear in *Proceedings of the Sixth International Workshop on Machine Learning*. Ithaca, NY: Morgan Kaufmann.

Fried, L. S., & Holyoak, K. J. (1984). Induction of category distributions: A framework for classification learning. *Journal of Experimental Psychology: Learning, Memory, and Cognition, 10*, 234–257.

McNulty, D. M. (1988). Extending moment analysis with directed attention to handle structural variations in character recognition. In *Proceedings of the Seventh Biennial Conference of the Canadian Society for the Computational Studies of Intelligence* (pp. 206–212). Edmonton, Canada: Morgan Kaufmann.

Neumann, P. G. (1977). Visual prototype formation with discontinuous representation of dimensions of variability. *Memory & Cognition, 5*, 187–197.

Nosofsky, R. M. (1986). Attention, similarity, and the identification-categorization relationship. *Journal of Experimental Psychology: General, 15*, 39–57.

Nosofsky, R. M. (1987). Attention and learning processes in the identification and categorization of integral stimuli. *Journal of Experimental Psychology: Learning, Memory, and Cognition, 13*, 87–108.

Salzberg, S. (1988). *Exemplar-based learning: Theory and implementation* (Technical Report TR-10-88). Cambridge, MA: Harvard University, Center for Research in Computing Technology.

Shepard, R. N. (1987). Toward a universal law of generalization for psychological science. *Science. 237*, 1317–1323.

Tversky, A. (1977). Features of Similarity. *Psychological Review, 84*, 327–352.

Selective Associations in Causality Judgments II: A Strong Causal Relationship May Facilitate Judgments of a Weaker One

A. G. Baker and Dwight Mazmanian
McGill University and Concordia University.

ABSTRACT

Previous research had shown that a strong relationship between a causal factor and an outcome reduces estimates of the relationship between a second causal factor and the same outcome (two causal factors, one outcome). In the present experiment subjects judged the effect of one response (pressing a spacebar) on two outcomes (a ball and/or a box might change color). We used an operant-like procedure in which subjects did problems on the video screen of a computer. The response was involved in various contingencies with the ball and box. In the critical condition one outcome (changes in the color of the box) was highly correlated with the cause (pressing the spacebar) and the other, target, outcome (changing ball color) was only modestly related to the cause. In contrast to earlier work the concurrent strong causal relationship increased the perceived causal relationship between the target outcome and the cause. The present experiment was derived from and its results are partially accounted for by the Rescorla-Wagner model (1972), which is a simple connectionist model.

INTRODUCTION

In classical conditioning experiments animals which are asked to make judgments of the covariation between an outcome and two signals for the occurrence of that outcome often exhibit what are called selective associations. They "decide" that one signal is the cause and discount the other. They show that they have made this decision by showing a strong conditioned response to one stimulus and little or none to the other (e.g., Wagner, Logan, Haberlandt, and Price; 1968).

We (Baker, Mercier, Vallee-Tourangeau, Pam & Frank, unpublished manuscript) have recently demonstrated that if humans are asked to make judgments of the likelihood of an outcome given two possible causes they show a similar tendency. In one of our experiments subjects played a game which had two possible causes (airplanes or landmines) of an outcome (explosions). When one of the causes (the presence of the airplane) was very highly correlated with the outcome it caused a reduction in the judged effectiveness of the other cause which was moderately correlated with the outcome. The presence of a highly correlated causal factor reduced the judgments of the effectiveness of a second cause.This "error" in judgments is very interesting because it is predicted by the Rescorla-Wagner model (1972) which is a simple connectionist model of animal associative learning and which Shanks (1985) and others have suggested can be extended to the human judgment process.

The Rescorla-Wagner model (1972) explains the selective association effects in which a strong causal factor reduces judgments of a weaker one by claiming that there is a limited amount of associative strength to go around and that the causes compete for it. In our earlier studies the strong cause acquires much of the associative strength so the weaker cause gets little. This notion could be contrasted with a cognitive representational view that might claim that the interaction between the judgments occurs at the representational level when the subjects are processing the correlations between the events. We attempted to contrast these two explanations and to extend our results from the discrete trial procedures that we previously used which involved two causes and one outcome to a procedure modeled on free operant techniques and in which one response or causal factor produced two outcomes. According to the Rescorla-Wagner model unlike two causes, two outcomes should not compete with one another yet a simple representational account might predict that if they involve contingencies similar to those used in the earlier experiments they should require a similar amount or level of cognitive processing and thus might be expected produce an interaction that is similar to that found in our earlier experiments.

We modified a procedure that was developed by Wasserman and his colleagues (e.g., Wasserman, Chatlosh, & Neunabar; 1983). Subjects sit at a computer and press the spacebar and then estimate whether this action has an effect on a geometric figure. An outcome involves the figure changing color. The procedure is "free operant". It is not divided into a series of explicit trials as were our earlier multiple causality experiments. The session is divided into 1 second "bins". If one or more responses occurs in any bin it is called an instance of a response and the probability of an outcome is determined by the conditional probability of an outcome given a response. If no response occurs during any second then the outcome is determined by the conditional probability of an outcome given no response.

The contingency or covariation between two events is best described by what is called the delta P rule (dP) (c.f., Allan, 1980). The contingency can be either positive or negative; that is the cause may make the effect more likely to occur or it might make it less likely to occur. The dP rule describes the one way contingency of the cause on the effect and it is simply the difference between the conditional probability that the effect or outcome will occur given that the cause has occurred and the conditional probability that the outcome will occur in the absence of the cause. Delta P varies from -1 to + 1. A dP of 1 represents a perfect positive contingency, a dP of zero represents no relationship between the cause and effect, and a dP of -1 represents a perfect negative contingency.

In our experiment the outcomes involved the center of a square (box) and a circle (ball) changing color. The idea behind the experiment was to see if the presence of an outcome that was highly correlated (dP = 1 or -1) with the response would reduce estimates of a modestly correlated (dP = .5 or -.5) outcome. To this end every subject was asked to do nine problems in a factorial design in which three contingencies of the moderately correlated ball with the outcome (dPs = .5, -.5 and 0 as a control) were paired with three contingencies of the highly contingent box (dPs = 1,-1, and 0). The issue of most interest was whether a highly contingent box would reduce the estimates of the moderately correlated ball.

METHOD.

SUBJECTS AND APPARATUS

The subjects were 12 female and 6 male volunteers from Concordia University. The stimuli were presented on an IBM PC computer with a color display (color graphics adapter) and consisted of a circle (ball) and a square (box). The box and ball were presented in the center of the screen, side by side, with the ball on the left. The figures were outlines and their colors were from the IBM CGA palettes. The ball was green and the box was brown. On trials in which an "outcome" occurred the centers of the figures changed colors for 100 ms. The center of the ball changed from black to red and the center of the box changed from black to green. On alternating games the palettes were switched substituting the colors cyan, magenta, and white directly for green, red and brown respectively.

PROCEDURE

The subjects signed a consent form and then sat down at the computer and followed the online instructions. There were five screens of instructions. Between the first four screens were demonstrations of the essentials of the task. Following the first screen of instructions the subjects were shown the ball and box. When they pressed the spacebar the ball and box appeared. After 2 s the next page of instructions appeared. Following this page the subjects were shown how a response could make the centers of the ball and box change colors. They pressed the spacebar and the ball and box appeared. When the spacebar was next pressed the centers of the ball and the box changed color for 200 ms. The centers then cleared and 1 s later the next instructions appeared. Following them, the subjects were shown that the objects could change color with no response. They pressed the spacebar and the ball and box reappeared. One second later the centers of the ball and the box changed color for 200 ms and then cleared for 1 s.

The instructions described the task and introduced the above demonstrations. The subjects were explicitly told that it was a good strategy to refrain from responding some of the time in order to see what would happen in the absence of a response. They were also instructed that they should make their judgments on a scale of -100 to +100. The end points represented perfect negative and positive contingencies respectively and the midpoint represented zero contingencies. When the spacebar was pressed the screen cleared and the first problem began with the appearance of the ball and box. Each problem lasted for 180 s. The problems were divided into 1 s bins. If one or more responses occurred in a bin it was defined as a response and then the occurrence of an outcome was determined by the conditional probability of an outcome given a response for each figure. If there were no responses during a bin then it was defined as an occurrence of no response and the outcomes for both figures were determined by the conditional probability of an outcome given no response. The outcomes happened at the end of each bin (i.e., the center of one or both figures changed color for 100 ms).

The ball was the target figure (to be influenced by the box). There were three ball contingencies, a moderately positive contingency (dP=.5), a moderately negative contingency (dP=-.5), and a zero contingency (dP=0). For the dP=.5 contingency the conditional probability of an outcome given a response was .75 and the conditional probability given no response was .25. For the negative contingency these probabilities were reversed (P(Outcome|Response)=.25; P(Outcome|No Response)=.75). For the zero contingency the probability of an outcome was .5 given a response or no response.

There were also three contingencies for the box: a perfect positive contingency (dP=1), a perfect negative contingency (dP=-1), and a zero contingency (dP=0). For the dP=1 or -1 contingencies the probabilities of an outcome given a response were, of course, either 1 or 0 and the probabilities of a response given no outcome were either 0 or 1. The zero contingency was the same one used for the ball (i.e., probability of an outcome = .5 regardless of whether or not there was a response). All 9 combinations of the ball and box contingencies were given to each subject. Each subject received the contingencies in a different order with each contingency occurring in the first position twice.

Thus in this experiment a moderate positive, a moderate negative or a zero ball contingency was contrasted with either a strong positive, a strong negative or a zero box contingency. If the subjects were to exhibit selective associations as our previous subjects had done then the strong box contingencies would be expected to reduce the estimates of the ball contingencies.

RESULTS.

We analyzed the estimates of the ball and the box contingencies. The results of these analyses indicated that the subjects could discriminate among the contingencies. They discriminated the box contingencies from one another; $F(2,34) = 61.23$; and the ball contingencies did not affect these estimates; $F(2,34) = 0.28$. The subjects discriminated reliably among the three ball contingencies: $F(2,34) = 44.98$. Post hoc tests showed they discriminated each ball contingency from each other; minimum $F(2,34) = 12.02$. There was no reliable effect of the box contingency on the ball estimates; $F(2,34) = 1.62$; but the ball by box interaction was nearly reliable; $F(4,68) = 2.21$; $p < .1$. Thus these data do not extend our earlier results to this paradigm in fact the nearly reliable interaction came about because the estimates of the ball contingency were actually higher (in absolute value) when they were paired with the strong box contingencies (dPs= 1 or -1) than when they were paired with the zero box contingency. In addition to these analyses within the box and ball contingencies we also compared the estimates of the high box contingencies (dPs= 1 and -1) with the moderate ball contingencies (dPs= 5. and -.5) and found that the subjects discriminated between the positive contingencies; $F(1,17) = 26.29$. but that they did not reliably discriminate the -1 contingency from the -.5 contingency; $F(1,17) = 4.18$; $p < .1$.

The preceding analyses expose a potential problem with this experiment as a test of the hypothesis that strong concurrent contingencies might interact with weak ones. To test the hypothesis it would seem necessary to choose a preparation in which the subjects discriminate the strong from the weak contingencies. While this was true for the positive contingencies the discrimination between the negative contingencies was weak. A small number of subjects appeared to do poorly on the box estimates. To formalize this impression we calculated the correlation between each subject's box estimates and the nominal box contingencies. Generally these correlations were quite high. For 12 of the 18 subjects the correlations were higher than .9.

Because it is crucial that the subjects be sensitive to the box contingencies for them to influence the ball contingencies we decided to eliminate those subjects whose box estimates did not correlate significantly at the 5% level with the nominal contingencies. This rather conservative rule eliminated three subjects (maximum $r(8) = .404$, $p > .25$. Figure 1 shows the mean estimates of the ball contingencies with these three subjects removed. The pattern of the results is very clear. When the subjects experienced a strong positive or negative box contingency the absolute value of the ball estimates was higher. That is they judged the moderate but positive ball contingency to be more positive when it was paired with either a strong positive (dP = 1) or a strong negative (dP = -1) box contingency. They also judged the moderate negative contingency to be more negative when it was paired with either a strong positive or negative box contingency. These impression are confirmed by a statistical analysis of the ball estimates with the three subjects removed, there was a significant effect of the ball contingency; $F(2,28) = 66.68$; and no effect of the box contingency; $F(2,28) = 0.37$; but the interaction was now reliable; $F(4,56) = 3.17$. In order to analyze the interaction and to compare the absolute values of the estimates of the positive and negative dP = .5 contingencies we changed the signs of the estimates of the negative contingencies. This replaces the negative means of the -.5 contingencies with their absolute value but does not effect the variance so that

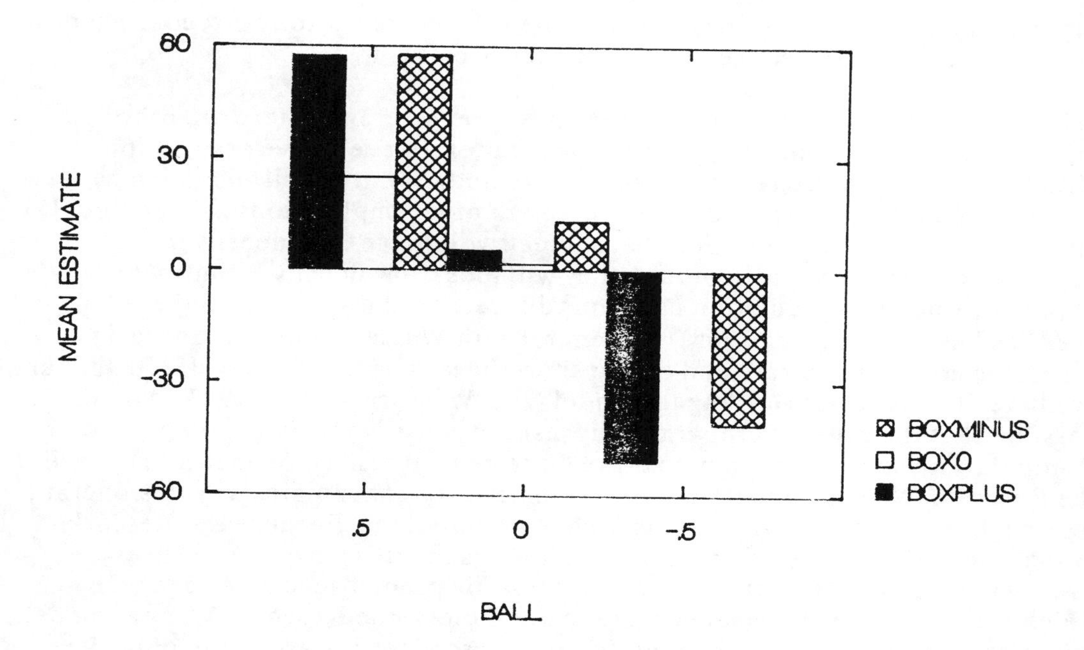

Figure 1: Mean estimates of the ball contingency for the 15 subjects with a high correlation between their box estimates and the nominal box contingencies.

the positive and negative ball contingencies can be directly compared. There was no main effect for ball contingency; $F(3,28) = 0.59$; indicating that the negative contingencies were judged to be as negative as the positive ones were positive. The main effect for Box contingency was now reliable; $F(2,28) = 6.11$; but the interaction was not; $F(2,28) = 0.37$; supporting the observation that the strong box contingencies increased the estimates of the nonzero ball contingencies.

DISCUSSION.

We (Baker et al; unpublished manuscript) have provided evidence that effects analogous to selective associations in animals can occur in human judgments of causality. We found that the presence of an airplane that was highly correlated with explosions reduced the absolute value of judgments of the contingency of landmines that were only moderately correlated with the outcome. This effect was quite robust and was maintained even with major modifications of the game which involved substituting abstract symbols for the airplane and the landmines and changing the instruction sets to ones which did not imply causality at all. Shanks (1986) has also provided evidence that experience with one contingency can reduce estimates of another. Contrary to the above findings, in the present experiment we have found that exposing the subjects to a strong box contingency enhanced rather than reduced ball contingency estimates.

It is of interest to ask why the present results are different. There are other differences between the two preparations. Our earlier selective association effects came from a discrete trials procedure and they are easily modeled by the Rescorla-Wagner (1972) model. But there are other implications of that model and these include the prediction that subjects will judge high density 0 contingencies to more positive than they will judge low density 0 contingency. We have confirmed this prediction using our discrete trial procedure (Baker et al 1989) as has Shanks (e.g., 1985). In general with Wasserman's operant tasks estimates are very accurate and do not show the sort of the density effects that are predicted by the Rescorla-Wagner model (c.f., Wasserman et al 1983). So it is possible that the present preparation is just not sensitive to associative manipulations in the same way that the discrete trial task is. As mentioned earlier the Rescorla-Wagner model provides a framework that explains why this operant task might not be sensitive to associative manipulations. Because the Rescorla-Wagner model explains selective associations as resulting from two causes competing for one effect it would not necessarily predict such an effect here in which two effects have the same cause. Nonetheless, the Rescorla-Wagner model does not easily account for the fact that the present results are in the opposite direction to those of our earlier experiments.

One traditional explanation from the animal literature that might be used to integrate the present results within the traditional associationist framework is that the subjects might generalize between the two figures and/or mistake one outcome for the other. While this is possible, it is really quite unlikely because the subjects clearly understood the tasks and, above and beyond the interaction between the ball contingency and box contingency, they easily discriminated the contingencies from one another.

A second alternative explanation might be that the cognitive load of the perfectly correlated box contingency was low compared to that required for the zero box contingency. Thus when the subjects were concurrently asked to make judgments of the zero box contingency they had less capacity available for making the ball judgments and this suppressed their judgments. The argument is that our results arise not from the strong box contingency facilitating the ball estimates but from the more difficult $dP = 0$ box contingency suppressing the ball estimates. This alternative relies heavily on the additional assumption that the subjects have a zero report bias. If their system is overloaded then they make estimates near zero. This does not seem unreasonable. It must be mentioned, however, that a typical error made in situations in which subjects do not accurately judge contingencies is to go with number of outcomes given a response (Ward & Jenkins, 1965;

Smedslund, 1963) and in the present case this number is quite high because the subjects receive an outcome on 50% of all trials with a response. We also have carried out an indirect test of this explanation. In an unpublished experiment we contrasted the dP=.5 ball contingency with a dP=.8 box contingency. This dP=.8 contingency was quite difficult to do compared to a perfect contingency (thereby increasing the load on the subjects) yet the estimates of the ball contingency in this experiment were very similar to those reported here which used the perfect box contingency. Finally it is our impression from the reports of the subjects that both preparations seem equally difficult.

REFERENCES

Allan, L.G. (1980). A note on measurement of contingency between two binary variables in judgment tasks. *Bulletin of the Psychonomic Society, 15*, 147-149.

Baker, A.G., Berbrier, M., & Vallee-Tourangeau, F. (1989). Judgments of a 2X2 contingency table: Sequential processing and the learning curve. *Quarterly Journal of Experimental Psychology, 41B*, 65-97.

Baker, A.G., Mercier, P., Vallee-Tourangeau, Pam. M., and Frank. M. Selective Associations in Causality Judgments I: A Strong Causal Relationship May Reduce Judgments of a Weaker one. Manuscript submitted for publication

Rescorla, R.A., & Wagner, A.R. (1972). A theory of Pavlovian conditioning: Variations in the effectiveness of reinforcement and non-reinforcement. In A.H. Black & W.F. Prokasy (Eds.), *Classical conditioning II: Current theory and research.* New York: Appleton-Century-Crofts.

Shanks, D.R. (1985). Continuous monitoring of human contingency judgments across trials. *Memory and Cognition, 13*, 158-167.

Shanks, D.R. (1986). Selective attribution and the judgment of causality. *Learning and Motivation,17*, 311-334.

Smedslund, J. (1963). The concept of correlation in adults. *Scandinavian Journal of Psychology, 4*, 165-173.

Wagner, A.R., Logan, F.A., Haberlandt, K., & Price, T. (1968). Stimulus selection in animal discrimination learning. *Journal of Experimental Psychology, 76*, 171-180.

Ward, W. & Jenkins, J. (1965). The display of information and the judgment of contingency. *Canadian Journal of Psychology, 19*, 231-241.

Wasserman, E.A., Chatlosh, D.L. and Neunaber, D.J. (1983). Factors affecting judgments of response-outcome contingencies under free-operant procedures. *Learning and Motivation, 14*, 406-432.

Correspondence to: A.G. Baker, Department of Psychology, McGill University, 1205 Dr. Penfield, Montreal, PQ, Canada, H3A 1B1. Research was supported by an NSERC of Canada grant to Baker and the McGill-IBM (Canada) cooperative.

REPRESENTATION AND ACQUISITION OF KNOWLEDGE OF FUNCTIONAL SYSTEMS

by

Serge BAUDET and Guy DENHIERE

Université de Paris VIII
Groupe TEXTIMA - U.R.A. 218

ABSTRACT

Many experimental studies have shown that learning and memorization of complex information are strongly influenced by the learners' prior knowledge. Thus, detailed analyses of the structures and the processes involved in learning and memorization require precise assessment of the learner's prior knowledge in relation to the characteristics of the domain to be acquired.
We have developed a formalization in terms of systems: relational, transformational, teleological (functional and intentional) which permits us to simultaneously describe that domain being acquired, the representaion of the acquiring organism, and our representation of that representation.
Here, we will report a study in which this formalization was employed in assessing the representation that students with different levels of knowledge about automobile mechanics have of a functional system: the starter system of an automobile.
The predictions made by this formalization were compared with the performances of three groups of students with different levels of knowledge on a series of four tasks: free interview, causal questioning, completing lacunary event triples, and a multiple choice questionaire on the existence of events and causal relations. The criterium used to choose these four tasks was that they differ according to the demands they make in the retrieval of stored information in memory.
The results show that:
(i) subjects with a good level of knowledge have a representation organized in a fuctional autonomous system organized in sub-systems, while
(ii) subjects with lower levels of knowledge do not have a representation organized as a functional system, and
(iii) subjects from the intermediate group built a representation organized as a functional autonomous system but containing less information and more poorly organized in sub-systems.

The emergence of cognitive research on the acquisition of knowledge from texts has led to a break from an approach centered exclusively on text and linguistic knowledge and to take into account the specific characteristics of those type-representations that are knowledge and beliefs (Denhière & Baudet, 1988). While processing a text, an individual constructs several types of representation from the textual information. In the description of those representations, an important step has been the introduction of the concept of mental model (Johnson-Laird, 1983) or situation model (van Dijk & Kintsch, 1983) to conceptualize the world representation that individuals build through their experiences and their learning, and which they activate during the reading of a text. The concept of a model, however, only has value if the model is rigorously defined and if the descriptions of the world and other representations that an individual has of it are clearly specified. So, we propose an analysis in terms of systems as an attempt to produce a conceptualization that allows for a precise description of the representation that we have of the world and of the representation of the representation that the learner builds for himself (Baudet & Denhière, in press).

RECOURSE TO THE NOTION OF SYSTEM

To characterize our description of a complex domain involving several individuals or objects, their characteristics and their relations, and our representation of the learner's representation, we have developed a model depicting relational, transformational or teleological systems, functional or intentional (see Baudet and Denhière, 1988).

A **relational system** represents complex stative situations : states in which are found individuals or objects for a possible world. Defined by intension, a relational system is a collection of individuals affected by the definition of one or several relations between these individuals. Formally, a relational system is a sequence <I, R1, ..., Rn> where I is a non-null set and R1, ..., Rn are relations that apply to elements of I (see Coombs, Dawes and Tversky, 1975).

A **transformational system** represents complex events: transformation sequences of stative situations. Defined by intension, a transformational system is used to transform; i. e. in an interval of time t : i, j, it is characterized by modifications in the " normal course of the world", changes in the "natural tendency" of successive states of the system either to remain as is (conservation of states) or to change (events) (von Wright, 1967; François, 1988).

A **teleological system** represents structures and behaviors of organisms : sets of interrelated functional units. When the functional units ---human beings and by extension, animals--- are credited with intentionality, they will be considered to be intentional systems; when they are components of a technical or biological device they will be referred to as functional systems. Defined by intension, these systems are teleological, i. e. they form a functional unit. In an interval of time t : i, j, the initial state of the system, defined by the individuals initially present, their relationships and the initial values of their attributes is modified so as to attain a configuration (final state) which constitutes the target goal of the system. Each modification intervening during interval of time t : i, j, functions as a means of achieving this goal,that is, it creates the necessary conditions in the circumstances (see Mackie, 1974) to reach this goal.

CAUSAL CONNECTIONS

Causal connections are crucial to transformational and teleological systems. The present model draws on the philosophy of action (von Wright, 1967; Mackie, 1974; Trabasso & van den Broek, 1985) by taking account of knowledge about the construction of state, event, and action representations, and naïve causality. Recent experimental work (Hilton and Slugoski, 1986) is in line with the hypothesis that the cognitive representation of causal relations is built up via a causal explanatory operation (search through a set of events for the cause of a given event or state) which implements contrafactual reasoning based on the criterium of necessary condition and judgment of naturalness of events in the situation. Thus, the naïve concept of causality which will be activated by the occurrence of a causal connection in language or in the world can be interpreted as (Mackie, 1974) : **X Causes Y : the occurrence of X is a necessary condition, in the circumstances, for the occurrence of Y.** Causal connections are built in relation to a specific context : the circumstances. The cause and the effect represent modifications in the normal course of the world: "Cause is an INUS condition (Insufficient but Necessary part of an Unnecessary but Sufficient condition), a modification introduced into the causal field which, in the absence of any other modification, is a necessary condition for the effect to occur" (Mackie, 1974). By causal field we mean the set of necessary conditions for the occurence of the effet which are not modification in the normal course of the world.

THE TELEOLOGICAL DESCRIPTION OF A FUNCTIONAL SYSTEM

In general, a teleological description of a system can be expressed as follows (see Mackie, 1974) : **I has C in E because C in E leads to B**, in which **I** = individual or set of individuals, **C** = behavior of a system described by the sequence of states or events, **E** = environment or circumstances, and **B** = goal of system (final state aimed at by the system). At the same level of analysis, in the case of a complex description, the system must be decomposed into subsystems whose description is more elementary. The teleological nature of the functional system, i.e. its hierarchically structured organization into goals/subgoals makes this decomposition possible. This decomposition reflects the structure of reality : the functional system is tangible evidence of problem solving activity implemented by the designer. Each subsystem, like the system itself, makes up a functional unit. It is characterized by its role in the general functioning of the system : the final state of the subsystem serves as a subgoal of the system. The system is thus analyzed as a set of hierarchically organized functional units, a tree structure. These units are related causally, temporally and topologically. This yields the following descriptions for a functional system:

(i) Causal path description of system functioning :
The description consists of establishing a sequence of actions, events and states which express a temporal sequence of system functioning. A state is described by a relational system and an event and an actions are described by a modification of a relational system. Local semantic coherence arises from the explanation of relations between actions, events, and states.

(ii) Teleological description of system functioning :

This is represented by a tree structure whose original node is the goal of the system. The subordinate nodes represent subgoals of the system, which must be attained for the main goal to be accomplished. These subordinate nodes are the macro-events of the system. The occurrence of these macro-events is itself conditioned by the occurrence of events represented by the nodes immediately below them. The construction of a structure of this type thus consists of a categorization and a hierarchization of events into goals as a function of the goals assigned to the system, which may or may not violate the temporal sequence. The global semantic coherence is ensured by this goal structure.

EXPERIMENTS TO TEST THE VALIDITY OF THE MODEL

We carried out four tasks (free interview, causal questioning, completing lacunary event triples, and multiple choice questionaires on the existence of events and causal relations) with three groups of students (n=7) having different levels of knowledge of car mechanics (G1>G2>G3). Our objective was to identify their representation of the starter system.
We put forward the two following general hypothesis :

H1 : The acquisition of knowledge about a functional system is an activity which results in the construction of a coherent signification which corresponds to the description of a functional system as proposed above.

H2 : Subjects in group G1 with a good knowledge of the starter system will have a representation of this system which corresponds to our description of a functional system. Subjects from group G3 will not have constructed a representation of the starter system as an autonomous functional system. The group G2, who have demonstrated a lower level of acquisition than group G1 should either lack a representation of the starter system organized as an autonomous functional system, even though they know more elements of this system than G3, or have a representation of the starter system organized as an autonomous functional system but, in relation to group G1, this should be less elaborated insofar as it should contain fewer elements and be less well organized with respect to sub-systems.

The following predictions are deduced from the hypothesis 1 :

Distance Effect (D). The majority of recalled and recognized information (objects, events, relations) in the interview protocols and the questionnaires will belong to the starter system. In the protocols, the number of intrusions belonging to systems other than the starter system will be inversely proportional to the distance of that system from the starter system : START SYST > ADJ SYST > OTHER SYST.

Position effect (P) in the sub-systems. The initial and final event of a sub-system will have a higher probability of being expressed in the interview protocols and questionnaires than the intermediate events (boundary effect). Furthermore, the teleological nature of the representation allows us to predict a higher probability of occurrence for the final event leading to the realization of the sub-system's goal: FINAL > INITIAL >INTERMEDIATE.

*Interaction T * S* between the type of task (T) (interview vs. questionnaire) and the level of structure of the information (S) (micro- vs. macro-proposition): providing assistance to access information (questionnaire) allows for easier recovery for that information which our analysis in terms of systems identifies as belonging to the micro-structure rather than the macro-structure.

From the second general hypothesis H2 we can predict the following interactions:

*Interaction D * K* between the factors distance (D) and knowledge level (K) predicted on the basis of the hypothesis (H2): the distance effect will not be observed for group G3 whose cognitive representation is not organized as a functional system.

*Interaction M * K* between the membership level (M) and the knowledge level (K): the effect of membership level in the system will not be observed for group G3.

*Interaction T * S * K* between the type of task (T), the level of structure (S) and the knowledge level (K): the interaction in prediction 5 will not be observed for group G3 whose cognitive representation is not organized as a functional system.

Tasks

The three groups participated in four tasks organized as follows:
- phase 1: free interview followed by causal questioning,
- phase 2: incomplete event triples; this immediately succeeds phase 1,
- phase 3: multiple choice questionnaire on the existence of events and causal relations; this follows phase 2 after a one week delay.

Tasks executed by the subjects are assumed to vary in terms of the activities involved in the recovery of knowledge from memory (Baudet, 1988).

Protocol analysis :

For each subject we thus have an interview protocol and a questioning protocol.

First, an inventory of all objects, states, events and actions mentioned in the protocols is made and they are categorized as a function of their system membership: starter system, systems adjacent to the starter system, other systems (Blaizet, Cheritel, Legros, 1988). States, events and actions are then categorized in terms of their membership level within a sub-system: initial, intermediate and final positions. Then they are categorized in micro- and macro-propositions depending on whether they represent micro- or macro-events. Finally, we make an inventory of the relations made by subjects among the states, events and actions. They are first classified with respect to their position in the structure analyzed in terms of systems: starter intra-system, inter-systems, and other intra-systems. The relations are then categorized in terms of their nature : CAUSE (C), ENABLING (E), GOAL (G), TEMPORAL (T), SPECIFICATION (SP).

Results :

We present only the results of the first three tasks. The results of the multiple choice questionnaires on the existence of events and causal relations confirm the results obtained with the previous ones.

1. Free interview and causal questioning :

1. 1. Objects :

1 : Distance effect (D) : The average number of objects mentioned in the interview protocols and questionnaires were ordered according to the predicted hierarchy : $F_{2,36} = 55.6$; $p<.001$. SYST (m=16.2) > ADJSYST (m=6.1) > OTHER SYST (m=1.0).

2 : Interaction K * D . There is a significant difference between the mean number of objects belonging to the starter system and those objects belonging to adjacents systems for groups G1 and G2, but not for G3 : $F_{4,36} = 9.33$; $p<.01$.

1. 2. Events :

1 : Distance effect (D): The mean number of events in the interview protocols and questionnaires was ordered according to the predicted hierarchy : $F_{2,36} = 33.6$; $p<.01$. SYST (m=4.9) > ADJSYST (m=2.0) > OTHER SYST (m= 0.4).

2 : Interaction K * D. There is a significant difference between the mean number of events belonging to the starter system and those events belonging to adjacents systems for groups G1 and G2, but not for G3 : $F_{4,36} = 7.8$; $p<.01$.

3 : Position effect for the events in the sub-system (P): The average number of events in the interview protocols and questionnaires was ordered according to the predicted hierarchy : $F_{2,36} = 115.0$; $p<.001$. FINAL (m=13.2) > INITIAL (m=6.4) >INTERMEDIATE (m=2.4).

4 : Interaction K * P. An analysis of the simple effects shows that only in the final position do significant differences occur between G1 and the other two groups : $F_{4,36} = 7.8$; $p<.01$.

5 : Interaction T * S. The questioning which facilitates the recovery of information, affects the micro-structure mainly : $F_{1,18} = 6.11$; $p=.02$.

6 : Interaction K * T * S approaches significance: $F_{2,18} = 2.7$; $p=.09$. The questioning resulted in a relative improvement of the recovery of information pertaining to the micro-structure for groups G1 and G2 but not for G3 (multiple comparisons of the means were all significant $p=.05$).

1. 3. Relations :

1 : Membership level in the system (M). The average number of relations mentioned in the interview protocols and questionnaires is ordered according to the predicted hierarchy : $F_{2,36} = 10.6$; $p<.01$. INTRASYST (m=10.6) > INTERSYST (m=3.8) > INTRASYST≠ (m=3.0).

2 : Interaction K * M. For groups G1 and G2 the number of relations internal to the starter system was significantly greater than the relations belonging to either of the other two system categories and this was not the case for group G3: $F_{4,36} = 4.124$; $p<.001$.

3: Interaction M * T. The questioning procedure was effective mainly in recovering relations internal to the starter system : $F_{2,36} = 13.50$ $p<.001$.

4 : Interaction M * T * K. The preceding interaction was not observed for group G3 : $F_{4,36} = 3.70$; $p=.01$.

5: Interaction M * R. Subjects use more CAUSE relations than GOAL relations within the system and this is not the case between systems : $F_{10,180} = 4.94$; $p <.001$.

6: Interaction M* R * K. The three groups of subjects use more CAUSE relations than GOAL relations within the starter system. However, with respect to the relations between systems one sees the contrary: subjects from groups G1 and G2 establish more GOAL relations than CAUSE relations while subjects in group G3 use more CAUSE relations than GOAL: $F_{20,180} = 2.54$; $p <.01$.

2. Incomplete event triples :

1: Distance effect (D) to the sub-system: . The frequency of response types follow the predicted hierarchy ($F_{3,54} = 11.9$; $p<.01$) :

S-SUBSYST	>	S-SYST	>	OTHER SYST	(OMISSIONS)
.363	>	.179	>	.095	(.363)

2: Interaction between D * K: $F_{6,54} = 12.0$: $p<.01$. Table 4 below shows the different patterns of response frequencies according to the groups:

G1: S-SUBSYST > S-SYST > OTHER SYST : .625 > .250 > .017
G2: S-SUBSYST = S-SYST > OTHER SYST : .375 > .232 > .054
G3: no significant difference : .090 > .050 > .021

3: Boundary effect of sub-systems (B): The significant interaction C * P: $F_{3,54} = 5.9$; $p<.01$ shows that the correct responses are more numerous when the gap occurs at the border of two sub-systems rather than within a system.

CONCLUSIONS

The four experiments provide a body of results compatible with the hypothesis that acquiring knowledge about a functional system is an activity which culminates in the construction of a coherent network which corresponds to the description of the proposed functional system. They also provide information as to what might be the appropriate steps necessary for achieving mastery of a complex technical system: from the incoherent representation of some events, states or actions to a cohesive organization. That cohesive unit is a functional system capable of differentiating this organization into sub-units of the same type (sub-systems units at a high level of the functional system). Actually when we compare the performances of the three groups of subjects having different knowledge levels, it seems that the group which was most knowledgeable constructed a representation organized in functional systems and sub-systems. On the other hand the group which received the same instruction as the previous one but which showed a less well developed knowledge about the system demonstrated by their performance that they built a representation organized as a functional system but not with sub-systems. Their cognitive representations of the starter systems differs from those of the preceding group both in terms of fewer real units represented and also by the structure of these units into a system which could be decomposed into functional sub-systems with difficulty, if at all. Finally, the group which received no instruction directly concerning the starter system but which has general knowledge and intuition about car mechanics following an introductory course, performs in such a way as to indicate that they do not differentiate the starter system from those other systems which make up a technical object like a car. In particular they make no distinction between the starter system and adjacent systems such as the thermal internal combustion engine, the ignition system, the energy supplying system.

Our analysis in terms of systems produces a conceptualization that allows for a precise description of the representation that we have of the world and of the representation of the representation that the learner builds for himself. It allows us to formulate in new terms, questions regarding comprehension and text production. It is a necessary condition for the detailed study of the processing of complex verbal information such as the interplay of the linguistic and logico-linguistic elements of the text, the cognitive characteristics of individuals and the characteristics of the world represented in a text. Our model allows us to seriously consider the construction of computerized systems to assist learning in complex domains (see Tapiero, Poitrenaud, Denhière, 1988).

REFERENCES

BAUDET, S. (1988). Relative importance of information and retrieval from memory. In MANDL H., DE CORTE E., BENNETT N. & FRIEDRICH H.F. (eds.), Learning and Instruction. London: Pergamon Press ltd.

BLAIZET, F., CHERITEL, J., & LEGROS, D. (1987). Représentation cognitive et compréhension du fonctionnement d'un système fonctionnel complexe : le moteur thermique à combustion interne, Communication au Colloque : Culture technique et formation, Cité des Sciences et de l'Industrie de la Villette, Paris, 17-18 Décembre 1987.

BAUDET, S., & DENHIERE, G. (in press) Mental models and acquisition of knowledge from text : Representation and acquisition of functional systems. In: G. Denhière & J.P. Rossi : Text and Text Processing. Amsterdam, North-Holland.

COOMBS, C.H., DAWES, R.M. et TVERSKY, A (1975). Psychologie mathématique, Paris: P.U.F.

DENHIERE, G. (1988).Story comprehension and memorization by children : the role of input-, conservation- and output processes. In: WEINERT F. & PERLMUTTER M. (eds), Memory development : Universal changes and individual differences, Hillsdale, N.J.: Erlbaum.

DENHIERE, G. et BAUDET, S. (in press). Cognitive Psychology and Text Processing: From Text Representation to Text-World, Semiotica, Special issue: Cognition and Artificial Intelligence.

FRANCOIS, J. (in press). Changement, Causation, Action : Trois catégories fondamentales de la description sémantique du lexique verbal à l'exemple de l'allemand et du français. Genève, Droz.

HILTON, D.J. & SLUGOSKI, B.R. (1986). Knowledge - Based Causal Attribution : The Abnormal Conditions Focus Model, Psychological Review, vol. 93, 1, 75-88.

JOHNSON-LAIRD, P.N. (1983). Mental models. Cambridge, MA: Harvard University Press.

MACKIE, J.L. (1974). The cement of universe. A study of causation. Oxford: Clarendon Press.

TAPIERO, I., POITRENAUD, S., & DENHIERE , G. (1988). Individualized acquisition of knowledge with the computer: interrogation and learning guided by the structure of knowledge. European Journal of Psychology of Education, Special Issue: Acquisition of knowledge from text.

van DIJK, T.A. & KINTSCH, W. (1983). Strategies of discourse comprehension. N.Y.:Academic Press.

Trabasso, T. & van den Broek, P.W. (1985) Causal thinking and the presentation of narrative events. Journal of Memory and Language, 24, 612-630.

van DIJK, T.A. & KINTSCH, W. (1983). Strategies of discourse comprehension. N.Y.:Academic Press.

von WRIGHT, G.H. (1967) : The Logic of Action : a Sketch. In N. RESCHER (ed.), The Logic of decision and action. Pittsburgh: University of Pittsburgh Press.

CONNECTIONISM AND INTENTIONALITY

WILLIAM BECHTEL

DEPARTMENT OF PHILOSOPHY
GEORGIA STATE UNIVERSITY

ABSTRACT

Connectionism offers greater promise than symbolic approaches to cognitive science for explaining the *intentionality* of mental states, that is, their ability to be *about* other phenomena. In symbolic cognitive science symbols are essentially arbitrary so that there is nothing that intrinsically relates them to their referents. The causal process of transduction is inadequate to explain how mental states acquire intentionality, in part because it is incapable of taking into account the contextual character of mental states. In contrast, representations employed in connectionist models can be much more closely connected to the things they represent. The ability to produce these representations in response to external stimuli is controlled by weights which the system acquires through a learning process. In multi-layer systems the particular representations that are formed are also determined by processes internal to the system as it learns to produce the overall desired output. Finally, the representations produced are sensitive both to contextual variations in the objects being represented and in the system doing the representing. These features suggest that connectionism offers significant resources for explaining how representations are *about* other phenomena and so possess *intentionality*.

THE PROBLEM OF INTENTIONALITY

Explaining the intentionality of mental states, the fact that they are *about* phenomena that are generally situated outside of the cognitive agent, has been a central concern in the philosophy of cognitive science. The challenge is to explain what it is in virtue of which a mental state is about a particular phenomenon and so has a particular content. One of the factors that makes this challenge difficult was identified by Brentano (1874/1973). He noted that a mental state such as a belief seems to involve a relation between the believer and external phenomena, but that this relation is unlike ordinary relations. If Sam believes that Sarah is a neurologist, Sam's state of mind seems to stand in a relation to Sarah. Normally, for a relation to exist both relata must exist. Yet, Sam could well have this belief and Sarah not exist. His mental state is still *about* Sarah, and not anyone or anything else. Thus, intentionality cannot be handled simply in terms of relations.

The problem of explaining intentionality is a serious one for symbolic cognitive science since it takes seriously an aspect of the ordinary logic of sentences about mental states. These sentences typically have the form of propositional attitudes, in which the verb (e.g., *believes*) represents a relation between a person and a *proposition*. The proposition then becomes the *bearer* of the intentionality since it is what represents the possible or actual condition in the world to which the person's belief is directed. To explain such states, many practitioners of symbolic cognitive have assumed that there are symbols in the mind corresponding to propositions and that the mind manipulates these symbols via procedures much like those posited in formal logic. The use of symbols as bearers of intentionality helps solve the problem of how mental states can be about non-existing entities, since there are a variety of procedures through which we can imagine formal symbols being introduced which do not correspond to actual entities. The challenge, however, is to explain how symbols, whether or not they do refer to real things, have the specific representational content they have. I will briefly examine why this problem is a difficult one for symbolic cognitive science. My main endeavor will then be to explore how connectionist approaches offer promise in explaining this aspect of intentionality.

Intentionality and Symbolic Cognitive Science

This is not the place to review in detail the difficulties that arise in explaining the intentionality of formal symbols (see Bechtel, 1988). Rather, I will try to capture some of the problems informally so as to set up the contrast with connectionist approaches. The main problem the symbolic approach faces in explaining intentionality is that primitive symbols are treated as *atomic* and *arbitrary*. As a result, there is nothing about the symbol itself that determines its referent. The question then arises as to what it is that determines the referent of a symbol. What makes the mental symbol for Sarah refer to Sarah? The most plausible approach is to treat the symbol for Sarah as having a particular referent because of the way it is employed by the cognitive system. The set of symbols is manipulated by formal rules in a manner that is appropriate to the referential function of those symbols. As a formal system, the cognitive system is construed as a *syntactic engine*. The model here is the manner in which formal proof procedures in logic are *truth* preserving because they mirror the relations between objects in the world. *Truth* is a semantic property, relating a proposition to the situation in the world that satisfies it. Proof procedures do not utilize semantic information but provide a formal means of manipulating symbols that respects the semantic property of truth. Similarly, the formal operations of the cognitive system's syntactic engine do not rely on the referents of these symbols but provide a means for properly manipulating symbols so as to facilitate the system's negotiation with these objects. Since reference is a semantic relation, the syntactic engine can be seen as simulating a *semantic engine* (Dennett, 1981).

According to the view just characterized, there is nothing about the formal symbols that determines their semantic content. This can be appreciated by the simple thought experiment in which a formal system, a computer program, that is satisfactorily performing one task is employed to perform another task and does it equally well. There is nothing about the formal symbols in the program that makes them more about the objects involved in the first task than those encountered in the second task. We, the users of the program, must supply the interpretation. This point is closely related to one Searle (1980) derives from his famous Chinese room argument in which he pictures himself manipulating symbols in a purely formal manner using a set of rules. He does this in such a manner as to carry on a conversation in Chinese without understanding a single word of Chinese or knowing that he is conversing in Chinese. The Chinese characters could have quite different semantics and that would not alter Searle's behavior. Since humans do know what their mental states are about, Searle objects that the formal symbol approach totally fails to capture the *intrinsic intentionality* of mental states.

While some theorists have been satisfied with the view that all there is to intentionality is accounted for whenever a syntactic engine simulates a semantic engine, many others have agreed with Searle that we need to explain how humans, at least, are real semantic engines. We must explain, they maintain, how our mental state have determinant contents and should not be subject to whatever reinterpretation an external party chooses to employ. However, few have been satisfied with Searle's own explanation of intrinsic intentionality, which appeals to the biological character of mental states. An alternative perspective, suggested by Dreyfus and Dreyfus (1986), is to focus the difficulty on the *context-free* character of formal symbols. In characterizing formal symbols as context-free we are noting that how symbols are processed depends only on what is formal represented and no other aspects of the environment. Dreyfus and Dreyfus attributed the reliance on context-free formal symbols to traditional philosophy, which has provided much of the theoretical framework for cognitive science:

> According to Heidegger, traditional philosophy is defined from the start by its focusing on facts in the world while "passing over" the world as such. This means that philosophy has from the start systematically ignored or distorted the everyday context of human activity. The branch of the philosophical tradition that descends from Socrates through Plato, Descartes, Leibniz, and Kant to conventional AI takes it for granted, in addition, that understanding a domain consists in having a *theory* of that domain. A theory formulates the relationships among objective, *context-free elements* (simples, primitives, features, attributes, factors, data points, cues, etc.) in terms of abstract principles (covering laws, rules, programs, etc.) (pp. 24-25).

For a formal symbolic system, the system's total knowledge about context must be provided in terms of formal symbols, that is, in other explicit representations in the system. The hope has been that we could build in enough explicit representations to enable the system to deal adequately with all contexts that arise in the real world, but this is precisely what Hubert Dreyfus has long been questioning (see Dreyfus, 1979). The problem for a formal symbol system is that there does not seem to be any other way to bring context into play.

The main alternative to trying to account for the intentionality of symbols in terms of formal relations between symbols has been to analyze their meaning or intentionality in terms of their relations to the objects that they represent. One possibility that has been pursued has been to treat the causal mechanisms that produce the symbols in us as the source of intentionality. Dretske (1981), for example, characterizes the causal relation between the object in the world and the symbol in the head in terms of the *information* that is transmitted and then tries to explain intentionality in terms of how the symbol bears information *about* the object. When a symbol is activated without being caused by its referent, it is still about the object which would normally cause its activation. This proposal has been challenged from a number of perspectives. In particular, it has been argued that such causal relations are inadequate to account for the possibility of error or misrepresentation (e.g., the possibility of representing non-existent objects), which, as we have already noted, is an important characteristic of intentional states (see Churchland & Churchland, 1983 and Fodor, 1984).

An additional objection to treating the causal relation between referent and symbol as the basis for intentionality is that such an approach is not able to accommodate the role of contextual factors such as those the Dreyfuses have emphasized. When we use representations intentionally, the particular referent that is intended for the system may vary with the context. This problem is readily seen when we consider the representational function of words in a natural language. Barsalou (1987) has shown surprising variability in people's prototypicality ratings of exemplars of concepts over time, suggesting that the representational function of words as well as their internal representations change with context. The problem for capturing this in a symbolic account is that symbols are fixed entities. Moreover, the relata in the causal link between an object and a symbol will have to involve something like the typical entity that generates the symbol in the cognizer. The causal theory cannot explain how on the different occasions when a symbol is used, there may be significant variation among intended referents. This variability in intended referents is an aspect of intentionality that cannot be accounted for either in terms of formal relations between symbols or in terms of the typical causal ancestor of the symbol. Contextual sensitivity is, however, something connectionist systems are more adept at dealing with. Hence, there is motivation to explore the potential of connectionism in accounting for intentionality.

A Connectionist Perspective on Intentionality

Part of the problem with the symbolic approach is that it limits contact with the world to a process of transduction through which a sensory input is transformed into a symbol. Some of the potential of connectionism in accounting for intentionality stems from the alternative perspective it provides on the transduction process. Sensory input will be provided to the network by activating certain nodes in the network. These nodes will then cause other nodes to activate. The initial activation process culminates in the activation of the units constituting the representation. This processing within the system is of a piece with the causal transmission of signals in the external world and so provides the potential for direct contact of the representational states of the system with their referents. Despite the fact that there is a direct continuity in the sort of processing involved, this process may still seem to be very like the kind of transduction envisaged in a symbolic model: the sensory input causes a representation to be activated in the system. But there are several crucial differences between this connectionist process and the type of transduction required in symbolic systems that render the connectionist approach better suited for explaining intentionality.

One of the ways in which connectionist models have an advantage over symbolic accounts is that in at least one respect connectionist representations will not be arbitrary in the way that symbolic representations are. This is a result of the fact that connectionist systems have the capacity to learn how to generate their representations and also what representations to employ. At the level of basic representations, only the first of these capacities is generally employed in current connectionist systems. In simple, two-level, feedforward networks trained through procedures such as the least mean squares learning algorithm, for example, the weights required to produce the output representation are learned. Through the learning process the network selects how to attend to features of the input. Only some input units are relevant for determining the weights of particular output units, and the weights from these input units adjust accordingly. Thus, the process of generating the representation involves an adaptation of the representational system to the external referent. Here is one initial respect in which the representations developed in connectionist systems are closely tied to that which they are supposed to represent. This linkage makes the relation between representation and represented somewhat less arbitrary than in symbolic systems.

The representations that simple networks learn, however, are chosen by the researcher. Since any input can be paired with any output, there is still a strong sense in which the representations are arbitrarily related to what they represent. To reduce this sense of arbitrariness we need to consider systems which possess the ability to create their own internal representations. Something like this capacity is found in multi-level feedforward networks trained through processes like backpropagation. The hidden units in such systems develop specific response characteristics in the course of training the output units to produce the desired patterns of activation. Sometimes it is possible to determine, through detailed analysis of when the hidden units become active, what representational function is performed by each of these units. For example, Hinton (1987) designed a network to learn information about relations in two family trees. The input units specified one person and a kin relationship, and the output units were to identify the person standing in that relationship. Between the input and output units were three layers of hidden units. The input and output units were coded in a localist fashion, one person or relationship per unit. However, because the number of hidden units was much smaller than the number of input units, the network was forced to find distributed representations for the input and output. For example, the twenty four input units encoding the possible individuals fed into a set of six hidden units. Through the course of learning via back propagation, the network had to find a way to represent all the information about these individuals that it required in order to determine the correct output person. The network developed a representational system that identified persons in terms of their tree (British or Italian), their generation, and the branch of the tree from which they came. The important point for our purposes is that in Hinton's simulation the network developed its own distributed representation in the course of adjusting connection strengths so as to minimize its error in solving the task for which it required the information. Since the network is determining these representations on the hidden units, they are far less arbitrary than do symbols in a symbolic system.

In existing networks the internal representations that are constructed are grounded in an already existing representation chosen by the researcher. Thus, in Hinton's simulations, one set of input units encodes the name of the person whose relative is being sought, and the other set of input units encodes the relations. Hence, the representations that are learned (i.e., the activation pattern over the hidden units) are comparable to higher order concepts or complex symbols that might be acquired in symbolic systems. (They are not fully comparable to these since they are far more sensitive to small variations in input information than are symbolic representations. For example, while one unit encodes whether or not the input person is English, it generates higher activation levels for some English persons than others.) This limitation, however, results from the fact that these systems do not use sensory stimuli directly as inputs. If one were to train a system that took as inputs the outputs of sensory receptors that directly picked up information from the environment, then the responses of hidden units could be thought of as defining the system's most basic categorization of inputs and hence as providing the system with its most basic representations.

The crucial point to be emphasized is that representations on hidden units result from the system's attempt to accommodate to its environment. They cease to be states which could have been causally connected to any sensory input and, hence, arbitrary as far as the operation of the system was concerned. Since these representations constitute a learned response of the system to a given set of inputs that the system then uses in order to respond in the desired way to those inputs, these representations are naturally seen as being *about* the entities supplying the input. (The tightness of this connection is evident in the fact that in order for researchers to analyze the operation of hidden units, they must try to identify what input patterns will in fact generate the response of particular hidden units.) A connectionist system such as I have described is thus able to develop representations in much the way Dreyfus and Dreyfus portray human systems as learning:

> By playing with all sorts of liquids and solids every day for years, a child may simply learn to discriminate prototypical cases of solids, liquids, and so on and learn typical skilled responses to their typical behavior in typical circumstances (Dreyfus and Dreyfus, 1987, p. 33).

The contrast between this process and the way interpretations are generally assigned to symbols in symbolic systems is clear. There are not separate processes of learning to use a symbolic representation and learning how to assign an interpretation to it. The connectionist representation is developed as part of the system's adaptation to its environment.

One of the failures Dreyfus and Dreyfus claimed befell symbolic representational systems was their lack of context sensitivity. The responses that connectionist systems make to their environments are quite sensitive to the particular stimuli they receive as well as to other processing that is occurring in the networks. Particularly when units can take on continuous activations, there is enormous variability in the responsiveness of individual units. As a result, the system does not need to have discrete symbols by which it can represent each variation in context. For example, consider a case in which a representation is produced not from an input, but from activity elsewhere in the network that causes it to activate a pattern much like it would for a particular type of input such as a ball. On one occasion this activity may result in a pattern more like that typically generated by a baseball, while on another occasion it might result in a pattern more like that typically produced by a basketball. This variation is then available to enable the system to adjust its response in light of differences in input circumstances and internal conditions. This ability to vary representations in appropriate manners may not be a unmitigated benefit since it will be necessary to ensure that the ultimate response of the system is appropriate to the context and is not a bizarre one. Thus, the responsiveness of the system to the representations must itself be tuned to the variability in the representation itself. But at least it is possible for such a connectionist system to represent objects differently depending upon context and so these systems are not restricted, as are symbolic systems, to representing context in yet other arbitrary symbols.

The connectionist approach to modeling cognition thus offers promise in explaining the *aboutness* or *intentionality* of mental states. Representational states, especially those of hidden units, constitute the system's own learned response to inputs. Since they constitute the system's adaptation to the input, there is a clear respect in which they are *about* those inputs. They are about the situations to which they are responses in much the way biological adaptations are adapted to situations like those which figured in the process of their selection. The fact that these representations are also sensitive to context, both external and internal to the system, enhances the plausibility of this claim that the representations are representations of particular states. The connectionist approach thus makes a start on explaining the *aboutness* of representations. Unfortunately, there is more to be done to explain intentionality. We must also explain how mental states can represent things that do not exist. This seemed relatively easy to do in symbolic systems, since we could simply incorporate a symbol to stand in for the non-existent object. Yet we could not explain why the arbitrary symbol had the referent it did. A detailed explanation of how connectionist systems could make reference to non-existing objects is beyond this paper. But the outlines of how this is possible can be sketched. In interactive networks, activations can be brought about by activity in the network itself, and not just from external inputs. It is conceivable that activation patterns could be induced that do not correspond to anything normally caused by input patterns. These would be representations of non-existent objects. We know they are *about* these objects, and not others, because they are the representations that would be produced if the system ever did confront such an object. Thus, if a representational pattern was created by internal processes in the system which would be produced by the system encountering a unicorn, then it would be a representation of a unicorn, not of Santa Claus. The network's response to the production of these states can be viewed as its further thinking about the non-existent objects.

The proposals advanced here are simply intended to show the promise of connectionism in helping us understand the intentionality of mental states. They do not show that connectionist accounts will be successful or that symbolic analyses cannot invoke similar strategies in order to explain intentionality themselves. (The causal analysis of the intentionality of symbolic states most nearly parallels the account proposed here and could conceivably employ some of the strategies outlined here to flesh out that account. What distinguishes the two accounts is that the causal account does not treat the representation as an adaptation on the part of the cognitive system, and so does not as clearly overcome the problem that the symbolic representation remains rather arbitrary and so not intrinsically linked to its referent. It is simply the symbolic state that happened to be caused by the sensory input.) There are challenges to be faced in devising connectionist networks that will have the right semantics to model cognition. For example, just designing a system that has a context sensitive representation of an external referent does not ensure that it can use this representation appropriately in solving other problems. But perhaps there is even a virtue here in that this constitutes an empirical research problem about the intentional representations in a network, and not simply a problem to be solved by *a priori* philosophical speculation. Since so little has been achieved in the attempt to explain the *aboutness* or intentionality of mental state, the fact that connectionism offers a plausible promissory note is one reason to take it seriously.

REFERENCES

Barsalou, L. (1987). The instability of graded structures: Implications for the nature of concepts. In U. Neisser (Ed.), *Concepts and conceptual development: Ecological and intellectual factors in categorization* (pp. 101-140). Cambridge, England: Cambridge University Press.

Bechtel, W. (1988). *Philosophy of mind. An overview for cognitive science*. Hillsdale, NJ: Lawrence Erlbaum Associates.

Brentano, F. (1874/1973). *Psychology from an empirical standpoint* (A.C. Pancurello, D. B. Terrell, & L. L. McAlister, Trans.). New York: Humanities.

Churchland, P. S. & Churchland, P. M. (1983). Stalking the wild epistemic engine. *Nous*, *17*, 44-52.

Dennett, D. C. (1981). Three kinds of intentional psychology. In R. Healey (Ed.), *Reduction, time and reality* (pp. 37-61). Cambridge: Cambridge University Press.

Dretske, F. I. (1983). *Knowledge and the flow of information*. Cambridge, MA: MIT Press/Bradford Books.

Dreyfus, H. L. (1979). *What computers can't do: The limits of artificial intelligence*. (2nd edition). New York: Harper & Row.

Dreyfus, H. L. and Dreyfus, S. E. (1987). *Mind over machine. The power of human intuition and expertise in the era of the computer*. New York: The Free Press.

Fodor, J. A. (1984). Semantics, Wisconsin Style. *Synthese*, *59*, 231-250.

Hinton, G. (1986). Learning distributed representations of concepts. *Proceedings of the eighth annual conference of the Cognitive Science Society*. Hillsdale, NJ: Lawrence Erlbaum Associates.

Searle, J. R. (1980). Minds, brains, and programs. *The Behavioral and Brain Sciences*, *3*, 417-424.

A Connectionist Model of Category Size Effects During Learning

Timothy J. Breen
Boeing Advanced Technology Center

ABSTRACT

This paper reports the results of category learning experiments in which the number of exemplars defining a category during learning was varied. These results reveal that category exemplars from larger sized categories are classified more accurately than those from smaller-sized categories. This was true both early and late in learning. In addition, subjects exhibited a response bias toward classifying exemplars into larger-sized categories throughout learning. A connectionist model is developed which exhibits these same tendencies.

INTRODUCTION

This paper reports the results of category learning experiments in which the number of exemplars defining a category during learning was varied. These results are then compared with the results of simulations using a connectionist model of category learning. Categorization has a special status for connectionist models, since the ability of connectionist systems to learn generalizations from specific instances is frequently cited as one of the most promising aspects of the connectionist approach (e.g. Norman, 1986, pp. 535-536). Although several examples exist in which connectionist models have been successfully applied to data from classification experiments (e.g. Knapp & Anderson, 1984; McClelland & Rumelhart, 1985; Gluck & Bower, 1988) the range of these cases is relatively narrow. Therefore, it is important to evaluate these models in light of additional empirical findings.

THE EFFECT OF CATEGORY SIZE ON LEARNING RATE

A robust finding in the classification literature is that increasing the number of exemplars representing a category during learning, under most circumstances, improves transfer performance on novel category exemplars (e.g. Homa & Vosburgh, 1976). What is not known is whether, or how, this variable influences category learning. For example, in a task in which subjects are required to learn the category assignments of members of three different categories, where the categories contain 3, 6, and 9 members respectively, is one category learned more quickly than the others? One might suspect for example, that the category with only three members would be easiest for subjects to learn.

EMPIRICAL FINDINGS

To examine this question, analyses of previously unreported data from a series of experiments conducted by Breen & Schvaneveldt (1986) are reported below. Breen & Schvaneveldt conducted three experiments in which subjects learned to classify dot patterns (Posner, Goldsmith & Welton, 1967) into three different categories. Dot pattern categories have been used extensively in the classification literature, and are constructed by first assigning dots (usually nine) randomly into cells of a matrix. This dot pattern is referred to the objective prototype of the category. To generate category exemplars, a statistical distortion rule is applied to the objective prototype that moves the dots to a new position in the matrix. Additional categories can be created by generating distortions of a new random objective prototype pattern.

In the these experiments, categories in the learning phase were represented by 3, 6, or 9 dot patterns. Subjects continued to classify patterns during the learning phase until all 18 patterns were classified correctly during a single block of trials. Conditions in the learning phase for all three experiments were identical, and because transfer performance was of primary interest, the learning data were not reported earlier. (See Breen & Schvaneveldt, 1986, for further details of the experimental procedure).

Out of 300 subjects participating in all three experiments, 44 failed to reach learning criterion (errorless performance in 30 blocks or less in Experiment 1, or 35 blocks or less in Experiments 2 & 3), and these data were excluded from the analyses. The average number of blocks to criterion for all remaining subjects was 15.5.

Figure 1 shows average correct responses over learning blocks for each of the three category sizes. To generate these learning functions, errorless performance was assumed after each subject achieved the learning criterion. For example, if a particular subject met the learning criterion after 10 blocks of trials, it was assumed that no errors would have occurred for blocks 11 through 35. Since this assumption is probably too strong, the right-hand side of the graph in Figure 1 is most likely artificially inflated for all category sizes. It is clear, however, that early in learning, classification accuracy was enhanced for exemplars of the larger categories.

Figure 2 shows a clearer picture of classification accuracy late in learning, in which classification accuracy is plotted as a function of the $-n^{th}$ block in relation to each subjects' learning criterion (backward learning curve, Trabrasso & Bower, 1968). The number of subjects contributing to each data point is also shown in the bottom of the figure. Surprisingly, Figure 2 suggests that the larger category sizes maintained their advantage late in learning.

To confirm these results, an analysis of variance was performed on data from the first three blocks of trials and for the last three prior to reaching the learning criterion for each subject. Because 46 subjects reached criterion in less than seven blocks, these data had to be excluded from this analysis. The analysis treated category size as a factor with three levels (3, 6, and 9), and blocks as a factor with two levels (early and late) in a (3 x 2) factorial design. The results revealed a main effect of blocks [$F(1,209) = 687.87$, $MSe = 29.881$, $p < .001$], and category size [$F(2,418) = 24.03$, $MSe = 0.791$, $p < .001$]. Category size did not interact with blocks [$F(2,418) = 0.34$,

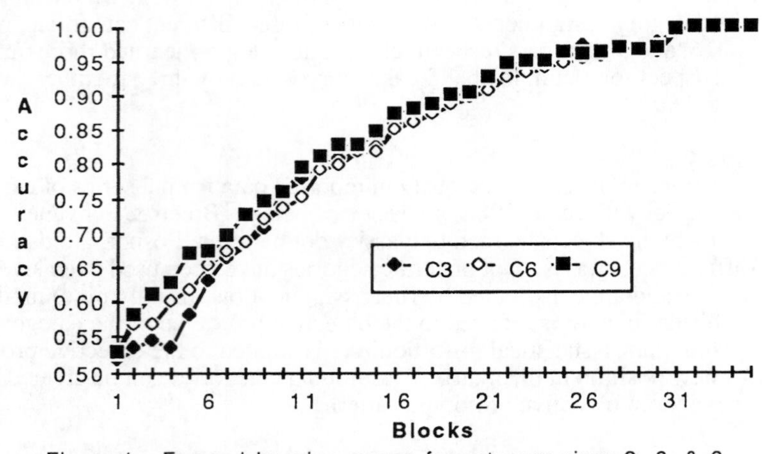

Figure 1. Forward learning curves for category sizes 3, 6, & 9.

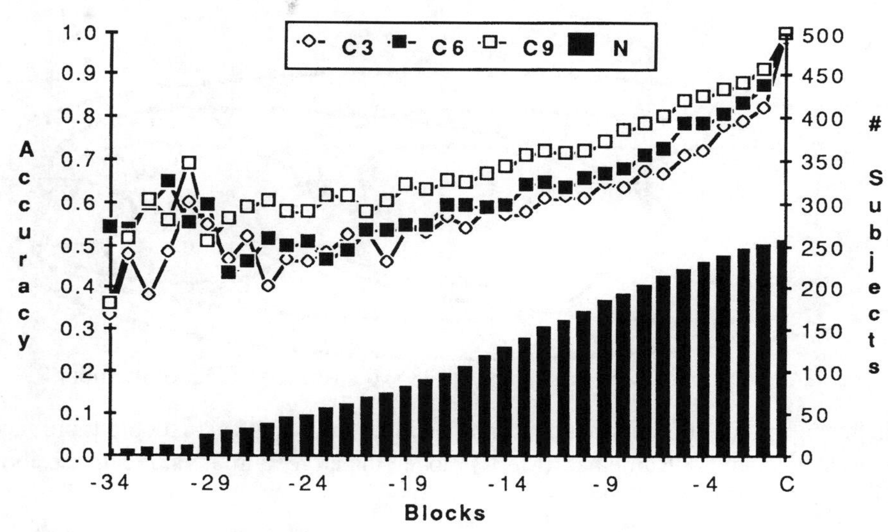

Figure 2. Backward learning curves for category sizes 3, 6, and 9.

MSe=0.006], suggesting that the effect of category size was the same both early and late in learning.

To summarize, these results suggest that those categories containing a larger number of exemplars were learned most quickly, and that subjects were more accurate in classifying exemplars from large categories both early and late in learning. These findings are problematic for at least some distributed models of learning and memory.

McCLELLAND & RUMELHART'S (1985) MODEL

For example, McClelland and Rumelhart (1985) have proposed a model of category learning and representation that employs the delta learning rule (Figure 3). Since this model has been described in detail elsewhere, only a brief description of the general properties of the model will be presented here. The model consists of a single layer of nodes, with each node in the model connected to every other node. Each node may receive activation from two sources. One is from outside the network when a pattern, in the form of a binary feature vector, is presented to the model. The other is from other nodes in the network through connections which have non-zero weights.

The model is trained by presenting a pattern to the model, allowing activation to spread throughout the nodes, and then applying the delta rule to adjust the connection weights such that the activity levels of the nodes match, or come progressively closer to matching, the input pattern. The delta learning rule is specified by:

$$W_n = W_{n-1} + \eta \delta_n i^T{}_n$$

where W_n is the weight matrix following trial n, η is a constant which determines the rate of learning, $i^T{}_n$ is the transpose of the input pattern on trial n, and δ_n is the difference between the desired and actual output on trial n:

$$\delta_n = t_n - W_{n-1}\, i_n$$

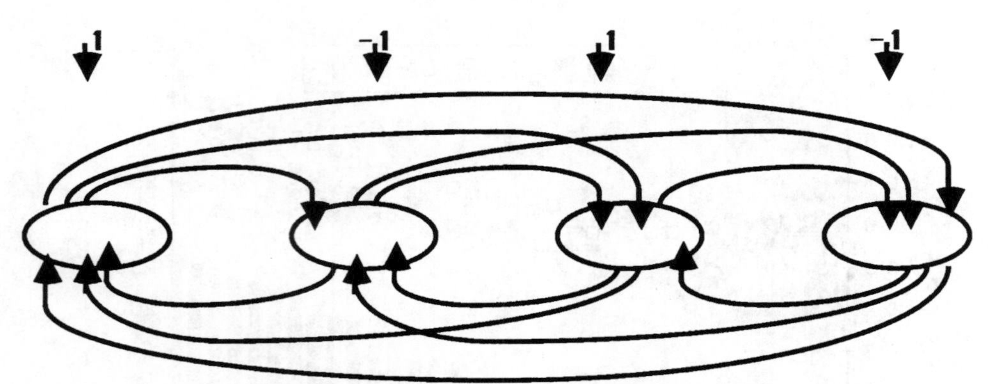

Figure 3. McClelland & Rumelhart's (1985) distributed model of memory.

where t_n is the desired or target output on trial n and $W_{n-1}\, i_n$ is the actual output produced on trial n. In the McClelland & Rumelhart (M&R) model, the target output value t in the above equation is the input pattern on a particular learning trial.

The performance of the model is evaluated in terms of the hacking distance between the input pattern and resulting node activations. This measure is referred to as *response strength.* The general idea is that when the pattern of activation produced by the model closely matches the input pattern, the input pattern has closely matched what is stored in the connection weights. In other words, if response strength is high, the model has recognized the input as something that it has learned or knows about. The response strength for input pattern p is the dot product over the activations of each node and the input pattern, normalized for the number of nodes in the model:

$$RS_p = \frac{1}{n} \sum_{i=0}^{i=n} a_i p_i$$

A SIMULATION

The ability of the M&R model to account for the above results is evaluated in the following simulation. For the simulation, training patterns from different categories were constructed by first generating three random binary feature vectors of length 20. These patterns become the category objective prototypes. Distortions of the objective prototypes were then generated by flipping the sign of each feature in the objective prototype with a probability of .15. The training set consisted of 3 distortions of one prototype, 6 distortions of a second, and 9 distortions of a third, for a total of 18 patterns.

During each trial in the simulation, a training pattern was presented to a model consisting of 20 completely connected nodes, activation was allowed to spread and stabilize throughout the model, then the connection weights were changed according to the delta learning rule. Each block of trials consisted of one pass through the 18 patterns, and each simulation run consisted of 30 blocks of trials. The number of simulation runs, consisting of stimulus generation-model training cycles, was 100.

Figure 4 plots response strength of the model over learning blocks. Average response strength is greater for members of the category containing nine patterns early in learning, but average response

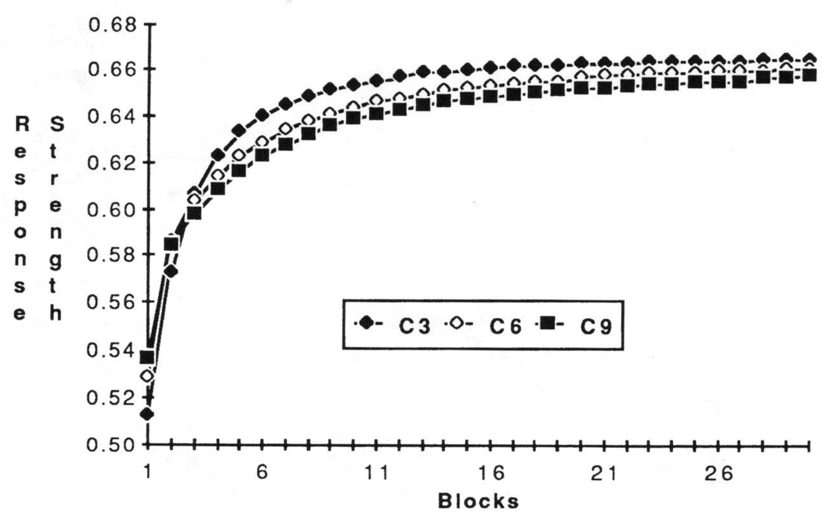

Figure 4. Response strength plotted over 30 learning blocks for category sizes 3, 6, &9.

strength for members of the category containing three members quickly overtakes response strength for other category members.

Considering the general properties of the model provides some insight into the simulation results. The model has the ability to represent both general, abstract information, along with specific, instance information in the same connection weights. In this sense, it is similar to a mixed-prototype model of categorization (e.g. Homa, Sterling, & Trepel, 1981). One factor which determines how strongly the model represents general or specific information about a category is how many distinct patterns comprise a category during learning. In general, the model retains highly specific information about small categories, and more abstract information about large categories. Under most circumstances, this results in more accurate generalizations to novel patterns when trained on greater numbers of distinct category exemplars (Breen, 1988).

The interaction shown in Figure 4 is made clear by considering that on each block of learning trials, half of the patterns belonged to the largest category. This caused the early advantage for the category with 9 members, because the model had relatively more experience with that category. Why the slope of the learning function is steepest for the smallest category is precisely because there were only three patterns to learn. That is, more interference among same category members is expected to occur as category size increases, producing a flatter learning function. This property of the model instantiates the mixed-prototype model assumption that processing capacity limitations (among other things) encourage abstract representations.

AN EXTENSION OF THE MODEL

A simple extension of the M&R model would involve the addition of a set of output nodes, with each output node responding to evidence concerning the presence of a particular category. In this model, shown in Figure 5, the input layer is completely connected and is trained the same way as before, by using the delta rule to produce a pattern of activity across the nodes that matches the input pattern. In addition, each node in the input layer is connected to each node in the output layer. The delta rule is also used to train the output nodes to produce a pattern of activity

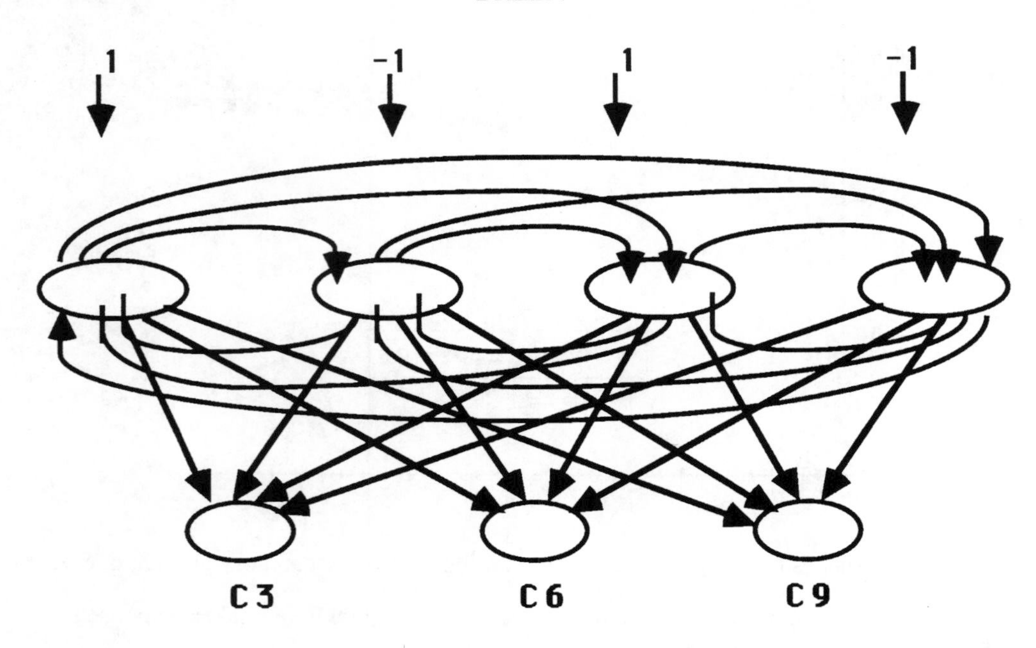

Category	Desired Response
C3	1 0 0
C6	0 1 0
C9	0 0 1

Figure 5. An extension of McClelland & Rumelhart's (1985) model.

that more closely resembles a categorization response. For example, consider the previous simulation in which the model is trained on patterns from three categories, with each category containing either three, six, or nine exemplars during learning. Each node in the output layer can be trained to take on positive activation depending on which category C3, C6, or C9, an input pattern belongs. For example, if a pattern from C3 (the category containing 3 exemplars) is presented to the model, the output layer is trained to produce the activity pattern [1 0 0] (see Figure 5).

The previous simulation in which category size was varied during learning was repeated using the model in Figure 5 (referred to as Model 2). All other methodological aspects of the simulation were identical to the method employed earlier. The sequence of events on each learning trial was as follows. A pattern was presented to Model 2, and activation was allowed to spread throughout the network (both input and output layers) until these activation levels stabilized. The activity levels in the input layer were then matched against the input pattern, and the weights connecting nodes in the input layer were adjusted using the delta rule. Simultaneously, the activity pattern in the output layer was compared to the desired category response, which is shown in Figure 5 for each category, with the delta rule again determining weight adjustments from the input to output layers.

Figure 5 shows the activity levels of nodes in the output layer for "correct" category nodes, for example, the average activity level for node C6 when a pattern from the category containing 6

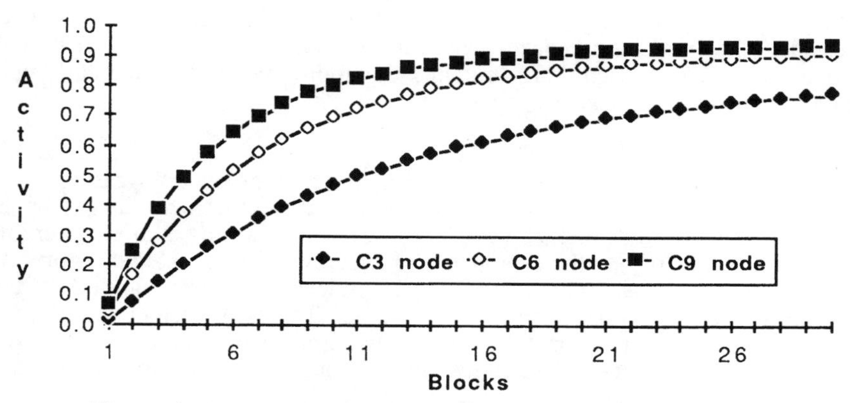

Figure 6. Average activity levels for "correct category" nodes.

exemplars was presented. The results of this simulation show that the activity level in the output nodes corresponding to the larger categories remained consistently higher than the activity levels of the nodes corresponding the smaller sized categories. This can be seen most clearly by comparing the activity levels of the C3 and C9 nodes in Figure 5. The results of this simulation are more in line with the results of the Breen & Schvaneveldt experiments.

Recall that one of the reasons cited for the inability of the M&R model to account for this result was that storing a large number of exemplars from the same category in the connection weights tends to produce interference in the input layer, producing a flatter learning function. This interference, however, only concerns the ability of the model to respond strongly to specific (old) input patterns. More exemplar experience also produces more accurate generalizations With increased experience, what the model gives up in representing specific information it gains in representing generality. Interference, per se, is thus not an undesirable quality. The same holds true for the input layer in Model 2. However, because the output layer of Model 2 is trained to produce a category level response, increased training on different patterns from the same category will only facilitate the acquisition of category-level information by the model.[1]

RESPONSE BIASES

Two further questions can be addressed by an analysis of the Breen & Schvaneveldt learning data that involve the particular kinds of errors that subjects make while learning to classify exemplars of categories which vary in size. The first question is whether category size influences the kinds of errors subjects make during learning. For example, when an error is made when classifying an exemplar from a category of size six, are subjects more likely to classify it as a member of the larger (size nine) category? This would be expected if subjects are using information about the relative size or likelihood of the three categories in making a response. The second question is that if subjects are prone to a response bias of this nature, will this bias be differentially reflected in errors occurring early and late in learning? One possibility is that such a bias would more strongly

[1]The connections between nodes in the input layer do not play a role in accounting for this category size effect. For example, an independant-cue model of the type proposed by Gluck and Bower (1988) is able to produce this same behavior, as well as the "response bias" tendencies in the following section.

influence responses early in learning, when subjects have less complete knowledge about category membership. For instance, when subjects are unsure of the correct category assignment when an exemplar is presented, they may base their response on knowledge about the relative probability of category exemplars occurring on each trial. And, this may more frequently occur early in learning, before much category information has been acquired.

EMPIRICAL FINDINGS

Figure 7 shows the breakdown of errors occurring during the first three learning trials (Early) and the last three trials before criterion (Late) for 210 subjects. It shows that when an exemplar from one of the three categories (C3, C6, or C9) was presented during learning, subjects were more likely to make an error by classifying the exemplar into a relatively larger sized category. In addition, this trend is equally apparent both early and late in learning. The magnitude of the bias appears to be greatest when a member from C6 is presented. This is consistent with the explanation that subjects were using probability information about the relative frequency of occurrence of category exemplars during learning, since C9 and C3 are the largest and smallest categories.

To confirm these results, an analysis of variance was performed treating Blocks as a factor with two levels (early and late), Response as a factor with three levels (C3, C6, and C9),and Correct Category (or category size) as a factor with three levels (C3, C6, and C9). In addition to the main effects reported above, this analysis revealed a main effect of Response [$F(1,209) = 31.010$, $MSe = 0.937$, $p < .001$]. The Response by Correct Category interaction approached significance [$F(2,418) = 2.797$, $MSe = 0.076$, $p < .1$], as did the three-way interaction of Blocks, Correct Category, and Response [$F(2,418) = 2.620$, $MSe = 0.041$, $p < .1$]. Blocks and Response did not interact [$F(1,209) = 1.935$, $MSe = 0.028$, $p > .1$].

It appears that subjects were prone to bias their responses toward the larger-sized categories to the same degree both early and late in learning. The finding that Blocks and Response did not interact was somewhat surprising, because it might be expected that a response bias would be reflected to a greater degree during the early blocks, when category learning is minimal. However, the acquisition of knowledge relating to the category membership of particular exemplars was confounded with the acquisition of knowledge about the relative sizes of each category in these experiments. Subjects were not told prior to the experiment that each category was represented by a different number of members during the learning phase. So early in learning, category size information may have been available to a lesser degree relative to later stages in learning.

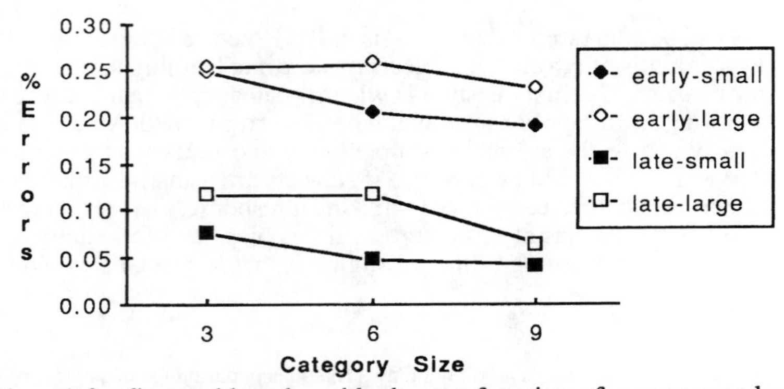

Figure 7. P(error) for first and last three blocks as a function of response and category size.

Therefore, a model that proposes that frequency information plays a stronger role in the absence of more "categorical" knowledge may still be consistent with these data. In these experiments, such a model would assume that with more experience in classifying exemplars during learning, the quality of both frequency and category information is enhanced. Early in learning, subjects rely to a relatively greater extent on poor quality frequency information. And late in learning, subjects rely to a lesser degree on high quality frequency information.

The above discussion, of course, lacks a connectionist flavor. Any model incorporating the notion of a response bias, which seems most naturally described in terms of rules or strategies, is inconsistent with the spirit of connectionist modeling. Ideally, a connectionist model's behavior should exhibit a tendency toward classification into larger sized categories and arise naturally from the structure of the input population and the architecture of the model.

SIMULATION RESULTS

The potential ability of Model 2 to account for these results can be examined in a straight-forward manner by observing the model's performance during the previous simulation. In particular, when a pattern from a particular category is presented during learning we can observe the activity levels in the nodes corresponding to the incorrect categories. For example, when a pattern from the category containing six members is presented (C6) to the model during learning, what are the activity levels of nodes corresponding to C3 and C9? Figure 8 shows these values across 30 learning blocks during the previous simulation.

Figure 8 shows that when Model 2 was learning to classify patterns from three categories containing either three, six, or nine patterns, and was presented with a pattern from the category containing six patterns, the activation of the C9 node was consistently higher than the activation of the C3 node. In fact, during learning, the model showed a general tendency to slightly inhibit those nodes corresponding to the two alternative categories, and the degree of inhibition depended upon category size. Nodes corresponding to smaller categories were inhibited to a greater extent than larger categories on those trials when an alternative category pattern was presented. This is somewhat interesting behavior from a model that contains no explicit mechanisms for producing a "response bias" for larger sized categories.

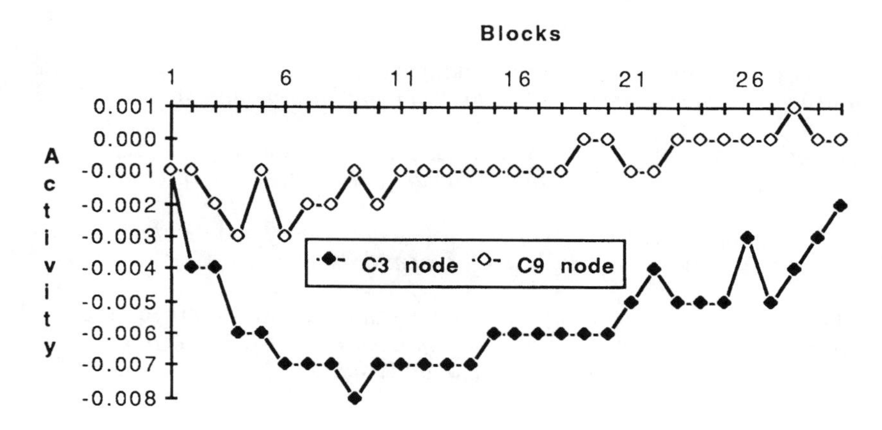

Figure 8. Activity levels of C3 and C9 node during learning trials when C6 pattern was presented.

Although the model as it stands is clearly too underdeveloped to make quantitative predictions about subjects behavior in this task, the model does exhibit a completely natural tendency toward inhibiting classification into relatively smaller-size categories. One further note is that when the learning procedure involves actively inhibiting alternate category responses, it will produce radically different behavior. For example, if on a particular trial the output layer is trained to produce the activity pattern [-1 1 -1] instead of [0 1 0] when presented with a pattern from C6, the model will learn to more strongly inhibit the C9 node, which produces response bias in the opposite direction than before. This finding produces a further constraint on the particulars of the learning procedure.

CONCLUSIONS

An extension of McClelland & Rumelhart's (1985) distributed model of learning and memory was shown to account (at least qualitatively) for subjects behavior in a category learning task in which category size was varied. Other researchers, no doubt, will fault the model for its inherent linearity. However, linear models have been found to be surprisingly robust over a variety of conditions in simulations of categorization tasks (Breen, 1988). All models can be pushed past their limit, and the present work is intended to provide some useful constraints for further model development.

REFERENCES

Breen, T. J. (1988). *An Evaluation of Connectionist Models of Categorization.* Unpublished doctoral dissertation. New Mexico State University, Las Cruces, New Mexico.

Breen, T. J., & Schvaneveldt, R. W. (1986). Classification of empirically derived prototypes as a function of category experience. *Memory &Cognition*, **4**, 313-320.

Gluck, M. A., & Bower, G. H. (1988). Evaluating an adaptive network model of human learning. *Journal of Memory & Language*, **27**, 166-195.

Homa, D., Sterling, S. & Trepel, L. (1981). Limitations of exemplar-based generalization and the abstraction of categorical information. *Journal of Experimental Psychology: Human Learning and Memory*, **7**, 418-439.

Homa, D., & Vosburgh, R. (1976). Category breadth and the abstraction of prototypical information. *Journal of Experimental Psychology: Human Learning and Memory*, **2**, 322-330.

Knapp, A. G., & Anderson, J. A. (1984). Theory of categorization based on distributed memory storage. *Journal of Experimental Psychology: Learning, Memory, & Cognition*, **10**, 616-637.

McClelland, J. L., & Rumelhart, D. E. (1985). Distributed memory and the representation of general and specific information. *Journal of Experimental Psychology: General*, **114**, 159-188.

Norman, D. A. (1986). Reflections on cognition and parallel distributed processing. In J. L. McClelland & D. E. Rumelhart (Eds.), *Parallel distributed processing: Explorations in the microstructures of cognition, (Vol. 2: Psychological and Biological Models).* Cambridge, Mass.: MIT Press.

Posner, M. I., Goldsmith, R., & Welton, K. E. (1967). Perceived distance and the classification of distorted patterns. *Journal of Experimental Psychology*, **77**, 353-363.

Trabasso & Bower, G. H. (1968). Attention in learning: Theory and research. New York: Wiley.

ACKNOWLEDGMENTS

This paper is based on portions of a PhD dissertation in psychology submitted to New Mexico State University. The research was supported by the Computing Research Laboratory at NMSU. I would like to thank Roger Schvaneveldt, Jim McDonald, Jordan Pollack, Ken Paap and Don Dearholt for many contributions during the dissertation work, and Mark Gluck, Keith Butler, and Colleen O'Neill for critical reading of an earlier version of this paper.

A connectionist model of phonological short-term memory

Gordon D. A. Brown
Department of Psychology
University College of North Wales
United Kingdom

ABSTRACT

A connectionist model of phonological short-term memory is described. The model makes use of existing connectionist techniques, developed to account for the production and perception of speech and other sequential data, to implement a model of the articulatory rehearsal involved in short-term retention of verbal information. The model is shown to be consistent with a wide range of experimental data, and can be interfaced with existing connectionist models of word recognition. The model illustrates, within a connectionist framework, how the mechanisms of speech perception and production can be recruited for the temporary storage of information. Advantages of this strategy are discussed.

INTRODUCTION

The inclusion of some limited-capacity speech based temporary store is near-universal within cognitive models of language processing, and the properties of this store have been extensively investigated by psychologists over the past three decades. Recent connectionist modelling work has naturally been concerned with the temporary storage of information, but a large body of existing experimental evidence from cognitive psychology cannot readily be interpreted in terms of existing connectionist models. This is partly because of the difficulty of dealing with certain types of temporal phenomena in connectionist models, and also because earlier cognitive psychological models have not always taken account of the temporal dimension in any explicit way (Elman, 1988). There is a need, then, for a psychologically well-motivated model of the temporal characteristics of human short-term memory.

Previous connectionist approaches to short memory have generally been concerned to characterize the types of architecture that can give rise to temporary information storage, either at a neural level or in terms of a cognitive-level working memory system (e.g. Grossberg & Stone, 1986; Schneider & Detweiler, 1987). Schreter and Pfeifer (1989) describe a simple localist architecture which gives rise to primacy and recency serial position curve effects, but their architecture is not intended to account for the detailed experimental results of the type outlined below. Our own approach focuses specifically on the phonological short-term memory store, which is normally viewed as just one subpart of a more complex working memory system (e.g. Baddeley & Hitch, 1974).

PSYCHOLOGICAL APPROACHES TO STM

Many early theorists held the view that short-term memory contained a constant number of "slots" that could be filled by material to be remembered. More than approximately seven items could not be held in short-term storage, but "item" came to be interpreted broadly, allowing for the possibility that large amounts of information could be chunked together in such a way that each slot could hold much information- a character, a word, even a well-learned sentence.

An alternative class of explanation of limited STM capacity comes from the time-limited **trace decay** model (e.g. Baddeley, 1986; Schweickert & Boruff, 1986). In this type of model, a trace is registered in immediate memory when each stimulus item is encountered, and this trace is subject to decay over time. The trace can be refreshed by using a subvocal rehearsal procedure, but if the traces of all the items are to be maintained then it must be possible to rehearse all the items to be remembered within the time taken for the trace of any item to decay to threshold. Thus, as Schweickert and Boruff make clear, the probability that a list will be correctly recalled will be equal to the probability that the time taken to recite the list is less than the variable duration of the trace. Many researchers have suggested that subjects' immediate memory span for familiar materials such as words and digits will be equal to the amount of that material that can be rehearsed subvocally in a fixed time interval. Estimates of this constant time interval vary, but average out at around two seconds.

There is considerable experimental evidence for the trace decay model. A correlation between articulation rate and span has been observed in a variety of contexts, across and within both languages and individuals. Developmental increases in memory span are paralleled by an increase in speech rate (Hulme & Muir, 1985), and adult span correlates with rate of articulation (e.g. Baddeley, Thomson & Buchanan, 1975). Memory span for long words is smaller than span for shorter words in the same language, where "length" is measured in terms of articulation duration (Baddeley et al., 1975). This word length effect is abolished when subjects are required to suppress articulation and are therefore unable to make use of the subvocal rehearsal procedure (Baddeley et al., 1975; Baddeley, Lewis & Vallar, 1984). A similar pattern of results is observed across languages: subjects using languages in which materials (usually digits) are more slowly articulated show reduced memory spans. These ubiquitous correlations between rate of articulation and memory span have been taken to support some version of the verbal trace decay model. In one specific version, Salame and Baddeley (1982) claim that the "articulatory loop" component of the working memory system consists of a phonological store (which gives rise to phonemic confusability effects in STM tasks) and an articulatory rehearsal process (which gives rise to word length effects). Information in the phonological store will decay unless rehearsed. Access to the store when material is presented visually can only be gained via the articulatory rehearsal procedure, and use of the rehearsal procedure will be prevented by articulatory suppression. The connectionist model we report here may be seen as an implementation of a phonological store and speech-based rehearsal process.

It can be seen that these models, which have received a great deal of support from the psychological literature, rely heavily on the temporal characteristics of both information decay and the speech-based articulatory rehearsal procedure. In order to implement this type of model using connectionist methodology, it is therefore necessary to have a way of representing the temporal flow of information. There have been considerable recent advances in the ability of connectionist models to account for temporal phenomena in plausible ways. Previous attempts involved recoding the temporal dimension as a spatial one (Elman, 1988), and sometimes required a reduplication of the entire network for each time-slice of input. However, a different approach involves making some of the input units to a network sensitive to the recent activation history of the network (McClelland & Rumelhart, 1988). In the following section we show how this type of architecture can be extended to produce a psychologically plausible model of the temporal characteristics of human short-term memory.

THE MODEL ARCHITECTURE

The heart of the model of STM is a model of the articulatory rehearsal process used to refresh traces in the phonological store. We model this by taking two separate connectionist networks, one designed for speech production and one designed for speech perception, and interfacing these two nets. The first net, based on an architecture developed by Jordan (1986), can take a temporally static, unordered plan (e.g. a representation of whole-word phonology) and translate this unchanging input into a temporal *sequence* of outputs (e.g. an ordered list of phonemes or articulatory commands). This type of architecture is illustrated by the left half of Figure One: the "production net plan units" are held constant throughout a given output sequence, and the "production net state units" or "context units" have their activations set on the basis of the previous network output. This architecture has been modified by Norris (1989) to *recognize* temporal sequences as single items (as occurs in speech perception).

The Norris model has the same basic architecture as the Jordan net, but is trained to associate a temporally constant pattern of activation on the output units with a time-varying sequence of inputs to the "plan" units. Thus a sequence of items can be input to the network, which will compute a single appropriate output. The resulting network has a number of attractive characteristics, including the ability to generalize in the time domain (e.g. to recognize words spoken at varying rates) and the ability to recognize items within a constant stream of sequential input without the need for reduplication of the net at every point where an item to be recognized might begin (see Norris, 1989, for a discussion of these issues).

When a speech production net and a speech recognition net of the types discussed above are interfaced, so that the output of the production net provides a source of input to the perception net, the architecture in Figure One results. This may be interpreted as a model of the subvocal articulatory rehearsal process in STM, in that the speech production system may direct its output into the speech perception system without overt spoken output ever resulting. Note that not all connections to other parts of the cognitive system are shown: for example, we assume that input and output lexica are separate but connected, and that production and perception mechanisms are connected at various stages (see Ellis & Young, 1988; and Monsell, 1987, for discussion of relevant architectural issues). Input to the rehearsal procedure is provided from a set of input nodes (those in the bottom left-hand corner of Figure One): these represent knowledge about word pronunciations and could be computed for example from the position-independent orthographic trigram units in the network discussed by Mozer (1987). In a complete model there would be input to the speech production net from both high-level and low-level spelling-to-sound correspondences (Brown, 1987a). Note that our "lexical input units" are labelled as input units simply because they provide input to the network we are modelling; in a complete model of the cognitive system they would be more properly characterized as output units. All that matters for present purposes is that there is a set of units that provides input to the speech production network, and that is all that is implemented at present. These units would themselves receive input from a number of different sources- the semantic system and visual short-term memory as well as the spelling-to-sound translation process.

In the present small-scale version of the model, there are 10 nodes in each oval drawn in Figure One- thus in each of the perception and the production nets there are 10 input/plan units, 10 context/state units, 10 hidden units and 10 output units. Individual nodes (other than hidden units) in the present model represent single phonemes, although in some of our experimental (and psychologically more plausible) versions of the model, nodes stand for individual articulatory features. Finally, and crucially for the present model, there are 10 phonological storage nodes which take as their (sequential) input the (sequential) output from the speech perception network (the right half of Figure One). These phonological storage nodes are partly responsible for

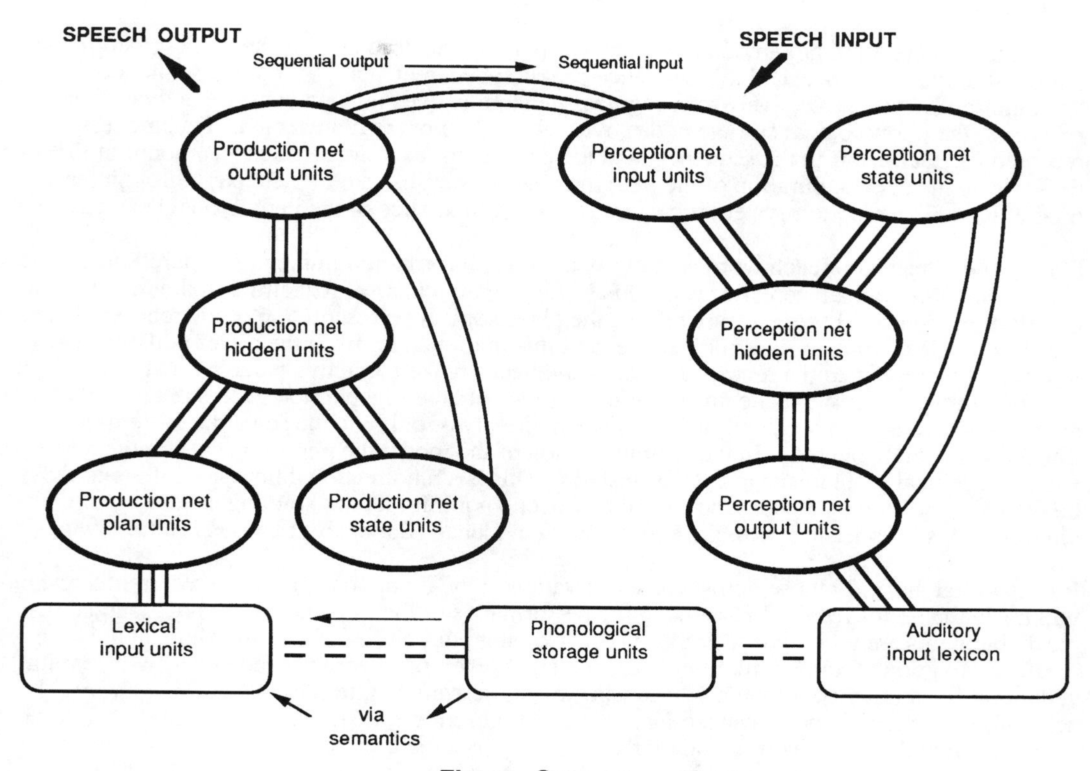

Figure One

temporary storage in the model, but they cannot be accessed directly from visual lexical input. As in the Salame and Baddeley (1982) account, it is assumed that the phonological store gives rise to phonemic confusability effects in short-term memory, and the articulatory rehearsal process gives rise to word length effects (see below).

The simulation of short-term memory processes in the model involves two quite separate phases. The model is first given "long-term memory" about the sequences of phonemes that make up words, and this information is assumed not to change during the later simulation of short-term memory for lists of whole words. Thus, in the first phase, the learning phase, the perception net and the production net separately learn to recognize and produce the same set of phoneme sequences. This learning takes place using the standard back-propagation algorithm described in Rumelhart, Hinton & Williams (1986); the precise training procedure for these nets is described in Jordan (1986) and Norris (1989). At present the nets are trained with a small vocabulary of items which vary in length from 2 to 5 phonemes, with the phonemes being drawn from the very limited (due to computational resource restrictions) pool with which the model currently operates. No psychological reality is claimed for this process.

The main phase of the simulation is the retention in STM of a sequence of items represented at the lexical input level. The input of the sequence of items to be remembered is given by clamping on sets of the lexical input units in sequence: this is analogous to the presentation of a sequence of words. While it is clamped on, each word in the input sequence acts as a (temporally constant) input to the production net side of the articulatory rehearsal process in Figure One. Thus each item in the list of material to be remembered can be input into the "production" network, emerging as a temporal output sequence, and this sequence can then be directed as input to the sequence "recognition" net that effectively re-recognizes the item in question and hence re-activates, or refreshes, the phonological storage nodes over which the item is represented. This process is repeated for each word in the sequence, and the process for each word takes an amount of time that depends on the spoken duration of the item in question, because a complete pass through the production and perception system is required for each time-slice of the item to be rehearsed.

During the rehearsal of each word as described above, information in the non-ordered input nodes, and in the phonological store, decays. This is the primary cause of forgetting in the model. The output of the rehearsal process may refresh the phonological representation of the rehearsed item in the phonological store, as described above, and this in turn can refresh the nodes at the lexical input level that initiated the rehearsal process and hence make the item available for spoken output or another rehearsal. We make no commitment as to whether the phonological storage units can gain this access to the speech production system directly or only via the semantic system (not illustrated or implemented). In the current version of the model the phonological storage nodes can excite the lexical input nodes in a linear fashion. This is a unidirectional link: lexical input nodes on the left hand side of Figure One can neither excite nor inhibit the phonological storage units directly. This is consistent with the experimental evidence (Baddeley, Lewis & Vallar, 1984).

It is assumed that only those items whose activation in the input nodes is above a certain threshold will be available for recall. In assessing the performance of the model, it is simply assumed that recallable items are those whose entries in the lexical input units are above threshold at the time of recall. Activation of an item represented in the input level may be reinforced either by incoming activation from other cognitive modules, such as the semantic system or visual STM, or by activation from the phonological storage units. (At present we are not concerned to model these cognitive modules, and in our simulations we simply assume a small but constant amount of activation arriving at the input to the speech production system from other sources, such as visual memory, while items are being rehearsed. Only a fixed amount of such activation is assumed to be available for all the items to be remembered.) If the level of activation for an item in the input lexical nodes decays below a certain level before the item can be rehearsed, that item will be forgotten. Thus, as in the trace decay model, short-term memory span is limited in capacity to those items whose activations can be refreshed by the articulatory rehearsal process described above before their activations decay to below threshold. During the continuous sequence of rehearsal, the next item to be rehearsed is always selected on the basis of which item's representation is most decayed while still being above threshold. Note that the phonological store in this model can be viewed as both pre-production and post-production, in that material in the store has been processed by much of the speech production apparatus, but can also, indirectly, be part of further sequences of speech production. Note also that the model incorporates both long-term and short-term storage without using both fast and slow weights as in some other accounts.

THE EXPERIMENTAL DATA

There is a wide range of empirical data relevant to evaluation of the model, not all of which can be covered here (see Baddeley, 1986, for a review). Most of our investigations to date have examined the model's ability to remember various sequence-lengths of items, where the items themselves can vary in length. The performance of the model with simulated visual and auditory input can readily be tested, with and without portions of the articulatory rehearsal procedure being made unavailable. For the sake of simplicity it is assumed that all possible phonemes take the same length of time to produce, and that a word containing six phonemes will take twice as long to articulate as words with only three phonemes. These simplifying assumptions are not critical to the operation of the model.

There are widely-observed **word length effects** in STM tasks (Baddeley, Thomson & Buchanan 1975): subjects can remember more items when the items to be remembered have a short spoken duration. Like the Salame and Baddeley (1982) model, our connectionist model behaves in the same way as human subjects because of the temporal characteristics of the rehearsal procedure: long items (those with many phonemes) take longer to rehearse, for rehearsal time is proportional to the number of phonemes (one pass through the network is necessary for each time-slice of the material to be remembered). And the longer the rehearsal time before an item can be refreshed, the more likely it is that the traces of earlier items will have decayed to the extent that they cannot be retrieved. The experimental manipulation **articulatory suppression**, which requires subjects to recite irrelevant material aloud at the same time as remembering a sequence of auditorily or visually presented items, has its effect in the model by making the speech production net unavailable. Thus the word length effect, reflecting the rehearsal procedure, is abolished by articulatory suppression. There is some residual memory capacity even under suppression conditions, arising from visual and semantic coding; we have not yet modelled these sources of capacity in any detail. (There is a need, for example, to account for the fact that articulatory suppression has differential effects across varying serial position.) **Phonemic confusability effects**, which are widely assumed, as here, to reflect the operation of the phonological store rather than the articulatory rehearsal procedure, are also abolished by suppression when material is visually presented, because visually presented material can only gain access to the phonological store via the rehearsal procedure. In contrast, auditorily presented material can show phonemic confusability effects, because this material can gain access to the phonemic store via the recognition side of the rehearsal procedure. This modality-dependent behaviour of the model is consistent with the observations and model of Baddeley et al. (1984). We have not yet examined the mechanisms of confusability effects in the model in detail, due to computational resource constraints and the need for a larger vocabulary, but they are assumed to arise due to interference in the phonological store. As in the interactive activation model of word recognition, the probability of being able to identify an item is assumed to reflect the level of activation of that item's units *relative to* the activation of units for other items. And when items share phonemes, their total levels of activations over phonemes are relatively more similar, leading to difficulty in identification. The **retention of order information** is generally believed to be an important function of STM (Healy, 1974); in our model (as in other models of STM) order information is represented simply in terms of the extent to which the activation if an item code has decayed in the phonological store. The model has ready access to this information for other purposes, and can use the decay levels as order markers without the need for further mechanisms inside the phonological store. This appears to provide a relatively efficient method of encoding order information for humans, for such information is more likely to be lost whenever phonological STM is made unavailable (but cf. Grossberg & Stone, 1986). Effects of **lexicality, imageability** and **visual confusability** on STM capacity are assumed in the model to result from non-phonological sources of activation that help to maintain the activation level of lexical input units. Thus, they simply provide an alternative source of input in addition to refreshment by the output of the articulatory rehearsal procedure. **Chunking** effects have a similar source, in that they are assumed to arise from the (as yet underspecified) coalitions of units that can be brought to bear on the recall process. It has been suggested that **item identification time** may be independently related to memory span for those items (Dempster, 1981): Our implementation assumes that the input to the rehearsal process can be seen as the output of a word identification process, and so if items take a long time to load into the rehearsal procedure, there will be correspondingly more time for the codes of other to-be-remembered items to decay. Indeed, the model reported here was designed as an extension and development of an earlier computational model of single word reading (Brown, 1987a, 1987b).

While the model can account for a wide range of data as it stands, it is assumed that a more complete model, which includes more sub-components of the working memory system, will be required to account for suffix effects and aspects of retroactive and proactive inhibition as well as the use of retrieval cues. Those parts of the **serial position curve** that are sometimes assumed to reflect rehearsal and transfer to LTM are consistent with the current version of the model, and it is assumed that there is an additional, passive storage mechanism responsible for recency effects. The model as it stands also assumes an outside source of strategic control (deciding when to rehearse), and some binding mechanism so that the model can distinguish different tokens of the same word. In addition, we note that the model builds on speech processing mechanisms that have been criticized for requiring a segmented input stream.

DISCUSSION

The model provides a connectionist, psychologically plausible account of the way in which mechanisms of speech perception and production can be recruited to serve as a temporary storage system. The suggestion that temporary phonological storage capacity is available as a by-product of the language processing system is a well-established one (Ellis, 1979), but computationally explicit mechanisms have been lacking. The model is essentially a connectionist implementation of the Baddeley model of the articulatory loop (Baddeley, 1986; Salame & Baddeley, 1982; cf. also Schneider & Detweiler, 1987). Our model accounts in a similar way for the limited capacity of human short-term memory, in that it is only possible for a temporally limited amount of material to be rehearsed by the network before information decays beyond recall. Similar reasoning can be used to explain the developmental increases observed in temporary memory capacity, as well as providing an explanation of word length effects and the ability of STM to encode order information. We are currently extending the model and investigating its ability to account for developmental phenomena in particular. The model is being trained with a larger vocabulary, represented in terms of acoustic features rather than phonemes as at present, for empirical evidence demonstrates that confusions in STM can occur at sub-phoneme levels.

Our approach is motivated by the belief that rehearsal processes, as characterized in current cognitive models, are a ubiquitous feature of human cognition, and there are good reasons for this which are illustrated by reference to our model. If a trace is refreshed via the normal perception and production mechanisms, which are available at no extra cost to the organism, the maintenance of the trace can take advantage of what is know about the perceptual structure of the world, for these regularities are encoded in the perception and production mechanisms. This contrasts with the case of simple resonance, where units can remain active simply by passing activation backwards and forwards without making use of perception and production mechanisms and the regularities implicit therein.

ACKNOWLEDGEMENTS

This research was supported by grants from the Medical Research Council (U.K.) (1989) and the Leverhulme Trust (1988-1990). I thank Dennis Norris for useful discussions.

REFERENCES

BADDELEY, A.D. (1986). *Working memory*. Oxford: OUP.

BADDELEY, A.D. & HITCH, G.J. (1974). Working memory. In G. Bower (Ed.), *Advances in the psychology of learning and motivation 8,* New York: Academic Press.

BADDELEY, A.D., THOMSON, N. & BUCHANAN, M. (1975). Word length and the structure of short-term memory. *Journal of Verbal Learning and Verbal Behavior,* 14, 575-589.

BADDELEY, A.D., LEWIS, V. & VALLAR, G. (1984). Exploring the articulatory loop. *Quarterly Journal of Experimental Psychology,* 36A, 281-289.

BROWN, G.D.A. (1987a). Resolving inconsistency: A computational model of word naming. *Journal of Memory and Language*, 23, 1-23.
BROWN, G.D.A. (1987b). Constraining interactivity: Evidence from acquired dyslexia. *Proceedings of the Ninth Annual Conference of the Cognitive Science Society*, 779-793. Hillsdale, NJ: Lawrence Erlbaum Associates.
DEMPSTER, F.N. (1981). Memory span: Sources of individual and developmental differences. *Psychological Bulletin*, 89, 63-100.
ELLIS, A.W. (1979). Speech production and short-term memory. In J. Morton & J.C. Marshall (Eds.), *Psycholinguistic series Vol 2: Structures and processes*. Cambridge, Mass: MIT Press.
ELLIS, A.W., & YOUNG, A.W. (1988). *Human cognitive neuropsychology*. Hillsdale, NJ: Lawrence Erlbaum Associates.
ELMAN, J.L. (1988). *Finding structure in time*. CRL Technical Report 8801, University of California, San Diego.
GROSSBERG, S., & STONE, G. (1986). Neural dynamics of attention switching and temporal order information in short term memory. *Memory & Cognition*, 14 (6), 451-468.
HEALY, A.F. (1974). Separating item from order information in short-term memory. *Journal of Verbal Learning and Verbal Behavior*, 13, 644-655.
HULME, C. & MUIR, C. (1985) Developmental changes in speech rate and memory span: A causal relationship? *British Journal of Developmental Psychology*, 3, 175-181.
JORDAN, M.I. (1986). Attractor dynamics and parallelism in a connectionist sequential machine. *Proceedings of the Eighth Annual Conference of the Cognitive Science Society*, Hillsdale, NJ: Lawrence Erlbaum Associates.
McCLELLAND, J.L., & RUMELHART, D.E. (1988). *Explorations in parallel distributed processing: A handbook of models, programs and exercises*. Cambridge, Mass: MIT Press.
MONSELL, S. (1987). On the relation between lexical input and output pathways for speech. In A. Allport, D. MacKay, W. Prinz & E. Scheerer (Eds.), *Language Perception and Production*. New York: Academic Press.
MOZER, M.C. (1987). Early parallel processing in reading: A connectionist approach. In M. Coltheart (Ed.), *Attention and performance XII: The psychology of reading*. Hillsdale, NJ: Lawrence Erlbaum Associates.
NORRIS, D. (1989). Dynamic net model of human speech recognition. In G.T. Altmann (Ed.) *Cognitive models of speech processing: Psycholinguistic and computational perspectives*. Cambridge, Mass: MIT Press (in press).
RUMELHART, D.E., HINTON, G.E., & WILLIAMS, R.J. (1986). Learning internal representations by error propagation. In D.E. Rumelhart and J.L. McClelland (Eds.), *Parallel Distributed Processing Vol 1*. Cambridge, Mass: MIT Press.
SALAME, P., & BADDELEY, A.D. (1982). Disruption of short-term memory by unattended speech: Implications for the structure of working memory. *Journal of Verbal Learning and Verbal Behavior*, 21, 150-164.
SCHNEIDER, W., & DETWEILER, M. (1987). A connectionist/control architecture for working memory. In G.H. Bower (Ed.) *The psychology of learning and motivation vol 21*. New York: Academic Press.
SCHRETER, Z., & PFEIFER, R. (1989). Short-term memory/long-term memory interactions in connectionist simulations of of psychological experiments on list learning. In L. Personnaz and G. Dreyfus (Eds.), *Neural networks: From models to applications*. Paris: I.D.S.E.T.
SCHWEICKERT, R., & BORUFF, B. (1986) Short-term memory capacity: Magic number or magic spell? *Journal of Experimental Psychology: Learning, Memory and Cognition*, 12 (3), 419-425.

Toward a Connectionist Model of Symbolic Emergence

YVES CHAUVIN

PSYCHOLOGY DEPARTMENT
STANFORD UNIVERSITY

This paper examines how and why empirical results related to first-word acquisition in infants can occur in a generic associative PDP model. During learning, a network is exposed to a micro-world composed of categories made of clusters of "images" and of labels attached to these clusters. The architecture of the network allows encoding of labels and images in a common level of representation and subsequent extraction of labels from images and images from labels. If (1) the learning rule is an error-correction/steepest descent algorithm, (2) the image clusters are sufficiently "fuzzy", (3) the mapping image/label is consistent and (4) the network capacity is adapted to the size of the micro-world, this simple generic model can be shown to account for a broad spectrum of first-word acquisition data including acquisition "burst", underextensions, overextensions, gradual generalization, comprehension before production and decontextualization.

INTRODUCTION

Acquiring the meaning of words may be seen as a categorization or pattern recognition problem. The task of the infant is to classify the world into labeled categories, in agreement with the categories and labels used by adults. In this sense, there is early symbolic emergence or meaning acquisition when an entity in a modality becomes consistently mapped to another entity in a different modality. In the model below, patterns of activations are presented to a PDP network. The model has two types of inputs corresponding to two different modalities. One of them can be seen as corresponding to the auditory modality, the other to a visual modality. The model is simply exposed to a micro-world made of a micro-set of categories. Each category is composed of a set of micro-images and of an associated label. This micro-world is structured: images associated with identical labels are similar. During learning, images and labels are presented to the network, separately or together. The network learns how to build internal representations of these labels and images, and under certain conditions, to associate images with the corresponding labels.

MODEL

Microworld.

Images are simple random dot patterns constructed on a grid composed of 61 rows and 21 columns. Nine random cells are turned on to form a pattern. Before being used as input to a connectionist network, the grid is preprocessed to reduce the computational demands and create a "smearing" effect allowing a notion a similarity between patterns (Knapp and Anderson, 1984). We can call "retina" a two-dimensional layer of units (or "cells") that transform these random dot patterns into another two-dimensional pattern of activations. The units of this "retina" form a regular lattice that is superimposed on the original grid and have their receptor fields centered on a grid cell. In all the simulations described below, the shape of the receptor fields is chosen as a bi-dimensional decreasing exponential of the form $exp(-d/k)$ where k is the spread parameter and d is the distance between the center of the field and a point of the "retina".

When a pattern is presented to the model, each unit computes its activation by summing the activations due to each of the grid cells in its receptor fields. The retinal units that are too far from the active cells of the original grid cannot get enough activation and are "filtered out" of the final retinal grid. Figure 1 shows an original pattern of dots and the resulting pattern after

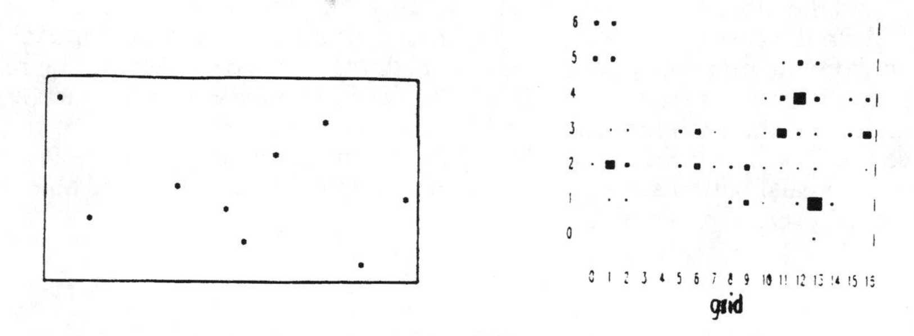

Figure 1. On the left, a random pattern of dots. On the right, a filtered pattern of dots represented on a 17x7 grid and stored into the pdp network. The size of each rectangle corresponds to the activation of the corresponding unit in the filtered grid. In this case, the filtering parameters are the following: the grain is 4, the profile is an exponential and the spread parameter is 1.2.

filtering. The filtered grid is then presented to a connectionist network for learning (see below). The microworld consists of 4 categories of such images. For each category, a basic random dot pattern was created. Out of each of these 4 basic patterns, 7 distorted patterns were generated by moving each dot around its original basic location. Each category of images is then associated to a single label (A, B, C or D).

Network Architecture.

The basic architecture of the network is shown in Figure 2. The learning rule used during the simulations is the back-propagation algorithm (Rumelhart, Hinton & Williams, 1986). The network is an auto-associative network. With this architecture, the input and output layers are identical and the network learns how to encode the incoming information in the hidden layers (Cottrell, Munro & Zipser, 1987; Zipser, 1987; Baldi & Hornik, 1988). In the present network, there are two pairs of input and output layers. One input layer theoretically corresponds to the

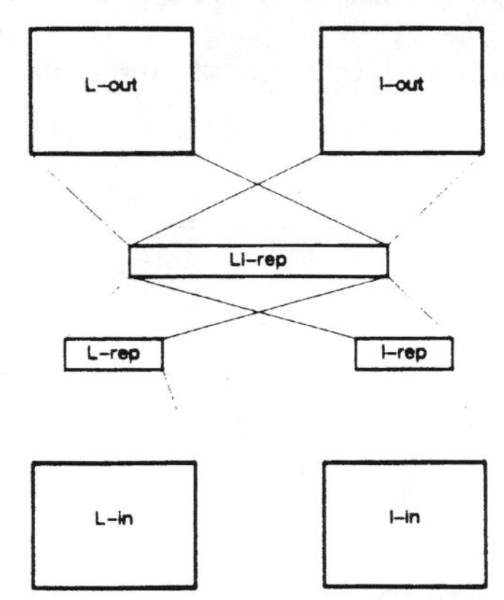

Figure 2. The network has two input layers, two corresponding output layers and three hidden layers: one for each input layer and one common to both. This last layer will encode the information that is necessary to reproduce the input patterns. Each layer is given a name that will be used in the paper. *L-in* stands for labels at the input level, *L-rep* for the representation of the labels, *L-out* for the labels at the output level, *L-in* for the "images" at the input level, *L-rep* for the representation of the "images", *L-out* for the "images" at the output level, and *LI-rep* for the representation common to both labels and "images".

"auditory modality" and the other one to the "visual modality". In the simulations, the "auditory modality" corresponds to the category labels used in the experiments. The "visual modality" will receive its input from the preprocessed random dot patterns. As we can see in Figure 2, the hidden layers *L-rep* and *I-rep* are specific to each "modality" and will specifically encode the corresponding stimuli. The common hidden layer *LI-rep* receives activations from both "modalities" and must have the capacity to regenerate the input patterns at the output level. If there is a correlation between the visual patterns and the labels, this common layer should be able to discover and represent it (Zipser, 1987).

Learning Dynamics.

Training consisted in three auto-associations: images to images, labels to labels, and images plus labels to images plus labels. With a linear auto-associative network using the delta rule, it is possible to show that the principal components of the input patterns (eigenvectors of the associated covariance matrix) are encoded "successively", in an order depending of the size of their respective eigenvalues (Chauvin, 1988). Thus, learning can be seen as a differentiation process where the "central tendencies" are encoded first. The present network is a multi-layer non-linear network using a generalization of the delta rule (back-propagation, sigmoid units). Formal analysis of this type of network have not been made possible so far. However, simulations show that, to some extent, similar processes happen during learning in both types of network.

Figure 3 represents a geometrical interpretation of the generic phenomena that happen in a simple linear network. In this case, the network is composed of two input units, 1 hidden unit, and 2 output units. The two input units correspond to two dimensions (weight and height) collected from a sample of people. The main principal component is represented in the figure by a 45 degree slanted axis. Because the considered network has only one hidden unit, only one principal component will be encoded after learning (Baldi and Hornik, 1988). This hidden unit will represent the projection of an input pattern on this major principal component. Two projections are shown in the figure. For the first one, a complete pattern is given as input to the network, corresponding to the data point x1. The activation of the hidden unit represents the projection of x1 to the major principal component. The activation of the output units represents the back-projection of this hidden unit to the original space. As we can see, the coordinates of x1 in the original space are basically retrieved by these projections. If we suppose now that only the height coordinate of x2 is given as input to the network, the coordinate becomes projected to the

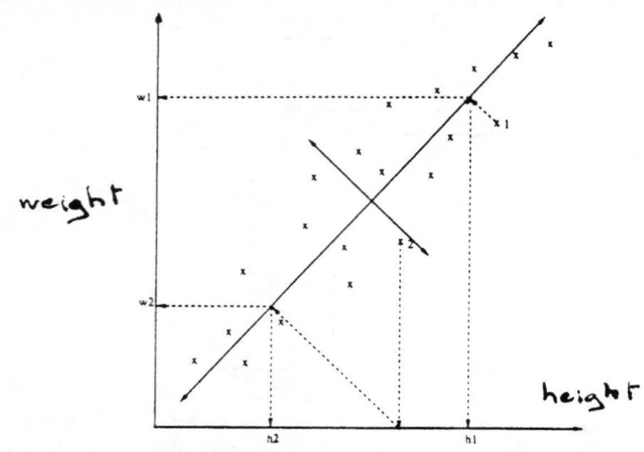

Figure 3. Geometrical interpretation of pattern completion by linear projection on the major principal component (see text). Two points are projected. The first one, x1, is projected from the complete original position to the major principal component. For x2, the "height" coordinate only is projected. Each of these principal component projections is then reinterpreted by back-projection in the original weight/height space.

major principal component and then back to the original space. As we can see, some information has been retrieved about the "weight" of x2. This corresponds to a pattern completion phenomenon by projection on the principal component.

SIMULATIONS

Categorization

After learning, a label presented to *L-in* reproduces itself in *L-out* and an image presented to *I-in* reproduces itself in *I-out*. The layers *L-rep, I-rep,* and *LI-rep* then represent the compressed information (Cottrell, Zipser, & Munro, 1987) of the input patterns. For a right amount of hidden units, presented with an image, the network is able to produce the label that corresponds to the associated category: there is *production*. Presented with a label, the network is able to give an image that basically corresponds to the average of all the images that have been stored with the same label: there is *comprehension*. For a sufficient number of images per category and a right set of low-level filtering parameters, the prototype effect can be observed for comprehension, as observed with infants (Thomson & Chapman, 1977), and production. Interestingly, because images form clusters, knowing the shape of an image provides some information about what the label should be. However, the network is not being trained to produce a label when an image is presented. The network does use the image information and automatically learns the cross association only because there is auto-association image to image and subsequent cluster extraction during learning: the internal representation of the images is *necessary* for the development of the labeling process.

Gradual Generalizations

Three levels of distortion are used to test generalization of categorization to new images (the network was trained on patterns created with the medium level only). These levels of distortions correspond to different standard deviations of a Gaussian noise added to each dot location of the prototypical images. Figure 4 shows the acquisition orders of each distortion level. As we can see, the network gradually learns how to generalize production and comprehension to more and more distorted patterns. Thomson and Chapman (1977) and others observed gradual generalization for comprehension with infants. Interestingly, generalization actually occurs earlier and faster for comprehension than for production.

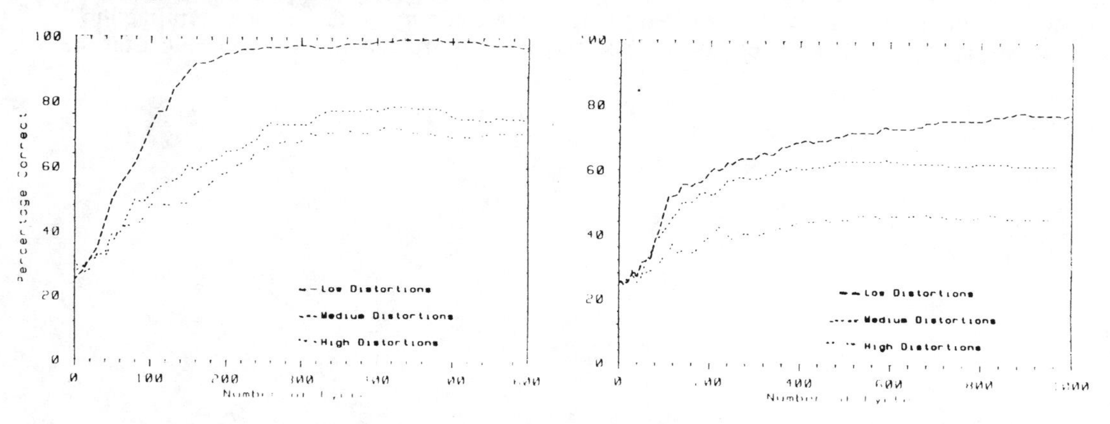

Figure 4. Gradual generalization for production and comprehension. The network gradually learns how to respond correctly to more and more distorted patterns.

Comprehension before Production.

Figure 5 shows production and comprehension data as a function of the number of learning cycles. We can see that production and comprehension performances are similar after sufficient training but that comprehension performance is clearly higher than production during early learning, in agreement with comprehension/production data observed during human first word acquisition (e.g. Bates, 1976). Label and image features can actually be considered as category features. Among these features, labels are the most "significant" because they are consistently present in all the examples of the category. For that reason, labels become good indicators of the category clusters and will allow good reconstitution of the images. In contrast, image features may be present or absent or "graded" among the examples and will not reconstitute the labels as well.

Acquisition Rates

Typically, categorization rates are low during early learning and suddenly increase as learning goes on. This initial period is usually longer for production than for comprehension and the production rate increase is not as sharp. During the differentiation process, the network actually learns how to distinguish the categories before distinguishing the exemplars within each category. As long as the categories are not distinguished, the network is still able to categorize some of the patterns correctly, "by chance", depending on their "projection" to the category averages. However, there is very little generalization during this period: the network is only able to generalize to patterns that are closely correlated to already stored patterns. When the network starts to "realize" that there exist category clusters, by "pulling apart" the corresponding averages, there is generalization and sharp increase in the acquisition rates. This sharp increase in comprehension and production rates can be compared to the well-known vocabulary explosion observed in production with humans (e.g. Barrett, 1983).

Decontextualization and Underextensions

Here, decontextualization is viewed as the process of shifting from temporarily associating a label with a single image to extending the association to the complete set of images corresponding to the label. Simulations show various cases of decontextualization depending on the initial weights of the network. In the most common case, a label is correctly mapped to only one image for some time and becomes slowly extended to the whole category while being generalized to new category examples. In another case, two category labels are decontextualized one after the

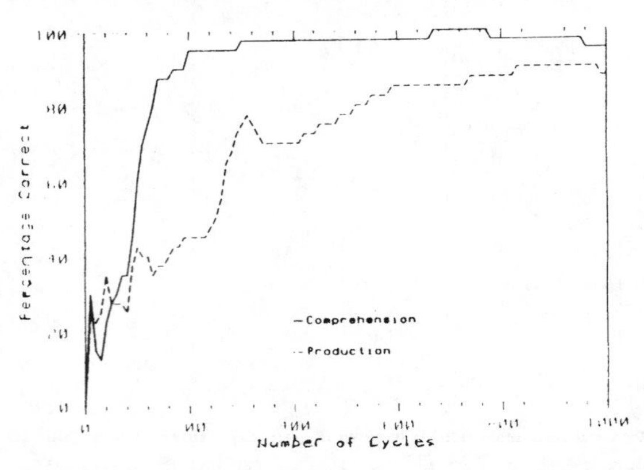

Figure 5. Comprehension versus production. During early learning, performance on comprehension is better than on production.

other: one is decontextualized much later than the other one, but also much faster. In other cases, the opposite phenomenon occurs, where a first category label is quickly decontextualized whereas another one is decontextualized much later and much more slowly. Interestingly, the simulations are very consistent with recent human data on decontextualization. There does not seem to exist an initial period where labels are first slowly decontextualized and a subsequent period where they are decontextualized from the onset (as previously suggested by Bates, 1979). In agreement with Barrett (1986, In Press), a label can be correctly mapped to a complete category early in learning while some other label might appear later and be slowly decontextualized. Furthermore, underextension followed by a forgetting stage followed by correct extension might occur, as observed by Bloom (1973).

Overextensions.

During very early learning, the network extracts the general average taken over the entire set of stored patterns. However, after this initial period, the network encodes the first principal component of the patterns and finds a steepest slope in a direction that might better correspond to one of the categories. Any other pattern correlated with this biased category will be similarly categorized by the network and overextensions might occur. In the model, if a label unit activation in *L-out* is above a given threshold but does not correspond to the label associated with a presented image, it can be considered as an over-extension of the indicated category. Simulations show that for production, over-extensions do occur for some of the categories and can be highly variable. When they occur, they are generally followed by periods of underextension, before being slowly readjusted to a correct "extension level". Overextensions are also much more likely to occur during early learning than during late learning. Figure 6 shows the total amount of overextensions and the total amount of correct extensions as a function of the number of cycles during a typical run. Overextensions also occur during comprehension. However, they start earlier, they end earlier, and they are not as numerous as overextensions during production. This difference between production and comprehension is also due to the fact that labels are good cluster indicators. Again, there are interesting similarities between the way the network learns and the way children acquire their first words. First, the network produces overextensions, in spite of equiprobable presentations (e.g. Rescorla, 1980). Second, the overextensions occur mostly during early learning: the late acquired categories are not overextended (Rescorla, 1976). Third, overextensions can be followed by a "recession" stage before correct extensions begin to take place. Fourth, overextensions are more frequent in production than in comprehension (Thomson & Chapman, 1977). Fifth, if a category is being correctly extended, then no other category can overextend to it (Leopold, 1949).

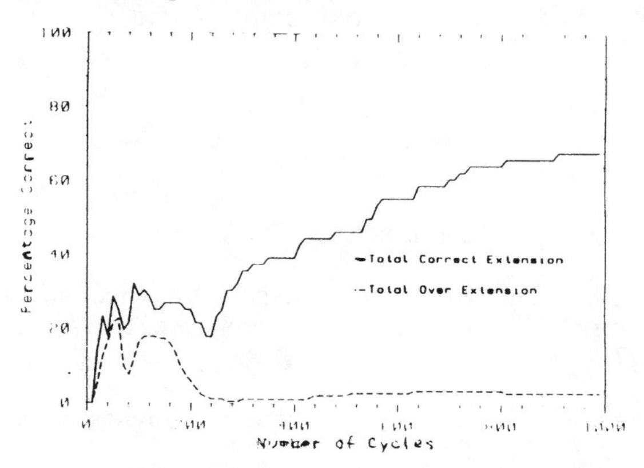

Figure 6. Total number of correct and over extensions as a function of the number of cycles for production during a typical run.

SUMMARY AND DISCUSSION

The patterns stored in the network can be viewed as multi-dimensional correlated vectors. The delta learning rule encodes these sets of vectors by first representing their major principal components. Figure 3 shows a geometrical interpretation of the phenomena occurring in a simple linear network for a low dimensional space. The projections represent the "knowledge" that the network has about the world. To retrieve the world knowledge from this representation means back-projecting these projections to the original space. If there is sufficient information compression in the hidden layers, labels will be retrieved from images and prototypical images from words (production and comprehension). The strictly consistent mapping between labels and image categories creates learning asymmetries between comprehension and production. In general, the direction of the main principal components depends on the image clusters and on the consistency between labels and image clusters. Therefore, a category prototype closer to the first principal component might dominate the whole set of examples during early learning, creating over-extensions to the related category. As the "category directions" are being discovered by the network, it becomes much easier to classify the examples belonging to the corresponding clusters (comprehension and production rate explosions). From this onset onwards, examples are really classified according to their prototypical directions. Finally, images can reproduce labels only because there is a differentiation process happening during auto-association of the images. During this process, the image clusters are reinforced in the internal representations and the labels can "understand" the information coming from the images. In this sense, the internal representation of the world, seen as a principal component or "central tendency" analysis, is necessary for the linguistic mapping.

The goal of this study is not to construct a realistic model of first word acquisition. Rather, it is to explore if phenomena related to symbolic emergence in infants could be "naturally understood" in a Parallel Distributed Processing framework. The differentiation process proposed by psychologists such as Piaget and Werner during early language acquisition is reminiscent of the phenomena occurring in simple linear networks using an error correction rule. Therefore, the original idea was to store in a network using such a rule, a set of patterns that would correspond to labels and images and to observe how and understand why associations between these labels and patterns could be built during learning. The network had to internalize the presented patterns in such a manner that resulting representations would be able to reproduce images and labels from images or labels. This constraint forced a level of representation that would compress labels and images into a common encoding layer. The present network can then be seen as a simple generic model that "embodies" these very general principles. Interestingly, the network was able to mimic quite a number of first word acquisition phenomena just by using these few principles.

Acknowledgments.
I am greateful to Dave Rumelhart and to the PDP research groups at UCSD and Stanford University for useful discussions. I am especially thankful to Yoshiro Miyata for the use of his simulator SunNet.

REFERENCES

Baldi, P., & Hornik, K. (1988). Neural networks and principal component analysis: Learning from examples without local minima. *Proceedings of the Conference on Neural Information Processing Systems, Denver, CO.*

Barrett, M. D. (1983). The course of early lexical development: A review and an interpretation. *Early child development and care, 11*, 19-32.

Barrett, M. D. (1986). Early semantic representations and early word usage. In S. A. Kucsaj, M. D. Barrett (Ed.), *The development of word meaning*. New York, NY: Springer-Verlag.

Barrett, M. D. (In Press). Early language development. In A. Slater, G. Bremer (Ed.), *Infant Development*. London: Erlbaum.

Bates, E. (1976). *Language and context: The acquisition of pragmatics*. New York, NY: Academic Press.

Bates, E., Benigni, L., Bretherton, L., Camaioni, L., & Volterra, V. (1979). *The emergence of symbols: Cognition and communication in infancy*. New York, NY: Academic Press.

Bloom, L. (1973). *One word at a time*. The Hague: Mouton.

Chauvin, Y. (1988). *Symbol Acquisition in Humans and Neural (PDP) Networks*. Unpublished Doctoral Dissertation. University of California, San Diego..

Cottrell, G. W., Munro, P., & Zipser, D. (1987). Learning internal representations from gray-scale images: An example of extensional programming. *Proceeding of the Ninth Annual Conference of the Cognitive Science Society, Seattle, WA*, 461-473.

Knapp, A. G., & Anderson, J. A. (1984). Therory of categorization based on distributed memory storage. *Journal of Experimental Psychology: Learning, Memory and Cognition*, *10*, 616-638.

Leopold, W. F. (1949). *Speech development of a bilingual child: A linguist's record* (Vol. 3). Evanston, Ill: Northwestern University Press.

Rescorla, L. (1976). Concept formation in word learning. *Unpublished doctoral dissertation*. Yale University

Rescorla, L. (1980). Overextension in early language development. *Journal of Child Language*, *7*, 321-335.

Rumelhart, D. E., Hinton, G. H., & Williams, R. J. (1986). Learning internal representations by error propagation. In D. E. Rumelhart, J. L. McClelland (Ed.), *Parallel distributed processing. Explorations in the microstructure of cognition. (Vol 1)*. Cambridge, Ma: MIT Press/Bradford Books.

Thomson, J. R., & Chapman, R. S. (1977). Who is "Daddy"? The status of two-year-olds' over-extended words in use and comprehension. *Journal of Child Language*, *4*, 359-375.

Zipser, D. (1986). *Programming networks to compute spatial functions* (Tech. Rep. No 8608). University of California, San Diego, Insitute for Cognitive Science.

Coherence Relation Assignment

K. Dahlgren
IBM/Los Angeles Scientific Center

Abstract. Three empirical studies of coherence in large corpora of commentary text are sketched, showing that cue phrases are infrequent, and that substantive coherence relations must be assigned in order to infer discourse structure. The notion of coherence is carefully defined in relation to the world, cognitive models of the world, and formal semantic representations of discourse. An efficient algorithm for assigning discourse coherence relations is described, which employs information from syntax, cue phrases, lexical items, formal semantics and naive semantics. The algorithm correctly assigns the coherence relations evident in an 8000 word corpus.

1.0 Introduction

Analyses of discourse structure in cognitive science have been dominated by two approaches. One examines syntactic and cue phrase information only, in order to avoid unsolved semantic puzzles [3, 13, 28, 32]. In this framework Grosz and Sidner have established that discourse is structured in a hierarchy, and that anaphora resolution is constrained by "focus spaces" or segments of discourse [13]. The other approach seeks to account for coherence---substantive relations between portions of a discourse [5, 11, 24, 17, 15, 27, 21, 31, 34, 36]. The coherence group divides into two camps, the top-downs [31], and the bottom-ups (all of the others). We are among the latter, that is, we aim to build discourse structure clause by clause, because a bottom-up approach will lead to more transportable, general results than will the (apparently) more tractable script scheme. This work is part of an ongoing project, NewSelector, for computational text understanding and precise text selection [5, 8]. The word meaning representation in NewSelector is based upon Naive Semantics (NS), a theory which identifies word meanings with commonsense theories of objects and events.

Studies of Coherence in Commentary. We have carried out three studies of coherence in an expanding corpus of *Wall Street Journal* (WSJ) commentary texts. Study 1 [5] of 8,000 words in six articles sought to examine what information is used in coherence relation assignment (CRA), and to determine whether syntactic markers and cue phrases were sufficient information for CRA. The coherence relation literature was reviewed [3, 10, 15, 17, 24], and 19 coherence relations (fully defined in [5]) which are relevant to the commentary genre were identified. In this paper we focus on just two of these, **cause** and **goal**. A coherence relation was assigned to each clause in the corpus by two judges. The syntactic and semantic properties of each clause were encoded. These properties included clause type, voice, mood, presence of negation, agentiveness of subject, type of subject and object, and aspectual class of the verb. The correlations between the coherence relation assigned to a clause, and syntactic/semantic properties of the clause form the basis of the algorithm described in Section 3. We found that the information used in CRA was: 1) syntax, 2) cue phrases, 3) lexical items, 4) tense, 5) aspect, 6) world knowledge.

Study 2 [6], of the same 8,000 words and 8,000 more, examined global coherence (or segmentation) to determine which factors influenced it. For each new S, the possibility of a new sister- or sub-segment arises. We found that change of coherence relation was the most reliable indicator of new segment and change of subject next most reliable. Other factors were paragraph indentation, length of segment with the same coherence relation to some other, cue phrases, and event anaphors. Significantly, there was a segmenting cue phrase such as, "turning to..." in only 16% of the cases of a new sister segment. Clearly any computational system which looks only for direct cues will miss most of the structure. Substantive coherence relations, if they can be extracted, are powerful indicators of structure.

Study 3 [22] of the same 16,000 plus 4,500 more words of *WSJ* text examined personal pronouns, demonstratives and definite NP anaphora. We found that when we segment text as proposed in Study 2 [6], the resulting structure predicts constraints on anaphora resolution. This work supports [13] empirically and also shows that event anaphora has very different constraints from individual anaphora.

2.0 Coherence

Why Compute Coherence? The reasons for computing coherence are several. First, it is uncontroversial that text understanding requires segmentation [13,28]. These segments or focus spaces can only be found using coherence, as indicated in Study 2. Second, our Study 3 shows that by computing coherence, anaphora resolution can be significantly constrained. Otherwise, you either have to use brute force, which leads to a combinatorial explosion, and still indeterminate results, or try cues like indentation, which will be correct only 50% of the time, and cue phrases, which are present only 16% of the time. Third, more intelligent text understanding is made possible by coherence inferences. Text is telescopic, and the reader fills in the gaps. A computational system which models such inferences will be able to reflect much more accurately the human understanding of text. Fourth, when considering whether one text is relevant to another, the more naive inferencing computed, the more accurate the relevance reasoning will be. Finally, because of this last point, a computational system with coherence can answer many more queries accurately, as in (1)-(3).

Why did John make a profit? --Because he invested. (1)
Why did John invest? --In order to make a profit. (2)
What did John invest in? --Typically, stocks or bonds. (3)

Problems with Coherence Theory. One of the reasons for the past emphasis on overt elements like structure and cue phrases, is that unsolved problems have plagued the coherence approach and made it a dubious notion. The first problem is one of *definition*. We have tried to rectify this below by giving a careful definition of what coherence is. Secondly, settling upon a set of coherence relations has been an elusive goal. Most studies have attempted to handle all genres with one big set [10, 15, 17, 24], but the set of relations varies with genre. The solution lies in assigning genre first, then computing coherence [27]. The third problem is informality. Much of the study of coherence has been descriptive [17,24] and has not attempted to provide a direct link between coherence theory and formal semantic theories. Recent developments in formal semantics provide a framework and ongoing research devoted to giving truth conditions for entire discourses as well as single sentences [20, 1, 35, 2]. It is now possible to integrate coherence structure with formal semantic representation (especially of temporal order and aspectual class which our Study 2 found are particularly significant indicators of coherence relations). The third problem is that no-one has proposed an algorithm for extracting coherence relations. This is because to do so, by all accounts, requires world knowledge, and it has heretofore seemed impossible to encode world knowledge in a non-*ad hoc*, transportable and practicable way. Our theory of lexical representation, Naive Semantics, offers a solution.

What is Coherence? We consider the notion of coherence for all types of discourse, spoken and written. It is based upon the intuition that the discourse (4) seems to "hang together", and that the discourse in (5) does not. Empirically, to the extent that discourses do not cohere, they are difficult to interpret and remember [16, 34, 11].

John invested heavily. He profited handsomely. (4)
John invested heavily. He ate pizza. (5)

The problems in coherence theory have been: 1) What is a coherent discourse? and 2) Which entities cohere: sentences, clauses, the propositions expressed, the real events denoted? In our view, a coherent discourse is one for which the hearer can build a cognitive representation such that the relations among events and individuals in the representation correspond with his understanding (theory) of the way actual world events and individuals relate.[1] Although the representation may contain a variety of types of sensory images, in general, the hearer's "understanding" amounts to a naive (in the sense of [14]) theory of the causal and other structure of objects and events [11, 34].

Consider a formal semantic representation for the discourse (4), shown in (6) as a Discourse Representation Structure (DRS) after Kamp [20] and Asher [1]. It has the content that there was an individual John and two events, the first of John investing heavily, the second of John profiting handsomely. Notice that there are two inferences in the DRS, one of temporal order between the investing and the profiting ($r1 < r2$) [26], the other concerning anaphor resolution of "he" to John. The cognitive picture of the events constructed by the hearer (and presumably, intended by the speaker) is indicated in English on the right-hand side of (6). It includes all of the content of the DRS plus the inference that John's goal in investing had been to make a profit. This goal inference is a coherence inference. The hearer brings the discourse into accord with his/her understanding or theory about investing. The reason for saying that "understanding" involves a theory (belief rather than knowledge) is that very often people, and cultures, are quite mistaken in such causal inferences. Nevertheless, they do use such structuring theories to manage the environment and to communicate via language. Because members of a subculture SHARE naive theories, the speaker can juxtapose just these two sentences, and know that the hearer will guess that John's goal had been profit. In summary, speakers in a given genre make a discourse (and thereby their reporting of events) understandable by choosing to report events using certain verbs in a certain sequence. This choice in a well-structured discourse makes it maximally possible for the hearer to build a cognitive picture of these events which coheres. It will cohere to the extent that he/she can bring it into accord with her/his theories about the way the world works. The relationships in the naive theory of the world are causal, intentional, comparative, part-whole, etc.

We claim that coherence belongs in a cognitive inference module, not in syntax or semantics [6]. Temporal order and anaphora resolution belong in the compositional semantics because they are explicitly and linguistically marked. Coherence is a gradient phenomenon in that the better-structured the discourse, the more readily and reliably a hearer will make coherence inferences. Similarly, the more knowledgeable and tuned in the hearer, the more accurately

Discourse Representation Structure

```
u1,e1,e2,now,r1,r2
------------------
John(u1)
e1 invest(u1)
heavily(e1)
e2 profit(u1)
handsomely(e2)
r1 < now
e1 ⊂ r1
r1 < r2
e2 ⊂ r2
```

Cognitive Representation (6)

John first invested heavily and then profited handsomely.

John's goal in investing had been to make a profit.

he/she will recover the speaker's intended cognitive representation. Thus CRA requires cognitive reasoning which goes beyond what the discourse says directly. In this paper we are offering two innovations: an account of the relationship between formal semantics and coherence, based upon [2], and an empirically-constructed algorithm for CRA.

In comparison with other work, ours is similar to van Dijk and Kintsch [34] in that they define coherence by whether sentences in a discourse describe related facts in some possible world, and they assume that large amounts of world knowledge are employed in building a cognitive model of a discourse. We differ in defining coherence as relating discourse events, rather than as relating sentences. Furthermore, we clarify the question of truth conditions as opposed to naive (or heuristic) inference regarding discourse interpretation. And we provide an algorithm. We draw upon Hobbs [16] and Mann and Thompson [24] for coherence relations. However, we define them as relating discourse events in a cognitive event model, rather than as relating utterances, clauses, or spans of discourse, as they do. For them, coherence is essentially a property of presentation style, of the speaker's intended effect on the hearer. In contrast, for us, coherence is essentially a property of mental models [19] which finds its origin in beliefs about relationships among real events. Our approach appeals to cognitive strategies and beliefs people use all of the time, whether thinking verbally or not. Yet another view defines coherence in terms of the speaker's goals [13,15]. We agree with Polanyi [27] that this aspect of coherence belongs in a level of theory above that of cognitive models of interpretation of discourse.

What are Coherence Relations? In particular, what are the relations **cause** and **goal**? A coherence predication cause(e1,e2) is a speaker/hearer theory about the causal connections between events. Starting with the basics, what is an event (denotationally)? One standard view, with many problems, is that an event is a spatially and temporally located occurrence in the real world. A more sophisticated view of events is as concrete particulars individuated by their causes and consequences [9]. This would explain the existence of real events in the world. Now consider a real event, say a car falling over a cliff. This can be broken into two causally related events as in (7).

e1. The car came to the edge. e2. The car fell over the edge. (7)

The car came too close to the edge, a critical point was reached in which the car was no longer balanced on the edge, and it fell over. We take cause as defined in [9], where cause is a two-place predicate relating events such that if the same event (with all of the relevant situation included) should reoccur, the caused event would reoccur. On this analysis we can assume the existence of causation in the world.

But in terms of the cognitive phenomenon of events and their structure in discourse, we must explain human interpretation of the actual world, not the world itself. Even the direct observation of some real event involves observer interpretation, minimally, of the idea that each frame or pixel he sees is part of the same real event and not a series of different events. The observer view that a certain thing is happening, e.g., that car is falling off of that cliff, is a theory---often a conscious verbal theory. "Oh, that car is falling off of that cliff". When the observer thinks, "Oh, an accident", we have even more theorizing and interpretation as actor goals (or lack of them) are inferred. So the predication of events is epistemological, heuristic, and retractable.

How shall we analyze observer construction of causal inferences? Given that there are cases where one event causes another (such as, the car comes too close to the edge, and falls over the cliff), in the cognitive interpretation of events (and of texts reporting events), people actively theorize and hypothesize about the causal and intentional structure of events as they unfold [11]. People are tentative about such inferences, but in order to function, they must guess. Such guesses are naive theories about the causal and intentional structure of events. Furthermore, the inferred causal structure is an important correlate of memory for the events [11]. In example (7), such a naive hypothesis would be formed when the observer uses naive physics to figure out that (e1) and (e2) are causally related. The point is that in understanding, interpreting and labelling observations of real world events, members of a Western culture (and probably of any culture) infer that the critical point was reached, and that the coming close to the edge (in the end) caused the falling over the edge. The same holds for discourse and text understanding. As they read, people infer causal structure and intentional structure (the goals of agents) [11]. In other words, cause, goal and enablement are salient relations hypothesized by readers about text events. Revising the definition, then, a coherence relation is a naive theory of the relation between events introduced into a discourse. It is a binary predicate whose arguments are discourse individuals, discourse events or states or sets thereof (see Asher [2]). A coherence theory (predication) arises from naive theories about the causal and other structure of the world.[2]

Naive Semantics. Turning to the third problem with coherence theory, we briefly describe our solution, a way of representing commonsense knowledge. Naive Semantics (NS) [5] is a theory of word sense meaning representation in which associated with each sense of each content word (noun, verb, adjective) is a naive theory of the sort of object, action or property named by the word. NS rejects a theory in which word meanings are broken up into atomic primitives which directly play a truth conditional role in sentence and discourse interpretation. Instead, these are supposed to contribute non-monotonically to the meaning representation, and further, they involve many unfired inferences. These rich naive theories are generalizations. Though not "true", they are and must be close enough to true, enough of the time, for people to refer correctly to real objects and events, and to communicate using language. NS representations are rich and open-ended. Anything at all can be there. The number of feature values could be as large as the number of words in English [33]. Word meanings are seen as the names of concepts, and concepts are mental representations which may take many forms - visual, motor, tactile or verbal. Obviously, at the present stage of computation, we are limited to the verbal aspects. NS representations of noun concepts come from the results of psycholinguistic studies of object concepts in the prototype theory [29, 4]. In principle, such representations could be quite extended. In practice, we use the first 1.5 minutes of subjects' freelisting of properties. These are typed (e.g., color(red)). An example is *banker*, shown below in English translation.

> *Typically, a banker is a well-dressed educated male who works in an office in a bank. He is trained in mathematics. He is dedicated, civic-minded, and has high status. He functions as a financier who lends money. Inherently a banker is a person in authority whose function is to engage in business and handle money.*

For verbs, we use the approach of Graesser [12], where it was shown that people conceive of actions in terms of their implications, such as cause, goal, result, location, manner and so on. We also classify verbs aspectually after Vendler [23]. The verb entry is based upon typical and inherent implications. An example is *invest*:

> *Typically, investing is done with capital in the form of money or other asset. One invests in stock, commodities, and real estate. Later, one may sell it or use it as collateral. Inherently, a sentient invests with the goal of making a profit.*

NS provides a means of representing the world knowledge attached to English words in a general, non-*ad hoc* way, resulting in transportable representations. From the engineering point of view, these representations, though painstaking, are in fact feasible, and they go a long way toward providing the information necessary for syntactic disambiguation [7], word sense disambiguation [5], relevance reasoning and coherence [6]. Fortunately, it is not necessary to encode all of commonsense knowledge in order to achieve significant and useful results in text understanding. With our independently derived representations, we succeeded with all of the CRA's we need NS for in the Study 1 corpus. We found and confirmed that discourse cue phrases, syntax, compositional semantics (tense and aspect) and NS (or conceptual knowledge) all contribute to discourse coherence.

3.0 Coherence Relation Assignment Algorithm

The CRA algorithm was developed by examining the information-bearingness of each of the factors found in Study 1 relative to each other for each coherence relation. Those with a high informational load were included as factors to be considered during processing. In addition, we considered the most efficient ordering of tests for the factors. Information-bearingness results follow. Cue phrases such as *in order to* for **goal** and *because* for **cause** [3] are decisive for CRA where present, but are only present in 9% of local coherence and 16% of global. Similarly, certain specific lexical items such as the verbs *contrast* or *oppose* for the **contrast** relation are highly indicative, but rare in the data. As for syntax, most constructions are merely suggestive of coherence relations. For example, a main clause is more likely to

Table I. Discourse Coherence Algorithm
Source and Target cohere under Relation if
  syntactic tests return Relation, or
  connectives indicate Relation, or
  Relation = **comment** if comment tests succeed, or
  Relation = **import** if import tests succeed, or
  causal tests return Relation and
    not both Source and Target are stative and
    source is temporally before target
      or
  Relation = **situation** if situation activity tests succeed, or
  Relation = **sequence** if sequence tests succeed and
    Source and Target are telic and
    source is temporally before target.

introduce an argument of certain coherence relations. However, such tendencies are not helpful in building an algorithm. A small number of syntactic structures, on the other hand, are decisive. These are the comparative for **contrast**, a generic sentence for a **generalization**, verb ellipsis for a **parallel** or **contrast**, relative clause, participial and appositive for **description**.

Turning to formal semantics, tense alone is not informative for CRA, because clauses in the simple past tense introduce events which can bear any coherence relation to other discourse events. Clauses in the simple present introduce events which bear all but one (**reported event**) of the coherence relations to other discourse events. However, temporal order, that is, whether or not the events or states introduced in two clauses overlapped in time, is informative. **Cause, goal, elaboration** and **comment** require temporal precedence, while **parallel, contrast, generalization, description**, and others can relate fully overlapping events or states. Thus lack of temporal order can be used to exclude the possibility of certain coherence relations.

Aspect is more decisive than temporal order in CRA. Aspect refers to the temporal perspective, the continuity and completion, of a clause. One of the two clauses introducing discourse events must be telic for certain causal coherence relations to hold between the events. For other relations to hold, clauses must be clause activity or clause stative. In NS, the aspect of a verb is listed as part of its lexical entry. But context affects aspect, so the aspect of the entire clause must be computed [25], taking into account factors such as progressive verb marking and quantified or unspecified subject or object. An algorithm for clause aspect assignment is under development.

A final factor which influences discourse coherence inferences is commonsense knowledge, which is required when a pair of clauses provide no or insufficient cue phrases, syntactic properties, temporal order or aspect information for CRA. An example is (4), which has two simple past tense clauses, both clause-telic, both main clauses with no discourse cues. These properties are consistent with **sequence, cause, goal, enablement, elaboration, import** or **comment**. Here NS can be used for CRA. The NS representation of the verb *invest* is powerful enough to drive the inference that goal(e_1,e_2). In the corpus, independently derived NS representations are sufficient for CRA in all of the cases where it is needed.

Coherence Relation Assignment Algorithm. The local algorithm, shown in Table I, considers each clause (Source) in relation to the others in a segment one at a time (Target). Another (global) algorithm builds the segment tree [6]. The information the local algorithm uses are syntactic properties of the source clause, connectives in either the source or target, the temporal order of the events in the source and target, NS information associated with the verbs, semantic information such as types of adverbials, mood, and agentiveness in the clauses. The algorithm was hand tested in the original corpus with 97.5% accuracy. A test on an additional corpus of 8,000 words is in progress.

Applying the Algorithm. Finally, we step through the algorithm on a complex sample text, which is a paraphrase of one of the articles in our corpus.

> *Levine, (e_1) charged with SEC violations last May, (e_2) was convicted (e_3) and sentenced here yesterday. Levine (e_4) had engaged in extensive insider trading. He (s_5) was greedy and (s_6) wanted more money. Levine's light sentence (s_7) reflects (e_8)an attempt by the court to (e_9) reward cooperation in such cases. The judge (e_{10}) said that Levine's (e_{11}) cooperation (e_{12}) had influenced him in his favor. Critics (e_{13}) argued that light sentences (e_{14}) will result in more violations.*

The coherence relations in this text that we explain are **reported event**(e_2), **sequence**(e_3,e_2), **situation activity**(e_1,e_2), **situation-activity**(e_4,e_2), **cause**(s_5,e_4), **goal**(s_6,e_4), **import**(s_7,e_2), **comment**(e_{10},e_2), and **comment**(e_{13},e_2). We use the notation C_i to denote the clause which introduces an event e_i or a state s_i. The first clause to be considered is C_2 in relation to the participial clause C_1. Referring to the algorithm in Table I, we see that the main clause C_2 will designate a **reported event** because C_2 will fail the syntactic tests (it is not a relative clause, appositive, nor any of the syntactic structures the algorithm looks for). There is no connective, no verb of saying for the comment test, and no modal, conditional, interrogative or import verb for the import test. When the algorithm tries in the causal tests to prove that C_2 expresses a **reported event**, it will succeed. Next, the algorithm considers C_1 in relation to C_2. Here tests succeed on the source clause C_1. Since C_1 is a participial it must be either **description** or **situation**. As C_1 contains a time adverbial, it is designated **situation**. Note that the time adverbial in the main clause C_2 did not result in the same assignment. Next the algorithm considers C_4 in relation to C_2. **Reported events** (C_2) are tried first as targets in commentary, because the commentary genre revolves around them. Considering C_4 in relation to C_2, syntactic tests, connectives, comment tests and import tests all fail. There is only an indirect relation between breaking the law and being convicted, so causal tests fail. Now the algorithm tries **situation_activity**, and succeeds because C_4 is in the perfect. Next the algorithm tries C_5 in relation to C_2. All tests up through import fail. Now the algorithm tries causal tests and finds in the NS representations that *greed* can cause people to break the law, so it assigns cause(s_5,e_2). Similarly, it finds that a typical goal of breaking the law is making money, so it assigns goal(s_2,e_4). Turning to C_7 in relation to C_2, the syntactic, connective and comment tests fail. The import test succeeds because (s_7) overlaps (e_2) in time, and *reflect* is an import verb. Finally, the two comment clauses C_{10} and C_{13} are discovered because they fail the syntactic and connective tests, and they contain non-performative verbs of saying.

Notes

1. We would claim that this is true even in the interpretation of metaphors and fiction.
2. This point of view has evolved in discussions with N. Asher, C. Lord, J.P. McDowell, B. Partee and E.P. Stabler, Jr. and the Symposium on Discourse Coherence and Segmentation, University of Texas, 1989.

References.

1. Asher, N. 1987. A Typology for Attitude Verbs and their Anaphoric Properties. *Ling. and Phil.* 10:125-198.
2. Asher, N. 1989. *Abstract Objects and Anaphora in Semantics*. Manuscript.
3. Cohen, R. 1984. A Computational Theory of the Function of Clue Words in Argument Understanding. *COLING* 251-258.
4. Dahlgren, K. 1985. The Cognitive Structure of Social Categories. *Cognitive Science* 9:379-398.
5. Dahlgren, K. 1988. *Naive Semantics for Natural Language Understanding*. Boston: Kluwer Academic Press.
6. Dahlgren, K. 1989. Formal Properties of Discourse Segmentation. In preparation.
7. Dahlgren, K. and J. McDowell. 1986b. Using Commonsense Knowledge to Disambiguate Prepositional Phrase Modifiers. *Proc. AAAI 86*.
8. Dahlgren, K., J.P. McDowell, and E.P. Stabler, Jr. 1989. Knowledge Representation for Commonsense Reasoning with Text. Forthcoming in *Computational Linguistics*.
9. Davidson, D. 1967. Causal Relations. *J. Phil.* 64:692-703.
10. Fox, B. 1984. *Discourse Structure and Anaphora in Written and Conversational English*. UCLA Dissertation.
11. Graesser, A. 1981. *Prose Comprehension Beyond the Word*. New York: Springer-Verlag.
12. Graesser, A. and L. Clark. 1985b. The Generation of Knowledge-Based Inferences during Narrative Comprehension. In G. Rickheit and H. Strohner, eds., *Inferences in Text Processing*, Amsterdam: North-Holland.
13. Grosz, B. and C. Sidner. 1986. Attention, Intensions and the Structure of Discourse. A Review. *Computational Linguistics* 7:85-98. 12:175-204.
14. Hayes, P. J. 1985. The Second Naive Physics Manifesto. In J. R. Hobbs and R. C. Moore, eds., *Formal Theories of the Commonsense World*, Norwood, NJ: Ablex.
15. Hirst, G. 1981. Discourse-Oriented Anaphora Resolution: A Review. *Computational Linguistics* 7:85-98.
16. Hobbs, J.A. 1979. Why is Discourse Coherent? SRI Tech. Note #176.
17. Hobbs, J. 1985. On the Coherence and Structure of Discourse. CSLI Report # CSLI-85-37.
18. Hopper, P. and S. Thompson. 1980. Transitivity in Grammar and Discourse. *Language*, Vol. 56, pp. 251-299.
19. Johnson-Laird, P.N. 1983. *Mental Models*. Harvard U. Press.
20. Kamp, H. 1981. A Theory of Truth and Semantic Representation. In J. Groenendijk, Th. Janssen, and M. Stokhof, eds., *Formal Methods in the Study of Language*, Amsterdam: Mathematisch Centrum, 277-322.
21. Lockman, A. and A.D. Klappholz. 1980. Toward a Procedural Model of Contextual Reference Resolution. *Discourse Processes* 3:25-71.
22. Lord, C. and K. Dahlgren. 1989. Tracking Participants and Events in Newspaper Articles. In preparation.
23. McDowell J. and K. Dahlgren. 1987. Commonsense Reasoning with Verbs. *Proc. IJCAI*.
24. Mann, W. and S. Thompson. 1987. Rhetorical Structure Theory: A Theory of Text Organization. ISI Reprint Series: ISI-RS-87-190.
25. Moens, M. and M. Steedman. 1987. Temporal Ontology in Natural Language. *Proc. ACL* 1-7.
26. Partee, B. 1984. Nominal and Temporal Anaphora. *Ling. and Phil.* 7:243-286.
27. Polanyi, L. 1988. A Formal Model of the Structure of Discourse. *J. Pragmatics* 12:601-638.
28. Reichman, R. 1985. *Getting Computers to Talk Like You and Me*. Cambridge, MA: MIT Press.
29. E. Rosch and B. B. Lloyd, eds., *Cognition and Categorization*. New York: Erlbaum.
30. Sanford, A.J. and S.C. Garrod. 1981. *Understanding Written Language*. New York: Wiley and Sons.
31. Schank, R. C. and R. P. Abelson. 1977. *Scripts, Plans, Goals and Understanding*. Hillsdale, NJ: Erlbaum.
32. Schiffren, D. 1987. *Discourse Markers*. Cambridge U Press.
33. Schubert, L. K., R.G. Goebel, and N.J. Cercone. 1979. The Structure and Organization of a Semantic Net for Comprehension and Inference. In N.V. Findler, ed., *Associative Networks*, New York: Academic Press.
34. Van Dijk, T. and W. Kintsch. 1983. *Strategies of Discourse Comprehension*. New York: Academic Press.
35. Wada, H. and N. Asher. 1986. BUILDRS: An Implementation of DR Theory and LFG. *Proc. COLING* 540-545.
36. Wilks, Y. 1975. Preference Semantics. In E. Keenan, ed., *Formal Semantics of Natural Language*. Cambridge U. Press.

A Model for Contextualizing Natural Language Discourse

John Dinsmore
Department of Computer Science
Southern Illinois University at Carbondale

Abstract

This paper describes a computational model of semantic processing in natural language discourse understanding based on the distribution of knowledge over multiple *spaces* as proposed by Fauconnier (1985), Dinsmore (1987a), Kamp (1980), Johnson-Laird (1985) and others. Among the claims made about such a partitioned representation of knowledge are the following: First, it promotes a more direct, more natural mapping from surface discourse sentence to internal representation. Second, it supports more efficient reasoning and retrieval processes over that internal representation. Finally, it provides an accurate account of many of the most recalcitrant problems in natural language discourse understanding. Among these are implicit information, presupposition, referential opacity, tense and aspect, and common-sense reasoning in complex domains.

The model identifies two fundamental levels of semantic processing: *contextualization,* in which an appropriate space for assimilating the information conveyed in a discourse sentence is located, and *construction,* in which the information is actually assimilated into that space. Contextualization allows the full semantics of the discourse to be realized implicitly in the internal representation. It also accounts for the use of moods, tenses, and various adverbials in discourse. The interaction of the contextualization processes with the semantics of aspectual operators provides an account of the discourse use of aspect.

INTRODUCTION

In partitioned representations (Dinsmore, 1987a) the information conveyed in a natural language discourse is distributed appropriately over multiple *spaces,* which function as small, distinct, logically coherent knowledge bases within which objects and relations can be represented, and reasoning processes can be performed. Spaces represent such things as hypothetical realities, belief systems, quantified domains, thematically defined domains, fictions, and situations located in time and space. Spaces in this sense differ from the focus or thematic spaces of Grosz (1977), Reichman (1985) and others in that

Once upon a time, there was a tailor named Siegfried.

Siegfried had once consulted a famous wizard. The wizard mistakenly thought Siegfried was an alcoholic. Still, if Siegfried would work hard, he would be very successful. The wizard assumed that anyone who was rich was happy. Well, Siegfried would be rich, and would even stop drinking.

Now the tailor Siegfried did work hard and had in fact become rich. But he was not happy, and he had actually become an alcoholic.

Fig. 1. The Siegfried story.

the former have a logical or semantic function not found in the latter, as detailed in Dinsmore (1988, 1987). During discourse understanding, knowledge is appropriately distributed over spaces, lower-level processes are delegated to spaces, and spaces are thereby allowed to accumulate knowledge. For instance, in understanding the story of **Fig. 1** a set of spaces are constructed as in **Fig. 2** and knowledge distributed over the spaces as indicated. A linear notation of the form **S | P** will be convenient to show that a proposition **P** belongs to a space **S**. We call such an expression a *statement.* For instance, one of the statements recognizable in **Fig. 2** would be,

sp_4 | Siegfried is rich

Each space has a role or function of known as its *primary context.* **Fig. 3** shows how the primary contexts of the Siegfried story embed spaces. Our convenient linear notation extends to contexts: a context looks like an ordinary statement, but contains a *space term* of the form ⟦S⟧. For instance, some of the contexts recognizable in **Fig. 3** are the following.

sp_0 | At time time_2, ⟦sp_2⟧
sp_2 | wizard_8 believes that ⟦sp_3⟧
sp_3 | Siegfried works hard ☛ ⟦sp_4⟧

Language understanding can be considered a transductive process whereby the discourse sentence is gradually transformed into its partitioned internal representation while passing through a series of intermediate representations. The transformation process involves identifying constituent structures, distributing structures over spaces, and processing structures at a low level within spaces. For a discourse sentence *P*, *contextualization* determines the space, **S**, that *P* is intended to say something about. That space is known as the *focus space* for **P**. In the story of **Fig. 1** the focus space starts at **sp_1** then moves to **sp_2** for *"Siegfried had once consulted a famous wizard,"* and for the

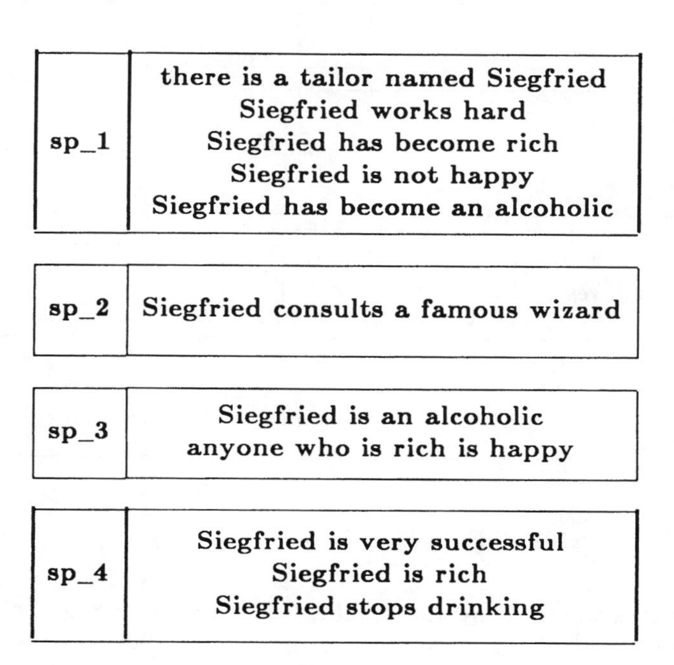

Fig. 2. Partitioned representation of the Siegfried story.

following sentence. It then moves to **sp_3** for *"But if Siegfried ...,"* then back to **sp_2**. It moves to **sp_4** for *"Well, Siegfried would be rich, ..."*, and finally returns to **sp_1** for the final two sentences.

Construction transforms the statement **S | P** through the progressive refinement of knowledge structures until a permanent internal representation is produced. During construction new spaces and their associated contexts will often be set up, and existing contexts will be used to access spaces for distributing information. At the same time various semantic processes will occur locally within spaces, such as determining referents for definite descriptions and satisfying the presuppositions of certain grammatical constructions. For instance, in the processing of the sentence *"The wizard mistakenly thought that Siegfried was an alcoholic,"* **sp_2** is used as the focus space. Within **sp_2** a referent for *"the wizard"*, call it **wizard_8**, is located. The belief space **sp_3** is then created along with the context **sp_2 | wizard_8 believes that ⟦sp_3⟧**, and the statement **sp_3 | Siegfried is an alcoholic** is further restructured.

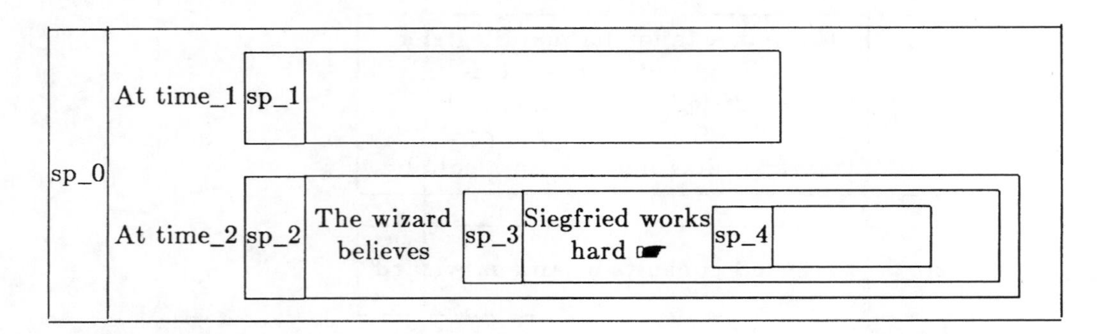

Fig. 3. The contexts used in representing the Siegfried story.

CONTEXTUALIZATION

Contextualization concerns the identification of the *focus space* in which to begin reconstructing the semantic content of the discourse sentence. It provides an associated context which is necessary for the full semantic significance of the discourse sentence to be realized. The contextualization step provides a key distinction between the current model and most other models of semantic processing.

For instance, in a fictional discourse like that excerpted below it is necessary to identify a focus space **sp_21** such that we have a primary context like **sp_2 | In** ***The Dog of the Burgervilles,*** **⟦sp_21⟧**.

> *Sherlock turned slowly around. Suddenly a poisoned dart whizzed by. "Yikes," said he.*

Since **sp_21** is in focus, the meanings of the sentences of the discourse are represented by statements specifically in **sp_21**. Accordingly, the full meaning of the discourse is represented, and questions like *"In the Dog of the Burgervilles, what made Sherlock say, 'Yikes'?"* can be answered when **sp_21** is no longer in focus. The following discourse is analogous to the last.

> *Arthur believes it is the duty of everyone to fight what he thinks is an invasion of space frogs. Before this situation gets out of hand, every homeowner should defrog his own yard, taking care to ...*

After the first sentence of the first discourse the focus space **sp_7** has a primary context something like **sp_3 | Arthur believes that ⟦sp_7⟧**.

Tracking the Focus for Contextualization

A main contribution of this paper is to define what the contextualization process is and to provide a framework in which it can be discussed. Nevertheless, a full account of the process awaits future research; like many interpretive tasks it involves a wide range of poorly understood cognitive factors. However, our initial model of the contextualization process identifies the focus space as:

- The most *active* space,
- that is consistent with the *focus cues* of the current discourse sentence, and
- that has a content *conceptually consistent* with the intermediate representation of the current discourse sentence.

Spaces are *active* to a degree dependent on how recently or how often they have been used in recent discourse processing. The reader will notice that in the Siegfried story the focus space for every sentence but the first corresponds to a space used or created shortly before the the sentence was processed. We also observe a tendency to return to a previous focus space, or to use the same focus space in successive contextualizations. We can model this by assuming varying levels of activation, with the last focus space most active, and spaces that have not been focused or recently accessed less active. More active spaces are thereby the best candidates for focus.

Focus cues are inflectional morphemes and other syntactic structures occurring in the discourse sentence that restrict the set of focus space candidates for contextualization. Focus cues are generally verb forms, like the Past tense or the conditional mood, and certain adverbials. We will return to this kind of grammatical conditioning of the contextualization process momentarily.

Ultimately, the current intermediate representation should be conceptually consistent with the contents of the focus space. This generally means that its presuppositions should be satisfied there, the objects it mentions should reside there, and it should not contradict knowledge that is already stored there. For instance, before we contextualize the sentence *"The wizard mistakenly thought Siegfried was an alcoholic,"* in **Fig. 1** we have **sp_0**, **sp_1** and **sp_2** as active spaces. Among the focus cues is **Past**, which is compatible with any of these spaces. Because a referent for *"the wizard"* can be found there, **sp_2** is strongly recommended as the focus space. Likewise, the focus space in the Sherlock Holmes discourse is readily identified as fictional since Sherlock Holmes is generally known not to exist in reality.

Focus Cues

A number of adverbials of little apparent semantic content seem to play a role in tracking the focus space. In the Siegfried story, *"Once upon a time, ..."* would seem actually to trigger the initialization of a *new* temporal/situational space embedded within a story space. *"Well"* seems to indicate that the focus space is different than that for the previous sentence. *"Now"* seems to indicate a return from a temporally prior focus space. However, the most consistently present type of cue seems to be associated with the form of the main verb of the discourse sentence: **Past**, **Present**, or **conditional**.

English requires the conditional (usually indicated by *"would"*) for any sentence or embedded clause assimilated into a counterfactual space **S1**, one whose primary context is of the form **S0 | P ☛ ⟦S1⟧** and prohibits its use in any other sentence or embedded clause. For instance, in the following discourse,

> *If cars had never been invented, people would still ride horses. Furthermore, shopping malls would not exist. At least there would be less smog.*

processing the first sentence will set up a space, call it **sp_12**, with a context something like **sp_10 | Cars have never been invented ☛ ⟦sp_12⟧**. The clause *"people would still ride horses"* uses the conditional, since **sp_12 | people ride horses** is constructed, where **sp_12** is a counterfactual space. This space then becomes the focus space for the next two conditional sentences. It is instructive to contrast the use of the conditional with the use of a non-conditional form in sentences that are otherwise identical. If the discourse were to continue,

We would have a lot to blame Henry Ford for.

sp_12 would likely remain in focus, since it is a counterfactual space as required. On the other hand, if the discourse were to continue,

We have a lot to blame Henry Ford for.

then a shift to some other space, probably back to the previous focus space **sp_10**, would be forced, giving the sentence almost the opposite semantic interpretation.

TENSE AND ASPECT

Researchers in the semantics of tense and aspect have looked at sets of sentences like the following,

Fred won $1,000,000 in the lottery.
Fred has won $1,000,000 in the lottery.
Fred had won $1,000,000 in the lottery.

and in view of their apparent truth-conditional identity have proposed semantic analyses which attribute the same explicit semantic content to them (cf., Taylor, 1977).

Reichenbach (1947) uses the term *reference time* to characterize such differences. If the event time is **E** (in this case, the time at which Fred wins the lottery), the time of speech **S**, and the reference time is **R**, then $\mathbf{R} = \mathbf{E} < \mathbf{S}$ for the first of these sentences, $\mathbf{E} < \mathbf{R} = \mathbf{S}$ for the second, and $\mathbf{E} < \mathbf{R} < \mathbf{S}$ for the third.

It turns out that we can show how Reichenbach's concept of *reference time* can be defined as an artifact of the more general discourse process of *contextualization*. This account additionally shows how the relationships of **R**, E and **S** (*reference time, event time*, and the *time of speech*) follow from the actual semantics of the aspects in a compositional way. Space limitations prohibit developing this account fully, but I can at least suggest what is involved here, and refer the reader to another paper for details.

A temporal space has the same role as any other space in the contextualization process, with tenses acting as focus cues. For instance, the following discourse exhibits the usual pattern of using the same focus space for consecutive sentence until a focus cue indicates a shift as well as the tendency to return to a previous focus space.

> *Fred's car was parked at the corner. Fred himself was looking under the hood. Fred has only recently learned anything about auto mechanics. It was already dark.*

Let us define a *temporal space* as any space **S** with a primary context of the form **S0 | At time T, [[S]]**. We define the's concept of *reference time* simply as the time mentioned in the context of a temporal focus space, i.e.:

- If there is a context of the form **S0 | At time R, [[S1]]** then **R** is the *reference time* of **S1**.

We also speak of the *reference time of a sentence* as shorthand for the reference time of the focus space into which the sentence is contextualized. In any case, English permits the Past tense only in a sentence or embedded clause that is assimilated into a temporal space with a reference time **R** before the time of speech S, i.e., **R < S**. English requires the Present tense in any sentence or embedded clause that is assimilated into a temporal space with a reference time **R** at the time of speech **S**, i.e., **R = S**.

In the current model, the sentences above do differ in the kinds of internal representations they give rise to, but their truth conditions collapse together because of the different focus spaces they are forced to contextualize to along with the differing semantic interpretations of Past and Perfect.

Dinsmore (1982, in press) presents and motivates the precise semantics. Dinsmore (in press) shows how these semantic rules interact with contextualization to account for the use and understanding of these sentences. This account generalizes to the *Prospective* and *Future* sentences that Reichenbach also describes, and to the other aspects *Inceptive, Terminative* and *Progressive* (Dinsmore, in press, 1987b). Both Dinsmore (1982) and Johnson (1981) have foreseen that Reichenbach's system might generalize in this way.

References

Dinsmore, J. (1982) On the Semantic Nature of Reichenbach's Tense System. *Glossa* 16, 216-239.

Dinsmore, J. (1987a) Mental Spaces from a Functional Perspective. *Cognitive Science* 11:1, 1-21.

Dinsmore, J. (1987b) Discourse Models and the English Tense System. *Cognitive Science Society 9*, 934-937.

Dinsmore, J. (1988) *Foundations of Knowledge Partitioning.* Tech. Report 88-16, Department of Computer Science, Southern Illinois University at Carbondale.

Dinsmore, J. (in press) The Use and Function of the English Past and Perfect. In Carol Georgopoulos & Roberta Ishihara (eds.), *Interdisciplinary Approaches to Language: Essays in Honor of Yuki Kuroda*, D. Reidel.

Fauconnier, G. (1985) *Mental Spaces: Aspects of Meaning Construction in Natural Language.* Cambridge, MA: Bradford/MIT Press.

Grosz, B. (1977) Focusing and Description in Natural Language Dialogs. In A. Joshi, B. Sag, & I. Weber (eds.), *Elements of Discourse Understanding*, Cambridge: Cambridge Univ. Pr.

Johnson, M. (1981) A Unified Theory of Tense and Aspect. In Philip Tedeschi & Annie Zaenen, *Tense and Aspect (Syntax and Semantics 14)*, New York: Academic Press, pp. 145-176.

Johnson-Laird, P. (1983) *Mental Models.* Cambridge, MA: Harvard University Press.

Kamp, H. (1980) A Theory of Truth and Semantic Representation. In J.A.G. Groenendijk, T.M.V. Janssen & M.B.J. Stokhhof (eds.), *Formal Methods in the Study of Language: Part I*, Amsterdam: Mathematisch Centrum, 277-322.

Reichenbach, H. (1947) *Elements of Symbolic Logic.* New York: MacMillan.

Reichman, R. (1985) *Getting Computers to Talk like You and Me.* Cambridge: Cambridge Univ. Pr.

Taylor, B. (1977) Tense and Continuity. *Linguistics and Philosophy* 1, 199-220.

An Intelligent Tutoring System Approach to Teaching People How to Learn

Richard G. Feifer

Center for the Study of Evaluation -- UCLA Graduate School of Education
UCLA Artificial Intelligence Laboratory

ABSTRACT

Sherlock is an intelligent tutoring system designed to teach people to build simplified knowledge representations (graphic maps) to facilitate learning of a text. Previous attempts to automate instruction in graphic mapping have had problems because they attempted to diagnose a learner's misunderstandings by looking at a finished graphic map. Sherlock uses a knowledge-based approach to diagnose a learner's misunderstandings by looking at the knowledge and processes that lead to a learner's graphic map, rather than the completed map.

In Sherlock's model a semantic network is used to represent the knowledge in the text. A production system models the strategy for constructing a graphic map by initiating spreading activation on the semantic network, and interpreting the resulting activation patterns. In a limited evaluation Sherlock was able to correctly determine if a construction was appropriate 96% of the time.

INTRODUCTION

In this paper I examine the problem of teaching people to use a learning strategy called **graphic mapping.** In graphic mapping the learner is taught a simplified knowledge representation scheme. The learner then uses this scheme to pictorially represent textual material. Figure 1 contains a sample graphic map construction.

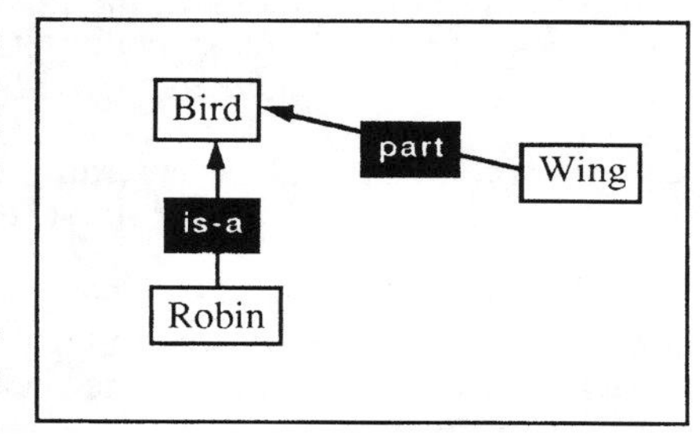

Figure 1: A Graphic Map

Researchers have shown that comprehension of text can be enhanced by having the learner construct a graphic map representing the text (Dansereau, 1978; Dansereau, Collins, McDonald, Holley, Garland, Diekhoff & Evans, 1979a,b; Anderson, 1979; Novak, Gowin & Johnson, 1983).

The decisions that a learner makes in constructing a map appear to be equally dependent on both the learner's strategy for building a graphic map and the learner's understanding of the text. Intelligent tutoring systems have been developed which attempt to model a learner's strategy knowledge or a learner's factual knowledge, but not both. Sherlock models the acquisition of both strategy and facts in an integrated manner (Feifer, Dyer, & Baker; 1988).

Even domains which seem to rely predominantly on one kind of knowledge involve, to at least some extent, both kinds of knowledge. Programming, for example, requires a knowledge of the syntax and commands of a computer language in addition to knowledge of how to build programs in that language. Thus, a tutoring system able to model the acquisition of both kinds of knowledge can more completely model the acquisition of knowledge in any domain.

SHERLOCK

The Sherlock tutoring environment provides the learner with three components: (a) a text to be represented pictorially, (b) a screen containing icons[1] representing concepts within the text, and (c) a set of gm-links[2] which the learner can use to connect the icons.

Sherlock has been programmed to facilitate learning of a text excerpted from an introductory business law text book describing consideration and its place in a contract. Sherlock offers the learner six gm-links: PART, IS-A, LEADS, EQUIV, PROP and NOT. Learners are instructed to find icons that they believe are related and then choose the gm-link that best represents the relationship. For example, if the learner believes that one icon represents a concept that is a generalization of a concept represented by a second icon, he should make an IS-A gm-link between the two icons.

Sherlock's Input and Output

Once the learner has specified a gm-link, Sherlock tries to evaluate it and provide meaningful feedback. What follows are excerpts of a transcript (Feifer, 1989) from actual interactions between Sherlock and a learner named Janey. The text in parentheses are descriptions of the interactions and the figures that illustrate the content of the screen at each point in the interaction. All other text are comments made by the learner.

"I was first looking at these icons here (Figure 2); instead I am going to look at the links (the list of link types) to try and link something together from these different links I have to choose from."

"Now they are equivalent according to this. So I am going to use an equivalent link (Figure 3)."

"According to this paragraph a consideration act is a lawful act. So a lawful act is a legal act. So I am going to link them as equivalents because they are both legal acts."

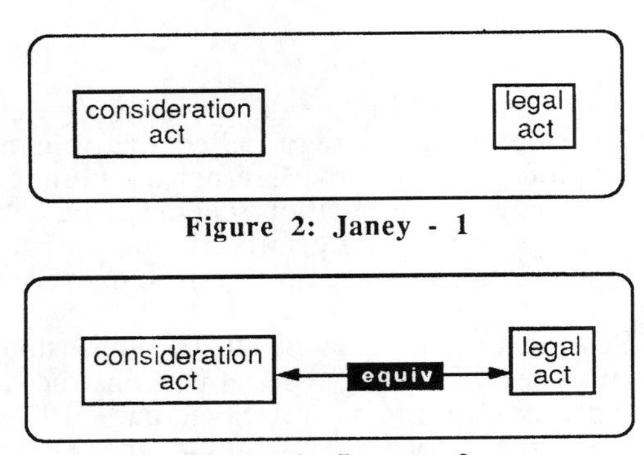

Figure 2: Janey - 1

Figure 3: Janey - 2

---

[1]I use the term icon to refer to a box containing text that the learner can use to represent a conceptual entity.

[2]To avoid confusion between the graphic map that the learner constructs and Sherlock's internal knowledge representation, links used in a graphic map are referred to as gm-links.

(Sherlock requests information regarding her reasons for making the link by presenting her with the menu shown in Figure 4.)

Why did you do that?
The likelihood of a legal act being a consideration act is equal to the reverse
Every legal act is a consideration act
Every consideration act is a legal act
legal act and consideration act refer to the same concept
The likelihood of a legal act being a consideration act is not equal to the reverse
legal act is another name for consideration act
It is not as likely that a legal act is a consideration act
DONE
ABORT

Figure 4: Janey - 3

"In general I wouldn't say that a 'consideration act' is a 'legal act'. In general. But this (the text) is telling me that it is. So I am answering these question in regards to the material here? Yes."

(She chooses "Every consideration act is a legal act" and "It is not as likely that a legal act is a consideration act.")

(Sherlock provides her with the plan feedback shown in Figure 5)

"Sounds like algebra, and I am just terrible at algebra."

"I guess that is what ... I used, but it doesn't really make good sense. That is the plan I used, but it doesn't seem like it is a very good plan or that it is going to be equivalent."

(Sherlock provides the comment shown in Figure 6)

"It means where I made the equivalent link? Huh. Let's check that out."

You used the plan:
if
every x is a y
it is not as likely that a y is a x
then
make an EQUIV link from x to y
that is not a good plan

Figure 5: Janey - 4

At times like this I would make an IS-A link.

Figure 6: Janey - 5

(Sherlock asks her if she would like to remove the link. She answers "YES". In Figure 7 the link is removed.)

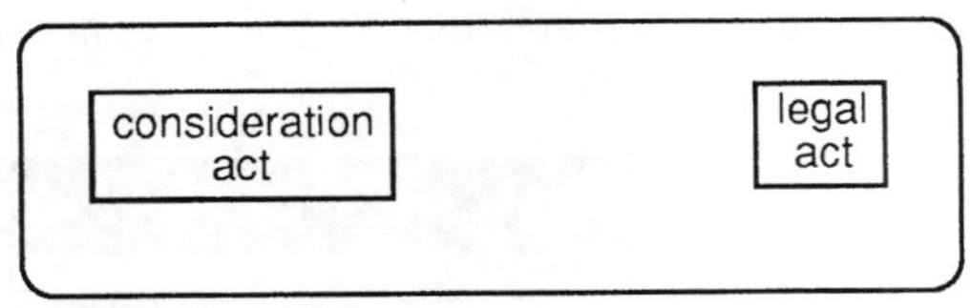

Figure 7: Janey - 6

"So, 'legal act' well... 'consideration act' would be... would be a subset of a 'legal act,' or vice versa. Or do I have to decide that? I guess I have to decide that. Huh, OK. I would say that a..."

"Well, according to this a 'consideration act' is a type of a 'legal act.' So I am going to connect 'consideration act.'" (Figure 8).

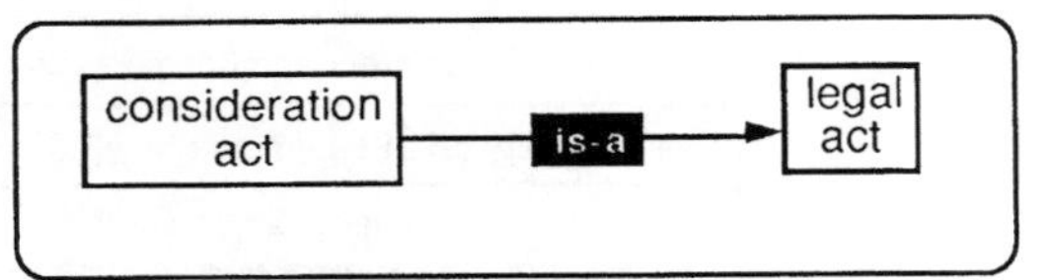

Figure 8: Janey - 7

"Well according to this a 'consideration act' is a 'legal act'. It is one type, it is a type of a 'legal act.' So it's got to be legal. So... it's some type, or kind of 'legal act.'"

(Sherlock provides the feedback shown in Figure 9)

Very good, that is what I would have done.

Figure 9: Janey - 8

In this sequence Sherlock determines that the learner seems to understand the relationship between a consideration act and a legal act, but has a bad strategy for representing that relationship. Sherlock decides that the problem is not with the facts used to choose the gm-link, but rather with the type of gm-link that those facts lead to.

Sherlock's Architecture

Sherlock uses the eight components shown in Figure 10.

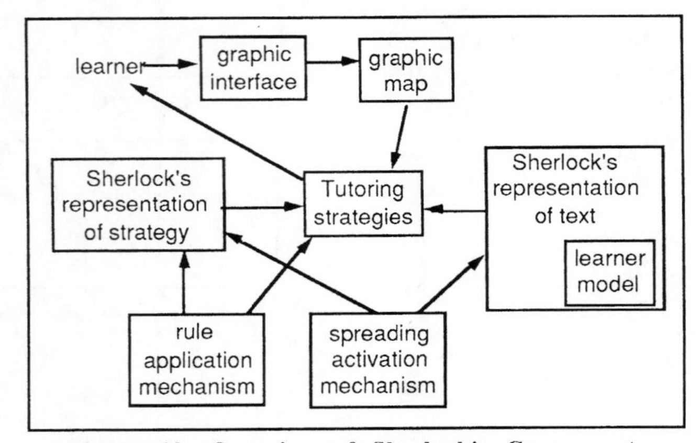

Figure 10: Overview of Sherlock's Components

The function of each of these components is briefly described below.

1. The **graphic interface** interprets the learner's clicks on the mouse buttons to build the graphic map.
2. The learner builds the **graphic map** using the icons provided by Sherlock. The icons are linked together using the six gm-links described above.
3. **Sherlock's representation of text** is a localist spreading activation network made up of nodes for concepts and links for the relationship between concepts. The semantic network is used to represent Sherlock's understanding of a text's content and background. The representation of the text is hand-coded into the network.
4. **Sherlock's representation of strategy** consists of rules or plans for building a graphic map. Each of the rules is of the form:

   IF the following things are true about the relationship between two icons
   THEN make this kind of gm-link between them

   These rules are hand-coded into Sherlock and are based on strategies described by subjects during initial pilot studies.
5. The **learner model** represents what Sherlock currently believes to be the learner's understanding of the text, graphic elements, and mapping skills. It is built by Sherlock by modifying elements in the hand-coded representations of the text content and graphic mapping strategy.

   The learner model is not fully implemented at this time. The only aspect of the learner model which Sherlock currently represents is the learner's interpretation of the screen icons.
6. The **tutoring strategies** are rules or plans in a form similar to that of the strategies for building a graphic map. The rules in the tutoring strategies are hand-coded to represent Sherlock's pedagogical knowledge.
7. The **spreading activation mechanism** operates on the semantic network to generate inferences. It is based on a mechanism developed by Michael Gasser (1988) for classifying concepts.
8. The **rule application mechanism** operates on the rules in Sherlock's representation of strategy and the tutoring strategies to determine what action Sherlock should take at any given time.

Sherlock's Tutoring Strategy

Sherlock determines the relationship between the two icons that the learner just linked by using spreading activation on a semantic network representation of the text. Sherlock then uses a production system representation of graphic mapping strategy to determine whether the learner's link is appropriate. If there is no plan that would justify the gm-link that the learner just made, Sherlock asks the learner to indicate the reasons for making the gm-link.

Sherlock uses the learner's answer to separately evaluate the learner's plan and the facts that the learner believes. Sherlock classifies the learner's plan as an instance of one its graphic mapping rules using the representations of these rules in the semantic network. If Sherlock cannot recognize the plan the learner used, it will inform the learner of this. If Sherlock does recognize the plan, but it is a bad plan, it will inform the learner that he has used a bad plan. If Sherlock recognizes the plan and it is a good plan, it will not give any feedback on the plan.

To evaluate the learner's factual beliefs, Sherlock compares the learner's answer to its own factual beliefs. If there is a good[3] match between the learner's fact beliefs and Sherlock's, no further action is taken on facts. If there is not a good match, Sherlock will consider the possibility that the learner is using an alternative interpretation for the icons. If any alternative interpretations for the icons exist, that have not already been tried, Sherlock will use one of these interpretations and start again from the top.

If all possible alternative interpretations have been tried, Sherlock will pick the interpretation that led to fact beliefs which were closest to the learner's fact beliefs. Using this interpretation Sherlock will determine two things:

1. Are there any false facts that the learner believes to be true, that led to the bad gm-link that the learner made? If so, Sherlock will bring them to the learner's attention.
2. Are there any true facts that the learner does not believe, which would have led to a better gm-link? If so, Sherlock will bring them to the learner's attention.

EVALUATION

To evaluate the accuracy of Sherlock's diagnosis a study was conducted in the summer of 1988. Four subjects were video taped during a two-hour session using Sherlock. Subjects were instructed to think aloud while building their map.

As a first step, I inferred the subjects' beliefs looking at their actions and words. Inferences were made without looking at Sherlock's feedback or the transcript of Sherlock's processing. There is no claim that the beliefs inferred actually reflect the subjects' beliefs; only that they represent one human tutor's best guess as to what the subjects believe. Sherlock's diagnosis is referred to as correct if it agrees with these inferred beliefs.

A total of 70 links were made by the subjects. Of these, 11 were aborted before Sherlock's final analysis. These 11 links were aborted because the subject decided that he or she was doing something wrong. Included in the analysis are the 59 links that the subjects allowed Sherlock to analyze.

Of the 59 completed links, Sherlock determined that 33 (55.93%) were appropriate. There were actually 32 appropriate links. I classified a link as appropriate if it reflected a correct understanding of the text and the graphic mapping strategy. Of the 26 links that Sherlock labelled as wrong, 25 were actually wrong. Thus Sherlock's determination of whether a link was right or wrong was correct for 96.61% of the links (Table 1).

---

[3]"Good" is currently defined as meaning that the learner and Sherlock agree on 80% of the facts.

For the 25 links which Sherlock correctly determined were wrong, the diagnosis matched only 56% of the time. This percentage of match means that Sherlock was able to correctly determine that a link was right or wrong and provide a correct diagnosis for a total of 77.97% of the links.

	# of links	% of total
good link correctly identified	32	54.24
good link incorrectly seen as bad	1	1.69
bad link correctly identified		
reason found	14	23.73
reason not found	11	18.64
bad link incorrectly seen as good	1	1.69
Total	59	100

Table 1: Overall Accuracy of Links

CONCLUSION

Accuracy is important in a tutoring system; wrong feedback can have negative impact on learning. Telling a learner he is wrong when he is right can lead the learner to a loss of self confidence. Telling a learner he is right when he is wrong can reinforce incorrect beliefs. Sherlock was able to correctly determine if a link was right or wrong over 96% of the time. The question is: Is this accurate enough? One way to answer this is to compare Sherlock to other forms of instruction.

A human tutor will certainly be more accurate that any machine-based tutor. In terms of automated tutoring, the highest accuracy can be achieved with multiple-choice CAI. If the questions and distractor choices in a multiple-choice format are carefully written, close to 100% accuracy can be reached. The problem is that multiple-choice responses are the least indicative of what a learner understands. Open-ended responses can be much more useful for ascertaining what a learner understands. But if even single-word responses are allowed in CAI the accuracy dramatically drops because it is difficult to anticipate every potentially correct response.

Sherlock offers a compromise in that there is a finite range of responses possible. That range, however, is quite large. With 25 icons there are 3600 possible learner actions[4]. It would be possible, but very difficult, to record in advance which of the 3600 possible actions is correct. Add the qualifier that certain responses are only acceptable if the learner is using particular interpretations, and it becomes impossible to completely anticipate correct responses. Considering the range of responses allowed, Sherlock's performance is certainly comparable to any automated tutoring approach that currently exists.

---

[4]Each learner action is a possible combination of from-icon, gm-link type, and to-icon. Thus there are 25 (number of possible from-icons) * 6 (number of gm-link types) * 24 (number of possible to-icons) possible combinations.

Sherlock was less successful at determining why an action was wrong. Comparing this ability to other forms of tutoring is more difficult. In automated tutoring, only intelligent tutoring systems make any claim for diagnosing the cause of a misunderstanding. And in intelligent tutoring systems research, evaluations have only been done on a system's ability to identify errors. No system has been evaluated for its accuracy in identifying the cause of an error.

Sherlock has demonstrated that it is possible to understand unanticipated responses and diagnose the cause of misunderstanding without degrading the system's ability to make a bottom-line determination of whether a learner's response is correct.

REFERENCES

Anderson, T.H. (1979). Study skills and learning strategies. In H.F. O'Neil and C.D. Spielberger (Eds.). *Cognitive and affective learning strategies.* New York Academic Press.

Dansereau, D.F. (1978). The development of a learning strategies curriculum. In H.F. O'Neil, Jr., (Ed.), *Learning Strategies.* New York: Academic Press.

Dansereau, D.F., Collins, K.W., McDonald, B.A., Holley, C.D., Garland, J.C., Diekhoff, G.M., & Evans, S.H. (1979a). Development and evaluation of a learning strategy training program. *Journal of Educational Psychology. 71*, 64-73.

Dansereau, D.F., McDonald, B.A., Collins, K.W., Garland, J.C.,Holley, C.D., Diekhoff, G.M., & Evans, S.H. (1979b). Evaluation of a learning strategy system. In H.F. O'Neil, Jr., & C.D. Speilberger (Eds.), *Cognitive and affective learning strategies.* New York: Academic Press.

Feifer, R.G., Dyer, M.G., & Baker, E.L. (1988). Learning procedural and declarative knowledge. *Proceedings of the Intelligent Tutoring Systems Conference - 88*, Montreal, Canada.

Feifer, R.G. (1989). *A intelligent tutoring system for graphic mapping strategies.* Doctoral dissertation. (Technical Report UCLA-AI-89-04). University of California, Los Angeles, Computer Science Department, Artificial Intelligence Laboratory.

Gasser, M.E. (1988). *A connectionist model of sentence generation in a first and second language.* Doctoral dissertation. (Technical Report UCLA-AI-88-13). University of California, Los Angeles, Computer Science Department, Artificial Intelligence Laboratory..

Novak, J.D., Gowin, B., & Johnsen, G.T. (1983). The use of concept mapping and knowledge vee mapping with junior high school science students. *Science Education, 67*, 625-645.

True and Pseudo Framing Effects

Deborah Frisch

University of Oregon

ABSTRACT

The term "framing effect" describes the finding that people often respond differently to different descriptions or "frames" of a single situation. Framing effects violate the principle of "invariance" which states that one's decision should not be affected by how a situation is described. An important question about framing effects is whether subjects agree that two versions are equivalent. The term "framing effect" assumes that subjects would agree that the two situations were equivalent. The study reported here tests this assumption. In this study, subjects were first asked to answer framing effect problems and then were asked to compare two versions of a problem and state whether the two versions should be treated the same. In some cases such as Kahneman and Tversky's (1984) lives lost/lives saved problem, subjects treated two versions differently but reported that they should be treated the same. This is called a "true framing effect." In other cases such as Thaler's (1980) reference point problem, subjects treated the two versions differently and stated that they should be treated differently. This is described as a "pseudo framing effect." The distinction between true and pseudo framing effects has implications for both normative and descriptive theories of decision making.

INTRODUCTION

For the last 30 years, researchers have studied human decision making by comparing people's choices to utility theory, a widely accepted normative model of decision making (Savage, 1954). A growing body of research demonstrates that people's choices systematically deviate from this model (see von Winterfeldt & Edwards, 1986 for a review).

Recently, a type of violation of utility theory has been demonstrated that is much more disturbing than other violations. The term "framing effect" describes the finding that people often respond differently to different descriptions or "frames" of a single situation (Kahneman & Tversky, 1984). Framing effects violate the principle of "invariance" which states that one's decision should not be affected by how a situation is described. Clearly, the principle of invariance is fundamental to the concept of preference. While other violations of utility theory cast doubt on the descriptive accuracy of utility theory, framing effects call into question the assumption that people have well-defined preferences.

A commonly cited example of a framing effect is the "lives lost/lives saved" problem from Kahneman and Tversky (1984) (see Appendix, Problem 7). In this example, the same situation is described either in terms of a loss (number of lives lost) or in terms of a gain (number of lives saved). Subjects are given a choice between a sure thing and a risky option. The majority of subjects choose the sure thing in the lives saved version, but choose the risky option in the lives lost version. This example demonstrates that a single situation described in two different ways can lead to different choices.

The term "framing effect" has been used in two different ways. There is a strict usage of the term that refers to pairs of situations that are objectively identical and that only differ in the way they are described. The term is also used more loosely to describe pairs of situations that are not identical but which differ in a way that is irrelevant from the perspective of utility theory.

Most research on framing effects has used a between subjects design. Although this paradigm has been useful in demonstrating the different types of framing effects that exist, it is somewhat limited. In particular, there are two questions about framing effects that have not been addressed:

1. Would a single person treat two versions of a framing effect differently? Perhaps if subjects answered both versions of a framing effect in a short period of time they would "see" the equivalence and therefore not respond inconsistently.

2. Do subjects agree that two versions are equivalent? The term "framing effect" assumes that subjects would agree that the two situations were equivalent. It suggests that different frames of the same problem lead to different choices. However, this assumption has not been tested. Given that the term has been used in the loose sense described above, it is possible that subjects do not agree that two situations should be treated the same. Specifically, subjects' intutions may conflict with utility theory about whether two situations "boil down" to the same question.

I shall use the phrase "true framing effect" to refer to the situation where a person treats two versions of a problem differently, but agrees that they should be treated the same when she directly compares them. I shall use the phrase "pseudo framing effect" to refer to the situation where a person treats two versions of a problem differently and states that they should be treated differently when she directly compares them.

The distinction between true and pseudo framing effects has implications for both normative and descriptive theories of decision making. True framing effects are evidence that the processes involved in decision making are influenced by irrelevant aspects of a problem. As several authors have pointed out (Kahneman & Tversky, 1984; Shafer, 1986) this seriously calls into question the notion of preference. If minor changes in the presentation of a decision affect people's choices, then we feel less secure that these choices are revealing anything stable or real about people's preferences.

In contrast, pseudo framing effects are more relevant to normative theories of decision making. Pseudo framing effects demonstrate that psychologists are wrong in their assumptions about what factors should affect decisions. In particular, they would suggest that situations that are equivalent from the perspective of utility theory are not necessarily viewed as equivalent by people. The present study was designed to examine whether previously demonstrated framing effects were "true" framing effects. In addition, I was interested in seeing which, if any, framing effects would disappear using a within subject design.

METHOD

Subjects. Subjects were 31 undergraduate students enrolled in Introductory Psychology courses who participated for course credit.

Procedure. The experiment consisted of two parts. In Part I, subjects were presented with 18 decision problems on an IBM XT computer. The 18 problems consisted of 9 pairs of framing effects. The problems were presented in 2 orders. Two members of a given pair were not presented consecutively. Other problems not related to the present study were also presented.

In Part II of the experiment, subjects were presented with both members of a pair. They were then asked whether "the two situations should be treated the same way or differently."

Stimuli. Five of the pairs of framing effects were taken from previous research by Kahneman and Tversky (1984) and Thaler (1980). The other four pairs were developed for this study. All pairs used are in the Appendix.

RESULTS

The first question was whether framing effects would occur using a within subject design. On 8 out of 9 pairs, there was a significant difference in subjects' responses to the two versions of the problem (See Table 1). There was no framing effect on Kahneman and Tversky's (1984) cash discount/credit card surcharge problem. Thus, framing effects do occur in a within subject design, even when subjects answer the questions within a brief time period.

The second question of interest was whether these framing effects were "true framing effects" or "pseudo framing effects."

This analysis was qualitative. A true framing effect refers to the situation where the majority of subjects treated the members of a pair differently, but stated that they should be treated the same. In contrast a pseudo framing effect refers to the situation where subjects treat two problems differently and state that they should be treated differently. This was assessed by looking at the percentage of subjects who stated the the two versions were equivalent. There was a great deal of variation across problems on this measure (See Table 1). At one extreme was the lives lost/lives saved problem which was a true framing effect. Although 65% of subjects treated the two versions differently, only 10% of the subjects said that the two situations should be treated the differently.

Table 1. Mean responses to problems and percentage of subjects saying problems should be treated differently.

Problem	Type	Mean response Version 1 (s.d.)	Mean response Version 2 (s.d.)	% of subjects treating 1 and 2 differently	% of subjects saying 1 and 2 should be treated diff.
1	R.P.	3.8 (3.6)	2.9 (1.8)	55	60
2	R.P.	5.3 (2.7)	4.1 (3.2)	58	36
3	R.P.	6.0 (3.6)	4.2 (3.2)	80	36
4	R.P.	13.0 (11.4)	19.0 (26)	52	43
5	L/G	173 (535)	89 (89)	77	80
6*	L/G	3.0 (2.5)	3.2 (2.6)	23	0
7	L/G	4.4 (2.8)	6.4 (2.5)	65	10
8	S.C.	10.2 (11.3)	5.8 (9.0)	77	73
9	S.C.	5.8 (3.3)	4.8 (3.1)	39	23

* No framing effect demonstrated
R.P. : Reference point problem
L/G : Loss/gain type problem
S.C. : Sunk cost problem

At the other extreme was Thaler's (1980) sunk cost example (Problem 8). The question was how many times you would play tennis in the next six months if you developed tennis elbow. Seventy - seven percent of the subjects estimated a higher number of times if they had paid to join a tennis club than if they hadn't. Eighty percent of the subjects said that one's decision about whether to play should be affected by whether one had paid to join the club. That is, the majority of subjects attended to sunk costs (counter to economic theory) and the majority also stated that they believed one should attend to sunk costs. Thus, this problem was a pseudo framing effect. Thaler's (1980) reference point problem (Problem 1) was another case that was a pseudo framing effect. Fifty-five percent of the subjects treated the two versions differently and sixty percent said that they _should_ be treated differently.

For the 8 problems on which a framing effect was demonstrated, there was a great deal of variation in the extent to which subjects stated that the two situations should be treated differently. Kahneman and Tversky's lives lost/lives saved example was the lowest (10%) and thus was the clearest example of a "true framing effect." Thaler's beer example was the highest percentage (90%) and an example of a "pseudo framing effect."

The problems used in this study could be grouped into three categories : reference point problems (Problems 1-4); loss/gain problems (Problems 5-7) and sunk cost problems (Problems 8-9). It is possible that some types of framing effects are true framing effects while other types are pseudo framing effects. To test this idea, I compared the mean answer to the question about whether the members of a pair should be treated differently for the three categories. The mean percentages were 43.7 for reference point problems, 30.0 for loss/gain problems and 48.0 for sunk cost problems. These differences were not significant. Thus, there is no evidence suggesting that these three categories differ with respect to the true-pseudo framing effect distinction.

DISCUSSION

This study provides evidence that framing effects differ in an important way. Some instances of framing effects are "true framing effects," that is, subjects who treat two problems differently state that that the two situations should be treated the same. Other instances of framing effects are "pseudo framing effects." Subjects treat them differently because they believe that the difference between the situations warrants different actions.

Future research might proceed in different directions for true and pseudo framing effects. An obvious question about true framing effects is "Which way of looking at the problem is the 'right' way?" That is, if a person responds differently to two frames of a problem, and agrees that the two frames are equivalent, which way is revealing the person's true preference? In contrast, pseudo framing effects suggest that people reject certain principles of economic theory (e.g. the principle that one should ignore sunk costs). Future research might examine which principles of economic theory people reject.

REFERENCES

Kahneman, D., & Tversky, A. (1984). Choices, values, and frames. American Psychologist, 39, 341-350.

Savage, L.J. (1954). The Foundations of Statistics. New York: Wiley.

Shafer, G. (1986). Savage revisited (with discussion). Statistical Science, 1, 463-501.

Thaler, R. (1980). Toward a positive theory of consumer choice. Journal of Economic Behavior and Organization, 1, 39-60.

von Winterfeldt, D., & Edwards, W. (1986). Decision analysis and behavioral research. New York:Cambridge University Press.

APPENDIX

For each problem, there are two versions: (1) and (2). For some of the problems, these are presented separately. For others, the text corresponds to the version (1) problem. The version (2) problem is obtained by deleting the **bold** text in version (1) and adding the text in [brackets].

Reference point problems

1. (1) You are lying on the beach on a hot day. All you have to drink is ice water. For the last hour you have been thinking about how much you would enjoy a nice cold bottle of your favorite brand of beer. A companion gets up to make a phone call and offers to bring back a beer from the only nearby place where beer is sold, **a fancy hotel** [(2) a small run-down grocery store]. He says that the beer may be expensive and so he asks you how much you are willing to pay for the beer.

2. (1) You go to a nice restaurant and notice that your favorite bottle of wine costs $5 more than it does in a liquor store.

(2) You go to a nice restaurant that doesn't have a liquor license. They charge you $5 corking fee if you bring wine to drink.

Would you **buy** [bring] the wine?
Use a number from 1 to 10 where 1 means you would definitely not buy the wine and 10 means you would definitely buy the wine.

3. (1) You go out to dinner in a nice restaurant. You order some baked clams for an appetizer and shrimp scampi for your main course. After 30 minutes, your waiter comes with the scampi and tells you that **he forgot to order your appetizer. If you want, he will order it now and you will get it in 15 minutes.**
[(2) the kitchen is really backed up and your baked clams aren't ready. If you still want them, they will be ready in 15 minutes.]

You have two options.
a. wait for it
b. cancel the order

What would you do? Use a number from 1 to 10 where 1 means you would definitely choose a and 10 means you would definitely choose b.

4. (1) Imagine that you go to purchase a jacket for $125. The jacket salesman informs you that the jacket you wish to buy is on sale for $120 at the other branch of the store.

(2) Imagine that you go to purchase a calculator for $15. The calculator salesman informs you that the calculator you wish to buy is on sale for $10 at the other branch of the the store.

How close would the other store have to be (in minutes of driving time) in order for you to make the trip to the other store?

Loss/gain problems

5. (1) Back in the 1950's you purchased a case of good wine for $5 a bottle. Today, a wine merchant offers to purchase it from you. How much would you be willing to sell a bottle for?

(2) You have just heard that a wine merchant has a case of good wine dated from the 1950's. He purchased the wine for $5 a bottle. He now wants to sell it. How much would you be willing to pay per bottle?

6. (1) You go to a gas station. They charge 90 cents a gallon for unleaded gas if you pay cash. They charge you 5 cents extra a gallon if you charge it.

(2) You go to gas station. They charge 95 cents a gallon for unleaded gas if you charge it. They give you a 5 cents a gallon discount if you pay cash.

Would you pay cash or use your charge?
Use a number from 1 to 10 where 1 means you would definitely pay cash and 10 means you would definitely use your charge.

7. (1) Imagine that the U.S. is preparing for the outbreak of an unusual Asian disease, which is expected to kill 600 people. Two alternative programs have been proposed. Assume that the exact scientific estimates of the consequences of the programs are as follows:

If Program A is adopted, 200 people will be saved.
If Program B is adopted, there is a one-third probability that 600 people will be saved and a two-thirds probability that no people will be saved.

[(2) If Program A is adopted, 400 people will die.
If Program B is adopted, there is a one-third probability that nobody will die and a two-thirds probability that 600 people will die.]

Which program would you choose? Use a number from 1 to 10 where 1 means you would definitely choose Program A and 10 means you would definitely choose Program B.

Sunk cost problems

8. (1) You have paid $300 to join a tennis club for 6 months. **During the first week of your membership, you develop tennis elbow.** [(2) You enjoy playing tennis. One day on the court, you develop tennis elbow.] It is extremely painful to play tennis. Your doctor tells you that the pain will continue for about a year.

Estimate the number of times you will play tennis in the next 6 months.

9. (1) You go out to a restaurant. The chocolate amoretto kahlua cheesecake sounds great so you order it. It is wonderful but very rich, and after two bites you are in sugar shock.

(2) You go out to a restaurant. It is the restaurant's one year anniversary and they are giving everyone free desert. You get the chocolate amoretto kahlua cheesecake. It is wonderful but very rich, and after two bites you are in sugar shock.

Would you eat more of it? Use a number from 1 to 10 where 1 means you definitely would not eat more and 10 means you definitely would eat more.

QUESTION ANSWERING IN THE CONTEXT OF CAUSAL MECHANISMS

Arthur C. Graesser, Darold Hemphill, and Lawrence E. Brainerd
Department of Psychology and the Institute for Intelligent Systems
Memphis State University
Memphis, TN 38152

Abstract

A model of human question answering (called QUEST) accounts for the answers that adults produce when they answer different categories of open-class questions (such as why, how, when, what-enabled, and what-are-the-consequences). This project investigated the answers that adults generate when events are queried in the context of biological, technological, and physical mechanisms. According to QUEST, an event sequence in a scientific mechanism is represented as a causal network of events and states; a teleological goal hierarchy may also be superimposed on the causal network in biological and technological domains, but not in physical systems (e.g., rainfall, earthquake).

When questions are answered, QUEST systematically operates on the causal networks and goal hierarchies that underlie a causal mechanism. Answers to how and enablement questions sample causal antecedents of the queried event in the causal network; consequence questions sample causal consequents. Answers to when questions sample antecedents to a greater extent than consequents even though events from both directions furnish sensible answers. Answers to why questions sample both causal antecedents in the causal network and superordinate goals from goal hierarchies that exist in technological and biological knowledge structures.

Graesser and Franklin (in press) have developed a model of human question answering called QUEST. This model accounts for the answers that are produced when individuals answer different categories of open-class questions: why, how, when, where, enablement, consequence, etc. Questions are answered in the context of different types of material, including stories, scripts, and expository texts on scientific mechanisms. The components of QUEST have foundations in some previous models that specify the Q/A processes which operate on structured databases representing world knowledge (Allen, 1987; Brachman, 1983; Graesser, Robertson, & Anderson, 1981; Graesser & Murachver, 1985; Lehnert, 1978; Lehnert, Dyer, Johnson, Yang, & Harley, 1983; McKoewn, 1985).

This research focuses on short scientific texts that depict causal event sequences in biological, technological, and physical mechanisms. For example, suppose that an individual reads the the following text about a nuclear power plant.

Event 1: Atoms are split.
Event 2: Heat energy is released.
Event 3: The water in the surrounding tank is heated.
Event 4: Steam drives a series of turbines.
Event 5: The turbines produce electricity.

After reading this text, individuals were probed with five different categories of questions:

WHY - Why is water in the surrounding tank heated?

HOW - How is water in the surrounding tank heated?
ENABLE - What enables water in the surrounding to be heated?
WHEN - When is water in the surrounding tank heated?
CONS - What are the consequences of water in the surrounding tank being heated?

QUEST accounts for the answers that are produced when particular events are probed with a particular category of question. This project focuses on the "answer likelihood scores" of explicit events in the text. For example, what is the likelihood that Event 3 is produced when Event 2 is probed with a CONS question?

Representation of Knowledge

QUEST assumes that causal networks organize the events that are explicitly mentioned in event sequences. In the example causal network below, there is an event sequence that unfolds chronologically and causally (events 1, 2, 3, and 4). There may be some loops in the event sequence (as in events 2 and 3). A set of enabling states (states 5, 6, 7, and 8) are needed for the event sequence to unfold.

The Consequence (C) arcs in a causal network denote a weak sense of causality. If a forward C-arc connects nodes X and Y, then the connection must satisfy both temporal and causal criteria. Regarding temporality, node X must occur or exist prior to node Y. Regarding causality, X must furnish one or more of several causal relationships with Y. For example, a necessity relationship exists whenever a counterfactual test is satisfied: if X is negated or removed from the system, then Y will not occur. Other types of causal relationships involve sufficiency (X is sufficient for Y to occur), and operativity (X must be operating/existing when Y occurs). The causal analysis is similar to Trabasso's causal chain theory (Trabasso & van den Broek, 1985) and some theories in qualitative physics (Forbus, 1985).

Our naive understanding of a scientific system may often be teleological. That is, events are organized according to a functional, purposeful, goal-oriented knowledge structure. For example, a nuclear power plant is designed to achieve the goal of producing electricity; the plan of achieving this goal is superimposed on the causal network of events and states. Technological systems are typically motivated by the goals and plans of animate agents. Biological systems are often interpreted teleologically. According to a naive view of evolution, for example, a species develops in order to acquire a superior capacity. Physical systems (e.g., rainfall, earthquakes) received a goal-oriented interpretation when the Greeks had myths about gods governing the natural events and processes.

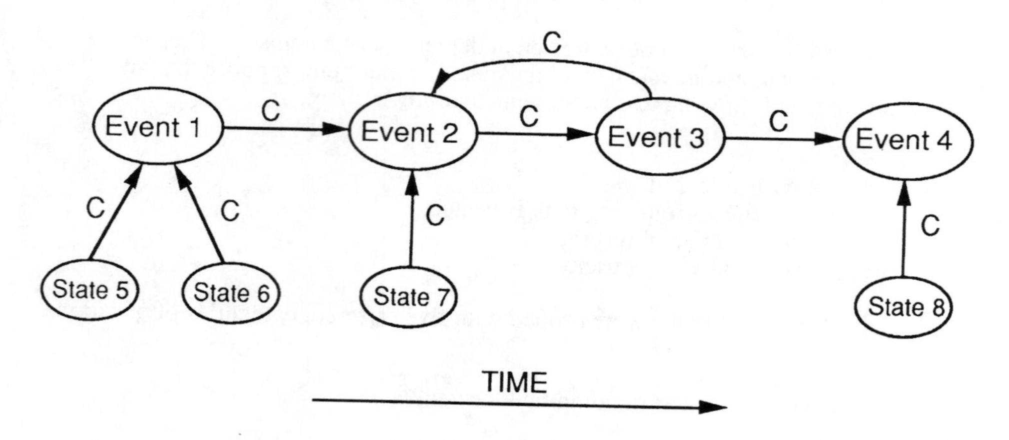

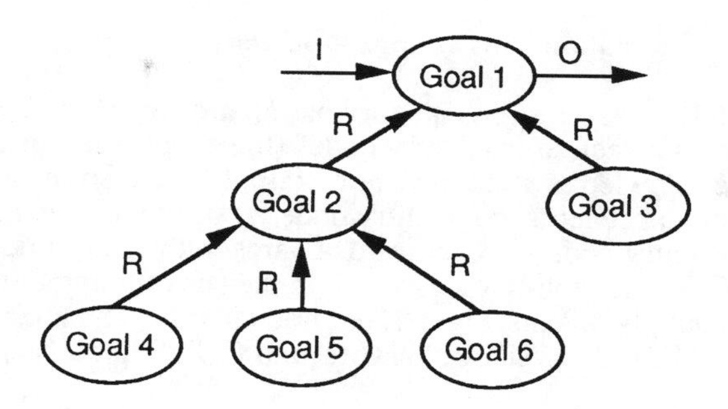

Goal-oriented knowledge is represented as a hierarchy of goals that are related by Reason (R) arcs, as shown above. The most superordinate goal (goal 1) is the primary goal that the agent wants to achieve. The subordinate goals correspond to intermediate plans and low-level actions or processes. States/events in the world initiate the goals (signified by the I-arc); the goals may have outcomes (signified by the O-arc) that are positive or negative. Goal/plan hierarchies are very popular in theories of action and problem solving (Miller, Galanter, & Pribram, 1960; Graesser & Clark, 1985; Newell & Simon, 1972)

When there is a teleological understanding of a causal mechanism, a goal hierarchy is superimposed on the causal network. This is illustrated below in the context of the short text on nuclear power. For every event, there is a corresponding goal. Just as event 5 is the final event in the event chain, goal 5 is the most superordinate goal in the goal hierarchy. Just as event 1 is the initial event in the chain, goal 1 is the most subordinate goal in the goal hierarchy.

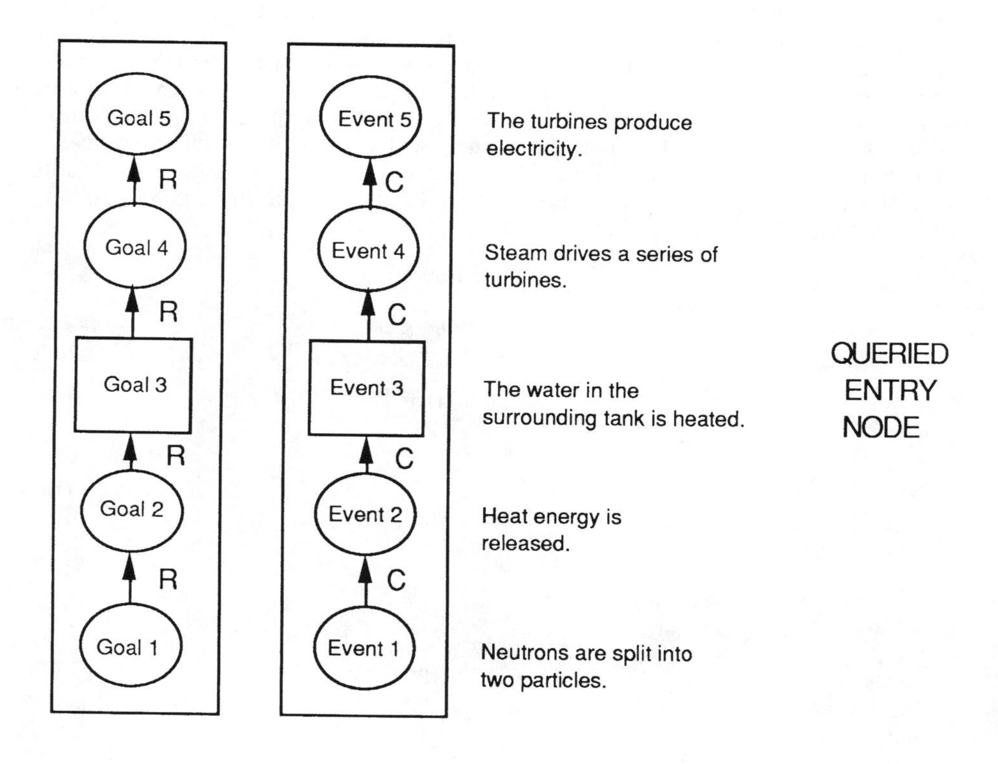

Question Answering Procedures

According to QUEST, each question category has an arc search procedure which specifies the legal path of arcs between (a) an "entry node" (the event being queried) and (b) a "good answer" node in the knowledge structure. For example, a question category might sample nodes that are causal antecedents to the entry node. Causal antecedent nodes are on paths that radiate from the entry node via backwards C-arcs in the causal network. When event 3 is probed with a HOW-question (How is water in the surrounding tank heated?), the antecedent nodes would be events 1 and 2, but not 4 and 5. The arc search procedures are specified for WHY, HOW, ENABLE, WHEN, and CONS questions in this paper.

Materials and Question Answering Protocols

The texts were 24 event sequences that were extracted from passages in the American Academic Encyclopedia. All texts had five events, as with the example on nuclear power. Eight passages were in the technological domain (e.g., television, nuclear power), 8 were in the biological domain (e.g., mitosis, photosynthesis), and 8 were in the physical science domain (e.g., earthquake, rainfall).

Question answering (Q/A) protocols were collected from college students at Memphis State University. Eight subjects provided Q/A protocols for each text, yielding 192 subjects altogether. Given that a text had 5 sentences and that there were 5 question categories (WHY, HOW, ENABLE, WHEN, and CONS), each subject answered 25 questions. The "answer likelihood" score for a particular answer was the proportion of subjects (out of 8) who gave that answer to a particular question.

Table 1 shows mean answer likelihood scores for those events that were causal antecedents versus causal consequents of the queried events. A causal antecedent occurred prior to the queried event (via a backwards C-arc or R-arc) whereas a causal consequent occurred subsequent to the queried event (via a forward C-arc or R-arc). The answer likelihood scores are segregated according to question category (averaging over the three knowledge domains). In addition, WHY-questions are segregated according to technological, biological, versus physical domains. These means are interpreted in the next section. In tests of statistical significance, the error term reflects the variability among items (i.e., a particular answer A to a question Q in a text T).

Table 1

Question Category	Antecedent Event	Consequent Event
Why?	.16	.17
How?	.21	.06
What enables?	.26	.08
When?	.36	.10
What are the consequences?	.08	.36
Why-Questions Segregated by Knowledge Domain		
Physical	.30	.10
Technological	.08	.20
Biological	.10	.20

Analysis of Five Question Categories

WHY-questions. The answers to WHY-questions were evenly divided between causal antecedents and causal consequents, according to Table 1. However, causal consequents were prevalent in technological and biological domains, but not in physical domains (see bottom of Table 1). In physical science domains, the nodes in causal networks are sampled by pursuing paths of backwards C-arcs from the entry node; goal hierarchies are not very prevalent. In technological and biological domains, goal hierarchies are more prevalent; the answers to why-questions sample superordinate goals via forward R-arcs (Graesser et al., 1981; Graesser & Clark, 1985; Graesser & Franklin, in press). Therefore, teleological interpretations are imposed on technological and biological domains, but rarely on physical science domains.

HOW-questions. Answers to HOW-questions included causal antecedents to the entry node in the causal network, as predicted by QUEST. The fact that causal consequents were occasionally sampled (answer likelihood = .06) can be attributed to occasional loops in the event chain and to answerers occasionally sampling the text in a haphazard manner. QUEST also predicts that some answers to HOW-questions specify the speed, force, intensity, and/or qualitative manner in which an event occurs (e.g., X occurred quickly, forcefully, in circles).

ENABLE-questions. Answers to these questions include causal antecedents to the entry node in the causal network, as predicted by QUEST. Thus, the answers to HOW and ENABLE questions are quite similar.

WHEN-questions. Strictly speaking, it is possible to relate a queried event temporally with either a causal antecedent (i.e., queried event occurred after the answer event) or with a causal consequent (i.e., queried event occurred before the answer event). However, there was a strong bias toward antecedent events in this study and in earlier research on narrative passages (Graesser & Murachver, 1985). The answers specified that a queried event occurs after its antecedent rather than before its consequent. According to QUEST, answers to WHEN-questions may also refer to higher-order, global event descriptions; the queried event would occur during the more global event.

CONS-questions. As predicted by QUEST, these answers included causal consequents of the entry node in the causal network (via paths of forward C-arcs). Answers to CONS-questions are essentially opposite of the answers to HOW, ENABLE, and WHEN questions.

Distance effects. Answer likelihood scores decreased as a function of the distance between the entry node and the answer node. A rather simple mathematical model provided a very good fit to the complete set of answer likelihood scores. The complete set includes 20 scores for each passage (5 queried events and 4 explicit answers per event), 24 passages, and 5 question categories (yielding 2400 scores altogether).

The mathematical model has three free parameters associated with each passage. Parameter a is the likelihood of pursuing a causal antecedent path whereas parameter c is the likelihood of pursuing a causal consequence path. Parameter t is the likelihood of traversing a single arc on a path whereas n is the number of arcs between the entry node and the answer node. The answer likelihood scores are closely predicted by $a*t^n$ for causal antecedents and $c*t^n$ for causal consequents. The overall mean value was .67 for t, the distance dampening parameter. Regarding the causal antecedent parameter (a), the mean value was substantially higher in those cells that are predicted as good answers by QUEST (.63) than in those cells that are not predicted to be good answers (.18). Regarding the causal consequent parameter (c), again the mean was much higher in good answer cells (.51) than in bad answer cells (.19).

To summarize, when distance effects are combined with the arc search procedures of QUEST, a very simple mathematical model provides an impressive fit to the answer likelihood scores. It should be emphasized once again, however, that an adequate account of answers to WHY-questions must assume the existence of (1) teleological goal hierarchies being superimposed on causal networks and (2) systematic differences among technological, biological, and physical science mechanisms.

References

Allen, J. (1987). Natural language understanding. Reading, MA: Benjamin/Cummings.

Brachman, R. J. (1983). What IS-A is and isn't: An analysis of taxonomic links in semantic networks. Computer, 16, 30-36.

Forbus, K. D. (1985). Qualitative process theory. In D. G. Bobrow (Ed), Qualitative reasoning about physical systems. Cambridge, MA: MIT Press.

Graesser, A.C., & Clark, L.F. (1985). Structures and procedures of implicit knowledge. Norwood, NJ: Ablex.

Graesser, A.C., & Franklin, S.P. (in press). QUEST: A cognitive model of question answering. Questioning Exchange.

Graesser, A.C., & Murachver, T. (1985). Symbolic procedures of question answering. In A.C. Graesser & J.B. Black (Eds.), The psychology of questions. Hillsdale, NJ: Erlbaum.

Graesser, A.C., Robertson, S.P., & Anderson, P.A. (1981). Incorporating inferences in narrative representations: A study of how and why. Cognitive Psychology, 13, 1-26.

Lehnert, W. G. (1978) The process of question answering. Hillsdale, NJ: Erlbaum.

Lehnert, W. G., Dyer, M. G., Johnson, P. N., Yang, C. J., & Harley, S. (1983). BORIS: An in-depth understander of narratives. Artificial Intelligence, 20, 15-62.

McKoewn, K. R. (1985). Discourse strategies for generating natural language text. Artificial Intelligence, 27, 1-41.

Miller, G. A., Galanter, E. & Pribram, K. H. (1960). Plans and the structure of behavior. New York: Holt, Rinehart, & Winston.

Newell, A., & Simon, H. A. (1972). Human problem solving. Englewood Cliffs, NJ: Prentice-Hall, Inc.

Trabasso, T., & van den Broek, P. (1985). Causal thinking and the representation of narrative events. Journal of Memory and Language, 24, 612-630.

LEARNING A TROUBLESHOOTING STRATEGY: THE ROLES OF DOMAIN SPECIFIC KNOWLEDGE AND GENERAL PROBLEM-SOLVING STRATEGIES

LEO GUGERTY
EDUCATIONAL TESTING SERVICE
PRINCETON, NJ

ABSTRACT

This research investigated how college students learned an efficient troubleshooting strategy, elimination. The subjects' task was to find the broken components in networks that were similar to digital circuits. With only minimal training in this task, subjects usually used a strategy of backtracking from the incorrect network outputs, instead of the more efficient elimination strategy, which involves backtracking but also eliminating (ignoring) components that lead into good network outputs. Computer simulation modeling suggested that in order for subjects to learn the elimination strategy on their own, they needed to apply (1) certain key domain-specific knowledge about how the components worked, and (2) the general reductio-ad-absurdum problem-solving strategy. An experiment showed that these two kinds of knowledge do enable students to increase their use of elimination, thus supporting the model.

INTRODUCTION

Imagine you have rented a one-room cottage for the weekend. Upon arriving, you turn on the radio and no sound comes out, even with the volume control up high. A little investigating shows that the radio and a desk lamp are plugged into a well-worn extension cord, which is plugged into a wall outlet. Nearby is a fuse box with some replacement fuses and a new extension cord. What would you do first to find the cause of the silent radio?

There are a number of problem-solving strategies you could use in this situation. Based on your past troubleshooting experience, you could try to recall some of the likely causes of problems with radios. Or you could focus on the current situation and backtrack from the evident problem (the silent radio). This might lead you to replace the extension cord or some of the fuses. However, a more efficient strategy than simple backtracking would be to turn on the lamp. If it works, you can then eliminate the extension cord and fuse box as possible causes of the problem. In this situation, the elimination strategy isolates the problem to the radio or its cord. More precisely, in backtracking, the set of possibly faulty components consists of all those components that lead into the bad system output. In elimination, this set of possibly faulty components is reduced by ignoring the components that lead into good system outputs. The elimination strategy has also been called dependency-directed backtracking (Stallman & Sussman, 1977).

This research focused on how people learn the elimination strategy in a novel troubleshooting task. In particular, it considered how domain-specific knowledge and general-purpose problem-solving strategies are used in learning elimination. Psychologists have recently debated the relative importance of domain-specific versus general-purpose knowledge in problem solving (Glaser, 1984; Perkins & Salomon, 1989). Some suggest that all problem-solving strategies are closely tied to the specific domains in which they are used. Others claim that people do have general strategies that they can transfer to novel problems. Those who have written on this topic often have noted the paucity of research examining how domain-specific and general knowledge might interact during problem solving, and have called for such research (Alexander & Judy, 1989).

This study focused explicitly on the interaction between domain-specific and general-purpose knowledge. I first developed a simulation model that highlighted the domain-specific and general knowledge needed for learning elimination. Then I conducted a training experiment to test the model. This experiment determined whether either domain-specific or general knowledge alone would improve use of elimination, or whether both together were necessary.

The task for this research was not taken from everyday experience, as is the electrical troubleshooting problem above. Since I planned an experiment requiring a high degree of experimental control over the subjects' domain-specific knowledge, I chose a task that would be novel for my subjects (college students). Subjects had to find the broken nodes in very simple networks that were similar to digital circuits (see Figure 1). The network shown passes 0's and 1's from left to right. The nodes act as AND gates; when working correctly they only pass on 1's if all their inputs are 1's. When nodes break, they pass on 0's regardless of their inputs. The subjects searched for the broken node by testing particular connections between nodes to see if they were passing 0's or 1's, and by replacing nodes. The networks were presented on paper and subjects made tests and replacements by typing node numbers into a computer. Tests and replacements were assigned costs (in imaginary money), with replacements costing four times more than than tests. Subjects were asked to keep costs to a minimum. The network task was taken from the work of Rouse (1978).

For the network in Figure 1, the backtracking strategy leads to considering the following set of 18 possibly-faulty nodes: 10 through 23, 25 through 27, and 31. The elimination strategy allows many of these nodes to be ignored because they lead to an output of 1, leaving a possibly-faulty set of 4 nodes: 18, 22, 26, and 31. Pilot testing showed that college students usually did not use elimination when troubleshooting the network problems. Most resorted to the less efficient backtracking strategy.

The next section presents the model of the domain-specific and general-purpose knowledge needed to learn elimination.

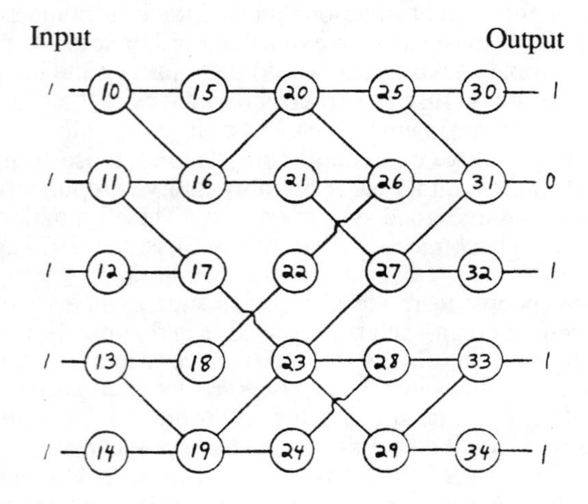

Figure 1. **Example network**

THE SIMULATION MODEL

I created separate production-system models for the backtracking and the elimination strategies. By looking at the knowledge that had to be added to the backtracking model to obtain the elimination model, I could predict what knowledge a person using only backtracking would need in order to learn elimination.

The backtracking model initially focuses on the node that gives the 0 network output, testing each input to this node (in a random order) until it finds a 0 input or discovers that all the inputs are 1. If all the inputs are 1, the model concludes that the current focus node is broken and replaces it. If a 0 input is found, the node outputting that 0 becomes the next focus node and the process is repeated.

When the backtracking model is looking for 0 inputs to a node outputting a 0, it generates hypotheses that each of the node's input lines are passing 0's and tests these by making actual tests of the network (as a subject would make on the computer). For example, given the network in Figure 1, it might generate the hypothesis that line 25 - 31 is passing a 0 and immediately test this. In the elimination model, this testing process is modified. Instead of immediately testing the hypothesis that 25 - 31 is 0, the elimination model uses knowledge of how the nodes work and a kind of "what if" reasoning to propagate the effects of the hypothesis through the network. Propagation leads to the further hypotheses that line 25 - 30 is passing a 0 and that node 30 is outputting a 0. Since this last hypothesis is contradicted by the fact that node 30 is outputting a 1, the original hypothesis is assumed to be false. Thus, the model concludes that line 25 - 31 is passing a 1 and this line is not tested on the computer. If after propagation, the original hypothesis is found to only agree with known network information, the model goes ahead and tests the line associated with this hypothesis.

The elimination model uses two kinds of knowledge in this reasoning process. The first of these is the knowledge of how the nodes work that is used to propagate a hypothesis through the network. The model uses two key rules about the nodes, both of which are used in the previous example. These are the rules that all outputs of a node are equal and that if a node has a 0 input, it will output 0's. The second kind of knowledge used in the elimination model is the overall process of propagating a hypothesis, noticing contradictions, and falsifying the original hypothesis. This is basically the reasoning process known as **reductio ad absurdum (RAA)**.

The general-purpose nature of RAA should be emphasized. It can be used in mathematics, legal reasoning, and science. Polya (1957) included it in his book on general problem-solving skills. On the other hand, the node knowledge used by the elimination model is domain specific. In addition, it should be noted that the model does not suggest that overall improvement in domain-specific knowledge will lead to the elimination strategy. Two, quite specific rules about how the nodes work are used. Other rules about the nodes would not be expected to lead to the reasoning needed for elimination.

To summarize, the model suggested that people using only backtracking will learn elimination if they: (1) learn particular domain-specific knowledge about how the nodes work, and (2) apply the general RAA reasoning strategy. According to the model, both of these kinds of knowledge are needed for learning elimination. The next section describes the experiment that tested the model.

THE EXPERIMENT

METHOD

To test the model, I designed an experiment with five conditions, based on five ways of training subjects to do the network task. In each condition, subjects first received brief instruction in how the nodes and networks worked and how to do the task. The initial instruction contained enough information for the subjects to induce the elimination strategy, but this information was not highlighted. After the initial training, each subject received one of five kinds of extra training and then solved 24 network problems.

I designed the training conditions to test whether either of the two types of knowledge highlighted by the model (domain-specific and general) could facilitate elimination by itself, or whether both had to be taught together. Thus I included conditions in which subjects received either no extra training (**baseline**), only the domain-specific node knowledge suggested by the model (**relevant node**), or both the domain-specific knowledge and the general RAA strategy (**relevant node/RAA**). In the relevant node/RAA condition, subjects learned RAA in the context of the network problems.

I also needed an RAA-only condition in which subjects learned RAA but not the relevant node knowledge. Since people are often bad at transferring knowledge across domains, it was important that subjects in the RAA-only condition learn RAA in the context of the network problems, as did the relevant node/RAA subjects. Thus, for the RAA-only condition, I taught RAA in the context of the network problems, but using domain-specific knowledge that was, according to the model, irrelevant to learning elimination. This is the **irrelevant node/RAA** condition. Finally, I added an **irrelevant node** condition where subjects learned only the irrelevant domain-specific knowledge.

The relevant domain-specific knowledge consisted of the two key rules about how the nodes worked that were used by the model to learn elimination. The irrelevant domain-specific knowledge consisted of rules about how the nodes worked that were true but, according to the model, irrelevant to learning elimination. (An example of an irrelevant node rule is: For a working node to have a 0 output, it must have at least one 0 input.) Comparing these two conditions (relevant node and irrelevant node) allowed me to test whether any increase in elimination after node training was due to the particular node knowledge indicated by the model or to general familiarity with how the nodes worked.

The main prediction from the model was that subjects in the relevant node/RAA condition would show the greatest use of elimination, since these subjects were explicitly taught all the knowledge sufficient for learning this strategy. Use of elimination in the irrelevant node condition was expected to be the same as in the baseline condition; since in both these conditions, subjects practiced none of the key knowledge needed for elimination. The model did not make a clear prediction regarding the relevant node condition and the irrelevant node/RAA condition, where subjects were taught only part of the knowledge sufficient for elimination. If subjects in these two conditions could infer the remaining needed knowledge from the initial training or from prior knowledge, then their use of elimination would increase. If not, it would stay the same.

Ten University of Michigan undergraduates participated in each condition. The overall procedure for each subject was: initial training, pretest (4 network problems), node training (depending on the condition), RAA training (depending on the condition), and post-test (24 network problems). After each post-test problem, subjects were told how much money they had spent and what would be a "good" amount to spend on that problem. The good scores were based on using elimination plus the half-split strategy, which involves testing near the middle of a chain of possibly faulty nodes. During the pretest, subjects' only feedback consisted of how much money they had spent on each problem.

In the node training, a subject would see, for example, a diagram of an individual node with one of its input lines passing a 0 and one of its output lines marked with a question mark. The subject had to indicate what was being passed along the line with the question mark, either "0", "1", or "Can't tell". The correct answer in this case is "0". This problem exemplifies the relevant node rule that if a node has a 0 input, it outputs 0's. Subjects in the node training conditions did 96 node problems, with immediate feedback after each problem.

In the RAA training, subjects saw diagrams like in Figure 2. They were told to assume that the lines marked with a 1 and a 0 were actually passing those values and that the "0?" was a hypothesis. Their task was to determine, if possible, what value was being passed along the line with the hypothesis. The experimenter first demonstrated on a few problems how the hypothesized value could be propagated, and how sometimes, as in this problem, the hypothesis would lead to a contradiction and could therefore be falsified. The correct answer for this problem is "1". This is an example of relevant RAA training. Subjects in RAA training conditions did 24 RAA problems, with immediate feedback after each problem. The instructions emphasized that subjects could spend less money on the network problems by using RAA to test some of their hypotheses instead of making tests on the computer.

I would like to stress that the RAA training did not directly teach the elimination strategy. In well-practiced use of elimination on the network problems, subjects first step in problem-solving is usually to cross off the nodes that lead into outputs of 1. Then they direct their search for the faulty node to the remaining set of nodes. In the RAA training, subjects did something rather different. They used RAA to determine whether certain hypotheses about the network are true or false.

RESULTS

A major advantage of the network task is that it allows easy measurement of subjects' strategy use merely by observing the tests they made. The main dependent variable for measuring use of

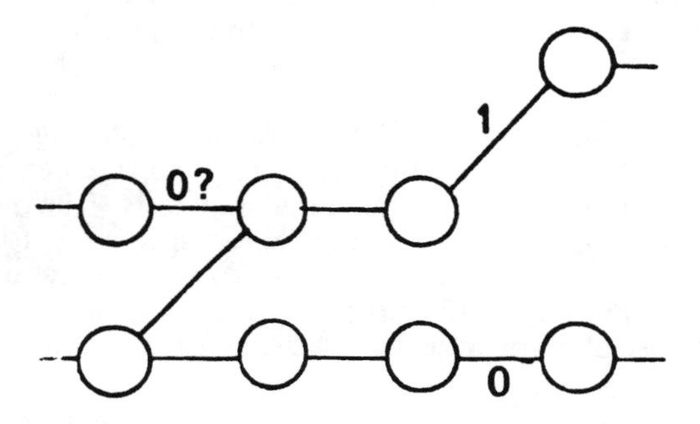

Figure 2. **Example of a relevant RAA training stimuli.**

backtracking was the percentage of tests on each problem that were within the backtracking set A test is in the backtracking set if the line tested leads into the 0 network output. For the elimination strategy, a similar variable was calculated using the elimination set, the set of lines that lead into the 0 network output but not any network outputs of 1. For example, in Figure 1, the only tests consistent with elimination were those of the lines connecting nodes 18, 22, 26, and 31.

However, because the elimination set is contained within the backtracking set, subjects using only backtracking will by chance make some tests in the elimination set. I therefore calculated another variable to represent subjects' use of elimination that factored out elimination tests that would be expected merely by use of the backtracking strategy. For each network, I calculated the percentage of elimination tests that would be expected if a subjects used the backtracking strategy described by the model. This percentage was subtracted from the subjects' actual percentage of elimination tests on that network to give a new variable, called the percentage of elimination tests beyond chance.

On the 4 pretest networks (before any extra training), subjects used the backtracking strategy almost exclusively. Considering all 50 subjects, the average percentage of backtracking tests was 99%; while the average percentage of elimination tests beyond chance was 3%. An analysis of variance showed that the subjects in the five training conditions did not differ significantly in their use of elimination prior to training. However, subjects in some conditions (including the relevant node/RAA condition) did use elimination slightly more on the pretest. To handle these differences, subjects' pretest scores on a dependent variable were used as a covariate when analyzing the post-test data.[1]

Subjects did quite well on the node and the RAA training. They answered 97% of the node problems and 92% of the RAA problems correctly, with no significant differences between the relevant and irrelevant training.

Figure 3 shows the subjects' use of elimination on the post-tests. The data for each subject were averaged over the 24 post-tests. The figure gives the adjusted means from the analysis of covariance, since these are the means that would be expected after any preexisting (i.e., pretest) differences in use of elimination have been factored out. As the figure shows, post-test use of elimination after relevant/RAA training was significantly greater than in the baseline condition ($p < 0.05$). The other three training conditions showed no improvement over the baseline. This was true for both the percentage of elimination tests and the percentage of elimination tests beyond chance.

To put these data in context, the straight line at 48% shows the percentage of elimination tests that would be expected given use of the backtracking strategy as implemented in the model. Using the modeled elimination strategy would lead to 100% elimination tests. The modeled backtracking and elimination strategies would result in values of 0 and 48%, respectively, for the percentage of elimination tests beyond chance. Thus it seems that the two kinds of training suggested by the model, relevant node and RAA training, did help people use elimination more often. In fact, they increased the above-chance use of elimination by at least a factor of two.

---

[1]The difference between pretest and post-test scores was not used as a dependent variable because different kinds of feedback were used on the pretests and post-tests, and there were many fewer pretests than post-tests (4 vs. 24).

This conclusion is further supported by analysis of other aspects of subjects performance on the post-tests. Subjects in the relevant node/RAA condition also made fewer tests and took longer to make their tests than subjects in the other conditions. The overall picture is that subjects in the relevant node/RAA condition were using elimination extensively, while subjects in the other four conditions used it only slightly above the levels expected due to chance.

Thus the experiment shows that in order to learn the elimination strategy in the network task, college students need explicit training that conveys both of the kinds of knowledge suggested by the model, domain-specific knowledge of how the nodes worked and knowledge of the general RAA strategy. The experiment supported the main conclusion based on the model - that learning elimination depends on the interaction of both domain-specific and general knowledge. Furthermore, not any kind of domain-specific knowledge will help. Only the key domain-specific knowledge highlighted by the model leads to increased use of elimination, when paired with the appropriate general strategy.

CONCLUSION

My initial question concerned how domain-specific and general-purpose knowledge interact to allow learning of problem-solving strategies in novel domains. Simulation modeling proved quite helpful in this research. It allowed precise identification of the kinds of domain-specific and general knowledge that might be involved in learning a particular troubleshooting strategy, elimination. The experiment supported the model and suggested that the general reductio-ad-absurdum strategy and certain key domain-specific knowledge, when learned together, substantially increase the use of the elimination strategy. The experiment reported here also provides empirical support for AI models such as SOAR, which suggest that problem-solving

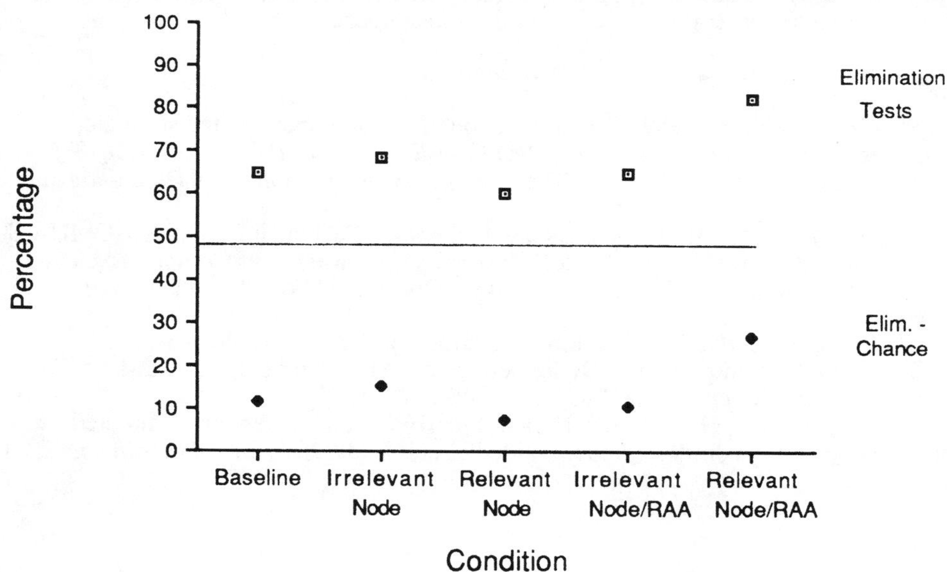

Figure 3. **Post-test use of elimination (adjusted means)**

strategies in a domain can be induced using domain-specific knowledge and very general problem-solving strategies (Laird & Newell, 1983). The students in this experiment were not taught elimination directly; rather, they induced it using domain-specific knowledge and RAA.

Because of the training design used in the experiment, this research can also suggest answers to educational questions concerning how general problem-solving strategies can be taught. One such question is whether general problem-solving strategies can and should be taught independently of domain-specific knowledge. This research argues against an extreme "independence" position, at least for the elimination strategy. Domain-specific knowledge was found to be essential to using the general RAA strategy to learn elimination.

Many avenues are open for further research. If research such as this is conducted on other strategies and other domains, we will begin to fill in the gaps in our understanding of how domain-specific knowledge and general strategies interact in problem solving. Also, one could address the question of whether the students who learned the elimination strategy in this experiment could transfer this knowledge to other domains. Elimination is a general-purpose strategy, which can be used in many kinds of troubleshooting tasks, such as computer-program debugging and medical diagnosis, as well as in searching for lost objects. Perhaps because these students induced the elimination strategy from more basic knowledge, they would have a deep understanding of it and thus be able to apply it in other domains.

This report is based on my dissertation, which was submitted to the Psychology Department at the University of Michigan. I would like to thank my doctoral committee for their help, and also Irving Sigel and Drew Gitomer for their comments on this report.

BIBLIOGRAPHY

Alexander, P. A. & Judy, J. E. (1989). The interaction of domain-specific and strategic knowledge in academic performance. *Review of Educational Research, 58(4),* 375-404.

Glaser, R. (1984). Education and thinking: The role of knowledge. *American Psychologist, 39(2)*, 93-104.

Laird, J. E. & Newell, A. (1983). A universal weak method. (Technical Report No. CMU-CS-83-141). Pittsburgh, PA: Carnegie-Mellon University, Department of Computer Science.

Perkins, D. N. & Salomon, G. (1989). Are cognitive skills context bound? *Educational Researcher, 18(1)*, 16-25.

Polya, G. (1957). *How to Solve It.* Princeton, NJ: Princeton University Press.

Rouse, W. B. (1978). Human problem-solving performance in a fault diagnosis task. *IEEE Transactions on Systems, Man & Cybernetics, SMC-8*, 258-271.

Stallman, R. M. & Sussman, G. J. (1977). Forward reasoning and dependency-directed backtracking in a system for computer-aided circuit analysis. *Artificial Intelligence, 9*, 135-196.

Representing Variable Information with Simple Recurrent Networks

Catherine L. Harris
Jeffrey L. Elman

Department of Cognitive Science
University of California, San Diego

ABSTRACT

How might simple recurrent networks represent co-occurrence relationships such as those holding between a script setting (e.g., "clothing store") and a script item ("shirt") or those that specify the feature match between the gender of a pronoun and its antecedent? These issues were investigated by training a simple recurrent network to predict the successive items in various instantiations of a script. The network readily learned the script in that it performed flawlessly on the non-variable items and only activated the correct type of role filler in the variable slots. However, its ability to activate the target filler depended on the recency of the last script variable. The network's representation of the script can be viewed as a trajectory through multi-dimensional state space. Different versions of the script are represented as variations of the trajectory. This perspective suggests a new conception of how networks might represent a long-distance binding between two items. The binding must be seen as not existing between an antecedent and a target, but between a target item and the current global state.

INTRODUCTION

Researchers interested in how networks might be used to model aspects of natural language have begun to explore the representational capacities of simple recurrent networks (Elman, 1988; Servan-Schreiber, Cleeremans, & McClelland, 1988). These networks are chosen for study because they require minimal assumptions about the structure of language data. If words of a language are represented as random binary strings presented one at a time to a network, then sentences are simply temporal sequences of words. Elman (1988; 1989) has shown that even as unassuming a task as that of predicting the next word in the sequence can result in the extraction of interesting regularities. Although the simplicity of SRN's (simple recurrent networks) places limits on their usefulness as realistic models of natural language, it is hoped that some of the principles governing their behavior will hold for more complex architectures, or architectures which include SRN's as sub-components.

The SRN used in the current work has three layers. On each time step, the pattern of activation on the middle ("hidden-unit") layer is *copied* to another bank of units called the context layer. On the next cycle, the context layer together with the input layer feeds the hidden units. Only the forward-feeding connections are modified during training. Although the SRN has immediate access to only the current word and to the preceding state, past work has shown that the hidden layer will often come to represent a condensed, prediction-relevant record of past items.

Previous successes with SRN's suggest two further avenues of investigation:

- It has been shown that SRN's can, with the right training environment, develop internal representations for a word which are sensitive to the word's sentential context. Under what circumstances (what types of patterns and training environments) would a network be motivated to color the representation of an item with aspects of the larger context, such as its position in a discourse?
- One feature of natural languages is that regularities exist between non-adjacent items. Examples are subject-verb agreement, the gender/number match between pronouns and their antecedents, and the relationship between script setting (e.g, "restaurant") and script entities ("waitress," "menu"). How do recurrent networks fare at extracting these long-distance relationships, and what representations do they construct in doing so?

The two questions do not have to be addressed together, but there are a number of reasons for exploring them at the same time. One is convenience: a script may be composed of sentences embodying a variety of linguistic regularities, some of which can include the long-distance relationships we are interested in. An additional reason is that some long-distance relationships, like the relationship between the gender of a pronoun and the gender of its proper-name antecedent, span sentence boundaries and thus are most naturally explored in the context of connected sentences.

INSTANTIATION OF SCRIPT VARIABLES

Connectionist models of language have yet to seriously confront the problem of how networks might represent variable bindings (Norman, 1986). Bindings such as those between pronouns and their world-referents require a mapping from one system (linguistic symbols) to another system (a representation of the referent world). The mapping between the name "Mary" and a specific individual in the world is a between-system regularity. But regularities also exist within a single representational system. For example, in the surface form of words, the gender of a name agrees with the gender of the pronoun.

By definition, SRN's can only capture regularities that exist within a single representational system. It is thus important to stress that they are not an adequate vehicle for exploring all of the complexities of the binding problem. Nevertheless, one important step is to understand what sequential co-occurrence regularities SRN's can capture and what representations they will construct in doing so.

The Script Skeleton

We began our exploration of the representation of script information and long-distance relationships by constructing the simplest type of script: a fixed sequence of items, where an item can be either a constant (an invariant item) or a variable. We used the following script skeleton:

person1 asked *person2* if *subj.pronoun2* wanted to go to a *place*
at the *place subj.pronoun2* saw a *thing1 subj.pronoun2* liked
subj.pronoun2 showed *person1* the *thing1* and asked *obj.pronoun1* if *subj.pronoun1* liked it
subj.pronoun1 told *person2 subj.pronoun1* liked the *thing1* but *subj.pronoun1* wanted to get a *thing2*

Selecting *Laura* and *Ralph* as the characters, and *restaurant* as the script yields:

Laura asked Ralph if he wanted to go to a restaurant
At the restaurant he saw a sandwich he liked
He showed Laura the sandwich and asked her if she liked it
She told Ralph she liked the sandwich but she wanted to get a salad

Four sets of script variables and 6 proper names were used to generate instantiations of the script skeleton.

Place	*Thing1*	*Thing2*
restaurant	sandwich	salad
furniture store	sofa	chair
clothing store	shirt	jacket
record store	record	tape

3 male names: Ralph, John, Jeff
3 female names: Mary, Sue, Laura

The variables, sixteen constant items, an end-of-sentence marker and an end-of-script marker added up to 40 lexical items. Items were represented as unique bits in a 40-bit vector, meaning that input and output layers contained 40 units. Scripts were constrained so that each passage contained a male and a female character, although which occurred first varied. All possible combinations of 4 scripts, 9 male-female combinations, and 2 orders (female first name or male first name) resulted in 72 different scripts. The 72 scripts were concatenated in a random order and joined to form a sequence of 3780 items. This sequence constituted the training set.[1]

Weights were changed after each presentation of an input-output pair. Training was stopped when the decrease in error was negligible. With a low learning rate (.01), this required about 600,000 presentations of an input-output pair.

NETWORK PERFORMANCE

Two aspects of network performance were examined.

- How well does the network solve the task of predicting the next word when the word is a variable compared to when the word is a constant?
- What internal representations are constructed in the service of this prediction task?

Ability to Activate the Correct Targets

Network performance on one instantiation of a script appears in Table 1. At each step in the sequence, the target output is shown, followed by all output units activated at greater than 0.20 ("threshold"). Blanks after a target word mean that no output reached threshold on this cycle. Activation values have been multiplied by 100.

[1] One idiosyncrasy is that three of the *place* names are composed of two words, while one ("restaurant") is a single word. This means that instantiations of the restaurant script will yield sequences of length 51 instead of 53. A second idiosyncrasy is that in the "record store" script, the name of thing1 is a repetition of a token in the place name.

TABLE 1: Activations for One Script Instantiation

	Target Output	Activated Outputs Units		Target Output	Activated Output Units
1	*Laura*		27	*sandwich*	24
2	asked	asked 93	28	and	and 90
3	*Ralph*		29	asked	95
4	if	if 93	30	**her**	**him** 46, **her** 42
5	**he**	**he** 70, **she** 23	31	if	if 94
6	wanted	wanted 92	32	**she**	**he** 26, **she** 75
7	to	to 97	33	liked	liked 93
8	go	go 86	34	it	it 89
9	to	to 96	35	end1	end1 98
10	a	a 93	36	**she**	**he** 50, **she** 47
11	*restaurant*		37	told	told 91
12	end1	end1 89	38	*Ralph*	
13	at	at 79, end2 25	39	**she**	**she** 80
14	the	the 88	40	liked	saw 20, liked 80
15	*restaurant*	*restaurant* 20	41	the	the 90
16	**he**	**he** 43, **she** 50	42	*sandwich*	*sandwich* 28, *sofa* 23, *shirt* 37
17	saw	saw 76, liked 24	43	but	but 85
18	a	a 97	44	**she**	**he** 48, **she** 31
19	*sandwich*	*sandwich* 21	45	wanted	wanted 97
20	**he**	**he** 56, **she** 32	46	to	to 97
21	liked	liked 91	47	get	go 31, get 73
22	end1	end1 88	48	a	a 96
23	**he**	**he** 72, **she** 41	49	*salad*	
24	showed	showed 91	50	end1	end1 93
25	*Laura*		51	end2	end2 87
26	the	the 97			

Activating constants. For all but four of the constant slots (slots 13, 17, 40, 47), only the target output unit was activated at greater than threshold. Note how the similarity in the sequences "*he/she* wanted to go/get" caused competition between two outputs in script position 47.

Activating proper names and script-entities. No proper names were activated in the script instantiation in Table 2 or in the rest of the corpus. The network was consistently mute at these slots in the script. Inspecting Table 1 might lead one to believe that the network did have some ability to activate the appropriate script entities. For example, *restaurant* and *sandwich* appear to be appropriately activated in 15 and 19. Sampling over a complete run through the 72 scripts of the training set revealed that the network always activated the appropriate category of filler (e.g., one or more of the *thing1* variables for a *thing1* slot). However, targets were not more reliably activated than non-targets.[2]

The difficulty in activating any class members for name slots, and in activating the target class member in the script variable slots, may be linked to the frequency of occurrence of the target items in the training set. A given proper name only occurred twice in one out of three instantiations, while *thing1* variables occurred slightly more frequently (three times in one out of four instantiations). The pronouns, on the other hand, were highly frequent variables in this training set. "He" and "she" each occurred four times per script instantiation. The network was more successful at activating pronouns than other variables. If an item appears infrequently during training, there will be few opportunities for the network to learn how to adjust the weights that will turn on the target unit in the output layer.

Activating pronouns. Comparing the relative activation of target and non-target pronouns in Table 1 shows that the network's ability to activate the target pronoun is limited. Pronouns occur in nine different script positions. Sampling over a complete run through the 72 scripts of the training set, it was found that in only three of these nine script positions (slots 5, 23, 39) was the network able to activate the target pronoun significantly better than the non-target pronoun.

Ignoring the script entities, the basic task of the network is to learn two variations on the script. In one variation, a male name occurs in the first name slot, dictating that the first four pronouns will be female and the remaining five pronouns slots will be male; in the second variation a female name occurs first. The network appears to need constant reminders of which of these two tracks it is on. For example, the reminder for the pronoun in position 44 is the pronoun in 39. What distinguishes the pronouns in slots 5, 23 and 39? The most recent reminder is either the current input (as in 39), or the immediately preceding item (5, 23).

Hidden Unit Analysis

A hierarchical cluster diagram of the 40 lexical items appears in Figure 1. Members of each variable class (*place, thing1, thing2*) are clustered together, suggesting that the network has extracted these type categories. (*Restaurant* may be grouped separately from the other place names because it is a one-word place name, rather than a two-word place name.) The male and female names are also clustered into separate categories, as one would expect if the network has discovered a correlation between these names and the values of pronoun slots. The tree's lack of balance and bushiness indicates that a number of items did not cluster into categories. For example, the two articles ("a" and "the") occurred in similar script positions, but were not similar to other items in the set. In general, the grammatical function words had such idiosyncratic environments that no abstract type could be extracted for them.

To better understand how the network carried information about pronoun identity forward from a cue like a proper name, we wanted a method of following the network's change of state over time. This was accomplished by reducing the dimensionality of the hidden unit layer by principal components analysis. Each input item activates a vector of 40 hidden units. By using the first two principal components of this vector, the state of the hidden-unit vector can be

[2] Why would *restaurant* and *sandwich* be actitvated regardless of what *place* name occurred in slot 11? In slot 42, why was *shirt* always most highly activated? One hypothesis is that at some point in training, these were the correct outputs, and the network slid down the error slope into a local minimum from which it was never able to emerge.

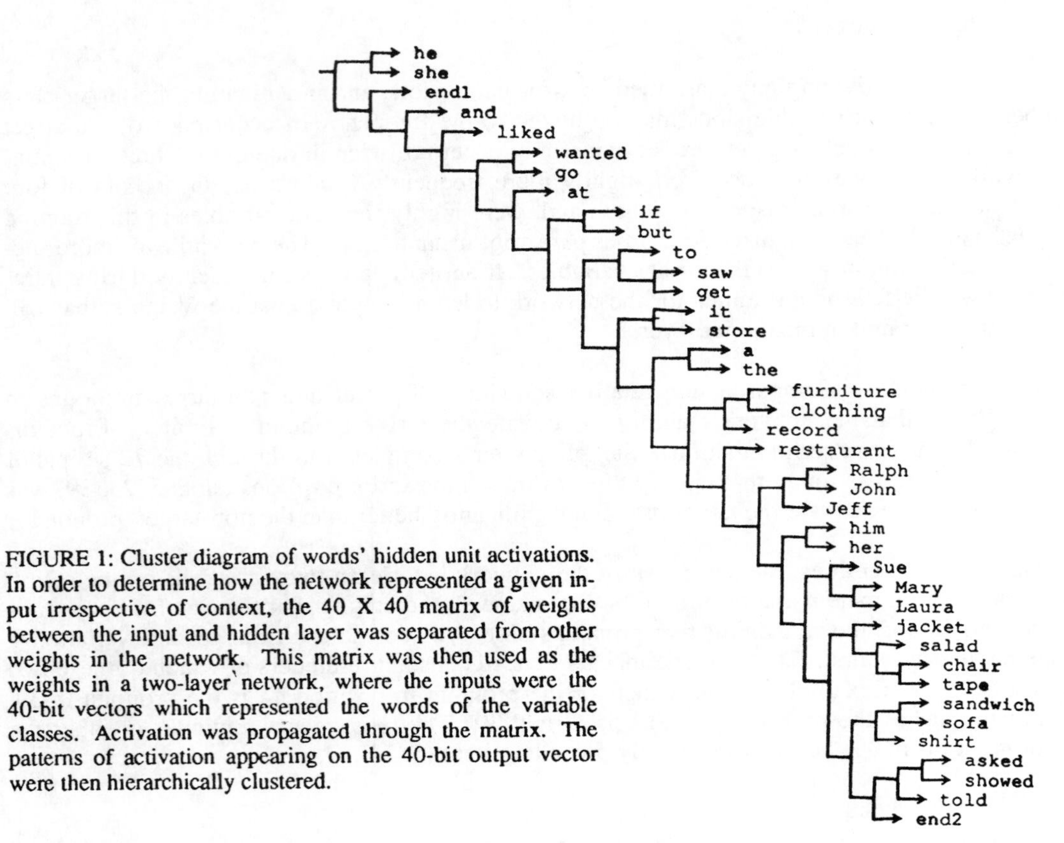

FIGURE 1: Cluster diagram of words' hidden unit activations. In order to determine how the network represented a given input irrespective of context, the 40 X 40 matrix of weights between the input and hidden layer was separated from other weights in the network. This matrix was then used as the weights in a two-layer network, where the inputs were the 40-bit vectors which represented the words of the variable classes. Activation was propagated through the matrix. The patterns of activation appearing on the 40-bit output vector were then hierarchically clustered.

approximated with a single point in a 2-D plot.

Figure 2 illustrates the state change in two versions of the first sentence of the skeletal script. The two versions are the two types of gender ordering, script setting held constant.

Following the trajectories from the starting point of "Laura" and "Ralph" one sees that the two versions are distinct early in the sentence. The difference in their paths becomes most marked immediately after getting the cue to gender ("Mary/John") and continues to be distinct through the first pronoun. The paths begin to come together after the fixed sequence "...wanted to go to a..." By the beginning of the next sentence (not depicted) the trajectories are identical. The paths diverge after receiving either "he" or "she" as input, collapse when "record" is encountered, and deviate again at the next pronoun. This good differentiation continues into the next sentence, which begins with a pronoun -- notably, one of the slots where the network was successful at activating the target pronoun (slot 23).

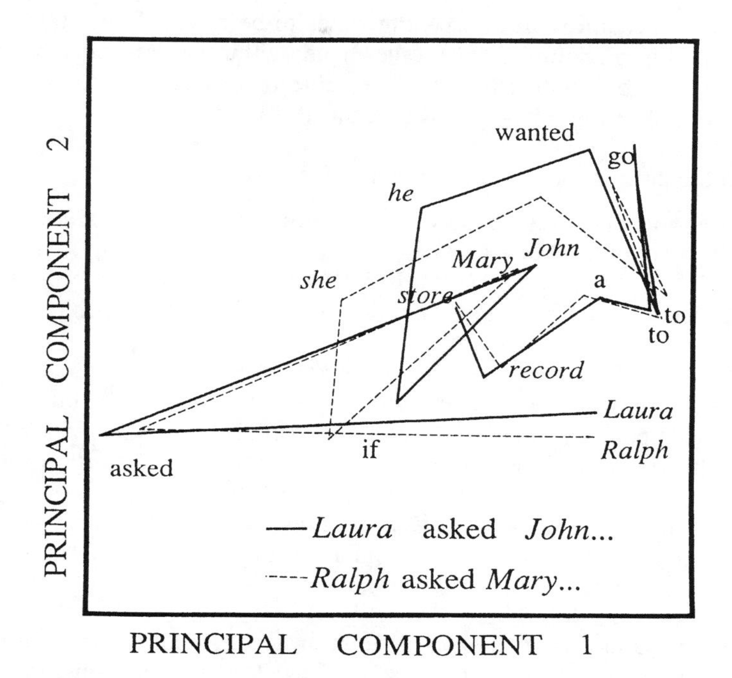

FIGURE 2: State change diagram for two versions of script sentence one. For a given state, labels indicate what word was the target. When versions had identical targets, only one label is given.

DISCUSSION

Studying how SRN's learn a skeletal script has allowed us to make the following observations about the properties of these networks:

- SRN's are good at extracting those distributional regularities which signal class membership. The current network did this even though the only clue to class membership was through co-occurrence relations with non-adjacent items. For example, the network learned that *thing2* variables form a class (Figure 3) even though the cue to class membership occurred 7 items previously.
- Although the network was able to construct long-term representations of the structure of the input, its ability to carry transient information about the value of a variable was limited. Information about the identity of a variable must be carried through the intervening items since the last cue. This information can be viewed as a path through state space. Information that the upcoming pronoun is to be a "he" will take the form of a slightly different trajectory than information that the upcoming pronoun is a "she."

To the extent that we want to view the rec net as having the ability to represent a long-distance relationship, we need to view the relationship as holding not between a temporally separated target and antecedent, but between the target and the current global state. This view is an intriguing one and merits further exploration. Nevertheless, the transiency of these relationships is sobering. It is difficult to imagine that speakers' ability to select the correct pronoun might be mediated by a mechanism which requires all intervening states to be flavored with information about the identity of the upcoming pronoun. On the other hand, within-system regularities may exist, such as subject-verb agreement, which might prove more amenable to modeling with a device capable of capturing only fleeting relationships (Elman, 1989).

Work in progress extends these preliminary findings in two ways:

- We examine what factors will encourage a network to construct a representation of items which is sensitive to script position. For example, for many stereotyped scripts, it is likely that generic verbs ("like," "see") and function words will not be sensitive to script position, while items which help define script structure ("menu," "eat," "pay") will acquire position-sensitive representations.
- What factors, beyond recency of last cue, influence the transiency of long-distance relationship? One possibility is that networks will have difficulty carrying information through parts of the script which have been poorly learned. For example, if the network never learns which *thing1* item to activate, then the *thing1* slot is a position of high error. Carrying information about gender through this high-error region could be problematic. Performance might be improved by changing the training regimen. Early in training, the network could be trained on sentences containing only dependencies between adjacent items. As these are mastered, non-adjacent dependencies could be added to the training set.

Viable connectionist models of natural language will require an understanding of the principles governing regularities *between* two representational systems as well as *within* a single representational system. Our long-term goal is to construct a model which maps between two systems. The contribution of the current work is that it explores some of the properties of a computational system that may eventually be a useful tool for achieving this goal.

REFERENCES

Elman, J. (1988). Finding structure in time. CRL Technical report 8801, Center for Research in Language, University of California, San Diego.

Elman, J. (1989). Structured representations and connectionist models. *Proceedings of the 11th Annual Cognitive Science Society Conference*. Hillsdale, New Jersey: Lawrence Erlbaum.

Norman, D. A. (1986). Reflections on cognition and parallel distributed processing. In J. L. McClelland and D. E. Rumelhart (eds.), *Parallel Distributed Processing, Vol. II*. Cambridge, MA: MIT Press.

Servan-Schreiber, D., Cleeremans, A., & McClelland, J.L. (1988). Encoding sequential structure in simple recurrent networks. Technical report CMU-CS-88-183, Carnegie Mellon University.

Device Representation for Modeling Improvisation in Mechanical Use Situations

Jack Hodges

Computer Science Department
University of California, Los Angeles

ABSTRACT

Improvisation requires an understanding and application of mechanical objects in broad contexts. The capacity to interpret a situation in terms of an object's capabilities requires the integration of functional and behavioral object representations. A model is presented which describes the integration of causal interactions between these levels of abstraction. The model maintains both intentional and behavioral representations to allow inferencing at each level, but integrates them by applying an inferencing mapping between the two. This model is used to reason about simple mechanical objects in the domain of improvisational mechanics.

INTRODUCTION

When people have to resolve problems involving mechanical objects in real-life situations, they must make decisions based on conflicting goals and constraints at both the functional and behavioral level[1]. Even though a problem-solver may recognize a behavioral advantage of one object over another, their higher-level personal goals may cause them to try objects based on functional capabilities. Consider the following example of improvisation where these differences lead to a goal failure:

Broken Knife

A man wants to polish one of his silver candlesticks. He must therefore pry open a can of silver polish in the kitchen, but doesn't want to brave winter weather to get a screwdriver from the garage. He reasons that he can use a screwdriver-like object and decides to try a carving-knife. What he doesn't realize is the knife is not strong enough in the dimension relevant for prying. The knife blade breaks.

There are many representational issues in **Broken Knife**, spanning the situational, intentional, functional and behavioral reasoning levels. At the situational level, planning choices are dictated by the relationships between the man and such contextual elements as the winter weather and objects available in the kitchen. On the intentional planning level, the man has chosen the POLISH-METALLIC plan to preserve his candlesticks. This plan requires that he have silver polish on his rag, a state which is blocked by the fact that the silver polish can is closed. Recognizing that the only resolution is to pry the can open, he realizes that the tool he usually uses for this function, a screwdriver, is in the garage. There is now a goal conflict: between his goal of preserving the candlesticks and his goal to preserve his own comfort.

Here the functional level becomes significant. A screwdriver works as a prying tool for the silver polish can because it fits into the slot between the can and lid and is strong in relation to the force necessary to pry open the lid. A carving-knife will fit into the slot and was strong enough for the functions that it was used for in the past. The knife therefore apparently matches the constraints for PRY-OBJECT, so the man uses it.

Finally there is the behavioral level. The knife is indeed strong, but only in the context of carving and along the width of the knife's blade. Along the thickness of the knife's blade, where the force of prying will be borne, the knife is not strong - not in relation to the friction force holding the lid onto the can. The knife blade therefore breaks.

We have been interested in modeling improvisation situations like **Broken Knife** in hopes of better understanding the creative process during problem-solving. Improvisation is a kind of invention where the problem-solver is constrained by circumstance. Improvisation thus encompasses the scope of EDISON, an on-going project to model the knowledge and reasoning of naive inventors, people whose knowledge and planning is based on experience rather than technical expertise [Dyer, Hodges & Flowers, 1986]. Our claim is that any approach to real-life problem-solving and decision-making must integrate each of the above levels of abstraction into a complete system. Previous object models have empha-

[1] Functional descriptions refer to the intended use of objects, as opposed to behavioral descriptions, which describe physical interactions between objects.

sized object representation at the functional or behavioral level, but none have integrated the two into a single representation and processing mechanism. EDISON has been designed to achieve this integration, and to support the associated multi-level reasoning.

REPRESENTING OBJECT FUNCTION AND BEHAVIOR

Intentional representation models have traditionally described objects with an emphasis toward their intended uses, while behavioral models have emphasized their behavioral capabilities. Each model type has been successful in its respective domain, but either could benefit from the capabilities of the other.

Intentional and Functional Object Models

Intentional object models, such as conceptual-dependency (CD) [Schank & Abelson, 1977], describe objects by an agent's intentions and how an object's function affects the outcome of those intentions (i.e. objects are black boxes). Using CD notation, the act of throwing a ball in a game of catch is represented by the thrower Propeling the ball toward the catcher while unGrasping it. The resulting state enables the ball to Ptrans from the thrower's location to the catcher's location. With this kind of model inferences can be made about the relationship between the people playing (e.g. "John threw the ball to Bill." vs. "John threw the ball at Bill."), but not about the ball involved (e.g. what if the ball never reaches Bill). This limitation presents a problem for predicting and explaining how plans are affected by object function and behavior.

Lehnert's object primitives [Lehnert, 1978] and Rieger's common sense algorithm (CSA) [Rieger, 1985] integrated object functionality into CD to describe how and when objects are used. These models introduced the idea of a functional representation level, between intentional and mechanical levels, which had properties found in both. Unfortunately, both models had weak behavioral representations and blurred the distinction between object function and behavior. They were therefore unable to take full advantage of their functional representations.

Behavioral Object Models

Behavioral object models describe objects' physical composition and interactions in lieu of their intended purpose or context. Instead of action primitives based on some form of agency, the primitives in behavioral models are simple qualitative physical process descriptions [Forbus, 1985] which describe objects and their interactions. The actor's Propel and Grasp actions (in a game of Catch) result in Force and Constraint states which enable the process, Transmit, of force to the ball. The ball unGrasping is paralleled by a Constrain process, and the resulting Force and Constraint states enable a Move process. Behavioral models are useful for predicting, explaining and simulating the ball's behavior (e.g. when the ball's weight, force and direction are known), but not for describing how or why it was thrown in the first place. Another problem with behavioral models is that they don't utilize contextual and intentional information for disambiguating, or predicting, object function during problem-solving.

Representing Objects In Edison

EDISON is an object-based representational model for reasoning about situations like **Broken Knife** by integrating object knowledge derived from intentional and behavioral points of view. The intentional part of EDISON'S bi-level model considers the object as an instrument to achieving specific goals in specific contexts. The behavioral part of EDISON considers the object and its behavioral dependencies with other objects. This integration is achieved by considering the structural continuity which must be maintained to support inferences between these abstraction levels, and by considering a third, *functional*, part which overlaps the intentional and behavioral abstraction levels and provides for a continuous inference path between them.

The objects described in EDISON are simple mechanical devices, such as screwdrivers, hammers, knives, can openers, and nail clippers. In EDISON, the representational emphasis is on the physical qualities and relations which support an object's functional description. Most of the reasoning in EDISON is done at higher levels, so the simulator is only used for diagnosis and explanation. This contrasts to detailed qualitative simulators, such as [Doyle, 1988], designed for this purpose. The EDISON model represents all objects as combinations of primitive devices (such as levers, springs, and wheels) which effect the leverage mechanism through the Transform process [Hodges, Dyer & Flowers, 1987. All object behavior can thus be described in terms of the transmission, translation, or magnification of force and motion.

Object *functions* refer to the tasks an object has been or could be applied to in a particular context, and have both intentional and behavioral qualities. Using a knife to carve turkey, to threaten someone, to tighten screws, or to pry can lids all describe knife functions. At the intentional level object functions describe this context sensitivity through *attributes*, which are qualities associated with an object's functional capability relative to other objects. For example, if we want to carve a turkey, then we need an object which has a *sharp* and *long* blade relative to the turkey.

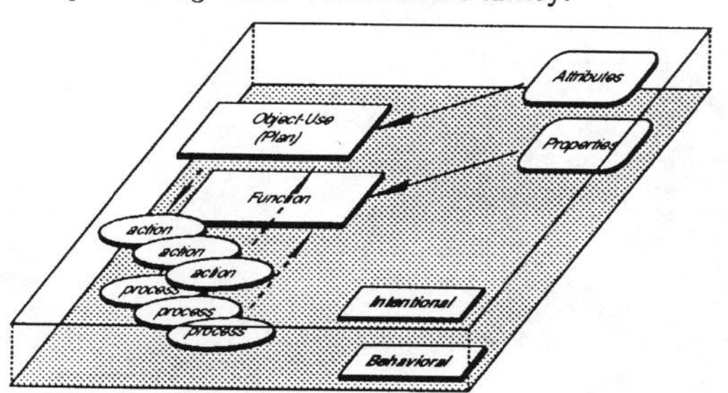

Figure 1: Knowledge structures and their causal relationships are isomorphic for intentional and mechanical representations.

An object's attributes direct planning choices in context by constraining applicable functions. At the behavioral level functions organize the processes (as process-state sequences) which effect the object's behavior. Processes are constrained by an object's physical properties and its relationships with other objects.

Intentional-Behavioral Representational Continuity

The relationship that object function plays in integrating intentional and behavioral models is depicted in figure 1. Whether viewed intentionally or behaviorally, the same object function is represented in a given situation. Each point of view provides different inferences about the object, so in EDISON the causal relationships are kept distinct. For example, in the game of catch we may want to make inferences about the ball Ptransing (such as why it was thrown), or its Moving (such as how and where it will go), depending on our goals. If we simply merge the representation levels one set of inferences is lost.

It is also important to remember that plans and functions in a given situation both describe the same behavior, but simply at different levels of abstraction. In EDISON these relationships are maintained by a structural isomorphism between intentional and behavioral knowledge structures. For example, consider the *plan-action-state* relationship which describes causality at the intentional level. This has a one-to-one correspondence with the *function-process-state* relationship at the behavioral level.

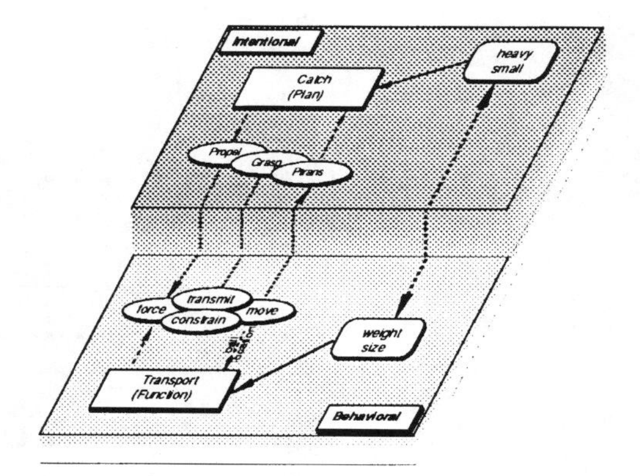

Figure 2: The bi-level representation for a game of catch shows the continuous, albeit separate, inference path between intentional and mechanical abstraction levels.

The bi-level model is designed to describe situations like the game of catch introduced above and depicted in figure 2. The intentional representation is shown on the upper level and the behavioral representation is shown on the lower level. The intentional description has a causal "gap" after the thrower's unGrasp action, whereupon the ball Ptranses to the catcher. The behavioral representation overlaps at this point, with the enabling and constraining conditions for the Transport function, and continues to describe the ball's behavioral path (paralleling the Ptrans action) until the Transport function terminates (i.e. the ball's motion ceases). The Transport terminating state is identical to the Catch plan's resulting state (arrival at the intended location). By integrating intentional and behavioral representations this way inferences can be made about object function and behavior not possible with either level alone.

Intentional-Behavioral Inference Continuity

There is a difference in generality between intentional and behavioral reasoning levels which, despite the structural continuity, obviates direct inferences between the two levels. However, because the same object is considered at both inference levels, its functions provide the necessary inference continuity through the associated constraining attributes and properties.

At the intentional level, attributes describe functional capabilities of an object learned through experience, and are specific to particular objects in particular contexts. Knowing the attribute enables high-level inferences about its functional capabilities if the context is reinstated. For example, knowing that a carving-

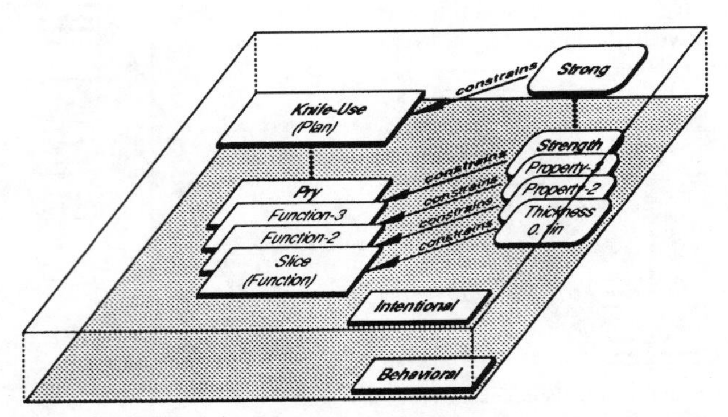

Figure 3: Functional attributes like *strong* are causally related to plan application through the constraints they place on object functionality. Likewise property values constrain the underlying processes. Different attributes will be associated with different situations, and different property values will support the associated functions.

knife was successful in transmitting force for carving a turkey, one might have concluded that the knife is a strong object (w.r.t. the turkey). The *strong* attribute of the knife is a relative term between like property values of the knife and bird, and is only valid for this situation. Other situations requiring *strong* objects, however, might remind the problem-solver of the carving-knife. Attributes thus affect planning, providing grist between context and a problem-solver's associated interpretation. Figure 3 depicts the relationship between different attributes, such as *strong* and *thin*, and how they constrain Knife-Use via the knife functions Pry-Object and Slice.

At the behavioral level the *strong* attribute is associated with the knife's value for the breaking-strength[1] property, which directly constrains the Pry-Object function's processes. Knowing the knife's value for breaking-strength guarantees inferences about its capacity to pry. The correspondence between the *strong* attribute and the breaking-strength property value enables inferences between levels. The difference between object functionality based on the attribute, *strong*, and that based on the property, breaking-strength, is that dimensionality (i.e. detail) is lost. If the problem-solver retrieves the knife based on the higher-level functionality (for example during planning), then the dimension of strength is unlikely to be remembered. In Broken Knife this leads to failure. However, the fact that a screwdriver was *strong* for its intended function for tightening screws, leads to an inference that it will be *strong* for other functions as well, such as prying a varnish-can or punching an oilcan for which it is an effective tool. If the knife's behavior is the basis for retrieval (for example during problem-solving experimentation), then dimension is remembered and predictions, inferences, or explanations can be made with confidence.

Attribute-Property Relationships

The ability to make correspondences between attributes and property values is important because of the different inferences that can be made at the functional and behavioral levels, respectively. If the correspondence is made, then the inferences can be compared and behavior modified. Each attribute defines a *range* in a property's quantity space. The two attributes, *light* and *heavy*, which describe the weight property of an object, illustrate a many-to-one relationship which is characteristic between attributes and property values. Many attributes are associated with object function through a specific property, such as *strong* to strength, or *long* to length. Attributes can also be described by combinations of properties or other attributes. The attribute *metallic*, for example, is described by the attributes *shiny, smooth, cold* and *hard*.

There are no exact correspondences between an attribute and its associated property value, since attributes are context-dependent. Nevertheless, some comparisons can be made based on how properties and attributes are represented. In EDISON property values are defined as (property, dimension, value) triples, and attributes as (property, reference) doubles. These relationships are illustrated in figure 4 for the carving-knife's *strong* attribute in **Broken Knife**.

[1] The equivalent force an object can withstand prior to failure.

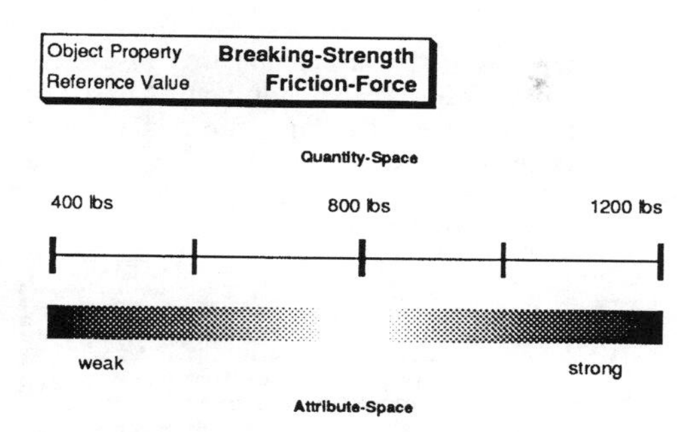

Figure 4: The attributes *weak* and *strong* illustrate the relative breaking-strengths (shown in pounds) of objects and their context dependency.

The attributes *weak* and *strong* map onto the material property describing breaking-strength. The numbered line segment in figure 4 represents a portion of quantity space describing breaking-strength values, with its central value being the Friction-Force attribute reference. There are two ways that attributes are referenced to property values in quantity-space:

1. To a known reference point or value (e.g. silver-polish can-to-lid friction force).
2. To a boundary value (e.g. the full-open position of a water faucet).

The reference point defines the context which an attribute is directly applicable, and is always found in the situational context. For instance, in **Broken Knife** the reference can be the can's or screwdriver's, breaking-strength, or the friction force between the Canlip and the Lidlip. Either way the knife is comparably weak. The shaded bars in figure 4 represent attributes, and show the variation of the terms *weak* and *strong* with respect to Friction-Force. The shading indicates the generalized relationship between what the man in **Broken Knife** knows about knife and can strength.

The attribute-property value relationship combined with the bi-level structural isomorphism provides a continuous inference path between intentional and behavioral levels of abstraction. If a situation exists in memory where a carving knife has successfully been used as a *strong* object, say to cut meat, then EDISON will likely try to use it again when the need for a *strong* object arises (e.g. in **Broken Knife**).

REASONING ABOUT OBJECTS IN CONTEXT

The **Open:varnish-can** situation shown in figure 5 illustrates the effect that attributes have at the intentional level. The associated property value and behavioral effects have also been depicted in figure 5, but a detailed description can be found in [Hodges, 1989]. At the intentional level varnishing a chair entails a number of preparatory steps, one of which is to get the varnish onto a paintbrush (a D-Cont goal). In figure 5 this step leads to a plan for opening the varnish can by prying the lid with the tip of a screwdriver.

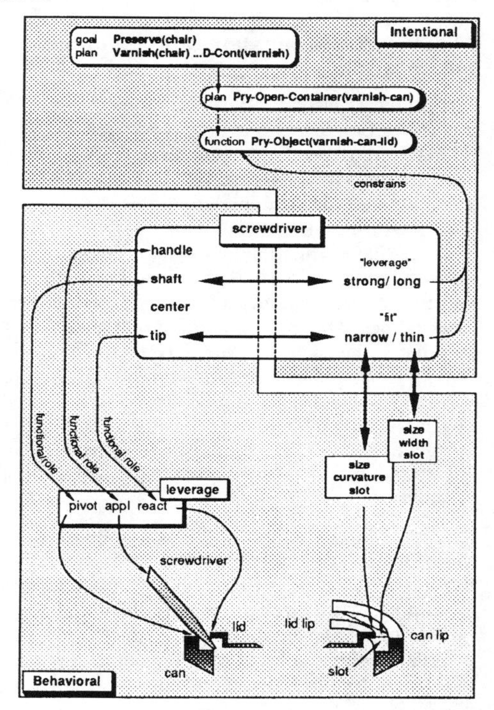

Figure 5: The attributes associated with "leverage" and "fitting" are instrumental in representing how a screwdriver is used to pry a varnish-can lid in **Open:varnish-can** by constraining its application. Attributes map both to object regions (such as handle, shaft and tip) and property values, which constrain functional interactions.

At the functional level the Pry-Object function is governed by two attribute groups, one for leverage and one for fit. The "leverage" requirement states that the screwdriver be *long*, so that sufficient mechanical advantage can be gained to overcome the friction holding the can and lid together, and *strong* so that it won't break under this force. The "fit" requirement states that the tip of the screwdriver must be *thin* and *narrow* compared to the slot between the canlip and lidlip, and constrains the Contact and Magnify processes in Pry-Object at the behavioral level. The leverage box in Figure 5 states that any object with regions of force application, pivot, and force reaction can be used to apply leverage. The screwdriver has these regions bound to its handle, shaft, and tip. In terms of prying these screwdriver regions are the only locations of interest. There are similar regions associated with the can (i.e. the lid, lidlip, can, and canlip). The regions on both objects are also used to define the attribute reference points for prying.

Bi-Level Representation and Situation Interpretation

The primary reason for describing object use at varying abstraction levels is to support different object interpretations depending on context. We want a representation model which describes how a screwdriver or knife is used as a utensil in one circumstance, a weapon in another, and a paperweight in a third. Each of these situations calls upon the same object property (weight), but with different required property values. Models that are context independent bar behavioral descriptions from addressing an actor's perspective in the same way that models that are context sensitive bar a functional description from making predictions about behavior. However, even when an object has only been used in a single context (such as using a carving knife for slicing), the attributes which enabled its functionality might enable its use in other contexts.

Knife breaking-strength provides a good example of this. Objects used to cut must be *strong* enough that they do not bend or break before the cut is completed. Of course, knife strength is only meaningful in the dimension of the intended cut. However, a person who naively uses a knife might generalize the extent of strength to all of its dimensions.

Figure 6 illustrates how **Broken Knife** is represented at the situational level. The upper window illustrates the information given. The lower window illustrates a number of situations where simple devices have been used in standard ways, and the attributes which constrain their functionality. The D-Cont goal to get silver polish onto a rag leads to an Open-Container plan. This information is provided to memory as a retrieval cue. The **Open:varnish-can** situation, where a screwdriver is used for prying, is the best functional match but conflicts with the man's P-Comfort goal. The result is that screwdriver-use, and screwdriver-related experiences, are unavailable for planning (with a screwdriver). This is shown with circle-ended dotted lines. The screwdriver attributes which are pertinent to prying are shared (situationally) with other devices (e.g. carving knife in **Slice:turkey**) which can be applied to the Pry-Object function. The **Flip:pancakes** situation is inappropriate because the spatula has attribute *broad*, which conflicts with the *narrow* attribute instrumental to Pry-Object. The carving-knife is also applicable based on availability, since the carving-knife resides in the kitchen setting of **Broken Knife**. The end result is a plan combining the Pry-Object function with the carving-knife object.

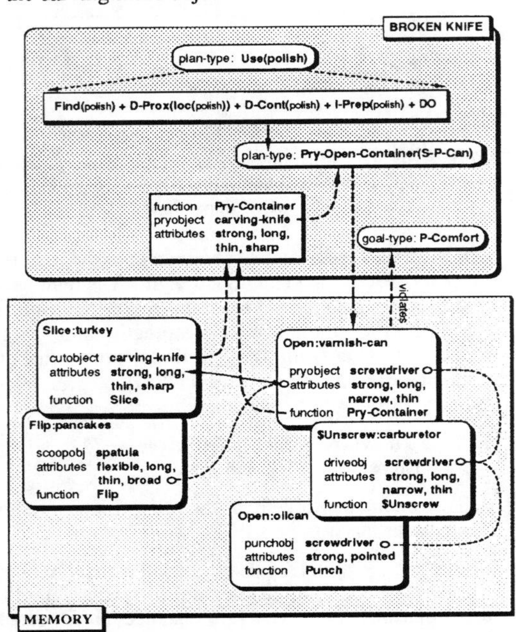

Figure 6: The **Broken Knife** situation illustrates situational interpretation of a carving knife based on its *strong* attribute. The Open-Container(S-P-Can) plan is indexed in memory to situations where objects have been used for opening. **Open:varnish-can** is strongly associated but cannot be applied directly because of a goal conflict. The screwdriver and carving knife share attributes instrumental to prying, so that an alternate Pry-Object plan using the carving knife can be applied to the situation.

A DETAILED EXAMPLE

The representation for the functional and behavioral inference paths in **Broken Knife** in figure 6 is fleshed out in figure 7. The behavioral description shown in figure 7 represents the process interactions supporting the Pry-Object function with the knife instantiated as the Pry-Object. The representation is shown instantiated with the carving knife after retrieval from memory and combination into the Pry-Object function. The attribute/property-value rela-

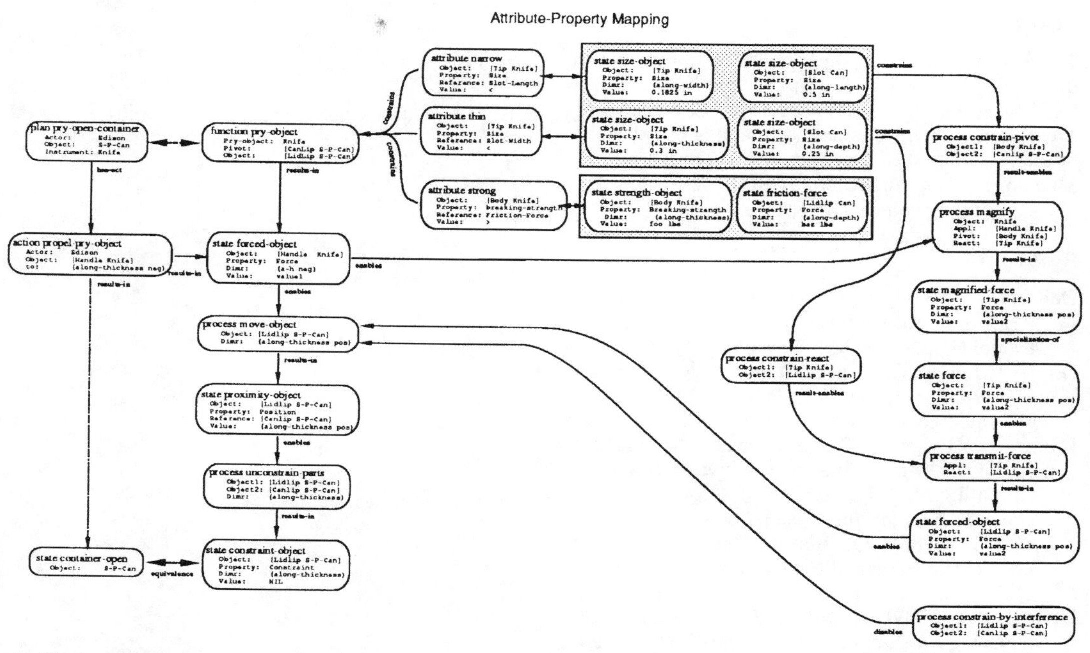

Figure 7: Functional-behavioral representation for **Broken Knife**. The attribute-property relationships constrain the Pry-Object function and the processes which comprise it. Attributes are associated with an object in context so the carving knife *strong*, *narrow* and *thin* attributes are associated with a retrieved situation, **Slice:turkey**. Some of the fillers illustrated (e.g. [Lidlip S-P-Can]) are simplifications of the actual representation.

tionship is shown as it affects the functional/behavioral description under the heading Attribute-Property Mapping. The *fit* requirement affects Pry-Object in two dimensions, so the comparison to size is made in two dimensions. The size values constrain the processes Magnify and Transmit-Force. The darkened two-way arrows between attributes and property values (states) represent a "many-to-one" link. The dashed and darkened two-way arrow between Pry-Object and Open-Container illustrates the inference cross-over between the functional and behavioral level.

The planning and interpretation involved in **Broken Knife** and the other situations illustrated in figure 6 are currently being implemented in ROBIN, a localist spreading-activation model of high-level inferencing [Lange & Dyer, 1989], which uses the DESCARTES connectionist simulator [Lange, Hodges, Fuenmayor, & Belyaev 1989]. In this implementation there will be equivalent inference paths for other devices which could be used as the Pry-Object filler, such as the candlestick itself. These inferences compete with the use of the knife through the spread of activation. The carving knife inference path will win out and be chosen as the plan for prying open the container, however, since its *strength* and *fit* attributes match the constraints on the Pry-Object role better than the other available objects.

CONCLUSIONS

Designing a knowledge representation model which supports the invention process requires an integration between intentional and behavioral object descriptions. The model must address how the environment and people's higher-level goals and intentions affect object choice during problem-solving, and how objects' properties support that functionality at the behavioral level. The bi-level representation used in the EDISON model provides the necessary integration and maintains the inferences from each abstraction level. The concept of attributes is introduced, and their relation to property values is discussed with respect to how they affect inferences between intentional and behavioral levels of abstraction.

Acknowledgements

This research has been supported by a contract with the Office of Naval Research, contract number N00014-86-0615. The author expresses thanks to Trent Lange for invaluable discussion and assistance in the preparation of this document. Thanks also to Michael Dyer, Colin Allen, and the anonymous reviewers for their editorial assistance.

References

DeKleer, J. & Seely-Brown, J.S. (1985): Qualitative Reasoning About Physical Systems, edited by Daniel G. Bobrow, MIT Press, pages 7-84.

Doyle, R.J. (1988): *Hypothesizing Device Mechanisms: Opening Up the Black Box*, MIT Artificial Intelligence Laboratory TR 1047.

Dyer, M., Hodges, J.B., & Flowers, M. (1986): EDISON: Engineering Design Invention System Operating Naively, *Journal of Artificial Intelligence in Engineering, Vol. 1 No. 1*, p. 36-44.

Forbus, K. (1985): Qualitative Reasoning About Physical Systems, edited by Daniel G. Bobrow, MIT Press.

Hodges, J.B. (1989): *Foundations for Creativity: Integrating Functional and Behavioral Object Representations for Problem-Solving*, Ph.D. Dissertation, Computer Science Department, University of California at Los Angeles (forthcoming).

Hodges, J.B., Dyer, M. G., & Flowers, M. (in press): Knowledge Representation for Design Creativity. In D. Sriram and C. Tong, editors, *Artificial Intelligence Approaches to Engineering Design*, Addison-Wesley, (in press).

Lange, T. & Dyer, M. G. (1989): Frame Selection in a Connectionist Model of High-Level Inferencing. *Proceedings of the Eleventh Annual Conference of the Cognitive Science Society (CogSci-89)*, Ann Arbor, MI, August 1989.

Lange, T., Hodges J., Fuenmayor, M., & Belyaev, L. (1989): DESCARTES: Development Environment For Simulating Hybrid Connectionist Architectures. *Proceedings of the Eleventh Annual Conference of the Cognitive Science Society (CogSci-89)*, Ann Arbor, MI, August 1989.

Lehnert, Wendy (1978): The Process of Question Answering. Lawrence Erlbaum Associates. Chapter 10.

Rieger, Chuck (1975): In *An Organization of Knowledge for Problem Solving and Language Comprehension*, Morgan Kaufmann, p. 487-508.

Schank, R. C. & Abelson, R. (1977): *Scripts, plans, goals and understanding*. Hillsdale, NJ: Lawrence Erlbaum Associates.

'Confirmation bias' in rule discovery and the principle of maximum entropy

Edward Hoenkamp
Computer Science Department
University of California, Los Angeles

ABSTRACT

In scientific research as well as in everyday reasoning, people are prone to a 'confirmation bias', i.e. they tend to select tests that fit the theories or beliefs they already entertain. This tendency has been criticized by philosophers of science as not optimal. The behavior has been studied in a variety of psychological experiments on controlled, small-scale simulations of scientific research. Applying elementary information-theory to sequential testing during rule discovery, this paper shows that the biased strategy is not necessarily a bad one, moreover, that it reflects a healthy propensity of the subject (or researcher) to optimize the expected information on each trial.

INTRODUCTION

The standard scientific paper backs up the presented theory with corroborating evidence, and does not discuss at length findings that could falsify it. This does not reflect a dishonesty on the part of the scientist but primarily that she found what she was looking for: once a theory takes shape, the scientist is prone to look for evidence that confirms rather than disconfirms the predictions. It has long been observed that in scientific research as well as in everyday reasoning people tend to test cases that confirm their currently held hypotheses or beliefs. This tendency is called 'confirmation bias', but is actually an aggregate of several distinct phenomena. Aside from behavior during rule-discovery, it ranges from biased reasoning in inference tasks, such as Wason's four-card problem [Wason & Johnson-Laird, 1972], to bias in social perception as studied by Snyder and Swann [1978]. It not only turns up in learning situations, but it is also an important factor in the perseverance of beliefs after evidential discrediting [Ross, Lepper, Hubbard, 1975; Hoenkamp, 1987]. This paper uses the term to mean the strategies people use to discover a rule governing a set of data. A thorough analysis of the phenomenon from a Bayesian perspective can be found in [Klayman & Ha, 1987], which contains some fine points not mentioned in the present article. Another Bayesian approach is [Fischhoff & Beyth-Marom, 1983], which emphasizes shortcomings in hypothesis evaluation. Since philosophers of science such as Popper [1962] and Platt [1964] stress the importance of seeking disconfirmation, there seems to be a discrepancy between what people actually do, and what they ought to do. This paper uses a measure of information to assess conditions for the appropriateness of these competing strategies.

EXPERIMENTS ON RULE DISCOVERY

Wason [1960] designed an experiment to study how people behave when their beliefs about a rule are corroborated. Subjects were told that they had to guess a rule governing a number triple, and that 2-4-6 conformed to this rule. They were to figure out this rule by proposing other number triples. After each one the experimenter would tell whether it conformed to the rule. If the subject announced a rule, the experimenter would tell her whether it was correct. The rule the experimenter had in mind was 'increasing numbers'.

The following protocol typifies the trend of subjects to generate number triples expected to confirm their hypotheses [Wason & Johnson-Laird, 1972]. The '+' or '-' is used by the experimenter to indicate correctness.

2-4-6 (+) given. 8-10-12 (+) two added each time. 14-16-18 (+) even numbers in order of magnitude. 20-22-24 (+) same reason. 1-3-5 (+) two added two preceding number. Announcement: 'starting with any number two is added each time' (incorrect). 2-6-10 (+) middle number is arithmetic mean of other two. 1-50-99 (+) same reason. Announcement: 'middle number is the arithmetic mean' (incorrect). 3-10-17 (+) same number, seven, added each time. 0-3-6 (+) three added each time. Announcement: 'the difference between two numbers next to each other is the same' (incorrect). 12-8-4 (-) same number subtracted each time. Announcement: 'adding a number, always the same one' (incorrect). 1-4-9 (+) any three numbers in order of magnitude. Announcement: 'any three numbers in order of magnitude' (correct).

This experiment has been replicated many times with simple to very intricate variations. Some researchers tried to induce a tendency to falsify [Mynatt et al., 1977; Tweney et al., 1982], or used a broader rule [Gorman & Gorman; 1984]. Others worked with groups [Gorman, Gorman, Latta, Cunningham, 1984]. Domains other than number triples have been used; Mynatt et al. [1977] simulated a universe on a computer screen, where subjects had to find the rules that governed the deflection of particles near objects. Kern [1982] used an imaginary planet, and subjects had to locate the place where creatures landing on the planet would stay alive. Time and time again the tendency to confirm showed up. And it seems representative for scientists' actual behavior, as was found by Mitroff [1974] who interviewed scientists at NASA before the first Apollo moon landing. Given that this proclivity is so pervasive, the question is: are people really doing it the wrong way? To find an answer we have to investigate if, or under what circumstances, there exists an optimal test strategy.

CHOOSING AN OPTIMAL TEST STRATEGY

There are at least two ways in which a strategy for sequential testing could be optimal [Tweney et al., 1981]. To decide which of two strategies is optimal, one could take the one that best complies with an established criterion for rationality, such as Popper's falsification principle. Or one could opt for the most efficient one (in terms of time, money etc.). The two criteria are independent, but if the most efficient strategy turns out the more successful on average, the established criterion is immaterial. But how can we quantify the efficiency of a strategy? I define a strategy to be the most efficient if the expected cost of testing is minimal. If every test costs the same, our goal would be to minimize the number of tests. Consequently, we want each test to be as informative as possible. But wait, informative as possible for what purpose?

Suppose a subject in Wason's task proposes a triple 10-12-14 to test 'subsequent even numbers'. Wason sees this as a confirmatory strategy. The concept is confusing however: the triple confirms the subject's rule, but it could disconfirm the experimenter's rule. In his criticism of Wason, Wetherick [1962] uses the term *positive test* for this case. A triple 1-3-5 to test 'subsequent even numbers' would then be a negative test, which in contrast could be confirmed by the experimenter. I will call a positive test strategy one that relies on positive testing to investigate a hypothesis (analogously for 'negative test strategy'). Klayman and Ha [1987], using the same distinction, investigate which strategy has the highest probability of falsifying the hypothesis. This is much in line with Popper's [1962] principle to strive for falsification: accumulating confirmatory evidence cannot prove a theory correct, but one falsification is enough to show the theory is incorrect. However, as other philosophers have shown [Kuhn, 1970; Feyerabend, 1975], scientists will not abandon their theories, but instead make changes to their theories that will account for the new findings. To understand this behavior, we should not look for test strategies that are most likely to show a theory is flawed. Instead, we should look for one that shows where the flaws are located, so as to make optimal changes. I will stay with the concepts of positive and negative test strategies, but compare them not by their probability to falsify, but by the information they provide per test.

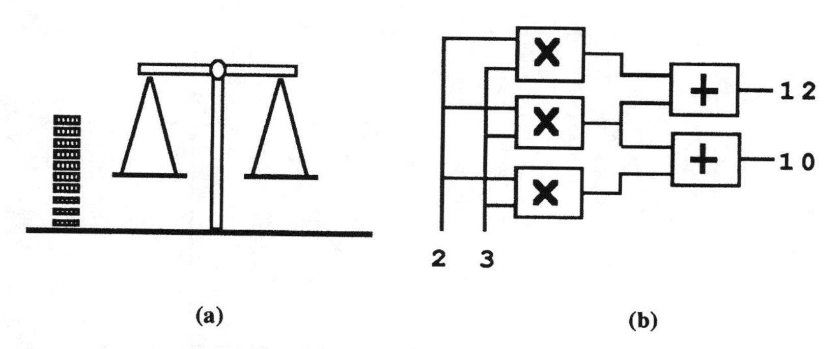

Figure 1. Two examples of sequential testing. **a.** Nine coins, one of which is lighter or heavier than the others. Determine this one in the least number of weighings. **b.** For the given three multipliers and two adders, make the minimum number of measurements to determine the malfunctioning component(s).

INFORMATION CONTENT OF A TEST

To measure the information content of a test, I will borrow concepts from information theory. We denote the possible outcomes a_i of an experiment with their probabilities p_i as the finite scheme A:

$$\begin{bmatrix} a_1 \; a_2 \ldots a_n \\ p_1 \; p_2 \ldots p_n \end{bmatrix}, \text{ e.g. for a 'true die' the scheme would be } \begin{bmatrix} 1 & 2 & 3 & 4 & 5 & 6 \\ \frac{1}{6} & \frac{1}{6} & \frac{1}{6} & \frac{1}{6} & \frac{1}{6} & \frac{1}{6} \end{bmatrix}.$$

The information contained in such a scheme is called entropy. For the finite scheme A above, the entropy is defined as:

$$\mathcal{H}(p_1, p_2, \ldots, p_n) = -\sum_{i=1}^{n} p_i * \log(p_i) \qquad (x1)$$

The entropy can be viewed as the uncertainty taken away after the outcome of the experiment becomes known. Consequently, if one of the probabilities is 1, the entropy is 0, since in that case the outcome is certain. Now, if a choice can be made among several different schemes, the one with maximum entropy reduces the most uncertainty. Figure 1 shows two applications of this idea to sequential testing. For example, in figure 1a the choice is among the numbers of coins to be put in each pan. (For example, to maximize the entropy on the first step, one has to put 3 coins in each pan). Another example is the proposal by De Kleer and Williams [1987] for diagnosing multiple faults in electronic circuits (see figure 1b).

The concrete examples above can be generalized to optimizing test strategies in general. Suppose a scientist (or a subject) generates an hypothesis to describe phenomena in some domain D. Let us denote the intended phenomena as T (target), and the set described by the hypothesis as H. Figure 2 shows the four possible locations of a new observation. The figure depicts the general case, but the reader can think of the 2-4-6 task as an example.

The black arrows show that the new observation may end up in either $H \cap T$, in which case the hypothesis is corroborated, or in $H \cap T^c$, and then the hypothesis is falsified. The positive and negative strategies can be represented as the following schemes for some p^+ and p^-:

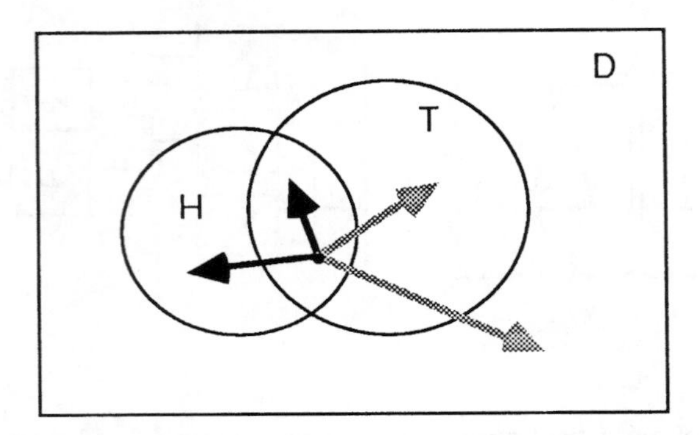

Figure 2. The places where the new observation may lie. H and T are the hypothesized set and the target set in domain D. The black and grey arrows indicate the positive and negative test strategies respectively.

$$S^+ = \begin{bmatrix} H \cap T & H \cap T^c \\ p^+ & 1-p^+ \end{bmatrix} \quad \text{and} \quad S^- = \begin{bmatrix} H^c \cap T & H^c \cap T^c \\ p^- & 1-p^- \end{bmatrix}$$

The p^+ and p^- can thus be written as the conditional probabilities $p^+ = P(T/H)$, and $p^- = P(T/H^c)$, with H^c to denote the complement of H. In comparing both strategies, a few qualitative remarks can be made. First, a scheme may contain no information at all, namely if one of the probabilities equals 1 (since then the outcome is certain). This is the case if p^+ or p^- equal 1 or 0. But note, there is an overlap between H and T containing the element(s) of T used to formulate H in the first place. This leaves $p^-=0$ and $p^+=1$ to consider. If $p^-=0$ then H includes T. In other words if the hypothesis is too general, a positive strategy is more efficient than a negative. For $p^+=1$, T contains H, and so in that case a negative strategy is better (we will come back to this).

A second observation is that both strategies contain the same maximum information (of 1 bit). $\mathcal{H}(S^-)$ depends on p^-, and thus on the size of the domain, whereas $\mathcal{H}(S^+)$ depends on the overlap of H and T only . All in all, it may be that the positive strategy is not as bad as it might have looked. How good or bad it is quantitatively, will be discussed in the next section.

COMPARING THE INFORMATION CONTENT OF BOTH STRATEGIES

To investigate under precisely which circumstances a positive strategy is the more efficient, i.e. produces the most information per test, the following inequality can be solved:

$$\mathcal{H}(S^+) > \mathcal{H}(S^-)$$

according to definition (x1) this means that

$$-(p^+ * \log(p^+) + (1-p^+) * \log(1-p^+)) > -(p^- * \log(p^-) + (1-p^-) * \log(1-p^-))$$

Using the property that $p*\log p + (1-p)*\log (1-p)$ is a convex function on [0,1] symmetric around .5 this simplifies to $p^- < p^+ < 1-p^-$, or equivalently

$$\frac{p^+}{p^-} > 1 \qquad \text{(x2)}$$

and

$$p^+ + p^- < 1 \qquad (x3)$$

Let's take a closer look at (x2). According to Bayes' rule, updating the probability of a hypothesis H upon receiving datum T satisfies

$$\frac{P(H/T)}{P(H^c/T)} = \frac{P(T/H)}{P(T/H^c)} * \frac{P(H)}{P(H^c)}$$

Writing out the fraction in formula (x2) as $P(T/H)/P(T/H^c)$ shows it is the likelihood ratio (the second term) in Bayes' rule. If this ratio is greater then 1, the datum is called diagnostic. So to rephrase formula (x2): for a positive strategy to be optimal, the target elements must be diagnostic for the hypothesis. At the end of the paper I will return to the relative merits of both conditions.

Noisy data. The experiments that make up most of the literature, are based on error-free feedback. Outside the laboratory the situation is often far from that ideal. Does this have an influence on which strategy should be preferred? In the rule-discovery tasks discussed here it means that the subject receives a 'correct' where an 'incorrect' would be in place and vice versa. In the presence of error, a strategy has to be chosen that maximizes information per test *on average*. In terms of information-theory what we have is a noisy channel of a particular kind (a binary symmetric channel) over which the feedback is sent. Given that enough tests can be performed and that the error-rate is less than .5, the actual feedback can be recovered (using an optimal coding scheme). Interestingly enough, under these circumstances the scheme that maximizes the information in the error-free case also maximizes the average information in the presence of error. It follows that the inequalities (x2) and (x3) remain valid.

It should be noted that formula (x1) can be derived from three very simple and plausible axioms [Khinchin, 1957], such as that adding impossible events to the scheme doesn't change the entropy[1]. So the results in this paper depend only on the acceptance of those axioms, and the cost function for sequential testing. Yet, as the next section will show, several interesting psychological findings can be easily understood this way.

APPLICATIONS OF THE THEORY TO EXPERIMENTAL FINDINGS

Recall that we are talking about tasks in which successive tests are needed for a discovery, and that reducing the number or the cost of tests is achieved by choosing a strategy that maximizes the entropy on each trial. We shall now see how an assorted sample of observations can be explained in this manner[2].

Wason's 2-4-6 induction task. As we saw before, in this task, the subject starts with a hypothesis (subsequent even numbers) that is a subset of the experimenter's rule (increasing numbers). In this case $P(T/H)=1=p^+$, so that inequality (x3) is not satisfied, and therefore a negative strategy is be preferable. This is exactly what the experiment showed.

The 'first confirm later disconfirm' strategy [e.g. Gorman & Gorman, 1984]. In rule-discovery tasks, the successful subject usually starts with a positive strategy, and later shifts more to a negative strategy. Suppose a set C of observations has been confirmed for hypoth-

---

[1]The other two are: the entropy is maximal if all probabilities are equal, and the entropy of two schemes equals the entropy of the first plus the expectation of the second given the outcome of the first.

[2]Which only shows how difficult it is to exorcise confirmation bias.

esis H. If the tester is not simply replicating observations, the p^+ has then decreased[1], namely from the initial P(T/H) to P(T/H-C), while p^- remains the same. After a while inequality (x2) will not be fulfilled any longer at which point the tester should switch to a negative strategy.

The 'win-stay, lose-shift' strategy. Studies in concept identification have shown that once learners have a hypothesis about reinforced responses, they will stick to that hypothesis even if later other responses are also reinforced. The hypothesis is changed only if falsifying information is encountered [Trabasso & Bower, 1968]. The rule cannot be true in general. The maximum entropy for S^+ occurs for $p^+=.5$. And as we have seen just before, p^+ decreases for an S^+, so the suggestion is justified if $p^+ > .5$, i.e. if more than half the hypothesis set is in the target. Indeed, this restriction holds in the cases discussed by Trabasso and Bower [1968].

Positive strategies work better for groups. Condition (x2) states that for a positive strategy to work the target elements must be diagnostic for the hypothesis. There is considerable literature about people's neglect in using the likelihood ratio in evaluating probabilities [Kahneman, Slovic, Tverski, 1982]. However, Trope and Bassok [1982] showed that diagnosticity is a major determinant in people's preference for a particular information-gathering strategy. That is, if given the opportunity to compare, they opt for the hypothesis with the highest diagnosticity. So one can expect if a group of people, such as a scientific team, generates various hypotheses, the one with highest diagnosticity will be recognized. In that case it seems probable that one satisfying (x2) will occur, and therefore will prevail. Indeed, groups using positive strategies are better in a rule-discovery task[2] than individuals [Gorman, Gorman, Latta, Cunningham, 1984].

A negative strategy doesn't work if the rule is too general. If T grows to cover a larger part of D, $\mathcal{H}(S^-)$ decreases. In other words, if the rule becomes more general the negative strategy will give less and less information per trial. This may explain the finding on a variation of the 2-4-6 task. Gorman and Gorman [1984] used two more general rules besides the 'ascending numbers', namely 'at least one even number' and 'no two numbers can be the same'. They indeed found that even subjects who were encouraged to use S^- were not successful in discovering the rule.

Feedback in the presence of noise. In most experiments the feedback is error-free. But as mentioned before, conditions (x2) and (x3) remain valid in the presence of error, if the subject (or researcher) is allowed to perform many tests. Two things change subject's behavior, however. First, the information per test is lower, so more tests have to be performed. Second, an optimal coding scheme requires that tests have to be replicated. Given that a positive strategy is appropriate, this should induce long stretches of positive tests. Kern [1982] asked subjects to partake in a computer simulation where creatures had to be placed on an imaginary planet. They had to discover a line on one of which sides the creatures died. She found that if the feedback was random on a proportion of the trials, a strong positive testing tendency ensued. A strong tendency to replicate was found in [Gorman, 1986], confirming the need for replications in the face of noise.

Klayman and Ha's approach. In the Bayesian approach taken by Klayman and Ha [1987], the preferred strategy is the one most likely to falsify the hypothesized prediction. In their formalization this means that the positive strategy is preferable precisely if $P(T^c/H) > P(T/H^c)$,

---

[1] Except for the degenerate case where $p_c=1$.

[2] The task was 'Eleusis' in which a rule governing the appearance of playing cards had to be discovered.

i.e. 1-P(T/H) > P(T/H^c), which is equivalent to inequality (x3). Klayman and Ha show that the inequality holds under realistic circumstances. In other words, people's positive strategy is very often appropriate. Their approach, however, misses inequality (x2), and thus leaves unexplained the phenomena mentioned above that depend on it. In addition, (x3) didn't have to be postulated, it follows automatically under the plausible assumption that a good strategy optimizes the cost of sequential testing. It would be interesting to design an experiment where (x3) holds, and (x2) doesn't. The prediction is that a positive strategy would give the highest probability for falsification, whereas a negative one would produce the best information to change the theory.

CONCLUSION

This paper compared people's actual behavior in a rule discovery tasks with the behavior they should exhibit according to some canon of rationality. It did so by describing people's discovery behavior as sequential testing for which the total cost of the trials has to be optimized. The paper showed that under that criterion, and given realistic circumstances, a positive strategy is often the best one. The derived conditions were shown to explain the degree to which people are successful in rule-discovery tasks in a spectrum of experimental settings. At the same time they may suggest variations on the task (such as changing the diagnosticity of the target).

Little attention has been paid in the psychological literature to other strategies of inquiry (but see [Tukey, 1986] for an exception). The next step in this research therefore is to analyze the relative merits of such strategies in the way it was done in the present paper for positive and negative strategies. If this also leads to the formulation of new conditions (analogous to (x2) and (x3)), this may suggest experiments that shed additional light on people's modes of inquiry.

Acknowledgements

This work was supported by a grant from the Netherlands Organization for Scientific Research (NWO), during a sabbatical leave from NICI, Nijmegen, the Netherlands. I'm grateful to Hector Geffner, Charles Wharton, Vicky Breckwich, Claudia Lange, and Trent Lange for comments on an earlier version of the paper.

REFERENCES

De Kleer, J. & Williams, B. (1987). Diagnosing multiple faults. *Artificial Intelligence,* 32, 97-130.

Fischhoff, B. & Beyth-Marom, R. (1983). Hypothesis evaluation from a Bayesian perspective. *Psychological Review,* 90, 239-260.

Gorman, M. (1986). How the possibility of error affects falsification on a task that models scientific problem solving. *British Journal of Psychology,* 77, 85-96.

Gorman, M. & Gorman, M. (1984). A comparison of disconfirmatory, confirmatory and control strategies on Wason's 2-4-6 task. *The Quarterly Journal of Experimental Psychology,* 36A, 629-648.

Gorman, M., Gorman, M., Latta, R., Cunningham, G. (1984). How disconfirmatory, confirmatory and combined strategies affect group problem solving. *British Journal of Psychology,* 75, 65-79.

Hoenkamp, E. (1987). An analysis of psychological experiments on non-monotonic reasoning. *Proceedings of IJCAI-87,* 115-118.

Kahneman, D., Slovic, P., & Tverski, A. (1982). Judgment and uncertainty: Heuristics and biases. New York: Cambridge UP.

Kern, L. (1982). The effect of data error in inducing confirmatory inference strategies in scientific hypothesis testing. Unpublished PhD thesis. Ohio State University.

Khinchin, A. (1957). *Mathematical foundations of information theory*. New York: Dover.

Klayman, J. & Ha, Y-W. (1987). Confirmation, disconfirmation, and hypothesis testing. *Psychological Review,* 94, 2, 211-228.

Kuhn, T. (1970). *The structure of scientific revolutions*. (2nd edition). Chicago: University of Chicago Press.

Feyerabend, P. (1975). *Against method*. London: Verso Editions.

Mitroff, I. (1974). Norms and counter-norms in a select group of the Apollo moon scientists: A case study of the ambivalence of scientists. *American Sociological Review,* 39, 579-595.

Mynatt, C., Doherty, M. & Tweney, R. (1978). Consequences of confirmation and disconfirmation on a simulated research environment. *The Quarterly Journal of Experimental Psychology,* 30, 395-406.

Popper, K. (1962). *Conjectures and refutations*. New York: Basic Books.

Platt, J. (1964). Strong inference. *Science,* 146, 347-353.

Ross, L., Lepper, M. & Hubbard, M. (1975). Perseverance in self-perception and social perception: Biased attributional processes in the debriefing paradigm. *Journal of Personality and social psychology,* 32, 880-892.

Snyder, M. & Swann, W. (1978). Hypothesis-testing processes in social interaction. *Journal of Personality and social psychology,* 36, 1202-1212.

Trope, Y. & Bassok, M. (1982). Confirmatory and diagnosing strategies in social information gathering. *Journal of personality and social psychology,* 43, 22-34.

Tukey, D. (1986). A philosophical and empirical analysis of subjects' modes of inquiry in Wason's 2-4-6 task. *Quarterly Journal of Experimental Psychology,* 38A, 5-33.

Tweney, R., Doherty, M., Worner, W., Pliske, D., Mynatt, C. (1980). Strategies of rule discovery in an inference task. *Quarterly Journal of Experimental Psychology,* 32, 109-123.

Tweney, R., Doherty, M., Mynatt, C. (1981). *On scientific thinking*. New York: Columbia UP. Introduction to chapter IV.

Trabasso, T. & Bower, G. (1968). *Attention in learning*. New York: Wiley.

Wason, P. (1960). On the failure to eliminate hypotheses in a conceptual task. *The Quarterly Journal of Experimental Psychology,* 12, 129-140.

Wason, P. & Johnson-Laird, P. (1972). *Psychology of reasoning: Structure and content.* Cambridge: Harvard UP.

Modeling of User Performance with Computer Access and Alternative Communication Systems for Handicapped People

Heidi M. Horstmann, M.S. and Simon P. Levine, Ph.D.

Rehabilitation Engineering Program
Department of Physical Medicine and Rehabilitation
University of Michigan

ABSTRACT

Disabled individuals who cannot use a standard keyboard require a special interface in order to use a computer. The GOMS model is used here to quantitatively evaluate three interfaces currently used in computer access systems for handicapped people. Each interface uses a row/column scanning technique for letter selection, and two of the interfaces employ word prediction in an attempt to improve text input rate. Techniques for modeling these interfaces are presented, and the resulting predictions for performance time, learning time, and working memory requirements are discussed. The models predict that the systems with word prediction actually have lower performance than one that allows only single letter selections. Factors contributing to this result include additional mental operators required for use of the word predictive interfaces and an insufficient probability of successful word prediction.

INTRODUCTION

The personal computer has tremendous potential for improving the functional abilities of physically and cognitively disabled individuals. Some of this potential has already been realized, and many new educational, vocational, and recreational opportunities have opened up for disabled individuals through the use of the computer. For a computer to be useful to disabled individuals, alternatives to the computer's hardware or software must often be developed. For example, a disabled user who cannot physically use the standard keyboard must have an alternative means of accessing the computer, referred to as a computer access system. In addition, use of the computer as an alternative communication aid for people who cannot speak requires a special user interface design, similar to that of a computer access system.

This paper addresses issues surrounding the design of these user interface alternatives. The GOMS (Goals, Operators, Methods, Selection Rules) model (Card, Moran, & Newell, 1983) is used to quantitatively describe and predict user performance for three interfaces currently used in computer access and alternative communication systems for handicapped individuals.

BACKGROUND

Handicapped individuals with physical impairments may need an alternative to the standard keyboard for computer access. The exact nature of the physical impairment determines what type of physical input technique is used (e.g., single switch, expanded keyboard). This in turn determines the physical component of the user's "typing" rate. Some users may have cognitive and/or perceptual impairments as well, which affect the mental component of their performance.

There are many communication and computer access aids that are either commercially available or in the final stages of testing, with more packages being developed each year. These incorporate a wide range of physical input methods, such as expanded keyboards, head pointing devices, and breath-controlled switches. In addition, a variety of methods designed to enhance rate, such as symbolic encoding, abbreviation expansion, and word prediction can be used. Unfortunately, developers' publications give only minimal attention to an analysis of their design goals and design decisions. Analyses of these issues that do exist focus almost exclusively on physical efficiency, without considering the mental load on the user in a rigorous or quantitative way (Goodenough-Trepagnier et al., 1982; Rowley, 1987).

METHODS

The GOMS Model

The GOMS model was developed by Card, Moran, and Newell (1983), and refined by Polson and Kieras (1985), among others (1986). The user's behavior is represented by a sequence of elementary steps (called "Operators") defined by the goals of the user and the constraints of the task. The final model is a list of statements that represent the Goals, Methods, Operators, and Selection Rules to provide a complete model of the user's behavior in pursuit of the overall goal, specifying each required step in the proper sequence.

The GOMS model can be used to predict both learning and performance times, as well as points of excessive long or short term memory load. These predictions can then be used during the design process to estimate the consequences of particular design decisions, or to compare the performance of a proposed design to alternative systems. Several studies, most of which use text editing as the paradigmatic task, have demonstrated that the GOMS model provides a good description of user behavior and predicts task performance time and learning time with reasonable accuracy (Card, Moran, & Newell, 1983; Polson & Kieras, 1985; Ziegler, Hoppe, & Fahnrich, 1986).

Estimation of Performance Time

The first step in predicting overall performance time for a task is to identify all possible ways in which the task can be achieved, represented by paths through the GOMS model. Each path is defined by statements in the model that are executed when the user follows the path. The execution time for a given path is estimated by summing the times required to execute each individual statement (Card, Moran, & Newell, 1983). The statement times are estimated as follows: one cognitive cycle time per statement plus any Operator time required for statement execution, (e.g., key-hit time, decision-making time), as determined by the analyst.

The overall performance time estimate is the weighted average of individual path times, based on the probabilities of individual path execution during general system use. In the case of the systems modeled here, the overall performance time is the text generation rate, and the individual paths are the different methods used to select letters or words.

Estimation of Learning Time

The empirical formula used to estimate learning time is the sum of 30 minutes for baseline learning time, 30 seconds for each statement in the model, plus any additional memorization time (Kieras, 1987). If two or more statements describe very similar or identical operations, they are counted only once to account for learning transfer gains. Long term memorization time is estimated as 10 sec/chunk of information memorized (Kieras, 1987).

Working memory storage requirements

The GOMS model provides a means of estimating the number of information chunks in working memory at any given time as well as the storage time between retention and retrieval for each chunk. The number of statements that must be executed between retention and retrieval yields an estimate of the necessary storage time for that information (Kieras, 1987).

Alternative Input Systems Modeled

Each of the three computer access interfaces modeled is designed for use by a severely disabled user who can activate only one or two switches. The standard row/column scanning interface consists of a letter matrix that is scanned automatically to allow the user to make a selection using a single switch. The user waits for the system to highlight a particular row, then hits the switch to select the row. The system then highlights successive letters in that row, until the user hits the switch again to select the desired letter. The letters are arranged in order of overall frequency of occurrence (Dabbagh & Damper, 1985), as shown in Figure 1, so that the letters with the highest frequency of use require the fewest number of scan steps for selection. This arrangement stays fixed which simplifies user memorization of letter position. Text is generated by selecting each letter from the letter matrix one by one.

The other two interfaces modeled add word prediction to simple letter scanning in an attempt to improve user performance. These systems exploit the redundancy of the English language in order to predict the user's desired word, thereby reducing the number of physical actions required of the user (Gibler & Childress, 1982). It is assumed that the predictive interfaces use the same letter matrix arrangement described above.

sp	E	A	R	D	U	V
T	O	I	L	G	K	
N	S	F	Y	X		
H	C	P	J			
M	W	Q				
B	Z					

FIGURE 1. Standard row/column letter matrix

The first predictive interface studied is a slight variation on the PACA system, developed at Northwestern University (Heckathorne & Leibowitz, 1985). The first two letters of every word are selected using standard single-switch row/column scanning. When the second letter is selected, the letter matrix is replaced by a list of the seven most likely words that start with the two selected letters. If the desired word is not in the first prediction list, the user can select a second prediction list and subsequently choose a word or return to row/column scanning.

The second predictive interface analyzed is the PAL system, developed at the University of Dundee, Scotland (Arnott et al., 1984). The major differences between it and the PACA system are that both its ten-word list and letter matrix are on the screen at the same time, and predictions are made even before a letter is selected and are refined as subsequent letters are selected. If a word is in the prediction list the user hits one switch to initiate one-dimensional scanning of the word list; if not, a second switch initiates row/column scanning of letters.

GOMS Models for the Three Interfaces

Standard row/column scanning. The GOMS model for the standard row/column scanning interface contains seven statements. The only selection path using this interface is a single letter selection from a static two-dimensional letter matrix requiring execution of all seven GOMS statements.

The PACA System. The GOMS model for the PACA system contains 29 statements. There are four possible paths through the PACA system model:

1. Single letter selection for first or second letter of each word.
2. Single letter selection following an unsuccessful search of both prediction lists.
3. Word selection when word is found in first prediction list.
4. Word selection when word is found in second prediction list.

The PAL System. With the PAL system, if the user searches the prediction list after every letter selection, there are only two possible selection paths, as follows:

1. Letter selection after deciding that the desired word is not in the prediction list. (T_1)
2. Word selection when the desired word is found in the prediction list. (T_2)

However, if the word is not present in the prediction lists after the 3rd letter selection, it is assumed that the user does not search the subsequent prediction lists and will select individual letters.

Model Input Parameters for Model Simulation. The first step in comparing system performance times is to establish a set of nominal parameter values to use in the performance prediction equations for each system. The parameters are:

Basic Processor Times
- cognitive cycle time
- perceptual cycle time
- motor cycle time

Operators
- switch hit
- word-found
- selection-is letter or word
- 1st-or-2nd-letter-of-word
- at-least-4th-letter-of-word
- search list for word
- decide if text is complete

System Parameters
- system scan rate
- ave. no. of letters/word
- ave. no. of scans/word selction
- prediction success parameters

Values for the cognitive, perceptual, and motor Processor times are taken from basic human information processing research (Card, Moran, & Newell, 1983). All three values can be estimated at 0.1 seconds for people without cognitive, perceptual, or motor impairments. These values were used for initial simulation trials as they also represent a wide range of disabled users whose cognitive, perceptual, and motor times (for operating one or two switches) is identical to able-bodied individuals. Time required to hit the switch can be modeled as a simple reaction time, taking one cognitive cycle and one motor cycle, or 0.2 sec.

All except one of the mental Operator times are estimated by determining the relative number of component Processor times. The text-complete Operator is one that cannot be readily subdivided into component Processor cycles. Therefore, a value of 1.35 seconds was used, taken from Card, Moran, and Newell's study (1983) of the generic **M** operator.

The minimum scan rate can be set at the time it takes to perceive a letter on the display and match it to an image of the desired letter plus the switch hit time, or 0.4 sec. Five letters/word was chosen as the nominal estimate for simulation trials (Goodenough-Trepagnier et al., 1982). An estimate of one-half the number of words in the prediction list is used as the nominal value for the number of scan steps/word selection. Overall prediction success parameters for PACA and PAL systems were based on developers' estimates of 70% prediction success (Arnott et al., 1984; Gibler & Childress, 1982).

RESULTS

Performance Time

The results of simulation trials to predict overall text generation rate using the nominal parameters values are shown in Figure 2. The predicted rate for the standard R/C system is 3.58 words/minute (wpm), with the PAL system at 3.16 wpm and the PACA system at 2.92 wpm. These simulation trials predict that the standard R/C scanning system is faster than the predictive interfaces.

Dependence on Number of Letters/Word

Figure 3 shows the predicted text generation rate for each system plotted against the number of letters/word, **L**, when it is varied from 4.5 to 6 and all other parameters are kept at nominal values. The standard R/C system is much more sensitive to changes in **L** than either of the predictive interfaces. This is because the standard R/C system has only one selection path so the number of letters/word is the same as the number of selection loops executed. With the predictive interfaces, a change in **L** affects only those selection loops in which the final letters of a word are individually selected (approximately 30% of the time).

Dependence on Prediction Parameters

The overall proportion of words in the dictionary (70%) can be subdivided into the distribution of words among the prediction lists. For the PACA system, $\mathbf{w_1}$ and $\mathbf{w_2}$ are the probabilities that a word is on the first or second word lists, respectively, given that the word is in the dictionary. Even with $\mathbf{w_1} = 1.0$, indicating that all words in the dictionary are presented on the first word list, the estimated rate is only 3.01 wpm. For the PAL system, $\mathbf{x_i}$ is the probability of successful word prediction following selection of the **i**th letter. When $\mathbf{x_1}$ and $\mathbf{x_2}$ are varied together from 0.25 to 0.40, the largest estimated rate is 3.22 wpm at $\mathbf{x_1} = \mathbf{x_2} = 0.40$.

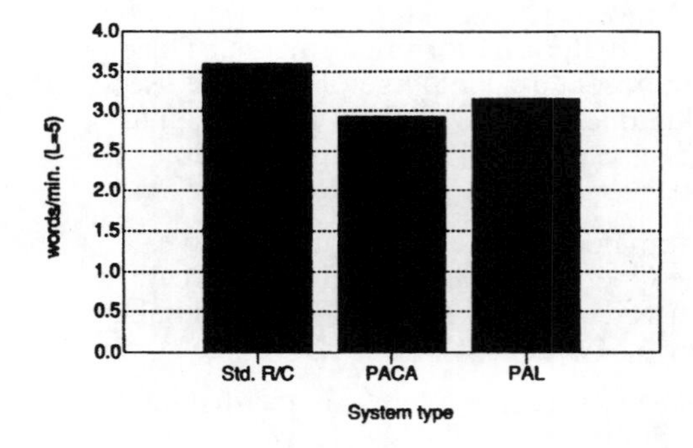

FIGURE 2. Estimated rates using nominal parameters

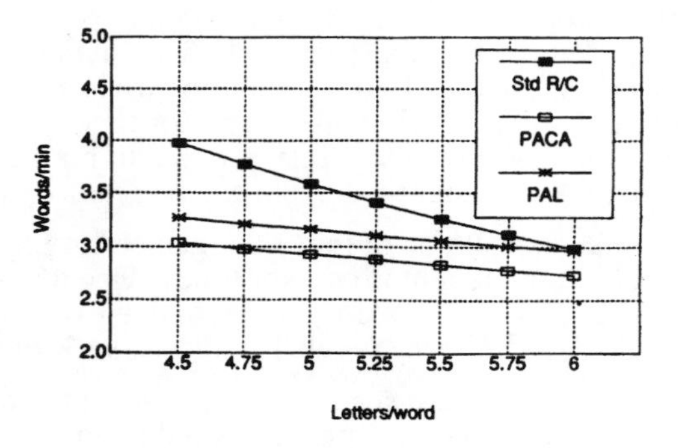

FIGURE 3. Estimated rates as functions of letters per word.

Learning Time Requirements

The GOMS model for the standard row/column scanning interface predicts a basic operational learning time of 33.5 minutes. The time required to memorize the 27 letter locations can be estimated at 22.5 minutes for a total learning time of 56 minutes. The PACA system operational learning time estimate is 43 minutes, and the memorization learning time 23.8 for a total of 66.8 minutes. The PAL system operational learning time estimate is 45.5 minutes, and the memorization learning time 22.5 for a total of 68 minutes.

Working Memory Requirements

None of the systems modeled here places excess demands on working memory capacity or retention time. The largest amount of storage required at any one time is three chunks, which is safely below the five chunk limit suggested by Kieras, and all required retention times are less than one second (Kieras, 1987).

DISCUSSION

Performance Time

Performance time refers to the time it takes to perform the overall task. In the case of an alternative input system, the overall task is to generate text to be spoken in a conversation or used as input to an application program. The ideal case is for the disabled user to approach rates achieved by able-bodied individuals, typically 35 - 40 words/minute for typing and 100 - 200 wpm for speaking. These are unrealistic for a single switch scanning system. The minimum acceptable rate should be above 3 wpm because at rates below this point, conversation breaks down due primarily to the receiver's impatience (Goodenough-Trepagnier et al., 1984). Goodenough-Trepagnier et al. (1984) have shown that receivers' impatience decreases markedly at a rate of 5 wpm, which makes this rate a reasonable target for a minimally acceptable rate.

The preceding GOMS analysis provides estimates of performance time for each system under a variety of conditions. The surprising overall result of this analysis is that none of the three interfaces approaches 5 wpm using nominal parameter values, even though user parameters correspond to those of an able-bodied user. In addition, the two predictive interfaces are at a consistently slower rate than the standard R/C system, with the PAL system somewhat faster than PACA, under almost all conditions.

There are three main factors that contribute to the estimated slowness of the predictive interfaces. First, the number of statements to be executed in use of the predictive interfaces is much greater than the mere 7 statements used in the standard R/C system; this reflects the relative complexity of the predictive systems. Second, use of the predictive systems requires additional mental operators, such as visual search time and word-found matching, which increase the overall text generation rate. Third, the relatively poor predictive ability of the PACA and PAL systems contributes to the slow rate estimate.

The proportion of words present in the dictionary is crucial to text generation speed with predictive interfaces. It should be noted that a major feature of both the PACA and PAL system is that the dictionary contents change dynamically based on the user's word usage. This feature may significantly increase the proportion of words present in the dictionary over time with a resulting increase in text generation rate. This is a user-specific system feature that cannot be easily modeled with the GOMS model. However, the GOMS model can be used to develop criteria for the proportion of words needed to be found in the dictionary in order to achieve a predefined performance level.

Learning

System learning time should be as short as possible, since systems that are difficult to learn will be less acceptable to the target user. Rubinstein and Hersh (1984) propose a "10 minute rule" as a criteria for learning the basics of a system. This may be impossible to achieve as some published estimators of learning time use a base learning time of at least 30 minutes (Polson & Kieras, 1985). A more reasonable design requirement for learning time may be to combine these for a total of 40 minutes.

None of the estimates for the three modeled interfaces meets this design requirement, with the closest being standard R/C scanning at 56 minutes. The two predictive systems have basically the same estimated learning times, at roughly 68 minutes. Note, however, that the estimated learning times include 22.5 minutes for memorization of the 27 letter matrix positions. Memorization of these positions is not essential for use of any system. Therefore, the time required for this memorization can be subtracted from the estimated learning time to give an absolute minimum learning time estimate.

Future Work

This research represents an initial stage in the development of a model that has the potential to become an extremely important tool in the design and prescription of computer access and communication aids for disabled people. The results presented here raise the question as to whether word prediction interfaces, developed as a faster alternative to row/column letter scanning, are actually less efficient than the row/column scanning interface. The model also provides insight into the reasons for this surprising result. First, an overall word prediction success of 70% does not provide enough word selection opportunities to counteract the mental overhead involved in using the more complicated predictive interfaces. Second, when a word is selected, the length of the average word is too short to provide enough switch hit savings.

The quantitative validity of these results is dependent upon the accuracy of the GOMS model descriptions and input parameters. Therefore, one direction for future research is to study the behavior of actual users to determine the validity of the GOMS model predictions.

If previous validation of this approach for analysis of text editing is assumed to carry over to the present application then further sensitivity analysis of input parameters can be expected to yield at least qualitative information about the value of one approach over another. By modeling various techniques common to many different systems, criteria can be developed for system optimization (e.g., determine efficacy of a linear vs. binary search strategy). Future work with the GOMS model is well justified by the potential benefits of an accurate model for human performance with an alternative input scheme for computer operation.

REFERENCES

1. Arnott, J.L., Pickering, J.A., Swiffin, A.L., & Battison, M. (1984). An adaptive and predictive communication aid for the disabled exploits the redundancy in natural language. *Proc 2nd Internat Conf Rehabil Tech*, Washington, D.C.: RESNA, 349-350.

2. Card, S., Moran, T., & Newell, A. (1983). *The Psychology of Human-Computer Interaction*. Hillsdale, NJ: Erlbaum Associates.

3. Dabbagh, H.H. & Damper, R.I. (1985). Average selection length and time as predictors of communication rate. *Proc 8th Ann Conf Rehabil Tech*, Washington, D.C.: RESNA, 404-406.

4. Gibler, C.D. & Childress, D.S. (1982). Language anticipation with a computer based scanning communication aid. *Proc IEEE Computer Society Workshop on Computing to Aid the Handicapped*, New York: IEEE, 11-15.

5. Goodenough-Trepagnier, C., Rosen, M.J., & Demsetz, L. (1982). Determinants of rate in communication aids for the non-vocal motor handicapped. *Proc 26th Ann Meet Human Factors Society*, 172-175.

6. Goodenough-Trepagnier, C., Galdieri, B., Rosen, M.J., & Baker, E. (1984). Slow message production rate and receivers' impatience. *Proc 2nd Internat Conf Rehabil Tech*, Washington, D.C.: RESNA, 347-348.

7. Heckathorne, C.W. & Leibowitz, L.J. (1985). PACA: Portable anticipatory communication aid. *Proc 8th Ann Conf Rehabil Tech*, Washington, D.C.: RESNA, 329-331.

8. Kieras, D.E. (1987). *A Guide to GOMS Task Analysis*. University of Michigan.

9. Polson, P.G. & Kieras, D.E. (1985). A quantitative model of the learning and performance of text editing knowledge. *Proc Comp Human Interface Conf*, 207-212.

10. Rowley, B.A. (1987). RPM for accessing large vocabulary files. *Proc 10th Ann Conf Rehabil Tech*. Washington, D.C.: RESNA, 165-167.

11. Rubinstein, R. & Hersh, H. (1984). *The Human Factor*. Bedford, MA: Digital Press.

12. Ziegler, J.E., Hoppe, H.U., & Fahnrich, K.P. (1986). Learning and transfer for text and graphics editing with a direct manipulation interface. *Proc Comp Human Interface Conf*, 72-77.

FOCUSING YOUR RST: A STEP TOWARD GENERATING COHERENT MULTISENTENTIAL TEXT

Eduard H. Hovy[1]
Information Sciences Institute of USC

Kathleen F. McCoy[2]
University of Delaware

Abstract

In multisentence texts, the order and interrelationships of sentence topics is of crucial importance if the reader is to understand easily. What makes paragraphs coherent? What strategies do people employ to control the presentation order and linking of material? Without a theory of coherence, text generation systems have little hope of producing acceptable texts. While various theories of text coherence have been developed, no single theory captures all the phenomena of human-generated paragraphs. In this paper we argue that the coherence of a paragraph does not result from the application of a single theory, but instead results from the cooperation of a number of different coherence strategies. We illustrate this claim by showing how two very different theories about the planning of coherent text — 1) Rhetorical Structure Theory, based on structural and semantic relationships that hold between pieces of the text, and 2) Focus Trees, based on how the focus of attention shifts during discourse — can be used within a single system to complement each other to best advantage.

1 Introduction

In multisentence texts, the order and interrelationships of sentence topics is of crucial importance if the reader is to understand easily. But what makes a paragraph, and by extension, a text, coherent? By what strategies do people control the presentation of material so as to develop their ideas intelligibly? Without answers to these questions, text generation systems have little hope of producing acceptable paragraphs. Various theories of text coherence have been developed (e.g., see [Hobbs 78, Reichman 78, Cohen 83, Mann & Thompson 88]), each based on valid but quite different considerations. Unfortunately, no single theory suffices to define coherence well enough to compare with paragraphs written by people. An adequate theory of text planning must incorporate several coherence strategies under one framework. Care must be taken that the text planner give proper preference to the most effective coherence strategy at each step in the process, lest its effect be precluded by an independent decision.

In this paper we discuss two strategies that contribute greatly to the planning of coherent texts: Rhetorical Structure Theory and Focus Trees. Rhetorical Structure Theory (RST) [Mann & Thompson 88] provides coherence to a text based on structural considerations about the rhetorical relationships that hold between adjacent pieces of a paragraph. Focus Trees [McCoy & Cheng 88] provide coherence to a text based on anticipated shifts in the focus of

[1]This author was supported in part by the Advanced Research Projects Agency under DARPA contract MDA903-87-C-641, and by AFOSR contract F49620-87-C-0005.

[2]This author was partially supported by UDRF Grant #LTR870112.

attention of the participants as the text proceeds. We first introduce these notions and illustrate how each is individually useful yet underconstraining to a generation system whose aim is to produce coherent multisentential text. Finally, we show how these two theories can be combined in a single text planning system that uses both strategies effectively. While we do not argue that combining these two methods into one system fully solves the coherence problem, we believe that it is a step toward a complete solution. We expect that ultimately other sources of guidance will have to be incorporated, and that the text planning methodology advocated here is general enough to support them.

2 Rhetorical Structure Theory and Coherence

The Penman project at ISI has been investigating the planning of coherent multisentential paragraphs of text by computer. The planner, a top-down hierarchical expansion planning system patterned on NOAH [Sacerdoti 77], uses plans which are operationalizations of some RST relations from Rhetorical Structure Theory [Mann & Thompson 88], which posits that approximately 20 relations suffice to relate adjacent blocks of text in the ways English speakers consider coherent. The planner is described in [Hovy 88a, Hovy 88b]. It operates antecedent to the natural language generator Penman [Mann & Matthiessen 83].

The text structure planner plans coherent paragraphs to achieve communicative goals to affect the hearer's knowledge in some way. It accepts one or more communicative goals along with a set of clause-sized inputs from the domain of discourse to be generated as an English paragraph. The planner assembles the input entities into a tree that expresses the paragraph structure. The nonterminals in the tree are RST relations while the terminal nodes contain the clause-sized inputs. Finally, the planner traverses the tree, dispatching the leaves (the input entities) to be generated by Penman.

The planner embodies a limited top-down hierarchical expansion planning framework. Figure 1 shows a typical relation/plan in this formalism. Each relation/plan has two parts, a *nucleus* and a *satellite*, and recursively relates some unit(s) of the input or another relation (cast as nucleus) to other unit(s) of the input or another relation (cast as satellite). In order to admit only properly formed relations, nuclei and satellites contain requirements that must be matched by characteristics of the input. In addition, nuclei and satellites contain growth points: collections of goals that suggest the inclusion of additional input material. On finding (an) RST relation/plan(s) whose effects include achieving (one of) the system's communicative goal(s), the planner searches for input entities that match the requirements holding for each of its parts. If fulfilled, the planner then considers the growth points of each part of the relation/plan. It tries to achieve each newly instantiated growth point goal by again searching for appropriate relation/plans and matching them to the input, recursively, adding successfully achieved goals to the paragraph tree structure. The planning process bottoms out when either all of the input entities have been incorporated into the tree or no extant goals can be satisfied by the remaining input entities. The tree is then traversed in a depth-first left to right manner, and the relation/plans' characteristic cue words or phrases are added to the appropriate input entities and transmitted to Penman to be generated as English clauses.

Up until now, the paragraphs produced by the system relied on a very important assumption about the growth points: their presence and order were treated as injunctions. That is to say, the structure planner always tried to achieve every growth point goal in the order given. As shown in [Hovy 88b], treating growth points this way is equivalent to using the relation/plans as schemas — structures that mandate the content of a paragraph-sized block of text [McKeown 85]. Though useful for many constrained applications, schemas do not support well systems that seek to exhibit dynamic and adaptive behavior. Since we are attempting to build such systems, we have

Figure 1: The RST relation/plan SEQUENCE

```
Name: SEQUENCE

Results:
  ((BMB SPEAKER HEARER (SEQUENCE-OF ?PART ?NEXT)))

Nucleus requirements/subgoals:
  ((AND (BMB SPEAKER HEARER (MAINTOPIC ?PART))
        (BMB SPEAKER HEARER (NEXT-ACTION ?PART ?NEXT))))

Nucleus growth points:
  ((BMB SPEAKER HEARER (CIRCUMSTANCE-OF ?PART ?CIR))
   (BMB SPEAKER HEARER (ATTRIBUTE-OF ?PART ?VAL))
   (BMB SPEAKER HEARER (PURPOSE-OF ?PART ?PURP)))

Satellite requirements/subgoals:
  ((BMB SPEAKER HEARER (MAINTOPIC ?NEXT)))

Satellite growth points:
  ((BMB SPEAKER HEARER (ATTRIBUTE-OF ?NEXT ?VAL))
   (BMB SPEAKER HEARER (DETAILS-OF ?NEXT ?DETS))
   (BMB SPEAKER HEARER (SEQUENCE-OF ?NEXT ?FOLL)))

Order: (NUCLEUS SATELLITE)
Relation-phrases: ("" "then" "next")
Activation-question:
  "Could ~A be presented as start-point, mid-point, or end-point
   of some succession of items along some dimension? -- that is,
   should the hearer know that ~A is part of a sequence?"
```

reconsidered the interpretation of growth point goals by treating them merely as (unordered) suggestions for additional paragraph growth.

Under the new interpretation, the paragraph structurer produces many more paragraph trees, some of which do not seem coherent. We take here an example from one of the three domains to which the paragraph planner has been applied, the Integrated Interfaces domain, a multimodal system which satisfies user requests for information from a Navy database [Arens et al. 88]. The Integrated Interface display planner furnishes a set of 6 related entities along with the goal of describing the sequence of events starting from the first event, including as much of the given information as possible. Using the RST relation/plan that achieves the goal to express a sequence given in Figure 1, but taking the nucleus growth points out of order, the paragraph structure planner produces the tree in Figure 2, from which Penman generates the text shown. While this text is well-structured according to RST, it lacks the coherence found, for example, in the following rendition of the same propositional content:

> With readiness C4, Knox is en route to Sasebo. It is at 79N 18E heading SSW. It will arrive 4/24 and will load for four days.

RST relation/plans do constrain the planner to produce only coherent paragraphs. Its valuable contribution to the coherence of a text must be supplemented with other coherence factors. One of these is focus.

Figure 2: RST Generated Navy text

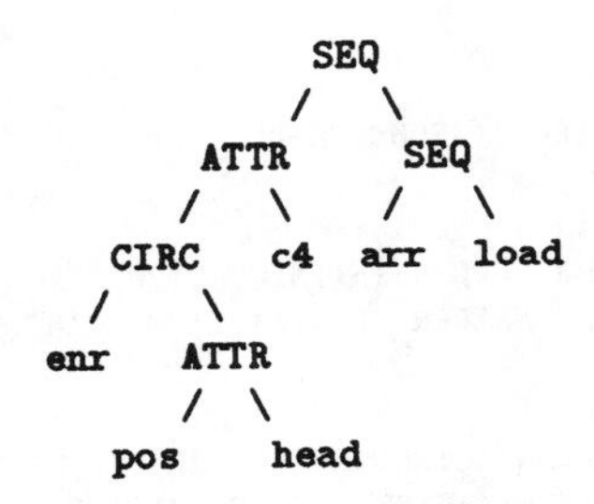


```
Knox is en route to Sasebo. It is at 79N 18E heading SSW.
It is C4. It will arrive 4/24, and will load for four days.
```

3 Focus Trees and Coherence

Discourse Focus Trees were introduced in [McCoy & Cheng 88] to capture the shifts in the focus of attention of discourse participants as a discourse progresses. They are an attempt to integrate into one unified approach the kinds of focusing phenomena noticed by researchers in specialized kinds of discourse [Schank & Abelson 77, Garrod & Sanford 83, Grosz 77, Carberry 83, McCoy 85]. During the discourse, a focus tree is constructed and traversed, one node being visited at a time. Based on the position of the visited node in the tree, entities from the knowledge base are highlighted. In deciding what to say next, the generation system must either choose an element from the highlighted set or make one of a small set of legal moves to another node in the focus tree. If another focus move must be made, the shift must be marked in the text lest it seem incoherent.

Each node in the Focus Tree points to an entity from the knowledge base. Thus the nodes in the focus tree are of different types, depending on the ontology of the domain. In general, Focus Tree nodes belong to one of five types: object, attribute (property), setting, action, and event. Each type of node causes highlighting of a particular set of knowledge base entities, and in so doing, furnishes different candidates for what may next be coherently included in the text. Figure 3 lists the permissible focus shifts for three node types.

The node type alone is not sufficient to determine knowledge base highlighting. In different conversations, for example, the very same object can support various focus moves. Therefore the highlighting depends also on the position of the currently visited node with respect to its ancestors (sibling nodes also play a role) in the focus tree. The focused knowledge can be thought of as the intersection of the knowledge related to information about the currently visited node and the knowledge related to each of its ancestor nodes in the tree. In this way, the parent nodes lend a perspective through which the currently visited node, and its children, are viewed.

Associated with this inheritance of perspective is the following rule: Focus candidates are always interpreted in the most specific context. That is to say, they migrate down the tree if they can: when in a topic shift a child node becomes the new currently visited node, and it has focus candidates (potential child nodes) in common with any of its ancestors, then those candidates migrate down the tree to appear *only* under the child node. Then, when the parent node is later returned to, a subsequent shift of focus to one of the migrated candidates would involve the

Figure 3: Candidate Focus Shifts for Selected Node Types

NODE TYPE	FOCUS SHIFT CANDIDATES
OBJECT:	attributes of the object, actions the object plays a prominent role in (e.g., is actor of)
ACTION:	actor, object, etc., of the action (any participant role; see [Fillmore 77]), purpose (goal) of action, next action in some sequence, subactions, specializations of the action
ATTRIBUTE:	objects which have the attribute, more specific attribute

revisiting of the intermediate node, a move that is incoherent unless linguistically marked.

As the discourse proceeds, a Focus Tree is built up and traversed. A node may be added to the tree either by explicit reference in the discourse or by inference which can happen in both top-down and bottom-up fashion. By top-down we mean that each particular node in the tree, when visited, furnishes candidate nodes to which the focus may later progress, based on its type and its position in the tree. Each progression causes an appropriate child node to be grown in the tree. Bottom up inferencing may also be necessary to connect several seemingly unrelated nodes under a unifying theme.

The traversal of the tree (shifting of focus) normally proceeds depth-first: what is said next is either an expansion of the currently visited node, or an expansion of one of its previously unexpanded children, or a new expansion of one of its ancestors. A major difference between this focusing theory and other theories of focus (e.g., [Grosz 77, Sidner 79, Grosz & Sidner 86]) is that a depth first walk of the tree is only expected, not required. Other focus moves are indeed possible, though they require explicit marking in the text (by the use of such phrases as "to go back to..."). The further away from the standard depth-first traversal the move is, the stronger the marking must be.

Focus Trees can be used in the generation of paragraphs by constraining what is said next to respect legal focus shift moves in the tree. However, the use of the Focus Tree for this purpose does not preclude the generation of incoherent text in all cases. For instance, using the above rules, the following text could be generated from the Navy text input entities, assuming the initial focus is on Knox:

> Knox, which is C4, will arrive 4/24 and load for 4 days. It is heading SSW and is at 79N 18E. It is en route to Sasebo.

The above text is not a coherent rendering of the text produced in the previous section. Prohibiting such text requires additional information not contained in Focus Trees.

4 Integration of the Two Methods

The preceding sections described the inability of either method alone — RST or Focus Trees — to fully control the generation of coherent paragraphs. In this section we describe a way of integrating these theories that uses each to best advantage.

The insight that focus and structural considerations can be combined to produce coherent text is not new. McKeown implemented a combined scheme in [McKeown 85]. Her TEXT system generated paragraphs by first partitioning off the portion of the knowledge base that might be included in the text using simple rules. This pool of relevant knowledge lent a "global focus" [Grosz 77] to the text. Once the potentially relevant knowledge was identified, the assembly of the paragraph was controlled by structural rules encoded in a schema. Variability, primarily in the inclusion of optional material, was controlled by a focusing mechanism based on [Sidner 79].

While it is clear that an RST planner would greatly benefit from the incorporation of a focusing mechanism, the mechanism used by McKeown is not sufficient because of the recursive method of planning employed by the RST planner. McKeown's algorithm always controls what should be said immediately following the text planned so far. Using the RST planner, two pieces of text may be planned under a particular RST operator, but then growth points in either the nucleus or the satellite may cause additional text to be inserted *between* the already planned parts. McKeown's algorithm provides no way to handle focus dependencies over discontinuous pieces of text. In addition, since her algorithm uses a stack, it does not maintain a record of popped entities. As a result, the algorithm would allow returning to a previously focused entity which had been popped off the stack without reference to its previous mention.

The use of focus trees avoids these problems: 1) inserting additional text corresponds to introducing new nodes into the Focus Tree, which is a routine operation, and, 2) a tree is precisely a stack that records its history.

We integrate the two methods as follows: While the RST planner constructs the paragraph structure tree, a focus tree is constructed in tandem. During the expansion of a node in the RST tree, the structurer applies all the growth point goals active at that point and collects the resulting candidate relations and their associated clause-sized input entities. Each candidate growth entity is then checked against the currently allowed focus shifts in the Focus Tree, and invalid candidates are simply removed from consideration. One of three possibilities ensues:

1. Only one candidate remains and growth proceeds straightforwardly.
2. More than one candidate remains. In this case all candidates are coherent based on rhetorical structure and focus but additional measures, still to be developed, must be employed to select the best of these. (As an interim practical solution, the growth points in the RST relation/plan can be ordered by typical occurrence, and the tree can be grown in this default order.)
3. No candidates remain. In this case the overall stylistic goals of the system may dictate to either stop tree growth at this point, or continue tree growth in the default order as above but linguistically mark the text to indicate a focus shift.

One further subtlety remains: Some RST trees are unacceptable to the Focus Tree criterion in their initial form, but can be made acceptable by reordering their parts (which may involve generating appropriate linguistic focus words in the text). Consider the planning of the RST tree in Figure 2, which is such a case, under the additional control of the Focus Tree. The initial goal to express a sequence starting with `enroute` and focusing on `Knox` generates the RST and Focus trees in Figure 4. Next, using the growth point calling for an ATTRIBUTIVE relation, the RST planner finds the `C4` readiness attribute of `Knox`. However, the Focus Tree requires that the `C4` clause precede the `enroute` clause in the text — otherwise, as is clear from Figure 4, generating `C4` causes a shift up the Focus Tree away from `enroute`, a shift that must be undone directly in order to generate the subsequent `arrive` and `load` clauses. The RST planner handles this requirement by inverting the ATTRIBUTIVE relation nucleus and satellite in the RST tree. After subsequent planning, the final result is the RST tree in Figure 5, which would give rise to the text shown. Note that simple reordering of the attributive information makes the text more coherent, and prevents both the text generated in Figure 2 and the unacceptable text allowed by the Focus Trees alone.

Figure 4: Initial Trees

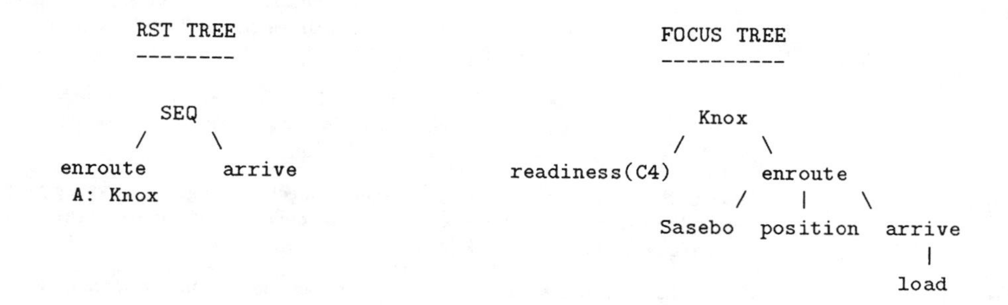

Figure 5: Joint RST and Focus Generated Navy text

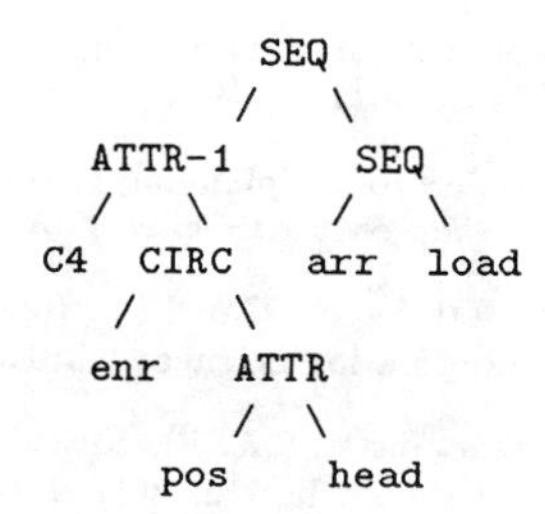


```
With readiness C4, Knox is en route to Sasebo. It is at 79N 18E
heading SSW. It will arrive 4/24 and will load for four days.
```

5 Conclusion

In this paper we illustrated how a text planner which relies on a single coherence method will not generate coherent paragraphs in all circumstances. We presented two coherence theories, RST and Focus Trees, and showed how they may be integrated into a single planning methodology to overcome problems that neither addresses alone.

Though a step in the right direction, this combination is not yet sufficient to guarantee coherent text in all cases. We envision that other aspects of text coherence will give rise to other theories which must ultimately be integrated into this framework. We believe the top-down hierarchical expansion method is powerful enough to support such additions. We hope to continue this investigation by identifying other coherence techniques useful for the generation task and integrating them into this framework.

References

[Arens et al. 88] Arens, Y., Miller, L., Shapiro, S.C. & Sondheimer, N.K. Automatic Construction of User-Interface Displays. In *Proceedings of the 7th AAAI Conference*, St. Paul, MN, 1988. Also appears as USC/Information Sciences Institute Research Report RR-88-218.

[Carberry 83] Carberry, S.M. Tracking user goals in an information-seeking environment. In *Proceedings of the 3rd AAAI Conference*, Washington, D.C., 1983 (59-63).

[Cohen 83] Cohen, R. *A Computational Model for the Analysis of Arguments.* Ph.D. dissertation, University of Toronto, 1983. Also appears as University of Toronto Computer Systems Research Group Technical Report no. 151.

[Fillmore 77] Fillmore, C.J. The Case for Case Reopened. In P. Cole and J.M. Sadock (editors), *Syntax and Semantics VIII: Grammatical Relations.* Academic Press, New York, 1977 (59-81).

[Garrod & Sanford 83] Garrod, S. and Sanford, A. Topic dependent effects in language processing. In G.B. Flores d'Arcais and R.J. Jarvella (editors), *The Process of Language Understanding.* John Wiley & Sons Ltd., 1983 (271-296).

[Grosz 77] Grosz, B.J. *The Representation and Use of Focus in Dialogue Understanding.* Technical Report no. 151, SRI International, Menlo Park CA, 1977.

[Grosz & Sidner 86] Grosz, B.J. and Sidner, C.L. Attention, Intentions, and the Structure of Discourse. *Computational Linguistics Journal* 12(3), 1986 (175-204).

[Hobbs 78] Hobbs, J.R. Why is discourse coherent? Technical Note no. 176, SRI International, Menlo Park CA, 1978.

[Hovy 88a] Hovy, E.H. Planning coherent multisentential text. In *Proceedings of the 26th ACL Conference*, Buffalo, 1988 (163-169).

[Hovy 88b] Hovy, E.H. Approaches to the planning of coherent text. Presented at the *4th International Workshop on Text Generation*, Los Angeles, 1988.

[Mann & Matthiessen 83] Mann, W.C. and Matthiessen, C.M.I.M. Nigel: A systemic grammar for text generation. USC/Information Sciences Institute Research Report RR-83-105, 1983.

[Mann & Thompson 88] Mann, W.C. and Thompson, S.A. Rhetorical structure theory: Toward a functional theory of text organization. In *Text* 8(3), 1988 (243-281). Also appears as USC/Information Sciences Institute Research Report RR-87-190.

[McCoy 85] McCoy, K.F. *Correcting object-related misconceptions.* Ph.D. dissertation, University of Pennsylvania, 1985.

[McCoy & Cheng 88] McCoy, K.F. and Cheng, J. Focus of attention: Constraining what can be said next. Presented at the *4th International Workshop on Text Generation*, Los Angeles, 1988.

[McKeown 85] McKeown, K.R. *Text generation: Using discourse strategies and focus constraints to generate natural language text.* Cambridge University Press, Cambridge, 1985.

[Moore & Swartout 88] Moore, J.D. and Swartout, W.R. A reactive approach to explanation. Presented at the *4th International Workshop on Text Generation*, Los Angeles, 1988.

[Paris 88] Paris, C.L. Generation and explanation: Building an explanation facility for the Explainable Expert Systems framework. Presented at the *4th International Workshop on Text Generation*, Los Angeles, 1988.

[Reichman 78] Reichman, R. Conversational coherency. *Cognitive Science* 2, 1978 (283-327).

[Sacerdoti 77] Sacerdoti, E. *A structure for plans and behavior.* North-Holland Publishing Company, Amsterdam, 1975.

[Schank & Abelson 77] Schank, R.C. and Abelson, R.P. *Scripts, plans, goals, and understanding.* Lawrence Erlbaum Associates, Hillsdale, 1977.

[Sidner 79] Sidner, C.L. *Towards a Computational Theory of Definite Anaphora Comprehension in English Discourse.* Ph.D. dissertation, MIT, 1979.

Individual differences in the revision of an abstract knowledge structure

Stephen Jackson
MRC Applied Psychology Unit,
Cambridge,
England

Abstract

Following the recent suggestion (Hockey, in press) that cognitive science has much to gain from the consideration of variability in cognitive functioning, this paper addresses the question of what aspects of memory performance underlie differences in cognitive 'style' such as 'Ambiguity Tolerance'. Subjects allocated to 'tolerant' and 'intolerant' groups on the basis of a traditional pencil & paper measure of 'Ambiguity tolerance' took part in a conceptual editing task which required them to disregard information learnt on a previous occasion. The results of the study show significant differences between groups, both in terms of recall and discrimination, and are interpreted as supporting the view that Ambiguity tolerance effects result from differences in the organisation and availability of the underlying conceptual representation.

Introduction

Our research focuses on two main issues: The circumstances under which abstract knowledge structures are revised or updated following particular learning episodes, and whether there are individual differences in the the processes which underlie such revisions. This paper focuses primarily on the second of these issues.

Despite the attraction of normative models of cognitive processing, it has been suggested by a number of authors (Hockey, in press; Robertson, 1985), that our understanding of many cognitive processes could be enhanced by taking into account the variability in cognitive functioning.

An approach which has been highlighted as being of particular importance to this endeavour is that of 'Cognitive Style' (Robertson, 1985), which concerns the way individuals' conceptually organise their environment (Goldstein & Blackman, 1978). This paper explores the effects of one such style variable [1], 'Tolerance of Ambiguity / Rigidity', on the revision of an abstract knowledge structure.

Tolerance of ambiguity

The concepts of 'Ambiguity tolerance / Rigidity' have a long history and have been investigated using a variety of techniques both within, and outside of, the psychological laboratory (for a review see Goldstein & Blackman, 1978). These include studies concerned with; Perceptual ambiguity, problem solving, category sorting, and concept learning. The results of such studies suggest that individuals vary in their ability to restructure the means by which they organise environmental input, particularly where input contains information which is inconsistent with either some prior knowledge structure or with other aspects of the input.

---

[1] As the terms Tolerance of ambiguity and Rigidity have often been used interchangeably by previous authors (Goldstein & Blackman, 1978), no distinction will be drawn between these concepts within this paper.

In addition, such studies have led to the general conclusion that: "Rigid individuals tend to have their cognitions 'walled-off' from each other which results in apparent behavioural inconsistency" (Goldstein & Blackman, 1978).

Rationale

The study made use of a variation on the general Person - Impression formation paradigm, which is a form of concept learning task which has been used several times previously to investigate Tolerance of ambiguity effects. In studies of this sort, subjects are presented with information, typically either behavioural descriptions or trait terms, which relate to one or more fictitious persons. Often aspects of the information are inconsistent with respect to either information presented earlier or else with other items within the same set. Although a number of dependent variables are applicable to this type of study, subjects most commonly are required to produce descriptions or judgments of the fictitious person or persons. Thus the experiment to be reported within this paper differed from earlier studies in two respects. Firstly the focus of the current study was on memory performance rather than trait or behavioural judgments, and secondly, the study was designed to investigate the effects of ambiguity tolerance at retrieval.

Design

The experiment was a between-subjects design and consisted of 4 treatment groups. The general experimental procedure was as follows:

Subjects were presented for one minute with a set of 10 trait adjectives (List 1) and were instructed to form an impression of a fictitious 'John Smith'. After a gap of 12 minutes, during which time subjects completed several intervening tasks, the subjects were presented with a further set of trait adjectives (List 2) describing the same fictitious person. The trait terms in List 1 were **not** manipulated in this experiment. The trait terms which made up List 2 comprised of a set of 10 synonyms to the items in List1. However, 50% of these terms were randomly varied to the antonym of the corresponding List 1 term, thus producing a set of List 2 items which contained 50% inconsistent items. Thus if the List 1 term was **mean**, and its synonym **stingy**, then the List 2 item, if selected for change, might be to **charitable.**

Following a further set of intervening tasks, subjects were tested for their recall of the **List 2 information only**, for their recognition accuracy (New - Old) of items from both lists, and for their discrimination accuracy (List 1 - List 2 - New). The experimental manipulation concerned the stage in the above procedure at which subjects were instructed to disregard the information given in List 1. The specific conditions were as follows:

Table 1: Experimental Design

Time	1	2	3	4	5
Condition 1	List 1	***	List 2	------	Test
Condition 2	List 1	------	List 2	***	Test
Condition 3	------------------		List 2	------	Test
Condition 4	List 1	------	List 2	------	Test

*** = Subjects instructed to disregard the items in List 1

Thus condition 3 constitutes a control where the List 1 information is never learned, and condition 4 an additional control, where no disregard instructions are given. Condition 4 also differs from the other treatment groups in that, at test, subjects are required to recall information from **both** List 1 and List 2.

Finally, scores on the McDonald (1970) scale for Ambiguity tolerance were obtained and a median split produced two groups of high and low scorers designated here as ambiguity TOLERANT and INTOLERANT.

Results

Condition 4 Recall

An analysis was carried out on the data from Condition 4. In this condition subjects learnt both List 1 and List 2, and were tested for their recall of items from both lists. Thus this condition forms a measure of the relative memorability of the two lists in the absence of any instructions to disregard items. The result of this analysis (ANOVA) revealed a main effect for List ($F_{1\ 14} = 22.67$, $P < 0.001$), and shows that in the absence of disregard instructions, the items from List 1 are significantly better recalled than those from List 2.

Recall

Figure 1 shows the mean recall performance, for List 2 information only, across the treatment groups. Analysis of variance (ANOVA) revealed a significant main effect for condition ($F_{2\ 41} = 4.53$, $P < 0.02$). Pairwise comparisons reveal no significant difference between recall in Condition 1, where disregard instructions were given prior to learning List 2 and in the Control condition (Condition 3) where List 1 is not presented for learning. However, recall in condition 2, where the disregard instructions were presented after **both** lists had been learnt, was significantly worse than for both of the other conditions ($P < 0.05$).

This result indicates that subjects only have difficulty in disregarding the information in List 1 when this instruction does not occur until after they have learnt List 2.

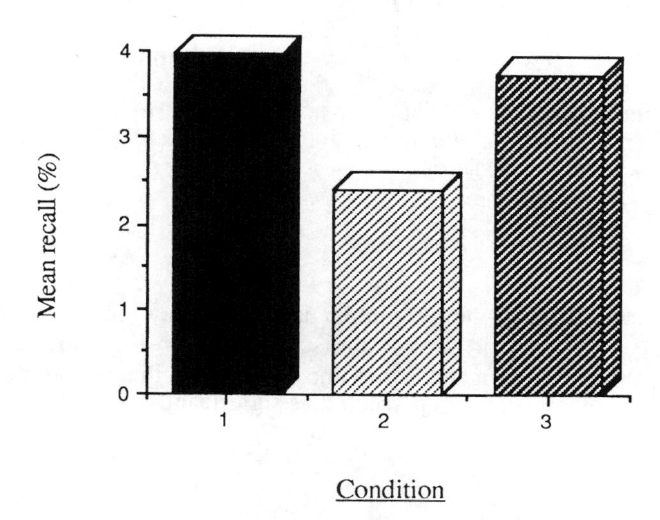

Condition

Figure 1: Mean level (%) of recall of List 2 items

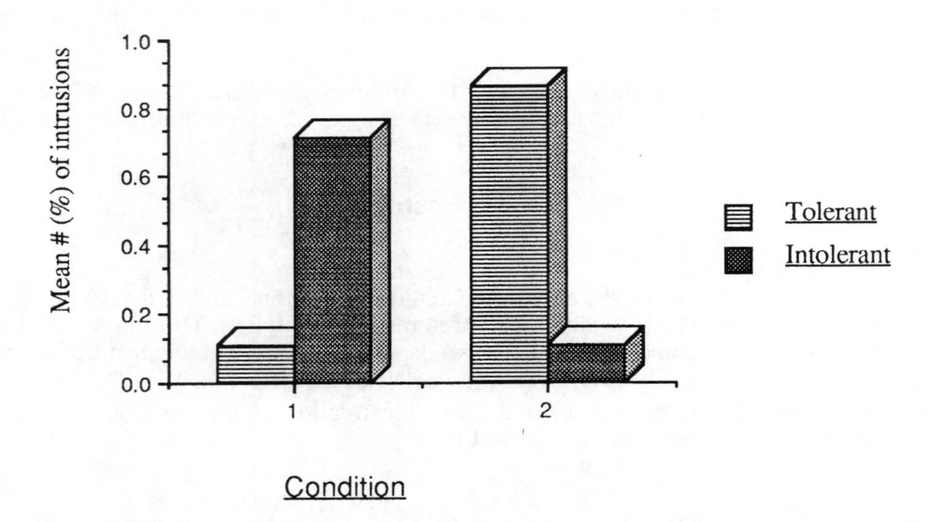

Figure 2: Mean number of List 1 intrusions occurring during subjects' recall of List 2 items

List 1 intrusion data

An ANOVA was carried out on the number of List 1 items recalled by subjects when instructed to recall List 2 items only (Fig. 2). Although the total number of intrusions was small, the results of this analysis were statistically significant. They reveal no main effect for Ambiguity tolerance or for Condition, but a significant interaction effect between Ambiguity tolerance and Condition ($F_{1\ 28}$ = 7.13, $P < 0.01$).

Analysis of the simple effects of this interaction reveal that Condition has a significant effect on the Ambiguity tolerant group ($F = 4.4$, $P < 0.05$) but not on the Intolerant group and that Tolerance of Ambiguity only has a significant effect ($F = 4.4$, $P < 0.05$) at Condition 2, where subjects are not instructed to disregard the List 2 information until after they have learnt List 2.

This result suggests that the Ambiguity tolerant group have greater difficulty in separating information given on different occasions and that the Intolerant group may be maintaining separate representations of the two sets of information.

Recognition Data

d prime

An Analysis of Variance carried out on the recognition data (Old - New) revealed a main effect for condition ($F_{3\ 45}$ = 8.08, $P < 0.001$). Pairwise comparisons (Newman-Keuls) reveal that Conditions 1,2, & 4 do not differ significantly from one another, but that recognition performance in Condition 3, where List 1 items were not presented, is significantly better ($P < 0.01$) than in all of the other conditions.

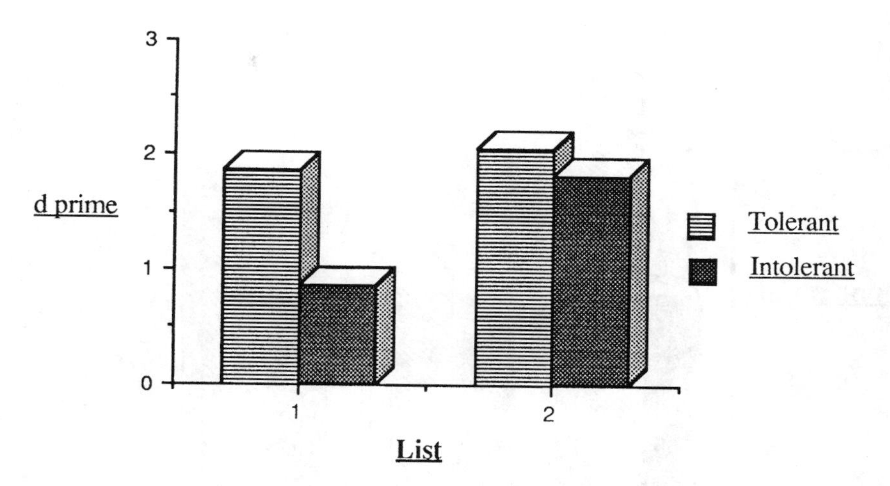

Figure 3: Discrimination performance for List 1 and List 2 items across the two levels of ambiguity tolerance

Discrimination data

d Prime
An Analysis of Variance carried out on the discrimination data (List 1 - List 2 - New) revealed the following effects:

A main effect for Ambiguity Tolerance ($F_{1\ 32} = 6.19$, $P < 0.02$), the ambiguity tolerant group showing more accurate discrimination performance overall.

A main effect for condition ($F_{2\ 32} = 3.53$, $P < 0.04$), which reveals that there was no significant difference in performance between Condition 1, where instructions to disregard List 1 are given prior to learning List 2, and condition 4 where no disregard instructions were given. In Condition 2 (disregard instructions given after List 2 items have been learnt, performance is significantly poorer than for both Condition 1 and condition 4 ($P < 0.05$).

A main effect for List ($F_{1\ 32} = 16.22$, $P < 0.001$), which reveals discrimination accuracy was greater for the items presented in List 2 than for those in List 1.

In addition to these main effects there were two significant interactions. Firstly, an interaction effect (Fig. 3) between Ambiguity tolerance and List type ($F_{1\ 32} = 7.07$, $P < 0.01$).

An analysis of the simple effects within this interaction reveal that Ambiguity tolerance has a significant effect on List 1 discrimination ($P < 0.001$) and that List has a significant effect on the Ambiguity intolerant group alone.

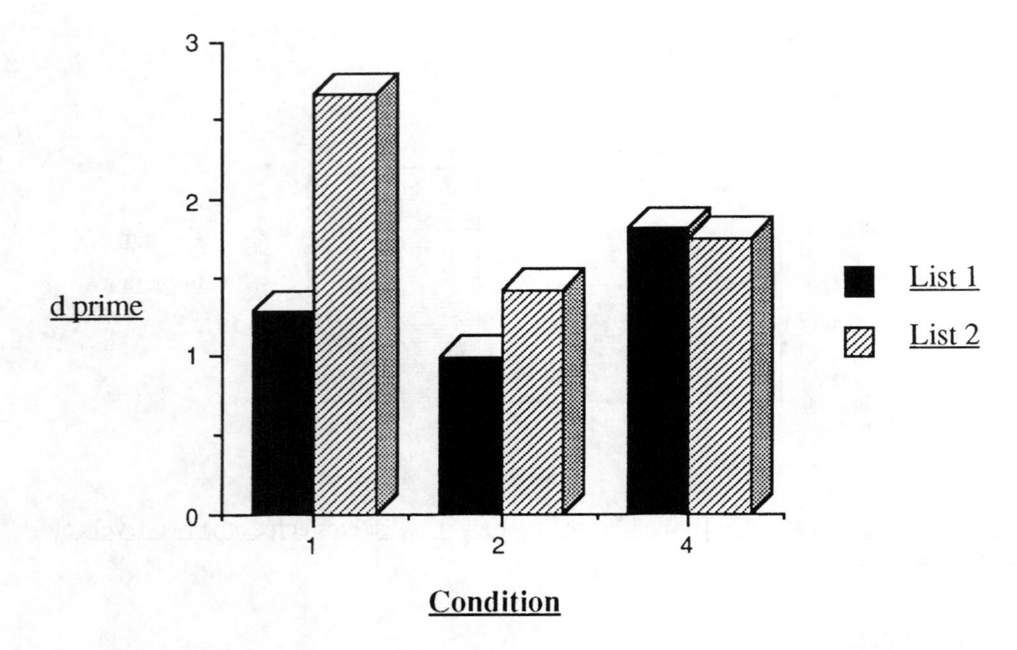

Figure 4: A comparison of list discrimination across the three relevant conditions

This result indicates that the Ambiguity intolerant group are effectively disregarding the List 1 items when instructed to do so, whereas for the ambiguity tolerant group discrimination performance for the List 1 items does not differ significantly from that of List 2. Again this result can be interpreted as evidence for the tolerant group forming a unified impression of the two sets of information.

There was also a significant interaction effect (Fig. 4) between Condition and List ($F_{2\ 32} = 8.8$, $P < 0.001$). The simple effects of this interaction reveal that Condition only has a significant effect on List 2 performance ($P < 0.002$) and that List only has a significant effect at Condition 1 ($P < 0.001$).

As with the recall data, this result shows that subjects can effectively disregard information if the instruction to do so is given prior to learning new, related information (Condition 1).

Beta Data
Analysis of the Beta data revealed only two main effects and no statistically significant interactions. These were:

A main effect for Ambiguity Tolerance ($F_{1\ 32} = 5.78$, $P < 0.02$), with the Tolerant group showing significantly higher Beta levels than the Intolerant group, and a main effect for List ($F_{1\ 32} = 10.28$, $P < 0.003$), with Beta levels greater for List 2 than from List 1.

Summary of Results

The results from this study show that in the absence of specific instructions to disregard information (Condition 4) there was a strong, statistically significant recall advantage for the information learnt first (List 1). However, when instructed to ignore this information (Conditions 1 & 2) these instructions only had a significant effect on List 2 recall when given after both lists had been learnt (Condition 2). This finding is also the case for the discrimination data where performance was impaired relative to the control group only for subjects performing within Condition 2. If these findings are interpreted within an Interference theory framework, then the results suggest that instructions to disregard given prior to new learning have the effect of eliminating PI to the level of a control group who do not receive the initial List (Figure 1).

Although the results in relation to the effect of disregard instructions are themselves of interest, the main focus of this study was on differences in memory performance which could underlie Tolerance of ambiguity effects. With regard to this issue the results reveal that the ambiguity tolerant group show greater discrimination accuracy and higher Beta levels than the intolerant group and that 'Ambiguity tolerance' interacts with task characteristics in a memory 'editing' task, as follows:

Whereas the ambiguity intolerant group show no difference in List 1 intrusions at List 2 recall, across different instruction conditions, the ambiguity tolerant group show a significant increase in List 1 intrusions where instructions to disregard List 1 items follow the presentation of both lists (Condition 2). Also, whereas the ambiguity intolerant group show significantly better discrimination performance for List 2 over List 1 items, the ambiguity tolerant group discriminate List 1 and List 2 items equally well.

Discussion

Although previous studies of 'Ambiguity tolerance' have principally made use of judgments as a dependent variable, this study has sought to explore the question of whether there may be memory performance differences which could account for 'Ambiguity tolerance' effects.

The results from this study can be interpreted as support for the hypothesis that, in contrast to ambiguity tolerant individuals who tend toward unified impressions, ambiguity intolerant individuals compartmentalise information which relates to a single concept but which has been learnt on separate occasions. Thus such 'Tolerance of ambiguity' differences which may exist between individuals may well be attributable to differences in both the structure and availability of aspects of the underlying knowledge representation.

Acknowledgments

This research was supported by a studentship awarded by the Medical Research Council of the UK. I would like to thank Debra Bekerian & Georgina Jackson for their comments on an earlier version of this paper and also to Sarah Hampson & Vernon Gregg for their assistance toward an earlier version of this experiment.

References

Goldstein, K. M. & Blackman, S. Cognitive Style: Five approaches and relevant research, N.Y. John Wiley & Sons, 1978.

Hockey, G. R. J. (in press) 'Styles, Skills and Strategies: Cognitive variability and its implications for the role of mental models in HCI' in M.Tauber & D. Ackerman (eds), Mental Models and Human Computer Interaction.

McDonald, A.P. (1970) 'Revised scale for ambiguity tolerance: Reliability & Validity', Psychological Reports, 26, 791-798.

Robertson, I. T., (1985). 'Human information processing strategies and style', Behaviour and Information technology, 4, 19-29.

EBL and SBL: A Neural Network Synthesis

Bruce F. Katz
The Beckman Institute for Advanced Science and Technology
University of Illinois

ABSTRACT
Previous efforts to integrate Explanation-Based Learning (EBL) and Similarity-Based Learning (SBL) have treated these two methods as distinct interactive processes. In contrast, the synthesis presented here views these techniques as emergent properties of a local associative learning rule operating within a neural network architecture. This architecture consists of an input layer, a layer buffering this input, but subject to descending influence from higher order units in the network, one or more hidden units encoding the previous knowledge of the network, and an output decision layer. SBL is accomplished in the normal manner by training the network with positive and negative examples. A single positive example only is required for EBL. Irrelevant features in the input are eliminated by the lack of top-down confirmation, and/or by descending inhibition. Associative learning then causes the strengthening of connections between relevant input features and activated hidden units, and the formation of "bypass" connections. On future presentations of the same (or a similar) example, the network will then reach a decision more quickly, emulating the chunking of knowledge that takes place in symbolic EBL systems. Unlike these programs, this integrated system can learn in the presence of an incomplete knowledge domain. A simulation program, ILℵ, provides partial verification of these claims.

INTRODUCTION
Learning is, and always has been, central to connectionist models of cognition. Numerous adaptive rules have been proposed that, in the context of their respective architectures, are able to improve the network's performance through observation of examples characteristic of a given domain. Although far removed in sophistication from Mill's (1843) system of induction, all such strategies are designed, like his, to extract the regularities by which similar causes are predictive of similar effects. Machine learning classifies such techniques, for obvious reasons, as Similarity-Based Learning. SBL continues to be of prime importance in both connectionist and "symbolic" models of intelligence.

Recently, however, non-connectionist learning research has placed equal emphasis on Explanation-Based Learning, and other more knowledge-intensive methods (DeJong & Mooney, 1986). In the classical formulation of the EBL problem (Mitchell, Kellar, & Kedar-Cabelli , 1986), one is given a set of domain rules, a training example, and a goal that can be inferred by the application of the domain knowledge to the example. An explanation structure is then constructed, with the input features at the leaves of this tree, and the goal node at the top. This structure may then be generalized using goal regression or other related techniques (Mooney & Bennet, 1987). The resulting structure may then be "flattened", so that a new rule is formed with the left hand side being the generalized example, and the right hand side the original goal. If the left-hand side is easily observable, then one will have a quick and easy way of predicting the goal concept given the appropriate inputs, without the need to produce what may be an extensive inference chain. To take a simple example, let us assume one knows that all professors are absent-minded, and that all absent-minded people misplace things. Suppose one sees Professor X misplacing his glasses. One forms the explanation of this event, and one emerges in the end with the general rule that professors will tend to misplace things. One may question the role of the example in the above, since, from a strictly logical point of view, it is unnecessary. The standard response to this objection (Mitchell, Kellar, & Kedar-Cabelli, 1986) is that the example indicates which type of knowledge it may be profitable to chunk; the full deductive closure of one's current knowledge is not readily computable given spatial and temporal limitations.

EBL, then, differs primarily with SBL in that it is a knowledge intensive approach. It eliminates features irrelevant to the classification task not by noticing their joint occurrence in both positive and negative examples, as there is typically only one positive example, but by noting which features are necessary for the generalized explanation. E.g., in the above example, the fact that Professor X's specialty was medieval history was not part of the explanation structure, and was therefore deemed irrelevant.

Theoretical parsimony alone would suggest the desirability of unifying both EBL and SBL in a single system. However, there is another concern which is of equal importance. Classical EBL can only work when the domain under study is complete; i.e., there is always an unbroken chain of inference from the example to the goal (Rajamoney & DeJong, 1987). Such a restriction seems overly stringent, and is unlikely to be met in many common situations. It would be desirable to have SBL patch the missing links in a partially broken inference chain. In addition, it would also be highly advantageous to induce primarily over the end-products of an inferential system, rather than raw input features. Think of learning from written text -- clearly, very little learning is occurring at the pixel or letter level; most if not all learning is ideational.

The symbolic learning literature offers a few approaches to integrated learning. Among these are OCCAM (Pazzani & Flowers, 1987), Liebowitz's (1986) adaptation of UNIMEM to integrated learning, and Danyluk's (1987) interactive approach. All of these systems, however, are decomposable into separate EBL and SBL modules. The purpose of this work is to show that a neural network model can account for both types of learning as *emergent* properties of a local adaptive rule operating in a particular architecture. A simulation program, ILℵ, is presented which partially verifies this claim.

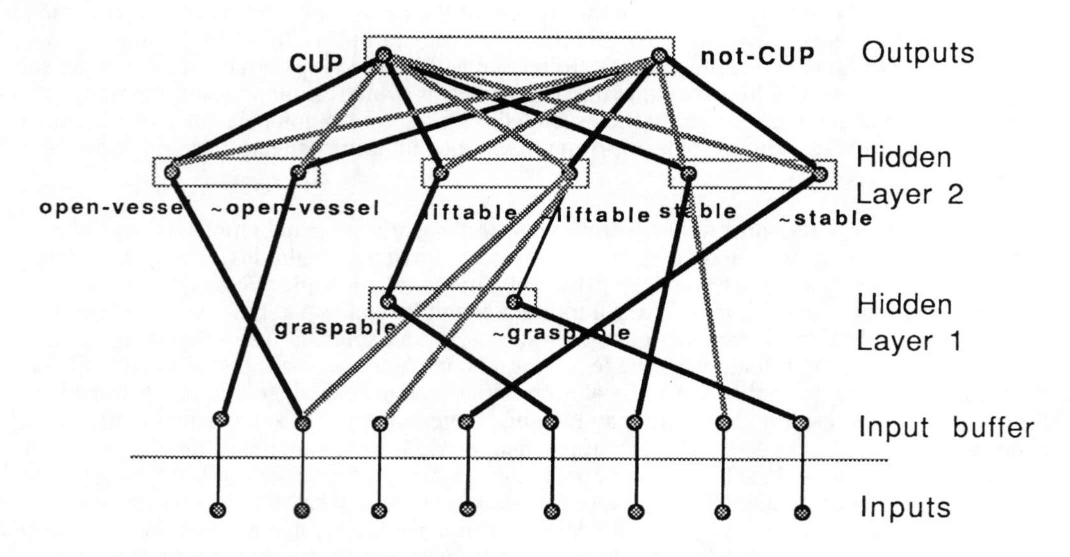

FIGURE 1. A SIMPLIFIED VIEW OF THE SYSTEM ARCHITECTURE

ARCHITECTURE
A sample network in ILℵ (for an example which is discussed more fully later) is shown in figure 1. Input nodes are activated by features in the environment. These inputs are buffered by another layer, with one node for each corresponding node in the input layer. Unlike input nodes, which are clamped on or off by the environment, nodes in the input buffer may be affected by top-down control. This will prove important in the mechanism for EBL.

Activation flows from the input buffer to sets of nodes in one or more hidden layers. Solid lines represent excitatory connections, while shaded lines represent inhibitory connections. In addition, the dotted boxes in the figure are shorthand representations for sets of mutually inhibitory nodes at the same layer. Nodes in these layers also have excitatory connections to themselves. This sub-architecture has been shown to produce winner-take-all networks (Rumelhart & Zipser, 1986), that is, the node in the set receiving the most activation will reach maximum value, while all others will be driven to zero activation. Activation spreads in parallel in all directions until one unit in the output layer "wins" and becomes the decision. In this case, the network decides whether the input is a cup or some other object. The relaxation process is described more fully in the next section.

INFERENCE
Inference is accomplished by the spread of activation. The activation of a unit is a weighted sum of its inputs, as in (1). In this equation, a_i represents the net activation level of unit i, w_{ij} is the weight between units i and j, and o_j is the output of unit j.

$$a_i = \Sigma\, w_{ij}\, o_j \qquad (1)$$

Weights may be either positive (excitatory), or negative (inhibitory), and are unbounded. In contrast, the output of a unit is held between 0 and 1 by the sigmoidal function in equation (2). In this formula, T is a free parameter representing the "temperature" (cf., Hinton and Sejnowski, 1986) of the network, and θ is a constant threshold. Lower temperatures make it more likely for a unit to reach extremal values at relaxation, while the threshold controls the amount of activation a unit needs to fire.

$$o_i = 1 / (1 + \exp(-(a_i - \theta) / T)) \qquad (2)$$

In addition to bounding a unit's output, this non-linear function controls for noise at sub-threshold activation levels (Rumelhart, Hinton, & Williams, 1986).

Activation propagates throughout the network, until the network reaches a steady state. Hopfield (1985) has shown that networks with symmetric weights (which are currently used exclusively) are guaranteed to converge to a fixed point. In addition, if the temperature in (2) is sufficiently low, one node in a group of competing nodes will always "win", and the network will make a discrete decision.

THE LEARNING RULE
In this section, a learning rule is offered, which, in conjunction with the architecture in ILℵ, performs both SBL and EBL. The starting point for the development of the learning rule is Hebb's (1949) observation that simultaneous activity of two units indicates that the weight between these units should be strengthened. This extensively used rule is shown in equation (3), where the change in weight between units is equal to the product of the outputs of the nodes at a given time multiplied by a learning rate constant, λ. The second term in (3) allows unlearning of connections and the development of inhibitory connections.

$$\Delta\, w_{ij} = \lambda\, o_i\, o_j - \delta\, |o_i - o_j| \qquad (3)$$

For reasons that will be made clearer in the next section, it is desirable that the network learn only after relaxation, as a means of controlling spurious correlations. One simple way to do this is to only apply (3) after the network relaxes. However, this would require a global "homunculus" watching the network that tells each unit when to learn. One local solution to this difficulty, and the one adopted here, is to divide the right hand side of (3) by the function

$$\mathcal{D}(o_i, o_j) = \begin{cases} 1 & \text{if } |d(o_i)/dt| + |d(o_j)/dt| < \varepsilon, \text{ and} \\ 1000 & \text{otherwise.} \end{cases} \qquad (4)$$

Thus, only when both units are no longer changing will the weight change be significant. It should be noted that (3) is capable of learning conjunctive concepts only; no disjuncts must appear in the target concept. Learning is not limited to classifying orthogonal input patterns, however, as is typical in Hebbian schemes (Jordan, 1986), because of the winner-take-all decision procedure.

EXPLANATION-BASED LEARNING

While Hebbian associative learning is a clear candidate for SBL, its performance on EBL tasks is less established. Figure 2 is a highly schematic view of how EBL is accomplished in ILℵ using the learning procedure outlined above. Panel **A** represents the state of the network before relaxation. Note that the input buffer is a veridical representation of the input vector. Panel **B** represents the network after relaxation. Descending inhibition has turned off the two rightmost units in the input buffer (the threshold in equation 2 can also be adjusted so that merely the lack of excitatory confirmation also results in a dampened unit.). The network has "decided" that these features were not crucial in the determination of the final decision, or in the final activated state of the intermediate units leading to this decision. It is suggested that the process of moving from **A** to **B** is equivalent, in effect, to forming a proof structure of the goal concept from the inputs in that previous knowledge is used to weed out irrelevant attributes in the data. Unlike symbolic techniques, where relevance is determined by the explicit computation of a proof structure, in ILℵ it is an emergent property of top-down attentional control. Like its symbolic counterpart, though, this method can profit by a single positive example, since large numbers of positive and negative examples are not needed to determine relevant features.

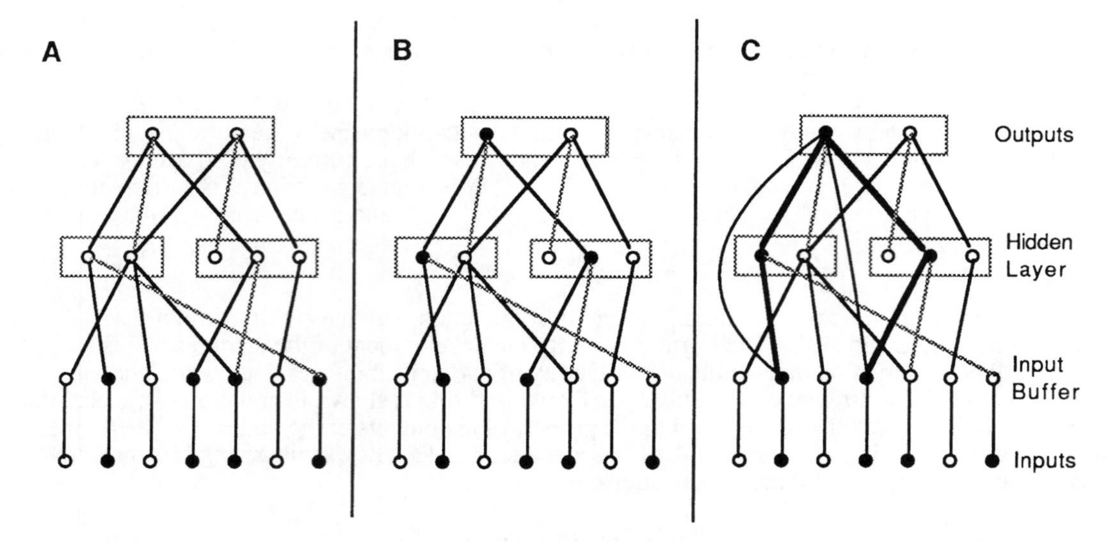

FIGURE 2. EBL IN ILℵ

Panel C represents the state of the network after learning. Recall that the learning rule constrains the network to learn primarily after relaxation. Thus no correlations are made between data that was originally present in the input buffer, but turned off during relaxation (no direct learning is permitted from the input layer to other layers). Existing connections between units active at relaxation are strengthened, and new connections may also form. These "bypass" connections can be seen in C as new lines between the input buffer and the activated output node. These new connections, along with strengthened old ones, cause the network to relax at a much faster rate given a similar input pattern. This occurs because the competition time between sets of mutually inhibitory nodes (those in the dotted boxes) is proportional to the difference in activation values of these nodes, and the strengthened and bypass connections increases this difference.

Existing EBL algorithms include a step in which the proof structure is generalized. In the current model, this type of generalization is a side-effect of the activation of higher-order nodes. For example, in an EBL task involving Clyde the elephant, if the mammal unit receives top-down confirmation and fires, its connections to other units would change in a manner similar to the connections emanating from the elephant unit. The system would then reap the rewards of the earlier training with Clyde in a similar context involving Sam the giraffe (also a mammal).

EXPERIMENTAL RESULTS

In the following experiment, eight examples of cups and non-cups (common household objects) were used. Horn-clause rules for cup recognition (as found in the EBL literature) were translated directly into the network in Figure 1. The connections were hardwired such that the network gave the correct response on each example. The examples were presented to the network in random order, and the number of synchronous cycles until network relaxation was measured for each example. The graph in figure 3 summarizes these results. Initially, the network took 19 cycles to relax; after the presentation of 200 examples, this figure was reduced to 7 cycles. An effect similar to rule compilation in EBL was achieved by the formation of bypass connections (and strengthened connections) in a neural network. Irrelevant features in the input pattern did not enter into learning, as they were in low states of activation at relaxation due to the lack of descending confirmation.

The second experiment focused on the relation between recognition errors and the completeness of the knowledge domain. Two cases were studied: the cup domain discussed above, and a randomly generated boolean formula with three disjunctive terms. They were examined under three conditions: full prior knowledge, partial prior knowledge, and no knowledge prior to learning. Table 1 summarizes these results. Naturally, in both cases, the complete domain yielded no

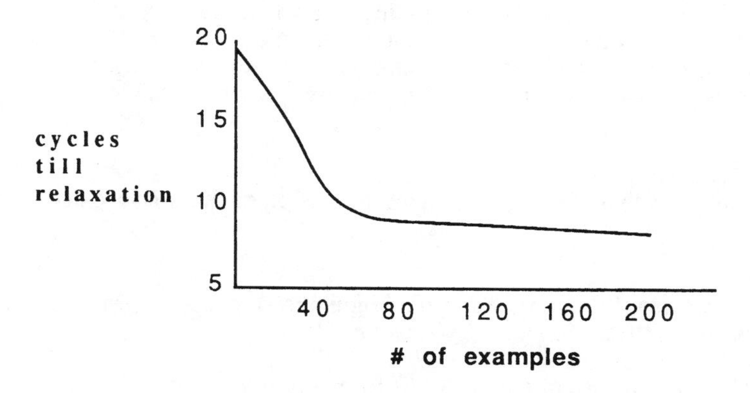

FIGURE 3. RECOGNITION TIME DECREASE IN A COMPLETE DOMAIN

recognition errors, and only one sweep through all the examples were needed to verify this. In the no knowledge case, no prior connections between the input buffer and the output layer existed, and no hidden units were used in the cup case. For the boolean formula, five hidden units were in place, and a modified reinforcement learning procedure, similar to Barto and Anandan's (1965) associative reward-penalty algorithm, that is capable of acquiring disjunctive concepts, was used. In the partial knowledge case, connections between the input buffer and hidden units were in place, as in figure 1, but the connections from the hidden units to the output units were removed. Note that this represents one of the traditionally difficult cases for EBL, that of an incomplete domain. The partial knowledge helped the network outperform, to a small extent, a network with no knowledge in the cup domain. More dramatic increases in performance were seen in the boolean case, as expected, with the hidden units doing the hard work of encoding the relevant disjuncts (cf. Rivest, 1984).

TABLE 1. MEAN SWEEPS UNTIL PERFECT RECOGNITION AS A FUNCTION OF PRIOR KNOWLEDGE

	complete knowledge	partial knowledge	no prior knowledge	partial/ none
CUP	1	3.6	5.2	69%
BOOLEAN	1	11.0	34.2	32%

DISCUSSION

A neural architecture has been outlined that provides seamless integration of Similarity and Explanation-Based Learning. Not fully treated in this paper are the following issues:

a) The acquisition of disjunctive concepts (as in backpropagation, e.g.), and the relation between disjunctive concept learning and EBL.

b) No unification is performed in the current model (as in symbolic EBL systems), yielding the binding problem (see Touretzky & Hinton, 1988 for a partial solution to this problem).

c) The relation between EBL in the above model and automaticity (Schneider, 1984) needs to be further explored.

d) The relation between sequential processing in a parallel network and EBL (extended chains of inference can currently be handled only by adding a new layer to the network for each link in the chain). Ultimately, one would like to show that the mind can convert lengthy sequential procedures into easily computable boolean functions by observing its own input-output relations. This research is the first step toward suggesting that this may be possible using a purely local algorithm.

ACKNOWLEDGEMENTS

I would like to thank Bob Stepp for his patient discussion of these issues and Marcy Dorfman for her suggestions.

REFERENCES

Barto, A.G., & Anandan, P. (1985). Pattern recognizing stochastic learning automata. *IEEE Transactions on Systems, Man, and Cybernetics, 15.*

Danyluk, A.P.(1987). The use of explanations for similarity-based learning. *Proceedings of the International Joint Conference on Artificial Intelligence.* Milan, Italy.

DeJong, G., & Mooney, R. (1986). Explanation-Based Learning: An alternative view. *Machine Learning 2.*

Hebb, D.O. (1949). *The Organization of Behavior.* Wiley: New York.

Hinton, G.E., & Sejnowski, T.J. (1986). Learning and relearning in Boltzmann machines. In Rumelhart, et. al. (Eds.), *Parallel Distributed Processing, Vol. I.* MIT Press.

Hopfield, J.J., & Tank, D.W. (1985). "Neural" computation of decisions in optimization problems. *Biological Cybernetics 52*, pp. 141-152.

Jordan, M.I. (1986). An introduction to linear algebra in parallel distributed processing. In Rumelhart, et. al. (Eds.), *Parallel Distributed Processing, Vol. I.* MIT Press.

Lebowitz, M. (1986). Integrated learning: Controlling Explanation. *Cognitive Science 10,* pp. 219-240.

Mitchell, T.M., Keller, R.M., & Kedar-Cabelli, S.T. (1986). Explanation-based generalization: A unifying view. *Machine Learning 1.*

Mill, J.S. (1843). *A System of Logic, Book III.* London.

Mooney,R. & Bennet,S. (1986). A Domain independent explanation-based generalizer. *Proceedings of AAAI.*

Pazzani, M., Dyer, M., & Flowers, M. (1987). Using prior learning to facilitate the learning of new causal theories. *Proceedings of the International Joint Conference on Artificial Intelligence.* Milan, Italy.

Rajamoney, S.A., & DeJong, G.F. (1987). The classification, detection, and handling of imperfect theory problems. *Proceedings of the International Joint Conference on Artificial Intelligence.* Milan, Italy.

Rivest, R.L. & Sloan (1988). Learning complicated concepts reliably and usefully. *Proceedings of the First Workshop on Computational Learning.*

Rumelhart, D.E., Hinton, G.E., and Williams, R.J. (1986). Learning internal representations by error propagation. In Rumelhart, et. al. (Eds.), *Parallel Distributed Processing, Vol. I.* MIT

Rumelhart, D.E., and Zipser, D. (1986). Feature Discovery by competitive learning. In Rumelhart, et. al. (Eds.), *Parallel Distributed Processing, Vol. I.* MIT Press.

Schneider, W., Dumais S.T., and Shiffrin R.M. (1984). Automatic and control processing and attention. In Raja and Davies (Eds.), *Varieties of Attention*, Academic Press.

Touretzky, D. S., and Hinton, G.E. (1988). A distributed connectionist production system. *Cognitive Science, Vol. 12.*

Competition and Learning in a Connectionist Deterministic Parser[1]

Stan C. Kwasny

Kanaan A. Faisal

Department of Computer Science
Washington University

ABSTRACT

Deterministic parsing promises to (almost) never backtrack. Neural network technology promises generalization, competition, and learning capabilities. The marriage of these two ideas is being investigated in an experimental natural language parsing system that combines some of the best features of each. The result is a deterministic parser that learns, generalizes, and supports competition among structures and lexical interpretations.

The performance of the parser is being evaluated on predicted as well as unpredicted sentence forms. Several mildly ungrammatical sentences have been successfully processed into structures judged reasonable when compared to their grammatical counterparts. Lexical ambiguities can create problems for traditional parsers, or at least require additional backtracking. With the use of neural networks, ambiguities can be resolved through the wider syntactic context. The results have shown the potential for parsing using this approach.

INTRODUCTION

Any plausible model of language processing should permit alternative linguistic structures to compete while inputs are processed left-to-right. Computer models based on backtracking (e.g., Augmented Transition Networks (ATNs) or Definite Clause Grammars (DCGs)) do not adequately capture the competitive nature of sentence processing. Furthermore, there is no evidence from human experiments that any conscious re-processing of inputs is routinely performed. The lone exception is perhaps for ''garden path'' sentences.

A good example of competition can be found in the TRACE model of speech perception (McClelland & Elman, 1986). In that work, competing interpretations of the pseudo-speech feature vectors are proposed and activation levels rise or fall as each potential interpretation is supported or contradicted. Parsers should permit syntax and other levels of processing to aid in resolving lexical ambiguities just as ambiguous phonemes were resolved in TRACE.

In most neural network or connectionist parsers, grammar rules are processed into a network of units connected with excitatory and inhibitory links. The number of units required to realize a given grammar is a function of the maximum input sentence length and the complexity of the grammar. Hence, a limitation is introduced on the number of elements that can be present in the input. Sentences are processed within such a framework by presenting them, possibly in a simulated left-to-right fashion, at the input side of the network and activations are permitted to spread through the network (Cottrell, 1985; Fanty, 1985; Waltz & Pollack, 1985). Alternatively, a stochastic method, such as simulated annealing, is used (Selman & Hirst, 1985).

[1] Partial support for this work was received from the Center for Intelligent Computer Systems at Washington University.

Classically, parsers process inputs iteratively from an unbounded stream of input. Neural network parsers typically do not work iteratively and have limits imposed artificially on the length of the sentence. There is, however, work underway on neural network iteration mechanisms that could be used in parsers of natural language. (Servan-Schreiber, Cleeremans, & McClelland, 1988; Williams & Zipser, 1988).

In classic approaches, natural language processing by computer is performed under the direction of a set of grammar rules. These are often executed as if following instructions in a program. If the intent is to model human sentence processing, then this method is incorrect. Rules should be permitted to play an advisory role only — that is, as descriptions of typical situations and not as prescriptions for precise processing. Control in the application of a rule or variant of a rule should be determined jointly as a data-driven and expectation-driven process.

Symbolic rules are an essential part of most linguistic accounts at virtually all levels of processing, from speech signal to semantics. But systems based literally on rules tend to be brittle since there is no direct way to process linguistic forms that do not strictly adhere to the pre-conceived rules. If a complete set of rules for all meaningful English forms existed, then this might be satisfactory. But no such set of rules exists, nor does it seem desirable or even possible to construct such a set. Furthermore, the rules would have a difficult time capturing ''degrees of grammaticalness'' (Chomsky, 1965)[2].

Another consequence of a rule-based grammar is that acquisition of new grammar rules often require tedious re-tuning of existing rules. Rarely can a rule be added to the grammar without it affecting and being affected by other rules in the grammar. To the credit of their creators, some grammars have been continually refined over a period of years, even decades, in an attempt to more accurately depict the processing requirements of English. The only solution to this problem in a practical and realistic manner is through learning.

APPROACH

Our connectionist parser supports competition among sentence structures and performs sequentially over an unbounded input stream. In addition to parsing well-formed sentences, the parser is capable of parsing some types of ill-formed sentences and resolving some lexical ambiguities using syntactic context. Our model is based on a multi-level neural network, trained through backward propagation (Rumelhart, et al., 1986). It combines both symbolic and non-symbolic processing with actions of the rules carried out symbolically and decision-making carried out non-symbolically. Rules of the grammar are presented as training patterns of processing strategies, not as packets of infallible advice to be memorized and followed literally. Our design is based on deterministic parsing (Marcus, 1980) and iteration is an integral feature of the design.

Experimentation with a medium-size grammar has produced results which have been encouraging. Once trained, the network is quick, robust, and permits competition among processing alternatives. Training sequences are derived from two sources: (1) the rules of a rule-based deterministic grammar; and (2) traces of sentence processing steps from actual sentences. The former training is deductive while the latter training is inductive.

Deterministic Parsing

Deterministic, or ''wait-and-see'' parsing (WASP)[3] requires in the worst case that several (3 to 5) constituents of the input sentence be in view before deciding on the appropriate structure for the current constituent. Once this decision has been reached, it cannot be reversed and once structures have been constructed, they are never thrown away. Deterministic parsers are also rule-based in that their actions are

[2] There have been several expressions of this idea in the literature. Several psycholinguistic studies have attempted to measure the reality of this notion, both from a use as well as an interpretation perspective. Chomsky was selected as an important reference and one that illustrates a classic viewpoint.

[3] Waltz & Pollack (1985) characterize this option as one based on ''delay'' as opposed to one based on backtracking.

controlled by a collection of rules. The rules are partitioned into rule packets which aid in conflict resolution.

A single processing step in a traditional deterministic parser consists of selecting a rule to be fired from the appropriate rule packet and firing the rule to alter the structure and positions of constituents in the model. As with most rule-based systems, rules whose left-hand sides are found to match the state of the system correctly are eligible to be fired. Rule packets are activated as a consequence of which portion of the structure is being built and, within the packet, conflicts are resolved through a pre-assigned numeric priority and from the static ordering of rules within each priority value. Once selected, the rule is fired and its actions are performed. The action effects changes on the stack and buffer. After a series of processing steps, a termination rule fires, and the final parse structure is left on the top of the stack[4].

LEARNING A RULE-BASED GRAMMAR

Training proceeds by presenting patterns to the network and teaching it to respond with an appropriate action. The input patterns represent encodings of the buffer positions and the top of the stack. The output level of the network contains a series of units representing actions to be performed during processing and judged in a winner-take-all fashion. The training data are derived as ''rule templates'' from rules in a deterministic grammar. These rule templates are instantiated once in each epoch of training. Network convergence is observed once the network can achieve a perfect score on the rule templates themselves and the error measure has decreased to an acceptable level (set as a parameter). Once the network is trained, the weights are stored in a file so that various experiments can be performed with the network.

Network Architecture

Patterns in the pattern/action rules of the grammar consists of a list of syntactic features, divided into four groups to match the three buffer positions and the top of the stack. These are represented in a localist manner in the network with each syntactic feature being represented by a unit. The choice of a localist representation allows the grammar to be represented in a very straightforward manner and permits experimentation with sentence processing in a direct way.

In the set of experiments described here, the network has a three-layer architecture with 37 input units, 20 hidden units, and 20 output units. The input layer consists of four pools of input units, the first three pools represent the buffer, with each containing the features of a buffer item, and the fourth pool represents the top of the stack including the current node of the parse tree. One hidden layer has proven sufficient in all of our experiments. The output layer represents the 20 actions that can be performed on each iteration of processing.

During sentence processing, the network is presented with encodings of the buffer and the top of the stack. The network produces the action to be taken. If the action creates a vacancy in the buffer and if more of the sentence is left to be processed then the next sentence component is moved into the buffer. Iteration is achieved in this fashion.

Sentences

The grammar used is capable of processing a variety of simple sentence forms which end with a final punctuation mark. Simple declarative sentences, yes-no questions, imperative sentences, and simple passives are permitted by the grammar. What the model actually sees as input is not the raw sentence but a canonical representations of each word in the sentence, in a form that could be produced by a simple lexicon. Such a lexicon is not part of the model in its present form.

For test purposes, several sentences were coded that would parse correctly by the rules of the deterministic parser. Also, several mildly ungrammatical sentences were coded to determine if the network was

---

[4] This is an over-simplification of the processing involved, but accurately reflects accounts in many texts. A more accurate view, including a discussion of attention-shifting (AS) rules, rule priorities, etc., can be obtained from Allen (1987).

generalizing in any useful way. Finally, sentences containing ambiguously coded lexical items were presented to test if the context could aid in resolving such ambiguities.

Coding of Grammar Rules

In the canonical input format of a rule template, word forms are represented as a list of syntactic features. The set of possible features was chosen as necessitated by the grammar. In general each word form is represented by an ordered feature vector in which one or more values is ON(**+1**) for features of the form and all other values are either OFF(**-1**) or DO NOT CARE (**?**). A rule template is instantiated by randomly changing **?** to **+1** or **-1**.

Each grammar rule has the following format:

{ <Stack> <1st Item> <2nd Item> <3rd Item> → Action on Stack}

For example, a rule for Yes/No questions would be written as:

{ < *S node* **> <** *Aux Verb* **> <** *NP* **> < >** → *Switch 1st and 2nd items* **}**

A grammar rule is coded as a training template, which is a list of feature values. Each template represents many training patterns. On each training epoch every template is instantiated once yielding a specific training case. Thus, each training epoch is slightly different. Further details are available in Kwasny (1988a; 1988b).

Each input pattern consists of three feature vectors from the buffer items and one stack vector. Each vector activates 15 input units in a pattern vector representing a word or constituent of the sentence. The stack vector activates seven units representing the current node on the stack. In our simplified version of the grammar, only two items are coded from the buffer and thus 37 input units are sufficient.

Training from Rule Templates

Training consists of the presentation of 200,000 epochs of 23 training cases generated from 23 grammar rule templates[5]. The templates are not organized into rule packets nor grouped in any way as in the deterministic grammar. The probability of a **?** becoming a **+1** or **-1** is equal and set at 0.5. All weights in the network are initialized to random values between -0.3 and +0.3. After the presentation of each pattern, an error signal is derived from comparing activation on the output layer (the network's prediction) with the desired output pattern. That error signal is back-propagated through all the connections and the weights adjusted before presenting the next pattern[6].

Each rule template containing n **?**'s can generate up to 2^n training cases. Some rule templates have over 30 **?**'s which means they represent approximately 10^9 unique training cases. It is obviously impossible to test the performance of all these cases, so testing from rule templates involves substituting a zero value for each **?**. Zero is used since it represents the mean of the range of values seen.

PERFORMANCE

Each sentence receives a score representing the overall average strength of responses during processing. The score for each processing step is computed as the reciprocal of the error for that step. The error is computed as the Euclidean distance between the actual output and an idealized output consisting of a **-1** value for every output unit except the winning unit which has a **+1** value. The errors for each step are summed and averaged over the number of steps[7]. The average strength is the reciprocal of the average

[5] A slightly modified version of the grammar from appendix C of Marcus (1980) was used for all experiments in this paper. This appendix contains the list of rules specifically discussed in his thesis and can be taken to represent illustrations of the basic mechanisms. These have been coded into rule templates within our system for training.

[6] A slightly modified version of VICE, a program developed by John Merrill, was used for all simulations reported in this paper. Values of learning rate and momentum (*eta* and *alpha* in Rumelhart, et al. (1986)) were chosen sufficiently small to avoid large oscillations and were generally in the range of 0.01 to 0.02 for learning rate and 0.5 to 0.9 for momentum over a range of test runs.

[7] This sum is just the total-sum-of-squares (tss) used, for example, in the PDP software (McClelland & Rumelhart, 1988).

TABLE 1: Grammatical Sentences Used in Testing

	Sentence Form	Average Strength
(1)	John should have scheduled the meeting.	283.3
(2)	John has scheduled the meeting.	240.8
(3)	Has John scheduled the meeting?	132.2
(4)	John is scheduling the meeting.	294.4
(5)	Schedule the meeting.	236.2
(6)	The boy did hit Jack.	298.2
(7)	John is kissing Mary.	294.4
(8)	Mary is kissed.	276.1
(9)	Tom hit Mary.	485.0
(10)	Tom will hit Mary.	547.5
(11)	They can(v) fish(np).	485.0
(12)	They can(aux) fish(np).	598.2

error per step.

Parsing Grammatical Sentences

Grammatical sentences, by our definition, are those which parse correctly in the rule-based grammar from which we derived the training set. Table 1 shows several examples of grammatical sentences which are parsed successfully along with their response strengths. Each example shows a relatively high average strength value, indicating that the rules used in training have been learned.

During parsing, the input sentence is presented in the input buffer from left to right. On each iteration, the network is presented with constituents from the input buffer and the entry from the top of the stack. The action specified by the network is performed and the buffer and stack are updated as required. New input items replace empty buffer positions as needed. The process then repeats until a stop action is performed, usually when the buffer becomes empty.

Parsing Ungrammatical Sentences

An important test of the system's generalization capabilities is its response to ungrammatical sentences. This is strictly dependent upon its experience since no relaxation rules were added to the original grammar to handle such ungrammatical cases. This experiment consisted of testing a few ungrammatical sentences that were close to the training data and within the scope of our encoding. Table 2 contains examples that have produced reasonable structures when presented to our system. Note that overall average strength is lower for ungrammatical sentences when compared to similar grammatical ones.

In sentence (13), the structure produced resembled that produced while parsing sentence (1). The only difference was that the two auxiliary verbs, *have* and *should*, were in reverse order. Sentence (14) contains a disagreement between the auxiliary *has* and the main verb *schedule* and yet the comparable grammatical sentence (3) parsed identically, but with more strength in the network's responses. Similarly, sentence (15) is comparable to sentence (4) in its processing steps. For sentence (16), Charniak (1983) reports that his system, PARAGRAM, produces a nonsensical parse structure. In our parser, this sentence succeeds and produces a structure which resembles one for sentence (6).

Lexical Ambiguity

In a final set of experiments, the parser was tested for its ability to aid in the resolution of lexical ambiguity. Grammatical sentences were presented, except that selected words were coded ambiguously to represent an ambiguously stored word from the lexicon. These examples are shown in Table 3. Several of these examples come from Milne (1986).

TABLE 2: Ungrammatical Sentences Used in Testing

	Sentence Form	Average Strength
(13)	*John have should scheduled the meeting.	25.1
(14)	*Has John schedule the meeting?	38.1
(15)	*John is schedule the meeting.	4.7
(16)	*The boy did hitting Jack.	26.6

TABLE 3: Lexically Ambiguous Sentences Used in Testing

	Sentence Form (Words in <> are presented ambiguously)	Average Strength
(17)	<Will> he go?	83.6
(18)	Tom <will> hit Mary.	118.7
(19)	Tom <hit> Mary.	39.0
(20)	They <can> fish.	4.5
(21)	They can <fish>.	172.2

Sentence (17) contains the word *will* coded ambiguously as an NP and an auxiliary, modal verb. In the context of the sentence, it is clearly being used as a modal auxiliary and the parser treats it that way. A similar result was obtained for sentence (18). In sentence (19), *hit* is coded to be ambiguous between an NP (as in playing cards) and a verb. The network correctly identifies it as the main verb of the sentence. Sentence (20) presents *can* ambiguously as an auxiliary, modal, and main verb, while *fish* is presented uniquely as an NP. *Can* is processed as the main verb of the sentence. Compare this example with sentence (11) of Table 1. Here, each word is presented unambiguously with *can* coded as a verb and *fish* coded as an NP. The same structure results in each case, with the average strength level much higher in the unambiguous case. By coding *fish* ambiguously as a verb/NP and coding *can* uniquely as an auxiliary, the result obtained is as shown for sentence (21), which is comparable to sentence (12).

In the cases shown, the lexically ambiguous words were disambiguated and reasonable structures resulted. Note that the overall average strengths were lower than comparable grammatical sentences discussed, as expected.

DISCUSSION

Robust language processing has been demonstrated in our model for selected, mildly ungrammatical sentence forms as well as for some types of lexical ambiguity. A network model of language processing has been trained on an encoded set of rules and tested on a variety of problematic forms. Results have been good with expected sentence forms evoking higher response strengths in general than unexpected forms.

The robust property of our parser is one of the most important reason for considering this approach. Attempts to process ill-formed inputs using conventional (symbolic) means, though successful in limited ways, have generally resulted in somewhat ad hoc methodologies that are tedious to use and have their own ''sharp edges'' in performance[8]. As mentioned earlier, Charniak (1983) attempted to provide for

[8] For further discussion of symbolic approaches, see Kwasny & Sondheimer, (1981); Weischedel & Sondheimer, (1983); Weischedel & Ramshaw, (1987).

parsing ungrammatical sentences in a deterministic grammar. His method is to score each possible test from the pattern portion of a rule and execute the rule with the best score. Our network provides its own scoring mechanism refined during learning.

Competition in our network among sentence processing alternatives has been observed. In our winner-take-all network, there can be only one action taken on each step. In ambiguous situations, however, there are often two or more competing actions which reflect alternative processing sequences. This is true in the ungrammatical and lexically ambiguous examples which often have multiple grammatical counterparts. This feature of the processing is a necessary part of parsing. With the absence of outside influences in our parser, e.g., semantics or the context of a dialogue, the network provides a choice based solely on its training experiences.

A single neural network-based parser trained on a deterministic grammar without rule packets has been shown to generalize to some cases not acceptable to the grammar. The grammar is therefore being used in an advisory role. Indeed, sentence forms which fall under the jurisdiction of the grammar parse with minimal error and thus universally earn a higher strength score than its ungrammatical counterpart.

In a brief experiment on inductive learning, the network was trained on the grammatical sentences used in our tests and its performance was tested on the rule templates. For those rule instances that were represented in the training data, the system did well, but overall exhibited less generalization due to the lack of extensive training cases. Overall strength was low, except for the precise sentences for which it was trained. As these experiments are continued and more sentence examples are used, better generalization is expected.

FUTURE DIRECTIONS

There are several directions in which our work is progressing. Some of the recent work on recurrent networks is being examined with the hope of improving the iteration properties of our system. Ultimately, it should be sufficient to present a final encoded structure as teaching data for a sentence and permit the system to organize itself into the appropriate number and kind of processing steps necessary to build it. Although achieving this will not happen soon, this work is expected to move away from the present very strong dependence on the organization associated with classic deterministic parsing.

Our choice of encoding was based on its simplicity and directness. Now that our experiments have shown how generalization can be achieved, our representation of the structures being built and the stack being used should be improved (Pollack, 1988). Our coding scheme is also being expanded to include a more complete set of features, for example, person and number as well as other labels that can appear in final structures. Eventually, the output layer should produce an updated encoding of the input and not require that the action be performed externally. As our understanding of the capabilities of this approach increases, the grammar will be scaled up to a much larger grammar of English. The limits of the generalization capability demonstrated here need to be further probed.

Still to be addressed are issues at the semantic and lexical levels. Our feature vectors purport to capture the patterns of activation that a lexical component would produce. Experiments are ongoing in this area.

Finally, garden path sentences need to be better understood. These should not be dismissed as simply different or anomalous. There is hope within our framework for an attack on these defiant sentence forms.

ACKNOWLEDGEMENTS

The authors express gratitude to William Ball, Steve Cousins, Georg Dorffner, Rose Fulcomer, David Harker, Dan Kimura, Ron Loui, John Merrill, Robert Port, and Guillermo Simari for thoughtful discussions and comments concerning this work. We, of course, are responsible for errors.

REFERENCES

Allen, J. (1987). *Natural Language Understanding.* Menlo Park: Benjamin/Cummings.

Charniak, E. (1983). A Parser with Something for Everyone. In King (Ed.), *Parsing Natural Language*, New York: Academic Press.

Chomsky, N. (1965). *Aspects of the Theory of Syntax.* Cambridge: MIT Press.

Cottrell, G.W. (1985). Connectionist Parsing. *Proceedings of the 7th Annual Conference of the Cognitive Science Society*, Irvine, CA, 201-211.

Fanty, M. (1985). Context-Free Parsing in Connectionist Networks. (Technical Report 174), Computer Science Department, University of Rochester, Rochester, NY.

Kwasny, S.C. (1988a). A PDP Approach to Deterministic Natural Language Parsing. *Neural Networks 1*, Supplement 1, 305.

Kwasny, S.C. (1988b). A Parallel Distributed Approach to Parsing Natural Language Deterministically. (Technical Report WUCS-88-21), Department of Computer Science, Washington University, St. Louis, MO.

Kwasny, S.C., & Sondheimer, N.K. (1981). Relaxation Techniques for Parsing Ill-Formed Input. *American Journal of Computational Linguistics* 7, 99-108.

Marcus, M. P. (1980). *A Theory of Syntactic Recognition for Natural Language.* Cambridge: MIT Press.

McClelland, J.L., & Elman, J.L. (1986). The TRACE Model of Speech Perception. *Cognitive Psychology 18*, 1-86.

McClelland, J. L., & Rumelhart, D. E. (1988). *Explorations in Parallel Distributed Processing: A Handbook of Models, Programs, and Exercises*, Cambridge: MIT Press.

Milne, R. (1986). Resolving Lexical Ambiguity in a Deterministic Parser. *Computational Linguistics 12*, 1-12.

Pollack, J. (1988). Recursive Auto-Associative Memory: Devising Compositional Distributed Representations. (Report MCCS-88-124), New Mexico State University Las Cruces, NM.

Rumelhart, D. E., Hinton, G., & Williams, R.J. (1986). Learning Internal Representations by Error Propagation. In Rumelhart & McClelland *Parallel Distributed Processing.* Cambridge: MIT Press.

Selman, B. & Hirst, G. (1985). A Rule-Based Connectionist Parsing System. *Proceedings of the 7th Annual Conference of the Cognitive Science Society*, Irvine, CA, 212-221.

Servan-Schreiber, D., Cleeremans, A., & McClelland, J.L. (1988). Encoding Sequential Structure in Simple Recurrent Networks. (Report CMU-CS-88-183), Carnegie Mellon University, Pittsburgh, PA.

Waltz, D.L. & Pollack, J.B. (1985). Massively Parallel Parsing: A Strongly Interactive Model of Natural Language Interpretation. *Cognitive Science 9*, 51-74.

Weischedel, R.M. & Sondheimer, N.K. (1983). Meta-Rules as a Basis for Processing Ill-Formed Input. *American Journal of Computational Linguistics 9*, 161-177.

Weischedel, R.M. & Ramshaw, L. (1987). Reflections on the Knowledge Needed to Process Ill-Formed Language. In S. Nirenburg (Ed.), *Machine Translation: Theoretical and Methodological Issues.* Cambridge: Cambridge University Press.

Williams, R. J., & Zipser, D. (1988). A Learning Algorithm for Continually Running Fully Recurrent Neural Networks. (ICS Report 8805), University of California, San Diego, CA.

DESCARTES: Development Environment for Simulating Hybrid Connectionist Architectures

Trent E. Lange, Jack. B. Hodges, Maria. E. Fuenmayor, Leonid. V. Belyaev

Computer Science Department
University of California, Los Angeles

ABSTRACT

The symbolic and subsymbolic paradigms each offer advantages and disadvantages in constructing models for understanding the processes of cognition. A number of research programs at UCLA utilize connectionist modeling strategies, ranging from distributed and localist spreading-activation networks to semantic networks with symbolic marker passing. As a way of combining and optimizing the advantages offered by different paradigms, we have started to explore hybrid networks, i.e. multiple processing mechanisms operating on a single network, or multiple networks operating in parallel under different paradigms. Unfortunately, existing tools do not allow the simulation of these types of hybrid connectionist architectures. To address this problem, we have developed a tool which enables us to create and operate these types of networks in a flexible and general way. We present and describe the architecture and use of DESCARTES, a simulation environment developed to accomplish this type of integration.

INTRODUCTION AND MOTIVATION

Within the connectionist approach there are three paradigms, each having its own advantages and disadvantages: Distributed Connectionist Networks (DCNs), Localist Connectionist Networks (LCNs), and Marker-Passing Networks (MPNs).

DCNs (such as the models in [Rumelhart & McClelland, 1986]) use simple, neuron-like processing elements which represent knowledge as distributed patterns of activation. DCNs, sometimes known as *Parallel Distributed Processing* or *subsymbolic* models, are interesting because they have learning rules that allow stochastic category generalization, they perform noise-resistant associative retrieval, and they exhibit robustness to damage. Distributed models, however, have (so far) been sequential at the knowledge level, lacking both the structure needed to handle complex conceptual relationships and the ability to handle dynamic variable bindings and to compute rules.

LCNs (as exemplified by the models of [Waltz & Pollack, 1985] and [Shastri, 1988]) also use simple, neuron-like processing elements with numeric activation and output functions, but represent knowledge using semantic networks of conceptual nodes and their interconnections. Unlike DCNs, localist networks are parallel at the knowledge level and have structural relationships between concepts built into the connectivity of the network. Unfortunately, they lack the powerful learning and generalization capabilities of DCNs. They also have had difficulty with dynamic variable bindings and most other capabilities of symbolic models.

MPNs (as exemplified by the models of [Charniak, 1986] and [Hendler, 1988]) also represent knowledge in semantic networks and retain parallelism at the knowledge level. Instead of spreading numeric activation values, MPNs propagate symbolic markers, and so support the variable binding necessary for rule application, while preserving the full power of symbolic systems. On the other hand, they do not possess the learning capabilities of DCNs or exhibit the inherent evidential constraint-satisfaction capabilities of LCNs.

Hybrid Connectionist Models

Research at UCLA has spanned the range from subsymbolic to symbolic connectionist models [Dyer, 1989]. A number of us have begun to construct hybrid architectures which use what we term Multiple Interacting Networks, or MINs, heterogeneous connectionist networks that communicate via shared elements. A neurophysiological approach [Nenov & Dyer, 1988] effectively uses MINs for visual/verbal association by modeling heterogeneous neuronal characteristics in separate networks. We have also been exploring the use of MINs for higher cognitive tasks, such as planning, creativity, story invention, and political negotiations. In political negotiations research, for instance, MINs are used to simulate the multiple perspectives of negotiating parties.

Another approach is to build models that combine the bottom-up processing features of DCNs with the top-down processing features of LCNs and MPNs. Figure 1 shows **Hiding Pot**, an example wherein elements from each paradigm are combined using MINs. This allows us to approach a problem that would be difficult, if not impossible, using a single paradigm. **Hiding Pot** shows a simplified network built to understand the sentence, *"John put the pot inside the dishwasher because the police were coming."*[1] Network-A in Figure 1 utilizes an MPN to do role-binding and an LCN to activate and combine evidence for individual schemas. These then combine their functionality to support predictions and perform inferencing and disambiguation.

One might also want to combine different connectionist approaches by having separate networks that communicate with each other, where each one performs a different cognitive task. Network-B in Figure 1 is a DCN, trained to recognize words from line segments [McClelland & Rumelhart, 1986, chap. 1]. By integrating these two approaches, we can simulate cognitive processes at the different levels of abstraction necessary for modeling reading and understanding.

Network-A interacts with Network-B through shared lexical nodes. Once a word has been recognized, it passes activation to the concepts related to the word. For example, the node for concept John gets activation from the word node "john" which is shared by both networks. Activation then propagates along the chain of related concepts in the network as contextual evidence for disambiguation. Markers are passed over the role nodes across marker passing links between corresponding roles to represent role-bindings and perform the needed inferencing.

While there are several existing connectionist simulators, none allows the simulation of multiple interacting hybrid networks, as in **Hiding Pot**, that integrate elements from more than one paradigm of connectionist modelling. We have developed the DESCARTES simulation environment specifically to address this kind of integration. DESCARTES enables researchers to design, simulate, and debug hybrid connectionist architectures that combine elements of distributed, localist, and marker-passing networks.

DESCARTES ARCHITECTURE

DESCARTES is a package designed for simulating network processing, network interaction, and integration of networks into an overall processing environment. The system consists of two interactive components: network *elements*, such as nodes and links, their associations, and their functionality, and *processing controllers*, which organize network elements and coordinate their processing. The components of this architecture, as applied to **Hiding Pot**, are shown in Figure 2.

---

[1]The inferencing and frame selection needed to understand sentences such as **Hiding Pot** is explained more thoroughly in [Lange & Dyer, 1989a] and [Lange & Dyer, 1989b], which describe ROBIN, a model of high-level inferencing using an LCN without marker-passing.

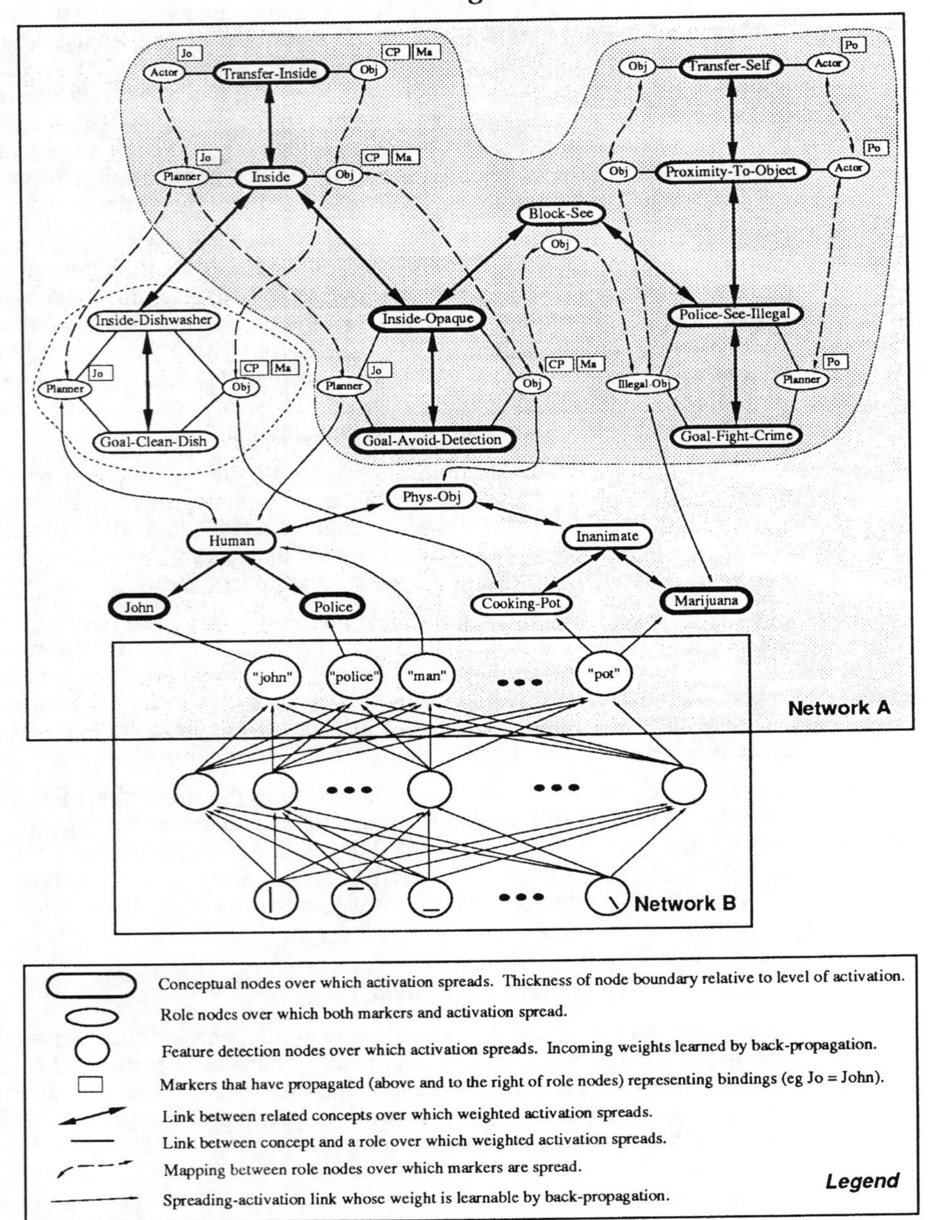

Figure 1: The sentence *"John put the pot in the dishwasher because the police were coming."* illustrates the utility of integrating semantic networks (Network-A) and distributed networks (Network-B). The darkest area represents the most highly-activated set of nodes representing the network's plan/goal analysis of the sentence. Not all markers are shown. Location role nodes and other parts of the network are also not displayed.

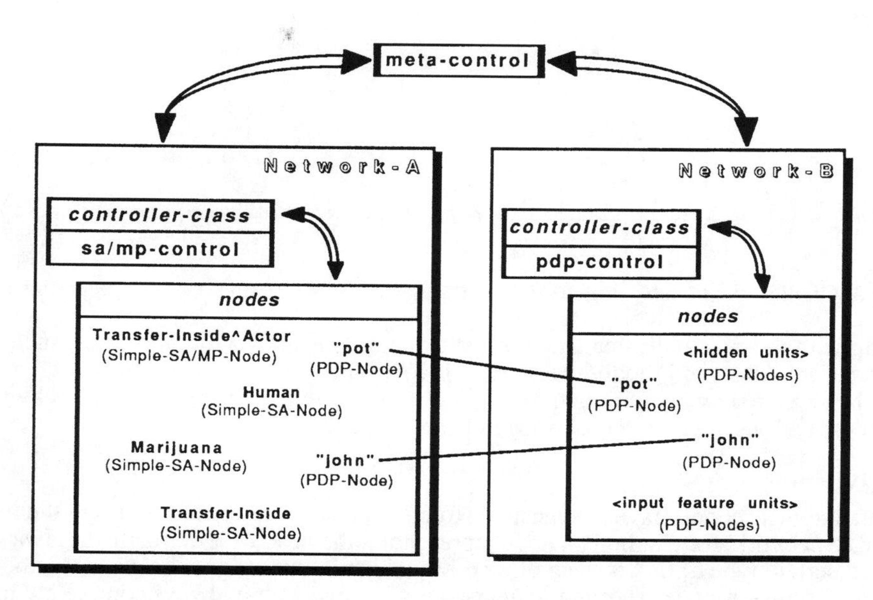

Figure 2: DESCARTES Processing Architecture applied to **Hiding Pot**. Shown in each network are a few of their nodes, with the class of each node being declared in parentheses below their names. PDP-Nodes "pot" and "john" are shared by both networks.

Processing Controllers

When DESCARTES is loaded and running, the required processing controllers are a *meta-controller* (a supervisor for all elements and sub-controllers present in the run-time system) and at least one *network controller* (a supervisor for an individual network and its elements). The architecture described in Figure 2, and implemented in **Hiding Pot**, is controlled by a meta-controller (Meta-Control) which coordinates the two networks (Network-A and Network-B). Each of these networks has a local network controller which coordinates the processing of its elements. In this case the controller for Network-A is of class SA/MP-Control, which combines both spreading-activation and marker-passing functionality.

Network Elements

The nodes shown in **Hiding Pot** are illustrative of the kinds of nodes provided in the system. Three of DESCARTES's predefined node classes are used in **Hiding Pot**: (1) Simple-SA-Node, used in **Hiding Pot** for conceptual elements, such as Human and Transfer-Inside, (2) Simple-SA/MP-Node, used for roles, such as Transfer-Inside^Actor, and (3) PDP-Node, used for feature detection in Network-B, such as the node representing lexical entry "pot". Figure 3 provides an example of node creation in DESCARTES.

Simple-SA-Node is a basic class of spreading-activation nodes with default activation and output functions. Simple-SA/MP-Node is another standard node class, which combines the functionality of Simple-SA-Node with that required for marker passing. Finally, PDP-Node is the simplest class of DCN-type nodes — spreading-activation nodes that modify the weights on their input links by backpropagation [Rumelhart *et al.*, 1986, chap. 8].

Many other common node and link types are predefined, with a variety of activation, threshold, and output functions. More complicated classes are also available, including gated nodes and

```
(Simple-SA-Node Transfer-Inside :in-links (SA-Link ("put"                   0.75)
                                                    (Inside                  1.00)
                                                    (Transfer-Inside^Actor 0.50)
                                                    (Transfer-Inside^Obj   0.50)
                                                    (Transfer-Inside^Loc   0.50)))

(Simple-SA/MP-Node Transfer-Inside^Actor :in-links (SA-Link (Transfer-Inside 1.0))
                                                    (MP-Link Inside^Planner))
```

Figure 3: Creation of Transfer-Inside and Transfer-Inside^Actor nodes, with forward-referencing.

links, along with more neurally-realistic nodes that communicate via output spikes, such as the artificial neural oscillators of [Vidal & Haggerty, 1987]. The functionality of DESCARTES objects can easily be extended by combining the default class definitions of the object hierarchy with user-defined modifications, a process described in [Lange *et al.*, 1989].

Structured Networks

Some connectionist models have a consistent structure between groups of nodes in the network. In a semantic network, for example, a node representing the head of a frame might always be connected via a certain type of link to each of its roles, which in turn might always have a node for their fillers. Groups of nodes forming winner-take-all networks are always completely interconnected with constant inhibitory weights. Rather than force the user to repetitively define all nodes and connections for each such structured group, DESCARTES has a facility that allows the programmer to optionally define a structured growing method for each node class. A node's growth method automatically creates the node's expected structured incoming and outgoing nodes and connections. This feature allows knowledge base definitions to act as keys for network creation rather than as exhaustive listings of the networks' nodes and their connectivity.

SIMULATION IN DESCARTES

Once the networks have been designed and built, the user starts the simulation by (1) optionally defining the cycling, termination, and display sequence for each network, (2) initializing the meta-controller to clear out all activation and markers, (3) activating or marking the desired nodes, and (4) starting the cycling sequence and specifying the number of global cycles to run. An example of this process is shown in Figure 4, but for a complete description see [Lange *et al.*, 1989].

Figure 4 shows the initial activation and markers needed to process the phrase *"John put the pot inside the dishwasher."* The first define-cycling command in the figure specifies that the meta-controller spread activation in Network-A once per global cycle, while only passing markers once per every three global cycles. Both activation and markers will cycle until stability, their default termination condition. For analysis of the network's activity, the user has defined that a trace of the markers' propagation be shown and that the status of the nodes be displayed every ten cycles. The second define-cycling command defines that Network-B is not to be cycled in this example.

In general, the networks' cycling sequences need only be set once per session (if at all), although all sequencing and displaying parameters may be re-specified in mid-simulation. Activations and markers of nodes may be changed at any time. The cycling sequence is further described below.

The Simulation Cycle

As shown, DESCARTES is designed in such a way that networks can be cycled in parallel or serially. The meta-controller provides for timing coordination between the networks. Networks cycled in parallel behave as if they were a single net, even though they need not operate at the same fre-

```
(define-cycling %Network-A :sa-cycle-every      1      ;; (1)
                           :marker-cycle-every 3
                           :marker-trace       T
                           :display-every      10)
(define-cycling %Network-B :sa-cycle-every     NIL)
(init meta-control)                                    ;; (2)

(clamp-activation %"put"      1.0)                     ;; (3)
(mark %Transfer-Inside^Actor (marker %John))
(mark %Transfer-Inside^Obj   (marker %Cooking-Pot)
                             (marker %Marijuana))
(mark %Transfer-Inside^Loc   (marker %Dishwasher))

(cycle 50)                                             ;; (4)
```

Figure 4: An example of the DESCARTES control language.

quency, or, in fact, with the same functionality. A particular model may have a network of inhibitory nodes cycling at a faster rate than a network of excitatory nodes with which it interacts, at the same time as symbolic markers are being passed over each, and backpropagation is being performed within sub-networks of the model. With serial cycling, one network may wait until another network completes a specified number of cycles or reaches stability before starting to cycle itself.

Each global network cycle is comprised of four steps: (1) determination of which networks need to be cycled, (2) update of active nodes in the cycling networks, (3) spread from active nodes in the cycling networks to their out-links, and (4) report any requested output.

Determining Active Networks: The meta-controller determines which of the networks in the system need to be cycled in parallel on the given cycle, according to defaults and any define-cycling commands. In Figure 4, spreading-activation nodes in Network-A will be cycled on every global cycle, while marker-passing nodes will be cycled only on global cycles 1, 4, 7, and so on, until termination (stability).

Update: Each active node in the cycling networks queries its incoming links for new activation and/or markers. Spreading-activation nodes calculate their new activation by applying their activation function, while marker-passing nodes store any new markers they have received.

Spread-To-Out-Links: Each active node in the cycling networks calculates its output (either activation or markers) and sends it to its outgoing links. The output of spreading-activation nodes is calculated by applying their output function, while the output of marker-passing nodes is generally their new markers.

Report Output: The final step of a cycle entails querying the cycling networks for results. Each network controller can optionally display the status of important nodes at specified cycles (Network-A's status will be displayed every 10 cycles in Figure 4) or trace new activation and/or markers. DESCARTES currently has a number of output options useful for system design and debugging.

IMPLEMENTATION AND SIMULATOR ACCESS

DESCARTES has been designed for portability, flexibility, and simplicity of use. Portability is achieved via the use of COMMONLISP, the ANSI Lisp standard. Flexibility is augmented by the use of the COMMONLISP Object System, CLOS, whose hierarchical class structure provides inheritance which enables users to utilize pre-defined functional classes to customize their own semantics. A complete description of currently available functionality and test-bed cases can be found in [Lange *et al.*, 1989]. The largest test case simulated to date is an implementation of a ROBIN [Lange & Dyer, 1989b] network in the domain of **Hiding Pot**. It consists of two interacting LCNs built from four node classes and five link classes, with a total of 12,400 nodes and 40,000 links.

DESCARTES's control language is simple and effective, enabling the designer to easily set up and test different network configurations using either pre-defined or user-defined elements. At the same time, the system has been designed with ease of network debugging in mind, with history and output facilities that offer researchers valuable methods for interpreting network behavior.

DESCARTES will be made available to all interested users. Enquiries about access to the simulator should be sent to DESCARTES@CS.UCLA.EDU.

RELATED WORK

Some of the recent tools constructed for building and simulating connectionist architectures are (1) the Rochester Connectionist Simulator (RCS) [Goddard *et al.*, 1987], (2) the PDP Software Package [McClelland & Rumelhart, 1988], (3) MIRRORS/II [D'Autrechy *et al.*, 1988], and (4) GENESIS [Wilson *et al.*, 1988]. RCS is a spreading-activation simulator which allows units to have any amount of associated data. There is no specification language for construction of the net, but the system provides a library of commonly used network structures and units. The PDP Software package includes a number of programs for simulating the DCN models in [Rumelhart & McClelland, 1986]. MIRRORS/II and GENESIS, the most recent of the four systems, have both features: a high level non-procedural language for network construction and an indexed library of commonly used networks. Both have more sophisticated and flexible control mechanisms than RCS and the PDP Software Package, with MIRRORS/II emphasizing simulations using LCNs and GENESIS emphasizing realistic, biologically-based models.

The flexibility and symbolic capabilities afforded by DESCARTES' object-oriented implementation in COMMONLISP and CLOS comes at a small expense in simulation speed in comparison to the C-based implementations of RCS, the PDP package, and GENESIS. The only case where the difference in speed should be significant, however, is in simple backpropagation networks requiring thousands of learning epochs, for which the PDP package might be more appropriate. Except for GENESIS, all of the above-mentioned simulators are geared toward monotonic distributed or localist spreading-activation networks. None of them have the concept of hybrid multiple interactive networks as part of their design, especially those which can pass symbolic markers.

CONCLUSIONS

We have presented a development tool, DESCARTES, which provides researchers with the capability to combine Distributed Connectionist Networks, Localist Connectionist Networks and Marker-Passing Networks within a single simulation environment. The most important theoretical contribution of DESCARTES is the concept of Multiple Interactive Networks with intra- and inter-network heterogeneity. As a tool, it provides a simple, portable, and versatile environment for designing and testing different cognitive models. These capabilities make DESCARTES a unique and powerful tool for researchers in Artificial Intelligence, Cognitive Modelling, and Connectionism.

Acknowledgements

This research has been supported in part by a contract with the JTF program of the DOD and the Office of Naval Research (no. N00014-86-0615). DESCARTES has been implemented on equipment donated to UCLA by Hewlett-Packard, Inc., and Apollo Computer, Inc. We would like to thank John Reeves, Colin Allen, Michael Dyer, and Eduard Hoenkamp for their helpful comments on previous drafts of this paper.

REFERENCES

D'Autrechy, C. L., Reggia, J. A., Sutton, G. G., & Goodall, S. M. (1988): A General-Purpose Simulation Environment For Developing Connectionist Models. *Simulation, 51(1)*, p. 5-19.

Charniak, E. (1986): A Neat Theory of Marker Passing. *Proceedings of the National Conference on Artificial Intelligence (AAAI-86)*, Philadelphia, PA, 1986.

Dyer, M. G. (1989): Symbolic Neuroengineering for Natural Language Processing: A Multi-Level Research Approach. In J. Barnden and J. Pollack, editors, *Advances in Connectionist and Neural Computation Theory*, Ablex Publishing, 1989. In press.

Goddard, N., Lynne, K. J., & Mintz, T. (1986): *Rochestor Connectionist Simulator*. Technical Report TR-233, Department of Computer Science, University of Rochestor.

Hendler, J. (1988): *Integrating Marker-Passing and Problem Solving: A Spreading Activation Approach to Improved Choice in Planning*, Lawrence Erlbaum Associates, Hillsdale, New Jersey.

McClelland, J. L. & Rumelhart, D. E. (1988): *Explorations in Parallel Distributed Processing: A Handbook of Models, Programs, and Exercises*, MIT Press, Cambridge, MA.

Lange, T. & Dyer, M. G. (1989a): Dynamic, Non-Local Role-Bindings and Inferencing in a Localist Network for Natural Language Understanding. In David S. Touretzky, editor, *Advances in Neural Information Processing Systems I*, p. 545-552, Morgan Kaufmann, San Mateo, CA (Collected papers of the IEEE Conference on Neural Information Processing Systems — Natural and Synthetic, Denver, CO, November 1988).

Lange, T. & Dyer, M. G. (1989b): Frame Selection in a Connectionist Model of High-Level Inferencing. *Proceedings of the Eleventh Annual Conference of the Cognitive Science Society (CogSci-89)*, Ann Arbor, MI, August 1989.

Lange, T., Hodges J. B., Fuenmayor, M., & Belyaev, L. (1989): *The DESCARTES Users Manual*. Research Report, Computer Science Department, University of California, Los Angeles.

Nenov, V. I., & Dyer, M. G. (1988): DETE: A Connectionist/Symbolic Model of Visual and Verbal Association. *Proceedings of the IEEE Second Annual International Conference on Neural Networks (ICNN-88)*, San Diego, CA, July 1988.

Rumelhart, D. E., & McClelland, J. L. (1986): *Parallel Distributed Processing: Explorations in the Microstructure of Cognition*. Volumes 1-2, MIT Press, Cambridge, MA.

Shastri, L. (1988): A Connectionist Approach to Knowledge Representation and Limited Inference. *Cognitive Science, 12*, p. 331-392.

Vidal, J. & Haggerty, J. (1987): Synchronization in Neural Nets. *Proceedings of the IEEE Conference on Neural Information Processing Systems — Natural and Synthetic (NIPS-87)*, Denver, CO, November 1987.

Waltz, D. & Pollack, J. (1985): Massively Parallel Parsing: A Strongly Interactive Model of Natural Language Interpretation. *Cognitive Science, 9(1)*, p. 51-74.

Wilson, M. A., Upinder, S. B., Uhley, J.D., & Bower, J. M. (1988): GENESIS: A System for Simulating Neural Networks. In David S. Touretzky, editor, *Advances in Neural Information Processing Systems I*, p. 485-492, Morgan Kaufmann, San Mateo, CA (Collected papers of the IEEE Conference on Neural Information Processing Systems — Natural and Synthetic, Denver, CO, November 1988).

Frame Selection in a Connectionist Model Of High-Level Inferencing

Trent E. Lange
Michael G. Dyer

Computer Science Department
University of California, Los Angeles

ABSTRACT

Frame selection is a fundamental problem in high-level reasoning. Connectionist models have been unable to approach this problem because of their inability to represent multiple dynamic variable bindings and use them by applying general knowledge rules. These deficits have barred them from performing the high-level inferencing necessary for planning, reasoning, and natural language understanding.

This paper describes a localist spreading-activation model, ROBIN, which solves a significant subset of these problems. ROBIN incorporates the normal semantic network structure of previous localist networks, but has additional structure to handle variables and dynamic role-binding. Each concept in the network has a uniquely-identifying activation value, called its *signature*. A dynamic binding is created when a binding node receives the activation of a concept's signature. Signatures propagates across paths of binding nodes to dynamically instantiate candidate inference paths, which are selected by the *evidential* activation on the network's semantic structure. ROBIN is thus able to approach many of the high-level inferencing and frame selection tasks not handled by previous connectionist models.

INTRODUCTION

High-level cognitive tasks, such as planning, reasoning, and natural language understanding, require the ability to perform inferencing to make explanations of and/or predictions from known states and actions. In natural language understanding, for example, a reader must often make multiple inferences to understand the motives of actors and to connect actions that are unrelated on the basis of surface semantics alone. Complicating the understanding process is the fact that language is often ambiguous on both the lexical and conceptual level. Consider the phrase:

P1: *"John put the pot inside the dishwasher"*

Most people will infer that John transferred a Cooking-Pot inside of a dishwasher in an attempt to get it clean. However, suppose P1 is followed by:

P2: *"because the police were coming."*

Suddenly, the interpretation selected for the word *"pot"* in P1 changes to Marijuana, and his Transfer-Inside action becomes a plan for hiding the Marijuana from the police.

The inferences needed to understand these two phrases (**Hiding Pot**) illustrate one of the fundamental problems in high-level inferencing, that of *frame selection*. When should a system make inferences from a given frame instantiation? Which of its related frames should it instantiate to make these inferences? Without being able to cope with these problems, a system will not be able to handle the following crucial tasks:

Word-Sense Disambiguation: Choosing the meaning of a word in a given piece of text. In P1, the word *"pot"* refers to a Cooking-Pot, but when P2 is presented, the evidence is that the interpretation should change to Marijuana.

Inferencing: Making inferences to understand the results of actions and the motives of actors. Nothing in **Hiding Pot** explicitly states that the police might see the pot, or even that the police will be in proximity to it and John. Nor is it explicitly stated what the police will do if they see he possesses Marijuana. All must be inferred from seemingly innocuous phrases P1 and P2.

Concept Refinement: Inferring a specific frame from a more general one. In P1, the fact that the pot was inside of a dishwasher told us much more than the simple knowledge that it was inside of a container. In **Hiding Pot**, however, the salient point is that it is inside of an opaque object, which allows us to infer that the police will not be able to see it.

Plan/Goal Analysis and Schema Instantiation: Recognizing the plan an actor is using to fulfill his goals. In P1, it appears that John put the pot into the dishwasher as part of the $Dishwasher-Cleaning script to satisfy his goal of getting it clean. In **Hiding Pot**, however, it appears that it is part of his plan to satisfy his sub-goal of hiding it from the police, which is part of his overall goal to avoid arrest.

Frame selection is complicated by the effect of additional context, which often causes reinterpretation to competing frames. The contextual evidence in **Hiding Pot** can conflict even more, and the explanation change again, if, for example, the next phrase is:

P3: *"They were coming over for dinner."*

As a result of P3, the word *"pot"* might be reinterpreted back to Cooking-Pot. These examples clearly point out two sub-problems of frame selection, *frame commitment* and *reinterpretation*. When should a system commit to one interpretation over another? And if it does commit to one interpretation, how does new context cause that interpretation to change?

PREVIOUS APPROACHES

Symbolic rule-based systems, such as BORIS [Dyer, 1983] and MOPTRANS [Lytinen, 1984], have had some success at performing the inferencing and frame selection necessary for high-level cognitive tasks. Their processing mechanisms, however, are often extraordinarily complex, being governed by large collections of brittle and sometimes ad-hoc rules that usually change with each type of knowledge structure modelled. Ambiguous input, such as that of **Hiding Pot**, has proven especially difficult for rule-based approaches, often requiring complicated and expensive backtracking rules when reinterpretation is required.

Distributed Spreading-Activation Networks

Distributed connectionist models, such as those of [McClelland & Kawamoto, 1986] and [Touretzky & Hinton, 1988], have lately been receiving much interest, mainly because of the learning algorithms available for their massively parallel networks of simple processing elements. Despite this attention, no distributed network model has yet exhibited the ability to handle inferencing having complexity even near that of **Hiding Pot**. The primary reason for this current lack of success is their inability to represent dynamic role-bindings and to propagate these binding constraints during inferencing. Distributed networks, furthermore, are sequential at the knowledge level and lack the representation of structure needed to handle complex conceptual relationships [Feldman, 1989].

Localist Spreading-Activation Networks

Localist spreading-activation models, such as those of [Cottrell & Small, 1983], [Waltz & Pollack, 1985], and [Shastri, 1988], also use massively parallel networks of simple processing units. Localist networks represent knowledge by simple nodes and their interconnections, with each node standing for a distinct concept. Activation on a conceptual node represents the amount of *evidence* available for that concept in the current context.

Unlike distributed networks, localist networks are parallel at the knowledge level and can represent structural relationships between concepts. Because of this, multiple inference paths are pursued simultaneously; a necessity to account for the understanding speed exhibited by people. Disambiguation is achieved automatically as related concepts under consideration provide evidence for and feedback to one another.

The main problem with previous localist models is that the evidential activation on their conceptual nodes gives no clue as to *where* that evidence came from. Because of this, previous localist models have had no more success than distributed models at handling dynamic non-local bindings — and thus remain unsuited to tasks requiring high-level inferencing.

Marker Passing Networks

Marker-passing models, such as those of [Granger *et al.*, 1986] and [Hendler, 1988], operate by spreading symbolic markers across semantic networks. Role-bindings are trivially represented using the symbolic pointers stored in their markers, whose propagation is used to generate plausible inference paths. Unfortunately, the logic and lisp-based symbolic mechanisms of existing marker-passing systems are far more complex than the simple processing units of spreading-activation networks. More importantly, marker-passing systems lack the natural constraint satisfaction abilities that allow localist networks to implicitly weigh contextual evidence in choosing a most highly-activated interpretation. They must therefore use a symbolic mechanism separate from the marker-passing process to apply a theorem prover and/or a heuristic path evaluator for path selection.

ROBIN

ROBIN (ROle Binding and Inferencing Network), is a localist spreading-activation model that has all of the advantages of previous localist approaches but, in addition, handles the problems of dynamic role-binding, inferencing, and frame selection. The localist networks in which ROBIN encodes its semantic networks consist entirely of connectionist units [Feldman & Ballard, 1982] that perform simple computations on their inputs: summation, summation with thresholding and decay, or maximization. Connections between units are weighted, and either excitatory or inhibitory.

ROBIN uses structured connections of nodes to encode frames [Minsky, 1975]. Each frame has one or more roles, with each role having expectations and logical constraints on its fillers. Every frame can be related to one or more other frames, with pathways between corresponding roles for inferencing. Activation spreads from frame to related frame when the constraints on their role fillers are met, thus automatically instantiating other frames and performing the processes of inferencing and frame selection.

As in previous localist models, ROBIN's networks have a node for every known conceptual frame in the network. Relations between concepts are represented by weighted connections between nodes. Activation on a conceptual node is *evidential*, corresponding to the amount of evidence available for the concept and the likelihood that it is selected in the current context.

Simply representing the amount of evidence available for a concept, however, is not sufficient for complex inferencing tasks. Role-binding requires that some means exist for *identifying* a concept that is being dynamically bound to a role in distant areas of the network. A network may have never heard about John having the goal of Avoid-Detection of his Marijuana, but it must be able to quickly infer just such a possibility to understand **Hiding Pot**.

Dynamic Role-Bindings With *Signature Activation*

To handle the problem of dynamic role-binding, every conceptual node in the network has associated with it a node outputting a constant, uniquely-identifying activation, called its *signature* [Lange & Dyer, 1989]. A dynamic binding is created when a role's *binding node* has an activation matching the activation of the bound concept's signature.

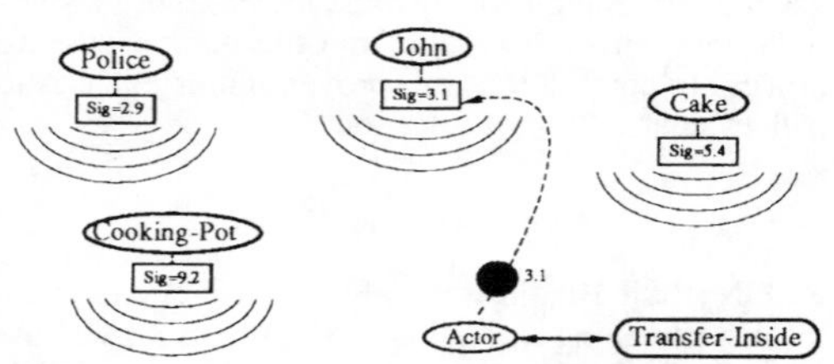

Figure 1. Several concepts and their uniquely-identifying signature nodes are shown, along with the Actor role of the Transfer-Inside frame. The dotted arrow from the binding node (black circle) to the signature node of John represents the virtual binding indicated by the shared signature activation, and does not exist as an actual connection.

In Figure 1, the virtual binding of the Actor role node of action Transfer-Inside to John is represented by the fact that its binding node, the solid black circle, has the same activation (3.1) as John's signature node. The complete Transfer-Inside frame is represented by the group of nodes that include the conceptual node Transfer-Inside, a conceptual node for each of its roles (only the Actor role shown), and the binding nodes for each of its roles.

Propagation of Signatures For Inferencing

The most important feature of signature activation is that it is spread across paths of binding nodes to generate candidate inferences. Figures 2a thru 2c illustrate how the network's structure automatically accomplishes this.

Evidential activation is spread through the paths between conceptual nodes on the bottom plane (i.e. Transfer-Inside and its Object role), while signature activation for dynamic role-bindings is spread across the parallel paths of corresponding binding nodes on the top plane. Nodes and connections for the Actor, Planner, and Location roles are not shown. Initially there is no activation on any of the conceptual or binding nodes in the network.

When input for P1 is presented, the lexical concept nodes for each of the words in the phrase are clamped to a high level of evidential activation, directly providing activation for concepts John, Transfer-Inside, Cooking-Pot, Marijuana, and Dishwasher.

To represent the role-bindings given by phrase P1, the binding nodes of each of Transfer-Inside's roles are clamped to the signatures of the concepts bound to them[1]. For example, the binding nodes of Transfer-Inside's Object are clamped to the activations (6.8 and 9.2) of the signatures for objects Marijuana and Cooking-Pot, representing the candidate bindings from the word *"pot"* (Figure 2a)[2].

The activation of the network's conceptual nodes is equal to the weighted sum of their inputs plus their previous activation times a decay rate, similar to the activation function of previous localist networks. The activation of the binding nodes, however, is equal

---

[1] ROBIN does not currently address the problem of deciding upon the original syntactic bindings, i.e. that *"pot"* is bound to the Object role of the phrase. Rather, ROBIN's networks are given these initial bindings and use them for high-level inferencing.

[2] An alternative input, such as *"John put the cake inside the oven"*, would be done simply by clamping the signatures of its bindings instead. A completely different set of inferences would then ensue. This is unlike previous localist models, where all instantiations must be hard-wired into the network.

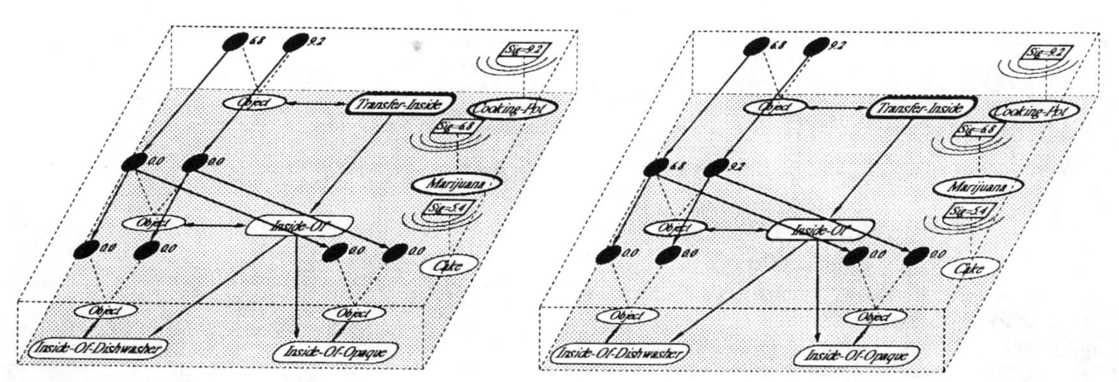

Figure 2a. Initial activation for P1.

Figure 2b. After activation has reached Inside-Of.

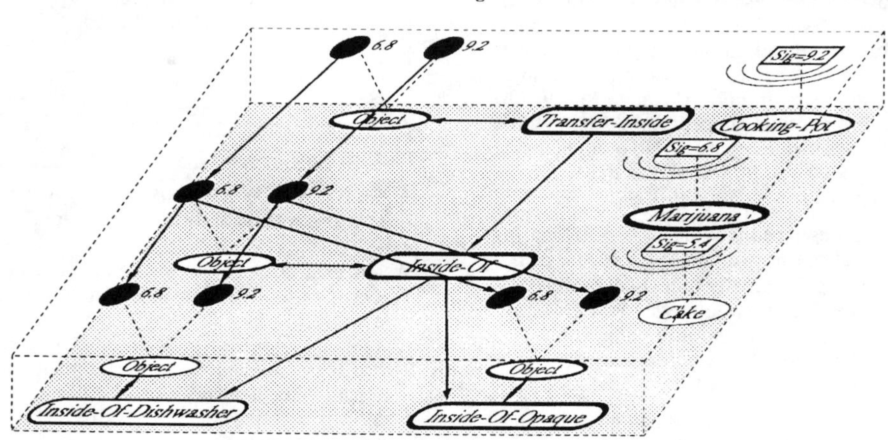

Figure 2c. Activation after quiescence has been reached in processing for **Hiding Pot**.

Figure 2. Simplified ROBIN network segment at three different cycles during processing of **Hiding Pot**. Each figure shows the parallel paths over which evidential activation (bottom plane) and signature activation (top plane) are spread for inferencing. Signature nodes (outlined rectangles) and binding nodes (solid black circles) are in the top planes. Thickness of conceptual node boundaries (ovals) represents their levels of evidential activation. (Node names do not affect the spread of activation in any way. They are simply used to initially set up the network's structure and to aid in analysis.)

to the maximum of their unit weighted inputs, allowing signatures to be propagated without alteration.

As activation starts to spread after the initial clamped activation values in Figure 2a, Inside-Of receives evidential activation from Transfer-Inside, representing the strong evidence that something is now inside of something else. Concurrently, the signature activations on the binding nodes of Transfer-Inside's Object propagate to the corresponding binding nodes of Inside-Of's Object (Figure 2b), since each of the binding nodes calculates its activation as the maximum of its inputs. The network has thus made the crucial inference of exactly which thing is inside of the other. Similarly, as time goes on, Inside-Of-Dishwasher and Inside-Of-Opaque receive evidential activation, with inferencing continuing by the propagation of signature activation to their corresponding binding nodes (Figure 2c).

Note that the actual activation values of signatures do not affect the network's processing. The signatures of Marijuana and Cooking-Pot were arbitrarily chosen to be 6.8 and 9.2 when the network was created, but could just as easily have been any other values. It is only necessary that each signature be different from all others — and so uniquely identify the concept bound to a role.

Frame	Binding Constraints	Used In
Inside-Of-Stove	(a Cooking-Pot is inside of a Stove)	$Stove-Cooking
Inside-Of-Dishwasher	(a Utensil is inside of a Dishwasher)	$Dishwasher-Cleaning
Inside-Of-Opaque	(a Phys-Obj is inside of an Opaque-Object)	Avoid-Detection

Figure 3. Three of the competing *refinements* of state Inside-Of.

FRAME SELECTION

Several paths of candidate inference chains are instantiated by the parallel propagation of signature and evidential activation. The path chosen as the network's interpretation at any given time is simply the one with the greatest evidential activation.

Consider how this process handles the problem of frame selection. Every frame in ROBIN's semantic knowledge base is related, through its roles, to one or more other frames. Some of those related frames compete, while others do not. The state Inside-Of, for example, has multiple concept *refinements*, three of which are described in Figure 3. No more than one of those refinements can be selected as the active *refinement* of a given instantiation of Inside-Of.

The mechanism described previously is sufficient for most examples of one or two phrases. Because of potential crosstalk from logically unrelated inferences[1], however, the network's structure is actually more complicated. Because of this, frame selection is a four part problem, controlled entirely by ROBIN'S structure of simple spreading-activation nodes:

1) *Choosing candidate frames:* When the role bindings of a frame match the logical binding constraints on the roles of a related frame, then that related frame becomes a *candidate frame* for instantiation. Related frames whose binding constraints are violated are rejected.

2) *Propagating bindings to candidate frames:* Candidate frames receive signature activation (representing role-bindings) from their instantiating frame. New candidate inferences can then propagate from each of the candidate frames to explore their respective inference paths.

3) *Propagating evidential activation to candidate frames:* Candidate frames receive weighted evidential activation from their instantiating frame. Candidates whose binding constraints are only partially matched receive proportionately less evidential activation than if their constraints were matched perfectly.

4) *Selection between candidate instantiation frames:* At any given time, the candidate frame with the most evidential activation represents the preferred interpretation. Commitments may change if new context gives more evidence to a competing frame.

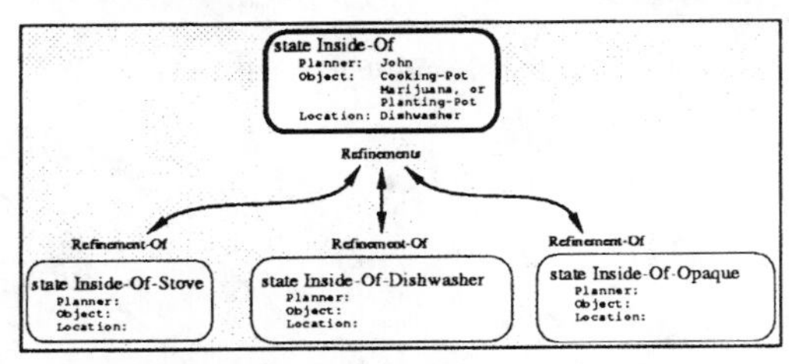

Figure 4. Overview of bindings instantiated with signature activation in Figure 2b.

As an example of how the frame selection process proceeds in ROBIN, consider Figure 4, which shows Inside-Of and three of its refinements. Evidential activation and signature role-bindings have reached Inside-Of (as in Figure 2b), so the candidates for its concept *refinement* need to be chosen. Inside-Of-Stove is rejected since a Dishwasher does not match the Stove constraint on its Location slot. Inside-Of-Dishwasher, however, is chosen as a candidate *refinement* frame, since its constraints are matched. Inside-Of-Opaque is also chosen as a candidate, since a Dishwasher *is-a* Opaque-Object.

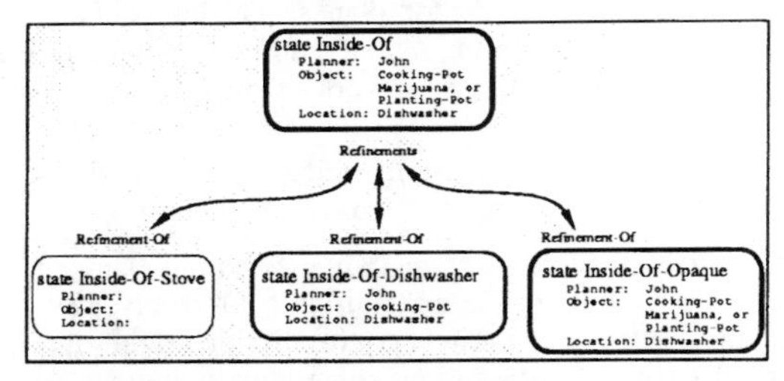

Figure 5. Overview after Inside-Of-Dishwasher and Inside-Of-Opaque become candidate *refinements* of Inside-Of (Figure 2c).

To implement this, the links allowing propagation of signature and evidential activation from one frame to another are gated by nodes that implement the frame selection process. Activation is only allowed to pass

[1]A problem not handled well by previous localist or marker-passing models.

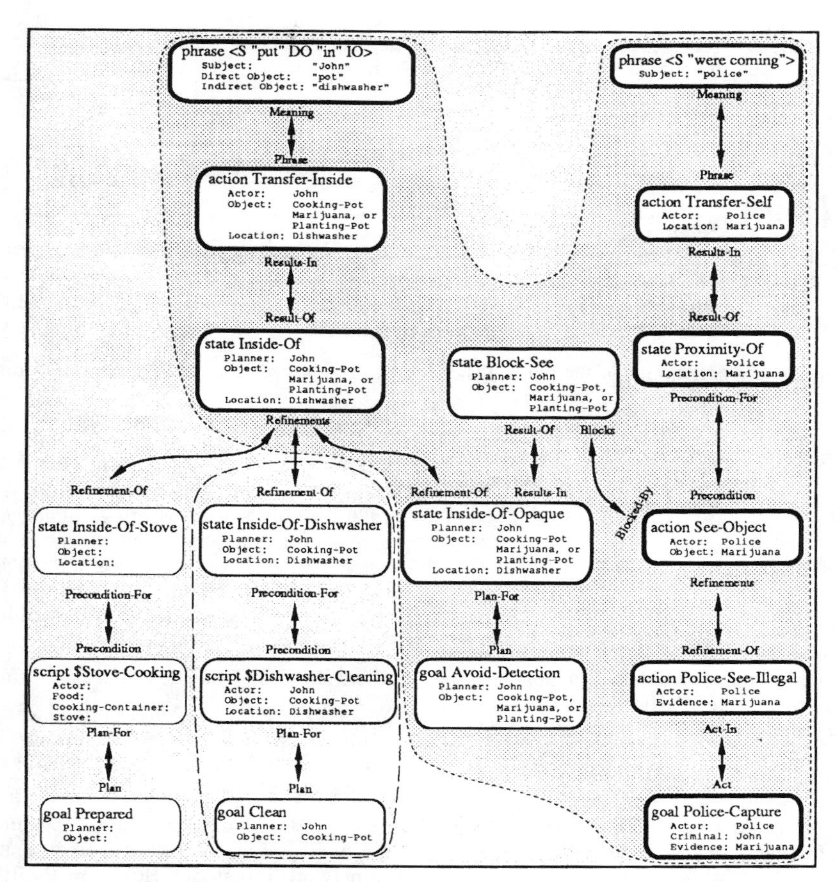

Figure 6. Overview of a small portion of a ROBIN semantic network showing inferences dynamically made after (syntactically pre-processed) input for phrases P1 and P2 of **Hiding Pot** have been presented. Thickness of frame boundaries shows the amount of evidential activation for the frames. Role fillers have been dynamically instantiated with signature activation. Darkly shaded area indicates the most highly-activated path of nodes representing the most probable plan/goal analysis of the input. Dashed area shows the discarded dishwasher-cleaning interpretation. Nodes outside of both areas show a very small portion of the rest of the network. These nodes received no evidential or signature activation from either phrase.

from a frame to one of its related frames when its role-bindings match the candidate frame's binding constraints. These logical binding constraints are calculated by groups of nodes that compare the frame's signature bindings to the candidate's binding constraints, and are described in [Lange, 1989].

As soon as Inside-Of-Dishwasher and Inside-Of-Opaque are chosen as candidate refinement frames, inhibitory gates (that disabled them from receiving signature or evidential activation from Inside-Of) are opened, performing steps 2 and 3 of the frame selection process. The result can be seen in Figure 5, where both have been instantiated. After activation has settled for **Hiding Pot**, Inside-Of-Opaque has the greater evidential activation (indicated by its thicker oval), and so is selected as the *refinement-of* Inside-Of, serving as the plan for hiding his Marijuana from the Police.

Selection of Ambiguous Role-Bindings

Note that all ambiguous meanings of a word are bound to a role with signature activation (Figures 2 thru 5). The network's interpretation of which binding is selected at any given time is the one whose concept

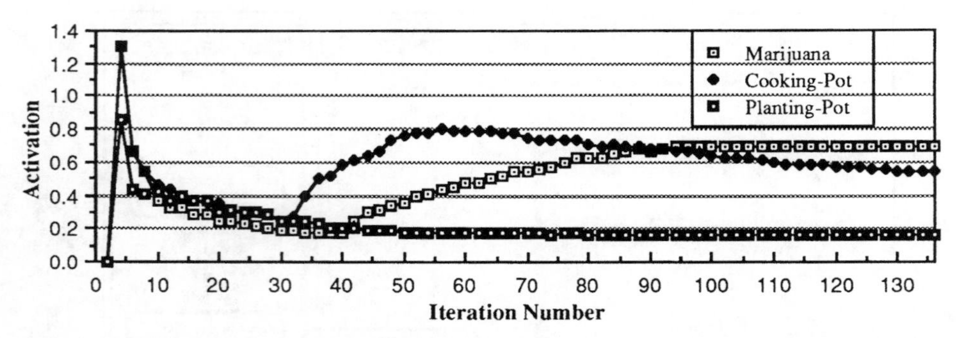

Figure 7. Evidential activations of the meanings of the word *"pot"* as activation spreads in **Hiding Pot**.

has greater evidential activation. Because all candidate bindings are propagated, with none being discarded until processing is completed, ROBIN is able to handle meaning reinterpretations without backtracking.

A DETAILED EXAMPLE

Figure 6 shows a segment of the semantic network embedded in ROBIN after input for both P1 and P2 have been presented and the network has reached stability, making the inferences needed to understand **Hiding Pot**. For example, the inference that the Marijuana is inside of an opaque object is represented by the instantiation of Inside-Of-Opaque. The role-bindings of the frames shown were instantiated dynamically with signature activation, with the final interpretation selected being the most highly-activated evidential path of frames inside the darkly shaded area.

During the interpretation of **Hiding Pot**, Cooking-Pot initially receives more evidential activation (Figure 7, cycles 40-70) than Marijuana by connections from the highly stereotypical usage of the Dishwasher for the Clean goal. The network's decision between the two candidate bindings at that point would be that it was a Cooking-Pot that was Inside-Of the Dishwasher. However, reinforcement and feedback from the inference paths generated by the Police's Transfer-Self eventually causes Marijuana to win out. The final selection of the Marijuana bindings over Cooking-Pot is represented simply by the fact that Marijuana has greater evidential activation. The resulting most highly-activated evidential path of frame nodes and propagated virtual bindings represents the interpretation of John hiding his Marijuana from the police (Figure 6).

Note that evidential activation remains on Cooking-Pot and Planting-Pot, available for possible reinterpretation given new input, such as phrase P3.

CURRENT STATUS AND FUTURE WORK

ROBIN has been fully implemented in the DESCARTES connectionist simulator[1] [Lange *et al.*, 1989]. ROBIN's inferencing, plan/goal analysis, schema instantiation, disambiguation, and reinterpretation abilities have been successfully tested on **Hiding Pot** and a number of other episodes in two domains, using syntactically preprocessed inputs of one or two sentences in length.

There are several directions for future work, including:

Signature dynamics: Currently, the identifying signatures are single arbitrary activations; instead, signatures should be distributed patterns of activation that are learned adaptively over time.

Embedded role-binding: Using signatures of pre-existing concepts, ROBIN can create and infer novel network instances. However, ROBIN currently cannot dynamically generate and propagate *new* signatures for one these instances. This ability is crucial for recursive structures, such as in: *"John told Bill that Fred told Mary that..."* Here each Object of the telling is itself a novel frame instance not having a pre-existing signature.

Network structure acquisition: Signatures allow ROBIN to create novel network instances over its pre-existing structure. The activation of these instances is transient. Over time, repeated instantiations should cause modification of weights and recruitment of underutilized units to alter network structure and create long-term memories.

[1] DESCARTES is a development environment that allows the flexible simulation of large-scale heterogeneous connectionist networks.

CONCLUSIONS

Inferencing and frame selection are fundamental problems in high-level reasoning. Unfortunately, previous connectionist models have been unable to approach these problems because of their inability to handle dynamic variable bindings and use them by applying general knowledge rules.

Although not completely solving the problems of role-binding and inferencing, we have presented a localist spreading-activation model that solves a significant subset of them. Using structure that holds *signature* activation, ROBIN is able to dynamically create novel frame instances by binding a role with any previously known concept in the network.

Since each signature is simply an activation value that uniquely identifies the concept bound to a role, it can be propagated across paths of binding nodes that preserve its activation, thus performing inferencing. This allows the encoding and "firing" of any general knowledge rule that states that the filler of one frame's roles can be inferred directly from the fillers of another. ROBIN's extra structure to handle dynamic variable-binding and rule-firing actually allows its networks to be smaller than other purely connectionist (non-marker passing) models, where all possible instantiations must be hard-wired into the network.

On the other hand, ROBIN's networks are not yet able to dynamically create new signatures, and thus cannot bind newly created recursive structures. This somewhat limits the model's inferencing capabilities in comparison to symbolic rule-based systems.

For the large portion of the inferencing process that it is able to handle, however, ROBIN has significant advantages over symbolic rule-based and marker-passing systems. The inherent constraint-satisfaction of ROBIN's normal *evidential* semantic network structure allows it to select the most plausible of the candidate frames and inference paths generated by the propagation of signature and evidential activation.

ROBIN is thus able to handle many of the high-level inferencing and frame selection tasks not approached by previous connectionist models, while at the same time perform disambiguation and semantic reinterpretation often difficult for symbolic systems.

Acknowledgements

This research has been supported in part by a contract with the JTF program of the DOD, and has been implemented on an Apollo DN4000 donated to UCLA by Apollo Computer Inc. Thanks to Jack Hodges, Eduard Hoenkamp, and the anonymous reviewers for their comments on previous drafts of this paper.

References

Cottrell, G. & Small, S. (1982): A Connectionist Scheme for Modelling Word-Sense Disambiguation. *Cognition and Brain Theory, 6*, p. 89-120.

Dyer, M. G. (1983): *In-Depth Understanding*. The MIT Press, Cambridge, MA.

Feldman, J. A., and Ballard, D. H. (1982): Connectionist Models and Their Properties. *Cognitive Science, 6:1*, p. 205-254.

Feldman, J. A. (1989): Neural Representation of Conceptual Knowledge. In L. Nadel, L. A. Cooper, P. Culicover, and R. M. Harnish (eds), *Neural Connections, Mental Computation*. The MIT Press, Cambridge, MA.

Granger, Eiselt, & Holbrook (1986): Parsing with Parallelism: A Spreading Activation Model of Inference Processing During Text Understanding. In *Experience, Memory, and Reasoning*, LEA Publishers, Hillsdale, New Jersey, p. 227-246.

Hendler, J. (1988): *Integrating Marker-Passing and Problem Solving*. LEA Publishers, Hillsdale NJ.

Lange, T. (1989): *High-Level Inferencing in a Localist Network*, Master's Thesis, Computer Science Dept., University of California, Los Angeles.

Lange, T. & Dyer, M. G. (1989): Dynamic, Non-Local Role-Bindings and Inferencing in a Localist Network for Natural Language Understanding. In David S. Touretzky (ed.), *Advances in Neural Information Processing Systems I*, p. 545-552, Morgan Kaufmann, San Mateo, CA.

Lange, T., Hodges J., Fuenmayor, M., & Belyaev, L. (1989): DESCARTES: Development Environment For Simulating Hybrid Connectionist Architectures. *Proceedings of the Eleventh Annual Conference of the Cognitive Science Society (CogSci-89)*, Ann Arbor, MI, August 1989.

Lytinen, S. (1984): Frame Selection in Parsing. *Proceedings of the National Conference on Artificial Intelligence (AAAI-84)*, August 1984.

McClelland, J. L. & Kawamoto, A. H. (1986): Mechanisms of Sentence Processing. In McClelland & Rumelhart (eds.) *Parallel Distributed Processing: Vol 2*. The MIT Press, Cambridge, MA.

Minsky, M. (1975): A Framework for Representing Knowledge. In P.H. Winston (ed.), *The Psychology of Computer Vision*. New York: McGraw-Hill, p. 211-277.

Shastri, L. (1988): A Connectionist Approach to Knowledge Representation and Limited Inference. *Cognitive Science, 12*, p. 331-392.

Touretzky, D. S. & Hinton, G. E. (1988): A Distributed Connectionist Production System. *Cognitive Science, 12*, p. 423-466.

Waltz, D. & Pollack, J. (1985): Massively Parallel Parsing. *Cognitive Science, 9:1*, p. 51-74.

A Symbolic/Connectionist Script Applier Mechanism

Geunbae Lee, Margot Flowers, Michael G. Dyer
Artificial Intelligence Laboratory
Computer Science Department, UCLA

Abstract

We constructed a Modular Connectionist Architecture which consists of many different types of 3 layer feed-forward PDP network modules (auto-associative recurrent, hetero-associative recurrent, and hetero-associative) in order to do script-based story understanding. Our system, called DYNASTY (DYNAmic script-based STory understanding sYstem) has the following 3 major functions: *(1) DYNASTY can learn distributed representations of concepts and events in everyday scriptal experiences, (2) DYNASTY can do script-based causal chain completion inferences according to the acquired sequential knowledge, and (3) DYNASTY performs script role association and retrieval while performing script application.* Our purpose in constructing this system is to show that the learned internal representations, using simple encoder-type networks, can be used in higher-level modules to develop connectionist architectures for fairly complex cognitive tasks, such as script processing. Unlike other neurally inspired script processing models, DYNASTY can learn its *own similarity-based distributed representations from input script data* using ARPDP (Auto-associative Recurrent PDP) architectures. Moreover DYNASTY's role association network handles both script roles and fillers as *full-fledged concepts*, so that it can learn the generalized associative knowledge between several script roles and fillers.

1 Background and Issues

A script is a knowledge structure of stereotypic action sequences [27]. According to psychological experiments[1], people use scripts to understand and remember narrative texts. But proposed symbolic AI models of script processing (e.g. SAM [2,26]) have many unresolved problems: (1) They are too rigidly defined, so they can not handle script deviations properly. (2) It is difficult to invoke the right script for the input story fragments. Proposed script headers[2] are unnatural and fragile.

A number of neurally inspired connectionist script processing models have been proposed to overcome weaknesses in the symbolic models [3,4,5], but none of them has the semantics needed for representing constituency of concepts and events. Dolan and Dyer [6] are the first to consider micro-feature based underlying representations in connectionist script processing to make their representations have similarity properties: similar concepts have similar representations. But as noted in [7] micro-features are unnatural and akward.

This paper proposes a modular distributed connectionist architecture called DYNASTY (DYNAmic script-based STory understanding sYstem) based on *automatically learned distributed semantic representations.* DYNASTY takes simple coherent groups of sentences as input, e.g.:

> John went to Sizzler. John ate steak and shrimp. John left a tip.

and produces causally completed groups of sentences as output:[1]

> John went to Sizzler. Waiter seated John. John looked at the menu. John ordered steak and shrimp. John ate steak and shrimp. John paid the bill. John left a tip. John left Sizzler for home.

There are three major tasks that DYNASTY must solve in order to handle this example: (1) DYNASTY must learn distributed semantic representations (DSR) for both concepts and events automatically from its input script data. (2) DYNASTY must learn sequential knowledge to do causal-chain completion inference. (3) DYNASTY must learn associations between script roles and their fillers for later retrieval of role bindings.

[1] The events in this output were mentioned by 55 - 75% of the human subjects in a psychological experiment [1].

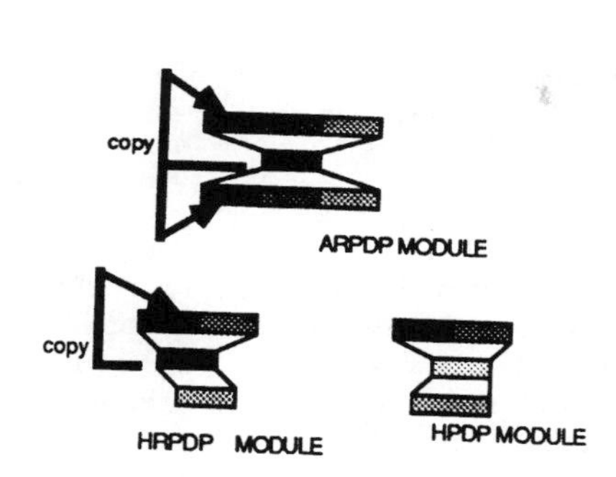

Figure 1: ARPDP, HRPDP, and HPDP modules.

2 DYNASTY System Architecture

DYNASTY has three different PDP (Parallel Distributed Processing) modules in its system architecture: ARPDP (Auto-associative Recurrent PDP), HRPDP (Hetero-associative Recurrent PDP) and HPDP (Hetero-associative PDP) modules. Figure 1 shows the three different modules in the system. Each module is not an entirely new architecture. For example, Pollack [8] used an ARPDP architecture[2] to generate recursive distributed representations of stacks and parse trees. HRPDP architecture has been used by many researchers, e.g. Elman [9], Allen [10], Hanson [11] and John [12] for several applications: natural language question-answering[10], parsing[11] and sentence comprehension[12]. HPDP architecture is an ordinary three layer PDP architecture. But what is new is that DYNASTY uses all these different PDP sub-architectures as modular components for a coherent system architecture, namely, a system for script application.

Figure 2 shows the overall DYNASTY architecture. DYNASTY modules communicate through a global dictionary [7] which has distributed representations of concepts and events. The ARPDP oval consists of two ARPDP modules, and their functions are to develop distributed semantic representations for concepts and events in an input script-based story. In the same way, the HRPDP oval consists of two HRPDP modules, and their functions are to learn sequential knowledge in the script and produce entire script events sequentially. Finally, the HPDP oval consists of one HPDP module with three symbolic buffers: event-match-list, script-instance-buffer, and script-buffer. Their functions are to learn the script

[2] He used a different name, i.e., RAAM (Recursive Auto Associative Memory).

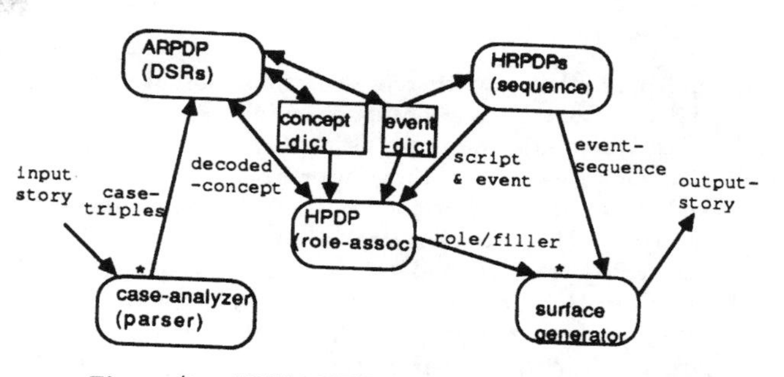

Figure 2: DYNASTY system architecture. The ovals represent PDP modules, while the boxes represent symbolic stores. The lines designate uni-/bi-directional data flow. Modules marked with * are not developed yet.

role and filler associations. The internal architectures and their functions will be described in detail.

3 Learning Distributed Semantic Representations

3.1 Criteria for a Distributed Semantic Representation

A distributed representation able to represent conceptual knowledge must have five features:

1.*Automaticity* – The representation must be acquired through some automatic learning procedure, rather than set by hand. For instance, the hand-coded microfeature based representation[15] does not meet this criterion.

2.*Portability* – The representation should be global rather than locally confined to its training environment. That is, the representation learned in one training environment should have structural/semantic invariant properties so that it can be applied in another task environment. For example, the representation in Hinton's family tree example[19] can be said to meet the automaticity criterion, but not the portability criterion, since it cannot be used in any other task.

3.*Structure Encoding* – Feldman[20] has argued that any conceptual representation must support answering questions about structural aspects of the concept. For example, part of the meaning of "irresponsible" is that there was an obligation established to perform an action and the obligation was violated. To answer a question about the meaning of "irresponsible" requires accessing these constituent structures. Any conceptual representation must have structural information in the representation itself about the constituents of the concept and purely holographic representations do not meet this criterion. This structure-encoding criterion implies systematicity, compositionality, and inferential coherence - the three properties that Fodor and Pylyshyn[18] mentioned when criticizing connectionism. The extended back-propagation method, FGREP[7], can be said to meet the first and the second criteria, but the resulting FGREP representation is purely holographic. We can not retrieve any structural information from the representation itself. Thus representations of lexical entries in the FGREP lexicon do not allow us to answer questions about the constituents of any word's conceptual structure. Hand-coded microfeatures are a good representation according to this criterion, since at least one can interpret the semantic content of each microfeature in the representation, but they are arbitrary, lack structure, and create a knowledge engineering bottleneck.

4. *Micro-Semantics* – Distributed representations gain much of their power by encoding statistical correlations from the training set, which are used to characterize the environment. These statistical correlations give connectionist models the ability to generalize. To support generalization, distributed representations should exhibit semantic content at the micro level, i.e. similar concepts should end up (by some metric) with similar distributed representations. This criterion provided the original impetus for microfeature-based encodings, since similar concepts are similar because they share similar microfeature values.

5. *Convergence* – A basic operation for any self-organizing (possibly chaotic) representation is convergence to a (possibly chaotic) attractor. At any one time, the representation should have a stable pattern of activation over the ensemble of units in a stable environment, and this pattern should converge to an attractor point in the feature space[14].

3.2 Forming Distributed Semantic Representations (DSRs) of Words

In this section we show how DSRs may be formed and demonstrate their validity for the task of encoding word meanings.

There are two alternate views on the semantic content of words: (1) The *structural view* defines a word meaning only in terms of its relationships to other meanings. (2) The *componential view* defines meaning as a vector of properties (e.g. microfeatures). We take an interim view – that meaning can be defined in terms of a distributed representation of structural/functional relationships, where each relationship is encoded as a proposition. Examples of propositions are verbal descriptions of action-oriented events in everyday experiences.

3.2.1 Representing DSRs

The intuition behind DSRs is that people learn the meanings of words through examples of their relationships to other words. For example, after reading the 4 propositions below, the reader begins to form a hypothesis of what kind of meaning the word "foo" should have.

- Proposition1: The man drinks foo with a straw.
- Proposition2: The company delivers foo in a carton.
- Proposition3: Humans get foo from cows.
- Proposition4: The man eats bread with foo.

The meaning of foo should be something like that of milk. The interesting fact is that the semantics of "foo" is not fixed, rather it is gradually refined as one experiences more propositions in varying environments. To develop DSRs based on propositions, we have to define the structural/functional relationships between concepts with respect to those propositions. For action-oriented events describing propositions, we use thematic case relations, originally developed by Fillmore[13], and extended in several natural language processing systems[21]. We use the following 8 thematic case relations which are similar to the ones defined in Fillmore[13] : agent, object, co-object, instrument, source, goal, location, and time. For example, the DSR of "milk" is now defined as the composition of relationships, e.g. with respect to the 4 propositions above. These are then combined as follows:

> *milk* = F_i (G_c (object, *proposition1*), G_c (object, *proposition2*), G_c (object, *proposition3*), G_c (co-object, *proposition4*),.....)

where *milk* is the meaning representation of "milk"; F_i is some integration function and G_c is some combination function of structural/functional relationships with respect to the corresponding propositions. In the same way, each proposition itself is defined as the composition of the constituent thematic case components *that are themselves combinations of structural/functional relationships* with their corresponding meaning representations of other words:

> *proposition1* = F_i (G_c (agent, *man*), G_c (verb, *drink*), G_c (object, *milk*), G_c (instrument, *straw*))

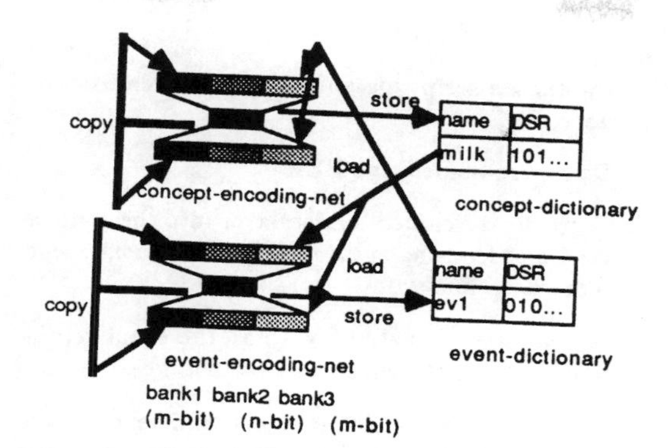

Figure 3: ARPDP Network Architecture for Learning DSRs

3.2.2 Learning DSRs

We have developed ARPDP (auto-associative recurrent PDP) networks for automatically learning DSRs. The basic idea is to *recirculate* the developing internal representation (hidden layer of the network) back out to the environment (input and output layers of the network).[3] Figure 3 shows our ARPDP architecture. The learning portion of the ARPDP architecture contains two symbolic memories (concept dictionary and event dictionary) and two 3-layer ARPDP networks. The input and output layers of each network has 3 banks of units: bank1, bank2, bank3. After each of the 3 banks is properly loaded with the elements of a proposition, the DSR emerges in bank1 by unsupervised auto-associative BEP (Backward Error Propagation)[16].

The DSR learning process consists of two alternating cycles: Concept Encoding and Proposition (Event) Encoding. Below we informally describe each cycle. In each, all concept and proposition representations start with a *don't care* pattern, e.g. 0.5, when the activation value range of each unit in network is 0.0 to 1.0. The structural/functional relationship representation is fixed, using orthogonal bit patterns (for minimizing interference).

Concept Encoding Cycle:

1. Pick one concept to be represented, say CON1.
2. Select all relevant triples for CON1. In the *milk* example, they should be triples like (*milk* object proposition1) (*milk* object proposition2) (*milk* object proposition3), etc.
3. For the first triple, load the initial representation for CON1 into bank1; load the structural/functional relationship into bank2, and load its corresponding proposition to bank3. In the *milk* example, for the first triple, bank1, bank2, and bank3 are loaded with bit patterns for *milk*, object, and proposition1, respectively.
4. Run the auto-associative BEP algorithm, where the input and output layers have the same bit patterns.
5. Recirculate the developed (hidden layer) representation into bank1 of both the input/output layers and perform step3 to step5 for another triple until all triples are encoded.
6. Store the developed DSR into the concept dictionary and select another word concept to be represented.

Proposition (Event) Encoding Cycle: Basically this cycle undergoes the same steps as the Concept Encoding Cycle except that, this time, we load bank1, bank2, and bank3 with (respectively) the proposition (event) to be represented, structural/functional relationship, and its corresponding concept representation (DSR). The result of the encoding is stored into the event dictionary.

Now the overall DSR learning process will be:

1. Perform the entire *concept encoding cycle.*
2. Perform the entire *proposition (event) encoding cycle.*
3. Repeat step1 and step2 until we get stable patterns for all concepts and events.

In this process,the composition function F_i is embodied in the dynamics of the Recursive Auto-Associative Stacking operation[8] and the combination function G_c is just a concatenation of two bit patterns. So what the ARPDP architecture does is form a representation by compressing propositions about a concept into the hidden layer and then use those compressions in the specification of propositions that define *other* concepts, and then recycle the compression formed for *this* concept back into the representation of the original concept (doing this over and over until it stabilizes). Thus each DSR has in it the propositional structure that relates it to other concepts, where each of those are also DSRs. This method produces what may be viewed as generalizations of Hinton's "reduced descriptions" [28].

[3] The idea of recirculation was first developed by Pollack[8] and Miikkulainen and Dyer[7].

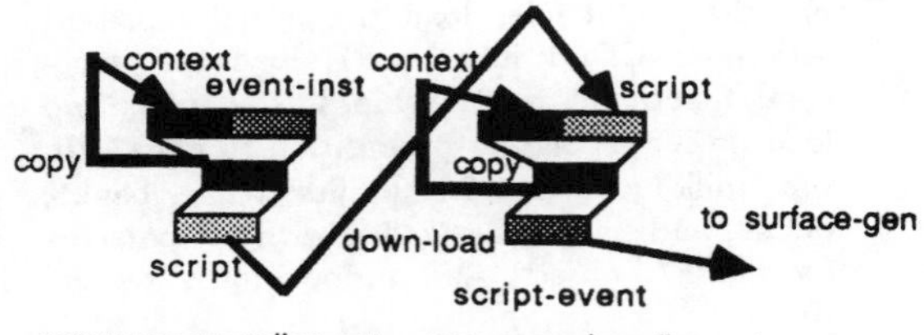

Figure 4: HRPDP architecture for learning the sequentaility of events

The decoding process is the reverse process of encoding: We load the concept representation in the hidden layer of the ARPDP concept encoding network and perform relaxation until we get the desired relationship in bank2 and proposition (event) in bank3 of the output layer. Next, we load the resulting proposition (event) in the hidden layer of the proposition encoding network and get back the constituent relationships and concept representations.

According to the evaluation and experiments reported elsewhere[17], the resulting DSRs meet all the 5 criteria: automaticity, portability, structure-encoding, micro-semantics, and convergence.

4 Learning Sequentiality of Events

Event sequences are encoded in two HRPDP networks, namely, a sequence encoding network and a sequence decoding network. Figure 4 shows this portion of the system architecture. The sequence encoding network has 2 banks in the input layer, namely, a context bank and an event bank, and has 1 script bank in the output layer. Similarly, the sequence decoding network has 2 banks: a context bank and a script bank in its input layer and 1 event bank in its output layer.

During the training phase, the system repeats the sequence encoding and decoding procedures for all the scripts defined in the system. For one script, the seqence encoding procedure is:

1. Select all relevant script instances (specific and incomplete event sequences with script roles already filled) and choose one instance.
2. Load *script bank* with the fixed orthogonal script representation.
3. Load *context bank* with *don't care* patterns and *event bank* with the first event representation in the chosen script instance from the event dictionary.
4. Do hetero-associative BEP.
5. Copy the developed hidden layer into the *context bank* and load the *event bank* with the next event representation.
6. Repeat step 4 to step 5 with all the event representations in the chosen script instance.
7. Choose another script instance and repeat step 2 to step 6 until all the selected script instances are encoded.

In this procedure, the weight vectors along with the context bank learn the correct encoding of the sequences for each script instance. For the same script, the sequence decoding procedure is:

1. Load the *context bank* with *don't care* patterns and load the *script bank* with the fixed orthogonal script representation.
2. Load the *event bank* with the first event representations of the chosen script. In this case, the generic event with the script roles unfilled is used.
3. Do hetero-associative BEP.
4. Copy the developed hidden layer into the *context bank* and load the *event bank* with the next event representation.
5. Repeat step 3 to step 4 with all the event representations in the script.

In the same way, the weight vectors along with the context bank learn the correct decoding of the sequences for the script.

In the performance phase, the system can do the causal chain completion inferences by using learned sequential knowledge. In this phase, the context bank is loaded with the don't care patterns and the event bank is loaded with the event representations from the input story. After a series of relaxations and copy actions, the script representation emerges in the script bank of the sequence encoding network. This is similar to the script recognition process in symbolic AI models. But here we don't need to worry about the script header problems: *All the events in the input story cooperate to invoke one script representation.* We load this script pattern into the script bank of the sequence decoding network and the same series of relaxations and copy actions make the completed event sequence emerge in the event bank. Since these

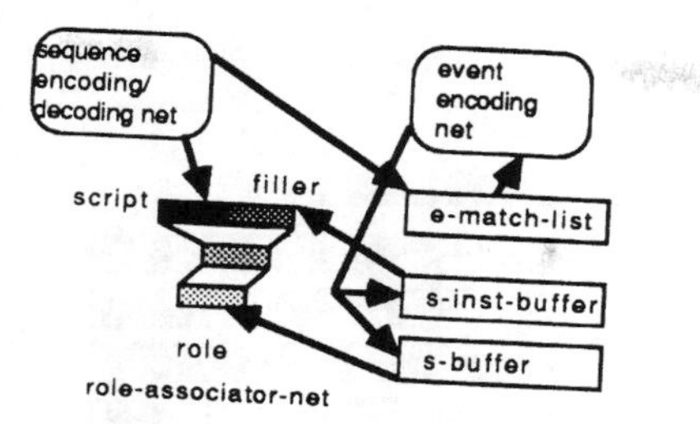

Figure 5: HPDP architecture for script role association.

events are role stripped, we need to fill the roles with fillers using a role associator network(Figure 5). After roles are filled, the output event sequences form the causal chain, i.e. the completed story output. This role binding operation will be addressed in the next section.

5 Role Association and Retrieval in DYNASTY

Role binding is not easy in a system using distributed representations since it is impossible to have context-free role variables. With similarity-based distributed representations, a solution using binding units, like in [22], will not scale up. In Smolensky's tensor approach [23], the superposition of several (schema role filler) triples in one cube makes *unorthogonal patterns* hard to be retrieved correctly.

We take a different approach to script role binding problems, namely, we consider both script roles and fillers as *full-fledged concepts*. So script roles are *associated* with their fillers rather than bound in the symbolic sense. This approach is in the same spirit as Wilensky's [24] frame/slot (or node/link) distinctions in his CRT (Cognitive Representation Theory), and as Touretzky and Geva [25], who used diffuse patterns for both slot names and fillers in their DUCS (Dynamically Updatable Concept Structures) architecture.

Figure 5 shows the role association/retrieval architecture in DYNASTY. While the HRPDP architecture is doing sequence encoding and decoding, the corresponding events in the input and output story are kept in the event-match-list. The event pairs are decoded using the ARPDP proposition (event) encoding network (see Figure 3) and stored into the script-instance-buffer and script-buffer respectively. The decoded results for the events in the input story (from the script-instance-buffer) are loaded into the filler bank, while the results for the events in the ouput story (from the script-buffer) are loaded into the role bank in the role associator network. The script bank in the same network is loaded with the patterns in the script bank in the sequence encoder network. After BEP training, the weight vectors learn the generalized features for script role and filler associations with the corresponding script representations. Then this role associator network is used to retrieve correct roles when the script and fillers are given. This is a new approach to the script role binding problem: By accumulating the associative knowledge between several roles and fillers while processing several scripts, the role associator network learns *the general role-filler associative features, not individual role-filler bindings*.

6 Experiment Results

We selected 4 scripts: *going to a restaurant, attending a lecture, grocery shopping, and visiting a doctor* from [1] and made 8 variations of each script. From the resulting 32 scripts, we extracted 122 events (propositions) to train our ARPDP modules. Figure 6 shows parts of our learned DSRs for the concepts and events.

In concept representations (CON-NAME in Figure 6), the first group designates script role concepts, while the second group designates their filler concepts. The filler concepts (e.g. John, Jack) for the same role (e.g. customer) develop similar representations. The third group designates some of the verb representations. Some of the concepts developed exactly the same representations, which is due to the limited number of propositions provided. The more propositions used in the training, the more refined are the representations.[4]

In event representations (EVENT-NAME in Figure 6), the first group designates events in the *restaurant* script, while the second group designates the same events in a specific instance (with script roles filled by proper filler concepts). The corresponding events in the second group also develop similar representations.

Next, we made up input stories (not causally completed ones) and fed them to our HRPDP and HPDP modules to get the causally completed stories with the correct role associations.

Figure 7 shows our results for the *restaurant* script when the system is fed with the input story *"John went to Sizzler. John ate steak-and-shrimp. John left a tip."* In each representation, the first row designates system output, and the second row shows the correct values for the comparison.

[4] 122 propositions are obviously insufficient in number to learn 70 concepts. We postulate that a child must experience a great number of propositions to learn a single concept correctly.

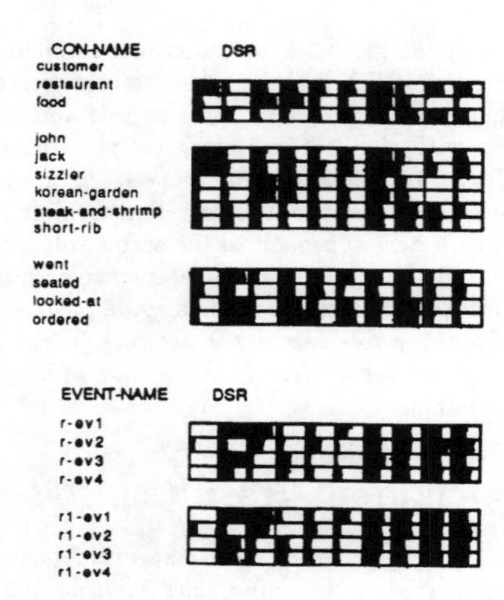

Figure 6: Learned DSRs of concepts (Nouns/Verbs) and events. The experiment is done using momentum accelerated back-propagation. Learning rate = 0.07,momentum factor = 0.5, 30 epochs for each concept and event; one epoch = 100 cycles of auto-associative backprop. The value range is 0.0 - 1.0 continuous which is shown by the degree of box fill-up.

As can be seen, the system is excellent at causal completion inference and script role retrieval.

7 Future Directions and Conclusion

A modular connectionist architecture with recursive, compositional distributed representations (the DSRs in DYNASTY) opens a new way to building practical connectionist systems that can do fairly high-level cognitive tasks. This type of neurally inspired cognitive architecture can bridge the gap between symbolic AI and the more numerical (statistical) neural network field. Usually symbolic AI systems lack in expandibility since they are brittle and break easily with large practical data. But our DYNASTY exhibits the reverse property: *The more data the system is fed, the more robust and refined its performance.* The next step is to extend this type of architecture from the prototype level to the practical level including parsing, generation and question-answering modules.

We have designed DYNASTY, a modular connectionist architecture for script processing. DYNASTY

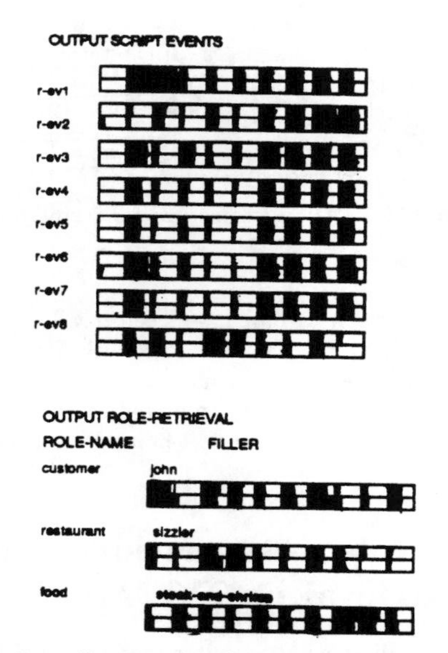

Figure 7: Causally completed output story with correct role-fillers retrieved.

can (1) automatically form distributed representations of the concepts (words) and events in the domain of script-based story understanding, (2) generate completed script event sequences from fragmentary input, and (3) successfully bind the roles in the script for the unstated events in the input. Moreover the representations formed contain constituent structure that can be extracted and events, roles, concepts with similar semantics end up with similar representations, i.e., they satisfy the 5 criteria for a DSR[17].

References

[1] Bower, G. H., Black J. B. and Turner, T. J. Scripts in memory for text. *Cognitive psychology.* 11, 177-220. 1979.

[2] Cullingford, R. E. SAM, in Schank, R. C. and Riesbeck, C. K. (Eds.) *Inside computer understanding: Five programs plus miniatures.* Lawrence Erlbaum Associates. 1981.

[3] Golden, R. M. Representing causal schemata in connectionist systems. *Proceedings of the eight annual conference of the cognitive science society.* Amherst, MA, 1986.

[4] Chun, Hon Wai and Alejandro Mimo. A model of schema selection using marker passing and connectionist spreading activation. *Proceedings of the ninth annual conference of the cognitive science society.* Seattle, WA. 1987.

[5] Rumelhart, D. E., Smolensky, P., McClelland, J. L. and Hinton, G. E. Schemata and sequential thought processes in PDP models. In Rumelhart and McClelland (Eds.) *Parallel Distributed Processing.* Vol. 2, Bradford Book/MIT Press, 1986.

[6] Dolan, C. P. and Dyer, M. G. Symbolic schemata, role binding, and the evolution of structure in connectionist memories. *Proceedings of the first international conference on neural network.* San Diego, CA, Volume II, 287-298. 1987.

[7] Miikkulainen, R. and Dyer, M. G. Forming global representations with extended back-propagation. *Proceedings of the IEEE second annual international conference on neural nets.* San Diego, CA. 1988.

[8] Pollack, J. Recursive auto-associative memory: devising compositional distributed reprsentations. *Proceedings of the tenth annual conference of the cognitive science society.* Montreal. 1988.

[9] Elman, J. L. Finding structure in time. Technical report 8801. Center for research in language, UCSD, San Diego. 1988.

[10] Allen, R. B. Sequential connectionist networks for answering simple questions about a micro-world. *Proceedings of the tenth annual conference of the cognitive science society.* Montreal. 1988.

[11] Hanson, Stephen J. and Kegl, Judy. PARSNIP: A connectionist network that learns natural language grammer from exposure to natural language sentences. *Proceedings of the ninth annual conference of the cognitive science society.* Seattle, WA. 1987.

[12] John, St. M. F. and McClelland, J. L. Applying contextual constraints in sentence comprehension. *Proceedings of the tenth annual conference of the cognitive science society.* Montreal. 1988.

[13] Fillmore, C. The case for case. In Bach, E. and Harms, R. (Eds.) *Universals in linguistic theory,* New York: Holt, Rinehart and Winston, 1968.

[14] Hopfield, J. J. Neural networks and physical systems with emergent collective computational abilities. *Proceedings of national academy of science,* Vol. 79, pp 2554-2558, 1982.

[15] McClelland, J. L. and Kawamoto, A. H. Mechanisms of sentence processing: assigning roles to constituents of sentences. In McClelland and Rumelhart (Eds.) *Parallel Distributed Processing.* Vol. 2. Bradford Book/MIT Press, 1986.

[16] Rumelhart, D. E., Hinton, G. E. and Williams, R. Learning internal representations by error propagation. In Rumelhart and McClelland (Eds.) *Parallel Distributed Processing.* Vol. 1, Bradford Book/MIT Press, 1986.

[17] Lee, G., Flowers, M. and Dyer, M. G. Learning distributed representations of conceptual knowledge. Research Report, Artificial Intelligence Lab, Dept. of Computer Science, Univ. of California at LA, 1989.

[18] Fodor, J. and Pylyshyn, Z. Connectionism and cognitive architecture: A critical analysis. *Cognition,* 28, 3-71, 1988.

[19] Hinton, G. E. Learning distributed representation of concepts. *Proceedings of the eighth annual conference of the cognitive science society,* Amherst, MA, 1986.

[20] Feldman, J. A. Neural representation of conceptual knowledge. Technical report, TR 189, Dept. of CS., Univ. of Rochester, New York, 1986.

[21] Schank, R. C. and Riesbeck, C. K. *Inside computer understanding: Five programs plus miniatures.* Lawrence Erlbaum Associates. 1981.

[22] Touretzky, D. and Hinton, G. E. A distributed connectionist production system. Technical report, CMU-CS-86-172. Computer Science Department, Carnegie Mellon Univ., Pittsburgh, 1986.

[23] Smolensky, P. A method for connectionist variable binding. Technical report, CU-CS-356-87. Dept. of Computer Science, Univ. of Colorado, Boulder, 1987.

[24] Wilensky, R. Some problems and proposals for knowledge representation. Technical report, UCB/CDS 86/294, Computer Science Division, Univ. of California at Berkeley, 1986.

[25] Touretzky, D. and Geva, S. A distributed connectionist representation for concept structures. *Proceedings of the tenth annual conference of the cognitive science society.* Montreal, 1988.

[26] Schank, R. and Abelson, R. *Scripts, plans, goals, and understanding.* LEA Press, Hillsdale, NJ. 1977.

[27] Dyer, M. G., Cullingford, R. and Alvarado, S. Scripts, in Shapiro (Eds.) *Encyclopedia of artificial intelligence.* John Wiley and Sons, Inc. 980-994, 1977.

[28] Hinton, G. Representing part-whole hierarchies in connectionist networks. *Proceedings of the tenth annual conference of the cognitive science society,* Montreal, 1988.

Distributed Problem Solving: The Social Contexts of Learning and Transfer

James Levin
Department of Educational Psychology
University of Illinois, Urbana-Champaign

Naomi Miyake
Faculty of Liberal Arts
Aoyama Gakuin Woman's College
Tokyo Japan

Michael Waugh
Department of Secondary Education
University of Illinois, Urbana-Champaign

ABSTRACT

The problem of transfer remains one of the most difficult challenges for schooling: knowledge and skills that students learn in a classroom is often not used in out-of-school contexts. To address this problem, this paper analyzes educational interaction conducted via long-distance electronic networks. We present a new methodology, called Semantic Trace Analysis. From our analyses, we present two possible solutions to the transfer problem. First, we describe an organizing framework for network interactions, which we call "receiver site transfer", which provides a functional environment for students' problem solving. In addition, we describe some initial explorations of "teleapprenticeships", instructional interactions through which students learn knowledge and skills by interacting with adults outside the school system. To the extent that adults increasingly use electronic networks for their work, we will be able to avoid the transfer problem by instructing students within the same context that they will use that instruction.

INTRODUCTION

Studies of problem solving have pointed to the problematic nature of transfer (Reed, Ernst & Banerji, 1974; Gick & Holyoak, 1980). Cognitive skills learned in one task are generally not used by subjects in "isomorphic" tasks (tasks perceived by the experimenters to be "the same task"). These experimental findings reinforce the widely expressed concern about the lack of transfer of skills and knowledge learned in school to out-of-school settings.

Pea (1987) has pointed to the limitations of locating the transfer problem solely in the task and the individual, and has suggested ways in which the social context is important in determining perceived similarity of problems and in selecting and applying previously learned skills to a novel problem. He draws upon a "cultural practices" theory (Laboratory of Comparative Human Cognition, 1983) for determining how skills will or will not be transferred.

We feel that this focus on the social context of problem solving, while an important first step, does not go far enough. The experimental findings described previously can be summarized crudely as

"Subjects will transfer skills and knowledge to a new task only when you tell them to transfer." This is somehow seen by the experimenters as a shortcoming of the subjects. If we view the experimental situation as an instructional one, we could instead blame the experimenters as inferior teachers, or blame the "educational system." However, viewed from the point of view of the subjects/students, transferring when being told to transfer is generally a very effective strategy, since the social context for most problem solving (both school-based and non-school-based) typically provides this sort of cueing support. Real problem solvers are often "told" by the social context what sort of problem they are facing and what sort of solution strategy might be appropriate.

The rationale for focussing on the "individual invention" aspect of transfer is so that problem solvers are not locked into a set of viewpoints suggested by a specific social context. In this way, innovative solutions can be reached. However, rather than focussing entirely on individual cognitive skills, a theory of transfer that takes social context into account needs to focus on ways that the naturally occurring *diversity* of social contexts which are available provides a more powerful means to suggest to problem solvers diverse, creative solutions for problems. We have developed one such model of the acquisition of transferrable skills, which we call *receiver site transfer*.

RECEIVER SITE TRANSFER

In our previous studies of instruction on electronic networks, we have developed a model of transfer, which we call "receiver site transfer" (Levin, Riel, Miyake, & Cohen, 1987; Levin, Waugh, & Kolopanis, 1988; Waugh & Levin, 1988; Waugh, Miyake, Levin & Cohen, 1988). It arose out of a goal to have students learn problem solving by tackling "real" problems (problems faced by the adults in the students' community), rather than by solving puzzles or other such problem solving exercises. The dilemma we faced was that "real" problems are *really* difficult and most often have no agreed-upon solution (otherwise they wouldn't still be problems for the adults in the community). We were concerned that conventional approaches to problem solving instruction when applied to such difficult problems would lead to frustration on the learner's part, and instead only teach them that they shouldn't try to solve real problems. Motivated by the theory of "dynamic support" (Riel, Levin, & Miller-Souviney, 1987), we considered how we might use other students, teachers, and adults linked to the students by electronic networks as a dynamically changing source of support for students' problem solving efforts.

For example, a shared "real" problem for a number of sites is a shortage of drinking water. A conventional approach to problem solving and instruction might have the students gather information about the problem, "brainstorm" ideas, and then evaluate their ideas (Polya, 1957). With this approach, most students would be unlikely to develop practical alternative solutions which passed even a superficial evaluation.

Instead, we took a "receiver site transfer" approach: 1) students in different geographic locations each described the ways that the problem is dealt with (partially) in their own location, 2) these descriptions were sent to the other participating locations, 3) students then analyzed the descriptions from the other locations, comparing them to their own descriptions, and 4) for those used elsewhere but not in their own location, students were asked to determine whether those techniques could in fact be applied in their own location. Thus, the diversity of sites served as a major source of potentially transferrable solutions to the problem.

We call this "receiver site transfer" because of its contrast to the usual form of advice giving in problem solving. Often when people have problems, they call upon an expert to tell them how to solve the problems. Typically an expert recommends that they use the way that a problem is solved in the expert's own location. We call this "sender site transfer", since the "transfer" is being carried out by the person from the place where the knowledge or skill originated.

In the case of "receiver site transfer", the individuals with a problem actively seek out others who have the same problem, and solicit from them descriptions of how they solve the "same" problem. Thus, the initiative for the transfer comes from the "receiving" site. Those seeking advice then try to determine which techniques are shared in common, and which are used elsewhere but not locally. The receiving site people are in a good position to examine specific differences between the two locations that might make a solution used elsewhere less useful locally. They may find relatively simple modifications to a solution used elsewhere that would make it useful locally. Or a given solution may suggest (through analogy or through similarity) other approaches that might work locally. The "receiver site transfer" model provides support for problem solving transfer that makes the problem solvers active participants in the generation of solutions, rather than passive receivers of "pat" solutions developed by "experts" elsewhere.

Levin, Kim and Riel (1988) found that the nature of the instructional interaction among students involved in electronic networking is different than that exhibited by students engaged in typical classroom instruction. Similarly, we have found that the nature of students' problem solving efforts in this medium are also quite different than typical classroom-based problem solving efforts of students. Electronic networks provide a medium which is qualitatively superior to the traditional classroom for helping students transfer practical problem solving skills and knowledge to new content domains.

THE WATER PROBLEM SOLVING PROJECT

The analyses of the problem solving activity discussed in this paper concern a project known as the *Water Problem Solving Project* (Levin & Cohen, 1985) which was conducted on a network called the InterCultural Learning Network. In this project, students in the United States, Mexico, Japan and Israel jointly tackled the problem of shortages of drinking water. In the initial phase of the project, the students conducted research and developed a description of how drinking water was obtained in the area where they lived. Next, these student-generated descriptions were sent via the network to the other project participants, and each of the groups of students were asked to analyze the techniques contributed by the other groups for acquiring and distributing potable water in order to identify patterns of similarity and difference. For those techniques used in other sites but not their own, students were asked to determine *why* the techniques were not used locally. In the final phase of the project, the students were asked to collect any additional information needed and then to make a judgement on the feasibility of utilizing one or more of these different techniques to help solve the water problem in their own location. They wrote up a report of their research, and sent it on the network to the other participants. This phase we call "post problem solving publication".

Receiver site transfer involves students in the process of acquiring information from diverse sources concerning the solution of some problem which is common among the various locations. The students then analyze the information in order to identify how the information might be applied in their location and share their analyses with the other network participants. The primary advantages of receiver site transfer are the following: it enables students to work on "real world" problems; it requires students to clearly articulate their thoughts in writing; it is interactive; it embodies the concept of peer tutoring; it requires students to analyze facts and synthesize new ideas. In addition, the technique seems to be highly motivating. Using this technique the emphasis in the problem solving activity is shifted away from simple attempts to brainstorm possible new solutions for a local problem, and instead toward comparing and analyzing solutions employed in other locations to solve similar problems and then attempting to adapt those solutions to fit the local situation.

Through engaging in activities which embody the receiver site transfer technique, students gain experience in using a practical method for solving "real" problems. In addition, because this technique is readily applied to a wide variety of specific problems, students can experience using the same technique in numerous problem solving activities. The flexibility of the technique provides students with a ready mechanism for exploring multiple points of view concerning the nature of and solutions for specific types of "meaningful" problems.

SEMANTIC TRACE ANALYSIS

Miyake developed the Semantic Trace Analysis as a technique for analyzing the network-based student interactions because the other types of analyses which we had previously employed focussed very specifically on syntactic or quantitative characteristics of the students' messages. The Semantic Trace Analysis is an attempt to focus on the nature of the content of the student interactions. What content were the students experiencing during the interaction? What was the purpose of their communication? In order to answer these questions, we needed a method of tracing the pattern of the development of students' ideas over the course of their project-oriented discussions in order to identify what contributed to the growth of the activity.

We applied this technique to the message interactions which were generated in the *Water Problem Solving Project.* We began by constructing a collective overview, or framework, consisting of all the ideas which were contributed by the students and other related concepts that have been mentioned in the discussion of the problem of obtaining drinking water. On this framework, we traced the course of the development of the students' ideas and graphically represented that pattern in chart form (see Figure 1). Using the chart as an activity map, one can identify information such as where a particular part of the interaction arose, how it became integrated into the previous discussion, and how the focus of the discussion shifted as a result of a particular communication.

Our analysis of the activity map for the *Water Problem Solving Project* reveals the importance of involving diverse groups of network participants. Whether it is the diversity among the participants or the nature of the activity or these characteristics in combination with others, this network-based activity resulted in significant contributions to the problem solving activity from multiple points-of-view. Whether or not the contributions were made because the activity compelled them to occur, or because the natural differences among the participants made it easy for each participant to contribute a unique and interesting observation remains a subject for further study. However, bringing multiple points-of-view to bear in problem solving efforts is highly desirable (Miyake, 1986) yet the practical difficulty of providing for these multiple viewpoints in functional settings in "typical" educational practice is significant.

Another valuable attribute of the Semantic Trace Analysis is its ability to serve as an evaluation mechanism for a network-based problem solving activity. By using the Semantic Trace Analysis map of the Water Problem Solving Project (Figure 1), one can easily see how the large number of ideas contributed to the ongoing discussion. In comparing these data to the summary message generated from any given site, one can gain a better perception of the influence that the network activity has had upon the students in that location. For example, a class of 8th grade students at Lincoln School in San Diego, California participated in the Water Project and twenty of those students contributed a summary message in which the students mentioned 71% of the ideas for solutions to the water problem which had been contributed by all of the network participants from around the world. Among those ideas mentioned by the San Diego students, 66% had been

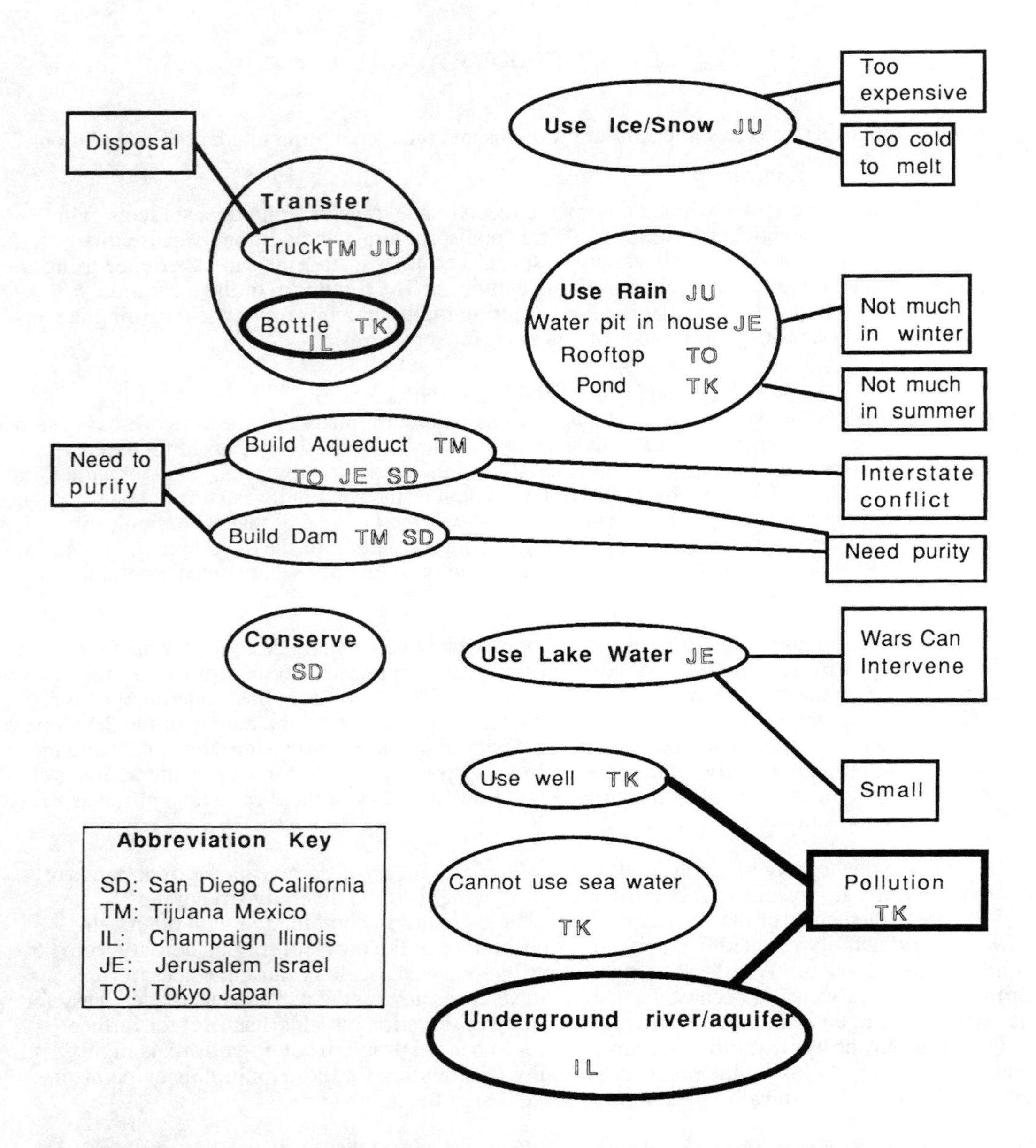

Figure 1: Semantic Trace Analysis of the Water Problem Solving Project

contributed by sites other than San Diego. Each student contributed between 0 and 4 ideas concerning techniques for water acquisition which might be used in the San Diego area. Almost half of the students (9 out of 19) contributed more than one idea on the topic (with an average of 1.7 ideas per student). Although these figures do not assess how much each individual student may have profited from the interaction among the network participants they do indicate a significant impact on the group as a whole.

TELEAPPRENTICESHIPS

We have observed a pattern in instructional electronic network interactions, teleapprenticeships, that resembles one found in traditional face-to-face apprenticeships. This pattern is characterized by a rich set of interactions between a diverse set of participants, a pattern quite different from that typically found in conventional classroom instruction (Levin, Riel, Miyake, & Cohen, 1987; Waugh, Miyake, Levin, & Cohen, 1988). Many of the recent research-based developments in instruction have been characterized as "cognitive apprenticeships" by Collins & Brown (Brown. Collins, & Duguid, 1989; Collins, 1988; Collins, Brown, & Newman, 1988). However, the instructional techniques described by Collins and Brown all take place within a conventional classroom. Telecommunications allows students within schools to interact with other students, teachers, and adults outside the school system in collaborative efforts to solve real, meaningful problems.

As more and more adults outside the school system begin using electronic message systems for their everyday work, we may see a new form of educational interaction evolve, in which students in schools spend more and more of their instructional time learning through their interactions with adults outside the schooling system. Students will learn in a functional learning environment by serving as "teleapprentices" to adults who are not professional teachers.

One of the major advantages of apprenticeship learning is that since skills and knowledge are learned in the same context in which they are to be used, the universal problem of "transfer" that afflicts all of schooling is minimized. If students acquire skills and knowledge in teleapprenticeships, then the problem of transfer is also minimized, since the context provided by the electronic network is the same context in which the skills and knowledge will be used.

Our analyses of instructional interactions on long-distance networks (Levin, Kim, & Riel, 1988; Waugh, Miyake, Levin, & Cohen, 1988) illustrate how such teleapprenticeship interactions can now be conducted. Since the interaction is in non-real time, it has become easier for both mentor and apprentice to participate, since they can control the time spent in the apprentice interaction. The network medium allows for a wider variety of people to interact than is typical of normal instructional settings.

SUMMARY

In this paper, we have presented a brief analysis of problem solving conducted via long-distance electronic networks. The analysis suggests two possible solutions to the transfer problem. The first solution is an organizing framework for network interactions, which we call "receiver site transfer". This framework provides a functional environment for students' problem solving, providing "dynamic support" for their efforts to tackle "real" problems. The second solution is "teleapprenticeships", instructional interactions through which students learn knowledge and skills by interacting with students, teachers and adults outside the school system. As adults increasingly use electronic networks for their work, we can avoid the transfer problem by instructing students within the same context that they will use what they learn.

REFERENCES

Brown, J. S., Collins, A., & Duguid, P. (1989). Situated cognition and the culture of learning. *Educational Researcher,* **18**, 32-42

Collins, A. (1988). Cognitive apprenticeship and instructional technology. Report No. 6899. Technical report. Cambridge, MA: Bolt, Beranek and Newman, Inc.

Collins, A., Brown, J. S., & Newman, S. E. (1989). Cognitive apprenticeship: Teaching the craft of reading, writing and mathematics. In L. B. Resnick (Ed.), *Knowing, learning, and instruction: Essays in honor of Robert Glaser*. Hillsdale, NJ: Erlbaum.

Gick, M., L., & Holyoak, K. J. (1980). Analogical problem solving. *Cognitive Psychology,* **12**, 306-365.

Laboratory of Comparative Human Cognition (1983). Culture and cognitive development. In W. Kessen (Ed.), *Mussen's Handbook of child psychology (4th edn.), Vol. 1* (pp. 295-356). New York: Wiley.

Levin, J. A., & Cohen, M. (1985). The world as an international science laboratory: Electronic networks for science instruction and problem solving. *Journal of Computers in Mathematics and Science Teaching,* **4**, 33-35.

Levin, J. A., Kim, H., & Riel, M. M. (1988). Analysis of instructional electronic message interactions. Paper presented at the American Educational Research Association Meetings, New Orleans.

Levin, J. A., Riel, M., Miyake, N., & Cohen, M. (1987). Education on the electronic frontier: Teleapprentices in globally distributed educational contexts. *Contemporary Educational Psychology,* **12**, 254-260.

Levin, J. A., Waugh, M., & Kolopanis, G. (1988). Science instruction on global electronic networks. *Spectrum: The Journal of the Illinois Science Teachers Association,* **13**, 19-23.

Miyake, N. (1986) Constructive interaction and the iterative process of understanding. *Cognitive Science,* **10**, 151-178.

Pea, R. D. (1987). Socializing the knowledge transfer problem. *International Journal of Educational Research,* **11**, 639-663.

Polya, G. (1957). *How to solve it.* Garden City, New York: Doubleday-Anchor.

Reed, S. K., Ernst, G. W., & Banerji, R. (1974). The role of analogy in transfer between similar problem states. *Cognitive Psychology,* **6**, 436-450.

Riel, M. M., Levin, J. A., & Miller-Souviney, B. (1987). Learning with interactive media: Dynamic support for students and teachers. In R. W. Lawler & M. Yazdani (Eds.), *Artificial Intelligence and education: Learning environments and tutoring systems (Volume One).* Norwood, NJ: Ablex Publishing.

Waugh, M., & Levin, J. A. (1988). Telescience activities: Educational uses of electronic networks. *Journal of Computers in Mathematics and Science Teaching,* **8**, 29-33.

Waugh, M., Miyake, N., Levin, J. A., & Cohen, M. (1988). Analysis of problem solving interactions on electronic networks. Paper presented at the American Educational Research Association Meetings, New Orleans.

A Framework for Psychological Causal Induction: Integrating the Power and Covariation Views

Yunn-wen Lien Patricia W. Cheng

Department of Psychology
University of California, Los Angeles

ABSTRACT

We propose a theoretical framework for interpreting the roles of covariation and the idea of power in psychological causal induction. According to this framework, the computation of inference is purely covariation-based, but covariation is computed only on a set of selected dimensions in a set of selected events. Whether or not a dimension has power or efficacy exerts an influence on whether or not that dimension is selected. We present an experiment testing two predictions based on this framework. Our experiment showed a strong bias towards inferring a movement by a human agent (compared to a state) to be the cause of an event. In support of our hypothesis, this bias was found only when the state was not salient and the inference was made within a relatively short time, suggesting that the bias occurred at the selection stage.

INTRODUCTION

Two views have dominated philosophical discussions on causation. According to the first view, which can be traced back to Aristotle's concept of an "efficient cause", causes produce their effects by virtue of their power or efficacy to do so. The idea of power or efficacy has often been associated with the concept of an active agent. Bishop Berkeley, for example, proposed that a person's ideas must be caused, not by either matter or other ideas, which are "inert" or passive, but by some "active" being (such as the person's own self or God, an all-powerful being). Similarly, the philosopher Thomas Reid considered voluntary actions by an agent to be the paradigm example of causation, and suggested that states can be called "causal" only in a loose and metaphorical sense. In the same vein, in their analysis of common-sensical causality, the legal philosophers Hart and Honore (1959) proposed that the concept of causation springs from the primitive notion that movements of our bodies bring about changes in the environment.

In opposition to the above view, David Hume proposed the radical idea that instead of explaining events in terms of causes having the power to produce them, we should simply note that certain events are found to be invariably conjoined with others. Hume's idea was extended by J.S. Mill, who proposed a prescriptive set of methods for causal induction based on the covariation between potential causes and effects. These methods form the basis of the ANOVA model (Kelley 1967, 1973), proposed by Kelley as a descriptive psychological model of causal induction.

Interestingly, although Kelley's covariational model has received some empirical support, there has also been reports of systematic deviations from the model . In particular, people appear to have a bias towards attributing an effect to a person rather than to a situation. This bias is considered so pervasive that it has been termed the "fundamental attribution error" (Ross, 1977). The error is clearly consistent with the idea that events are caused by active agents rather than passive situations. The philosophical debate on the power and covariation views has its psychological parallel. To explain both support for and deviations from Kelley's model, Cheng and Novick (1989, in press) proposed that a distinction ought to be made between the rules of inference computation and the data on which such rules operate. They argued that psychological rules of inference are covariational, and that they operate in an unbiased manner on a set of relevant dimensions in a set of relevant events. Biases reported in the literature, they argued, are due to the selection of relevant events and dimensions characterizing those events, rather than due to the process of inference computation. Cheng and Novick found empirical support for their view.

In the present paper, we propose that within the framework of the above distinction, the power and covariational views of causation can be regarded, not as *competing* explanations of the process of causal induction, but as *complementary* components of the process. More specifically, people may have a bias towards selecting an action as a dimension on which to compute covariation. The computed covariation on the selected dimensions then determines causal inferences. The bias for an action may be particular to actions per se, or may reflect a more general propensity to attend to salient dimensions.

EXPERIMENT TESTING THE INTEGRATION OF POWER AND COVARIATION

We tested two hypotheses within the above framework. If a bias towards attributing an effect to an action is due to a bias towards selecting that dimension for covariation computation, we hypothesize that (1) the bias will be most prominent when there is insufficient time or information for covariation to be computed for other potentially causal dimensions (and as a corollary, the bias may decrease or even disappear when there is sufficient time and information for covariation to be computed for other potential causal dimensions), and (2) the bias for an action may be a specific case of a more general propensity to attend to more salient dimensions.

To test our hypotheses, we presented subjects with animated sequences of events involving a fictional causal relation in which an action by an agent (a human figure's movement) and a state (the figure's shade) jointly cause a bird to chirp. The rule governing the chirping of the bird is: The bird chirps if and only if the figure moves and is dark grey in shade. The bird's chirp therefore covaried equally with an action and a state. An event is defined as an occasion on which the human figure (varying along the three dimensions of movement, size, and shade) and the bird appeared on a simple scene drawn on a black-and-white computer screen, and the bird either chirps, or does not chirp. We created a fictional causal relation to be sure that subjects responded by making a causal inference rather than by retrieving previous knowledge. To assess the role of covariation, we also included a third dimension (the figure's size), a state that did not covary with the effect. We assume that subjects' real-world knowledge would bias them towards interpreting the movement of the human figure as an action which has a high degree of power, and the human figure's size and shade as states which have low degrees of power.

To measure the bias towards attributing an effect to a human movement in an experimental situation, we needed to create conditions under which this bias might be manifested. As mentioned earlier, we predicted that if a bias for a dimension exists, it would most likely be manifested under conditions in which the dimension is more salient than other causally relevant dimensions. It seems to us that the rate at which a value on a dimension changes may be one of the primary determinants of salience. We thought that if a dimension is kept constant across a block of events, it would more likely be perceived as part of the background information, and hence less likely to be selected for covariation computation. Thus, to obtain a bias for inferring a movement as the cause of an effect, for one group of subjects we kept shade (the other causally relevant dimension) constant across a block of events while we let movement vary from one event to the next. However, to test that any preference that exists is for a movement in particular, rather than for more salient information in general, for a second group of subjects we let both movement and shade vary from one event to the next. Because both dimensions were salient for this group, if salience -- rather than bias for an action per se -- is what determines whether a dimension is selected for covariation computation, then there should be no bias in causal inference in this condition.

As mentioned earlier, we also predicted that if a dimensional preference exists, it would be likely to manifest itself most strongly when there is insufficient time or information to compute covariation for other potential dimensions. To measure subjects' causal inferences at various points as they accumulate information on the events, we asked them to answer the question, "What causes the bird to chirp?", after every four events -- our definition of a block. Subjects were told that they could give a specific positive answer, indicate that they did not know the answer, or that they thought there is no possible answer.

Method

Subjects. Thirty-four UCLA students participated in this experiment, 15 in the "change in shade between events" group, and 18 in the "change in shade between blocks of four events" group. One subject was excluded due to experimenter error.

Materials, Design, and Procedure. The human figure varied on three dimensions: movement, shade, and size. Each dimension has two values: The figure could either be still or wave an arm and a leg; be light grey or dark grey in shade; and be big or small. Because there were three dimensions with two values each, there were eight possible types of events defined by the configuration of values along the three dimensions of the figure. The animated sequences of events were presented on a Macintosh Plus microcomputer using the Video Works II software package.

The bird chirped whenever the figure was dark and was waving its arm and leg; it did not chirp otherwise. That is, the chirping of the bird covaried with movement and darkness in combination, but not with size. All subjects were presented the same set of eight events (with repetitions). The rate of change in shade, however, was varied between subjects. This rate was manipulated by arranging the set of eight possible events so that shade changed either from one event to the next or only between blocks of four events. The causally irrelevant dimension of size varied between events for both groups. The eight possible events were presented consecutively, with a star in the middle of a blank screen separating each event from the next. Each set of eight events were divided into two blocks of four. The subject paused after each block to write his or her answer to the question, "What causes the bird to chirp?" The blocks were repeated until the subject decided he or she would not change his or her answer if given more trials. The order of the events was counterbalanced across subjects in each of the two rate-of-change conditions.

Each subject was told to imagine that the computer screen was a window from which he or she saw a sequence of events. They were told that an event would involve a human figure and a bird, and that their task was to "figure out what makes the bird chirp". Nothing was mentioned about the dimensions that would be varied. Subjects were told that there was no "right" or "standard" answer, and that they should answer according to what felt right or natural to them.

Results and Discussion

Our results are presented in Table 1 on the next page. In the top half of the table, subjects in the two rate-of-change conditions are classified according to whether they initially judged the cause of the bird's chirp to be (1) movement only, (2) shade only, (3) movement and shade, or (4) other. The bottom half of the table presents an analogous frequency analysis for subjects' final causal judgments.

Both of our hypotheses were confirmed. As can be seen in the first row, there was a strong initial bias towards attributing the bird's chirp to the movement of the human figure in the condition in which its shade was kept constant within blocks of four events. Most of the subjects initially chose the figure's movement to be the cause. Corroborating this finding, the mean number of blocks on which subjects initially considered the cause to include the movement was 1.88, whereas the mean number of blocks on which subjects initially considered the cause to include the shade was 3.88, two blocks (i.e., 8 events) later. In contrast, this bias in initial judgments did not appear in the condition in which shade varied at a faster rate, from event to event, as can be seen in the

Table 1. PERCENTAGE OF TYPES OF INITIAL AND FINAL CAUSAL JUDGMENTS IN THE TWO RATE-OF-CHANGE CONDITIONS.

	Initial causal judgments			
rate of change of shade	movement only	shade only	movement & shade	other
between blocks of 4 events (n=18)	78	0	0	22
between events (n=15)	13	27	47	13

	Final causal judgments			
rate of change of shade	movement only	shade only	movement & shade	other
between blocks of 4 events (n=18)	0	0	89	11
between events (n=15)	13	7	73	7

second row. This pattern of results is consistent with our hypothesis that it is the salience of the dimension (as defined by the rate of change of values on the dimension) that determines selection for covariation computation, rather than whether or not the dimension involves a movement. Because movements are salient, they are more likely to be considered as a potential cause.

Note that although salience has an enormous effect on causal judgments, it is by no means a sufficient criterion for inferring that a dimension is a cause: Very few subjects chose size, which did not covary with the effect, as the cause either initially or finally, even though size changed at the faster rate (from event to event) for both groups of subjects.

Our other prediction was that the bias towards attributing an effect to a movement should decrease or disappear when there is sufficient time to compute information on other dimensions. As we predicted, there was no dimensional bias in subjects' final causal judgments. Most subjects reached the final conclusion that the combination of movement and shade was the cause, a conclusion consistent with the covariation between these dimensions and the effect.

Many real life situations may resemble conditions under which our subjects made their initial judgments, because one may have to form judgments under time and information constraints. The bias towards actions, and towards salient dimensions in general, could therefore be quite widespread.

FURTHER RESEARCH

In the above experiment, we manipulated the salience of shade by manipulating its rate of change. We have interpreted the lack of bias towards attributing an effect to movement when shade changed at a rapid rate to be due to a general propensity to attend to more salient dimensions. However, it seems that increasing the rate of change of shade, besides increasing its salience, may also increase the tendency to perceive the change as an action. This explanation requires further testing.

We have proposed a framework for understanding causal induction. Within this framework, the notion of power plays a role in selecting the relevant sets of dimensions or events, and covariation is then computed on these selected sets. Although our results show support for this framework, it seems to us that this framework is incomplete. Cheng and Novick (1989) discussed the hypothetical case (adapted from Hilton & Slugoski, 1986) of a person whose alarm clock has rung when and only when the sun rises. For this person, the ringing of the alarm clock covaries perfectly with sunrise. This person, however, is unlikely to conclude that the sun causes the alarm clock to ring, or that the alarm clock causes the sun to rise. Cheng and Novick proposed that this is because the person is unlikely on the basis of prior knowledge to select sunrise and the ringing of the alarm clock as dimensions on which to compute covariation. It seems to us that even if that person is to compute covariation on the two dimensions, and moreover succeeds in doing so, he or she is still unlikely to conclude either of the above causal relations. It seems that there may be an influence from a third stage, at which new inferences are evaluated according to its coherence with the rest of a person's knowledge. The evaluation of explanatory coherence (see Thagard, in press) is, of course, not particular to causal induction. Efficacy may play a role at that stage as well as in the initial selection stage.

ACKNOWLEDGEMENTS

The research reported in this paper was supported by Grant BNS87-10305 from the National Science Foundation to Patricia Cheng. We thank Rochel Gelman, Harold Kelley, and Michael Waldmann for their valuable comments.

REFERENCES

Cheng, P.W., & Novick, L.R. (1989). Covariation and pragmatics: A qualitative contrast model of causal induction. Manuscript in preparation, Department of Psychology, UCLA.

Cheng, P.W., & Novick, L.R. (in press). Where is the bias in causal attribution? In K.J. Gilhooly, M. Keane, R. Logie, & G. Erdos (Eds.), *Lines of thought: Reflections on the psychology of thinking*. Chichester, England: Wiley.

Hart, H.L., & Honore, A.M. (1959). *Causation in the law.* Oxford, England: Clarendon Press.

Hilton, D.J., & Slugoski, B.R. (1986). Knowledge-based causal attribution: The abnormal conditions focus model. *Psychological Review, 93,* 75-88.

Kelley, H.H. (1967). Attribution theory in social psychology. In D. Levine (Ed.), *Nebraska symposium on motivation*, 15, (pp. 192-238). Lincoln: University of Nabraska Press.

Kelley, H.H. (1973) The processes of causal attribution. *American Psychologist, 28,* 107-128.

Ross, L. (1977). The intuitive psychologist and his shortcomings: Distortions in the attribution process. *Advances in Experimental Social Psychology, 10,* 174-220.

Thagard, P. (in press). Explanatory coherence. *Brain and Behavioral Sciences.*

Lexical vs. Nonlexical Cognitive Processing: Is General Slowing Domain-Specific?

SUSAN D. LIMA

Department of Psychology
University of Wisconsin-Milwaukee

SANDRA HALE AND JOEL MYERSON

Department of Psychology
Washington University

The results from several meta-analyses place new constraints on the general slowing hypothesis of age-related changes in the rate of cognitive processing. It was found that in the lexical domain, a linear function described the relationship between the response latencies of older (age 65 - 75) and younger (age 19 - 29) adults with great precision: O = 1.48 Y - .067, where O and Y refer to older and younger latency, respectively, and the unit is the second; adjusted $r^2 = .976$. This function was based on data from lexical decision experiments and accurately predicted performance in an independent set of experiments employing other lexical tasks. In contrast, performance in nonlexical tasks spanning the same range of task difficulty was described by a nonlinear, positively accelerated power function: $O = 1.60\ Y^{1.26}$, adjusted $r^2 = .951$. It was concluded that although general slowing is observed in both the lexical and the nonlexical domains, latencies in the former are consistently shorter than would be predicted based on performance in the latter. These results are interpreted within the framework of the Information Loss Model, a mathematical model of age-related cognitive slowing (Myerson, Hale, Wagstaff, Poon, & Smith, in press).

One of the most striking observations of adult aging is that older adults perform cognitive tasks more slowly than younger adults. Is this age-related slowing a consequence of qualitative changes in cognitive processes, or is it more aptly characterized as a generalized quantitative slowing of cognitive processes that remain qualitatively stable with age? The purpose of this paper is to compare the quantitative and qualitative nature of age-related slowing in two cognitive domains, the lexical and the nonlexical, and to explain the findings within the framework of the Information Loss Model (Myerson, Hale, Wagstaff, Poon, & Smith, in press).

Age-related slowing has been found in experiments employing lexical tasks (e.g., lexical decision, category judgment, naming) as well as those employing nonlexical tasks (e.g., choice reaction time, memory scanning, mental rotation). The results of these experiments indicate that as task difficulty increases, so does the difference in response latencies between older and younger adult groups. The ubiquity of this "complexity effect" led to the development of the general slowing hypothesis, which states that all cognitive processes slow at the same rate with advancing adult age (e.g., Birren, 1965).

The existence of general slowing has been elegantly corroborated in meta-analyses in which the mean latencies of the older group were plotted as a function of the mean latencies of the younger group in the same experimental conditions, following the method of Brinley (1965). In the first major meta-analysis of this type, Cerella, Poon, and Williams (1980) suggested that the relation between old and young latencies was linear. An expanded and more systematic meta-analysis by Hale, Myerson, & Wagstaff (1987), which encompassed data from a remarkably wide variety of nonlexical tasks, demonstrated that the relation was actually a nonlinear, positively accelerated power function (the data are shown in Figure 1); this function accounted for 98.9% of the variance. Such precision of prediction suggests that general quantitative slowing was responsible for the greater latencies of the older adults. If it had instead been the case that task-specific cognitive processes differed between old and young, or that qualitatively stable cognitive processes slowed at different rates, then there would have been no single mathematical function relating old and young latencies across the

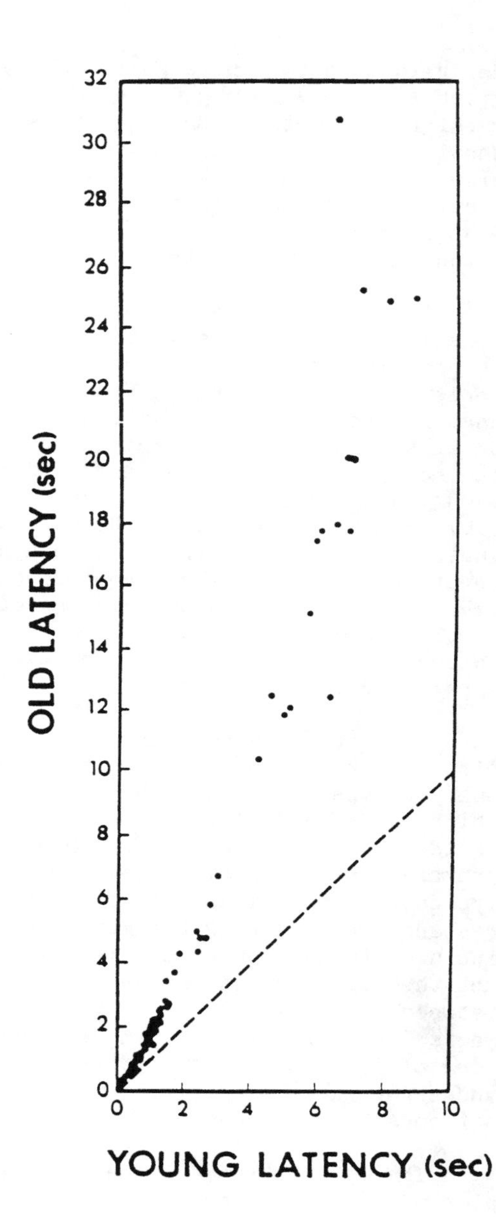

Figure 1. Old latency as a function of young latency (nonlexical tasks). The figure is taken from Hale et al. (1987).

entire data set. The significance of the single function is that the older group's latency in any nonlexical experimental condition can be reliably predicted from the younger group's latency in that condition without knowledge of the exact nature of the task. For example, if a young adult group performs a nonlexical task with a latency of 1.25 seconds, then an older adult group will perform that task with a latency of approximately 2.16 seconds, regardless of whether the task is choice reaction time, memory scanning, or mental rotation.

Evidence from psychometric testing indicates that verbal ability is less susceptible to age-related decline than nonverbal ability, suggesting the possibility that lexical slowing may be lesser in quantity than nonlexical slowing and that there will exist no single mathematical function that relates old and young latencies in both the lexical and the nonlexical domains. In order to compare lexical and nonlexical slowing, we conducted two meta-analyses in the lexical domain analogous to the one Hale et al. (1987) had conducted in the nonlexical domain. In their study, Hale et al. surveyed all issues of the *Journal of Gerontology* from 1975 to 1984; included in the meta-analysis were all experiments involving nonlexical reaction time tasks that required the pressing or releasing of a response key and that employed a younger group (mean age between 20 and 25 years) and an older group (mean age between 65 and 75 years). Nine studies met the inclusion criteria, yielding a data set consisting of results from 86 experimental conditions.

The data base for our two lexical meta-analyses included all issues of nine different journals from the years 1975 through 1987. The first meta-analysis was restricted to studies employing the lexical decision task, in which subjects decide as quickly as possible whether visually presented letter strings are words or nonwords. This task was by far the most prevalent reaction time task used in studies of word recognition and aging. Typically, the lexical decision response is signaled by pressing one of two response keys, making the motor component equivalent to that of the studies included in the nonlexical meta-analysis of Hale et al. (1987). Ten studies met the following inclusion criteria: the mean age of the younger group fell between 19 and 29 years and that of the older group fell between 65 and 75 years; the lexical decision response was based on one or two letter strings per trial; the authors reported both word and nonword response latencies; and error rates were similar for young and old subjects. The resulting data set consisted of results from 90 experimental conditions.

The mean latency of the older group in each experimental condition was plotted as a function of the mean latency of the younger group in the same condition; the results are shown in Figure 2, in which lexical decision response latencies are indicated by closed circles. Because word responses and nonword responses yielded statistically equivalent regression functions, functions based on all responses were calculated. The exponent of the best-fitting power function was not reliably different than 1.0, indicating that the relation between old and young latencies was essentially linear. The linear regression equation that best fit the data was

$$O = 1.48\ Y - .067$$

(represented by the solid line in Figure 2); O and Y represent the latencies of old and young groups respectively and the unit of time is the second. The adjusted r^2 was .976.

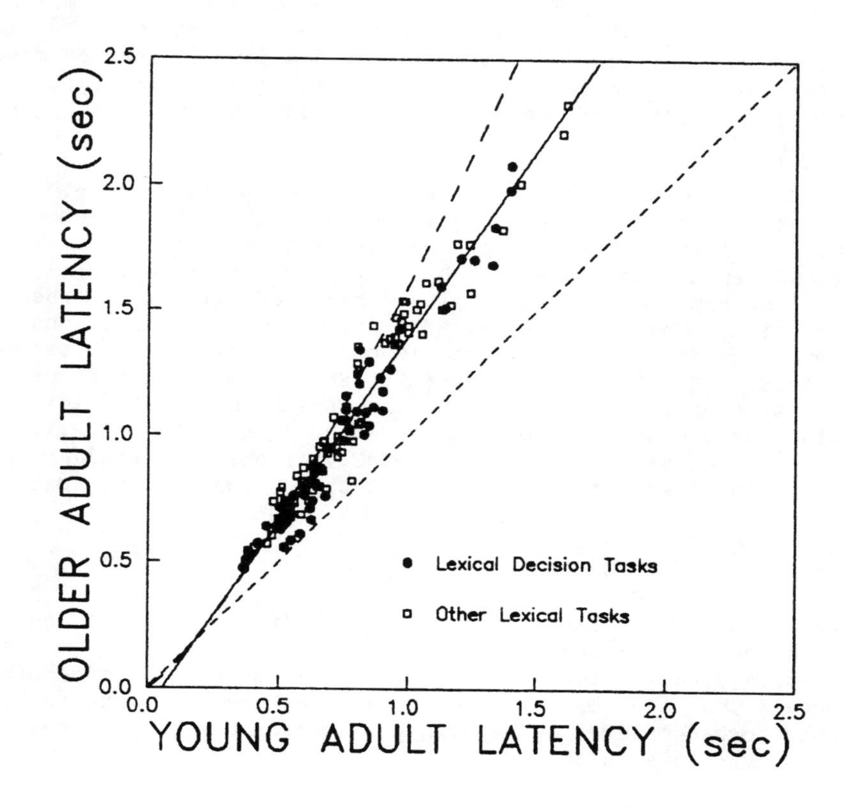

Figure 2. Old latency as a function of young latency (lexical tasks). If the performances of older and younger adult groups were equal, the data points would fall along the dashed diagonal line.

Because the younger adult latencies in the nonlexical meta-analysis of Hale et al. (1987) spanned a much wider range (0.2 s to 9.0 s) than those in our lexical decision meta-analysis (0.4 s to 1.6 s), we computed a best-fitting function for the 62 nonlexical conditions in which the younger adult latency fell between 0.4 s and 1.6 s; the equation of this function was

$$O = 1.60\ Y^{1.26}$$

with an adjusted $\underline{r}^2$ of .951. This positively accelerated function is indicated by the dashed curve in Figure 2. (The function is very similar to that found by Hale et al., 1987, across their entire data set: $O = 1.62\ Y^{1.29}$.) A comparison of the lexical decision data and the nonlexical function makes it apparent that lexical decision performance shows less age-related slowing than nonlexical performance; 74.4% of the lexical decision data points fall below the nonlexical curve.

Are the results from the lexical decision meta-analysis unique to the lexical decision task, or do they capture a general slowing trend common to the entire domain of lexical processing? To answer this question, we conducted a second lexical meta-analysis by surveying our nine-journal data base for all lexical experiments that employed reaction time tasks other than lexical decision. This survey yielded a data set of 76 conditions from nine studies employing four tasks: naming, same-different judgment, category membership judgment, and relatedness judgment. When older latencies were plotted as a function of younger latencies, the resemblance to the lexical decision function was striking. The results can be seen in Figure 2, in which latencies from the second lexical meta-analysis are indicated by open squares. The regression equation that best fit this second set of lexical data was

$$O = 1.47\ Y - .100$$

with an adjusted $\underline{r}^2$ of .960. The close similarity of this equation and the the equation from the lexical decision meta-analysis implies that essentially one rate of cognitive slowing characterizes lexical processing. It cannot be argued that the results from the lexical decision meta-analysis were attributable to age-related changes in post-access decision processes unique to the lexical decision task.

The results of the two lexical meta-analyses thus indicate that although older subjects process words more slowly than younger adults, the degree of age-related decrement is less than that found in nonlexical processing. The finding that the lexical domain is associated with a different function than the nonlexical domain indicates that age-related cognitive slowing is not so general that one rate of slowing characterizes performance in both domains. On the other hand, the existence of a precise mathematical relationship between old and young latencies within each domain indicates that the rate of cognitive slowing _is_ general across experimental conditions within that domain. It appears, then, that the rate of general slowing is domain-specific, with a lesser rate of slowing in the lexical domain than in the nonlexical domain.

The meta-analysis of Hale et al. (1987) showed that complexity effects in performing nonlexical tasks are nonproportional; not only does the difference between old and young latency increase as a function of task difficulty, but the ratio of old latency to young latency also increases as task difficulty increases. Recently, Myerson et al. (in press) developed the Information Loss Model of age-related slowing, a mathematical model that rests on three assumptions:

(a) the more complex the task, the more information processing steps required to complete the task;

(b) the duration of each processing step is inversely proportional to the amount of information available at that step; and

(c) a constant proportion of information is lost at each processing step.

Based on these assumptions, the equation for the relation between latencies of older and younger adults is

$$O = \{[1 + Y \cdot P_y / D_y (1-P_y)]^b - 1\} D_o (1-P_o)/P_o$$

where

$$b = \underline{ln}(1-P_o)/\underline{ln}(1-P_y),$$

D_o and P_o are, respectively, the duration of a processing step without information loss and the proportion of information loss per step for the older group, and D_y and P_y are the corresponding parameters for the younger group. If P_o is greater than P_y, then b is greater than 1.0, and the relation between older and younger latencies is positively accelerated. However, if P_o equals P_y, then the equation for the relation between latencies of older and younger adults simplifies to

$$O = Y \cdot D_o/D_y.$$

In this case, all processing steps in the older adults are proportionally greater than those of the younger adults by the general speed factor D_o/D_y, and the relation between the latencies of older and younger adults is linear.

Thus, according to the Information Loss Model, the linearity of the relation between old and young lexical latencies can only arise if the information loss proportion does not increase with advancing age. If the information loss proportion does increase, then the prediction is that the relation between old and young latencies will be positively accelerated. Therefore, in the lexical domain, the rate of information loss during cognitive processing appears to remain stable as an adult ages, whereas in the nonlexical domain, it appears to increase with age.

REFERENCES

Birren, J. E. (1965). Age changes in speeded behavior: Its central nature and physiological correlates. In A. T. Welford & J. E. Birren (Eds.), Behavior, aging and the nervous system. Springfield, IL: Charles C. Thomas.

Brinley, J. F. (1965). Cognitive sets, speed and accuracy of performance in the elderly. In A. T. Welford & J. E. Birren (Eds.), Behavior, aging and the nervous system. Springfield, IL: Charles C. Thomas.

Cerella, J., Poon, L. W., Williams, D. M. (1980). Age and the complexity hypothesis. In L. W. Poon (Ed.), Aging in the 1980s: Psychological issues (pp. 332-342). Washington, DC: American Psychological Association.

Hale, S., Myerson, J., & Wagstaff, D. (1987). General slowing and nonverbal information processing: Evidence for a power law. Journal of Gerontology, 42, 131-136.

Myerson, J., Hale, S., Wagstaff, D., Poon, L. W., & Smith, G. A. (in press). Aging and information loss: A mathematical model of cognitive slowing. Psychological Review.

Does Function Provide a Core for Artifact Concepts?

Barbara C. Malt and Eric C. Johnson

Department of Psychology
Lehigh University

Mental representations of everyday categories include many features that are neither necessary nor sufficient for membership in the category. Recent proposals have suggested, however, that there may be "core" features in the representation that are critical to category membership. Several researchers have suggested that for artifact categories (*chair*, *pencil*, *toy*, etc.), function serves as the concept core. We conducted two experiments testing whether the function typically associated with an artifact category provides clear boundaries for category membership. We found that some objects that do possess the function typically associated with a category are excluded from category membership, and we also found that some objects that do not possess the standard function are still considered to belong to the category. These results suggest that function may not provide a core for artifact concepts.

INTRODUCTION

The traditional view of concepts assumed that concepts could be described in terms of necessary and sufficient features, while the more recent family resemblance view holds that they consist of a set of features associated with a category with some probability (see Smith & Medin, 1981). Each view has had trouble accounting for all the observed facts about classification, however, and these problems have led a number of researchers to propose a hybrid view of concepts (e.g., Armstrong, Gleitman, & Gleitman, 1983; Medin & Smith, 1984; Rey, 1985). The hybrid view assumes that concepts contain both probabilistically associated features, used primarily for quick identification, and a concept "core" that can be called on when use of non-defining features is inadequate.

A hybrid model provides a convenient resolution to some of the problems associated with either pure view. However, it also resurrects an issue dropped in the move from the traditional view to the family resemblance view. One of the persistent problems for the traditional view was the difficulty of identifying features that would apply to all and only the exemplars of a given category (Wittgenstein, 1953; Rosch & Mervis, 1975). The hybrid view faces the same challenge the traditional view did in specifying exactly what the "core" features for various concepts might be. In addressing this issue for natural kind concepts (e.g., *tiger*, *gold*, *water*), many psychologists have adopted a view of the core derived from Putnam's (1975) analysis of word meaning, and they take the core to be an underlying trait such as a genetic code in the case of species concepts, and chemical composition or atomic weight in the case of inorganic substances (Putnam, 1975; see also Carey, 1985; Keil, 1986; Smith, in press; among others). For artifact concepts such as *chair*, *pencil*, or *toy*, however, the philosophical literature is less helpful (Putnam, 1975, refers only to an "artifactual nature"), and most psychologists have looked elsewhere for ideas about the core.

The primary psychological hypothesis about a core for artifacts is that it is the artifact's function (Keil, 1986, 1987; Rips, 1986). Intuitively, function seems to be a central aspect of artifact concepts; the function of chairs, for instance, seems to vary less than their appearance. Empirically, function appears to play an important role in classification decisions about artifacts. For instance, Rips (1986) found that if something umbrella-like in appearance is described as having been manufactured for use as a lampshade, subjects tend to classify the object as a lampshade; the function information appears to be weighted more heavily than the appearance information.

Nevertheless, there is reason to question whether function is truly a core for artifact concepts in the sense of providing a clear criterion for category membership. In general, people do seem to treat natural kinds as if they at least believe in a core of some sort (Barr & Caplan, 1987; Keil, 1986, 1987; Rips, 1986), but it is less clear that they do so for artifacts. For instance, even the most atypical members of natural kind categories are held to truly belong to their category (e.g., a penguin is a full-fledged bird, no matter how atypical), while atypical members of artifact categories seem to only "sort of" belong to their category (e.g., a lamp is a marginal piece of furniture). People are also more willing to accept hedges such as "loosely speaking" with artifact terms than with natural kinds, and they are more willing to say "you can call it whichever you want" when confronted with a difficult-to-classify artifact than a difficult-to-classify natural kind (Malt, 1985, 1988). These various observations suggest that artifact concepts may not conform well to the hybrid view that all concepts have a core providing clear category boundaries.

Furthermore, with respect to function in particular, intuitions suggest that it is possible to invent objects that have the function of a particular artifact category yet might not be considered a member of that category. For example, suppose that the function of a bench is to provide economical seating for several people outdoors. If someone satisfies this function by building a 6-foot high platform holding seats for several people, accessed by a rope ladder, and shielded from the sun by an awning, is the object a bench? It is likely that many people would feel it is not, which suggests that appearance can be critical to the classification of an artifact. This sort of example argues that even if a core of some sort does exist for artifacts, function per se may not be the core.

Thus the status of function as providing a core for artifact concepts is unclear. We conducted two experiments aimed at providing more definitive evidence about whether function truly provides a core for artifact categories; that is, whether it provides clear boundaries for category membership. The first experiment tested whether having the function typically associated with a particular category is *sufficient* for membership in the category. The second tested whether having that function is *necessary* for membership in the category. If the function associated with a category serves as a core, then it should be both necessary and sufficient for membership in the category.

EXPERIMENT 1: SUFFICIENCY

This experiment tested whether having the function normally associated with a particular category was sufficient to cause an object to be considered a member of the category. We first collected detailed descriptions of the functions of a number of common artifact categories. Then we constructed descriptions of objects that preserved the original function but replaced several standard physical features with new features. We were interested in whether or not these novel objects would be considered members of the original category on the basis of their function.

Method

Pretests. We used a three-phase procedure to arrive at the function statements for our descriptions. A fourth phase of pretesting provided a check on the physical features used in the descriptions.

Phase 1: Generating Contrast Categories. As a first step in eliciting the functions associated with common artifact categories, we gave 24 subjects a set of 28 common basic-level artifact names and asked them to list other categories that were similar to, but not the same as, each target category. Of the 28 categories, 17 yielded at least one response produced by 1/3 or more of the subjects. (For example, for "boots," 16 subjects listed "shoes," and for "couch," 16 listed "chair.") These 17 categories were used in the next phase of the experiment.

Phase 2: Eliciting Function Statements. We gave a new group of 20 subjects the 17 categories along with the contrast categories generated for each one in Phase 1. We asked subjects to describe the function of each target category in enough detail to distinguish it from the other similar categories. We tabulated responses, and used them to create a function statement for each target category.

Phase 3: Verifying Function Statements. To be sure that our derived function statements really did reflect the function of the intended category, we gave the statements to a new group of 24 subjects and asked them to list the category or categories each brought to mind. The target category was listed by at least half the subjects for each function statement, and in most cases by two-thirds or more of the subjects. Subjects thus did clearly perceive our function statements as belonging to the target categories.

Phase 4: Verifying Physical Features. We also wanted to be sure that the physical features for descriptions of the normal objects would be perceived as associated with the appropriate categories. For each target category, we constructed a 3- or 4-feature statement describing the appearance of a typical category member. We then gave 20 subjects the feature statements and asked them to list what object they thought the features belonged to. For 12 statements, the target category was the most frequent response, being listed by at least 1/2 of the subjects and in most cases substantially more. For these 12 categories, then, the feature statements are strongly associated with the target categories. For the remaining 5, the statements elicited the target category less than half the time, and these categories were eliminated from the stimulus set.

Sufficiency test. Having arrived at statements of both function and appearance that were reliably associated with particular artifact categories, we then constructed two kinds of artifact descriptions: normal and unusual. One description of each kind was constructed for each target category. The normal descriptions consisted simply of the physical feature statement pretested as described above, followed by the function statement pretested as described above. To construct the unusual descriptions, we took each physical feature mentioned in the normal statement and replaced it with an unusual one. We were careful to select only unusual features that would allow the object to serve the stated function. The unusual features were followed by the normal function statement, as in the normal descriptions.

We asked 40 subjects to read these descriptions and respond whether or not they thought each item described was a member of the specified target category. Subjects made their responses on 1-to-7 scale, where "1" was labelled "definitely is not," "7" was labelled "definitely is," and "4" was labelled "can't decide." Each subject saw a given target category in only one of its two versions. All subjects received the descriptions mixed with filler descriptions that varied functions as well as physical features to varying extents. Subjects were asked to read each item carefully, and they were given as much time as they wished to complete their ratings.

A sample description for "sweater" in its normal and unusual version is as follows:

> (Normal) "This thing is made of wool, has buttons down the front, and has sleeves ending in small openings. It is used to provide extra warmth for the arms and the upper body by being worn over a shirt. Is this thing a sweater?"
>
> (Unusual) "This thing is made of rubber, has buckles across the back, and has sleeves ending in gloves. It is used to provide extra warmth for the arms and the upper body by being worn over a shirt. Is this thing a sweater?"

Results

Descriptions with normal features were consistently rated as belonging to the target category, with a mean rating of 6.58 on the 7-point scale. Descriptions with unusual features received a mean rating of 4.35, which differed significantly from the normal feature mean, $F\ (1,38) = 315.68, p < .001$. This difference confirms that we were successful in creating descriptions for the unusual set that were perceived as different from normal category members.

The rating for unusual feature descriptions falls just above the midpoint of the scale. It is therefore important to look at ratings for individual items. If all items are rated on the positive side of the scale, this result would be consistent with the idea that having a particular function is sufficient to cause an item to be considered a member of a category. On the other hand, if this middle-of-the road overall mean reflects a combination of items included in the category and items excluded from it, the result would argue against the sufficiency of function.

Inspection of individual items showed that ratings conform to the latter possibility. Of the 12 target categories, 7 had mean ratings above the midpoint of the scale, but 5 had mean ratings below the midpoint. Of the 7 that did receive positive ratings, in retrospect it seems that at least several may have had features that were not perceived as very different from normal features. Since 5 of the items clearly were denied membership in the target category, it appears that function alone cannot have been determining membership, and that subjects must have also been influenced by physical features in the descriptions. The finding that a substantial number of items with standard functions were excluded from category membership strongly suggests that while function information may be important in membership judgments, it alone is not *sufficient* to determine category membership.

EXPERIMENT 2: NECESSITY

If function provides a core for artifact categories, then having a particular function should also be necessary for membership in a category. In Experiment 2, we tested whether an object must have the function usually associated with a category in order for it to be considered a member of the category. To test the necessity of a particular function, we generated descriptions of objects with the physical appearance of typical members of target categories, but with functions other than the normal one. We were interested in whether or not these items would be excluded from category membership on the basis of their unusual functions.

Method

Physical features for descriptions in this experiment were identical to those pretested in Experiment 1. To create descriptions of objects that retained normal appearance but varied in function, we used 4 different variations of function. *Normal* functions were simply those pretested in Experiment 1. *Related* functions overlapped with the normal function somewhat, but differed from it in some noticeable way. *Bizarre* functions diverged more strongly from the normal function. *Denial* functions were ones that explicitly mentioned that the object could not be used to satisfy the standard function of the target category.

Fifty-six subjects read descriptions containing the normal physical features and either the standard function from Experiment 1 or one of the three types of changed functions. As in Experiment 1, subjects responded on a 7-point scale whether or not they thought the item was a member of the target category. They were again asked to read each item carefully and take as much time as necessary to complete their ratings. Each subject saw a given target category in only one of the four conditions (Normal, Related, Bizarre, or Denial).

A sample description for "boat" in each of its four versions is as follows:

> (Normal) "This thing is wedge-shaped, with a sail, an anchor, and wooden sides. It is made to carry one or more people over a body of water for purposes of work or recreation. Is this thing a boat?"
>
> (Related) "This thing is wedge-shaped, with a sail, an anchor, and wooden sides. It is made as a holding area for dangerous criminals or persons in exile by detaining them a certain distance off-shore. Is this thing a boat?"
>
> (Bizarre) "This thing is wedge-shaped, with a sail, an anchor, and wooden sides. It is made to provide a temporary shelter and transportation for marine animals being reintroduced to their natural habitat. Is this thing a boat?"
>
> (Denial) "This thing is wedge-shaped, with a sail, an anchor, and wooden sides. It is made for collecting samples of marine flora and fauna under sterile conditions, and is totally mechanized so that no people are allowed onboard under any circumstances. Is this thing a boat?"

Results

The mean rating for items with normal features and the standard function was 6.54 on the 7-point scale, in line with ratings for similar items in Experiment 1. The mean rating for Related items was 5.17; for Bizarre items, 4.67; and for Denial items, 4.14. An ANOVA showed that ratings for the four types of descriptions differed significantly among themselves, $F(3,156) = 79.00, p < .001$. The overall trend, with Related closest to Normal, followed by Bizarre and then Denial, confirms that we were successful in creating descriptions that systematically varied in how closely the function matched the function typically associated with each category.

Most importantly, these results show that for all three types of function changes, mean ratings of category membership remain positive, indicating that items with atypical functions may still be granted category membership. Examination of individual item ratings shows that 11 out of 12 Related items were rated above the midpoint, and 9 out of 12 Bizarre items were also. Perhaps most striking is the fact that 7 out of 12 items were above the midpoint even in the Denial condition, where descriptions explicitly stated that the item cannot serve the normal function. Thus subjects considered the majority of the items to be members of the target category even though the items did not possess the normal function. These results demonstrate that having the function normally associated with a category cannot be strictly *necessary* for category membership.

GENERAL DISCUSSION

The results of Experiments 1 and 2 together suggest that having a particular function does not constitute either a necessary or a sufficient condition for membership in an artifact category. They indicate that while function may be an important factor in determining classification for artifacts, it may not provide a core for artifact concepts in the sense intended in current hybrid views of concepts.

One might object to the conclusion of these experiments by arguing that function was defined too narrowly for each category. Thus, perhaps the reason some Related, Bizarre, or Denial items in Experiment 2 were included in the target category is that those functions were actually within the normal scope of the category function. This line of argument does not, however, salvage the function-as-core position, for it makes it more difficult to see how a function could provide the basis for classification decisions. If the function of "boat," for instance, is taken to be generally to carry or suspend any sort of objects above water, then the function is also compatible with a number of other categories, such as rafts, life preservers, and cruise ships. This problem is likely to arise for most or all categories. For instance, expanding a function for "couch" from the specific "made to seat 3-4 people comfortably, or for relaxing in a fully prone position" (used in our experiments), to a more general "for people to sit on," results in a function compatible with chairs, stools, etc. Thus it appears that to entertain the possibility that functions can serve as a concept core, function must be taken to be quite specific and restricted.

A related concern about the general viability of functions as concept cores is whether they could serve as cores for superordinate level categories. Our experimental stimuli were restricted to basic level categories such as "couch," "boat," and "tractor" for which it was not difficult to obtain detailed function statements. However, for superordinates such as "furniture," "toy," or "vehicle," it is less clear what function could be given that would encompass most common exemplars while excluding members of other categories. A broad function for "vehicle" such as "made to get people from one place to another without much effort on their part" might apply to most vehicles, but it would also apply to escalators, moving sidewalks, and time warp machines that most likely would not be called vehicles. More restricted versions of the function, with appeals to the use of engines or wheels, would exclude various exemplars such as horse-drawn buggies or sleighs (with the precise subset excluded depending on the formulation of the function). Furthermore, it is not clear that such restricted versions are really pure function statements, since they gain their specificity by adding information about appearance. Thus finding a function that could conceivably serve as a true core appears to be even more difficult for superordinates than for basic level categories.

In sum, while appeals to function may appear to solve the dilemma of what could serve as a core for artifact concepts, closer examination suggests that function alone may not provide the answer to membership in artifact categories. Although our experiments do not directly address what the basis for classification might be, they do suggest that wide variations in both physical appearance and function can be acceptable for artifact categories. Membership might be determined by the sort of family resemblance relationship described by Rosch and Mervis (1975); by more complex relationships such as those described by Lakoff (1987); or by a core composed of still-to-be discovered sorts of information.

REFERENCES

Armstrong, S. L., Gleitman, L. R., and Gleitman, H. (1983). What some concepts might not be. *Cognition, 13*, 263-308.

Barr, R. A. and Caplan, L. J. (1987). Category representations and their implications for category structure. *Memory & Cognition, 15*, 397-418.

Carey, S. (1985). *Conceptual Change in Childhood.* Cambridge, MA: MIT Press.

Keil, F. (1986). The acquisition of natural kind and artifact terms. In W. Demopoulos & A. Marras (Eds.). *Language Learning and Concept Acquisition: Foundational Issues*, 133-153. New Jersey: Ablex Publishing.

Keil, F. (1987). Conceptual development and category structure. In U. Neisser (Ed.). *Concepts and Conceptual Development: Ecological and Intellectual Factors in Categorization.* New York: Cambridge University Press.

Lakoff, G. (1987). *Women, Fire, and Dangerous Things: What Categories Reveal about the Mind.* Chicago: University of Chicago Press.

Malt, B. C. (1985). Hedges and the mental representation of categories. *CC - AI: The Journal for the Integrated Study of Artificial Intelligence, Cognitive Science, and Applied Epistemology, 2*, 13-23.

Malt, B. C. (1988). Features and beliefs in the mental representation of categories. Manuscript under review.

Medin, D. L. and Smith, E. E. (1984). Concepts and concept formation. *Annual Review of Psychology*, *35*, 113-138.

Putnam, H. (1975). The meaning of 'meaning.' In H. Putnam, *Mind, Language, and Reality: Philosophical Papers, vol. 2.* Cambridge, England: Cambridge University Press.

Rey, G. (1985). Concepts and conceptions: A reply to Smith, Medin, and Rips. *Cognition*, *19*, 297-303.

Rips, L. J. (1986). Similarity, typicality, and categorization. Paper presented at the Workshop on Similarity and Analogy, Univ. of Illinois, June 1986.

Rosch, E. R. and Mervis, C. B. (1975). Family resemblances: Studies in the internal structure of categories. *Cognitive Psychology*, *7*, 573- 605.

Smith, E. E. (in press). Concepts and induction. In M. Posner (ed.) *Foundations of Cognitive Science.*

Smith, E. E. and Medin, D. L. (1981). *Categories and Concepts.* Cambridge, MA: Harvard University Press.

Wittgenstein, L. (1953). *Philosophical Investigations.* New York: MacMillan.

Planning in an Open World:
A Pluralistic Approach.*

Mitchell Marks, Kristian Hammond and Tim Converse
Department of Computer Science
University of Chicago
Chicago, IL 60637

Abstract

Recent work in planning has rejected the assumption of a closed, stable world, and the associated paradigm of exhaustive preplanning, which encounters serious problems trying to plan in a world where that assumption does not hold. Several alternative strategies have been proposed, responding to these new problems in a variety of ways. We review this spectrum, finding the various approaches in part incompatible but not bereft of some common themes and complementary strengths. We suggest factors in the application domain which should influence the appropriate mix, and describe the **TRUCKER** project to illustrate some of the problems and benefits in implementing such a mix.

Problems with Traditional Planning

The classical development of the theory of planning and problem-solving emphasized exhaustive preplanning, with the goal of being able to guarantee that an optimal or near-optimal plan would be found if one existed. Planners in this paradigm required certain assumptions to hold:

- The world will be stable; it will behave as projected.
- Time consumed in planning is independent of the time that can be devoted to execution, so that the efficiency of the planner has no side-effects on the feasibility of the constructed plan.
- The information available to the planner is complete, and execution will be flawless.
- Any initially correct plan will remain correct and can in fact be carried out.

In the real world, however, these assumptions simply do not hold. The world is not stable; agents must trade off planning time against execution time; and planners generally have to function under conditions of spotty rather than complete information. The simplifying assumptions were made in order to initiate progress in the serious investigation of planning. The harsh realities were consciously abstracted out of the theories initially, not merely overlooked. But with advancing theory, researchers have recently begun finding it feasible to explore the problem of planning in more realistic situations where these assumptions do not hold.

New problems in planning

In this paper we will attempt to classify the different kinds of issues that any planner must confront as we relax these traditional assumptions. We will discuss the different theories of planning that have arisen in

*This paper was submitted for presentation at the *1989 Meeting of the Cognitive Science Society*. It was also presented as a paper at the 1988 DARPA Workshop on Case-based Reasoning. This work was supported in part by the Defense Advanced Research Projects Agency, monitored by the Air Force Office of Scientific Research under contract F49620-88-C-0058, and the Office of Naval Research under contract N0014-85-K-010.

response to these issues. And we will present **TRUCKER**, a planner that combines features of many of these theories in an attempt to deal with the complexities of combining planning and acting in one system.

We now give a rough classification of the major sorts of problems a traditional planning system can encounter when required to deal with a more realistic domain. These problems, in turn, provide a basis for understanding what motivates the departures taken by theorists in recent work.

The Immediate Complexity Problem. This concerns the computational effort required in constructing one plan. If the planner searches for a correct and safe plan by projecting forward the effects of early steps to compare with preconditions of later steps, goals, and preservation conditions, the computational complexity can rise to a high order.

The Asymptotic Complexity Problem. As a planner interacts with the world, it is confronted with a stream of goals, or sets of conjunctive goals, rather than independent problems. If these are all treated singly, independently, the total planning and execution effort would be at least the sum of the separate costs (possibly worse, due to unfavorable interactions). But if the planner can somehow convert the interdependence from a problem to an advantage, then the average cost per goal can be reduced in the long run, offsetting the Immediate Complexity Problem.

The Execution-time Failure Problem. A plan which looked correct when it was constructed may turn out to be incorrect during execution. This may be because conditions in the world have changed in the meantime, invalidating the preconditions of a plan step, or because the plan was incorrect in the first place, based on incorrect assumptions in the planner's limited world-knowledge. To cope with this, a planner must have some facility for replanning, recovery, and repair.

The Planning/Execution Crowding Problem. If planning and execution are to be carried out by the same agent, essentially without parallelism, then time consumed in planning can deplete the time available for execution. This can create a situation where some series of actions would be a correct response to the goals and the world state, and could be feasibly executed within the total time available, but become infeasible within the time left after planning.

The Costly Information Problem. The planner cannot count on having complete information about a domain, either its underlying causal "physics" or its current state. To minimize the effects of this information shortage (namely inefficient plan construction and inaccurate plans), the planner should have information-gathering as a background goal. But understanding the world correctly, and storing new information in a usable form, can be expensive operations.

The Missed Opportunities Problem. A corollary to the Execution–time Failure problem is the Missed Opportunities problem. Because the world does not necessarily match the planner's understanding of it, it is often the case that opportunities to satisfy goals are missed at planning time and must be noticed and exploited at execution time.

NEW APPROACHES TO PLANNING

Several new directions in planning have arisen in response to problems like those enumerated earlier. All of them address the Immediate Complexity problem in one way or another, but differ in the additional emphasis they give to the various other problems. The outlook we propose here is that in most realistic environments, all of the problems will have to be addressed; so an ideal planner would combine the strengths of these different approaches, marshalled against the respective problems they most directly ameliorate.

One such new approach has come to be known as *reactive planning* (Agre & Chapman 1987) or *situated activity* in the preferred terminology of Agre and Chapman, following Suchman (1986). The major assumption of the traditional paradigm challenged by these authors is that adequate planning time is always available; along with the Immediate Complexity problem they are most directly concerned with the Planning/Execution Crowding problem. To function in a fast-changing world, a planner may have to pay more attention to execution or interpretation of plans and less to construction of plans. In the purest realizations of this idea, the planner will end up working from reflex-like stored responses for each immediate situation rather than true goal-directed plans. These are useful ideas, even when complexity or sensitivity of the problem domain dictates that they cannot be applied in pristine, radical form.

A key point from this line of thought is that planning and execution cannot be as neatly separated as traditionally supposed. This is not just because planning and execution share the same pool of available time (though that is an important aspect); rather, this represents a change in the very fundamentals of how to think and talk about planning. There isn't planning plus execution, there is one combined activity.

Various researchers have tried to address these same problems without completely abandoning the classical orientation that views activity as the execution of plans. *Reactive planning* systems (Firby 1987, Georgeff & Lansky 1987) are an attempt to combine plan construction and plan execution under a single control structure, in such a way that the systems will be robust to changes in the world while at the same time leaving room for genuine planning. The system described by Firby (1987) works with units of action called reactive action packages or **raps**. A **rap** "is essentially an autonomous process that pursues a planning goal until that goal has been achieved." Each **rap** has a number of methods that it knows about for achieving its goal, and will try methods until it can verify that one has succeeded. **raps** that are to be executed wait in a linear queue, and execution of a **rap** may involve a sequence of primitive actions or may in turn invoke other **raps**. In the latter case this provides some hierarchical structure to the plans specified by **raps**, without demanding elaboration to the level of primitive actions before execution can begin. The combination of multiple methods and verification of success results in a system that is very robust to execution failure.

The *procedural reasoning system* described by Georgeff and Lansky (1987) is an architecture for control of a mobile robot, in which the goals, beliefs, plans, and intentions of the robot are separately and explicitly represented. The current goals and beliefs about the state of the world determine which plans are chosen to be put on the execution stack. These plans hierarchically structure sub-plans, and may be addressed either to actions in the world or to manipulations of goals, beliefs and intentions themselves. The fact that new goals may be constructed in response to information gained during execution, and in turn push new plans onto the "intention" stack, makes possible a "shift of focus" in execution in response to new information. In particular, this permits the robot to interrupt the performance of a routine task in response to the detection of an emergency, and then resume the original task once the emergency has been dealt with.

An approach generally called case-based reasoning has become an emergent paradigm in several areas of AI, including planning, natural language understanding, diagnosis/repair systems, and problem-solving (Hammond 1989, Kolodner *et al.* 1985). As an approach to planning, *case-based planning* departs from traditional methods via an emphasis on the rôle of memory; more specifically, an episodic memory of past goals and the plans that succeeded or failed in satisfying them. This emphasis is directed at taming the Immediate Complexity problem and especially the Asymptotic Complexity problem.

In the purest form of case-based planning, new plans are *always* derived from plans in old cases, and are *never* computed purely from scratch (world knowledge and inference rules). A pristine case-based planning approach is best suited to a domain where execution failures or at least suboptimal execution can be tolerated. When a less fault-tolerant domain or task requires giving up this purity of approach, the correct response, we argue, is not to retreat to a full-scale projection of the plan's effects in the world. In the first place, that would mean giving up the efficiency advantages which form part of the motivation for case-based planning. Second, such a course is not in general possible; it depends on several of the assumptions we are trying to do without—assumptions of a stable world and complete knowledge. What is needed, instead, is a capability for *plan repair.*

The *adaptive planning* approach of Alterman (1985), and the *generate-test-debug* approach of Simmons and Davis (1987) are directed especially against the Execution-time Failure problem, as is (Hammond 1987). In adaptive planning, failure leads to replanning using semantically linked features; in generate-test-debug, replanning is guided by a causal description of the failure. Case-based planning also uses a causal description of plan failure, both to repair the current plan and to discover the features that will predict the problem in the future.

We have so far been treating the issue of failure as though it exclusively meant failure of a single plan to work correctly in execution, either through simple bad planning or through confrontation with unexpected conditions in the world. A planner dealing with multiple goals must also deal with possible failures deriving from the interactions of the plans for two or more goals. Interactions where plans may interfere with each other have long been a focus in planning research. Here we will place some emphasis on another sort of interaction between plans, interactions in which some benefit could be derived from combining plans. If a useful interaction could be obtained, but the planner does not take advantage of this possibility, it has fallen into another sort of interactive failure. This failure to take advantage of potentially beneficial plan interactions constitutes the Missed Opportunities problem.

Clearly, the necessity for making use of opportunities—avoiding the Missed Opportunities problem—springs ultimately from considerations of efficiency; that is, from the concerns we have labeled the Immediate Complexity and Asymptotic Complexity problems. Indeed, our whole taxonomy of problems has been revealed as a tangled network of mutual dependencies. The moral is obvious: they cannot be solved singly and piecemeal. Active planning in a realistic domain requires combined work on all these fronts simultaneously.

Strategy mix depends on domain

In the previous sections we listed several fundamental problems encountered in the traditional approach of full preplanning under a closed-world assumption; examined several recent directions in planning, each one aimed at ameliorating selected items from that list of problems; and called for efforts to develop an integrated approach. But we will not get very far by arguing about these issues at the level of generality in the previous sections. There is no best (and of course this could only mean "currently-best") integrated approach to planning in general, for the simple reason that there is no such thing as planning-in-general.

As happens almost anywhere in AI or computer science, we have reached the point of confrontation with trade-offs. A planner trying to operate in an unstable world, of which it has incomplete knowledge, is forced to trade correctness for efficiency, first-time success for long-run success, planning time for execution time. If the planner is trying to solve an NP-hard problem in the real world, the dilemma can only become sharper.

The best—or let us only say the least unsatisfactory—resolution of these trade-offs is not given by general considerations but instead depends on the domain, the task, and perhaps an externally-decided performance-level criterion. To make our discussion more concrete, we will focus on the choices stemming from the domain and task used in the **TRUCKER** project, whose implementation is described in the latter sections of this paper.

TRUCKER is a planner operating in the domain of messenger-service scheduling. A dispatcher controls a fleet of trucks which roam a city or a neighborhood, picking up and dropping off parcels at designated addresses. (Our implementation uses Chicago and its Hyde Park neighborhood.) Transport orders are "phoned in" by customers at various times during the simulated business day, and the parcel delivery sequence and truck routing are adjusted to efficiently accommodate the new orders. The relevant sense of efficiency here includes both the cost of the planner's own efforts and the evolving delivery sequence and routing.

TRUCKER's task involves receiving requests from customers, making decisions about which truck to assign a given request to, deciding in what order given parcels should be picked up and dropped off, figuring out routes for the trucks to follow, and monitoring the execution of the plans it constructs. A number of limited resources must be managed, including the trucks themselves, their gas and cargo space, and the planner's own planning time. **TRUCKER** starts off with very little information about the world that its trucks will be negotiating; all it has is the equivalent of a street map, an incomplete and potentially inaccurate schematic of its simulated world.

Thus, this is the sort of domain and task where the problems contemplated in our earlier list all naturally arise. Traditional approaches to planning, with emphasis on exhaustive preplanning, would therefore be inadequate to this task for a number of reasons:

- **TRUCKER** lacks perfect information about its world.
- **TRUCKER** does not know all of its goals in advance – new calls come in that must be integrated with currently running plans.

- Planning time is limited. **TRUCKER**'s world does not wait for it to complete plans before new events occur.
- Even given perfect advance information, an optimal solution to the problem **TRUCKER** faces is computationally intractable. Even scheduling the pickup and dropoff points for a single truck to minimize travel time is a variant of the traveling salesman problem, which is known to be NP-complete.

To stave off the effects of the Planning/Execution Crowding problem, we might try a situated-activity approach. But the complexity of the domain rules out a pristine situated-activity/reactive-planning approach to this task. Very few pickups and deliveries would get done if the trucks were commanded by a frenetic dispatcher constantly issuing new instructions based only on the current locations of the trucks and the last transport-request received.

However, an appropriate modification within the reactive-planning school of thought, we believe, can be derived along the lines taken in (Firby 1987). We separate out classes of actions which require temporally-extended control (routing) from those which can be but the matter of a moment (navigation), and assign execution of the latter to semi-autonomous agents.

To deal with Asymptotic Complexity, we might want to cast our planner in a case-based mold, storing and re-using plans. The relevant plans here are the routes for driving from one given block to another. That's fine, as far as it goes, and indeed **TRUCKER** has a route-memory. But by itself this technique doesn't go nearly far enough. A delivery truck cannot afford to work sequentially through its list of orders, driving directly from the pickup point of each request to the corresponding dropoff point before dealing with the next request, even if the list has been put in some rational order. There will be a clear case of interaction failure, contributing to the Missed Opportunities problem, if the planner is not able to combine nearby stops. On the other hand, the planner will be swamped in the Immediate Complexity problem if it checks for all route-combination possibilities every time a new request is phoned in. Clearly, it needs something beyond the situated-activity and case-based components demanded so far, something to help it select reasonable occasions for making the computational effort to detect advantageous combinations.

To deal with these combinations, then, we would want to give the planner an opportunistic component, whose job it is to detect apparent opportunities for route-combination. But if hammered together in isolation, such a facility would introduce its own new computational costs. It would be at least problematic, and perhaps no net gain at all, if this component were introduced as a new planning expense on top of everything else—say, as a collection of daemons attached to each pending delivery request.

This consideration takes us from *opportunism* in general to the more specific model of *opportunistic memory*.

A pending delivery goal gets attached to memory structures which will be used or activated anyway when an appropriate opportunity for dealing with that goal arises in the normal course of other activity. In the **TRUCKER** domain, the relevant normal activity is simply that of (simulated) driving. With that step, we have asked for another component, an observing/understanding component which "parses the world" from the raw stream of incoming information. In the course of interpreting the presence of a certain recognizable building or other landmark as meaning that the truck has reached a now-identifiable location, it must find and access a memory structure corresponding to that location. Waiting in that memory structure is a notation about other delivery goals associated with that place—but waiting quietly, as a notation, not waiting busily, as a daemon. Thus our response to the Missed Opportunities problem has demanded that we deal with the Costly Information problem at the same time.

When an opportunity for route-combination arises, the planner must be able to take advantage of it by reorganizing the delivery plans. (And of course it should store the combination for later re-use.) Besides the potential interaction failures represented by missed opportunities, **TRUCKER** must also be prepared to deal with direct execution failures. For both these reasons, it requires a replanning component.

Structure of the TRUCKER Program

The **TRUCKER** planner is embedded in a demonstration program consisting of three modules: the world simulation, the map, and the planner itself. Trucks move through the world, along routes constructed by the planner, assuming that the directions are valid, that there is gas in the tank, and so on (they may find out otherwise). The map is a schematic of the simulated world, but with considerably less information, lacking buildings, "visual" cues, one-way streets and other features. The simulated world, on the other hand, does contain cues of those sorts, which play an essential role in navigation. Though the program has to know where all the trucks are at any given moment, this information is not directly available to the planner; instead, it must construct and maintain this information as it goes along, "parsing the world." This intimate connection with locality provides the basis for having places remind the planner of possible opportunities.

The high-level agenda for a truck is a sequence of instructions about where to travel and what to do there. Typically it consists at any one time of alternating instructions for travel-steps and parcel transactions:

```
(GOTO (5802 S-WOODLAWN))
(PICKUP PARCEL-3)
(GOTO (920 E-55TH))
(DROPOFF PARCEL-5)
```

Plans of this sort are created as needed, and consumed piecemeal as each portion is executed. Each truck has such a plan. Portions not yet executed are available for reordering, cancellation, addition of new steps along the way, or transfer to another truck.

The planner also provides specific plans for the routes that trucks follow when executing a GOTO step. A route is represented as a series of turns, using street names and compass directions (with a start and stop instruction at the beginning and end). In particular, it is *not* a series of step-by-step or block-by-block instructions; a truck driving under the guidance of a route can travel several blocks without using a new portion of the route, until it must turn or make a stop. The route expanding the travel step `(GOTO (920 E-55TH))` in the delivery plan given above would be the following:

```
(START NORTH (5802 S-WOODLAWN))
(TURN EAST E-57TH)
(TURN NORTH S-CORNELL)
(TURN EAST E-55TH)
(STOP (920 E-55TH))
```

These pieces of knowledge are indexed by the place in the world with which they are associated.

Together, these provide the material on which the several active components demanded in the previous section do their work.

Reactive-planning component: central planning agenda

At the center of the **TRUCKER** implementation lies a "main loop" planning and execution supervisor, corresponding to the dispatcher in the domain model. The implementation is intended to connect with the ideas of (Firby 1987). The basic task of this component is to answer the phone, examine each new delivery order, and either assign it to a truck immediately or else decide to temporarily lay it aside.

The planner controls its own agenda by means of a request-based action queue, ordered by predefined priorities for various types of tasks. The central planning component is treated as time-bound. That is, almost all of the actions it can take, both those involving its own state and those involving the domain more directly, have costs in the simulated time-stream. As a consequence, it is designed to act in units of atomic actions that require little time singly; the atomic components of a complex action are placed in a priority queue, to be carried out when time allows. The contents of this queue at any given moment constitutes a tentative plan for the planner's actions in the near term. To achieve this atomization, most of the action-types built into the planner are molecular.

The most important molecular action is to try assigning a delivery request to a truck which will be able to handle it well. These are "or" packets. When a new order is received, the planner's only immediate response is to place such an assign-delivery-to-truck action somewhere in its queue. At some point that action is interpreted, and the result of that interpretation is to place four new packets into the queue.

```
handle-new-req-expansion:
      try-assign-to-truck-going-near    ; if reminded
      try-assign-to-idle-truck
      try-combine-with-unassigned-reqs ; if reminded
      dump-in-unassigned-reqs
```

By keeping the atomic actions generally inexpensive individually, even at the cost of multiplying their number, we prevent the planner from being tied up and uninterruptible when it should be noticing events in the world, a particular version of the Planning/Execution Crowding problem. But the main contribution of this architecture is against the Immediate Complexity problem, by avoiding projection of effects and enforcing an early (indeed, immediate) linearization of implicitly hierarchical structures.

Case-based component: route and combination memory

When a truck, working through its delivery agenda, completes one pickup or dropoff and prepares to drive on to the next, it requires a driving route from the dispatcher. If necessary, the dispatcher will consult the map and its memory of road conditions and typical speeds (a memory quite distinct from the map) in order to compute, by two-way best-first search, a near-optimal route from the truck's current location to its next stop. This computation is one of the two inherently expensive operations in **TRUCKER**, and the planner will avoid undertaking it if possible. The computation can be skipped if the planner already knows the desired route, having previously computed it and stored it. This, of course, is the core idea of case-based planning and we employ it very directly here: the planner cannot entirely avoid this expensive search, but it can avoid repeating it for the same locations. [1]

When two delivery requests are opportunistically combined and their routes are merged, the merged route is stored, along with the fact that these two pickup-dropoff location pairs proved combinable. This provides some interesting challenges in memory indexing, but otherwise the basic idea is still the same, and addresses especially the Asymptotic Complexity problem.

Opportunistic memory and replanning components: detecting and constructing plan combinations

TRUCKER merges requests in an effort to optimize over travel time. But it does so only when it encounters an opportunity to satisfy one request while it is actually running the route for a previous one, or if it has learned from a previous such opportunity that two requests are combinable. Initially, the effect of the queued action packets in the dispatcher is that **TRUCKER** runs requests in order of "call-in," assigning them singly to idle trucks until all trucks are occupied. It also links each new request with the memory nodes in its representation associated with the locations that would serve as opportunities for satisfying the request, *i.e.*, the pickup and delivery location. As the planner executes each stage of its plan, recognizing locations, it sometimes finds requests associated with locations that it is passing. When this happens, **TRUCKER** considers the possibility that the new request could be merged with the current plan—as well as the possibility that the resulting route should be stored and re-used.

Situated-activity and Understanding components: driving and navigating

Like these real drivers, **TRUCKER** cannot preplan all the driving steps involved in carrying out a sequence of deliveries. It first supplies the trucks with highest-level plans, a sequence of the locations where they are to stop for pickups and dropoffs. Only when such a step is ready for execution is it expanded into a plan at the next lower level, a sequence of major travel legs punctuated by turns or change of street name.

[1] This aspect was not our main theoretical emphasis in **TRUCKER**, so we did not implement certain interesting variations which suggest themselves as additional time-saving measures. New routes, for example, could be constructed by extending old ones; or the planner could model the city in terms of neighborhood centers, major intersections, and local "feeder" streets, and try to adapt any route found in memory which has the same start and end neighborhoods as the desired new route, or the same nearby major intersection.

This gives the planner the flexibility to rearrange the higher-level plans as needed for repair or opportunity, without wasting the effort of repeatedly changing the expansions at the lower level when the major steps get interleaved differently.

Summary

Recent developments in planning have separately addressed various of the major problems that arose when traditional planning ideas were presented with domains and tasks for which the assumptions of a closed world and complete knowledge do not hold. The new theories have shown considerable success in taming some of those problems, by regarding plan construction and execution as intimately tied together, and thus monitoring and guiding the execution of their plans. But even with this measure of success, no one of these theories can claim complete success, and none can be taken as the unique best direction in which planning research should go. We call for a pluralistic spirit and close attention to the dictates of the particular domains and tasks as a way of developing suitable planning systems.

References

Agre, P. E. and D. Chapman (1987). Pengi: An implementation of a theory of activity. In *Proceedings of AAAI-87*, AAAI, Seattle, WA, July 1987, 268-272.

Alterman, R. (1985). Adaptive planning: refitting old plans to new situations. In *Proceedings 7th Cognitive Science Society.*

Birnbaum, L., and G. Collins (1984). Opportunistic Planning and Freudian Slips. In *Proceedings of the Sixth Annual Conference of the Cognitive Science Society*, Boulder, CO, 1984.

Chapman, D. (1985). *Planning for Conjunctive Goals*, Technical Report TR 802, MIT Artificial Intelligence Laboratory.

Firby, R. J. (1987). An investigation into reactive planning in complex domains. In *Proceedings of AAAI-87*, AAAI, Seattle, WA, July 1987, 202-206.

Georgeff, M. P. and Lansky, A. L. (1987). Reactive Reasoning and Planning. In *Proceedings of AAAI-87*, AAAI, Seattle, WA, July 1987, 677-682.

Hammond, K. (1987). Explaining and Repairing Plans that Fail. In *Proceedings of the Tenth International Joint Conference on Artificial Intelligence*, Milan, Italy, August 1987.

Hammond, K., T. Converse and M. Marks (1988). Learning from opportunities: Storing and re-using execution-time optimizations. In *Proceedings of AAAI-88.*

Hammond, K. and N. Hurwitz (1988). Extracting diagnostic features from explanations. AAAI Symposium on explanation-based learning, Palo Alto, CA, March.

Hammond, K., *Case-based Planning: Viewing planning as a memory task.* Academic Press, Cambridge, MA, 1989.

Hayes-Roth, B., and F. Hayes-Roth (1979). A cognitive model of planning. In *Cognitive Science*, 2, 1979, 275-310.

Kolodner, J. L., R. L. Simpson, and K. Sycara-Cyranski (1985). A process model of case-based reasoning in problem solving. In *The Ninth International Joint Conference on Artificial Intelligence.*

Simmons, R. F., and R. Davis (1987). Generate, test, and debug: combining associational rules and causal models.

Suchman, L. (1987). *Plans and Situated Actions.* Cambridge University Press, 1987.

Lexical Ambiguity Resolution in a Constraint Satisfaction Network

Michael E. J. Masson

University of Victoria

ABSTRACT

Behavioral evidence supports the claim that in the absence of a strongly biasing context multiple meanings of an ambiguous word are activated, particularly when the two meanings occur with equal frequency. A simple constraint satisfaction system, based on a Hopfield network and incorporating a distributed memory scheme, is shown to account for results from a cross modal priming paradigm typically interpreted as evidence for multiple access. The model demonstrates that the power of an ambiguous word to facilitate identification of targets related to either of its two meanings may be produced by *selective* activation of just one meaning. Selective activation is driven by simultaneous processing of the ambiguous prime and the associated target word, with the unambiguous target determining the appropriate interpretation of the prime. The model also provides the basis for a reinterpretation of a number of other empirical results concerning lexical ambiguity resolution.

INTRODUCTION

The identification of a word that has at least two clearly distinct interpretations presents a serious challenge to models of word identification. The critical issue is whether all or only one of an ambiguous word's meanings are activated upon presentation of the word. Although certain kinds of contextual information apparently produce a form of selective access of a homograph's lexical entries (Duffy, Morris, & Rayner, 1988; Seidenberg, Tanenhaus, Leiman, & Bienkowski, 1982; Tabossi, 1988; Van Petten & Kutas, 1987), there is evidence to suggest that multiple access occurs in the absence of biasing context. Using a cross modal priming paradigm and balanced homographs (items with two equally frequent meanings), Seidenberg et al. (1982) found that hearing a homograph at the end of a nonbiasing sentence context produced equal priming of visual targets related to either of the homograph's two interpretations. Similarly, Duffy et al. (1988) found longer gaze durations, relative to control words, on balanced homographs that appeared following a nonbiasing phrase. The additional processing time was attributed to required selection of one of the two activated entries for integration with the context.

Simultaneous activation of multiple lexical entries is fully compatible with the classic semantic network view of the lexicon (e.g., Collins & Loftus, 1975; Collins & Quillian, 1972). This view holds that each lexical entry is represented as a unique node in the network, and it is quite possible for multiple nodes to be highly active. In fact, priming effects are assumed to be the result of activation spread across links between nodes. But strong, simultaneous activation of concepts, particularly unrelated concepts as in the case of distinct meanings of an ambiguous word, is problematic for models based on a distributed memory scheme (e.g., Eich, 1985; McClelland & Rumelhart, 1985). In a distributed memory system a concept is expressed as a pattern of activation across an entire network of nodes. Only one pattern of activation can be instantiated at any moment, therefore it would be impossible for two unrelated concepts (representing the two different meanings of an ambiguous word) to simultaneously dominate the network's pattern of activation. For this reason, demonstrations of multiple access constitute a serious challenge to this class of models.

Kawamoto and Anderson (1984) developed a neural network model incorporating a distributed memory representation that produced simultaneous activation of multiple meanings of an ambiguous word. In keeping with the limitations on multiple activation imposed by a distributed memory scheme, however, their reported simulations included no instance of two concepts simultaneously achieving activation levels greater than .5, where asymptotic activation was 1.0. Although this could be considered a case of multiple activation, it is not clear from their simulations whether this rather low level of activation would be adequate to produce priming effects equal in magnitude to those obtained with an unambiguous word (Seidenberg et al., 1982).

A CONSTRAINT SATISFACTION NETWORK MODEL

I have attempted to apply a simple constraint satisfaction model, based on a Hopfield network (Hopfield, 1982; Hopfield & Tank, 1986), to the problem of simulating cross modal priming results that have been taken as evidence for multiple access in the lexicon (Seidenberg et al., 1982). The network consists of a group of binary valued nodes, and concepts are represented as unique patterns of on/off states across these nodes. Only one pattern of activation can be represented in the system at a given instant, implying that the system will not allow multiple concepts to be fully activated simultaneously. But this restriction does not mean that multiple concepts cannot be partially activated at the same time. Degree of activation of a concept in this system is conceived as the proportion of nodes in the currently instantiated pattern that match the pattern defining the concept. When a pattern of activation is instantiated in the network it may partially match a number of different concepts. The maximum amount of simultaneous activation of a set of concepts, however, is limited by the similarity of their defining patterns of activation.

The system's knowledge about and potential for instantiating different concepts lies in the strengths of connections between nodes. New concepts are acquired by adjusting the connection weights according to a prescription of the general type proposed by Hebb (1949). The weight of the link connecting any two nodes is altered as a function of the on/off states adopted by the two nodes when a new concept is instantiated. Specifically, if both nodes are in the same state (both on or both off) then the link between them is increased in strength, but if the two nodes are in different states (one on and one off) their link is reduced:

$$\Delta w_{ij} = n_i n_j ,$$

where w_{ij} represents the weight of the link between nodes i and j, and n_i and n_j represent the states taken by those nodes when the new concept is activated. A node in the on state takes the value 1 and a node in the off state is assigned the value -1.

Pattern Recognition

Simulation of word identification is treated as a pattern completion problem in the model. Once the system has encoded a set of concepts, it can be provided a pattern of activation that partially matches a target concept. The system can then gradually change the pattern of activation until it reconstructs the entire pattern of the target concept. This is accomplished through a process of asynchronous updating of each node in the network. If the net activation sent to a node from all other nodes in the network exceeds some threshold, the node is set to the *on* state, otherwise it is set to the *off* state. The activation received by a node is a function of the on/off states of the other nodes in the system and the weight of the links between those nodes and the node selected for updating:

$$a_i = \sum_{j \neq i} w_{ij} n_j ,$$

where a_i represents the amount of activation directed to the selected node. In the simulations reported here the threshold for setting a node to the *on* state was zero. This updating scheme acts as a constraint satisfaction network, driving the network to a pattern of activation that represents a local maximum goodness of fit, and is stable in the sense that any further updates will not produce adjustments in the pattern. Under appropriate circumstances (e.g., the concepts learned by the network are few in number relative to the number of nodes in the network, and are not highly similar to one another), the stable pattern that is achieved will correspond to one of the concepts learned by the system (Hopfield, 1982).

To simulate word identification, a network consisting of two sets of nodes was constructed. One set of nodes represents the perceptual (visual and auditory) characteristics of a word, and another set represents its conceptual features. Each perceptual node is linked to each conceptual node, and the conceptual nodes are fully interconnected as well. Upon presentation of a word, perceptual input is immediately read into the appropriate subset of perceptual nodes (e.g., visual) and the other subset of perceptual nodes (auditory) are set to zero, indicating no relevant input is present in the other modality. No attempt is made in the current version of the model to simulate interactive effects in perception. Asynchronous updating is applied to the conceptual nodes, which begin in either a random state or a pattern determined by a previously presented stimulus. The perceptual nodes continue to hold the pattern of activation dictated by the sensory input. The updating scheme drives the pattern of activation among the conceptual nodes from the initial state to a stable pattern representing the concept designated by the perceptual input. Reaching a learned stable state constitutes full activation and identification of the target concept, and the number of updating cycles required to move the network to the stable state is taken as a measure of word identification time.

SIMULATION OF LEXICAL AMBIGUITY RESOLUTION

The critical issue was whether a system that inherently prohibits strong, simultaneous activation of unrelated concepts could simulate cross modal priming results that have been taken as evidence for multiple access of an ambiguous word's meanings. An attempt was made to simulate the results of Experiment 1 reported by Seidenberg et al. (1982). In this study subjects heard neutral phrases ending with an ambiguous or unambiguous prime word, then named aloud a visually presented target (e.g., *Joe buys the straw-HAY*). Presentation of the target occurred either immediately after the prime was pronounced or 200 msec later. In the case of an ambiguous prime the target was related to one of its meanings and when an unambiguous prime was used the target was either related or unrelated to it. When the target appeared immediately after the prime, homograph primes produced facilitation in naming equal to that produced by unambiguous primes. After a 200-msec delay, however, greater facilitation was obtained with unambiguous primes. Seidenberg et al. concluded that immediately after hearing an ambiguous prime both meanings were activated, thereby producing facilitation to either target. But after a delay one interpretation was arbitrarily selected so only one of the targets would be facilitated and the other would not. The average facilitation, then, would be smaller than that obtained with the unambiguous prime.

Simulation of these results involved a version of the network described earlier, consisting of 45 auditory, 40 visual, and 40 conceptual nodes. An ambiguous word was simulated by constructing two items with identical patterns of activation among perceptual nodes, and unrelated patterns in the conceptual nodes. These two items were encoded using the Hebbian learning rule. In addition, two unambiguous words related to each meaning of the homograph were also encoded. The patterns of activation in the conceptual nodes of related words overlapped in 29 of the 40 nodes. These items were used to simulate the three priming conditions tested by Seidenberg et al. (1982). The homograph and one of the unambiguous words related to each of its meanings served as primes and the other unambiguous words were targets. It was assumed that information in the neutral phrase would leave the conceptual nodes in a random pattern of activation because none of

TABLE 1

MEAN CYCLES REQUIRED TO IDENTIFY A VISUAL TARGET IN THE SIMULATION OF THE CROSS MODAL PRIMING PARADIGM

	Prime		
Target delay	Related ambiguous	Related unambiguous	Unrelated unambiguous
0 msec	174.8	175.2	208.4
200 msec	140.7	128.4	167.5

its constituents were strongly related to the primes or targets. Presentation of the prime was simulated by loading its auditory pattern into the network and onset of the visual target was simulated by loading the appropriate visual pattern into the network.

In the immediate condition it was assumed that some minimal processing of the prime would occur as it was being pronounced and that additional processing would continue during the early stages of target processing. Therefore the network was updated for 10 cycles using only the prime's auditory pattern, with the visual nodes set to zero. Then the visual pattern for the target was loaded and the network was updated under the influence of both perceptual patterns for a further 65 cycles. Finally the auditory pattern was set to zero to reflect selective processing of the visual target and updates continued until the system reached a stable state or 400 updates had occurred since target onset. In the 200-msec delay condition, the prime's auditory pattern was allowed to influence the system for 75 cycles at which point the target's visual pattern was loaded and the auditory pattern was set to zero. The system then continued to update until the target was identified or the system ran for 400 update cycles since target onset. This sequence was formulated on the assumption that in the delay condition processing of the auditory prime was terminated by onset of the visual target.

The simulation was run 100 times for each of the two delay conditions, with each run based on a set of words randomly selected within the constraints described earlier. Each run involved 10 trials in each priming condition. Despite the high degree of similarity among the concepts encoded by the system, only 13% of the trials failed to move into the stable state that defined the target word. The mean number of cycles required to identify the target as a function target delay and type of prime is shown in Table 1. These results very closely approximate the data reported by Seidenberg et al. (1982), with the exception that the simulation produced shorter response times in the delay condition. Seidenberg et al. found longer response times after a 200-msec delay in their first experiment, but the delay variable was manipulated between subjects and a within-subject manipulation would be needed to obtain a more reliable assessment of the overall effect of delay on response time. Moreover, other experiments they reported are consistent with the simulation, as are independent replications of their experiment (e.g., Van Petten & Kutas, 1987). The model produces faster identification in the delay condition because the target's visual pattern unilaterally influences activation in the conceptual nodes as soon as it appears. There is no competition from the auditory prime trying to move the system to a slightly different activation pattern in the conceptual nodes.

The model's success in producing equal facilitation with ambiguous and unambiguous primes in

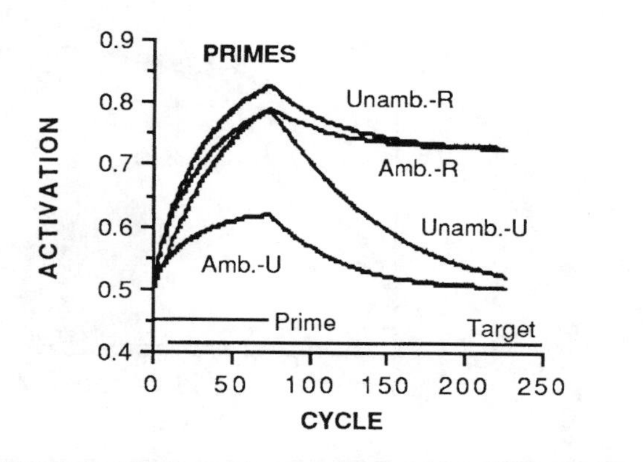

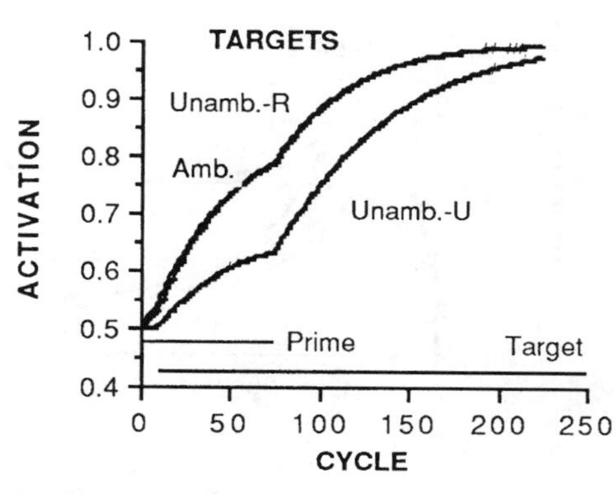

FIGURE 1. ACTIVATION VALUES FOR PRIMES (LEFT PANEL) AND TARGETS (RIGHT PANEL) IN THE IMMEDIATE CONDITION OF THE CROSS MODAL PRIMING PARADIGM. AMBIGUOUS AND UNAMBIGUOUS PRIMES WERE EITHER RELATED (R) OR UNRELATED (U) TO THE TARGETS. HORIZONTAL LINES INDICATE TIME COURSE OF SENSORY INPUT FROM PRIME AND TARGET.

the immediate condition was not due to multiple activation of both meanings of an ambiguous prime. Rather, simultaneous processing of the auditory prime and visual target in the immediate condition allowed the target to drive the system toward the relevant interpretation of the ambiguous prime. This process can be seen in Figure 1, which represents the activation values for prime (left panel) and target (right panel) concepts in the immediate condition. The activation value for a concept at a given instant is the proportion of the network's conceptual nodes that currently match the pattern of on/off states corresponding to that concept. A value of .5 indicates that a concept is at resting level in the sense that a concept would be expected to have half its nodes in common with a randomly chosen pattern of activation. The behavior shown in Figure 1 is not an example of *backward* priming, where the target activates a related meaning of the ambiguous prime, then the selected meaning sends activation back to the target (Glucksberg, Kreuz, & Rho, 1986). The mutually supportive activation of the conceptual nodes produced by simultaneous processing of the ambiguous prime and the target is more closely related to what Van Petten and Kutas (1987) referred to as *mutual* priming. In a distributed memory system this kind of interaction between closely coupled inputs involves simultaneous influence over the entire network of nodes. The influence is symbiotic when the two inputs represent conceptually related items. Equal priming by ambiguous and unambiguous primes occurred despite slightly lower activation of the relevant interpretation of the ambiguous prime. This is because patterns of activation representing homographs generally have higher goodness of fit values than unambiguous items, giving them greater power to influence the direction of change in the network's pattern of activation. The goodness of fit advantage for homographs is a product of the two encodings of their perceptual patterns (once for each meaning of a homograph) compared to only one encoding of the perceptual pattern for an unambigous word.

When the target was delayed the system had no basis for selecting the appropriate interpretation and was therefore incorrect in its selection on about half of the trials. In those instances the auditory prime moved the conceptual nodes toward a pattern of activation irrelevant to the target. Consequently, the average level of activation of relevant and irrelevant interpretations of the ambiguous primes were similar and lower than activation of the unambiguous primes, as seen in the left panel of Figure 2. Moreover, the ambiguous prime was effective in facilitating target identification only half the time, that is, on those occasions when the relevant interpretation

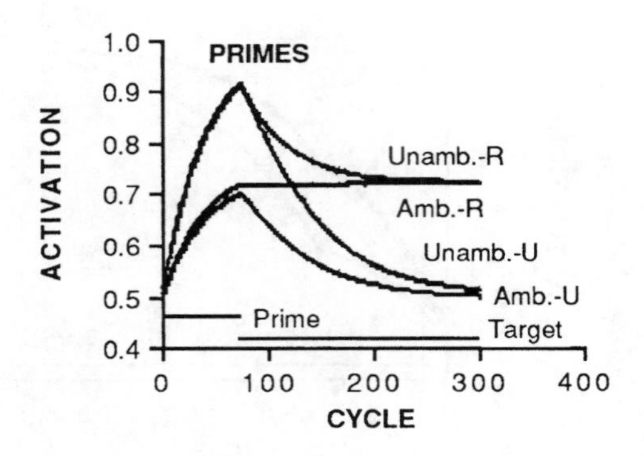

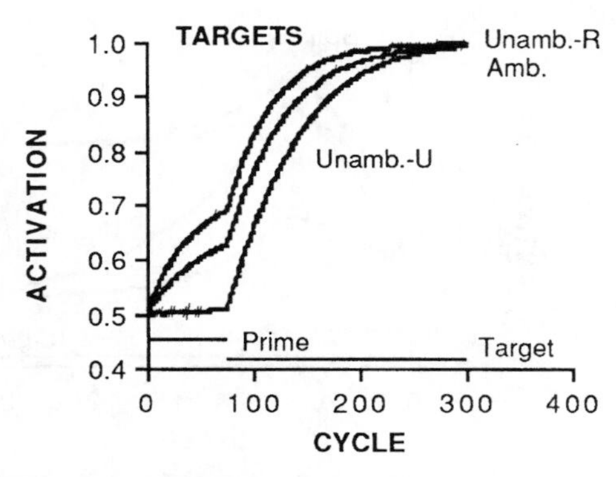

FIGURE 2. ACTIVATION VALUES FOR PRIMES (LEFT PANEL) AND TARGETS (RIGHT PANEL) IN THE DELAYED CONDITION OF THE CROSS MODAL PRIMING PARADIGM. AMBIGUOUS AND UNAMBIGUOUS PRIMES WERE EITHER RELATED (R) OR UNRELATED (U) TO THE TARGETS. HORIZONTAL LINES INDICATE TIME COURSE OF SENSORY INPUT FROM PRIME AND TARGET.

happened to be selected. The average growth of activation values of target items is shown in the right panel of Figure 2 and reflects the differences in observed facilitation effects.

Other Empirical Results

The model could be extended to account for another effect reported by Seidenberg et al. (1982). Using a biased context, they found evidence for selective activation of one interpretation of an ambiguous prime even when the target followed immediately after the prime. The context phrase contained a word strongly related to one interpretation of the ambiguous prime (e.g., *Although the farmer bought the straw-HAY*). Context effects of this form could be simulated by assuming that context words are identified without driving the conceptual nodes completely into the appropriate pattern of activation. Rather, an approximation to the known pattern would be sufficient to identify the word. This would allow parts of the pattern established by earlier context words to survive in the network until the ambiguous prime was presented. At that point the system would be in a state that slightly favored the relevant interpretation and that is the meaning that likely would be selected. The model could similarly account for results such as those obtained by Duffy et al. (1988) and Tabossi (1988) in which contexts not containing words directly associated with an ambiguous word nevertheless influenced which interpretation was selected. For example, context could activate elements of the conceptual nodes relevant to a salient feature of one meaning of the homograph causing that meaning to be selected when the homograph was presented (Tabossi, 1988).

In their study of event related potentials, Van Petten and Kutas (1987) replicated the Seidenberg et al. (1982) study except that contexts and targets both were visually presented and the contexts contained information to bias one interpretation of the homograph prime. The interesting result was that when a target related to the unbiased interpretation was presented immediately after termination of the homograph prime, event related potentials indicated that the target was initially responded to as though it were a contextually unrelated word. But 500 msec after target onset cortical activity suggested that the alternative interpretation of the homograph had been instantiated. This is the result that would be expected of the constraint satisfaction network model proposed here. Presentation of the target would eventually change the interpretation applied to the homograph prime, overriding the early influence of the preceding context.

There is a second kind of evidence that supports the multiple access view of lexical ambiguity resolution. In their study of eye movements during reading of ambiguous words, Duffy et al. (1988) found that balanced homographs were viewed an average of 18 msec longer than control words, provided that the preceding context was neutral with respect to the homograph's interpretation. Their explanation was that both meanings had been activated and a time consuming selection process was required in order for the word to be integrated with ongoing comprehension processes. But the viewing time effect could have resulted from an important difference between the homograph and control words. Duffy et al. equated these items for frequency, but they did so on the basis of occurrences of tokens rather than types. Thus for a balanced homograph, each of its meanings would be experienced in a relevant context by an average reader only half as many times as the control word. The longer viewing times for homographs may actually reflect the lower frequency of the arbitrarily selected interpretation of the homograph, rather than activation of both interpretations.

CONCLUSION

Results from the cross modal priming paradigm have significantly influenced theories of lexical ambiguity resolution and, more generally, theories of lexical access and language comprehension. These results have encouraged the assumption that multiple meanings of ambiguous words are initially activated then a context appropriate sense is selected (e.g., Kintsch, 1988; Seidenberg, 1985). The constraint satisfaction network model described here, however, was able to reproduce the results on which this assumption was founded even though it clearly involved selective access of lexical ambiguity. Although this demonstration does not prove that lexical ambiguities are processed by selective activation, it does show that a multiple access interpretation is not dictated by the available empirical evidence, and that a selective access account of the data is plausible. In addition, the model represents one example of how distributed memory systems can account for data that imply simultaneous instantiation of incompatible patterns of activation.

The present version of the model makes no claims about the key theoretical idea behind the multiple access proposal: modularity of the lexicon. A modular view of the lexicon assumes that lexical activation is independent of contextual information provided by sentence comprehension (Fodor, 1983; Seidenberg, 1985). Therefore, identification of an ambiguous word should involve multiple activation of its meanings unless *lexical* processes influence selection of one meaning (Seidenberg et al., 1982). In the simulations reported here, lexical activity was influenced only by sensory input directly impinging on the lexicon or by activity within the lexicon itself. No influence from contextual information based on sentence comprehension was incorporated and in this sense the model preserves the assumption of modularity in the lexicon. The fact that this system was able to simulate relevant empirical results while engaging in selective activation suggests an uncoupling of the issues of modularity and lexical ambiguity resolution.

REFERENCES

Collins, A. M., & Loftus, E. F. (1975). A spreading activation theory of semantic processing. *Psychological Review*, **82**, 407-428.
Collins, A. M., & Qullian, M. R. (1969). Retrieval time from semantic memory. *Journal of Verbal Learning and Verbal Behavior*, **8**, 240-248.
Duffy, S. A., Morris, R. K., & Rayner, K. (1988). Lexical ambiguity and fixation times in reading. *Journal of Memory and Language*, **27**, 429-446.
Eich, J. M. (1985). Levels of processing, encoding specificity, elaboration, and CHARM. *Psychological Review*, **92**, 1-38.
Fodor, J. A. (1983). *The modularity of mind.* Cambridge, MA: MIT Press.

Glucksberg, S., Kreuz, R. J., & Rho, S. H. (1986). Context can constrain lexical access: Implications for models of language comprehension. *Journal of Experimental Psychology: Learning, Memory, and Cognition*, **12**, 323-335.

Hebb, D. O. (1949). *The organization of behavior*. New York: Wiley.

Hopfield, J. J. (1982). Neural networks and physical systems with emergent collective computational abilities. *Proceedings of the National Academy of Science*, **79**, 2554-2558.

Hopfield, J. J., & Tank, D. W. (1986). Computing with neural circuits: A model. *Science*, **233**, 625-633.

Kawamoto, A. H., & Anderson, J. A. (1984). Lexical access using a neural network. *Proceedings of the Sixth Annual Conference of the Cognitive Science Society* (pp. 204-213).

Kintsch, W. (1988). The role of knowledge in discourse comprehension: A construction-integration model. *Psychological Review*, **95**, 163-182.

McClelland, J. L., & Rumelhart, D. E. (1985). Distributed memory and the representation of general and specific information. *Journal of Experimental Psychology: General*, **114**, 159-188.

Seidenberg, M. S. (1985). The time course of information activation and utilization in visual word recognition. In D. Besner, T. G. Waller, & G. E. MacKinnon (Eds.), *Reading research: Advances in theory and practice* (Vol. 5, pp. 199-252). New York: Academic Press.

Seidenberg, M. S., Tanenhaus, M. K., Leiman, J. M., & Bienkowski, M. (1982). Automatic access of the meanings of ambiguous words in context: Some limitations of knowledge toward processing. *Cognitive Psychology*, **14**, 489-537.

Tabossi, P. (1988). Accessing lexical ambiguity in different types of sentential contexts. *Journal of Memory and Language*, **27**, 324-340.

Van Petten, C., & Kutas, M. (1987). Ambiguous words in context: An event-related potential analysis of the time course of meaning activation. *Journal of Memory and Language*, **26**, 188-208.

ACKNOWLEDGEMENT

This research was supported by a grant from the Natural Sciences and Engineering Research Council of Canada and by computing facilities provided by the University of Victoria.

The Role of Computational Temperature in a Computer Model of Concepts and Analogy-Making

Melanie Mitchell and Douglas R. Hofstadter
Center for Research on Concepts and Cognition
Indiana University

ABSTRACT

We discuss the role of computational temperature in Copycat, a computer model of the mental mechanisms underlying human concepts and analogy-making. In Copycat, computational temperature is used both to *measure* the amount and quality of perceptual organization created by the program as processing proceeds, and, reciprocally, to continuously *control* the degree of randomness in the system. We discuss these roles in two aspects of perception central to Copycat's behavior: (1) the emergence of a *parallel terraced scan*, in which many possible courses of action are explored simultaneously, each at a speed and to a depth proportional to moment-to-moment estimates of its promise, and (2) the ability to restructure initial perceptions — sometimes radically — in order to arrive at a deeper understanding of a situation. We compare our notion of temperature to similar notions in other computational frameworks. Finally, we give an example of how temperature is used in Copycat's creation of a subtle and insightful analogy.

1. DESCRIPTION OF THE PROJECT

In our research, we are attempting to model the mental mechanisms underlying the fluid nature of human concepts. Humans are able to perceive and categorize situations very flexibly, to see beyond superficial details and understand the essence of a situation, and to make analogies between situations, fluidly translating concepts from one situation into the other. These abilities are central to every facet of human intelligence, from perception and learning, to recognition of concrete and abstract objects and situations (faces, letters of the alphabet, artistic and musical styles), and even to acts of great insight and creativity.

In order to isolate and study the mechanisms underlying these abilities, we have developed a microworld in which analogies are to be made between idealized situations consisting of strings of letters. We believe that analogy-making in this microworld requires the essence of abilities central to perception and analogy-making in real-world situations. A simple analogy problem is this: If the string **abc** changes to **abd**, what is the analogous change for **ijk**? A reasonable description of the initial change is "Replace the rightmost letter by its successor", and straightforward application of this rule to the target string **ijk** yields the commonsense answer **ijl** (other, less satisfying answers, such as **ijd**, are of course possible). However, given the alternate target string **iijjkk**, a straightforward, rigid application of the original rule would yield **iijjkl**, which ignores the strong similarity between **abc** and **iijjkk** when the latter is seen as consisting of three *letter-groups* rather than as six *letters*. If one perceives the role of *letter* in **abc** as played by *letter-group* in **iijjkk**, then in making a mapping between **abc** and **iijjkk** one is forced to let the concept *letter* "slip" into the similar concept *letter-group*. The ability to make appropriate *conceptual slippages* — in which concepts in one situation are identified with similar concepts in a different but analogous situation — is central to analogy-making and to cognition in general (Hofstadter, 1985), and our research centers on investigating how concepts must be structured and how perception must interact with concepts to allow the fluidity necessary for insightful slippages.

The letter-string microworld was designed to capture the essence of the issues of concepts and perception that we are investigating. Although the analogies in this microworld involve only a small number of concepts, they often require considerable insight. An example of such an analogy is the following: if **abc** changes to **abd**, what does **xyz** change to? At first glance, this problem is essentially the same as the one with target string **ijk** discussed above, but there is a snag: **Z** has no successor. (Notational note: in this discussion, lowercase boldface letters designate *instances* of letter categories, and uppercase boldface letters designate the categories themselves. For example,

z is an instance of the category **Z**.) Many people answer **xya**, but in our microworld the alphabet is not circular; this answer is intentionally excluded since the snag forces the analogy-maker to restructure their original view, to make conceptual slippages that were not initially considered, and hopefully to discover a more useful and insightful way of understanding the situation. One such way is to notice that **abc** is "wedged" against the beginning of the alphabet, and **xyz** is similarly wedged against the far end of the alphabet. Thus the **A** in **abc** and the **Z** in **xyz** can be seen to correspond, and then one naturally feels that the **C** and the **X** correspond as well. Underlying these object correspondences is a set of conceptual slippages that are mutually parallel: *alphabetic-first* ⇒ *alphabetic-last*, *right* ⇒ *left*, and *successor* ⇒ *predecessor*, which together yield an insightful answer: **wyz**. (For a detailed discussion of the microworld and a large number of sample analogy problems, see Mitchell, 1988.)

This example illustrates how problems in the microworld can contain the essence of many issues central to perception in general: in order to understand a situation, one must choose from a large number of possible ways in which the objects in the situation can be described and related to one another, and in which similarity to other situations can be perceived. It must be decided which concepts are relevant to the situation at hand, what is salient and what can be ignored, at what level of abstraction to describe objects, relations, and events, which descriptions to take literally and which to allow to slip, and so on. And if these choices lead to a impasse that seems to block progress towards understanding, then one may be required to fluidly restructure one's original perceptions, to shift one's view in unexpected ways, and hopefully to arrive at a deeper, more essential understanding of the situation. We are developing a computer model of the mental mechanisms we believe underlie these abilities, in which a notion of *temperature* has a central role.

2. THE ARCHITECTURE OF COPYCAT

Our computer model, called "Copycat", solves analogy problems in the microworld. (Earlier versions of the program have been described by Hofstadter, 1984, and Hofstadter & Mitchell, 1988a and 1988b.) In Copycat, concepts are modeled using what we call a "Slipnet": a network in which a node represents the "core" of a concept (e.g., *first*) and a link simultaneously represents a resemblance or relationship between two nodes and a potential slippage from one to the other. For example, *first* is the opposite of *last*, and thus in some circumstances they are similar and one can be slipped to the other. Each link has a label that roughly classifies the resemblance or relationship the link encodes. Each type of label is itself represented by a node. Thus, the nodes *first* and *last* are connected by a link with label *opposite*. During a run of the program, nodes become activated when perceived to be relevant, and decay when no longer perceived as relevant. Nodes also spread activation to their neighbors. The amount of similarity encoded by a link also can vary during a run of the program. Since the plausibility of slippage between two concepts depends on context (e.g., *right* ⇒ *left* is plausible in "**abc** ⇒ **abd**, **xyz** ⇒ ?" but not in "**abc** ⇒ **abd**, **ijk** ⇒ ?"), the degree of similarity encoded by a link depends on the relevance of the link's label to the problem at hand, which is measured by the activation of the node representing the label (e.g., the activation of the node *opposite* determines the degree of similarity between concepts linked in the Slipnet by an *opposite* link).

In our model, a concept is a region in the Slipnet, centered on a particular node (its core), having blurry rather than sharp boundaries: any other node is included in the concept *probabilistically*, to the degree that it resembles (or can be reached by a slippage from) the core node of the concept (Hofstadter & Mitchell, 1988a). The result is a network in which concepts are associative and dynamically overlapping (in Copycat, overlap is modeled by links), and in which the time-varying behavior of concepts (through dynamic activation and degree of similarity) reflects the essential properties of the situations encountered.

At the beginning of a run, Copycat is given the three strings of letters; it initially knows only the category membership of each letter (e.g., **a** is an instance of category **A**), which letters are spatially adjacent to one another, and which letters are leftmost and rightmost in each string. In order to formulate a solution, the program must perceive what is going on in the problem. To accomplish this, the program builds various kinds of structures that represent its high-level perception of the problem. (This is similar to the way the Hearsay-II speech-understanding system built perceptual structures on top of raw representations of sounds; see Erman et al., 1980.) These structures represent Slipnet concepts of various degrees of generality being brought to bear on the problem, and accordingly, each of these structures is built of parts copied from the Slipnet. The flexibility of the program rests on the fact that concepts from the Slipnet can be "borrowed" for use in perceiving situations, and that the Slipnet itself is not rigid but fluid, adjusting itself (via dynamic activation and degrees of similarity) to fit the situation at hand. An essential part of our model is this interaction of top-down and bottom-up processing: while the program's perception of a given problem is guided by the properties of concepts in the Slipnet, those properties themselves are influenced by what the program perceives.

The types of perceptual structures built by the program include descriptions of objects (e.g., the **Z** in **xyz** is the "alphabetic-last" letter), relations between objects (e.g., the **Z** in **xyz** is the successor of its left neighbor, the **Y**), groups of objects (e.g., **abc** is a group increasing in the alphabet), and correspondences between objects (e.g., the **A** in **abc** corresponds to the **Z** in **xyz**). (See section 4 for examples of these structures in a run of the program.) The actual building (and sometimes destroying) of perceptual structures is carried out by large numbers of simple agents we call "codelets". A codelet is a small piece of code that carries out some small, local task that is part of the process of building a structure (e.g., one codelet might estimate how important it is to describe the **A** in **abc** as "alphabetic-first", another codelet might notice that the **B** in **abc** is the alphabetic successor of its left neighbor in the string, and another codelet might build a data structure corresponding to that fact). Each perceptual structure is built by a series of codelets running in turn, each deciding on the basis of some local evaluation of the structure being built whether to continue by allowing the next codelet in the series to proceed, or to give up the effort at that point. If the decision is made to continue, an "urgency" value is assigned to the next codelet in the series. This value helps determine how long the codelet has to wait before it can run and continue the building-up of that particular structure.

All codelets waiting to run are placed in a single pool, and the system interleaves the building of many different structures by probabilistically choosing the next codelet to run. The choice is based on the relative urgencies of all codelets in the pool. Thus many different structures are built up simultaneously, but at different speeds. The speed of such a process emerges dynamically from the urgencies of its component codelets. Since those urgencies are determined by moment-to-moment estimates of the promise of the structure being built, the result is that structures of greater promise will tend to be built more quickly than less promising ones. There is no top-level executive directing processing here; all processing is carried out by codelets. Codelets that take part in the process of building a structure send activation to the areas in the Slipnet that represent the concepts associated with that structure. These activations in turn affect the makeup of the codelet population (for details, see Mitchell, 1988). (Note that though Copycat runs on a serial computer and thus only one codelet runs at a time, the system is roughly equivalent to one in which many activities are taking place in parallel at different spatial locations, since codelets work locally and to a large degree independently. Copycat's distributed asynchronous parallelism was inspired by the similar sort of self-organizing activity that takes place in a biological cell; see Hofstadter, 1984.) In summary, processes that build up structures are interleaved, and many such processes — some mutually supporting, some competing — progress in parallel at different rates, the rate of each being set by the urgencies of its component codelets. Almost all codelets make one or more probabilistic decisions, and the high-level behavior of the system emerges from the combination of thousands of these very small choices. The result is a *parallel terraced scan* (Hofstadter, 1983): many possible courses of action are explored simultaneously, each at a speed and to a depth proportional to moment-to-moment estimates of its promise. (Note that since the program uses nondeterminism to arrive at a solution, different answers are possible on different runs.)

3. THE ROLE OF TEMPERATURE

In addition to the Slipnet and codelets, an essential element of Copycat's architecture is a *temperature* variable, which plays two roles. It measures the amount of disorganization (or entropy) in the system: its value at a given time is a function of the amount and quality of structure that has been built so far. Thus temperature starts high, and falls as more structure gets built, rising again if structure gets destroyed. Temperature's other role is to control the degree of randomness used in making decisions (such as which codelet should run next, which structure should win a competition, etc.). The idea is that when there is little perceptual organization (and thus high temperature), the information on which decisions are based (such as the urgency of a codelet or the strength of a particular structure) is not very reliable, and decisions should be more random than would seem to be indicated by this information. When a large amount of good structure has been built (and thus temperature is low), the information is considered to be more reliable, and decisions based on this information should be more deterministic.

The solution to the well-known "two-armed bandit" problem (Given a slot machine with two arms, each with an unknown payoff rate, what is the optimal strategy for profit-making?) is an elegant mathematical verification of these intuitions (Holland, 1975). The solution states that the optimal strategy is to sample both arms but with probabilities that diverge increasingly fast as time progresses. In particular, as more and more information is gained through sampling, the optimal strategy is to exponentially increase the probability of sampling the "better" arm relative to the probability of sampling the "worse" arm (note that one never knows with certainty which is the better arm, since all information gained is merely statistical evidence). Copycat's parallel terraced scan can be likened to such a strategy extrapolated to a many-armed bandit, where each potential path of exploration corresponds to an arm. (This is similar to the search through schemata in a genetic algorithm; see Holland, 1975). There are far too many possible paths to do an exhaustive search, so in order to guarantee that in principle every path has a non-zero chance of being explored, paths have to be chosen and explored probabilistically. Each step in exploring a path is like sampling an arm, in that information is obtained that can be used to decide the rate at which that path should be sampled in the near future.[1] The role of temperature is to cause the exponential increase in speed at which promising paths are explored as contrasted with unpromising ones; as temperature decreases, the degree of randomness with which decisions are made decreases exponentially, so the speed at which good paths crowd out bad ones grows exponentially as more information is obtained. This strategy, in which information is used as it is obtained in order to bias randomness and thus to speed up convergence toward some resolution, but to never *absolutely* rule out any path, is an optimal strategy in any situation in which there is a limited amount of time in which to explore an intractable number of paths. This appears to be an ubiquitous principle in adaptive systems of all kinds (Holland, 1975), which supports our belief that the temperature-controlled parallel terraced scan is a plausible description of how perception takes place in humans.

---

[1] It should be made clear that in Copycat, "paths of exploration" are defined as any of the possible ways in which the program could structure its perceptions of the situation in order to construct an analogy. Thus possible paths are not laid out in advance for the program to search, but rather are constructed by the program as its processing proceeds, just as in a game of chess, where paths through the tree of possible moves are constructed as the game is played. The evaluation of a given move in a game of chess blurs together the evaluation of many possible look-ahead paths that include that move. Similarly, any given action in building a structure by a codelet in Copycat is a step included in a large number of possible paths toward a solution, and an evaluation obtained by a codelet of a proposed structure blurs together the estimated promise of all these paths.

Temperature allows Copycat to close in on a good solution quickly, once parts of it have been discovered. In addition, since high temperature means more randomness, raising the temperature gives Copycat a way to get out of ruts or to deal with snags; it can allow old structures to break and restructuring to occur so that a better solution can be found. This idea is similar to the use of temperature in simulated annealing, a technique used in some connectionist networks for finding optimal solutions (Kirkpatrick et al., 1983; Hinton & Sejnowski, 1986; Smolensky, 1986). Note, however, that the role of temperature in Copycat differs from that in simulated annealing; in the latter, temperature is used exclusively as a top-down randomness-controlling factor, its value being set by a rigid "annealing schedule", not by the state of the network, whereas in Copycat, the value of temperature reflects the current quality of the system's understanding, and is used as a feedback mechanism to determine the degree of randomness used by the system. Ideas about such a role for temperature were originally presented in Hofstadter (1983, 1984).

4. A RUN OF THE PROGRAM

The following set of screen dumps shows the role of temperature in a run of Copycat on the problem "**abc** ⇒ **abd**, **xyz** ⇒ ?", initially helping the system to quickly arrive at a seemingly good solution that unfortunately has a snag, and then helping it to get out of that "local minimum" to create a deeper understanding of the situation and allow a more insightful answer (**wyz**) to emerge from that understanding. Note that since the program is nondeterministic, different answers are possible on different runs. At present the program produces this answer rarely; it more commonly produces **xyd** (using the rule "Replace the rightmost letter by **D**"), **xyz** ("Replace all **C**'s by **D**'s"), and **yyz** ("Replace the *leftmost* letter by its successor"). These answers, along with several other possibilities, are discussed in Hofstadter (1985).

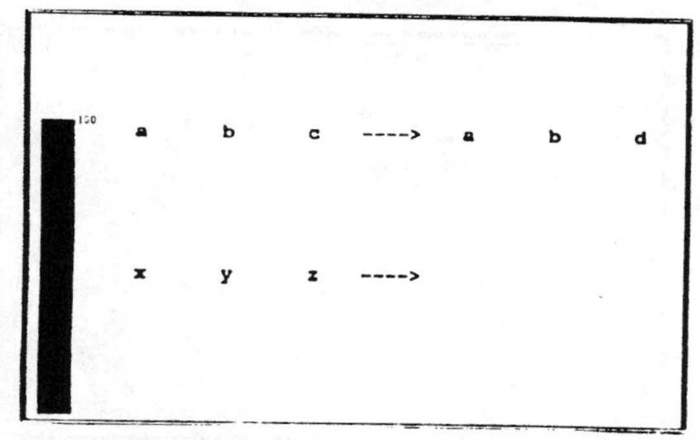

1. The program is presented with the three strings. The temperature, initially at its maximum of 100, is represented by a "thermometer" at the left.

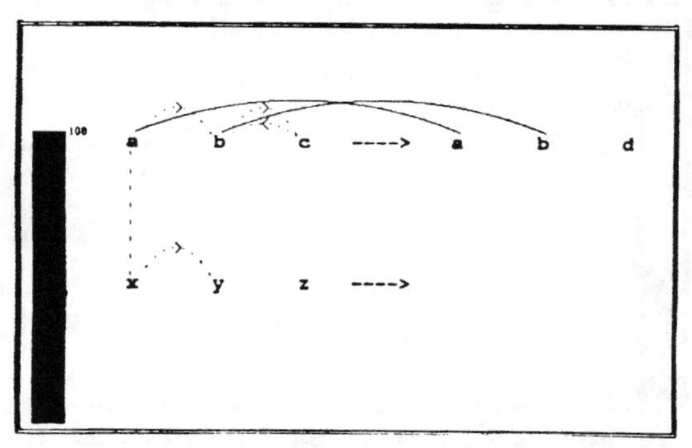

2. Codelets begin to build up perceptual structures. Dashed lines and arcs represent structures in the process of being built, and solid lines and arcs represent fully built structures. Once fully built, a structure is able to influence the building of other structures and the temperature. A fully built structure is not necessarily permanent; it may be knocked down by competing structures. Here the two solid arcs across the top line represent correspondences from the **A** and **B** in **abc** to their counterparts in **abd**. The shorter dashed arcs inside each string represent potential *successor* and *predecessor* relations in the process of being built, and the vertical dashed line represents a potential correspondence between the **A** and the **X**.

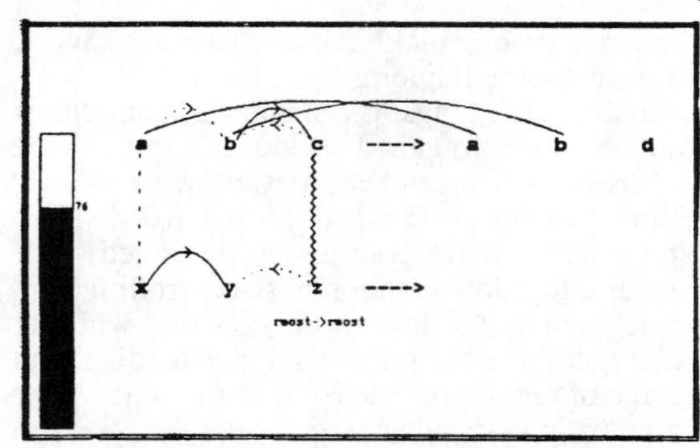

3. Some relations between letters within each string have been built and others continue to be considered. Copycat, unlike people, has no left-to-right or alphabetic-first-to-last biases, and in general is equally likely to perceive relations in either direction, although here, *successor* tends to be activated early when the C-to-D change is noticed, causing the system to tend to perceive the letters as having left-to-right successor relations rather than right-to-left predecessor relations. A correspondence between the C in **abc** and the Z in **xyz** (jagged vertical line) has been built. Both letters are *rightmost* in their respective strings: this underlying concept mapping is displayed beneath the correspondence. In response to these structures, the temperature has dropped to 76.

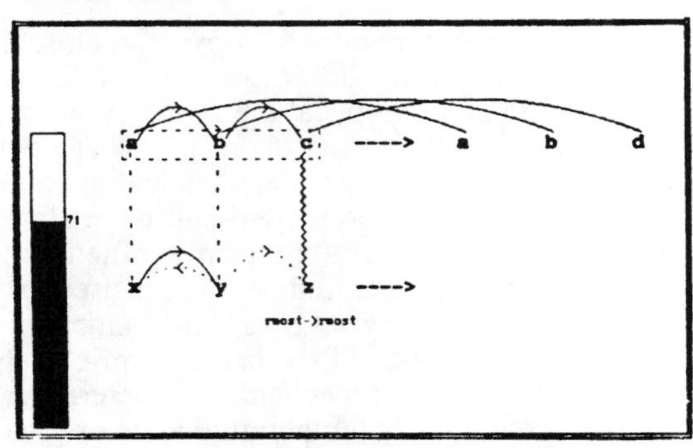

4. More relations have been built. Note that the potential predecessor relation between the **Z** and the **Y** shown in the previous screen has fizzled, and a potential successor relation has taken its place. This demonstrates the top-down pressure on the system to perceive the situation in terms of concepts it has already identified as relevant: since successor relations have been built elsewhere, the node *successor* in the Slipnet has become active, causing the system to more easily notice new successor relations. The program is also considering a left-to-right grouping of the letters in **abc** (represented by a dashed rectangle with a right arrow at the top), and other correspondences between the letters in **abc** and in **xyz**. The temperature has dropped to 71.

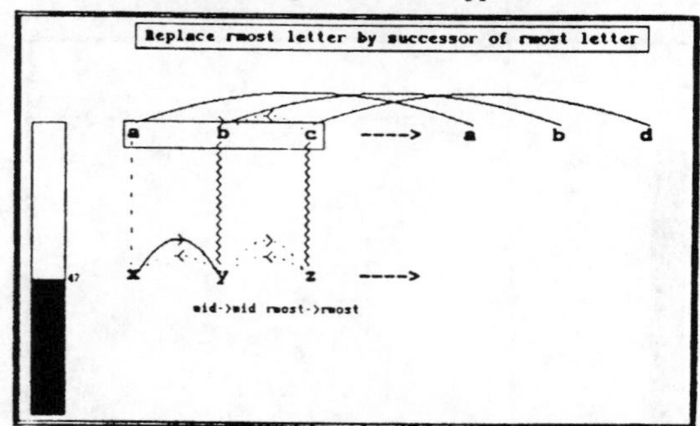

5. **abc** has been identified as a ***successor-group***, increasing alphabetically to the right (the relations between the letters still exist, but are not displayed). A **B-Y** correspondence has been built, and a rule (top of screen) has been constructed to describe the **abc–abd** change. Note there is no internal structuring of **abd**. Copycat currently expects the change from the *initial string* (here **abc**) to the *modified string* (here **abd**) to consist of exactly one letter being replaced. Thus no structures are built in the modified string except to identify what has changed and what has stayed the same. The program constructs the rule by filling in the template "Replace ____ by ____". As was mentioned at the beginning of section 4, there are several possible rules for describing this change. Note that a right-to-left predecessor relation between the **B** and the **C** in **abc** is being considered (dashed arc), and will have to compete against the already built left-to-right successor group. The latter, being much stronger than the former, will survive, especially since the temperature is now fairly low, reflecting that a high-quality mutually consistent set of structures is taking over.

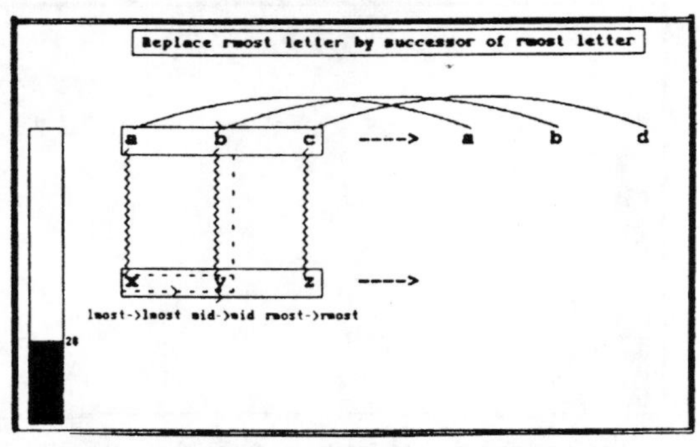

6. **xyz** has now been described, like **abc**, as a left-to-right successor group. (The direction of a group is indicated by an arrow at the top or bottom of the rectangle representing the group.) A strong set of correspondences has been made between the letters in **abc** and **xyz**, and a correspondence between the two groups (dashed vertical line) is being considered. The temperature has fallen very low, reflecting the high degree of perceptual organization, and virtually ensuring that this point of view will win out.

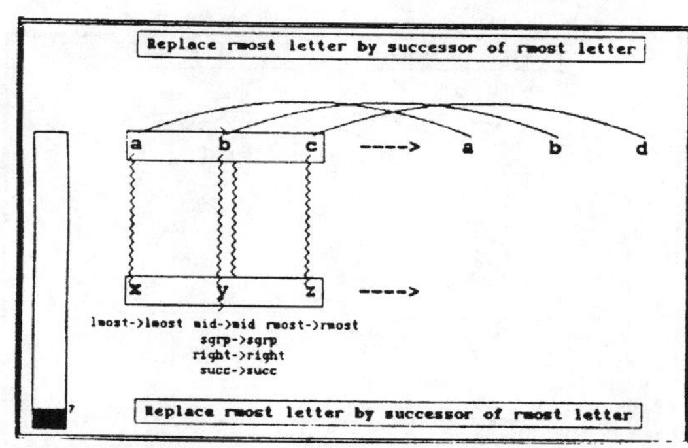

7. All the correspondences have been made. The correspondence between the two groups is supported by concept mappings expressing the facts that both are successor groups (displayed as "sgrp -> sgrp") based on successor relations ("succ -> succ") and both are increasing alphabetically toward the right. The concept mappings listed below the correspondences can be interpreted as instructions on how to translate the rule describing the initial change so it can be used on the target string. Here the concept mappings are identities, so the translated rule (appearing at the bottom of the screen) is the same as the original rule: "Replace rightmost letter by its successor". The temperature is almost at zero, indicating the program's satisfaction in its understanding of the situation. But then it hits a snag: it is unable to construct an answer according to the translated rule, since **Z** has no successor.

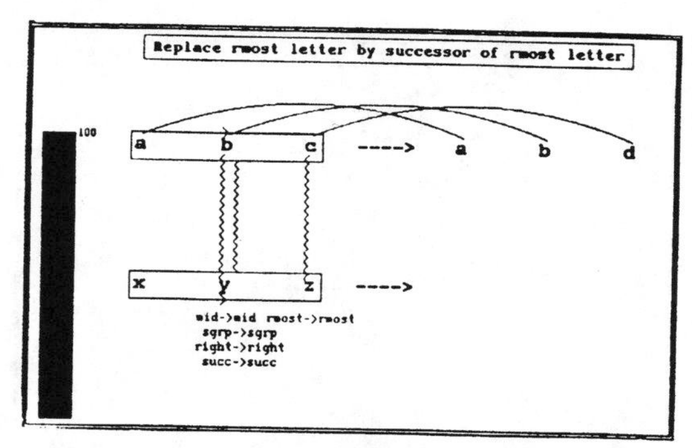

8. Being unable to take the successor of **Z**, the program has hit an impasse, which causes the temperature to go up to 100. This causes competitions between structures to be decided more randomly, and allows structures to be destroyed more easily (as can be seen, the **A** - **X** correspondence has been broken). In addition, since the **Z** was identified as the cause of the impasse, the node **Z** in the Slipnet becomes highly activated, which spreads activation to ***alphabetic-last***, making this concept relevant to the problem. In turn, ***alphabetic-last*** spreads activation to ***alphabetic-first***.

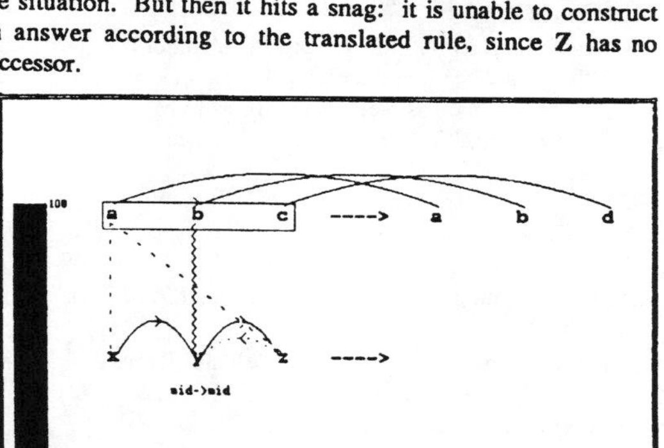

9. After breaking more structures and making other ineffectual attempts at restructuring (not shown), the program has noticed the relationship between the letters **A** and **Z**, and is trying to build a correspondence between them. Underlying it are two *slippages*: "leftmost -> rightmost" and "first -> last". Before the impasse was reached, the descriptions *first* and *last* were neither seen as relevant nor considered conceptually close enough to be the basis for a correspondence. But the combination of high temperature and the focus on the **Z** make this mapping possible, though still not easy, to make. In fact, on most runs of program on this problem, this mapping is either never made, or quickly destroyed once made. But in this run, this correspondence, once made, is perceived to be strong.

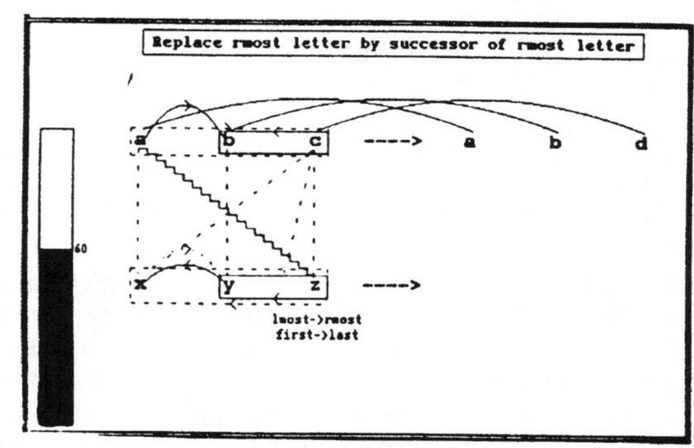

10. Many possible ways of restructuring the situation are being considered simultaneously, but the program is beginning to develop an understanding of the situation based on the **A-Z** correspondence. Under pressure from this correspondence, the program is now beginning to perceive **xyz** as a right-to-left *predecessor* group (yz has already been perceived as such, and the direction of the relation between the **X** and the **Y** has reversed). This new way of structuring the problem seems promising; the new structures have caused the temperature to fall to 60.

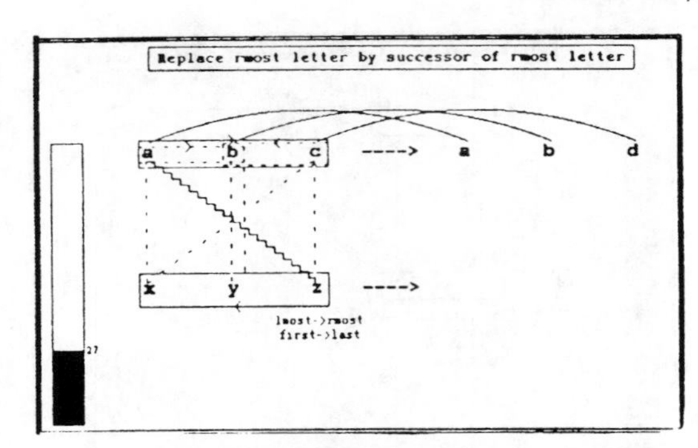

11. The "first -> last" slippage has engendered a complete restructuring of the program's perception of **xyz** (which is now understood as a right-to-left predecessor group, opposite in direction from the group **abc**) and the program is closing in on a solution. Alternative ways of structuring the situation are still being considered, but the low temperature reflects the program's satisfaction with its current understanding, and will make it hard for any alternatives to compete at this point.

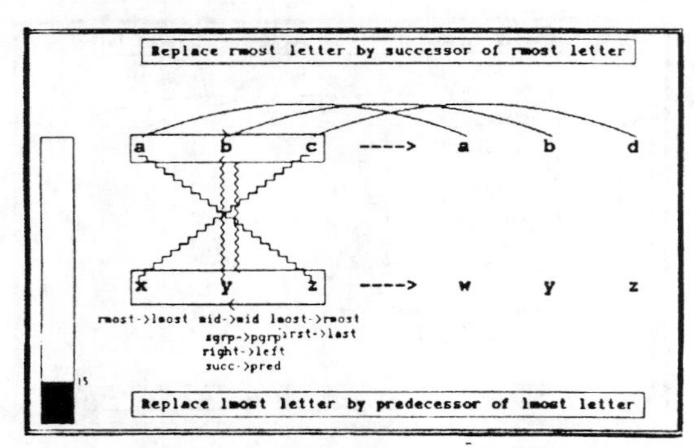

12. The mapping is complete and all attempts at building rival structures have ceased. The concept mappings listed underneath the correspondences give the slippages needed to translate the rule. The translated rule ("Replace *leftmost* letter by *predecessor* of *leftmost* letter") appears at the bottom of the screen, and the answer **wyz** appears at the right.

ACKNOWLEDGEMENTS

We thank David Chalmers, Robert French, Liane Gabora, Kevin Kinnell, David Moser, and Peter Suber for their ongoing contributions to this project and for many helpful comments on this paper. This research has been supported by grants from Indiana University, the University of Michigan, and Apple Computer, Inc., as well as a grant from Mitchell Kapor, Ellen Poss, and the Lotus Development Corporation, and grant DCR 8410409 from the National Science Foundation.

REFERENCES

[1] Erman, L.D., F. Hayes-Roth, V. R. Lesser, and D. Raj Reddy (1980). The Hearsay-II speech-understanding system: Integrating knowledge to resolve uncertainty. *Computing Surveys*, **12** (2), 213-253.

[2] Kirkpatrick, S., C.D. Gelatt Jr., and M. P. Vecchi (1983). Optimization by simulated annealing. *Science*, **220** (4598), 671-680.

[3] Hinton, G.E. and T.J. Sejnowski (1986). Learning and relearning in Boltzmann machines. In McClelland, J. and D. Rumelhart (1986) (Eds.). *Parallel distributed processing* (pp. 282-317). Cambridge, MA: Bradford/MIT Press.

[4] Hofstadter, Douglas R. (1983). The architecture of Jumbo. *Proceedings of the International Machine Learning Workshop*. Monticello, Il.

[5] Hofstadter, Douglas R. (1984). The Copycat project: An experiment in nondeterminism and creative analogies (AI Memo #755). Cambridge, MA: MIT AI Laboratory.

[6] Hofstadter, Douglas R. (1985). Analogies and roles in human and machine thinking. In *Metamagical Themas* (pp. 547-603). New York: Basic Books.

[7] Hofstadter, Douglas R. and Melanie Mitchell (1988a). Concepts, analogies, and creativity. In *Proceedings of the Canadian Society for Computational Studies of Intelligence*. Edmonton, Alberta: Univ. of Alberta.

[8] Hofstadter, Douglas R. and Melanie Mitchell (1988b). Conceptual slippage and analogy-making: A report on the Copycat project. *Proceedings of the Tenth Annual Conference of the Cognitive Science Society*. Hillsdale, NJ: Lawrence Erlbaum Associates.

[9] Holland, John (1975). *Adaptation in natural and artificial systems*. Ann Arbor, MI: Univ. of Michigan Press.

[10] Mitchell, Melanie (1988). A computer model of analogical thought. Unpublished thesis proposal. University of Michigan, Ann Arbor, MI.

[11] Smolensky, P. (1986). Information processing in dynamical systems: Foundations of harmony theory. In McClelland, J. and D. Rumelhart (1986) (Eds.). *Parallel distributed processing* (pp. 194-281). Cambridge, MA: Bradford/MIT Press.

An Interactive Activation Model for Priming of Geographical Information

Paul Munro
Stephen C. Hirtle

University of Pittsburgh

ABSTRACT

Clustering effects in observed performance on spatial recognition tasks give evidence that the judgment of spatial relationships is not based solely on Euclidean proximity, but can depend on other similarity relationships to an equal, or even to a greater, extent. Thus, the representation of spatial information must be coded as one of many features of an object, and these features are expected to interact with one another. A recurrent network using the interactive activation architecture of McClelland & Rumelhart (1981) is presented to illustrate the interaction of these featural representations, including a coarse coding representation of a Euclidean metric. The experiments of McNamara (1986) and McNamara, Ratcliff, and McKoon (1984) are simulated; the model results are in qualitative agreement with the data.

Introduction

The location of an object is certainly one of its most salient features. This is especially true for objects which are geographically fixed, since features which are invariant tend to have greater salience. Using a model of positional information, we can consider the representation to be topographic, in that objects that are sufficiently proximal should have similar (overlapping) representations.

However, recording geographical positioning is not enough, as several recent studies have demonstrated that the memory for locations of landmarks is biased by hierarchical, and other non-spatial, information (Hirtle & Jonides, 1985; McNamara, Hardy, & Hirtle, 1989; Stevens & Coupe, 1978). For example, Stevens and Coupe (1978) showed that subjects judged Reno, Nevada to be north*east* of San Diego, California, even though it is north*west*, presumably because Nevada lies to east of California. That is, the superordinate relationship altered the memory of the subordinate locations. Further research has shown similar effects for areas without explicit boundaries, where clusters arise from differences in terrain (Allen, 1981; Allen & Kirasic, 1985), perceptions of neighborhoods (Hirtle & Jonides, 1985; Merrill & Baird, 1987), or semantic features on artificial maps (Hirtle & Mascolo, 1986).

Spatial Priming within Regions

In order to model in a connectionist framework the contributions of both spatial location and cluster membership, we chose a more basic paradigm than that of distance and orientation judgments. In recent work, McNamara and his colleagues have shown that a priming paradigm can be used to infer spatial knowledge, in that items that prime each other are judged closer (McNamara, 1986; McNamara, Hardy, & Hirtle, 1989; McNamara, Ratcliff, & McKoon, 1984).

As one example, McNamara (1986) showed the effects of clusters on spatial memory. Subjects in this experiment learned either the locations of objects in a layout or the location of object names on map, where the spaces were divided into a two by two grid creating four regions, as seen in Figure 1a.

McNamara (1986) showed not only differences in standard spatial tasks due to region membership, but also differences in recognition times. Specifically, he showed that items are recognized faster if preceded with a item that was close in distance, and that items are recognized faster if preceded with an item from the same region. In the experiment, there were twelve pairs of locations in six experimental conditions (two pairs per condition) and eight filler locations, for a total of 32 locations, or eight locations per region. The three main independent variables were: distance between the two locations in a pair (either close or far), whether both locations are in the same region, and for locations in different regions, whether the locations were aligned or misaligned with respect to the region (cf., Stevens & Coupe, 1978). The results showed a strong effect of both distance and cluster membership. However, the effect of alignment was not consistent, in that alignment resulted in faster recognition times for far points, but slower recognition times for close points.

Network Structure and Function

The model follows the interactive activation scheme introduced by McClelland and Rumelhart (1981) in their model of letter perception. This implementation consists of three sets of units (see Figure 2):

The **place** units each specify a particular site. In our simulations, these are labeled points on a map. More generally, they correspond to salient geographical locations.

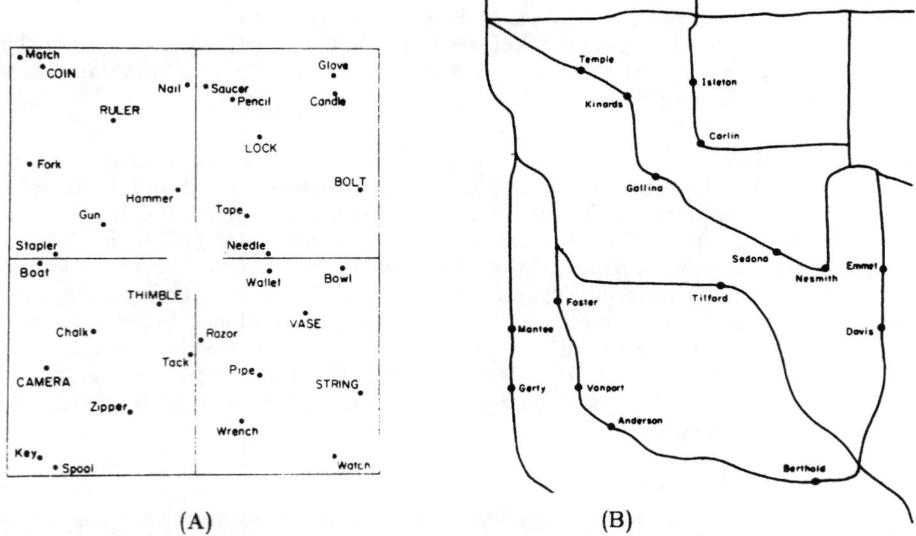

Figure 1. (A) Space of locations used by McNamara (1986). (Copyright 1986 by the Academic Press. Reprinted by permission.) (B) Space of locations used by McNamara, et al (1984). (Copyright 1984 by the American Psychological Association. Reprinted by permission.)

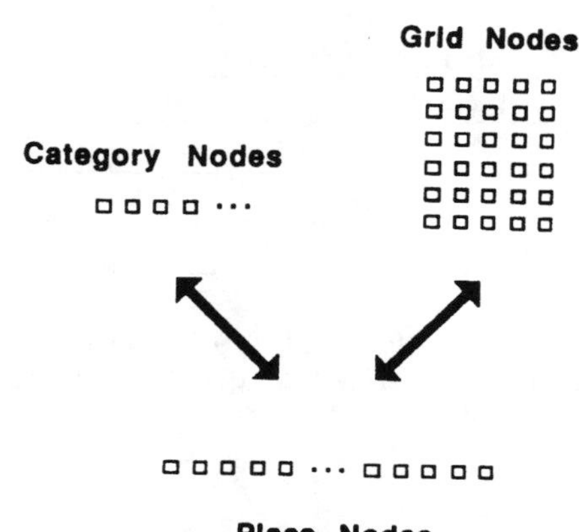

Figure 2. Network architecture for geographical priming.

The **category** units specify a particular category. Category membership is a binary function and is coded by positive and negative connections between category and place units.

The **grid** units represent a uniform rectangular grid across the map. The connections from a particular place unit to the grid units is determined by a Gaussian peak about the coordinates corresponding to the place unit.

Thus, connections exist in both directions between the place and category units (connection matrix **M**) and between the category and grid units (connection matrix N), with reciprocal connections having equal strength. The activity level of each unit is updated iteratively, by summing a decay term with an interactive term (Grossberg, 1978; McClelland and Rumelhart, 1981). The interactive term includes weighted sums of the activities of other units plus an occasional externally applied signal corresponding to an experimental stimulus. Thus, the activity $a(t)$ of a unit at time t receiving net activation $x(t)$ from the other units is updated according to the following differential equation:

$$\frac{da(t)}{dt} = -\gamma a(t) + \begin{cases} x(t)(1-a(t)) & x(t)>0 \\ x(t)a(t) & x(t)\leq 0 \end{cases}$$

Each iteration consists of two strokes: [1] update of the place node activities, $P_i(t)$, integrating decay with input from the category units, grid units, and the external stimuli, $E_i(t)$ and [2] update of the category and grid node activities, $C_i(t)$ and $G_{ij}(t)$, integrating decay with input from the place units. The coupling of the activation equations is given in Table 1.

The connection matrices, M and N are determined as functions of the distance between places and grid sites, and membership of places in the various categories, respectively. Since two indices are used to denote position of grid nodes, the activities G_{ij} have two indices indicating row and column in the grid, and elements of the matrix **M** have three

Table 1
Activity Notation and Input Computation

Unit	Activity $a(t)$	Net Input $x(t)$
place unit i	$P_i(t)$	$\sum M_{ijk} G_{jk}(t) + \sum N_{ij} C_j(t) + E_i(t)$
category unit i	$C_i(t)$	$\sum N_{ji} P_j(t)$
grid unit ij	$G_{ij}(t)$	$\sum M_{kij} P_k(t)$

indices; M_{ijk} denotes the connectivity of place node i to the grid node in row j, column k. The elements of the other matrix, N_{ij} are set to a positive constant, α_1 if place i is in category j, and to a negative constant, $-\alpha_2$, otherwise:

$$M_{ijk} = \beta \exp\left[-\frac{D_{ijk}^2}{\sigma^2} \right]$$

$$N_{ij} = \begin{cases} -\alpha_2 & i \notin j \\ \alpha_1 & i \in j \end{cases}$$

where D_{ijk} is the Euclidean distance between the points represented by P_i and G_{jk}. The representation of a place by the grid units is a regularized form of coarse coding, as described by Hinton, McClelland and Rumelhart (1986). The network parameters α_1, α_2, and β are scale factors on the connection matrices, and are generally small, to keep the system stable. The parameter σ sets a distance scale on the Gaussian sampled by the grid matrix **M**. In our experiments, σ was usually about 1/3 the size of a map edge.

It is important to realize that both the set of grid nodes and the set of category nodes represent positional information; these representations differ in a number of respects, but from an abstract point of view, they are equivalent.

Simulation Results: Spatial Priming within Regions

Each simulation consisted of three stimulus intervals: stimulus of the prime, relaxation, and stimulus of the target. These stimulus intervals consisted of maintaining the external input to the appropriate place node at a constant level (usually 0.1) for a fixed number of iterations. No external stimulus was applied in the relaxation period; this allowed the activity levels to decay (due to γ). Reaction time data was simulated by measuring times for activities to reach a criterion level. Parameters were determined empirically by examining the time courses of node activities from selected simulations. A particular activity level (the response criterion) was estimated to correspond to the ability to name the place in the experimental paradigm.

The three phases were typically 200 iterations, 50 iterations, and 200 iterations. The time courses of several place nodes are plotted in Figure 3 for a simulation of the experiment by McNamara (1983). For this simulation, the grid was 6 by 5 and there were 4 category units representing the four categories.

Figure 3 contains three "snapshots" of the place node activities in their corresponding locations (cf. Figure 1a). In the simulation, place unit 21 was stimulated for 200 iterations, stimulation ceased for the next 50 iterations, and place unit 25 was stimulated for

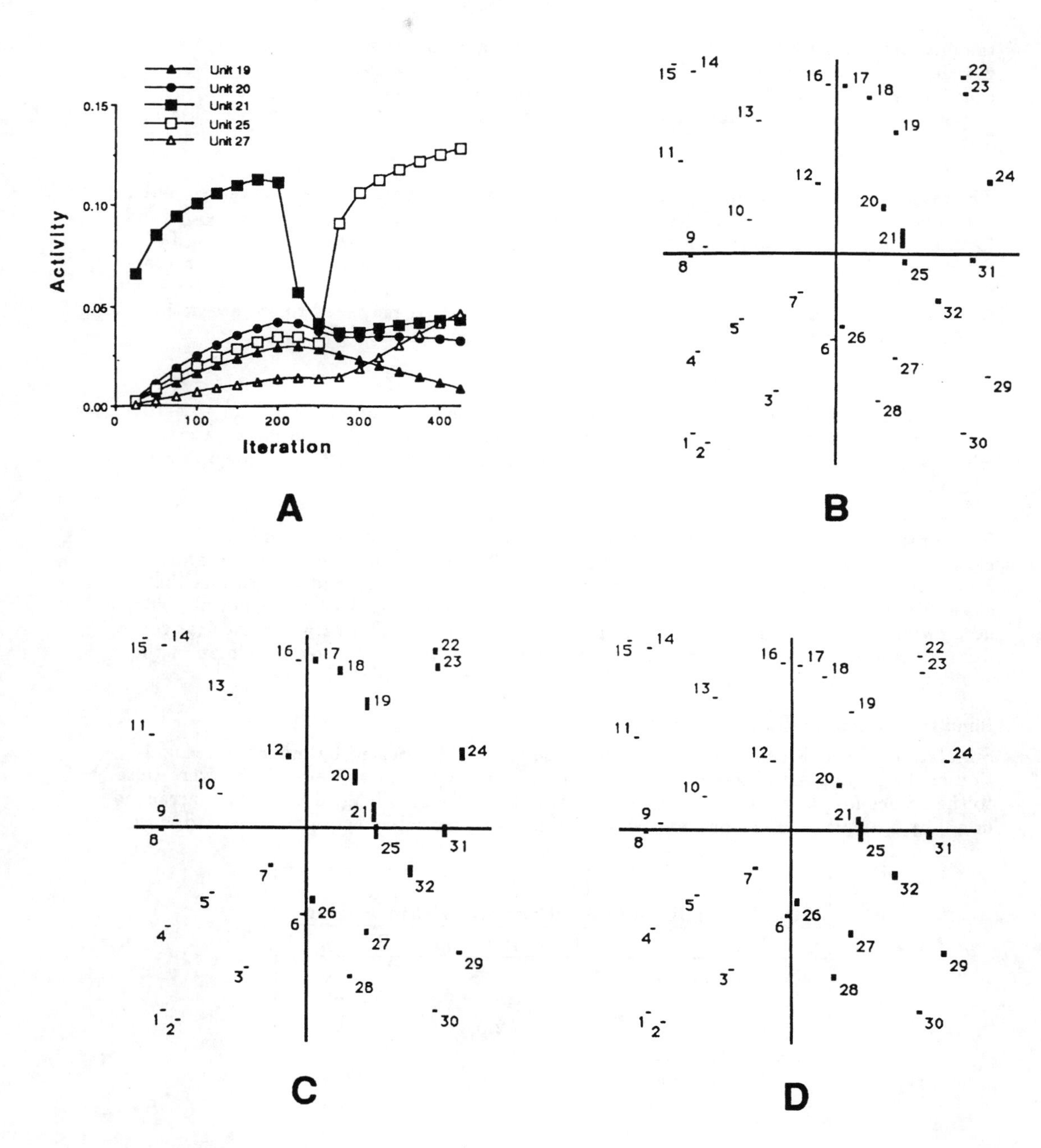

Figure 3. Time course of place node activity when stimulating node 21 for 200 iterations, followed by 50 iterations of relaxation, followed by stimulating node 25 for 200 iterations. (A) Plot of place node activity for 5 of the 32 nodes, and snapshots of activation levels of all place nodes after (B) iteration 200, (C) iteration 250, and (D) iteration 450.

the final 200 iterations. For this simulation, parameter values were $\alpha_1 = 0.4$, $\alpha_2 = 0.0$, $\beta = 0.3$, $\gamma = 1.2$, $\sigma = 4$, and the time step in our approximation to the differential equation was $\Delta t = 0.05$. In comparing our model with McNamara's data, we set the response level 0.11. The simulation results are compared with the experimental data in Table 2.

The results from the simulation correspond with the experimental data to a degree, but not in close detail. They match well for the close and far conditions within a region, and for the comparison of same-region to different-regions. However, whereas the data indicated a mild interaction of alignment with distance, the simulations show a mild interaction in the other direction. The weights in our model assumed an isotropic metric (Euclidean); generation of weights using a city block metric, may lead to an interaction consistent with the data.

Spatial Priming Along Routes

As a second example domain for the network, we turned to a related study. In an earlier experiment, McNamara, Ratcliff, and McKoon (1984) showed similar effects for a map where hypothetical cities were located along one of six different routes, as shown in Figure 1b.

The three main conditions were close in both Euclidean and route distance (CE-CR), close in Euclidean, but far in route distance (CE-FR), and far in both Euclidean and route distance (FE-FR). (The fourth logical condition of far in Euclidean distance, but close in route distance is geometrically impossible.) In addition, McNamara, et al (1984) used two distinct learning protocols (Experiment 1 versus 2). The data suggest that route distance is the critical determinant of psychological distance in the cognitive map of the subject, and that these results are not dependent on the learning protocol.

Simulation Results: Priming along Routes

Simulations of the McNamara, et al. (1984) study were performed by modeling recognition of the same pairs of items. The parameter values used for this simulation were close to the values for the previous simulation, but not identical. The grid units were arranged in a 6 by 5 array as in the previous simulation. Here, six category units were used, each

Table 2
Simulation Results for Priming within Regions

Condition	Mean Iterations	RT (*msec*)
Same Region		
Close	45.0	705
Far	52.0	768
Different Regions		
Close/Aligned	61.0	773
Close/Misaligned	87.5	753
Close/Overall	74.3	763
Far/Aligned	155.0	782
Far/Misaligned	104.0	797
Far/Overall	129.5	790

Table 3
Simulation Results for Priming along Routes

Condition	Mean Iterations	RT (*msec*)
CE-CR	13.3	624
CE-FR	26.0	670
FE-FR	47.4	673

corresponding to one of the routes. We used $\alpha_1 = 0.4$, $\alpha_2 = -0.08$, $\beta = 0.3$, $\gamma = 1.2$, $\sigma = 4$, and set the response criterion 0.08. The simulated results show a similar ordering as the data (Table 3). However, there is again a small discrepancy in that the simulations show a greater effect due to distance than appears in the experimental data.

Discussion

The network was able to represent both the locational information given by the geographic coordinates and the semantic information encoded by category membership, whether the categories are regions or routes. The model presented is in contrast to a spreading activation model that McNamara (1986) presents to account for his data. It has an advantage over the implementation proposed by McNamara in that the time component is made explicit.

These results point to a framework for representing positional information over a set of maps, rather than a single one. These representations may be orthogonal or overlap to various degrees. For example, the routes in the second simulation could be represented such that intersecting routes have common features. This could be implemented by having each category unit correspond to an intersection. We did not choose this representation because it has a problem of non-uniqueness (see Figure 1b).

The model presented complements previous connectionist models on related topics, such as examining the role context on spatial references in language (see, Cosic & Munro, 1988; Douglas, Novick, & Tomlin, 1987), and models examining spatial search (e.g., Barto & Sutton, 1981, Zipser, 1986).

Further research is planned to extend the model to more complex semantic structures. For example, McNamara, Hardy, & Hirtle (1989) have demonstrated that the ordered tree paradigm (see Hirtle & Jonides, 1985) can be used to determine the semantic structure imposed by subjects on an otherwise nonstructured array of landmarks. Thus, a small modification to the strategy above would be required as the resulting structure is hierarchical rather than a single set of regions or routes. However, the general approach should prove beneficial in the modeling of spatial knowledge.

Acknowledgements. This research was supported by NSF grant BNS-8617732 to the second author. The authors may be reached via email at munro@idis.lis.pittsburgh.edu and sch@idis.lis.pittsburgh.edu, respectively.

References

Allen, G. L. (1981). A developmental perspective on the effects of "subdividing" macrospatial experience. *Journal of Experimental Psychology: Learning, Memory and Cognition, 7,* 120-132.

Allen, G. L., & Kirasic, K. C. (1985). Effects of cognitive organization of route knowledge on judgments of macrospatial distance. *Memory & Cognition, 13,* 218-232.

Barto, A. G., & Sutton, R. S. (1981). Landmark learning: An illustration of associative search. *Biological Cybernetics, 42,* 1-8.

Cosic, C., & Munro, P. (1988). Learning to represent and understand locative prepositional phrases. In *Proceedings of the 10th annual conference of the Cognitive Science Society,* Montreal, Canada, 257-262.

Douglas, S. A., Novick, D. G., Tomlin, R. S. (1987). Consistency and variation in spatial reference. In *Proceedings of the 9th annual conference of the Cognitive Science Society,* Seattle, WA, 417-426.

Grossberg, S. (1978). A theory of visual coding, memory, and development. In E. L. J. Leeuwenberg & H. F. J. M. Buffart (Eds.), *Formal theories of visual perception.* New York: Wiley.

Hinton, G. E., McClelland, J. L., & Rumelhart, D. E. (1986). Distributed representations. In D. E. Rumelhart & J. L. McClelland (Eds.), *Parallel distributed processing: Explorations in the microstructure of cognition, Volume 1* (pp. 432-470). Cambridge, Mass: Bradford.

Hirtle, S. C., & Jonides, J. (1985). Evidence of hierarchies in cognitive maps. *Memory & Cognition, 13,* 208-217.

Hirtle. S. C., & Mascolo, M. F. (1986). The effect of semantic clustering on the memory of spatial locations. *Journal of Experimental Psychology: Learning, Memory and Cognition, 12,* 181-189.

McClelland, J. L., & Rumelhart, D. E. (1981). An interactive activation model of context effects in letter perception: Part 1. *Psychological Review, 88,* 375-407.

McNamara, T. P. (1986). Mental representation in spatial relations. *Cognitive Psychology, 18,* 87-121.

McNamara, T. P., Hardy, J. K., & Hirtle, S. C. (1989). Subjective hierarchies in spatial memory. *Journal of Experimental Psychology: Learning, Memory, and Cognition, 15,* 211-227.

McNamara, T. P., Ratcliff, R., & McKoon, G. (1984). The mental representation of knowledge acquired from maps. *Journal of Experimental Psychology: Learning, Memory, and Cognition, 10,* 723-732.

Merrill, A. A., & Baird, J. C. (1987). Semantic and spatial factors in environmental memory. *Memory & Cognition, 15,* 101-108.

Stevens, A., & Coupe, P. (1978). Distortions in judged spatial relations. *Cognitive Psychology, 13,* 422-437.

Zipser, D. (1986). Biologically plausible models of place recognition and goal location. In J. L. McClelland & D. E. Rumelhart (Eds.), *Parallel distributed processing: Explorations in the microstructure of cognition, Volume 2* (pp. 432-470). Cambridge, Mass: Bradford.

Apprenticeship or Tutorial: Models for Interaction with an Intelligent Instructional System

Denis Newman
BBN Systems and Technologies Corp.

ABSTRACT

Conventional intelligent tutoring systems are based on the individual tutorial as a model of instructor-student interaction and use a model of the student's understanding as a principal component guiding instruction. Apprenticeship provides quite a different model of interaction in which a model of the student is not essential. Instead, the instructor, interested in making use of the student's work, provides demonstrations and feedback in terms of the product toward which they are both working. Recent advances in the cognitive science of instruction provide insights into the interactive processes by which instructors appropriate the work of apprentices. An intelligent instructional system that instantiates apprenticeship interaction illustrates an alternative to tutorial-based systems that make use of a student model.

Conventional intelligent tutoring systems are built around a model of the student's partial understanding of the expert knowledge which is used to direct instruction (Sleeman & Brown, 1982; Wenger, 1987). The model of instructional interaction on which this approach is based is the *individual tutorial* in which knowledge or skills are transmitted from the tutor to the student. There are many other ways of organizing instruction, for example, collaborative learning or apprenticeships, which could provide models for intelligent instructional systems with characteristics very different from student model-based systems. In addition, the use of these systems in the context of human instructor-student interaction releases extensive human resources (instructor and students) for monitoring progress and directing next steps making some tutoring system features unnecessary. Tracking an individual student's cognitive change may be one of the features which can be dispensed with when advanced technologies are put into use in actual instructional contexts.

This paper examines the properties of intelligent instructional systems developed recently at BBN for use in training contexts. The goal of these projects was to apply known artificial intelligence techniques to training. The results of the work, however, provide cases that illustrate a different theoretical approach to instructional interactions. The instructional format supported by the systems more closely resembles an apprenticeship than an individual tutorial. That is, students work at simulated problems resembling those they will confront in the field while the system gives them feedback and expert demonstrations. The systems do not create a model of the student. They present a model of expert performance through direct modeling as well as by showing how the student actions fit into a framework that the expert uses to evaluate them. It is assumed that students, supported by human instructors, can carry out the interpretive work required to form the expert concept based on the information provided by the system.

A THEORY OF APPRENTICESHIP LEARNING

Cognitive science has traditionally taken the view that the mind of the individual is the appropriate unit of analysis (Gardner, 1985). The individual tutorial is a natural extension of this view of human cognition since the tutor is in the role of the cognitive scientist, diagnosing the individual misconceptions and presenting just the right stimuli to move the individual to a new understanding. Work on intelligent tutoring systems has shared this traditional view in its attempt to simulate the individual's tutor as well as the tutor's model of the individual. A less traditional approach to human cognition, however, may lead to new ways of using artificial intelligence in instructional interactions.

Recent work in the cognitive science of instruction has suggested that a unit of analysis larger than the individual person may be of value in understanding how cognitive change occurs (Hutchins, in press; Lave, 1988; Newman, Griffin & Cole, 1989; Resnick, 1987). The cognitive processes are seen as entirely intertwined with the social organization of instruction. Recent interest in apprenticeship learning (Lave, in preparation; Collins, Brown & Newman, in press) follows from this reformulation since apprenticeships are a part of the organization of work. This fact leads to important constraints (e.g., the sequence of apprentice tasks has to allow for useful work to get done) and provides essential motivations (e.g., the apprentice sees the components of the task in the context of creating a product) which makes apprenticeship a potentially powerful method of instruction. The student-instructor interactions in this context do not resemble Socratic dialogues. The instructor, wanting to be able to make use of what the student is doing, provides demonstrations and feedback in terms of the product toward which they are both working.

Vygotsky's (1978, 1986) developmental psychology provides important insights into instructional interactions relevant to this approach. Vygotsky introduced the concept of a zone of proximal development in which children can work at problems that are beyond their competence as individuals. With "scaffolding" provided by others, children can solve problems interactively while they are in the process of learning how to solve them themselves. Observations of instructional interactions in which a teacher is helping a student or group of students indicate that teachers often do not have, or apparently need, an understanding of exactly how the students are approaching the task. Newman et al. (1989) describe teaching and tutorial sessions in which the teacher appropriates the students' actions into her own way of understanding the task. The teacher has to find some way for the students to play at least a minimal role in the accomplishment of the task and give feedback in terms of the expert understanding of the task: what the goal is, what is relevant, why his move was not optimal and so on. In instructional interactions, both the student and teacher are necessarily somewhat ignorant of each other's mental state. All the student has to do is produce some move that in some way contributes (or can be understood as an attempt to contribute) to the task. The teacher does not have to know exactly what the student thinks he or she is doing as long as she can appropriate what the student does into the joint accomplishment of the task. Seeing how his or her action is appropriated provides the student with an analysis of task as the teacher understands it. Thus the basis for appropriation is the notion that the meaning of an action can be changed retrospectively by the actions of others that follow it (Fox, 1987; Newman & Bruce, 1986).

The concept of appropriation provides a model for a range of interactions between two parties that have different interpretations of the initial situation. An apprenticeship, for example, involves a novice and expert where the expert makes use of the novice's work even at the earliest stages of training when the novice has little understanding of the overall process. An "intelligent" tool can also appropriate the actions of an inexperienced student. For example, a system that provides a trace of the student's algebra problem-solving activities in effect takes the students actions and displays them in a framework that the student may not initially understand (Collins & Brown, 1987). By seeing how his or her actions are displayed, the student can come to understand, for example, that problem-solving is a process of successive attempts and backtracking.

Our design for intelligent instructional systems is based on the notion that students can come to understand the expert approach to the problem by observing examples of expert problem-solving and by seeing how their actions are interpreted within the framework of the expert understanding. This instructional format, which resembles an apprenticeship, depends on the interpretive work of the student in seeing what the system made of his or her actions and on the supportive role of the human instructor (Newman, in press). A theoretical approach focusing on the characteristics of instructional interactions among the student, instructor and computer points to practical uses for relatively simple artificial intelligence.

APPLICATION OF APPRENTICESHIP TO INSTRUCTIONAL SYSTEMS

Three instructional systems implemented on Symbolics AI workstations illustrate these properties. TRIO (Ritter & Feurzeig, 1988) trains F-14 navigators to carry out air intercepts. MACH-III (Kurland & Tenney, 1988; Kurland, 1989) trains mechanics to troubleshoot a complex radar system. INCOFT (Intelligent Conduct of Fire Trainer) trains surface-to-air missile operators in the identification of aircraft (Newman, Grignetti, Gross & Massey, in press). A description of INCOFT illustrates how features of apprenticeships are instantiated in intelligent feedback and articulate expertise of the knowledge-based simulation.

The Missile Operator's Task

INCOFT is designed to train soldiers to perform a complex real-time task of monitoring the operation of an automated missile system in which errors can have tragic consequences. In modern air defense surface-to-air missile systems, radar information is processed and presented to the operators in highly abstract form. The system itself can assign identities to aircraft as friendly or hostile based on flight patterns and transmitted signals. The operator must understand what is happening during the few minutes that a track takes to traverse the radar's area of coverage and be prepared to override the system in cases where local exceptions to the tactics built into the system are required and where a higher echelon calls in information not available to the local computer.

The missile system for which INCOFT trains operators uses a point system for determining identities of aircraft picked up on its radar. The airspace surrounding the missile site and any assets it is defending is divided into volumes. Aircraft lose a certain number of points for each volume they penetrate. Friendly aircraft presumably know the exact location of these volumes as well as of safe passage corridors which cut through them. Flying so that they are aligned with the corridor, for example, is worth positive points as a friendly indicator. Depending on the specific tactical situation, there are also speed and altitude limits which cause points to be added or subtracted. Finally, there are codes which friendly aircraft can transmit that supply additional evidence of friendly status. For each of hundreds of tracks that the radar can follow, the missile system computer can assign an identity as a friend, assumed friend, unknown, or hostile depending on the predefined thresholds.

The task of manual identification is used in training operators. The assumption is that if an operator can do what the computer does, then he or she must understand how the computer works and be able to monitor its operation. The task is to learn the algorithm used by the computer and be able to reproduce it. Given the complex set of criteria and the mental arithmetic this learning task is not trivial. Interviews with students after several hours of conventional instruction indicated that they often did not understand the criteria or utilize the algorithm (Newman, 1989). Tracks which had a positive indicator were declared friendly before sufficient points were accumulated, and tracks with a single negative indicator were declared hostile while the PATRIOT computer would have still considered them unknown according to the given point values and thresholds. Students do not see the task as understanding an algorithm but rather as determining the identity of the aircraft picked up on their radar. An initial step in training, therefore, is to communicate the expert view that there is an algorithm on which these decisions must be based. INCOFT simulates the operator's console, presents scenarios, and provides speech synthesized feedback on the student's actions as well as demonstrations of how the automatic system would have handled the situation. The feedback and demonstrations appropriate and reflect back the student's actions within a framework represented both graphically and in the form of tables that displays the expert's perspective.

Replay of the Exercise

As in conventional intelligent tutoring systems, INCOFT compares the student performance to an expert performance, in this case the missile system's computer. The student is presented with a scenario of between 2 and 13 minutes in which he or she must manually identify a number of tracks. When the exercise is complete, the scenario, exactly as carried out by the student, is replayed in "fast forward", pausing for each student action. Each action is compared to the expert action and commented upon, right or wrong. Where possible, INCOFT provides an analysis of incorrect actions, and of actions that happened to be correct but for which the operator made a procedural error or failed to gather all the necessary data. For example, if the difference between the expert identification and the student identification can be accounted for by one feature or by a piece of information the student failed to gather, then that is pointed out. In all cases, the verbal feedback is accompanied by a graphic representation of the point values and thresholds involved in the arithmetic calculation.

Summary Table

When the replay is complete, a table is displayed listing the actions the missile system would have taken for each track and comparing the student actions. In addition to summarizing the replay feedback, the table displays the time lag between the missile system identification action and the student's action and relates this to the time available for making an identification action before some disaster occurs. The table also provides a summary score of percentage of correct identifications and average time to make the identification.

Expert Demonstrations

The table also serves as a menu for selecting demonstrations of the identification process for any target on which an error was made or for which the process was not understood. Unlike the replay, the expert demonstration shows the scenario as the missile system would process it in automatic mode. The action is shown in "fast forward" up to the time that there is a change in the point total for the track being demonstrated. INCOFT explains each change in terms of volume penetration, corridor alignment, exceeding speed thresholds and so on. A scale indicating the accumulated points and the thresholds for the identifications is also displayed.

FORMATIVE RESEARCH RESULTS

Formative research with students and instructors in the current program of instruction guided the design of scenarios and feedback. It also provided initial information on the potential effectiveness of INCOFT in contrast to conventional simulator-based training. This research was not intended as a summative evaluation of the effectiveness of the system but does point to areas of strength. Students who had completed the relevant portion of the course were interviewed during and after operating a scenario. We also observed two instructors use INCOFT in actual instruction with students who were learning the material for the first time.

INCOFT's Representation of the Task

Students found the replay to be a great improvement over the conventional simulator and over-the-shoulder instruction since the usual student-instructor ratio makes it impossible to obtain feedback on most actions. But beyond simply providing detailed feedback and analysis, a powerful feature of INCOFT's articulate expert became evident in the students' responses to the single track expert demos of the identification process. Students had never before seen a scenario decomposed into separate tracks. Many students remarked on being able to see the precise point at which, for example, a track dealigned with a corridor and was declared hostile. While following any single track is just a matter of straightforward adding and subtracting, the missile system is able to do that for hundreds of tracks simultaneously. A novice human operator faced with, for example, 15 tracks, will have to look at each track, one time, in some sequence and make identifications. This snapshot approach does not take in the continuous history of a single track, yet it is the patterns of motion and activity that reveal a track's identity and intention. Interestingly, interviews with experienced air defense operators who were being reassigned from different systems, indicated that it is the perception of these patterns for particular tracks that seems to mark expertise in air defense operation. By decomposing what the missile system's computer does simultaneously, INCOFT demonstrates part of human expertise in this task.

By presenting the student's task in terms of its own framework, INCOFT utilizes features of apprenticeship in its style of student-machine interaction. The system essentially shows the student how the missile system would deal with the same cases and what aspects of the simulated situation are relevant to it. Operating a simulation is not productive work so, unlike an apprentice's master, the system does not literally make use of the student's work. The feedback, however, shares features with an apprenticeship in that it relates the student's output to the expert performance rather than to the student's internal states. For example, the replay feedback presents the aircraft identifications in terms of a graphically represented arithmetic calculation and the summary table presents the student's decision-making time in relation to the urgency of the situation as an expert would understand it. In this sense, the output is appropriated by the system's interpretive framework providing a reflection for the student in the expert's terms.

The Instructors' Role in the Apprenticeship

It is assumed that human instructors are part of the training context and assist the student in interpreting the feedback and in suggesting additional practice. For example, the instructor can suggest to the student that he or she see a particular expert demonstration. A field test of INCOFT in actual instruction--supervised by instructors rather than researchers--demonstrates the reasonableness of putting this power at the disposal of real instructors and the students rather than attempting to build the entire presentation into an automatic tutor. The summary table provides an opportunity for students to ask questions of the instructors and for instructors to give meta-analyses to the students. INCOFT does not process the data further or make decisions about what the student ought to do next. These decisions are handed over to the people involved.

The following example is taken from a session in which INCOFT was being used in instruction with students who were learning the task for the first time. The instructor is a highly experienced teacher but working with INCOFT for the first time. In this segment, the student has finished a relatively complex scenario and is looking at the summary table.

S: What's the 84 mean? [referring to the summary score at the bottom of the table]

T: That's your average time, average time that you did things, 84 seconds. A minute and a half almost.

S: And it should have all been done in 30 seconds?

T: Well, remember now, 30 seconds is operator override time, and that's maximum operator override time and what we're saying there is that you have that little time to make a decision on critical things that need to be done. If you've got a target, that is if you'd put into- which tab do you have override time?

S: Uh, tab, I got it wrote down in my notes.

T: Tab zero one. And what ever you have down in your operator override time that's the amount of time you have to do something before the system automatically engages the target. Now what this says, what this says to me is that you definitely need to improve and work on your decision making ability and capability, cause 84 seconds average time in order to make a decision is a long time. If you get an aircraft going 800 meters a second,

S: Uh huh.

T: he can go a loong way in a minute and a half, a long way.

S: Okay, I want to try this one again.

This is a complex interaction in which the student displays a misconception about a 30 second time limit introduced in another context and the instructor uses the student question as an occasion to review the concept and the location in the database of the relevant parameter. The instructor returns to the initial topic and presents a graphic case for the need for the student to act more quickly.

Two kinds of instructor-student interaction are evident in this transcript. The instructor conducted a brief *tutorial* on operator override time after having recognized that the student mistook the "average time you did things" for this feature of the system which has to do specifically with time available to override the computer in automatic engagement. Clearly, the instructor recognized the misconception and engaged in an aside to try to clarify the distinction before returning to his main topic.

The other kind of instructor-student interaction evident in the transcript is an amplification of the system's appropriation of the student's actions. The system reflected back to the student the number 84 which is a way of seeing the student's actions peculiar to the expert system which is capable of comparing each student action with the "expert" treatment of the track and coming up with an average time lag. The instructor reformulated the 84 seconds as "a minute and a half almost" and later made his evaluation explicit in terms of a real world concern for PATRIOT operators. This interaction is very different from the tutorial in that it is not based on an understanding of the student in his own right but on an evaluation of the students actions in terms of how it fits into an expert performance. This is more than just feedback on the "correctness" of the performance because it is introducing and motivating considerations that become evident to the student only after he sees how the system (including the instructor) appropriates his actions. The instructor and machine work together in the appropriation: INCOFT provides the student and instructor with detailed feedback on which to base this interaction but it is the instructor, not the machine, who handles the more complex misconceptions and places the task in a motivational context.

CONCLUSION

Instructional interactions in which a tutor is attentive to the student's understanding of the task can be a valuable form of instruction but is only one of many forms in which intelligent technology can be employed. While perhaps an interesting theoretical problem, creating a machine to model human tutoring is very difficult as a practical concern. Our work on INCOFT demonstrates some simplifications of the conventional tutoring system model that make the concept practically useful in instruction. Apprenticeship provides a model of instructor-student interaction that guides our design of feedback. In an apprenticeship, the instructor is interested in appropriating the student actions into productive work. Feedback shows the student whether his or her actions are productive in the framework of the task as understood by the instructor. INCOFT does not attempt to mimic a tutorial interaction. It also does not attempt to carry the entire weight of instruction. By putting various decompositions or representations of the processes in the hands of students and human instructors, we might expect useful instructional interactions to ensue between the people involved.

ACKNOWLEDGEMENTS

The INCOFT project involved the efforts of Wally Feurzeig, Mario Grignetti, Mark Gross, Laura Kurland, Ben Lubetsky, Dan Massey and others. We are grateful to John Lockhart and Laurel Allender for their comments. INCOFT was sponsored by the Joint Services Manpower and Training Technology Development (JS/MTTD) Program and monitored by the Army Research Institute (ARI) under Contract MDA903-86-C-0382. The views, opinions, and findings contained in this report are those of the author and should not be construed as an official Department of the Army position, policy, or decision, unless so designated by other official documentation.

REFERENCES

Collins, A. & Brown, J. S. (1987). The computer as a tool for learning through reflection. In H. Mandl and A. M. Lesgold (Eds.), *Learning Issues for Intelligent Tutoring Systems.* New York: Springer-Verlag.

Collins, A., Brown, J. S. & Newman, S. (in press). Cognitive apprenticeship: teaching the craft of reading, writing, and mathematics. In L. B. Resnick (Ed.), *Cognition and instruction: Issues and agendas.* Hillsdale, NJ: Lawrence Erlbaum Associates.

Fox, B. (1987). Interactional reconstruction in real-time language processing. *Cognitive Science, 11 (3),* 365-387.

Gardner, H. (1985). *The mind's new science.* New York: Basic Books, Inc.

Hutchins, E. (in press). The technology of team navigation. In J. Galegher, R. Kraut, and C. Egido (Eds.), *Intellectual teamwork: Social and technical bases of cooperative work.* Hillsdale, NJ: Lawrence Erlbaum Associates.

Kurland, L. C. (1989). *Design, development and integration of an ITS in the real world.* Paper prepared for the annual meetings of the American Educational Research Association, San Fransisco.

Kurland, L. C., and Tenney, Y. J. (1988). Issues in developing an intelligent tutor for a real-world domain: training in radar mechanics. In J. Psotka, L. D. Massey, and S. A. Mutter (Eds.), *Intelligent tutoring systems: Lessons learned.* Hillsdale, NJ:Lawrence Erlbaum Associates.

Lave, J. (1988). *Cognition in practice: Mind, mathematics and culture in everyday life.* Cambridge: Cambridge University Press.

Lave, J. (in preparation). *Tailored learning: Education and everyday practice among craftsmen in West Africa.* Palo Alto: Institute for Research on Learning.

Newman, D. (1989). *Application of Intelligent Tutoring Technology to an Apparently Mechanical Task.* Paper presented at the annual meetings of the American Educational Research Association, San Fransisco.

Newman, D. (in press). Cognitive change by appropriation. In S. Robertson and W. Zachary (Eds.), *Cognition, computation, and cooperation.* Norwood, NJ: Ablex Publishing.

Newman, D., & Bruce, B. C. (1986). Interpretation and manipulation in human plans. *Discourse Processes. 9,* 167-195.

Newman, D., Griffin, P., & Cole, M. (1989). *The construction zone: Working for cognitive change in school.* Cambridge: Cambridge University Press.

Newman, D., Grignetti, M., Gross, M., and Massey, L. D. (in press). Intelligent Conduct of Fire Trainer: Intelligent technology applied to simulator-based training. *Machine Mediated Learning.*

Resnick, L. B. (1987). Learning in school and out. *Educational Researcher, 16* (9) 13-20.

Ritter, F. & Feurzeig, W. (1988). Teaching real-time tactical thinking. In J. Psotka, L. D. Massey, and S. A. Mutter (Eds.), *Intelligent tutoring systems: Lessons learned.* Hillsdale, NJ: Lawrence Erlbaum Associates.

Sleeman, D., & Brown, J. S. (Eds.), (1982). *Intelligent tutoring systems.* New York: Academic Press.

Vygotsky, L. S. (1978). *Mind in society: The development of higher psychological processes* (M. Cole, V. John-Steiner, S. Scribner, & E. Souberman, Eds.). Cambridge: Harvard University Press.

Vygotsky L. S. (1986). *Thought and language.* (A. Kozulin, Ed.) Cambridge, MA: MIT Press.

Wenger, E. (1987). *Artificial intelligence and tutoring systems: Computational and cognitive approaches to the communication of knowledge.* Los Altos, CA: Morgan Kaufmann Publishers, Inc.

ABDUCTION AND WORLD MODEL REVISION [1]

Paul O'Rorke
University of California, Irvine

Steven Morris
University of California, Irvine

David Schulenburg
University of California, Irvine

ABSTRACT

Abduction is the process of constructing explanations. This paper suggests that abduction is a key to "world model revisions" — dramatic changes in systems of beliefs such as occur in children's cognitive development and in scientific revolutions. The paper describes a model of belief revision based upon *hypothesis formation by abduction.* When a contradiction between an observation and an existing model or theory about the physical world is encountered, the best course is often simply to suppress parts of the original theory thrown into question by the contradiction and to derive an explanation of the anomalous observation based on relatively solid, basic principles. This process of looking for explanations of unexpected new phenomena can lead by abductive inference to new hypotheses that can form crucial parts of a revised theory. As an illustration, the paper shows how one of Lavoisier's key insights during the Chemical Revolution can be viewed as an example of hypothesis formation by abduction.

BELIEF REVISION USING HYPOTHESES FORMED BY ABDUCTION

"World model revision" is at the more difficult, more creative end of the spectrum of belief revision problems. We all make simple changes in beliefs during everyday life, but dramatic changes in systems of beliefs such as occur in scientific revolutions appear to require extraordinary creative genius. Great changes in our way of looking at the world represent the height of human intellectual achievement and are identified with intellectual giants such as Galileo, Newton, Lavoisier, and Einstein.

James Bryant Conant argues in his introduction to the *Harvard case histories in experimental science* (Conant, Nash, Roller, & Roller, (Eds.), 1957) that case studies of revolutionary advances in science can facilitate the understanding of science by non-scientists. Cognitive scientists take this one step further and argue that case studies based on the history of science can be used to achieve a deeper understanding of the cognitive processes underlying scientific discovery (see, e.g., Bradshaw, Langley, & Simon, 1983; Langley, Simon, Bradshaw, & Zytkow, 1987). One immediate aim of such case studies of scientific revolutions is to develop computational models of the evolution of specific scientific theories over time. However, the ultimate goal is not so much to capture individual case histories — the main goal is to improve our understanding of how theory shifts are, or can be, made.

[1]This paper is based on work supported by an Irvine Faculty Fellowship from the University of California, Irvine Academic Senate Committee on Research and by grant number IRI-8813048 from the National Science Foundation to the first author.

The claim of this paper is that *hypothesis formation by abduction* can play a crucial role in world model revision. Abduction is the process of constructing explanations (Peirce, 1931-1958; Pople, 1973; Reggia & Nau, 1984; Schank, 1986; Charniak, 1988; Josephson, Chandrasekaran, Smith, & Tanner, in press). This paper focuses on abduction as a theory driven process. If a prediction of a given theory contradicts an observation, and if methods exist for identifying questionable details of the given theory, this form of abduction can be used to derive an explanation of the anomalous observation based on relatively solid, basic principles of the domain. The claim is that the process of looking for explanations of unexpected new phenomena can lead by abductive inference to new hypotheses that can form crucial parts of new theories.

THE CHEMICAL REVOLUTION

As an illustration, we present some initial results of a case study of the Chemical Revolution — the replacement of the phlogiston theory by the oxygen theory. This particular theory shift has attracted a great deal of interest partly because it occurred in the early days of chemistry, while the theory and the experiments were still close to common knowledge and everyday experience, and were not too highly technical. In addition, the Chemical Revolution has the advantage that a great deal is known about it, because of detailed records left by the scientists involved and due to the large number of books and papers on the subject by historians and philosophers of science (see, for example, Guerlac, 1961; Thagard in press-a; Ihde, 1980; in addition to Conant, 1957).

Prior to the Chemical Revolution, the phlogiston theory of chemistry provided the predominant explanation of the processes of combustion and calcination. Under this theory developed by the German chemist G. E. Stahl (1660 - 1734), it was thought that all combustible substances contained an element called phlogiston. Combustion was thought of as a sort of flow of phlogiston from combustible substances into the surrounding air. Calcination (e.g., rusting) was also thought of as a loss of phlogiston from metals and metallic calxes[2]. Lavoisier, the 18th century French chemist who was the driving force behind the Chemical Revolution, placed great importance on the observation that the weights of some substances increase in combustion and calcination. Just after this augmentation effect was demonstrated conclusively by experiments, Laviosier deposited a sealed note on November 1, 1772 with the Secretary of the French Academy of Sciences:

> *About eight days ago I discovered that sulfur in burning, far from losing weight, on the contrary, gains it; it is the same with phosphorus... This discovery, which I have established by experiments, that I regard as decisive, has led me to think that what is observed in the combustion of sulfur and phosphorus may well take place in the case of all substances that gain in weight by combustion and calcination; and I am persuaded that the increase in weight of metallic calxes is due to the same cause.*[3]

Lavoisier went on to discover that — contrary to the century old phlogiston theory — a gas contained in the atmosphere combines with burning combustibles and calcinating metals. This gas was first isolated by heating mercurius calcinatus (red calx of mercury; now called red oxide of mercury) until the gas in the calx was liberated. Lavoisier named the new gas "oxygen."

In the next section, we show how advances in research on qualitative physics provide a language for describing some important ideas associated with the phlogiston theory of combustion.

[2] A calx is a substance produced by calcination.

[3] Translation by Conant (Conant, 1957). The dots indicate text omitted by the authors.

Direct Influences:

GL1: deriv-sign(Q1, Sign) ← process(Process), active(Process), influence(Process, Q1, Sign).

Indirect Influences:

GL2a: deriv-sign(Q1, Sign) ← qprop(Q1, Q2, pos), deriv-sign(Q2, Sign).

GL2b: deriv-sign(Q1, Sign1) ← qprop(Q1, Q2, neg), deriv-sign(Q2, Sign2), opposite(Sign1, Sign2).

The Law of Sums:

GL3: qprop(Q, Q_i, pos) ← qty-eq(Q, qty-sum(Qs)), member(Q_i, Qs).

The weight of an object is qualitatively proportional to the amount.

GL4: qprop(weight(P), amount(P), pos).

~~**Combustion is a negative influence on the amount of phlogiston in charcoal.**~~

~~GL5a: influence(combustion, amount-of-in(phlogiston, charcoal), neg).~~

~~**Calcination is a negative influence on the phlogiston in mercurius calcinatus.**~~

~~GL5b: influence(calcination, amount-of-in(phlogiston, m-c), neg).~~

The amount of a complex substance equals the sum of the amounts of the components.

GL6: qty-eq(amount(C), qty-sum(Qs)) ← complex(C), is-a-set-of-amounts-of-components-of(Qs, C)

GL7a: is-a-set-of-amounts-of-components-of([Qi | Qs], C) ← is-an-amount-of-a-component-of(Qi, C), is-a-set-of-amounts-of-components-of(Qs, C).

GL7b: is-a-set-of-amounts-of-components-of([ ], C).

GL8: is-an-amount-of-a-component-of(Qi, C) ← complex(C), component(Ci, C), Qi = amount-of-in(Ci, C).

Observation: The weight of mercurius calcinatus increases.

O1: deriv-sign(weight(m-c), pos).

Case facts: Calcination is an active process.

CF1: process(calcination).

CF2: active(calcination).

Figure 1: A Fragment of a Phlogiston Theory, An Observation, and Some Case Facts

SOME ASPECTS OF THE PHLOGISTON THEORY ENCODED AS RULES

Figure 1 shows a fragment of the phlogiston theory describing the effects of combustion and calcination coded in terms of facts and rules. (Ignore the black lines in Figure 1 for now.) Also shown is an observation O1 which describes an increase in weight of a partially calcinated piece of mercury, so-called mercurius calcinatus (here abbreviated m-c). Additionally, case facts CF1 and CF2 indicate that calcination is taking place in some specific situation. This theory, observation and case facts, are expressed in a language derived from Ken Forbus's *Qualitative Process Theory* (Forbus, 1984). In the remainder of this section we briefly describe the individual statements in the fragment of the phlogiston theory.

In Figure 1, rules GL1 and GL2 are general laws of QP theory. GL1, *The Law of Direct Influences*, states that a quantity may be changing because some process is directly influencing it. The quantity increases or decreases according to whether Sign is "positive" or "negative." In this law, "deriv-sign(Q1, Sign)" means "the sign of the derivative of quantity Q1 is Sign".

GL2a and GL2b, *The Laws of Indirect Influences*, are meant to capture the notion that a quantity may change because it is qualitatively proportional to some other quantity. Here "qprop(Q1, Q2, pos)" means "quantity Q1 is positively qualitatively proportional to the quantity Q2." A qualitative proportionality may be either positive or negative. A change in one quantity may be accounted for by a similar change in some other quantity if there is a positive qualitative proportionality between them. In the case of a negative qualitative proportionality, a change in one quantity may be accounted for by an opposite change in another quantity.

Rules GL3, GL4, and GL5 are meant to capture some important aspects of the phlogiston theory. GL3, *The Law of Sums*, states that a quantity is qualitatively proportional to a second quantity if the first quantity is equal to a sum of a number of quantities one of which is the second quantity. "qty-eq(Q, qty-sum(Qs))" means "Q is a quantity equal to the sum of quantities Qs," where Qs is a list of quantities. "member(Qi, Qs)" means "Qi is a member of the list of Qs." GL4 states that the weight of any substance is proportional to the amount of the substance.

Phlogiston theorists viewed all combustible substances as complex substances containing phlogiston. In our qualitative process description of the phlogiston theory, rule GL5a states that combustion is a process that influences the amount of phlogiston in charcoal negatively. That is, if combustion is active, it drives down the amount of phlogiston in a partially burned piece of charcoal. Similarly, rule GL5b states that calcination drives down the amount of phlogiston in a partially calcinated piece of mercury. According to the phlogiston theory, pure metallic calxes were more primitive substances than metals. Metals were formed by heating calxes in the presence of a source of phlogiston such as charcoal; the calxes combined with the phlogiston to form the metals. On the other hand, metallic calxes resulted when phlogiston, which was viewed as a "metallizing principle," flowed out of metals.

Rules GL6, GL7 and GL8 provide some facts about complex substances. These rules state that the amount of a complex substance is equal to the sum of the amounts of its components.

ABDUCTION OF ASPECTS OF THE OXYGEN THEORY

In this section we show how the facts and rules in Figure 1 can be used to construct explanations of observations involving changes in the weights of burning and calcinating substances. In particular, we illustrate the role of abduction in theory formation by showing how Lavoisier's insight can be seen as abductive inference. This is done by showing how a specific "abduction engine", called AbE, generates an explanation of the increase in the weight of calcinating mercury. AbE is a PROLOG meta-interpreter that constructs explanation trees, evaluates partial explanations, and uses best-first heuristic search.

Let us assume as *given* the phlogiston theory shown in Figure 1. The phlogiston theory explains and predicts a *decrease* in the weight of substances undergoing combustion or calcination. This prediction contradicts the given observation that the weight of mercurius calcinatus *increases* during calcination. Assume that, as a result, questionable parts of the theory responsible for the contradiction have been identified and deleted as indicated by the black lines through offending statements in Figure 1.[4] Assume then, that our abduction engine AbE is given the reduced phlogiston theory and the observation and case facts shown in Figure 1. In the reduced theory, phlogiston is no longer considered to be an essential component of combustible substances and no mention is made of the effects of combustion or calcination on amounts of phlogiston.

[4]Existing contradiction backtracing and truth maintenance methods could contribute to identifying candidates for deletion or temporary suppression, but some method of evaluating plausibility will be needed in order to decide that a candidate should be suppressed. Basic principles which contribute to many explanations (e.g., conservation laws), should be preferentially retained.

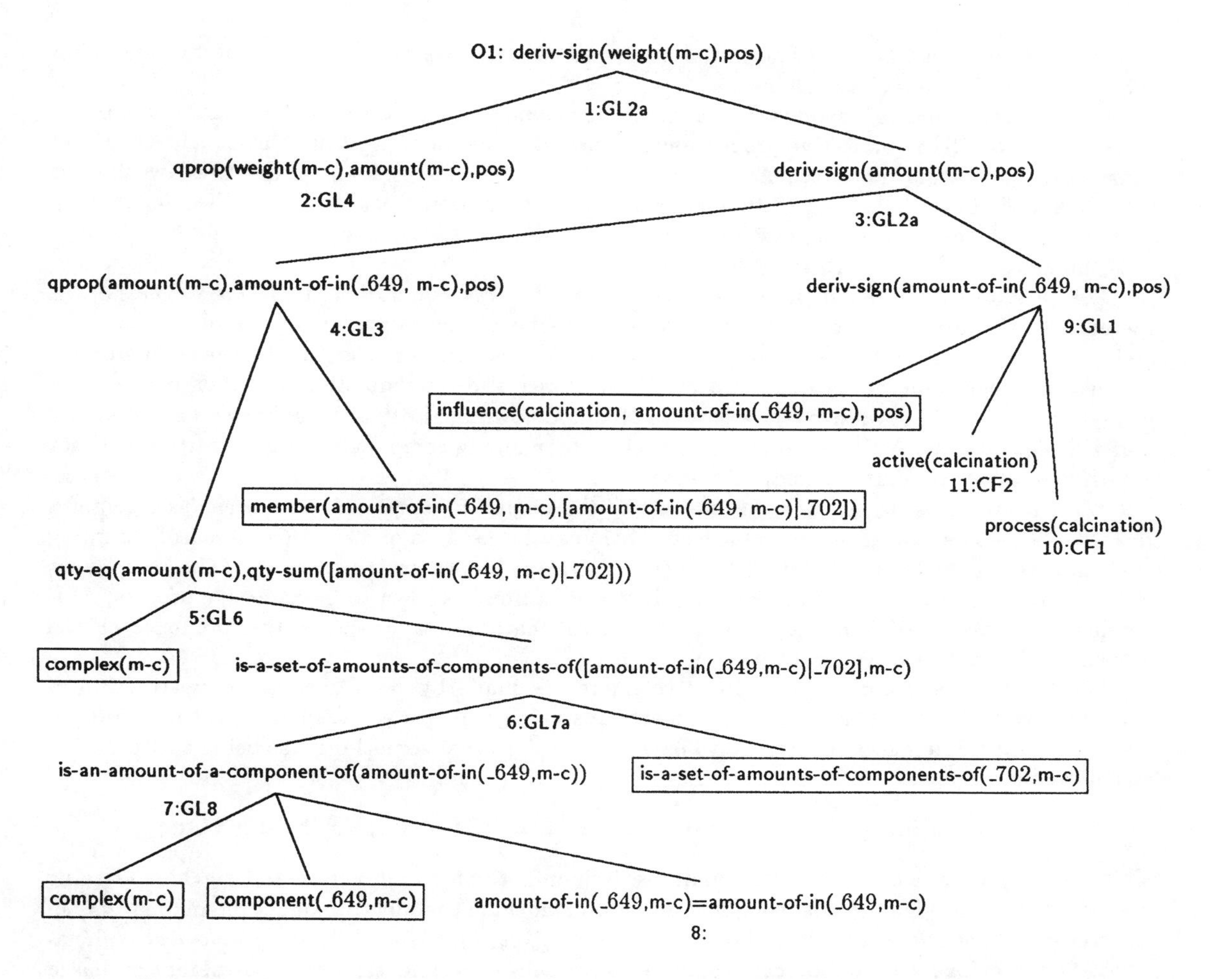

Figure 2: Why the weight of mercurius calcinatus (m-c) increases in calcination.

AbE is asked to explain, in terms of the given laws of qualitative physics and the ablated phlogiston theory, the observation that, during calcination (CF1 & CF2), the weight of mercurius calcinatus increases (O1). AbE does this by attempting to reduce the observation to the given facts, but if this is not possible it will propose some hypotheses in an effort to explain the observation. Figure 2 shows one explanation arrived at by AbE. We now briefly describe how this explanation tree was constructed.

The initial query is: *Why is the weight of the mercurius calcinatus increasing?* According to the laws of indirect influences (GL2), a change in some quantity may be explained by a change in some other quantity provided the two quantities are qualitatively proportional. Backward chaining on this law, AbE proposes that the weight of the mercurius calcinatus may be positively qualitatively proportional to another quantity. The question of whether there is any such quantity is answered as an instance of the general fact that the weight of any object is positively proportional to the amount of that object (GL4). The initial query can thus be explained in terms of an increase in the *amount* of the mercurius calcinatus.

Why is the amount of mercurius calcinatus increasing? To explain this, AbE again uses GL2a to propose a positive qualitative proportionality between the amount of mercurius calcinatus and some other increasing quantity. An appropriate proportionality is found using the law of sums (GL3). Recall that this law states that some quantity Q is proportional to some other quantity Qi if Q is equal to the sum of some set of quantities Qs and Qi is a member of that set. In this case, Q is the amount of the mercurius calcinatus.

The question is whether there is some set of quantities whose sum is equal to the amount of the mercurius calcinatus. This question is answered in terms of knowledge about complex substances (GL6, GL7, GL8). AbE backward chains on these laws to hypothesize that the amount of mercurius calcinatus is increasing because it is a complex substance and the amount of one of its components is increasing. AbE hypothesizes the existence of an unknown quantity of an unknown component of mercurius calcinatus. AbE also hypothesizes a set of remaining components and quantities, without identifying any particular elements of this set.

The question now is whether the amount of the unknown component of mercurius calcinatus is increasing. The law of direct influences (GL1) can be used to explain this increase, assuming that an active process can be found to have a *positive* influence on the amount of the component of the mercurius calcinatus. At this point, since calcination is known to be an active process, AbE completes its explanation by hypothesizing that calcination is a direct positive influence on the amount of the unknown component.

The hypotheses generated by abductive inferences made by AbE during its construction of this explanation of the augmentation of mercurius calcinatus are enclosed in boxes in Figure 2. These abductive inferences correspond to Lavoisier's insight that something was being added during calcination.

RELATION TO OTHER WORK IN COGNITIVE SCIENCE

This work is part of a coherent program of research on automated abduction and machine learning underway at Irvine. Our goal is to explore domain-independent models of abduction and learning in the context of specific examples and domains involving *logical*, *physical*, and *psychological* explanations. Our previous work on logical explanations includes experimental work on explanation-based learning in logical domains such as Principia Mathematica (O'Rorke, 1987). In collaboration with Andrew Ortony and Gerald DeJong of Illinois, we are investigating psychological explanations involving emotions. Initial progress on this research has been reported in (O'Rorke & Cain, 1988). The present paper describes initial progress of our work involving physical explanations. It fits into the theoretical framework for learning in physical domains sketched in Forbus and Gentner (1986). The learning taking place in our chemical revolution example appears to fit in the third stage ("learning naive physics") of Forbus and Gentner's four stage model.

Recent scientific discovery work by Jan Zytkow and Herbert Simon, followed up by Don Rose and Pat Langley, resulted in systems that can automatically detect and correct errors in chemical theories. These artificial intelligence programs, STAHL (Zytkow & Simon, 1986) and STAHLp (Rose & Langley, 1986) are similar, in that they both represent chemical theories in terms of *reaction and component models.* These systems could conceivably model the shift from the phlogiston to the oxygen theory as a change from a set of reaction rules and component models involving phlogiston to a set of reaction rules and component models involving oxygen. In our opinion, however, such an account of the theory shift would be incomplete; if only because the models of the phlogiston and oxygen theories would be incomplete if limited to reactions and component models. For example, both the phlogiston theory and the oxygen theory explained why a flame burning in an enclosed place eventually expires — but these explanations cannot be expressed in terms of component models and reactions alone.

While some revisions in STAHLp amount to hypothesizing the existence of unobserved substances in the input reactions (adding substances), and retracting previously believed observations of substances in the input reactions (deleting substances), all such substances must have been named in previous input reactions. STAHLp is not capable of hypothesizing the existence of a new substance — one that has not previously appeared in an input to STAHLp. This is in contrast to the example we have presented, in which a new component substance is hypothesized on the basis of general qualitative physical laws.

Paul Thagard has also done closely related research. Thagard (in press-b) presents a theory of explanatory coherence and a connectionist implementation. His program, ECHO, is given data representing observations and the phlogiston and oxygen theories. Using activation and inhibition links between data and theoretical statements, the program attempts to determine which of the two theories best "coheres" with the data. Thagard's ECHO focuses on the ***evaluation*** of ***existing*** theories. In another paper, (Thagard in press-a) he looks at the conceptual changes that occurred during the overthrow of the phlogiston theory, and gives a fairly detailed conceptual map of several important intermediate stages of chemical theory in the transition from the phlogiston theory to the oxygen theory. In this paper, Thagard suggests that the mechanisms for concept formation and rule abduction present in a program called PI can be used to form conceptual networks that can chart the conceptual changes which occurred during the Chemical Revolution. Our contribution is that we have shown a detailed example of how abduction can be used in concert with ideas from work on qualitative physics to make some crucial inferences associated with the discovery of oxygen.

CONCLUSION

Theory revision can profitably be viewed as a process that involves hypothesis formation by abduction. When an anomaly is encountered, the best course is often simply to forget or suppress questionable details of the original theory and to derive an explanation of the anomalous observation based on more solid, more basic principles. In this way, the process of looking for explanations of unexpected new phenomena can lead by abductive inference to new hypotheses that can form crucial parts of a revised theory.

The main result of this paper is that recent progress on abduction and qualitative process theory makes it possible to automate significant aspects of the reasoning that occurred in the Chemical Revolution. We believe that the language for describing processes and causal relationships resulting from work on qualitative physics together with inference mechanisms such as automated abduction will enable automation of many crucial but relatively common-sense insights associated with scientific revolutions. If this proves true, it suggests that automated abduction is a key to understanding "world model revision."

ACKNOWLEDGEMENTS

Special thanks are due to Pat Langley and Deepak Kulkarni for numerous discussions of scientific discovery. Discussions with Pat Langley and Don Rose on the STAHLp program sparked our interest in modelling the Chemical Revolution. Thanks also to Paul Thagard, of the Princeton University Cognitive Science Laboratory, for several useful discussions of the Chemical Revolution and of scientific revolutions in general.

REFERENCES

Bradshaw, G. F., Langley, P. W., & Simon, H. A. (1983). Studying scientific discovery by computer simulation. *Science, 222*, 971–975.

Charniak, E. (1988). Motivation analysis, abductive unification, and nonmonotonic equality. *Artificial Intelligence, 34*, 275–295.

Conant, J. B. (1957). The overthrow of the phlogiston theory: The chemical revolution of 1775-1789. In J. B. Conant, L. K. Nash, D. Roller, & D. H. D. Roller (Eds.), *Harvard case histories in experimental science.* Cambridge, MA: Harvard University Press.

Conant, J. B., Nash, L. K., Roller, D., & Roller, D. H. D. (Eds.). (1957). *Harvard case histories in experimental science.* Cambridge, MA: Harvard University Press.

Forbus, K. D. (1984). Qualitative process theory. *Artificial Intelligence, 24*, 85–168.

Forbus, K. D., & Gentner, D. (1986). Learning physical domains: Toward a theoretical framework. In Michalski, R. S., Carbonell, J. G., & Mitchell, T. M (Eds.), *Machine Learning: An Artificial Intelligence Approach, Volume II.* Los Altos, CA: Morgan Kaufmann.

Guerlac, H. (1961). *Lavoisier — the crucial year — the background and origin of his first experiments on combustion in 1772.* Ithaca, NY: Cornell University Press.

Ihde, A. J. (1980). Priestley and Lavoisier. In *Joseph Priestly symposium, Wilkes-Barre, Pa., 1974.* London: Associated University Presses, Inc.

Josephson, J. R., Chandrasekaran, B., Smith,Jr., J. W., & Tanner, M. C. (in press). A mechanism for forming composite explanatory hypotheses. *IEEE Transactions on Systems, Man and Cybernetics, Special Issue on Causal and Strategic Aspects of Diagnostic Reasoning.*

Langley, P., Simon, H. A., Bradshaw, G. L., & Zytkow, J. M. (1987). *Scientific discovery.* Cambridge, MA: MIT Press.

O'Rorke, P. (1987). LT revisited: Experimental results of applying explanation-based learning to the logic of Principia Mathematica. In *Proceedings of the Fourth International Workshop on Machine Learning,* (pp. 148–159). Irvine, CA: Morgan Kaufmann Publishers, Inc.

O'Rorke, P., & Cain, T. (1988). Explanations involving emotions. to appear in *Proceedings of the AAAI-88 Workshop on Plan Recognition,* St. Paul, MN: Morgan Kaufmann Publishers, Inc.

Peirce, C. S. S. (1931-1958), *Collected Papers of Charles S. Peirce (1839-1914).* Hartchorne, C., Weiss, P., & Burks, A. (Eds.)., Cambridge, MA: Harvard University Press.

Pople, H. E. (1973). On the mechanization of abductive logic. In *Proceedings of the Third International Joint Conference on Artificial Intelligence,* (pp. 147–152).

Reggia, J. A., & Nau, D. S. (1984). An abductive non-monotonic logic. In *Proceedings of the Workshop on Non-Monotonic Reasoning,* (pp. 385–395).

Rose, D., & Langley, P. (1986). Chemical discovery as belief revision. *Machine Learning, 1,* 423–452.

Schank, R. C. (1986). *Explanation patterns: Understanding mechanically and creatively.* Lawrence Erlbaum and Associates.

Thagard, P. (in press-a). The conceptual structure of the chemical revolution. *Philosophy of Science.*

Thagard, P. (in press-b). Explanatory coherence. *The Behavioral and Brain Sciences.*

Zytkow, J. M., & Simon, H. A. (1986). A theory of historical discovery: The construction of componential models. *Machine Learning, 1,* 107–137.

A LINGUISTIC APPROACH TO THE PROBLEM OF SLOT SEMANTICS

H. Van Dyke Parunak
Industrial Technology Institute
Ann Arbor, MI

ABSTRACT

Most frame-based knowledge representation (KR) systems have two strange features. First, the concepts represented by the nodes are nouns rather than verbs. Verbal ideas tend to appear mostly in describing roles or slots. Thus the systems are *asymmetric*. Second, and more seriously, the slot names on frames are arbitrary and not defined in the system. Usually no metasystem is given to account for them. Thus the systems are *not closed.*

Both these features can be avoided by structures inspired by case-based linguistic theories. The basic ideas are that an ontology consists of separate, parallel lattices of verbal and nominal concepts, and that the slots of concepts in each lattice are defined by reference to the concepts in the other lattice. Slots of verbal concepts are derived from cases, and restricted by nominal concepts. Slots of nominal concepts include *conducts* (verbal concepts) and derivatives of the slots of verbal concepts.

Our objective in this paper is not to define a new KR language, but to use input from the study of natural cognition (case grammar) to refine technology for artificial cognition.

TERMINOLOGY AND NOTATION

Concepts are predicates over instances (Hayes 1979), and are named with a prefixed "C-". Variables over concepts are lower-case letters near 'n' (a mnemonic for "intension"), while variables over instances ("extensions") are lower-case letters near 'x'. $x \epsilon m$ means "x is an instance of concept m." This paper is limited to the problem of defining concepts, and does not discuss how to make assertions about them (Woods 1975).

The links between concepts fall into two general categories, depending on whether or not they indicate subsumption (Brachman 1983). One concept C-1 *subsumes* another C-2 just when $\forall x.(C\text{-}2\ x) \rightarrow (C\text{-}1\ x)$. A non-subsuming link from one concept to another is a *slot*.

A slot is a two-place predicate over instances, and links two concepts, its *parent* (the concept to which it belongs) and its *restriction*. For the application of a slot to two instances to be true, it is necessary (but not sufficient) for the first argument to be an instance of the slot's parent, and the second to be an instance of its restriction. Slot names begin with "S-". To identify a slot's parent in cases of ambiguity, postfix the name of the parent concept, omitting the prefixed "C-". Thus the slot recording a lathe's workpiece is S-Workpiece.Lathe.

A functional notation (cf. Vilain 1985) describes manipulations of concepts and slots. For example, **CMeet** combines two concepts to form a concept that meets the restrictions of them both. (CMeet C-1 C-2) has the semantics $\lambda x.(C\text{-}1\ x)\ \&\ (C\text{-}2\ x)$. For example, C-Son = (CMeet C-Child C-Male). **CRestrict** builds a new concept from an old one by restricting the eligible slot-fillers for some slot of the older concept. (CRestrict C-1 S-1 C-2) has the semantics $\lambda x.(C\text{-}1\ x)\&\forall y.(S\text{-}1\ x\ y) \rightarrow (C\text{-}2\ y)$. If C-Machine has a slot S-Status, C-AvailableMachine = (CRestrict C-Machine S-Status C-Idle) describes exactly those machines that are idle. **CMeet** and **CRestrict**, though not a complete set, suffice to illustrate the ideas in this paper. See Vilain 1985 for a fuller set.

THE PROBLEM OF LACK OF CLOSURE

The main problem addressed by this paper is that the semantics of common frame formalisms lack closure both within individual frames and between frames.

Intra-Frame Closure

In

```
C-Lathe
   S-Workpiece
   S-SerialNumber
   S-Location
   S-Size
```

the various slots stand in different relations to C-Lathe. The filler of S-Workpiece changes as the lathe removes chips of metal. The filler of S-Location can change, too, but as a result of reorganizing the factory, not of the normal operation of the lathe. S-Location and S-Size are attributes of the lathe, yet they differ in their semantics from one another, and from S-SerialNumber.

The use of natural language names to identify slots is seductive, since it suggests that the structure has more meaning than the system can actually access. Formally, S-Workpiece has no more meaning than S-G10032. In common net formalisms, slot semantics are defined only implicitly through the inference code, in direct violation of the KR agenda of separating domain knowledge from processing strategy.

Inter-Frame Closure

A factory knowledge base will describe C-Workpiece as well as S-Workpiece, but the only connection available between these in many models is in pseudo-English slot names. S-Workpiece.Lathe should be more rigorously defined as the C-Workpiece associated with C-Lathe.

KRYPTON's role restrictions (Brachman *et al.* 1985) and KODIAK's MANIFEST operation (Wilensky 1984) address the inter-frame slot problem. For example, (MANIFEST C-Machine C-Tool) produces the concept "Tool-Of-Machine," so that C-

Machine gains a S-Tool slot pointing to the associated C-Tool. But the intra-frame closure problem remains. The same operation that produces *Tool-of-Machine = (MANIFEST C-Machine C-Tool)* also produces *Size-of-Machine = (MANIFEST C-Machine C-Size)* and *Action-of-Machine = (MANIFEST C-Machine C-Action).* Yet the relationship between C-Machine and its dependent concept in each of these cases is very different from the others.

TWO LINGUISTIC CONCEPTS

The linguistic concepts that suggest a solution to the closure problem are the distinction of nouns and verbs, and the grammatical theory of case.

The first concept simply observes that every known human language distinguishes nouns from verbs (Longacre 1976). Furthermore, natural languages universally distinguish three kinds of predication: statives (represented in English by adjectives and the verb "to be"), processes ("to become"), and actions ("to do," "to happen"). Any system that emulates human intelligence should mirror these distinctions.

The second concept, of verbal cases, is a sort of typing scheme for the arguments (nouns) of predicates (verbs) (Bruce 1975). Typical verbal cases include Agent, Object, Dative, Locative (From, To, At), Temporal, Material, Range, and Instrument. In the sentence "John hit the ball to Bill yesterday", "John" is the Agent, "the ball" is the Object, "Bill" is the Dative, and "yesterday" is Temporal. A restricted set of such cases (about 20 in most systems) suffices to define all the roles that nouns play toward verbs in a natural language. As a form of "slot" on low-level verbal concepts, cases were an inspiration for frames (Minsky 1974). This paper uses them to define slots for all concepts.

DEALING WITH ASYMMETRY

Early net systems treat nominal and verbal concepts symmetrically, with separate subsumption lattices for each (Quillian 1968; Hays 1973; Szolovits, Hawkinson, and Martin 1977). Modern net and hybrid formalisms are overbearingly noun-oriented in their representation of concepts. The ultimate root of modern subsumption lattices is typically "thing," forcing events to be nominalized if they are to be represented at all. Nodes representing events are typically named as gerunds, betraying their nominalization. KL-ONE and its descendents view concepts as playing "roles" instead of filling slots, further emphasizing that these concepts are construed as things.

Maintaining separate subsumption lattices for concepts derived from nouns and verbs respectively is consistent with the universal human distinction between such concepts. More pragmatically, it opens the way to define slot semantics within the system, by defining the slots in each lattice in terms of concepts in the other. Specifically, we let C-SummumGenus subsume C-Thing and C-Predication. C-Predication in turn subsumes C-Be for stative concepts, C-Become for process concepts, and C-Do for action concepts.

DEALING WITH LACK OF CLOSURE

Closing the definition of slots within a frame system requires addition of a third component, the *slot-maker*, to concepts and slots. In this section we discuss the general concept, then illustrate three kinds of slot-makers that we have found useful.

The Slot-Maker

A slot-maker maps two concepts to a slot, as does the MANIFEST operation in KODIAK (Wilensky 1984). The argument concepts are the parent and restriction of the slot, respectively. Some slot-makers require a third argument, defined below.

Having a slot-maker provides inter-frame closure. Having a set of slot-makers allows each to induce a distinct semantics on the slot created from its arguments, and thus provides intra-frame closure. So far, three kinds of slot-maker appear useful: one to define case slots, one to define conduct slots, and one to define component slots. In these descriptions, C-N(ominal) denotes some subset of C-Thing, and C-V(erbal) denotes some subset of C-Predication.

1. *(M-Case <case> C-V C-N)* defines slots of verbal concepts from nominal concepts, on the basis of linguistic cases. *C-V* is the parent of the slot, and *C-N* is its restriction. M-Case can be viewed as a set of slot-makers, one for each case. For example, (M-Case Agent C-Cut C-Thing) produces the slot that represents the agent of a cutting action as a thing. Each case has a distinctive semantics that it conveys to slots it defines.

2. *(M-Conduct C-N C-V <Slot of C-V>)* defines slots of nominal concepts from verbal concepts. *C-N* is the parent of the slot, and *C-V* is its restriction. For example, (M-Conduct C-Machine C-Cut S-Agent) produces the slot that describes a machine's cutting action. The third argument of M-Conduct tells what slot of the verbal concept the nominal concept occupies in performing the conduct. A nominal concept may have several conduct slots. Since stative predications of color and size are verbal concepts, (M-Conduct C-Machine C-Color S-Object) is the appropriate way to generate a slot to describe the color of a machine.

3. *(M-Part <aggregate concept> <component concept>)* describes a concept in terms of its component parts. The aggregate concept is the parent, and the component concept is the restriction. Nominal concepts can have nominal components, and verbal concepts can have verbal components.

Slot-makers close the universe of slots and concepts, but constitute a new component with respect to which the system remains open. The closure problem has moved up a level, not disappeared. Still, many problem domains need no more than M-Conduct, M-Part, and a dozen or so M-Case slot-makers. Few domains can be satisfied with this few primitive slots. Also, the slot-maker concept lets systems reason explicitly about the relation of slots to concepts, something that traditional architectures do not allow.

Case Slots

Case slots offer a natural mechanism for recording the interaction between the nominal and verbal semilattices. The M-Case slot-maker defines them in the first place:

```
S-Agent.Do =  (M-Case Agent C-Do C-Thing)
S-Instrument.Do = (M-Case Instrument C-Do C-Thing)
S-Object.Do = (M-Case Object C-Do C-Thing)
```

Beginning with these slots of C-Do, C-Cut is defined as a subclass of C-Do whose agent is a machine, whose instrument is a tool, and whose object is a part:

```
C-Cut      = (CMeet
                (CRestrict C-Do S-Agent C-Machine)
                (CMeet
                  (CRestrict C-Do S-Instrument C-Tool)
                  (CRestrict C-Do S-Object C-Part)))
```

Conduct Slots

Just as case slots of a verbal concept have nominal restrictions, conduct slots of a nominal concept have verbal restrictions. For instance, the slot on C-Lathe that describes its intended action is

```
S-Action.Lathe = (M-Conduct C-Lathe C-Cut S-Agent)
```

That is, a lathe's action is the cutting of which it is the agent.

Since S-Action.Lathe represents a verbal concept, it has its own case slots, which can relate C-Lathe to other nominal concepts. A slot on a nominal concept C-1 that refers to an instance of another nominal concept can be derived from a case slot of some conduct of C-1. Nominal concepts can be related to one another only by way of some predication (or by another slot-maker, such as M-Part).

For example, the lathe's workpiece slot S-Workpiece.Lathe is defined in terms of the S-Object case slot in S-Action.Lathe.

```
S-Workpiece.Lathe =
  λ x y. ∃ z.
   (S-Action.Lathe x z) & (S-Object.Cut z y)
```

This definition captures the semantics that a lathe's workpiece (**y**) is the object of some cutting action (**z**) performed by the lathe (**x**), thus achieving intra-frame closure. In general, if S-1 is a conduct slot of nominal concept C-N derived from verbal concept C-V, and S-2 is a case slot of C-V, a slot S-3 of C-N with a restriction in the nominal lattice can be defined

```
S-3 = λ x y. ∃ z. (S-1.N x z) & (S-2.V z y)
```

The conduct slot generated for C-Lathe (S-Action) is derived from the frame for C-Cut.

For each slot in C-Cut, C-Lathe now has an associated slot. The slots in C-Cut, in turn, are generated from the slots of C-Do by restriction relative to concepts in the nominal semilattice. As the system grows, slot definitions tend to "zig-zag" back and forth between the nominal and verbal semilattices. Among other mechanisms for specialization, verbal concepts specialize by taking more restricted nominal concepts as case slots, while nominal concepts specialize by taking more restricted verbal concepts as conduct slots.

Examples of Component Slots

Component slots describe an entity as a component of a larger aggregate. Such aggregation can be either temporal or spatial. Typically, verbal concepts aggregate temporally to form more complex verbal concepts, and nominal concepts aggregate spatially to form more complex spatial concepts. Examples of languages that can be used to describe aggregates include Allen 1983 for temporal structures and Eastman 1973 for spatial ones.

As an example, consider a verbal aggregate, C-Deliver. Intuitively, a delivery takes place when someone receives something from one party and later gives it to another party. With C-Deliver defined in this way,

```
S-Reception.Deliver = (M-Part C-Deliver C-Receive)
```

That is, the slot S-Reception of C-Deliver takes an instance of the concept C-Receive that is a part of the concept C-Deliver.

This construction assumes the formalization of C-Deliver. It is produced by an *aggregation function* that maps component concepts into a composite concept. Given this aggregation function (call it AF-Deliver),

```
C-Deliver = (AF-Deliver C-Receive C-Give)
```

Then the construction

```
S-Reception.Deliver = (M-Part C-Deliver C-Receive)
```

simply names the reception that is already built into the delivery.

The specific aggregation function in question is:

```
AF-Deliver =
λ m n.
 λ x. ∃ r ∈ m, g ∈ n, y, z, w, v.

  (S-Agent r v) & (S-Dative g w) & (v <> w) &          ;0
  (S-Agent x y) & (S-Dative r y) & (S-Agent g y) &     ;1
  (S-Object x z) & (S-Object r z) & (S-Object g z) &   ;2
  (S-Dative x w) &                                     ;3
  (Before r g)                                         ;4
```

The outer lambda binds `m` and `n` to the arguments of AF-Deliver, which are intended to be concepts of receiving and of giving, respectively. When these are bound, the value of AF-Deliver is the inner lambda, which is a predicate on `x`. The existentially quantified variables in this inner lambda represent an instance of receiving and giving (**r** and **g**, respectively), and four others used in clauses 1-4 to relate the concepts of the aggregate. Clause 0 insures that the source and destination of the delivery are not the same. Clause 1 constrains the agent of C-Deliver to be the same as the dative (recipient) of the component action of reception **r** and also the agent of the component action of giving **g**. Clause 2 identifies the object delivered with that both received and given by the deliverer. Clause 3 identifies the recipient of the delivery with the recipient of the component giving action. Clause 4 constrains the reception component of the delivery to take place before the giving component.

There are countably infinitely many aggregation functions, each typically useful for defining only one or a small family of composite concepts. AF-Deliver, for example, is only defined when its arguments are verbal concepts with case slots for datives, objects, and agents. The aggregation function makes the composition of an aggregate concept from its elements explicit, so that the M-Part slot-maker can name these components in relation to the aggregate.

CONCLUSION

Ontologies with separate subsumption lattices for nominal and verbal concepts permit the closure of slot semantics. A generalization of the linguistic notion of case permits definition of the slots in each branch of the ontology by reference to concepts in the other branch. Slots of verbal concepts are derived from linguistic cases, restricted by nominal concepts. Slots of nominal concepts include conduct slots restricted by verbal concepts; derivatives of the case slots of the verbal concepts defining a conduct slot, restricted by nominal concepts; and components of aggregate concepts.

The programs of the Industrial Technology Institute are partially supported by the W.K. Kellogg Foundation.

REFERENCES

Brachman, R.J. (1983). "What IS-A Is and Isn't: An Analysis of Taxonomic Links in Semantic Networks." *IEEE Computer* **16**, 30-36.

Brachman, R.J.; Fikes, R.E.; & Levesque, H.J. (1985). "KRYPTON: A Functional Approach to Knowledge Representation." In Brachman and Levesque, eds., *Readings in Knowledge Representation* (Los Altos: Morgan Kaufmann), 411-430.

Bruce, B. (1975). "Case Systems for Natural Language." *Artificial Intelligence* **6**, 327-360.

Hayes, P.J. (1979). "The Logic of Frames." in D. Metzing, ed., *Frame Conceptions and Text Understanding*, Berlin: Walter de Gruyter, 46-61.

Hays, D.G. (1973). "Types of Processes on Cognitive Networks." *International Conference on Computational Linguistics*, Pisa, Italy, 523-532.

Longacre, R.E. (1976). *An Anatomy of Speech Notions*. Lisse: Peter de Ridder.

Minsky, M. (1974). "A Framework for Representing Knowledge." MIT AI Memo No.

306.

Quillian, M.R. (1968). "Semantic Memory." in M. Minsky, *Semantic Information Processing*, Cambridge: MIT Press, 227-270.

Szolovits, P.; Hawkinson, L.B.; & Martin, W.A. (1977). "An Overview of OWL." MIT/LCS/TM-86, Cambridge, MA.

Vilain, M. (1985). "The Restricted Language Architecture of a Hybrid Representation System." *IJCAI-85* **9**, 547-551.

Wilensky, R. (1984). "Knowledge Representation--A Critique and A Proposal." *Proceedings of the First Annual Workshop on Theoretical Issues in Conceptual Information Processing*, Atlanta.

Woods, W.A. (1975). "What's in a Link: Foundations for Semantic Networks," in Bobrow, D.G. and A. Collins, *Representation and Understanding: Studies in Cognitive Science* (New York: Academic Press) 35-82.

Parsing and Representing Container Metaphors

R. Pascale
J. W. Roach
R. S. Virkar

Department of Computer Science
Virginia Polytechnic Institute and State University
Blacksburg, VA 24061

Abstract

We report the successful construction of a pattern based parser to recognize the class of container metaphors. Recognition of a metaphor in this class triggers a transformation that substitutes a correct, literal meaning form in the final representation of the utterance or sentence. The final meaning form reflects a theory of metaphors suggesting bodily experiences as the source of metaphor. A large set of primitives serves as the basic representation language. We conclude that pattern parsers with attached transformations work well for many normally difficult constructions such as metaphors, cliches and idioms.

I. Introduction

The frequency of metaphors in natural language has been reported to be as high as one in three utterances while some report occurrences in almost every utterance (Lakoff & Johnson, 1980). Recognizing, parsing and representing the meaning of a metaphor is therefore a major problem for any natural language parser.

Transformational syntactic parsers have little relevance to the problem, syntactic patterns of metaphors are not special, and normal methods of semantic analysis have not really found a method for determining the "real" meaning of a metaphor from its literal meaning. Syntactic patterns such as noun phrases, verb phrases and prepositional phrases do not allow a parser to distinguish between metaphorical and non-metaphorical uses of words. However, a parser that uses patterns of semantic primitives can detect whether or not a concept is used in its literal sense. The non-literal senses can thus be categorized as metaphorical.

In this paper, we present a parser based on patterns of primitives that can recognize and parse a class of metaphors known as container metaphors ("John is in love," for example). We also devise a means to represent the meaning of container metaphors appropriately.

II. What Are Metaphors?

By a metaphor we mean any non-literal use of a word or words. People normally use metaphors to express less concrete, less clear concepts, such as mental or emotional states, in terms of tangible concepts that are more easily visualized because of bodily experiences. The assimilation of concrete attributes by an abstract concept, however, must be only a partial structuring. A total assimilation of concrete properties would turn the abstract concept into a subcategory of a concrete object.

Metaphors tend to be cohesive. Orientational metaphors, for example, use direction and position in a (mostly) consistent manner to express meaning. "Down" metaphors have to do with lesser things or unhappy states while "up" metaphors refer to power and greater, happier concepts.

Metaphors such as orientational metaphors have their genesis in our culture and our experiences in the world. The fundamental theory we employ here, due to Lakoff and Johnson (1980), suggests that bodily experiences, for example, are responsible for the origin of metaphors. "Up is good" and "down is bad" then would derive from standing tall when we are happy and slouching when we are depressed. Being "in love" is having love surround and engulf our thoughts.

Lakoff and Johnson (1980) classify metaphors into four categories: orientational, structural, ontological and imaginative. Ontological metaphors express events, activities, emotions and other abstract concepts as entities and substances. An example of this category of metaphors is "mind is a machine." This metaphor gives rise to sentences such as "I am a little rusty today," and "My mind just isn't operating today." This type of metaphor implies that an abstract object and some other object to which it is being compared have the same qualities.

The ontological metaphors serve the purposes of referring (e.g. "That was a beautiful catch"), quantifying (e.g. "Dupont has a lot of power in Delaware"), identifying aspects (e.g. "The brutality of war dehumanizes us all"), identifying causes (e.g. "He did it out of anger"), and setting goals and motivating actions (e.g. "He went to New York to seek fame and fortune"). There are many sub-classes of ontological metaphors. These sub-classes are container metaphors, personifications and metonymy.

In the sub-class of container metaphors, each concept has an in-out orientation, bounding surface, container object, substance and other qualities. Some of these are land areas (e.g. "There is a lot of land in Kansas"), visual field (e.g. "He is in my view") and states (e.g. "He is in love"). In the sub-class of personifications inanimate objects are allowed to possess human qualities. An example of such a metaphor is "The feather was dancing in the wind." The feather (an inanimate entity) is given the human quality of dancing. The sub-class of metonymy is similar to personifications, however, in metonymy one entity is substituted for another. An example of such a metaphor is "The sax is out sick today." Here, the sax actually refers to the person who plays the saxophone.

In this paper, we shall concentrate on the container metaphors. Container metaphors are often used by people without fully being aware of the non-literal sense of the words. Examples of this sub-class are abundant in written text as well as spoken language.

III. Pattern-based Parsing

The use of a pattern-based approach for parsing natural language input was first exploited on a large scale by Parkison, Colby and Faught (1977). Their approach entailed matching pieces of input to elements of a large base of prestored patterns, and successful matches resulting in changes in the original sentence such as simplification and replacements. It has been shown since that purely syntactic means are not sufficient to relate meaning to utterances (Gross, 1979). We have already used pattern-based parsing approach in conjunction with semantic primitives (Virkar & Roach, 1988a, 1988b; Sanford & Roach, 1988). Now, we shall describe our approach for metaphors.

Linguistic expressions are generated from the lexicon and we hypothesize that most of the every-day lexicon can be represented by a large, yet finite, number of semantic primitives. Sentence forms can be classified by the patterning of semantic primitives and function words. We hypothesize that all simple sentence forms can be captured by a very large, yet finite, set of patterns.

A semantic primitive represents a set of words that refer to the same concept. Concepts interact with each other and these relationships are seen through the expressions of natural language. Our classification has four basic classes of semantic primitives: events, entities, abstracts and relationals. A meaningful expression is an expression that describes an event with the help of other associated basic classes. To describe an event, one or more of these associated elements may not be required. A meaningful expression cannot be anomalous, indeterminable, nor contradictory (Allan, 1986).

If we denote the set of all semantic primitives by P. Then, P^+ denotes the set of all sequences, of length ≥ 1, of semantic primitives. The language L, the set of all meaningful expressions, can now be viewed as a subset of the set of all possible sequences derived from P. In other words, $L \subset P^+$. Natural language understanding can now be defined as a mapping, U, that translates all meaningful expressions in L onto the set of sentence meaning structures, S; i.e., $U: L \rightarrow S$.

We use semantic mappings to translate an utterance, based on its semantic pattern, into a possible interpretation. Mappings use axioms to eliminate the incorrect interpretations of an utterance. We say that a function word is a word that, in its position in the utterance, signals the beginning of a new (possibly primitive) meaningful expression. The set of function words F contains logical connectives such as 'and' and 'or', and prepositions such as 'for', 'of', etc. It is also important to note that two meaningful expressions can be connected without the presence of a function word when one expression is embedded in another in a subordinate fashion.

A primitive utterance is a sentence that conveys only one "meaningful expression" in a language. We shall call it a primitive meaningful expression. A complex utterance, on the other hand, is a sentence that expresses two or more (related) meaningful expressions connected by one or more function words. A simple complex utterance is one that has two primitive meaningful expressions connected by one function word. Hence, by recognizing the function word, the two expressions can be transformed into two primitive meaningful expressions.

A semantic transformation can be defined as the process of decomposing a complex utterance into two primitive meaningful expressions using the function word appearing in the complex utterance, without altering the 'meaning' expressed by the original complex utterance. It should be noted, however, that several semantic transformations may exist for a given function word, and the one that is applied is selected based on the semantic pattern of the sentence. It should also be noted that a semantic transformation on an utterance that does not contain any function words is equivalent to applying a semantic mapping.

It is possible that after applying a semantic transformation, one or both of the resulting sentences will be complex. This can occur only in the presence of more function words. These function words can now be used to apply other semantic transformations and further reduce the sentences. Since every execution of a semantic transformation reduces the complexity of the sentence, a finite number of semantic transformations guarantees convergence to primitive sentences.

IV. Representation

In the previous section we have described the basic steps in the working of the parser. We acknowledged that multiple interpretations exist for words within the context of an utterance. The problem of resolving these ambiguities becomes evident in the treatment of metaphors.

The representation language we use is based on a set of semantic primitives. This set has been adapted from a linguistic effort (Nida, 1975) of developing a thesaurus. The parsing of an utterance produces a meaning form consisting of a many-sorted representation. This representation involves the event and other components, namely entities, relationals and abstracts.

In the case of container metaphors, the containing object is not physically (or spatially) containing some other object. Thus, a relational form such as

SPATIAL :: < object1 > < object2 >

is improper and hence must be discarded. If the containing concept is an emotion, then the parser should represent the affecting state of experience. If the containing concept is an activity or a state of affairs, then the parser should show the involvement. Similarly, if the containing concept is a class of objects, then the parser should represent the membership. Based on the type of the container metaphor our parser produces a representation that conveys appropriate meaning.

A container metaphor involving 'time' allows expressions such as 'in an hour' and 'in seconds'; and our representation scheme produces

{ Event X } :- Abstract (DURATION 1 hour)
{ Event X } :- Abstract quickly

respectively. Thus, the container-like use of time is deciphered correctly where time is actually an abstract primitive that describes the duration of events.

A container metaphor involving social groups allows expressions such as 'in a fraternity' and 'in computer science'; parsing of such metaphorical expressions results in

Membership :: < Entity Y > < Social Group fraternity >
Membership :: < Entity Y > < Profession comp sci >

respectively. The groups expressed as containers can be represented by using the membership relational.

A container metaphor involving emotional states provides expressions such as 'in love' and 'in pain.' The representation scheme we employ produces the following form for such expressions

Experience State love [< Entity Y >]

Thus, the container-like use of experiential states can be represented by states of entities.

A container metaphor with activities and events gives rise to expressions such as 'in the race' and 'in Watergate.' Our representation scheme generates the following form for these expressions

Involvement :: < Entity X > < Event race >

Involvement is a relational that captures emotional, physical as well as conceptual entanglement. Our scheme represents it appropriately and the event, used as a container, is shown to involve the entity X. It should be noted that this Involvement relational has nothing in common with the constraint relation defined by Barwise and Perry in situation semantics (Barwise & Perry, 1983).

Our representation scheme is based on four classes of semantic primitives. This allows it to differentiate between different types of container metaphors. As can be seen from the examples above, the trigger word for the container metaphors, "in", can relate an entity to an affecting relational, an affecting event, or an affecting abstract.

V. Results

We found that there was a one-to-one correspondence between sub-classes of container metaphors and transformation rules. Every container metaphor that we could figure out was correctly parsed by the rules we constructed. We identified fifteen sub-classes of container metaphors and added transformation rules for these sub-classes. These transformation rules can parse a large number of sentences with container metaphors. The rules we constructed are based on patterns of semantic primitives, and as such, each rule accounts for all utterances that fit the pattern associated with that rule.

Obviously, we cannot guarantee completeness of the rules, but for any example not covered by the rule, there will be no difficulty adding a pattern and its associated transformation to the rule base. Table 1 contains a sampling of the sentences that our system can handle.

VI. Discussion

The system we have built is one of the few computational linguistics systems to take prepositions seriously. By that we mean that our system can parse a very large number of word senses (captured as patterns) for each preposition. The only other previous system to our knowledge to work seriously with prepositions studied only the word 'for' (Hemphill, 1981). No previous system, for example, has attempted to capture over one hundred senses for the word 'over' (data source: Brugman, 1981) or any of the other prepositions. In fact, few systems have really attempted to deal with the polysemy problem at all. Most of our data for the voluminous number of prepositional word senses comes from Hill (1968). Our system derives its power to recognize metaphors precisely from this ability to account for the numerous senses of prepositions. To the extent that metaphorical use of language can be associated with prepositional phrases, our system can handle metaphors.

Container metaphors account for only one set of preposition triggered metaphorical phrases; we expect to extend our work to other prepositional metaphorical phrases. We hypothesize that pattern based parsers based on a large set of primitives and designed to help solve the polysemy problem will help solve the metaphor recognition problem. Solving the metaphor representation problem, of course, requires a theoretical stance, such as the one put forth in Lakoff and Johnson (1980).

VII. Conclusions

This paper has presented a parsing technique based on patterns of primitives that can recognize and parse metaphorical container phrases. The representation techniques used here reflect a theory of metaphors that requires metaphorical expressions to originate in bodily experiences. Experiments with the system indicate excellent results for the class of metaphors that were the target. Extensibility of the parsing techniques depends on the applicability of pattern based parsing to the recognition of metaphorical structures. We hypothesize that a large set of metaphorical structures can be parsed using pattern based techniques.

References

Allan, K. 1986. Linguistic Meaning: Vol. 1. New York: Routledge and Kegan Paul.

Barwise, J. and Perry, J. 1983. Situations and Attitudes. Cambridge, Massachusetts: The MIT Press.

Brugman, C. 1981. "Story of Over," Master's Thesis, University of California, Berkeley.

Gross, M. 1979. "On the Failure of Generative Grammar," Language, vol. 55, no. 4, pp. 859-885.

Hemphill, L. G. 1981. "A Conceptual Approach to Automated Language Understanding and Belief Structures: With Disambiguation of the word 'For',"Dissertation submitted to the Department of Computer Science, Stanford University.

Hill, L. A. 1968. Prepositions and Adverbial Particles. London: Oxford University Press.

Lakoff, G. and M. Johnson. 1980. Metaphors We Live By. Chicago: The University of Chicago Press.

Nida, E. A. 1975. Componential Analysis of Meaning: An Introduction to Semantic Structures. The Hague: Moulton.

Parkison, R. C., K. M. Colby and W. S. Faught. 1977. "Conversational Language Comprehension Using Integrated Pattern-Matching and Parsing," Artificial Intelligence Journal, vol. 9, no. 2, pp. 111-134.

Sanford, D. L. and J. W. Roach. 1988. "A Theory of Dialogue Structures to Help Manage Human-Computer Interaction," IEEE Transactions on Systems, Man and Cybernetics- Special Issue on Human-Computer Interaction and Cognitive Engineering, vol. 18, no. 4 (July/August), pp. 567-574.

Virkar, R. S. and J. W. Roach. 1988a. "Pattern-Based Parsing for Word Sense Disambiguation," Proceedings of The Tenth Annual Conference of the Cognitive Science Society, pp 688-694.

Virkar, R. S. and J. W. Roach. 1988b. "Direct Assimilation of Expert-Level Knowledge by Automatically Understanding Research Paper Abstracts," International Journal of Expert Systems, vol. 1, no. 4, pp. 281-305.

Table1. Expressions classified by what is being metaphorically represented

1. TIME
    a. She ran the mile in five minutes.
        RUSH-MOTION [{<PERSON>}:- DISTANCE
            {<PERSON>}:- DURATION]

2. EMOTION
    a. Fred is in love.
        EXPERIENCE STATE love [<PERSON>]

    b. She is in a panic.
        EXPERIENCE STATE panic [<PERSON>]

3. GEOGRAPHICAL AREAS
    a. The dog is in the field.
        POSITION:: [<ANIMAL> <PLACE field>]

    b. The tree is in the yard.
        POSITION:: [<PLANT> <PLACE yard>]

    c. The house is in Delaware.
        POSITION:: [<DWELLING> <PLACE Delaware>]

4. SOCIAL GROUPS
    a. He is in a fraternity.
        MEMBERSHIP:: [<PERSON> <SOCIAL GROUP fraternity>]

    b. She is in biology.
        MEMBERSHIP:: [<PERSON> <PROFESSION biology>]

5. EVENTS and ACTIVITES
    a. He was in Watergate.
        INVOLVEMENT:: [<PERSON> <EVENT Watergate>]

    b. She is in the race.
        INVOLVEMENT:: [<PERSON> <EVENT race>]

The Influence of Prior Theories on the Ease of Concept Acquisition

Michael J. Pazzani & David Schulenburg
Department of Information and Computer Science
University of California, Irvine

Abstract

The finding that conjunctive concepts are easier for human subjects to learn than disjunctive concepts is reported in most introductory books on cognitive psychology. In this paper, we report some conditions under which this finding may not be true. In particular, we demonstrate that the prior causal knowledge of subjects can influence the rate of concept learning. We report on an experiment that indicates that disjunctive concepts which are consistent with prior knowledge take fewer trials to learn than conjunctive concepts which are not consistent with prior knowledge. We present a computer model of this learning task.

Introduction

In concept identification tasks, it has been found that conjunctive concepts require fewer trials to learn than disjunctive concepts (Bruner, Goodnow, & Austin, 1956). More recently, it has been suggested (e.g., Murphy & Medin, 1985; Schank, Collins, & Hunter, 1986; Pazzani, in press) that a person's prior knowledge influences the speed or accuracy of learning. These claims are in part responsible for interest in explanation-based approaches to learning (DeJong & Mooney, 1986). More recently, a number of experiments have shown that with proper background knowledge people are capable of the single-instance generalization predicted by explanation-based learning (Ahn, Mooney, Brewer, & DeJong, 1987).

In this paper, we explore the interaction between the prior knowledge and the logical form of concepts. We first present an experiment in which these factors interact. Then, we present a computer model of this learning task.

Ease of Concept Acquisition: An Experiment

The purpose of this experiment was to investigate the interaction between prior knowledge and the acquisition of conjunctive and disjunctive concepts. Subjects were divided into two groups. The *Inflate* group had to perform a prediction task. This group observed photographs of a person and a balloon and had to learn to predict under which conditions a balloon could successfully be inflated. The second group, *Alpha,* used the same materials, but had a concept identification task that required learning which photographs belonged to a category called "alpha." These groups were then divided into conjunctive and disjunctive groups. The conjunction to be learned was that a balloon whose size is small <u>and</u> whose color is yellow was an alpha (or could be inflated). The disjunction to be learned was that a person whose age is adult <u>or</u> a person who is stretching a balloon is an alpha (or could inflate the balloon). Note that for the prediction task, the conjunctive concept is not consistent with prior knowledge while the disjunctive concept is. It is also important to stress that the prior background knowledge[1] (e.g., adults are stronger than children, stretching a balloon makes it easier to inflate) is not sufficient for subjects to deduce the

1. In a prior experiment (Pazzani, 1987), we asked subjects a series of True-False question about which balloons are easier to inflate. Almost all subjects indicated that adults could inflate balloons more easily than children and that a balloon that had been stretched was easier to inflate. Subjects also indicated that the color of a balloon, or dipping a balloon in water did not affect the ease of inflation. Some subjects also responded that long skinny balloons were harder to inflate than round balloons.

correct relationship in the absence of any data. There are a number of possible consistent relationships including a conjunctive one (adults can only inflate balloons that have been stretched).

The *Alpha* subjects serve as a control group to rule out the possibility that age and stretching are more salient than color and size. In a previous experiment (Pazzani, 1987), we have shown that for single attribute discriminations (e.g., action = stretching), prior background knowledge does not affect the concept identification task but does affect the prediction task. Subjects in this prior experiment took approximately the same number of trials to learn that a photograph of a person stretching a balloon was an alpha as to learn that a photograph of a person measuring a balloon with a ruler is an alpha. However, subjects required fewer trials to learn that a person could inflate a balloon that had been stretched than to learn than a person could inflate a balloon that had been measured.

We made the following predictions about the outcome of the experiments.

- Subjects in the *Alpha* conjunction category would take fewer trials than subjects in the *Alpha* disjunction category. (Conjunctions are easier to learn than disjunctions.)
- Subjects in the *Inflate* disjunction category would take fewer trials than those in the *Inflate* conjunction category. (Consistent concepts are easier to learn than inconsistent concepts.)
- Subjects in the *Inflate* disjunction category would take fewer trials than those in the *Alpha* disjunction category. (Prior knowledge facilitates learning.)

Subjects. The subjects were 88 male and female undergraduates attending the University of California, Irvine who participated in this experiment to receive extra credit in an introductory psychology course. Each subject was tested individually. Subjects were randomly assigned to one of the four conditions.

Stimuli. The stimuli consisted of pages from a photo album. Each page consisted of a close-up photograph of a balloon which varied in color (yellow or purple) and size (small or large) and a photograph of a person (either an adult or a 5 year-old child) doing something to the balloon (either dipping it in water or stretching it). For the *Inflate* subjects, the back of the page of the photo album had a picture of the person with a balloon that had been inflated or a balloon that had not been inflated. For the alpha subject, a card with the words "Alpha" or "Not Alpha" was on the reverse side of each page.

Procedures. Subjects were shown a page from the photo album and asked to make a prediction (or classification). Then the card was turned over and the subject saw the correct answer. Then the subject was presented with another card. This process was repeated until the subjects were able to predict or classify correctly on 6 consecutive trials. We recorded the number of the last trial on which the subject made an error. The pages were presented in a random order, subject to the constraint that the first page was always a positive example. If the subject exhausted all pages, the process was repeated until the correct answer was made or until 50 cards were presented. If the subject did not obtain the correct answer after 50 trials, we recorded this as the last error being made on trial 50.

Results. The results of this experiment (see Figure 1) confirmed our predictions. Figure 1 clearly illustrates that the task of learning a predictive relationship is influenced by prior theory. This effect is so strong, that it dominates the well-known finding that conjunctive concepts are easier to learn than disjunctive concepts. The interaction between the learning task and the concept to be acquired is significant at the 0.01 level $F(3,84) = 22.07$. However, the overall effect of either variable is not significant.

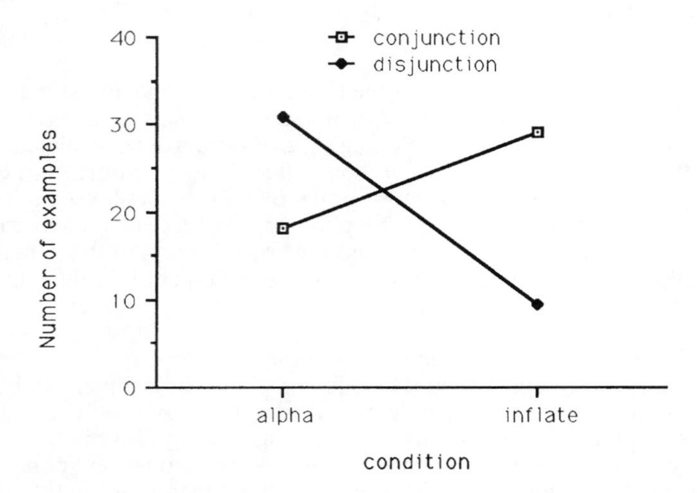

Figure 1. The ease of acquiring predictive (inflate) and descriptive (alpha) concepts. The disjunctive relationship is consistent with prior knowledge on the ease of inflating balloons, while the conjunctive relationship violates these beliefs.

Analysis of the data with a Scheffe´ test confirmed our three predictions (the results are significant at the 0.05 level):

- The *Alpha* conjunction category required significantly fewer trials than the *Alpha* disjunction category (18.0 vs. 30.8).
- The *Inflate* disjunction category required significantly fewer trials than the *Inflate* conjunction category (9.4 vs 29.1).
- The *Inflate* disjunction category required significantly fewer trials than the *Alpha* disjunction category (9.4 vs 30.8).

Discussion . The findings are consistent with our previous finding that concepts consistent with prior knowledge require fewer examples to learn accurately than concepts that are not consistent with prior knowledge. The result is especially important since it demonstrates that prior knowledge dominates the commonly accepted view that disjunctive concepts are more difficult to learn than conjunctive concepts. The result of the classification task with the same stimuli rules out an alternative explanation for these findings based on cue salience (Bower & Trabasso, 1968). This experiment raises important issues for empirical learning methods including neural network models (Rumelhart, Hinton, & Williams, 1986). The learning rules of purely empirical methods do not take the prior knowledge of the learner into account.

The experiment also points out inadequacies of current explanation-based methods (e.g., Mitchell, Kedar-Cabelli, & Keller, 1986) that assume that the background theory is sufficiently strong to prove why a particular outcome occurred. Purely explanation-based approaches to learning predict that subjects would be capable of learning from a single example. The background knowledge of our subjects seems to be able to identify what factors of the situation *might* influence the outcome of an attempt to inflate a balloon. However, they needed a number of examples to determine which of these factors were relevant and whether the factors were necessary or sufficient. In the next section, we discuss a method of integrating empirical and explanation-based learning that makes use of this weaker sort of domain knowledge.

Explanation-based Learning with Weak Theories of Tendencies

Much knowledge about the world does not consist of universally true generalizations (Mackie, 1974; Goodman, 1983). Instead, it consists of less certain *ceteris paribus* generalizations of tendencies that occur in the absence of other factors. Research in cognitive psychology has demonstrated that prior background knowledge influences the rate or accuracy of learning. However, computational models of learning that make use of prior knowledge have for the most part assumed that this background knowledge consists of universally true generalizations. Here we relax this assumption by considering that background knowledge consists of tendencies or influences.[2] We have constructed a learning system called POSTHOC that uses this sort of background knowledge to propose hypotheses that are then tested against further data. This background knowledge is also used to revise hypotheses that fail to make accurate predictions. POSTHOC is also capable of performing classification tasks for which its background knowledge is irrelevant.

To model the previous experiment, the following two influences are used as background knowledge:

```
(easier (strong-actor)  (inflate balloon))
(easier (less-elastic)  (inflate balloon))
```

An example in POSTHOC consists of a set of attributes and an outcome. For example, an adult successfully inflating a small yellow balloon that had been stretched is represented as:[3]

```
((size . small) (color . yellow) (age . adult) (act . stretch)) =>
   (inflate balloon)
```

and a small purple balloon that had been dipped in water by a child that is classified as a *not alpha* is represented as:

```
((size . small) (color . purple) (age . child) (act . dip)) =>
   (not alpha)
```

In addition, POSTHOC has a set of inference rules that indicate which features used to describe an example are needed to identify when an influence is present in an example. The following inference rules are used to model the results of the previous experiment:

```
(influence (act . stretch)  (less-elastic))

(influence (old-actor) (strong-actor))
(influence (age . adult) (old-actor))
```

These rules state that stretching a balloon tends to make it less elastic; that older actors tend to be stronger actors; and that adults are old.

POSTHOC maintains a single hypothesis that consists of a disjunction of conjunctions. For example, the following represents the hypothesis that adults can inflate any balloon, or children

2. In Pazzani (in press), we consider how this sort of knowledge might be acquired.

3. This representation of the potentially salient features of an example is admittedly over simplistic. Here, we concentrate on the processes of learning and this simple uniform representation facilitates the implementation of the empirical learning component of POSTHOC at the expense of over-simplifying the representation of background knowledge.

can inflate a yellow balloon:

```
( ((age . adult))  ((age . child)(color . yellow)) ) =>
   (inflate balloon)
```

When the current hypothesis makes an error, a set of rules examine the hypothesis and the incorrectly classified example, and revises the hypothesis. Thus, POSTHOC is an incremental hill-climbing model of human learning of the type advocated in (Langley, Gennari, & Iba, 1987).

There are three sets of rules. One set deals with errors of commission in which a positive example is falsely classified as a negative example. This rule set makes the hypothesis more general. The second rule set deals with errors of omission in which a negative example is falsely classified as a positive example. This rule set makes the hypothesis more specific. The final rule set creates an initial hypothesis when the first positive example is encountered. Within each rule set, the rules are ordered by priority. The rule sets in POSTHOC are:

Initializing Hypothesis:

```
1.    IF there is an influence that is present in the example
      THEN initialize the hypothesis to a single conjunct
      representing the features of that influence.

2.    IF TRUE
      THEN initialize the hypothesis to a conjunction of all
      features of the initial example.
```

The first rule determines if there are features of the example that would influence the outcome of a positive example. This is accomplished by chaining backward from the rules that indicate that a certain outcome (e.g., inflating a balloon) is easier under certain conditions. The conditions are verified by chaining backward via influence rules to find features that are indicative of an influence. For example, if the initial positive example is an adult successfully inflating a small yellow balloon that had been stretched, POSTHOC would try to establish that the strength of the actor is an influential factor. This can be established by showing that the actor is strong. The fact that the actor is strong can be verified because the example indicates that the actor is adult. The initial hypothesis is that adults can inflate balloons. In this example, since there is more than one influence present, one is selected at random. This is true of all of the rules in all of the rule sets. The second rule in this rule set initializes the hypothesis to the first positive example. This occurs if there are no influences present that would account for outcome. This is true for the classification task because there are no rules that indicate factors that influence whether or not something is classified as an alpha. This can also occur for the prediction task if no influence predicted by prior knowledge is present in a positive example.

Errors of Omission

```
1.    IF the hypothesis was formed with background knowledge
      AND there are features that indicate an additional influence
      THEN create a new conjunct of the features indicative of the
      influence.

2.    IF the hypothesis is a single conjunct
      AND a feature of the conjunct is not in the example
      AND the conjunct consists of more than one feature
      THEN drop the feature from the conjunct
```

```
3.      IF TRUE
        THEN add a new conjunct consisting of a random feature from
        the example and simplify the hypothesis.
```

The first rule applies only if the current hypothesis is consistent with prior knowledge and the features of the example indicate the presence of an additional factor. This additional factor is assumed to be a multiple sufficient cause (cf. Kelley (1971)) and a new conjunct is added. This rule would add a second conjunct `(act . stretch)` to the hypothesis `(age . adult)` if an example of a child inflating a balloon that had been stretched is encountered. The new hypothesis indicates that adults can inflate a balloon or anyone can inflate a balloon that has been stretched.

The second rule is a variant of the wholist strategy in (Bruner, et al., 1956) that drops a single feature rather than all features that differ between the misclassified example and the hypothesis. In case of ties, one is selected at random. Subjects in the Alpha group of the experiment learned conjunctive concepts more slowly than the wholist strategy would predict.

The final rule forms an additional conjunct from a random feature of the example when hypotheses consistent with background knowledge and conjunctive hypotheses have been ruled out. The simplification of the hypothesis affects the form of the hypothesis to make it more concise and understandable but does not affect the rate or accuracy of the hypothesis. It consists of a number of simplification rules (e.g., `X or XY <=> X`).

Errors of Commission

```
1.      IF the  hypothesis was formed with background knowledge
        AND for each true conjunct there are features not present in
        the current example that would be necessary for an influence
        THEN modify the conjuncts by adding the additional features
        that are indicative of the influence.

2.      IF TRUE
        THEN specialize each true conjunct of the hypothesis by
        adding the inverse of a feature of the example that is not in
        the conjunct and simplify.
```

The first rule adds a multiple necessary cause to the hypothesis (Kelley, 1971). For example, if the hypothesis is that all adults can inflate balloons, an error will occur on an example of an adult not inflating a large yellow balloon that has been dipped in water. The hypothesis is modified by finding an additional factor which could affect the outcome that is not present in the example (stretching the balloon) and asserting that this is necessary to inflate the balloon. The new hypothesis consists of a single conjunct that represents the prediction that adults can only inflate balloon that have been stretched.

The second rule specializes a hypothesis by adding additional features to each true conjunct. For example, if the hypothesis were yellow balloons or purple balloons that had been dipped in water are alphas:

```
( ((color . yellow))  ((color . purple) (act . dip)) ) =>
   alpha
```

and the following example is encountered:

```
((size . small) (color . yellow) (age . child) (act . dip)) =>
   (not alpha)
```

then the example will be falsely classified as an alpha because `(color . yellow)` is true.

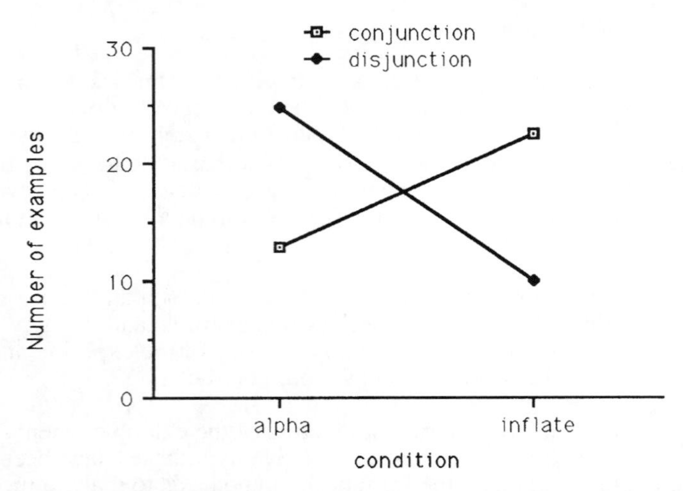

Figure 2. The result of a computer simulation of the learning experiment.

This hypothesis is modified by finding the inverse of a feature of the example (e.g., size) and asserting that this is necessary when the color is yellow. If this change turns out to be incorrect, later examples will force further revision of the hypothesis.

```
( ((color . yellow)(size . large)) ((color . purple)(act . dip)) )
   => alpha
```

Results

We ran 200 trials of the POSTHOC on each of the four conditions from the experiment. The results of this simulation are shown in Figure 2. Analysis of the data from this simulation confirms the same three predictions from the human learning experiment. In the absence of prior knowledge, conjunctions are easier to learn than disjunctions, concepts consistent with background knowledge are easier to learn than concepts that violate prior knowledge, and prior knowledge facilitates learning. Inconsistent conjunctive concepts (e.g., only small yellow balloons can be inflated) are more difficult for POSTHOC to acquire because the initial hypothesis typically includes a number of irrelevant attributes (e.g., `(age . adult))` predicted to be relevant by the weak domain theory. These irrelevant attributes are incrementally dropped from the hypothesis when they cause errors.

Conclusions

We have presented experimental evidence that prior knowledge influences the ease of concept acquisition. This experiment suggests additional experiments which we are in the process of running. Our model predicts that consistent conjunctive concepts are easier to acquire than inconsistent conjunctive concepts or inconsistent disjunctive concepts. In addition, if there are redundant relevant cues (Bower & Trabasso, 1968), our model predicts that subjects will attend to features consistent with their prior knowledge. Initial results on these experiments appear to confirm these predictions. A computer model of this task has practical applications as well since it extends the capabilities of explanation-based learning systems to deal with weaker domain theories by including an empirical component to test and revise hypotheses.

Acknowledgements

Comments by Caroline Ehrlich on an earlier draft of this paper were helpful in improving the presentation. Discussions with Ed Wisniewski helped develop some of the ideas in the paper. This research is supported in part by a Faculty Research Grant from the University of California, Irvine.

Bibliography

Ahn, W., Mooney, R., Brewer, W., & DeJong, G. (1987). Schema acquisition from one example: Psychological evidence for explanation-based learning. *Proceedings of the Ninth Annual Conference of the Cognitive Science Society.* Seattle, WA: Lawrence Erlbaum Associates.

Bower, G., & Trabasso, T. (1968). *Attention in learning: Theory and research.* New York: John Wiley and Sons.

Bruner, J.S., Goodnow, J.J., & Austin, G.A. (1956). *A study of thinking.* New York: John Wiley and Sons.

DeJong, G. & Mooney, R., (1986). Explanation-based learning: An alternate view. *Machine Learning, 1,* 145-176.

Goodman, N. (1983). *Fact, fiction and forecast, (4th ed.).* Cambridge, MA: Harvard University Press.

Kelley, Harold H. (1971). Causal schemata and the attribution process. In E. Jones, D. Kanouse, H. Kelley, N. Nisbett, S. Valins & B. Weiner (Eds.), *Attribution: Perceiving the causes of behavior.* Morristown, NJ: General Learning Press.

Langley, P., Gennari, J., & Iba, W., (1987). Hill climbing theories of learning. *Proceedings of the Fourth International Machine Learning Workshop.* Irvine, CA: Morgan Kaufmann.

Mackie, J. (1974). *The cement of the universe: A study of causation.* Clarendon Press: Oxford.

Mitchell, T., Kedar-Cabelli, S., & Keller, R. (1986). Explanation-based learning: A unifying view. *Machine Learning, 1,* 47-80.

Murphy, G. & Medin, D. (1985). The role of theories in conceptual coherence. *Psychology Review, 92,* 289-316.

Pazzani, M. (1987). Inducing causal and social theories: A prerequisite for explanation-based learning. *Proceedings of the Fourth International Machine Learning Workshop.* Irvine, CA: Morgan Kaufmann.

Pazzani, M. (in press). *Learning causal relationships: An integration of empirical and explanation-based learning methods.* Hillsdale, NJ : Lawrence Erlbaum Associates.

Rumelhart, D., Hinton, G., & Williams, R. (1986). Learning internal representations by error propagation. In D. Rumelhart. & J. McClelland (Ed.), *Parallel distributed processing: Explorations in the microstructure of cognition. Volume 1: Foundations.* MIT Press.

Schank, R., Collins, G. & Hunter, L. (1986). Transcending inductive category formation in learning. *Behavioral and Brain Sciences, 9,* 639-686.

Recognition of Melody Fragments in Continuously Performed Music

Robert Port and Svën Anderson
Department of Linguistics, Department of Computer Science
Indiana University, Bloomington, Indiana 47405

Abstract

The processing of continuous acoustic signals is a challenging problem for perceptual and cognitive models. Sound patterns are usually handled by dividing the signal into long fixed-length windows—long enough for the longest patterns to be recognized. We demonstrate a technique for recognizing acoustic patterns with a network that runs continuously in time and is fed a single spectral frame of input per network cycle. Behavior of the network in time is controlled by temporal regularities in the input patterns that allow the network to predict future events.

INTRODUCTION

An important step in the application of neural networks to perceptual problems is performance that runs continuously in time. Relevant perceptual tasks include (1) labelling of sequential patterns and (2) the prediction of stimulus events. Only recently have attempts been made to experiment with networks that handle sequential inputs [Elman, 1988,Gallant and King, 1988]. Achievement of these goals must be attempted in the context of several additional constraints. First, the network should receive only a single frame of input at a time. This implies that the system must construct a temporary memory of past inputs or reach a distinctive state that allows recognition of patterns that extend over a number of input frames. The employment of a long static input window (cf., [Elman and Zipser, 1988, Prager et al., 1986]) is an unsatisfactory solution for biological perceptual systems since response time must then be delayed to the end of the window, preventing optimal reaction time [Port et al., 1988]. A second constraint is that the system must be prepared to deal with patterns distributed in time that partially resemble each other yet have varying durations. This constraint prevents use of a built-in restart signal to begin analysis from a common initial network state, such as at the beginning of each perceptual trial. External reset, as found in unfolded networks ([Elman and McClelland, 1986]), fixed window networks ([Elman and Zipser, 1988]) or fixed length dynamic windows greatly reduces the biological plausibility of a system. Some means for resetting the system that can be partly controlled from the bottom up is required (cf., [Grossberg, 1980]).

We have been designing network architectures with a limited number of recurrent connections (inspired by [Jordan, 1986]) for processing continuous input signals, with the intention of eventually handling speech. We demonstrate in this paper that a modification of Real-Time Backpropagation [Williams and Zipser, 1988] permits generalization of the sequential network in interesting ways. In the simulations described below, we employ recurrent loops of nodes to store information about the history of the signal by training the system to predict the next input. This contrasts with memory that is either a record of previous inputs (as in delay-line systems [Waibel et al., 1988]) or a record of previous node activations ([Jordan, 1986,Elman, 1988,Anderson et al., 1988]). To support reset of the network when a partially recognized pattern is to be rejected, we use sigma-pi nodes [Rumelhart et al., 1986].[1] These allow the activation of nodes in one clique to gate the activity of another clique. In experiments with this system, we have attempted recognition of melodic patterns produced by hand on a keyboard instrument. In this way, we deal with some forms of natural variation and demonstrate the robustness of our system without tackling the magnitude of variability observed in speech.

DYNAMIC GRADIENT DESCENT FOR SIGMA-PI UNITS

Willaims & Zipser [1988] derive a gradient descent alogorithm for computing weight changes in continuously running recurrent networks. The technique requires maintaining a matrix of activation partials that is updated at each time step. In this section we extend the gradient descent algorithm to networks that contain modules composed of sigma-pi units. These are units that receive weighted activation products from 2 or more other units.

Suppose that the network contains m inputs and n nodes. Let I index the set of all external inputs, and N index each node in the network. We can then label input activations using the variable x and node activations with the variable y. It is straightforward to write the input to the node indexed k at a time t.

The input to a sigma-pi unit k can be written:

$$a_k(t) = \sum_{l \in I} x_l(t) + 1/2 \sum_{s \in N} \sum_{r \in N} w_{ksr} y_s(t) y_r(t)$$

Note that sigma-pi nodes simplify to the case of sigma nodes in the case where $y_r(t) \equiv 1 \ \forall t$, so that this derivation applies as well to combined modules of sigma and sigma-pi nodes. For clarity we have assumed that the external inputs k are weighted by a constant 1. The activation of node k at the next time step is

$$y_k(t+1) = \phi_k(a_k(t))$$

where ϕ_k is a C^1 function. If we know what the output values should be for some group of nodes at time τ, then we can define an error function for the network's performance using the sum-squares metric.

$$E(\tau) = 1/2 \sum_{k \in N} (e_k(\tau))^2$$

[1] Williams [1986] has shown that sigma-pi connections can compute any monotonic function of their inputs. They have been used to generate and maintain simple rhythms by Dehaene et al. [Dehaene et al., 1987].

where the error for output node k (e_k) is the difference between the desired value and the actual output for node k.

$$e_k(t) = \begin{cases} d_k(t) - y_k(t) & k \in T(t) \\ 0 & \text{else} \end{cases}$$

where the set $T(t)$ is the (possibly time varying) set of indices for nodes for which there exist desired values at time t.

Because the node activations vary at each time step, we wish to minimize the total error over a time frame beginning at t_i and ending at t_f by changing the weights. This implies changing the weights in the direction of the negative gradient of the total error with respect to the weights. The total error over this time frame is the sum of the network error at each time frame.

$$E_{total}(t_i, t_f) = \sum_{\tau=t_i+1}^{t_f} E(\tau)$$

Since

$$E_{total}(t_0, t_2) = E_{total}(t_0, t_1) + E_{total}(t_1 + t_2)$$

induction yields

$$\nabla_W E_{total}(t_i, t_f) = \sum_{\tau=t_i+1}^{t_f} \nabla_W E_{total}(\tau)$$

This means that the error at each time point in the time frame can be calculated and these values summed to yield the total gradient. At the end of the time frame, the ijth weight should be adjusted by

$$\Delta w_{hij}(t) = -\alpha \frac{\partial E(t)}{\partial w_{hij}} \quad h, i, j \in N$$

But

$$-\frac{\partial E(t)}{\partial w_{hij}} = \frac{\partial}{\partial w_{hij}} \left[1/2 \sum_{k \in N} (e_k(\tau))^2 \right] = \sum_{k \in N} \frac{\partial y_k(t)}{\partial w_{hij}} e_k(t)$$

Thus, computing the changes to be made to the weights boils down to calculating $\frac{\partial y_k}{\partial w_{hij}}$.

$$\frac{\partial y_k(t+1)}{\partial w_{hij}} = \frac{\partial}{\partial w_{hij}} \phi_k(a_k(t)) = \phi_k\prime(a_k(t)) \frac{\partial a_k(t)}{\partial w_{hij}} \tag{1}$$

and then

$$\frac{\partial a_k(t)}{\partial w_{hij}} = \sum_{s \in N} \sum_{r \in N} \left[1/2 \delta_{kh} y_i(t) y_j(t) + w_{ksr} y_r \frac{\partial y_s(t)}{\partial w_{hij}} \right]$$

where δ is 1 when $k = h$ and otherwise 0. At this point we have an iterative solution to the gradient that allows computation of future $\frac{\partial y_k}{\partial w_{hij}}$ if we assume that the initial partials are zero. At each time step this matrix of partials must be updated according to

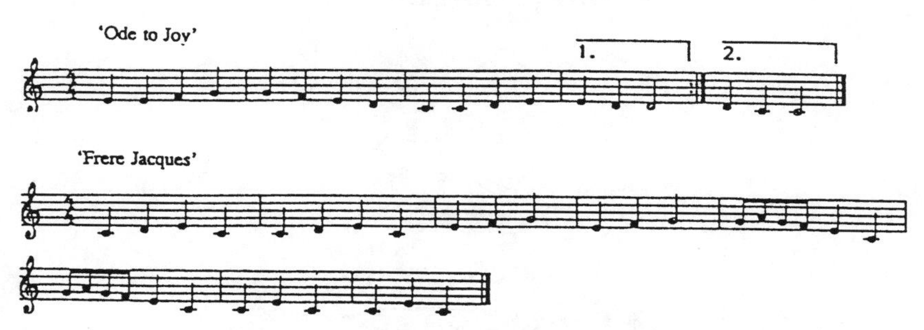

Figure 1: The two melodies used in the experiment are slightly edited familiar tunes. Note that measures 1 and 5 of 'Ode to Joy' are similar to measures 3 and 4 of 'Frere Jacques'

equation 1. Because the computation of the partials necessary for the learning algorithm scales as n^4, in actual implementations it is important to severely limit the number of sigma-pi units used.

In the simulations reported here weight updates were carried out at each time step. Output activations for supervised nodes were set to their desired values after each time step and the corresponding elements of the matrix of partials was set to zero (cf. [Williams & Zipser, 1988]).

MELODY RECOGNITION EXPERIMENT

We applied this architecture and algorithm to a problem in auditory sequence recognition. We recorded productions of two melodies on an electronic keyboard and trained a network to recognize two measures selected from the melodies. The measures have the same note sequence, differing only in the rhythm of the note patterns. This task requires robustness across natural temporal variability due to human performance while still restricting the difficulty of frequency discrimination required through use of the keyboard.

Stimuli

One of the experimenters produced 2 repetitions of the two familiar 8-measure melodies (slightly edited) shown in Figure 1. The melodies were played in the key of C, using a 6-note scale from C_4 (261 Hz) to A_4 (440 Hz) at a tempo of 132 beats/minute on a Casio Model C-140 keyboard. The tempo of performance was stabilized by use of a visual metronome and the performance was done in a staccato style to minimize note overlap. Statistical measures on the productions showed that the mean duration of each measure was 452 ms (SD=11 ms). There was a total of 10 different measure types. The training corpus was restricted to all of the measures from 2 of the repetitions; target measures in the 3 different repetitions of the melodies were used as testing data. Based on the duration of the shortest measure, a 1024 point fast-Fourier transform (FFT) was performed with Hamming window spacing that provides 8 equally spaced FFT frames for the shortest measure (that is, approximately one per 1/8th note). The windows were 64 ms wide with their centers fixed 48 ms apart. Figure 4 shows 8 successive FFT frames for

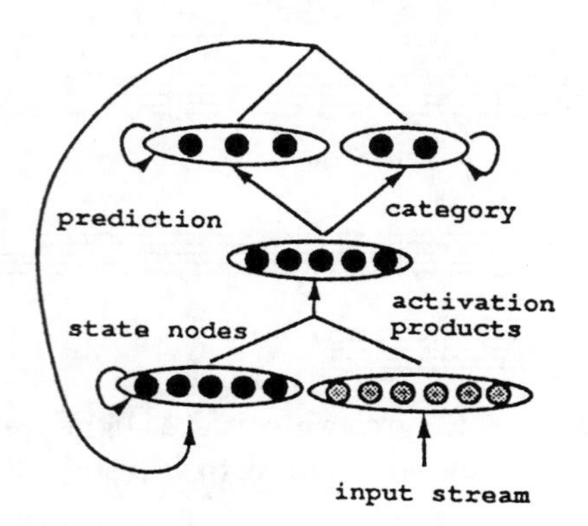

Figure 2: The architecture of the network employed.

two sample measures. Six frequency bins were centered approximately over each note in the 6-note scale that we employed. The highest 40 dB of dynamic range was retained for each bin; all values more than 40 dB down were replaced with 0. The dB values were then mapped linearly onto the range [0,1] which served as input to the network.

Procedure

For our experiments, the first measure of tune 'Ode to Joy' and the third measure of 'Frere Jacques' were selected as targets A and B respectively. This provides a challenging temporal discrimination task for the network in contrast to the easier task of differentiating each target from the other measures. The network was presented with a continuous random sequence of measures. As can be seen in Figure 4, the productions exhibited many variations that reduced the quality of the inputs. In order to be able to test on different productions of the target measure than were employed in the training, only half of the 10 instances of the target measure were used. The other 5 were employed only in the testing phase.

The network was as shown in Figure 2 with 6 input nodes, 5 hidden nodes, 5 output nodes (2 of which were trained to the category labels, and 3 trained to predict the subsequent input) and 4 state nodes that received connections from the prediction and category nodes. Connections to nodes on the hidden layer paired the input and state node cliques. These sigma-pi nodes weighted the product of the activation pairs as input. All weights were learned using real-time back propagation. The target function for the category node was a monotonic ramp from 0 to 1 during the presentation of the target measure. The prediction node targets rose to 1 and fell to 0.1 at appropriate times during each target measure.

Results

After training, the network was able to correctly identify occurrences of the target syllables in the input stream. Percent correct identification by itself, however, is not a suitable statistic for performance since both missed targets and 'false alarms' are possible

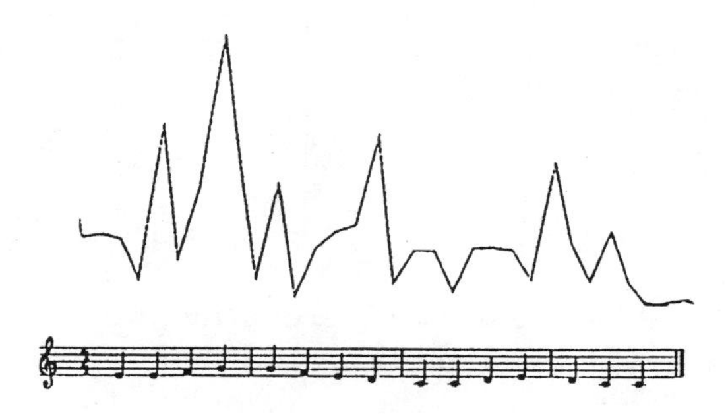

Figure 3: The output activation of the category node trained to recognize measure 1 during presentation of measures 1-4 of 'Ode to Joy'. The activation begins to climb every time an E (the first note in the target measure) occurs in the input, but it quickly falls for false positives.

errors. Reducing the frequency of targets missed invariably increases the number of false alarms. The statistic d' from signal detection theory is designed to provide a performance score that is independent of response criterion and which is thus a robust discriminability measure [Swets, 1961]. The units of d' represent z-scores along a hypothetical discriminant continuum. Thus a d' of 2 means that the mean values of the likelihood of 'target present' and 'target not present' are 2 standard deviations apart.

We apply d' here to evaluate two properties of performance: first, the ability of the network to differentiate each target measure from the measures in the data that do not include either target, and, second, to differentiate the two targets from each other. The second task should be more difficult. Figure 3 shows the output of the category node for Target A during presentation of 4 measures of the first tune. A threshold activation level was defined on the activity of the category nodes and each measure from a sample was classified as either a hit (correct labelling of the pattern), a false alarm (where the activation exceeded the threshhold during the measure but there was no target), a miss (target occurred but response was below threshhold) or a correct rejection (no target, no response).

When the test tokens of Target A were differentiated from nontarget measures ($n = 116$ measures), $d' = 2.03$. This value means, for example, that, if the ratio of misses to false alarms is 1, there will be about 85% correct identification of the target against about 15% false alarms. For test tokens of Target B versus all nontargets, d' was somewhat better, 2.75 (with $n = 96$). This implies about 91% correct identification and 91% correct rejection.

The most difficult discrimination, however, is between the two similar measures, Targets A and B. As mentioned above, the system was trained on a set of 10 tokens of each measure. When it is tested on two new sets of tokens, $d' = 1.64$ ($n = 87$),illustrating poorer discriminability for the two similar target measures. This implies about 80% correct with 20% false alarms. By testing the ability of the network to identify the same

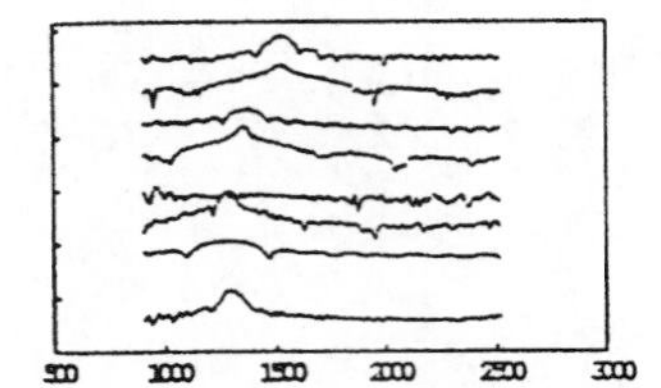

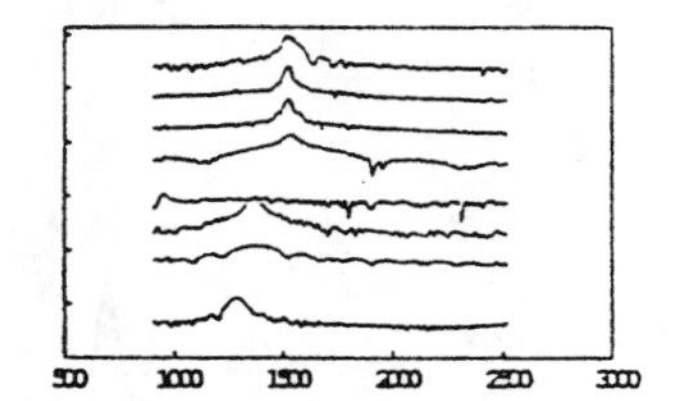

Figure 4: The FFT sequence for one token of each of the two targets for Experiment 2. Frequency increases from left to right, and time-ordering from bottom to top. The left-hand panel is measure 1 of 'Ode to Joy' while the right-hand panel is measure 3 of 'Frere Jacques'.

tokens it was trained on, we can evaluate the robustness of the system to the kinds of natural noise that existed in the data. Here $d' = 1.84$ ($n = 69$), not too much better than on the novel tokens. This suggests that our system did not greatly overlearn the training data and was able to generalize effectively.

CONCLUSIONS

This network is able to recognize real auditory patterns that were produced with characteristic human inaccuracy. The system 'listens' continuously, without an *a priori* input window other than the minimum time frame for the spectral analysis. This input sampling rate was also the rate of internode communication within the network itself, but this 'clock' does not control the point of reset of the network. Instead, we allowed periodicity in the input pattern to entrain the output behavior of the network. Then the targets themselves control the resetting function.

These perception experiments using acoustic input demonstrate that it is possible to use sparsely connected recurrent networks to continuously monitor inputs for particular patterns. This was achieved by use of a training technique that emphasized prediction of the next input signal and sigma-pi nodes to support rapid reset when a partial pattern is violated. This distributes control of the system toward the lowest levels—near the input—rather than having it externally specified by the design of the system. Apparently this system is robust enough to handle considerable natural variation in inputs. This is a step toward a continuously functioning dynamically controlled perceptual system for auditory inputs.

Acknowledements

We are grateful to Chan-Do Lee and William Mills for assistance with this project. This research was supported in part by the National Science Foundation, Grants DCR-8505635 and DCR-8518725.

References

[Anderson et al., 1988] Anderson, S., Merrill, J., and Port, R. (1988). Dynamic speech categorization with recurrent networks. In *Proceedings of the 1988 Connectionist Summer School*, pages 398–406. Morgan-Kauffmann, San Mateo, California.

[Dehaene et al., 1987] Dehaene, S., Changeux, J.-P., and Nadal, J.-P. (1987). Neural networks that learn temporal sequences by selection. In *Proceedings of the National Academy of Science*, volume 84, page 2727. National Academy of Science.

[Elman, 1988] Elman, J. (1988). Finding structure in time. Technical Report 8801, Center for Research in Language, University of California at San Diego, La Jolla, CA.

[Elman and Zipser, 1988] Elman, J. and Zipser, D. (1988). Learning the hidden structure of speech. *Journal of the Acoustical Society of America*, 83:1615–26.

[Elman and McClelland, 1986] Elman, J. L. and McClelland, J. L. (1986). Exploiting the lawful variability in the speech wave. In Perkell, J. S. and Klatt, D. H., editors, *Invariance and Variability of Speech Processes*, chapter 17, pages 360–381. Erlbaum, Hillsdale, NJ.

[Gallant and King, 1988] Gallant, S. I. and King, D. J. (1988). Experiments with sequential associative memories. In *Proceedings of the Tenth Annual Conference of the Cognitive Science Society.* L. Erlbaum, Hillsdale, NJ.

[Grossberg, 1980] Grossberg, S. (1980). How does a breain build a cognitive code? *Psychological Review*, 87(1):1–51.

[Jordan, 1986] Jordan, M. (1986). Serial order. Technical Report 8604, Institute for Cognitive Science, U. of California at SanDiego, La Jolla, CA.

[Port et al., 1988] Port, R., Anderson, S., and Merrill, J. (1988). Temporal information and memory in connectionist networks. Technical Report 265, Indiana University Computer Science Department.

[Prager et al., 1986] Prager, I., Harrison, T. D., and Fallside, F. (1986). Boltzmann machines for speech recognition. *Computer Speech and Language*, 1:1–20.

[Rumelhart et al., 1986] Rumelhart, D., Hinton, G., and Williams, R. (1986). Learning internal representations by error propagation. In Rumelhart, D. and McClelland, J., editors, *Parallel Distributed Processing*, volume 1. MIT Press, Cambridge, Massachusetts.

[Swets, 1961] Swets, J. A. (1961). Is there a sensory threshold? *Science*, 34:168–177.

[Waibel et al., 1988] Waibel, A., Hanazawa, T., Hinton, G., Shikano, K., and Lang, K. (1988). Phoneme recognition: Neural networks vs. hidden markov models. In *Proceedings of the ICASSP*, pages 107–110. IEEE.

[Williams and Zipser, 1988] Williams, R. and Zipser, D. (1988). A learning algorithm for continually running fully recurrent neural networks. Technical Report 8805, ICS, UCSD, La Jolla, CA.

[Williams, 1986] Williams, R. J. (1986). The logic of activation functions. In Rumelhart, D. E. and McClelland, J. L., editors, *Parallel Distributed Processing, Vol. 1*, chapter 4, pages 423–443. Mit Press, Cambridge, Massachusetts.

Computing Value Judgments During Story Understanding

John F. Reeves

Computer Science Department
University of California, Los Angeles

ABSTRACT

During story understanding readers make value judgments—judgments of the 'goodness' or 'badness' of characters' actions. This paper presents the representational structures and processes used to make value judgments by the computer program THUNDER. THUNDER creates evaluative beliefs about characters' plans based on a set of universal pragmatic and ethical judgment rules. To account for subjective differences in evaluative belief, THUNDER has a specific ideology to represent the idiosyncratic aspects of evaluation. There are two components in the representation of ideology: (1) a set of important, long term goals called values, and (2) a collection of planning strategies for each value. This representation for ideology allows THUNDER to reason about what is 'good', and what it believes to be 'good ways to get what is good.' The representation and rules for value judgments are used to (1) make inferences about character belief and ideology, (2) represent expectation knowledge based on personality traits, and (3) reason about the obligations that characters acquire.

INTRODUCTION

Plan evaluation is the process of deciding whether or not a plan should be used. Two types of reasons are used in plan evaluation: (1) *pragmatic* reasons, reasons about the consequences of the plan for the planner, and (2) *ethical* reasons, reasons about the consequences of the plan for people other than the planner. As an example of the two types of reasons, consider the reasons that the following two plans are 'bad':

EX-1: To save money, John decided never to change the oil in his new car.

EX-2: To get the money to buy a new car, John decided to rob a bank.

In EX-1, John's plan to save money is 'bad' because it will end up costing him more to replace the car engine when the bearings seize up than to perform regular maintenance. In EX-2, John's plan to get money is 'bad' because of the loss of property he is causing to the bank depositors. These two senses of the word "bad" correspond to the questions (1) will the plan work? and (2) is the plan ethically right?

THUNDER (Thematic UNDerstanding From Ethical Reasoning) (Reeves, 1988) is a story understanding program that reads short narratives and answers ethical and thematic questions. Value judgment is the primary task of THUNDER during story understanding. THUNDER uses its value judgments to recognize *belief conflict patterns*: abstract situations where the ethical judgments of the reader and story characters conflict. THUNDER uses belief conflict patterns to (1) organize the representation of the story, (2) focus attention on the thematically interesting elements of the story, and (3) identify the theme of the story by resolving the belief conflict. By judging story character's plans, THUNDER can answer the following questions (from EX-1 and EX-2, respectively):

> Why was John wrong not to put oil in his car?

It is wrong because not putting oil in the car will damage the car, and the car is more expensive than the oil.

> Why was John wrong to rob the bank?

It is wrong because John is taking money from the bank depositors.

In order to make evaluative judgments about story characters' actions, THUNDER has to (1) have knowledge about what is 'good' and 'bad', and (2) be able to reason about how actions are evaluated. THUNDER's *evaluative beliefs* about different types of human goals and ways for achieving those goals represent knowledge about normative value. Evaluative beliefs are organized in THUNDER's *ideology.* Expected goal successes and failures are used to determine normative goodness; goal successes are evaluated positively, and goal failures are evaluated negatively. To make evaluations of situations, THUNDER has a set of *judgment rules* which are applied to situations to create evaluative beliefs about story characters and what they have done.

This paper presents the structures and processes that are used in THUNDER's evaluative reasoning model. When references are made to the program's beliefs or values, these terms refer to the data structures that are used in the computer program to implement psychological functions. The usefulness of these structures is shown by (1) using them to make value judgments, and (2) identifying the components of the value judgment process. In addition to making judgments, the processes in the model are used to represent and reason about personality traits and obligation.

FACTUAL AND EVALUATIVE BELIEF

Representing and reasoning about beliefs is a fundamental problem for Artificial Intelligence (AI) systems. Previous approaches have addressed belief in terms of uncertainty and truth maintenance (e.g. (Cohen, 1985; Pearl, 1988)). However, there is more to belief than just the degree of certainty with which a proposition is held. Part of the problem is that these systems have not made the distinction between *factual* and *evaluative* belief. Factual beliefs are evaluated in terms of truth, and evaluative beliefs are evaluated in terms of 'good' and 'bad.'

In THUNDER, a *belief* is a conceptual object attributed to a person. The person (the believer) can be the reader/system or a story character. The *content* of a belief is a constituent conceptual object that the belief is about, such as a plan or a future state of affairs. The *strength* of a belief is the degree on either the factual or evaluative scale with which the believer holds the belief.

A *factual belief* is a belief that the content of the belief is true or false (has a truth strength). Factual beliefs can be held with degrees of certainty or probabilities.

An *evaluative belief* is a belief that the content of the belief is positively or negatively evaluated (has a positive or negative strength). Most of the evaluative beliefs used in THUNDER are about plans; evaluative beliefs about actions are handled by reference to beliefs about the plans in which they are a part. Positive and negative evaluations of plans correspond to beliefs that the plan should or should not be used, respectively.

A *judgment* is an evaluative belief that a person creates and is the product of a judgment process. A pragmatic judgment is the creation of a evaluative belief for pragmatic reasons, and an ethical judgment is the creation of an evaluative belief for ethical reasons. The process of making an ethical judgment is termed *ethical reasoning*.

The distinction between factual and evaluative beliefs is a metaethical philosophic position called *noncognitivism* (Boyce and Jensen, 1978, pp. 76-81). The basic precepts of noncognitivism are:

- Evaluative statements are not evaluated in terms of truth.
- There is no method of ultimate justification of evaluative statements (as in scientific or mathematical proof).
- The function of evaluative statements is to express emotions (Ayer, 1935), to influence other's attitudes (Stevenson, 1944), or to rationally guide human conduct (Hare, 1952).

The problem for noncognitivist philosophers is defining how evaluative statements are justified, and what constitutes a good reason for holding a evaluative belief (Toulmin, 1950). In the construction of THUNDER, 'good' is defined in terms of the values of an individual, and then character actions are evaluated in terms of the values. Using different value systems will produce different evaluations. For example, a Catholic and a Samurai would have different evaluations of the following story:

EX-3: A high school student killed himself after flunking out of school.

The Catholic believes that suicide is a mortal sin, and therefore the student's plan is wrong, but the Samurai believes that death is preferable to living in disgrace.

Once THUNDER makes an evaluative judgment, it is not concerned with establishing the truth of the statement, but rather with the reasons for the judgment, and how the judgment can be used in story understanding.

MODELING READER IDEOLOGY

An *ideology* is an organization for goals and plans in memory based on evaluative beliefs about states that should be desired, and how to go about achieving those states. The representation for ideology in THUNDER has two components: (1) the *value system*, a set of abstract, high-level evaluative beliefs about goals (called *values*) ordered by their relative importance (Rokeach, 1973), and (2) a set of *planning strategies* for each value, representing the ways that a person believes the value should be achieved. The values are based on Rokeach's terminal human values (Rokeach, 1973), and represented in terms of Schank and Abelson's goal primitives [1977].[1]

[1] In the notation used for goals, the goal type is signified by the letter preceding the goal name. Achievement goals (A) are a motivations to attain valued acquisitions

THUNDER's representation for ideology is an extension of Carbonell's system in the POLITICS program(Carbonell, 1978; Carbonell, 1979) where ideologies were represented by *goal trees.* A goal tree is a hierarchy of goals ordered by *subgoal* and *relative importance* relations. THUNDER divides the goal importance and instrumentality functions of ideology into separate structures: the value list and planning strategies, respectively. By making this separation, THUNDER loses the advantage of having one unified structure for representing ideology (the goal tree), but is able to reason more effectively about the end states that the program believes are 'good' and about the value of types of plans.

Another difference between POLITICS and THUNDER is that THUNDER makes a distinction between the role of pragmatic and ethical belief in the representation of ideology. POLITICS evaluated the consequences of events in terms of goal trees, so a 'good' plan was an effective plan for an important goal which avoids failures of other important goals. This is only the pragmatic side of evaluative belief—an ethical plan evaluator also has to consider the goals and goal failure effects on parties other than the planner. In THUNDER, the value system represents only the relative importance of the reader's *values*, and general judgment rules are used to evaluate goal successes and failures. Thus, the value system doesn't include instrumental goals, and separates the concept of 'what is good' from 'good ways to get what is good.'

Values

There are two types of values: (1) *preservation* values, and (2) *achievement* values. Preservation values are the things that everyone wants to keep: their health, freedom, possessions, self esteem, and social esteem. Achievement values are the things that people want out of life, such as a successful career, spiritual salvation, or excitement and good times. Preservation values are things that people should not have threatened, or worse, have fail, while achievement values are the things that people believe are valuable to try to get.

Preservation values are positive evaluative beliefs about having and keeping something. Having a preservation value allows the individual to evaluate actions that threaten the value. For example, if a person values their health, then threats and damage to their health are evaluated negatively. In a value system, preservation values can be held for a particular group of people: the individual, their family, friends, a social group (a community, nation, or race), or everybody. A white supremacist, for example, believes that freedom should be preserved only for the Caucasian race, and a patriot believes in freedom preservation for his nation.

Achievement values are positive evaluative beliefs about things that people try to get. There are four classes of achievement values: (1) *acquirement* values, like achieving power, money, or status, (2) *personal* values, such as achieving salvation, tranquillity, or wisdom, (3) *interpersonal* values, such as achieving love, respect, or friendship, and (4) *entertainment* values, such as pleasure, excitement, or enjoyment.

THUNDER's value system contains preservation and achievement values ordered by their relative importance. There are five preservation values: P-Health, P-Freedom, P-Possessions, P-Self-esteem, P-Social-esteem. Each preservation value is believed to be important for an ordered list of people: THUNDER, family, friends, social group, nation, and everyone else. The achievement values are less important than the preservation values, and are in the following order: the interpersonal values A-Love and A-Friendship, the personal values A-Intellect, A-Tranquility, and A-Salvation, the acquirement values A-Respect, A-Status, A-Power, and A-Possessions, and the entertainment values E-Excitement, and E-Enjoyment. Note that the value system can be reordered to represent different ideologies. For example, a spiritual person would have A-Salvation relatively higher in the list, while a patriot might have P-Freedom(nation) above the other preservation values.

Because there are a small set of goal primitives that are used in the value system, the system can monitor the goals for activation, threats, and failures. There are three points to notice in the construction of the value system: (1) the set of values that the program has is fairly short (Rokeach, 1973), (2) not all goals that the program knows about are included in the value system, and (3) the value system does not represent instrumental relations between the values because the system represents what is valuable, not how to maintain or achieve those valuable states.

Since the value system represents what the reader believes to be valuable, actions that threaten or cause values to fail are believed to be bad. When a story character does something that threatens a goal or causes a goal failure, the character's plan can be evaluated for how bad the plan is. In the evaluation, the following factors are used:

1. *Importance of the failed goal.* How important is the failed goal to the person whose goal it is? It is worse to violate an important goal of a person than a less important goal.
2. *Duration of the goal failure.* How bad is the

or social positions. Other goal types are preservation (P), delta (D), and enjoyment (E).

goal failure? The duration of a goal failure can be measured by how hard it is to recover: loss of property is replaceable, but consumes resources that the person suffering the goal failure would not have had to expend. Some goal failures are non-recoverable, such as loss of life.

3. *Scope of the goal failure.* How many goal failures does the plan cause? If John punches Jerry, he has caused a goal failure for just one person, but if John dumps toxic waste in the old swimmin' hole, he has causes goal failures for anyone who wants to use the swimmin' hole in the future.

Values are positive evaluative beliefs about goals. When THUNDER makes judgments about goal failures and successes it uses the goals that are in the values in the value system. Successes and failures of the goals in the value system are called *value successes* and *value failures*, respectively.

Planning Strategies

The second element of ideology involves beliefs about the ways that the values should be achieved. For example, in EX-1 John believes that a good way to save money is to not put oil in his car. John's plan is an instance the general strategy of being thrifty: John believes that a good way of possessing money is to avoid spending it. From EX-1, the reader knows that John values saving money, and also how he goes about saving money. An alternate strategy would be to avoid risking the money, as in:

EX-4: To save money, John invested in treasury bonds.

Planning strategies are associated with the various values in the ideology to make the distinction between value and instrumentality. Planning strategies are evaluative beliefs about plans for values in the value system. The content of a planning strategy is an abstract kind of plan, such as plans involving prevention for preservation of health.

By associating planning strategies with values, the system can quickly find good plans for a given value. Planning strategies can be used to organize plans for values by providing intermediate nodes in a plan hierarchy where plans are indexed by the ways in which the planner believes that they are valuable. If, for example, a person believes that prevention is a positive pragmatic strategy for preservation of health, then specific plans for preservation of health can be indexed under the planning strategy by their appropriate context, such as going to the doctor regularly, exercising and eating right, and avoiding situations were their health can be threatened. By organizing plans by the values that they achieve, and by their relative value, the system can reason about instrumental relations between the plans and planning trade-offs. For example, a person who believes in the prevention-for-health strategy will not believe that health threatening activities (such as skydiving or hangliding) are effective plans for entertainment, and that a good doctor is worth an additional cost.

PRAGMATIC AND ETHICAL REASONING

Evaluation of a person's actions consists of creating evaluative beliefs about their plans. In order to create evaluative beliefs, THUNDER has to (1) understand what the character is doing (his plan) and why he is doing it (his goal), (2) evaluate the character's plan by generating reasons for an evaluative belief about the plan, and (3) generate the reasons for the character's positive evaluative belief about the plan.

In EX-2, there are three pragmatic reasons that John's plan for getting money by robbing a bank is positively evaluated: (1) it helps achieve his goal of buying a car by getting a lot of money, (2) the plan has low resource consumption—it takes less time than working for the money, and is less expensive than investing, and (3) the plan is highly effective—better than mugging or robbing a 7-11. There is one pragmatic reason that robbing a bank is negatively evaluated: the liability of capture and imprisonment. Ethically, robbing a bank is wrong because of (1) the loss suffered by the people who have their money in the bank, and (2) the threatened loss of life to the people who were working in the bank.

Each reason for an evaluation of a plan can be broken down into two components: (1) a factual belief about the plan, and (2) a pragmatic or ethical *judgment rule* that is used to derive an evaluative belief from a factual belief. To generate appropriate factual beliefs about a character's plan, the following factors have to be considered:

1. *Plan availability.* What other plans are available to the planner? What are the relative merits of the other available plans?

2. *Goal importance.* How important is the planner's goal? If the plan causes goal failures for others, how important are the goals that fail?

3. *Intention.* If the plan causes goal failures, does the character realize that he is causing a goal failure? If a character is executing an action that will cause a goal failure for himself, such as locking the car door with the keys inside, then the action should be evaluated as stupid, but not as evil.

When THUNDER reads about a character's action, it infers a plan that that action is a part of.

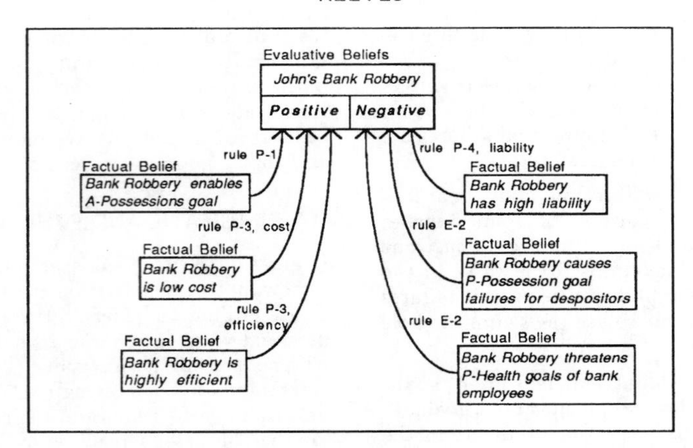

Figure 1: Pragmatic and Ethical Reasons for THUNDER's Evaluative Belief about Bank Robbery

Once a belief graph has been constructed, THUNDER makes a determination of its actual evaluative belief about the plan. In the determination, ethical reasons take precedence over pragmatic reasons. Because there is an ethical reason that John's bank robbery is evaluated negatively, THUNDER holds the evaluative belief that the bank robbery is wrong, even though there are pragmatic reasons that bank robbery is positively evaluated.

INFERRING CHARACTER BELIEFS AND IDEOLOGY

In addition to creating its own evaluative belief about the character's plan, THUNDER has to figure out why the character believed that the plan was justified. For a plan that THUNDER believes is pragmatically wrong, THUNDER can make inferences about the character's beliefs. For a plan that THUNDER believes is ethically wrong, inferences about the character's ideology can be made. When a character executes a plan that is evaluated negatively for pragmatic reasons, THUNDER uses the following *pragmatic inference rules* (PI rules):

> PI-1: The character doesn't have the factual belief about the plan that THUNDER used to make its evaluative assessment.
>
> or
>
> PI-2: The character believes that the goal that they are achieving is more important than the goal that they are causing to fail.

These two inference rules are mutually exclusive, and depend on the character's intention. For example, in EX-1 either John doesn't know that not changing the oil in his car will damages the engine (rule PI-1), or he knows it and believes that the short term goal success of saving money by not changing the oil is more important than the long term goal failure of having to buy a new car (rule PI-2).

When a character executes an ethically wrong plan, the following *ethical inference rules* (EI rules) are used:

> EI-1: The character believes that their value is more important than the value failure that they caused.
>
> and
>
> EI-2: The character believes that the ethically wrong plan is the only way to achieve their value.
>
> or
>
> EI-2': The character believes that the ethically wrong plan is a less expensive (in time or resources) way of achieving their value than other available plans.

These inferences are based on observations that people do not go out of their way to do ethically wrong actions; they must have a motivation (rule EI-1) and a rationale (rules E1-2 and EI-2'). From these inferences about what the character believes to be valuable, THUNDER can begin to construct the character's ideology. From EX-2, THUNDER can infer that John believes that his goal of getting a car is more important than the bank depositor's goal of preserving their money, and that John has pragmatic beliefs about bank robbery that make it better than other available plans.

If the goal of the plan is not an instance of a value in THUNDER's value system, THUNDER assumes that the goal is the subgoal of a larger plan schema, and continues to infer plans until a plan for a value is found. For example, if THUNDER reads:

EX–5: John robbed a bank.

THUNDER infers that that John is robbing the bank to get money. However, the goal of getting money is not a value. So THUNDER continues to find plans that are instrumentally enabled by getting money, such as A-Possessions plans, or plans that bank robbers use their money to pursue, such as plans for entertainment goals (by spending the money on parties or drugs.)

The inferred plan chain from action to a value is made up of one or more individual plan schemas. Each plan schema contains the goal failures that the plan causes; for example the 'threaten' plan schema (PS-Threaten) contains the motivated P-Health goal for the person threatened. PS-Threaten is a sub-plan of the bank robbery schema (PS-Bank-robbery), so when John robs a bank, THUNDER knows that the bank employees are suffering a P-Health value failure. The goal at the top of of the complete plan is called the *value of the plan*, or the value that the plan achieves. When complete plans are inferred, they can be evaluated both for planning failures (Dyer, 1983) and the ethical and pragmatic consequences. Even thought the plan may not have been completely executed, an evaluation can be made from the values that reader expects to succeed and fail.

THUNDER uses the following pragmatic judgment rules for evaluating story characters' plans:

P-1: If plan P1 achieves its value, then P1 is positively evaluated.

P-2: If plan P1 causes value failure VF for the planner, then P1 is negatively evaluated.

P-3: If plan P1 is better on plan metric[2] I than competing plan P2, then P1 is positively evaluated.

P-4: If plan P1 is worse on plan metric I than competing plan P2, then P1 is negatively evaluated.

The following ethical judgment rules are used in making ethical judgments about plans:

[2]A *plan metric* (Dyer, 1983) is a measurement unit for plans. For example, the "cost" metric measures how many resources are used during plan executions. Other plan metrics are enablement, efficacy, risk, coordination, availability, legitimacy, affect, skill, vulnerability, and liability.

E-1: If plan P1 achieves value V for another party, then P1 is positively evaluated.

E-2: If plan P1 causes value failure VF for another party, then P1 is negatively evaluated.

E-3: If plan P1 achieves value V while intentionally causing value failure VF and V is more important than VF, then P1 is positively evaluated.

E-4: If plan P1 achieves value V while intentionally causing goal failure VF and V is less important than VF, then P1 is negatively evaluated.

The reasons that rules E-3 and E-4 are ethical, rather than pragmatic, is that even if both of the goals in V and VF are the planner's goals, the importance measure is the understander's. For example:

EX–6: John took steroids to improve his physique.

If John is understood to be improving his physique to feel better about himself, and both John and reader knows about the harmful side effects of steroid usage, then V is John's P-Self-esteem goal, and VF is John's P-Health goal. Rules P-1 and P-2 evaluate the pragmatic consequences of the plan, while E-4 evaluates the plan as unethical because THUNDER believes that John should value his health more than his self-esteem.

These judgment rules can serve as deductive rules in plan evaluation, and as preferences or advice in plan selection or creation. For example, rule E-2 says to prefer plans that do not cause goal failures for others over those that do. Using these rules and factual beliefs about bank robbing, a belief graph can be constructed for EX-2 as shown in figure 1.

The beliefs in figure 1 are THUNDER's. The factual beliefs are THUNDER's knowledge about bank robbery, and how bank robbery can be compared to other plans for getting money. The links between factual and evaluative beliefs are labeled by judgment rules. For example, one reason that THUNDER has for believing that John's bank robbery is positively evaluated is that (1) THUNDER believes that the bank robbery will help achieve the A-Possessions goal by providing John with the money to buy a car (the factual belief), and (2) there is a pragmatic rule that plans that achieve values are positively evaluated (judgment rule P-1). Notice that THUNDER has reasons for both a positive and negative evaluation of John's bank robbery. However, THUNDER is not holding contradicting beliefs, but has reasons for believing both sides of the evaluation.

VALUE JUDGMENTS ABOUT CHARACTERS

Value judgments about story characters can be represented by value judgments about the plans that the characters execute or will be expected to execute. Carbonell [1980] recognized the relationship of values to personality traits. In his model of personality traits, Carbonell used a prototypical goal tree to represent the normative orientation of people's goals. Personality traits were then represented as modifications to the prototypical goal hierarchy. For example, the modifications to the goal tree for an "ambitious" person are to have their achievement goals moved higher in the tree, and preservation goals for others moved lower. This represents that an ambitious person will sacrifice family and friends to get ahead. Carbonell [1980, p.67] notes that goal trees do not completely represent personality traits; some traits have *means-oriented* components, meaning that they describe the planning choices that a character is expected to make. An "ambitious" person is expected to use deceptive plans, and will be hesitant to compromise, while a "capable" person will make correct decisions in plan selection and carry out plans without making errors.

The means-oriented components of personality traits can be represented by including the method by which a character achieves goals, or causes goals to fail. In THUNDER, the reasons that a character is expected to do 'good' or 'bad' actions are represented by *character assessments.* Character assessments are representations of the reasons for evaluative beliefs about characters, and provide the reader with a moral context in which to judge their actions.

There are two types of character assessments, corresponding to the ends of the evaluative scale: (1) *positive* character assessments, that represent how the character achieves goal successes, and (2) *negative*, that represent how the character causes goal failures. Character assessments have three components: (1) the type of goal that the character will achieve, or cause to fail, (2) the planning situation in which the assessment applies, and (3) the action that the character does in that situation to cause the goal consequences. For example, in the negative assessment for a "coward", the goal that the person will have fail is preservation of self esteem, the plan-situation where the failure occurs is during plan-execution in reaction to adversity, and the method of failure is that person abandons their goal when faced with an adverse situation. In contrast, an "imaginative" person has a positive assessment for all goals that apply in plan creation situations, and an "affectionate" person has a positive assessment for achieving other people's friendship and love goals by executing plans for those goals.

There are two sources of character assessments in story understanding: (1) *direct* character assessments, which are generated from the goal successes and failures that characters have in the story, and (2) *background* character assessments, which are associated with lexical entries, such as "coward", "affectionate, and "imaginative", or with other knowledge sources containing expectations about people, such as Schank and Abelson's [1977] role themes.

Direct character assessments provide reasons for evaluative beliefs about characters from goal successes and failures in the story, and background character assessments provide reasons based on a character's *capability* to cause goals to succeed or fail. For example, compare:

EX–7A: John beat up Jerry and took his lunch money.

EX–7B: John was a mean, spiteful sixth grader.

In EX–7A, John is bad because of what he did: a direct negative character assessment is built because he violated Jerry's P-HEALTH goal. In EX–7B, John is bad because the reader expects him to do things like beat people up; based on his description as mean and spiteful, a background negative character assessment is built for John that represents the expectation that John will cause P-HEALTH goal failures for others.

Character assessments provide (1) reasons for the reader's evaluation of the character, and (2) expectations about future character behavior. The expectation information associated with personality traits can be accessed from static knowledge of background assessments, or created dynamically by THUNDER as direct character assessments. Thus, expectations can be generated both from character descriptions and their actions.

REASONING ABOUT OBLIGATION

In addition to having goals, story characters may incur *obligations.* An obligation is a belief that someone should have a goal, but not that that person necessarily has that goal. An obligation is represented as a positive evaluative belief where the content of the belief is that the character has a goal. For example, if THUNDER reads the sentence:

EX–8A: John borrowed $5 from Bill...

From knowledge about 'borrowing', THUNDER knows that John has an obligation to pay Bill back. This obligation is represented as a goal that John should have, so THUNDER positively evaluates the situation where John has the goal of paying Bill $5. John may not share the belief; if the sentence continued:

EX–8B: ..., which John never intended to pay back.

THUNDER would make the judgment that John's intention not to repay the loan is ethically wrong, because THUNDER has the belief that John should have the goal, but John does not have the goal.

Since the content of an obligation is a goal for another party, characters that achieve these goals are evaluated positively for ethical reasons. Similarly, characters that violate obligations are evaluated negatively for ethical reasons. Story characters acquire obligations from the relationships that they become involved in, and from their description. Obligations are associated with knowledge structures for relationships, such as 'lovers', 'teacher/student' and 'employer/employee', and role-themes, like 'policeman' or 'bank president.' For example, in the 'teacher/student' relationship, the teacher has the goal that the students learn the material, and the students have the goal of showing the teacher that they have learned the material. Thus, one ethical reason that cheating on a test is wrong is that it violates the student's obligation to the teacher.

The values and obligations that THUNDER believes are good are distinguished from the goals that characters have, so that what a character wants and what the system believes that a character *should* want do not get confused. The goals that a character has provide their motivations, and the THUNDER's values and understanding of obligations provide a moral context in which to evaluate the character's actions.

CONCLUSIONS

The process of making value judgments has been implemented in THUNDER by modeling the creation of evaluative beliefs. Story characters' plans are evaluated using a general set of pragmatic and ethical judgment rules. These rules are independent of any particular individual. The parts of the model that are idiosyncratic to the individual are the data that the rules operate on: the factual and evaluative beliefs that the system has. THUNDER's primary task during story understanding is to make evaluative judgments about story characters' actions, and then to use those judgments to (1) focus attention, (2) control inferencing, and (3) recognize the thematic elements of the story. In addition, the representation for the reasons for evaluation of characters' plans can also be used to represent (1) the reasons for evaluation of characters, and (2) expectations and rationale for character behavior. By representing obligations as beliefs about goals for others, THUNDER can reason about violations of interpersonal relations.

ACKNOWLEDGMENTS

This work is supported in part by a grant from the Hughes Artificial Intelligence Center. Thanks to Dr. Michael Dyer, Jack Hodges, Trent Lange, Seth Goldman, Stephanie August, and the reviewers for their comments on an earlier version of this paper.

REFERENCES

Ayer, A. J. (1935). *Language, Truth and Logic.* Dover Publications, New York, second edition.

Boyce, W. D. and Jensen, L. C. (1978). *Moral Reasoning: A Psychological-Philosophical Integration.* University of Nebraska Press, Lincoln, NB.

Carbonell, J. G. (1978). Politics: Automated ideological reasoning. *Cognitive Science*, 2(1):29–51.

Carbonell, J. G. (1979). *Subjective Understanding: Computer Models of Belief Systems,.* PhD thesis, Department of Computer Science, Yale University, New Haven CT. Technical Report 150.

Carbonell, J. G. (1980). Towards a process model of human personality traits. *Artificial Intelligence*, 15:49–74.

Cohen, P. R. (1985). *Heuristic Reasoning about Uncertainty: An Artificial Intelligence Approach (Research Notes on Artificial Intelligence 2).* Pitman Advanced Publishing, London.

Dyer, M. G. (1983). *In-Depth Understanding: A Computer Model of Integrated Processing for Narrative Comprehension.* MIT Press, Cambridge, MA.

Hare, R. M. (1952). *The Language of Morals.* Oxford University Press, Oxford.

Pearl, J. (1988). *Probabilistic Reasoning In Intelligent Systems: Networks of Plausible Inference.* Morgan-Kaufman, San Mateo, CA.

Reeves, J. F. (1988). Ethical understanding: Recognizing and using belief conflict in narrative understanding. In *Proceedings of AAAI-88*, St Paul, MN.

Rokeach, M. (1973). *The Nature of Human Values.* Free Press, New York.

Schank, R. C. and Abelson, R. P. (1977). *Scripts Plans Goals and Understanding.* Lawrence Erlbaum, Hillsdale, NJ.

Stevenson, C. L. (1944). *Ethics and Language.* Yale University Press, New Haven, CT.

Toulmin, S. (1950). *The Place of Reason in Ethics.* Cambridge University Press, Cambridge.

Dynamic Reinforcement Driven Error Propagation Networks with Application to Game Playing

Tony Robinson and Frank Fallside
Cambridge University Engineering Department,
Trumpington Street, Cambridge, England.
(ajr@dsl.eng.cam.ac.uk)

ABSTRACT

This paper discusses the problem of the reinforcement driven learning of a response to a time varying sequence. The problem has three parts: the adaptation of internal parameters to model complex mappings; the ability of the architecture to represent time varying input; and the problem of credit assignment with unknown delays between the input, output and reinforcement signals. The method developed in this paper is based on a connectionist network trained using the error propagation algorithm with internal feedback. The network is viewed both as a context dependent predictor of the reinforcement signal and as a means of temporal credit assignment. Several architectures for these networks are discussed and insight into the implementation problems is gained by an application to the game of noughts and crosses.

INTRODUCTION

Of the three major types of learning: supervised; reinforcement driven; and unsupervised; it is reinforcement driven learning which is most applicable to to the formulation of models of animal behaviour and to the design of 'intelligent' machines which must operate with no a priori knowledge of their environment. Under this scheme a model is presented with a time varying input and it generates a time varying output. Feedback for adaptation comes from a single scalar which measures the past performance of the model. In this paper is it assumed that there is a maximum frequency at which these signals change and so the signals may be sampled at a constant rate without loss of information. It is also assumed that the input and output signals have a fixed dimensionality, and can therefore be represented by a sequence of vectors. These are common assumptions in the field of digital signal processing.

Connectionist reinforcement driven learning of arbitrary functions has three main prerequisites:

- The computational power of the model must be sufficient to represent the desired mapping and a suitable learning algorithm must exist. Models with restricted computational power, such as the linear mapping of the input space to the output space, are insufficient for learning complex tasks. However, the class of non-linear functions known as error propagation networks or multi-layer perceptrons [Rumelhart *et al.*, 1986] have the power to represent arbitrary mappings, and the parameters in these models may be trained using the technique of gradient descent.

- The model must have the capacity for sequence recognition and generation, and for a self-contained system the storage must be provided internally. Within the framework of error propagation networks there are many candidates. The first recurrent error propagation network was formulated by Rumelhart, Hinton and Williams [1986] and employs full connection from all units to the next time frame using an external buffer to store past activations during training. Partial connectivity and partial feedback of the error signal has been presented by Jordan [1986] and Robinson and Fallside [1987a] which has the advantage that no external buffer is needed. Full feedback of the error signal without an external buffer but with considerably increased internal storage has been formulated by Robinson and Fallside [1987a] and implemented by Williams and Zipser [1988].

- Finally, a mechanism is needed for credit assignment, that is which elements of the output vector and at what delay are to be assigned the credit for the reinforcement signal. Sutton and Barto have provided a means for credit assignment in a single node network by applying a first order filter to the input and defining the error signal as the difference of successive outputs [Sutton and Barto, 1981] or as the difference of successive predictions of future reinforcement [Sutton and Barto, 1987]. Barto, Sutton and Anderson [1983] developed a two node network where the function of the second node is to assign credit to the output of the first node. Sutton [1984] evaluates several of these models for temporal credit assignment. In the case where the reinforcement signal is a complex function of the input and output signal an error propagation network may be used to learn the required mapping. Munro [1987] and Jordan [1988] have both trained a network in this manner by presenting random pairs of inputs and outputs.

Whilst previous work has incorporated two of these aspects, it is the aim of this paper to combine all three. The following description assumes familiarity with error propagation networks, begins by describing feedback within these networks and proceeds to the joining of two networks so that they may be trained with a reinforcement signal. Two architectures for this type of network are given, and one of these is applied to the game of noughts and crosses.

ARCHITECTURES

There are many approaches to the architecture and training of error propagation networks with feedback. Common to all of these is that three distinct vectors can be identified: the input vector, $u(t)$; a state vector, $x(t)$; and an output vector, $y(t)$. The vectors $u(t-1)$ and $x(t-1)$ are used as input to an error propagation net whose output is $y(t)$ and $x(t)$, as in figure 1. In some models the state vector has common elements with the output vector or the vector of hidden unit activations, but this paper will consider the general case where the only necessary relationship is though the mapping made by the network.

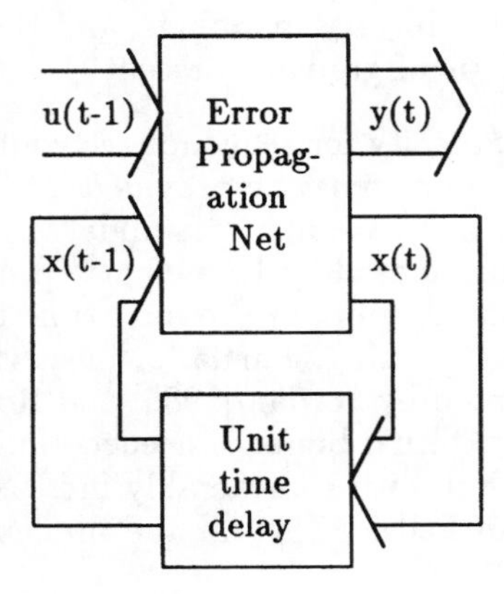

Figure 1: The Dynamic Net

The error propagation network is deliberately shown as a 'black box'. All that is required of the non-linear function contained within it is that given the partial derivative of the cost function (or 'energy') with respect to the value of each element of the vectors $y(t)$ and $x(t)$, it is possible to calculate the same derivative with respect to each element of the vectors $u(t-1)$ and $x(t-1)$ and also with respect to every parameter (or 'weight') within the network. Whilst it is most common to populate the network with nodes which compute a weighted sum of their input vector and pass this through a sigmoidal non-linearity, many other node types are also possible [Robinson, 1989].

A reinforcement driven dynamic net can be formed from two such dynamic nets and this architecture is given in figure 2. The first dynamic net (net Y) computes the overall output of the system from the sequence of input vectors. This net corresponds to the 'Associative Search Element' of Sutton and Barto. After training the complete behaviour of the network is specified by this network alone. However, during training a second dynamic net (net Z) is used for credit assignment of the reinforcement signal. This network corresponds to the 'Adaptive Critic Element' of Sutton and Barto. The function of the second net is to compute the expected reinforcement by modelling the behaviour of the environment in which the first net is placed (including of course the effect of the first net on the environment).

Unlike the two phase training schemes presented by Munro and Jordan, in this architecture both networks are trained at the same time. This is done by formulating the problem in terms of a single cost function which is a linear combination of two quantities: the expected squared difference between the prediced reinforcement signal and the observed reinforcement signal; and the expected squared difference between the prediced reinforcement signal and the desired reinforcement signal. Thus the cost function is minimised if the model can accurately predict the reinforcement signal, and that this reinforcement signal is close to the desired reinforcement (assumed to be the 'high' state).

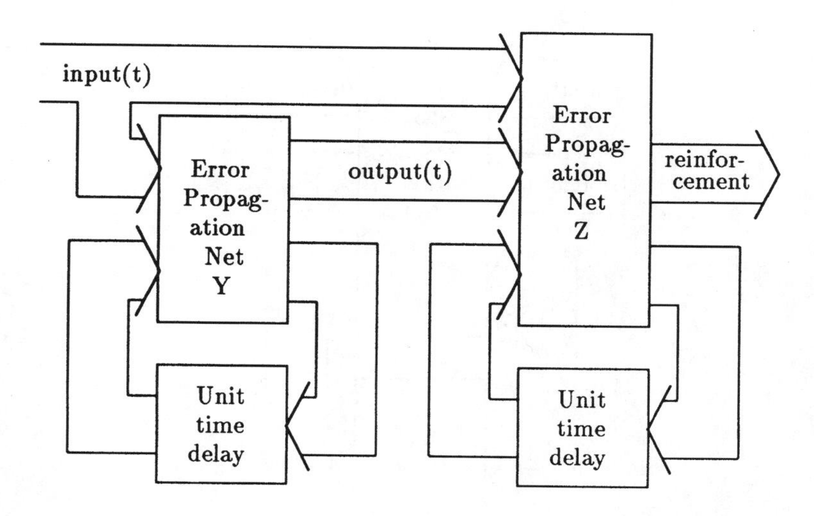

Figure 2: The Reinforcement Driven Dynamic Net

The training may be achieved in two passes for each input vector. In one pass the prediced reinforcement signal is compared with the observed reinforcement signal to calculate the derivative of the cost function with respect to the observed reinforcement output. This derivative signal is propagated back through net Z for all previous times that have influence on the observed reinforcement output and the corresponding derivative of the weights in this net is calculated. In the other pass the prediced reinforcement signal is compared with the desired reinforcement signal and this signal is propagated back through both nets and the derivative with respect to the weights in net Y is calculated. As with standard error propagation networks the derivatives may be used immediately to update the weights in a stochastic gradient descent, or alternatively the weights maybe changed after every pass through the complete training set.

In practice the two nets may be combined to achieve a more compact net, as in figure 3. This is desirable as the back-propagation of errors is a linear process and so the two error signals may be combined and propagated back as a single signal, so reducing the computation. A simple example of this network has previously been presented [Robinson and Fallside, 1987b] in which the net received a high reinforcement if the output had the same sign as the previous input, otherwise the reinforcement was low. Thus it has already been demonstrated that these networks can model a unit time delay.

A GENERAL GAME PLAYING PROGRAM

A subclass of the general net outlined above can be used for game playing, in which case the reinforcement signal is defined only at the end of the game. The technique adopted here is to play a game using the network of figure 2, storing the intermediate activations of all units. At the end of the game two separate computations are performed, one to make a more accurate

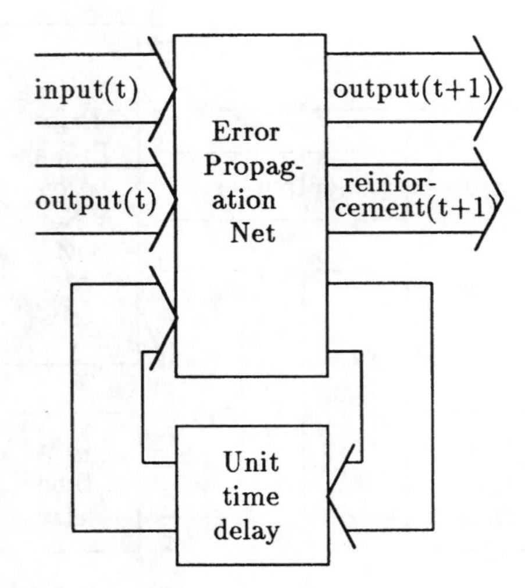

Figure 3: A Compact Reinforcement Driven Dynamic Net

prediction of the reinforcement signal the end of the game, and the second to bias this signal to the high reinforcement state.

NOUGHTS AND CROSSES

The game of 'noughts and crosses' or 'tic tac toe' was chosen for several reasons:

- It is well known and regarded as a 'simple' childrens game. However, it may be classified as 'difficult' when judged by the current standard of connectionist learning procedures.
- The mapping of a board position onto the optimal next move is a complex non-linear function requiring the learning of disjoint pattern classes.
- The state of the game is uniquely defined by the board position, so that net Y does not need any state units.
- The board may be represented in relatively few bits. Each of the nine locations may be unoccupied or occupied by either a 'O' or a 'X'. Thus an upper bound on the number of legal states is $3^9 = 19683$, which can be represented in 15 bits.
- The game has a short duration as no player may place more than five pieces on the board. Thus as far as assigning credit or blame for the outcome of the game, the error signal must be propagated back through a maximum of five states.

The 'opponent' to the net was a simple algorithm that would win by completing a line of two if possible, otherwise a piece would be placed randomly. If the net places pieces randomly, as is the case before any learning, then the net wins about 30% of the games which are not drawn. A suitably experienced player would never loose and only occasionally draw against this algorithm.

IMPLEMENTATION

Two 3x3 matrices were used to represent the board position. One has each element set high if the corresponding board position is occupied, the other is used to record the owner of the piece placed on the occupied site. The output representation was another 3x3 matrix, the legal move with the largest value in this matrix (after the addition of noise as discussed later) was taken as the move to be made. No attempt was made to take advantage of the symmetry of the game.

The machine was trained a 65 processor array of T800 transputers running at about 50 Mflops. Forty games were played per processor per update, so the weights were updated on gradient information collected over 2600 games. Each net had 144 hidden units with a sigmoidal activation function ranging from -1 to $+1$. The target values for the outputs were chosen to be in the linear region of the activation function, $+0.1$ for positive reinforcement and -0.1 for negative reinforcement.

PROBLEMS

Reinforcement driven learning is a harder task than supervised learning for the simple reason that less information is provided about the desired output. For the game playing program presented here there is the additional problem that changes to the weights change the response given to early moves, so the whole style of the game can change. For example, the initial moves are random, so the prediction and maximisation of the reinforcement signal is carried out for nearly fully populated boards of randomly placed pieces. However, towards the end of the learning period the game length has become shorter and there are correspondingly fewer pieces on the board. Thus the prediction and maximisation functions must relearn for this new set of training data. Because the form of the training set is dependent on the current performance, the net does not perform a gradient descent in a single function throughout the training, but performs a gradient descent in a continually changing function. Thus there is no guarantee of convergence or stability.

The algorithm used as an opponent to the net employed a random number generator to pick a legal move if it could not place a piece to win the game. This randomness means that some responses would be given more often than others in an unpredictable way and this hinders the learning by the introduction of noise into the error signal.

A strict pick-the-biggest rule to convert the output of the net into a symbolic form was found to lead to unstable behaviour during training. This is because the magnitude of the difference between the largest and second largest element is unimportant which results in a discontinuity in the weight space. For example, a small difference of activity in an output unit might change the move made during a game, and change the outcome of the game. So, for the same reason as step activation functions can not be used within a network, a step response in interpreting the output must be avoided. A probabilistic representation of the the output vector was used to improve the stability. This was implemented by adding random noise to the output vector before choosing the largest element. The noise was generated by the difference of two random numbers with range 0.1. Thus if one output was more than 0.2 above all the others this noise has no effect, otherwise the noise results in random decisions which, when averaged, blur out the discontinuities in the weight space. An alternative deterministic solution to this problem has been proposed by Boothroyd [1989, personal communication] in which a connectionist net is used to warp the output space closer to the form expected by the pick-the-biggest rule. Some preliminary investigations have been reported by Robinson [Robinson, 1989]. In a 'real world' environment, such as that of autonomous robot control, an analogue output may be appropriate and this would avoid the problem.

RESULTS

The initial performance of the net was to win about 30% of the games played. After playing 300,000 games this figure improved to 59%, and playing a further 3,000,000 games produced no further improvement. Whilst the performance of the net is lower than the optimal performance, the net did learn sufficiently to perform better than the opponent algorithm which it played against.

CONCLUSION

This paper has presented a scheme for implementing reinforcement driven learning for arbitrary sequences of input and output vectors. Three necessary conditions have been identified: the ability to make arbitrary mappings; the ability to store contextual information; and the ability to do credit assignment. This approach has used error propagation networks for the mappings, feedback of state information to provide context and a new cost function to perform credit assignment. The new cost function is a linear sum of that required to form a good predictor of the reinforcement signal and that required to maximise the reinforcement signal.

A dynamic reinforcement driven error propagation network has been applied to the game of noughts and crosses. The final performance was slightly better than the opponent algorithm but lower than the optimal performance. This has raised issues related to changing environmental conditions during training, statistical fluctuations in gradient descent techniques and the interfacing of a distributed machine to a symbolic environment.

ACKNOWLEDGEMENTS

One of the authors, Tony Robinson, would like to acknowledge financial support from the UK Science and Engineering Research Council, Cambridge University Engineering Department and Trinity Hall, Cambridge. Technical support was received from the ParSiFal project IKBS/146 which developed the transputer array, and considerable academic support was received from all members of the connectionist group in Cambridge University Engineering Department.

REFERENCES

[Barto *et al.*, 1983] Andrew G. Barto, Richard S. Sutton, and Charles W. Anderson. Neuronlike adaptive elements that can solve difficult learning control problems. *IEEE Transactions on Systems, Man, and Cybernetics*, 13(5):834–846, 1983.

[Boothroyd, 1989] C. B. Boothroyd. January 1989. Department of Material Science, Cambridge University. Personal communication.

[Jordan, 1986] Micheal I. Jordan. *Serial Order: A Parallel Distributed Processing Approach.* ICS Report 8604, Institute for Cognitive Science, University of California, San Diego, May 1986.

[Jordan, 1988] Michael I. Jordan. *Supervised learning and systems with excess degrees of freedom.* COINS Technical Report 88-27, Massachusetts Institute of Technology, May 1988.

[Munro, 1987] P. W. Munro. A dual back-propagation scheme for scalar reinforcement learning. In *Proceedings of the Ninth Annual Conference of the Cognitive Science Society*, Seattle, WA, 1987.

[Robinson, 1989] A. J. Robinson. *Dynamic Error Propagation Networks.* PhD thesis, Cambridge University Engineering Department, February 1989.

[Robinson and Fallside, 1987a] A. J. Robinson and F. Fallside. Static and dynamic error propagation networks with application to speech coding. In Dana Z. Anderson, editor, *Proceedings of Neural Information Processing Systems*, American Institute of Physics, Denver, November 1987.

[Robinson and Fallside, 1987b] A. J. Robinson and F. Fallside. *The Utility Driven Dynamic Error Propagation Network.* Technical Report CUED/F-INFENG/TR.1, Cambridge University Engineering Department, 1987.

[Rumelhart *et al.*, 1986] D. E. Rumelhart, G. E. Hinton, and R. J. Williams. Learning internal representations by error propagation. In D. E. Rumelhart and J. L. McClelland, editors, *Parallel Distributed Processing: Explorations in the Microstructure of Cognition. Vol. I: Foundations.*, chapter 8, Bradford Books/MIT Press, Cambridge, MA, 1986.

[Sutton, 1984] Richard S. Sutton. *Temporal Credit Assignment in Reinforcement Learning.* PhD thesis, University of Massachusetts, Department of Computer and Information Science, February 1984.

[Sutton and Barto, 1981] Richard S. Sutton and Andrew G. Barto. An adaptive network that constructs and uses and internal model of its world. *Cognition and Brain Theory*, 4(3):217–246, 1981.

[Sutton and Barto, 1987] Richard S. Sutton and Andrew G. Barto. A temporal-difference model of classical conditioning. In *Proceedings of the Ninth Annual Conference of the Cognitive Science Society*, Seattle, WA, 1987.

[Williams and Zipser, 1988] R. J. Williams and D. Zipser. *A Learning Algorithm for Continually Running Fully Recurrent Neural Networks.* ICS Report 8805, Institute for Cognitive Science, University of California, San Diego, October 1988.

A Case for Symbolic/Sub-symbolic Hybrids

Daniel E. Rose
Richard K. Belew

Cognitive Computer Science Research Group
Computer Science and Engineering Department
University of California, San Diego

Abstract

This paper considers the question of what qualities are necessary for an AI system to be a hybrid of symbolic and sub-symbolic approaches. Definitions of symbolic and sub-symbolic systems are given. SCALIR, a hybrid system for information retrieval, is presented, and then used to show how both symbolic and sub-symbolic processing can be combined. Arguments against SCALIR's hybrid nature are presented and rejected.

INTRODUCTION

Several times in the history of artificial intelligence (AI), researchers have divided up into rival camps arguing for or against certain approaches to various problems. The procedural vs. declarative knowledge dispute (Winograd, 1985) is one past instance of this. In many cases the disputes are resolved over time. One way this happens is that new conceptual frameworks arrive which encompass rival approaches, or simply show that one approach subsumes the other. Another way is for new techniques to be developed which merge the two sides.

Today, the rival camps are arguing for "symbolic" or "connectionist" AI systems. As supporters of the connectionist approach, we hope that the long-range solution to the debate will be the first one described above: symbolic processing will be shown to be an emergent property of large-scale sub-symbolic processing. In the mean time, however, we are investigating the second solution: developing a hybrid system which takes advantage of the strengths of both approaches.

SCALIR is a hybrid[1] system for legal informational retrieval currently being developed by one of the authors. When we first began to describe the system to others, we discovered an interesting phenomenon. Rather than arguing for or against the hybrid nature of the system, some members of our audience claimed that the system was not really a hybrid at all. Even more notably, some claimed that it was essentially just symbolic, while others said it was just connectionist.

In this paper we will outline the system in question, and then present and refute arguments challenging its dual symbolic and connectionist nature. In doing this, we will examine the question of what it means to be a symbolic or sub-symbolic system — and what it takes to be a hybrid.

THE SUB-SYMBOLIC/SYMBOLIC DICHOTOMY

The term "symbolic," as used in this paper, refers to the dominant approach to AI research for much of the past thirty years. From a cognitive perspective, the symbolic approach rests on Newell's Physical Symbol System Hypothesis (which says in essence that symbol manipulation is a necessary condition for intelligence) (Newell, 1980), but the use of symbolic AI systems predates this exposition of its premises.

Many traditional AI tools and techniques, such as expert systems, frames, and heuristic search do some form of symbol manipulation. We wish to characterize computational properties of symbolic systems, independent of accounts (such as Newell's) of their role in cognition.

[1]Throughout this paper, we use "hybrid" as shorthand for "symbolic/sub-symbolic hybrid."

We will focus on a narrow view of symbols rather than attempting to incorporate the vast philosophical tradition associated with them.

Our account begins with the following:

Definition 1 *A label is a unique identifier belonging to a previously enumerated, fixed set.*

With this definition in mind, we can say what it means to be a symbolic system:

Definition 2 *Symbolic systems are those in which the next state is selectively determined by labels associated with the objects of computation.*

This definition works for all systems generally considered symbolic, not just those with explicit logical rules. For example, the definition explains why a semantic network with spreading activation search is essentially a symbolic system. First, links as well as nodes in the network are labeled (and thus are symbols). Second, "activation" is typically a discrete marker (symbol), whose label affects its treatment. The decision to pass or not pass a marker depends solely on the links' labels.

For our other level of processing, we need another definition:[2]

Definition 3 *A class C is interchangeable if and only if all functions which operate on elements of C (i.e. whose domains are C^n for any integer n)*

1. *map only to range C, and*
2. *are infinitely many-to-one.*

Note that any computation using a member x of such a class will proceed identically regardless of which of the infinitely many possibilities which map to x were used, hence the name "interchangeable."

The term "connectionist" refers to the class of approaches based on neurally-inspired computer models. We will use the term to be representative of a broader class of sub-symbolic models which have the following property:

Definition 4 *Sub-symbolic systems are those in which the mechanism for mapping from input(s) to output(s)*

1. *is expressed in terms of interchangeable, continuous quantities, and*
2. *is modulated by continuous parameters determined by specific characteristics of the data (as opposed to general properties of the computational mechanism).*

Connectionist nets are fundamentally sub-symbolic; the interchangeable quantities is generally called "activations" and the modulating parameters are called "weights." But connectionist nets are not the only examples of sub-symbolic systems. The Classifier system (Holland et al., 1986) uses message "intensity" as its quantity and classifier "strength" as its modulating parameter, and so has sub-symbolic characteristics.

Armed with these definitions, we can now be clear about what we mean by "hybrid." A *hybrid system* is simply one which contains both symbolic and subsymbolic components. A degenerate case of a hybrid system is a connectionist net and an expert system put in the same box, each doing something different with the same input and producing its respective portion of the box's output. We will generally be interested in *tightly-coupled* systems, in which the components interact before the final output is produced.

OVERVIEW OF SCALIR

SCALIR (for Symbolic and Connectionist Approach to Legal Information Retrieval) is an AI system for full-text document retrieval. It uses techniques similar to Belew's AIR (Belew, 1986) but adds a symbolic mechanism useful for the legal domain. We claim that SCALIR is a tightly-coupled hybrid system.

The legal system has an interesting dual nature which makes it especially amenable to a hybrid approach. On the one hand, statutes are sets of rules to be applied in specific cases, and explicit symbolic relationships exist in almost every aspect of the law. On the other hand, the use of precedent to decide court cases means that the law is made in a parallel and distributed way; each case is decided on the basis of all relevant decisions in the past. Furthermore, statutes and court decisions are written in natural language, whose ambiguity makes it resistant to symbolic approaches. (These arguments are developed further in another paper (Rose and Belew, 1989)).

SCALIR's retrieval mechanism uses two interleaved networks, one connectionist and one symbolic. Nodes

[2] We use mathematical notation here for conciseness, not mathematical rigor.

representing terms, court cases, and statute sections are shared between the two networks. However, they are connected with two separate sets of links.

C-links are weighted, unlabeled connectionist links which use the microfeatures of the law (e.g. the individual words which appear in a court decision) to form associative relationships between legal documents. The resulting C-network is similar to the associative network in AIR.

S-links are labeled, unweighted symbolic links which use explicitly encoded knowledge about the law for inference. The S-links form a kind of semantic network which describes the relationships of the different types of nodes. For example, the well-known "key number" taxonomy of the law produced by West Publishing Co. provides a hierarchic structure for SCALIR's term nodes.

User queries can involve both associative and symbolic components. For example, the user could essentially ask the system to retrieve all cases which disputed a certain decision. Activity would propagate only through symbolic links which corresponded to negative citations, e.g. to an overruling case. From there it might spread to other cases generally related to the overruling ones.

Hybrid activity propagation is implemented by separating the activity into several components, which metaphorically can be viewed as different colored light. C-links are like grey filters which modify the intensity of the light. Each type of S-link is like a different colored filter, which allows only its corresponding type of light (i.e. activity) to pass. This means that the symbolic inference process — deciding whether or not to pass on activity depending on the type of S-link — can be done locally at each node. Figure 1 shows the process schematically.

Input to SCALIR takes the form of real-valued activations placed on a set of nodes. These activations spread through both C-links and S-links, and are combined numerically along the way. Finally, nodes which reach a high enough level of activity are considered outputs. Thus all processing debts are ultimately cashed in connectionist coin.

As in AIR, learning occurs as a result of negative and positive reinforcement from the user. Since there is no exact right answer in information retrieval, the user's browsing behavior becomes the feedback signal. In other words, when a user indicates that the search is to be pruned in a certain direction ("I don't want any more documents like this") or expanded ("I want to see more about this topic"), this results in negative or positive feedback to the system.

It is a relatively simple matter to use the feedback to train the weights on the C-links. S-links, on the other hand, do not have weights, since they represent explicit knowledge. Hybrid learning suffers from the traditional credit-assignment problem. When the system performs well (or poorly), how do we know whether the C-links or the S-links are primarily responsible? SCALIR's solution is to also learn the appropriate contributions of each component.

BUT IS IT CONNECTIONIST?

In this section we shall examine various versions of an argument that SCALIR is essentially a symbolic system. We will begin with general objections and move gradually to more specific ones:

> "Your system is simulated on a Von Neumann architecture using a program written in symbols. Therefore it is symbolic."

There is always an implementation level below the level of interest. One could equally well say that a theorem-prover was sub-symbolic because it depended completely on continuously varying electric fields in the circuits of the computer. But the most accurate description of the behavior of a theorem-prover is at the level of symbols. Similarly, SCALIR's C-network is best understood as sub-symbolic.

> "Even so, any processing done with symbolic nodes is symbolic processing."

If this were true, than essentially all connectionist systems would be symbolic. Inputs and outputs must represent something in the world in order to be useful, thus they are necessarily symbols. The designer of any connectionist net must explicitly code the meaning of input and output nodes. Having some nodes being symbolic does not make the system symbolic.

> "Yes, but the nodes in other connectionist systems form distributed representations, while SCALIR's are localist."

While distributed representations have many virtues in connectionist systems (see (Hinton et al., 1986), for example), this issue is a red herring with respect to the symbolic/sub-symbolic question. In fact, local is a subjective concept. For example, an ASCII code is a representation of a character distributed over seven bits. Yet some of the bits are localist representations of features of the character (such as case and printability).

> "Okay, but at least most connectionist systems have hidden nodes. SCALIR's nodes are all visible."

This claim presupposes a certain network architecture which SCALIR does not have. In networks with hidden units, such as layered feedforward nets or Boltzmann machines, these units are not accessible from the environment in any way. In this sense, it is true to say that SCALIR has no hidden units. However, in these systems, hidden units are usually defined as those which are neither inputs nor outputs. Input units and output units are all manipulated and examined every time the network is used. In SCALIR, only a fraction of the network is activated by a query as input, and only a fraction becomes active as output. But for the purposes of that query, all the remaining nodes in the network can serve as hidden units which do sub-symbolic processing.

> "But these so-called hidden units are still symbols. They represent features, rather than microfeatures."

Again, feature-hood is a subjective concept; one net's feature is another's microfeature. For example, a net trained to recognize handwriting might learn microfeatures corresponding to various arcs at various orientations, with letters as features to be detected. At the same time, a word-recognition net could use those letters as microfeatures. In SCALIR, terms are viewed as microfeatures of the law.

> "As long as the nodes have meaningful labels, *they are still symbols!*"

The question is not whether there are labels. The question is the labels are used in processing. SCALIR's connectionist component ignores the labels entirely.

It is a truism in connectionism that "the knowledge is in the weights." This being the case, it is the existence of these weights, communicating only interchangeable continuous activation, which should be our litmus test for sub-symbolic processing. The fact that the nodes are labeled is irrelevant. As Fodor and Pylyshyn explain:

> Strictly speaking, the labels play *no role at all* in determining the operation of the Connectionist machine; in particular, the operation of the machine is unaffected by the syntactic and semantic relations that hold among the expressions that are used as labels. To put this another way, the node labels in a Connectionist machine are not part of the causal structure of the machine. (Fodor and Pylyshyn, 1988)

BUT IS IT SYMBOLIC?

As in the previous section, we will now consider more arguments which dispute the hybrid nature of SCALIR. This time, however, the claims are that SCALIR doesn't really do any symbolic processing. These arguments rest on some the previously noted observation that "all processing debts in SCALIR are ultimately cashed in connectionist coin."

We begin with what is essentially the complement of one of the arguments from the previous section:

> "Connectionism pervades even the allegedly symbolic parts of SCALIR. Therefore SCALIR does no symbolic processing."

To begin with, we will concede that connectionist "baggage" plays more of a role in SCALIR's symbolic component than the reverse. This is simply because activation is the *lingua franca* chosen for communication between the two components of the system. Nevertheless, the presence of one thing (traces of connectionism) does not prove the absence of another (symbolic processing).

> "But whatever the reason, it is real-valued activations, not symbols, which flow though S-links. What is symbolic about them?"

It is true that real-valued activations are passed along by S-links. In fact, to prevent activity from spreading to the whole network, S-links cause a slight attenuation of the activity, and can thus be considered to have a "weight" just like connectionist links. Despite this, two qualities make S-links symbolic.

First, *knowledge is not in the weights.* Not only are the weights unlearned, they are unrelated to the data. Weights in connectionist nets are either learned (e.g. via back-propagation) or are set to pre-computed values designed to produce a certain behavior with respect to the data. The "weights" on SCALIR's S-links are set at a fixed value designed only to prevent infinite spread of activity. This is similar to the constraints on the distance markers can be passed in some semantic network implementations.

Note that systems which use pre-computed weights may still be sub-symbolic. Two examples are Hopfield nets (in which weights are determined algorithmically) (Tank and Hopfield, 1987) and the interactive activation model of McClelland and Rumelhart (McClelland and Rumelhart, 1981; Rumelhart and McClelland, 1982) (in which the weights were set "by hand" in order to model certain empirical phenomena).

Second, *S-links respond selectively to symbols.* Specifically, the presence or absence of various types of activation determines whether those components are passed along those S-links. The filtering done by the S-links is a symbolic process, for it is exactly by virtue of having a specific label that an S-link allows or does not allow certain activity to pass. Returning to the comments of Fodor and Pylyshyn:

> ... [T]he state transitions of Classical [symbolic] machines are causally determined by *the structure ... of the symbol arrays that the machines transform*: change the symbols and the system behaves quite differently. (Fodor and Pylyshyn, 1988)

In SCALIR, the symbols being transformed are the symbolic components of activation at each node, and it is the S-links, by their filtering ability, that do the transformation.

THE LIMITS OF THE DICHOTOMY

While we have constructed our definitions of symbolic and sub-symbolic processing as robustly as possible, we do not believe the two approaches are mutually exclusive. In fact, there is a continuum from sub-symbolic to symbolic. In this section we will examine some of the harder cases which fall closer to the center of the continuum.

As explained in Section 2, semantic networks fall squarely into the realm of symbolic systems. What happens when we begin to add more "connectionist" attributes to a semantic network? (Systems with these attributes actually exist (Hendler, 1987).)

As a first step, suppose that the designer of a semantic network wishes to prevent too much of the network from being marked each time. We can imagine passing a number along with the marker. This number could be a counter for measuring path length. It could be incremented each time a link was traversed, and then used to terminate the search when it reaches a certain threshold.

Now, for computational simplicity, imagine that each node decrements this counter, rather than incrementing it, and stops if the value reaches zero. This way the parameter becomes easily tunable; the programmer can change the desired path length of searches by starting the initially marked nodes with various quantities in the counters.

Suppose that too many nodes are still being marked. The programmer might want to introduce a penalty for fan-out as well as path length. Each time markers leave a node, their counters can be set to the incoming marker's counter divided by the out-degree of the node.

One last modification: subtraction is too crude a control for path length; its effect is not proportional to the current magnitude of the counter. Instead of subtraction, we will multiply each counter by a value slightly less than one as it traverses a link. As an implementation detail to prevent roundoff errors, we will replace the integer counter with a real-valued one, and use real arithmetic for all our multiplications and divisions.

If we call the counters "activation" and the product of the divisors and the multipliers "weights", do we now have a connectionist system? Our claim is that we do not. As with SCALIR's S-links, the "weights" bear no relationship to the data; there is no knowledge in them. The currency of the system, markers, are not interchangeable, because the system responds selectively to them depending on the link labels. Symbolic inference remains the fundamental processing operation.

Now considering the other extreme, imagine a connectionist network in which each node in the input gets different kinds of activation — colored blue or yellow, perhaps. All computation is done in some standard connectionist fashion, except that active nodes become tagged with the color of their activation: blue, yellow, or green (where the colors have mixed). Nodes which become sufficiently active after a certain time (say, when the network reaches equilibrium) are considered outputs, with the following proviso: only green-tagged nodes are candidates for output. Do we now have a symbolic system?

In this case, we believe we have a tightly-coupled hybrid system. It still meets the conditions for sub-symbolic systems; its weights are either learned or constructed to produce a certain mapping on the data, using interchangeable activation. But it also meets the conditions for symbolic processing; the mapping from input to output depends on a differential response to labels.

There are many variations of this exercise, in which various attributes are added or removed to traditional symbolic or sub-symbolic systems. We will consider only one more case: a system which we claim lies at the boundary of the two approaches.

The system can be characterized in two ways. It is a semantic network in which there is only one kind of link (IS-A), and only one kind of marker. Alternatively, it is a connectionist network in which all nodes are localist and labeled, and all weights have the value one. Since there is only one type of link and marker, there can be no selective response on the basis of labels and the system is therefore not symbolic. Since all weights are equal and independent of the data, the network cannot do meaningful sub-symbolic processing. This illustrates that hybrid systems result from combining symbolic and sub-symbolic features, not by averaging them.

The Classifier system provides another example of a tightly-coupled symbolic/sub-symbolic hybrid. While this system shares many of the continuous, sub-symbolic qualities of connectionist nets, the fact that it also *broadcasts* messages globally (i.e., without the attenuation associated with path traversal) and typically performs a *discontinuous* match of messages with classifier conditions make the system have significant symbolic characteristics as well.

DISCUSSION

Along with its corresponding approaches to AI, the Symbolic/Sub-symbolic dichotomy is often described in terms of two views of cognition; Table 1 shows an informal characterization of the two views. Recently, many have suggested that both views are helpful in understanding cognition. As Norman explains:

> People interpret the world rapidly, effortlessly. But the development of new ideas, or evaluation of current thoughts proceeds slowly, serially, deliberately. People do seem to have at least two modes of operation, one rapid, efficient, subconscious, the other slow, serial, and conscious. (Norman, 1986, p. 542)

Since these two levels both have important roles to play, we believe it is useful (at least for the present) to design hybrid systems which take advantage of techniques designed for both levels. (Similar arguments have been made by other proponents of hybrid systems, such as Hendler (Hendler, 1989) and Dyer (Dyer, 1988).)

We have outlined some criteria for what it means to be a symbolic or sub-symbolic system, and what a hybrid of the two approaches might look like. Our work on SCALIR has given us an informal existence proof that such hybrids are feasible.

One practical benefit of a hybrid system is obvious: the techniques developed for the two paradigms have different strengths and weaknesses. In particular, connectionist systems are much better at learning, while it is much easier to store explicit knowledge in symbolic systems. In addition, we believe that hybrid systems will exhibit emergent properties not found in either of their single-paradigm components.

References

Belew, R. K. (1986). *Adaptive Information Retrieval: Machine Learning in Associative Networks.* PhD thesis, University of Michigan.

Dyer, M. G. (1988). Symbolic neuroengineering for natural language processing: A multilevel research approach. Technical Report UCLA-AI-88-14, Computer Science Department, University of California, Los Angeles.

Fodor, J. A. and Pylyshyn, Z. W. (1988). Connectionism and cognitive architecture: A critical analysis. *Cognition*, 28:3–71.

Hendler, J. A. (1987). *Integrating Marker-passing and Problem Solving: A spreading activation approach to improved choice in planning*. Lawrence Erlbaum Associates, Hillsdale, NJ.

Hendler, J. A. (1989). Marker-passing over microfeatures. *Cognitive Science*. To appear.

Hinton, G. E., McClelland, J. L., and Rumelhart, D. E. (1986). Distributed representations. In Rumelhart, D. E. and McClelland, J. L., editors, *Parallel Distributed Processing: Explorations in the microstructure of cognition. Volume 1: Foundations*, pages 77–109. MIT Press, Cambridge, MA.

Holland, J. H., Holyoak, K. J., Nisbitt, R. E., and Thagard, P. (1986). *Induction: Processes of learning, inference and discovery*. Bradford Books, Cambridge, MA.

McClelland, J. L. and Rumelhart, D. E. (1981). An interactive activation model of context effects in letter perception: Part 1. an account of basic findings. *Psychological Review*, 88:375–407.

Newell, A. (1980). Physical symbol systems. *Cognitive Science*, 2.

Norman, D. A. (1986). Reflections on cognition and parallel distributed processing. In McClelland, J. L. and Rumelhart, D. E., editors, *Parallel Distributed Processing: Explorations in the microstructure of cognition. Volume 2: Psychological and Biological Models*, pages 531–546. MIT Press, Cambridge, MA.

Rose, D. E. and Belew, R. K. (1989). Legal information retrieval: A hybrid approach. In *Proceedings of the Second International Conference on Artificial Intelligence and Law*, Vancouver, Canada. To appear.

Rumelhart, D. E. and McClelland, J. L. (1982). An interactive activation model of context effects in letter perception: Part 2. the contextual enhancement effect and some tests and extensions of the model. *Psychological Review*, 89:60–94.

Tank, D. W. and Hopfield, J. J. (1987). Collective computation in neuronlike circuits. *Scientific American*, 6(257).

Winograd, T. (1985). Frame representations and the declarative/procedural controversy. In Brachman, R. J. and Levesque, H. J., editors, *Readings in Knowledge Representation*, pages 357–370. Morgan Kaufmann, Los Altos, CA.

	SYMBOLIC	SUB-SYMBOLIC
AI Approach	Traditional	Connectionist/PDP
Inference	Rule-based	Statistical
Processing	Sequential	Parallel
Speed in brain	Slow (> 100ms)	Fast (< 100ms)
Robustness	Brittle	Graceful degradation
Precision	High	Low
Representation	Features	Microfeatures

Table 1: Comparison of two paradigms.

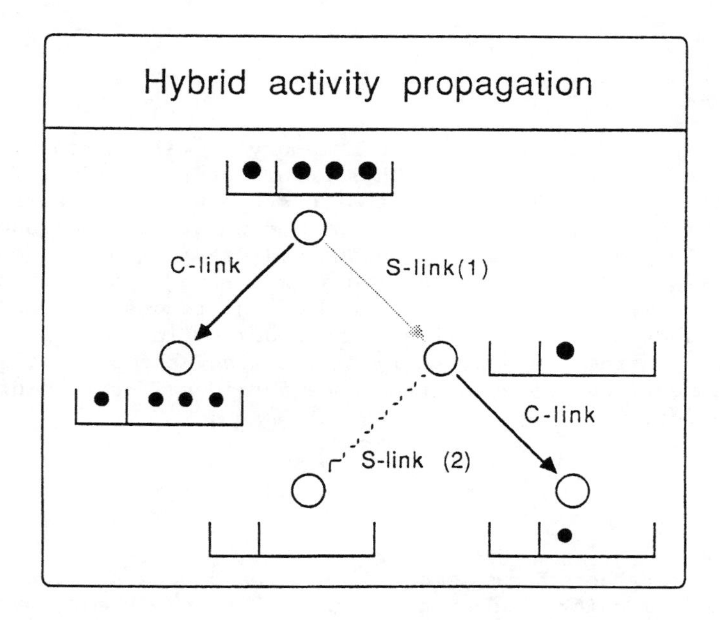

Figure 1: The row of filled dots represents different components of activation; the first is unspecified (i.e. strictly connectionist) while the others correspond to certain symbolic relationships. Larger dots indicate more activity. C-links allow all components to pass, attenuated by weight. S-links pass only the component of activity which corresponds to the link type.

Neural Network Models of Memory Span

Richard Schweickert

Lawrence Guentert

Lora Hersberger

Department of Psychological Sciences

Purdue University

Abstract

A model is presented in which short term memory is maintained by movement of vectors from one layer to another. This architecture is ideal for representing item order. Two mechanisms for accounting for serial position curves are considered, lateral inhibition, and noise from neighboring items. These also account for effects of grouping by inserting pauses during presentation. Two other effects, a reverse word-length effect and the effect of phonological similarity, are attributed to the reconstruction of items from partially decayed traces. If all the phonemes in an item are intact at recall, the item is recalled correctly. Otherwise, the subject guesses according to a model developed by Paul Luce for identification of words presented in noise.

Introduction

Several methods for short term memory storage have been proposed for neural networks, including quickly decaying weights (Hinton & Plaut, 1987), sustained activation, and moving activation (Hebb, 1949). Fast weights are useful for maintaining temporary learning, but not for the roughly 2 second duration of immediate memory (Mackworth, 1963). Sustained activation is possible, but it seems unlikely that it would not spread to neighboring units. Activation moving from layer to layer is not only likely, but accounts for several phenomena of short term memory in a natural way.

Memory span for a type of item, such as digits, is the number of items that a subject can immediately recall in order half the time. A key finding is that many errors are transpositions, rather than omissions or substitutions. The usual primacy and recency effects found in free recall are also found in immediate recall. Moreover, if there is an empty time interval between two items at presentation, there is a recency effect prior to the gap and a primacy effect after the gap (e. g., Huttenlocker & Burke, 1976). This suggests interference between items presented close together in time.

Interference could be explained by lateral inhibition of temporally adjacent items. Primacy and recency would occur because items at the extremes receive inhibition only from neighbors on one side. Recently, a way of accounting for effects such as Mach bands in vision without lateral inhibition has been proposed (Cornsweet & Yellot, 1985). With constant volume operators, excitation spreads from each unit, with the extent of the spreading inversely proportional to the intensity exciting the unit. Edge enhancement is one result. Yet another proposal for interference is that the positions of items are perturbed, so items are recalled in the wrong order (Lee & Estes, 1981). Items at the extremes can only move in one direction, and so are less likely to move.

If excitation spreads to neighboring items, excitation favoring an item could be strongest at a position different from the one the item was presented in. Hence, perturbations can be explained in terms of spreading excitation. A further simplification of the possibilities is that when lateral inhibition is combined with constant volume operators, erroneous predictions are made for vision (Yellot, 1989). The explanations are likely to be mutually exclusive for memory also. It is difficult to distinguish the effects of lateral inhibition from those of constant volume operators, even in vision (Yellot, 1989, p. 33), so we will present an example of a model of each kind.

A Lateral Inhibition Model

A model based on lateral inhibition is shown in Figure 1. It explains primacy and recency effects, and the effects of temporal gaps in presentation. When a phoneme i is presented to the input layer, its strength is s_i. After time t its strength decays to $s_i \exp(-t)$. The node in the output layer corresponding to phoneme i receives excitation from the input node for phoneme i, and receives inhibition from all the other nodes in the input layer. The closer the time of presentation of phoneme j is to the presentation of phoneme i, the greater the inhibition between them. Let t_{ij} be the time elapsing from presentation of i to presentation of j (regardless of which came first). For simplicity, assume the onset to onset interval for each phoneme is the same, t. If k phonemes intervene between phonemes i and j, then $t_{ij} = kt$. The inhibition of item j on item i is $s_j \exp(-t_{ij})$. The output of the node for phoneme i in the memory layer at time t is the log odds of correctly identifying phoneme i, based on the trace itself.

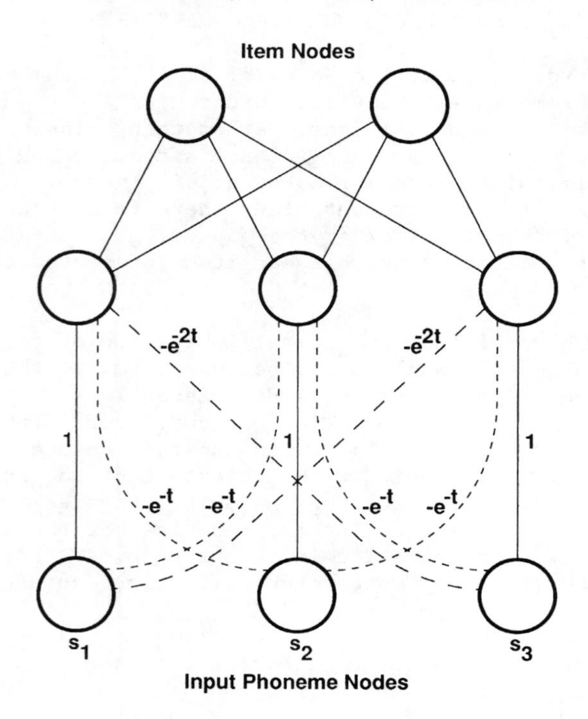

Figure 1. Phonemes in the bottom layer send excitation and inhibition to nodes in the next layer. Inhibition between two phonemes decays as a function of the time intervening between them.

Strengths in the memory layer also decay exponentially with time. These are the input to the word layer at the time or recall. Then at a time T,

$$\log [p_i(T)/(1 - p_i(T))] = (s_i \ - \ \ s_j \exp(-t_{ij}))) \exp(-T).$$

Here $p_i(T)$ is the probability that phoneme i is recalled correctly at time T.

For simplicity, suppose the time to read each word is the same as the time to recite it during recall. Then it is easy to see that the time elapsing between presentation of phoneme i and its recall is L, where L is the total time to pronounce all the items in the list.

A Spreading Excitation Model

Consider an array of rows and columns of neural units. A phoneme is a column vector, where each component is the strength of some feature. When a phoneme is input to the first column of the array, the excitation in a row is transferred to the next column, and to the next and so on. Suppose the time required for transfer is shorter, and has smaller variance, the stronger the excitation. When excitation spreads from a column to an adjacent column, the original excitation remains, but decays over time. After a while, the excitation for a given feature will be spread over a set of columns. If excitation from features of two or more phonemes arrives at the same column, the excitations are summed. This mode of spreading is close enough to that of constant volume operators to produce the "edge enhancement" analogous to primacy and recency. Items at the extremes only have neighbors on one side, so they have less noise added to their representations.

It is plausible that excitation would spread, and at different rates for different features. This gives a mechanism for assumptions of some models in the literature. First, the perturbations of Lee & Estes (1981) occur because excitation for one item may spread faster than that for another, so a later item may overtake an earlier one. Second, according to Glenberg and Swanson (1986), visually presented items are less distinct in terms of temporal order than auditorially presented items, resulting in better recall for the auditory items (the modality effect). The difference in temporal distinctiveness may be due to differences in the extent of the spread of excitement. Finally, the TRACE model for speech recognition by McClelland and Elman (1986) proposes that the activation for entities is spread over neighboring units. Their model is static, but a snapshot of the model sketched above would look like the neural array in the TRACE model.

Primacy, recency, and grouping effects are due to the mechanisms by which traces deteriorate. A subject processing a partially degraded trace will try to reconstruct the original item. The next two effects to be discussed are explained in terms of reconstruction.

The Reverse Word-Length Effect

Ordinarily, memory span is shorter for items taking longer to pronounce (the word-length effect). As a rule, the memory span for a type of item is the length of a list of such items that can be pronounced in about 2 seconds (Baddeley, Thomson, & Buchanan, 1975; Mackworth, 1963; Schweickert & Boruff, 1986). The span is slightly greater for familiar items. To learn about the role of familiarity, we investigaged memory span in highly practiced subjects.

Two subjects completed 30 sessions in a memory span experiment. There were twenty items in each of five types of item. The lengths of the lists were from 3 to 9 items. At the beginning of each trial, a list appeared on a CRT. Subjects read the list aloud, and speaking durations were measured. Subjects then tried to recall the list in order.

Each subject produced a reverse word length effect, that is, the slower the speaking rate in items per second, the more items that could be recalled in a given time period. The data for subject 1 are in Table 1, the other subject's data are similar.

Table 1.

Material	letters	words	prepositions	colors	shapes
Rate	3.11	2.77	2.75	2.62	1.94
Recall	50%	60%	69%	78%	90%

The Phonological Similarity Effect

In a pronunciation task, Chase (1975) found that subjects pronounce phonologically similar items more slowly than dissimilar ones. The difference in speech rate raises an interesting question. Does the rate difference account for the effect of phonological similarity on span?

We carried out an experiment to investigate this question. Phonologically similar lists were made of items from the set {b, c, d, g, j, k, p, t, v, z}. Dissimilar lists were made from the set {b, d, f, h, k, l, m, q, r, z}. Names of letters in the first set all end in long e or long a, making them more similar than those in the second set.

Eighteen subjects served individually for one hour. The session began with a practice block of digits, followed by two blocks each of similar and dissimilar items. Subjects were randomly assigned to six groups, corresponding to the six possible orderings of two similar and two dissimilar blocks.

The span for the similar items was 5.62, that for the dissimilar items was 7.06, a significant difference in an analysis of variance ($p < .001$). The pronunciation rates were almost identical, 3.01 items per second for the similar items, and 2.92 for the dissimilar. In short, when the task is not only to pronounce the items, but to recall them as well, speaking rates are the same for the similar and dissimilar items. The conjecture that the effect of phonological similarity on memory span is due to a slower pronunciation rate for phonologically similar items is not supported.

Redintegration

If the phonemes in item are not all recalled, a guess is made from the set of possible items. Identifying an item from a noisy memory trace is analogous to identifying an auditorially presented word in noise. A model for the latter task was developed by Paul A. Luce (1986). In this model, the probability of correct recall of all the phonemes in a word is the product of the probabilities of correctly recalling the phonemes individually. Further, the probability of a correct guess depends on the phonological similarity of items to their neighbors, and on word frequency. The model seems well suited to the present situation, and will be used here as the mechanism whereby a guess is made at recall of a noisy memory trace.

According to the Luce model, if all the phonemes of a word w are not recalled, then

$$g_w = \frac{h_{ww}\, b_w}{\sum h_{wv}\, b_v}.$$

Here, g_w is the probability of guessing word w correctly and h_{wv} is a parameter which increases as the phonological similarity between words w and v increases. The bias b_v in favor of responding with word v is influenced by word frequency.

Learning

The subject will improve his ability to guess considerably if he can tune his bias to match the actual presentation rates of the items in the experiment. Bush, Luce & Rose (1963) proposed a learning rule with two desirable properties in the limit as the number of trials approaches infinity. First, the probability of responding w approaches the value given in the formula above according to the ratio rule. Second, the biases become proportional to the presentation rates actually used in the experiment.

For every v and w, let $g_{wv,i}$ be the probability of guessing w on trial i, given that v was presented. Suppose on trial i, v' was presented. Then on trial i + 1, for every v and w

$$g_{wv,i+1} - g_{wv,i} = ch_{vv'}[d_{vv'} - g_{wv,i}],$$

where c, a constant, is the learning rate, and $d_{vv'}$ is 1 if v = v' and 0 otherwise.

Matters would be more complicated if the guessing probability depended on word length. However, the first and last phonemes are the most crucial for identifying a word (Garner, 1962) so the number of phonemes in the middle may not have much influence. Empirically, Luce and Pisoni (1986) found a very low correlation between word length and accuracy of word identification.

Correct recall of item i occurs either from the trace directly, with probability $p_w(L)$, or, by guessing. That is,

$$P(\text{recall } w) = p_w(L) + [1 - p_w(L)]g_w.$$

Note that $p_w(L)$ is influenced by word length and g_w by phonological similarity. In this way, the model uses different mechanisms for the effects of similarity and word length.

The subject can control the spoken duration of each item, and L is the sum of the durations of all the items on the list. Laugherty (1969) reports that immediate memory performance is not monotonic with presentation rate. The value of L which optimizes the probability of recall of item i does not depend on phonological similarity, however. Therefore, phonologically similar items will be pronounced at the same rate when immediate recall follows.

References

Baddeley, A. D., Thomson, N., & Buchanan, M. (1975). *Journal of Verbal Learning and Verbal Behavior*, *14*, 575.

Bush, R. R., Luce, R. D., & Rose, R. M. (1963). Learning models for psychophysics. In R. C. Atkinson (Ed.), *Studies in mathematical psychology*, Vol. 1. Stanford: Stanford University Press.

Chase, W. G. (1975). In S. Dornic (Ed.), *Attention and Performance VI*, Erlbaum, Hillsdale, NJ.

Cornsweet, T. N., & Yellot, J. I., Jr. (1985). Intensity-dependent spatial summation. *Journal of the Optical Society of Amerika-A*, *2*, 1769-1786.

Garner, W. R. (1962). *Uncertainty and structure as psychological concepts*. New York: Wiley.

Glenberg, A. M., & Swanson, N. G. (1986). A temporal distinctiveness theory of recency and modality effects. *Journal of Experimental Psychology: Learning, Memory, and Cognition*, *12*, 3-15.

Hebb, D. O. (1949). *The organization of behavior*. New York: Wiley.

Hinton, G. E., & Plaut, D. C. (1987). Using fast weights to deblur old memories. *Program of the Ninth Annual Conference of the Cognitive Science Society*. Hillsdale, HJ: Erlbaum.

Huttenlocker, J., & Burke, D. (1979). Why does memory span decrease with age? *Cognitive Psychology*, *8*, 1-31.

Laugherty, K. R. (1969). Computer simulation of short term memory: A component decay model. In G. Bower & J. T. Spence (Eds.), *The psychology of learning and motivation*, Vol. 3, 135. Orlando, FL: Academic Press.

Lee, C. L., & Estes, W. K. (1981). Item and order information in short-term memory: Evidence for multilevel perturbation processes. *Journal of Experimental Psychology: Human Learning and Memory*, *7*, 149-169.

Luce, P. A. (1986). Research on speech perception. Speech Research Laboratory, *Technical Report No. 6*, Department of Psychology, Indiana University.

Luce, P. A., & Pisoni, D. B. (1986). Paper presented at Psychonomic Society Meeting, New Orleans.

Mackworth, J. F. (1963). The duration of the visual image. _Canadian Journal of Psychology_, _17_, 62-81.

McClelland, J. L., & Elman, J. L. (1986). Interactive processes in speech perception: The TRACE model. In J. L. McClelland & D. E. Rumelhart (Eds.), _Parallel distributed processing: Explorations in the microstructure of cognition_, pp. 58-121. Cambrige: MIT Press.

Schweickert, R., & Boruff, B. (1986). _Journal of Experimental Psychology: Learning, Memory, and Cognition_, _12_, 419.

Yellot, J. I., Jr. (1989). Constant volume operators and lateral inhibition. _Journal of Mathematical Psychology_, _33_, 1-35.

The Lexical Distance Model and Word Priming

Noel E. Sharkey
Centre for Connection Science
University of Exeter

The Lexical Distance (LD) model, presented here, functions as the front end of a connectionist Natural Language Understanding system (e.g. Sharkey, 1989a and b). The lexicon consists of a vector of microfeatures which are divided among 3 classes: orthographic, semantic and situational. Treating lexical space as an energy landscape, the entry for each word is learned as a minimum of the energy function E (see Kawamoto, in press for a similar treatment). Initial access to the lexicon is via the graphemic microfeatures. When these are activated by the visual presentation of an word, the lexical net is destabilised and the system begins gradient descent in the energy function until it relaxes in an attractor basin which represents the meaning of the input word. The model characterises context effects in word recognition experiments by deriving time predictions based on the movement of the system from its initial state to the target state. Two classes of context are discussed along with their interactions with word frequency and stimulus degradation. The research demonstrates how these effects fall quite naturally out of the processing specifications of the LD model without need for *ad hoc* parameters.

Contextual effects on word recognition may be divided into two classes: those that occur as a result of processes within the lexicon (*lexical effects*) and those that occur as a result of processes occurring after proposition construction (*textual effects*). The class of effect is determined by the priming stimulus used. Lexical effects are found when single-word primes such as DOCTOR precede targets such as NURSE. Alternatively, textual effects occur only when the priming comes from complete propositions. For example, Sharkey and Mitchell (1985) found that sentences such as, 'Colonel Jones realised that he was late as he rushed into the station.' could be used to prime words such as BENCH. The resulting effects are textual in the sense that they rely on the construction (or activation) of related propositions. In the 'Colonel Jones example', BENCH is primed by propositions containing the reader's knowledge about stations i.e. people waiting for trains sit on benches.

The distinction between textual and lexical effects may be maintained empirically as follows: The lexical effects are instantaneous (Neely, 1976) and can be disrupted by one intervening item (e.g. Meyer, Schvaneveldt & Ruddy, 1972; Gough, Alford, & Holly-Wilcox, 1981; Foss, 1982; A.J.C. Sharkey, 1989). The textual effects have a slow onset i.e. they appear only after an unfilled delay (Kintsch & Mross, 1985) or a filled delay (Till, Mross, & Kintsch, 1988; A.J.C. Sharkey, 1989). In addition, textual priming has been shown to sustain over a number of unrelated items (Foss, 1982; Sharkey & Mitchell, 1985; A.J.C. Sharkey, 1989), and is deactivated only when textual cues indicate that a new knowledge domain is in focus (Sharkey & Mitchell, 1985).

In the new model presented here, lexical effects (from single-word primes) are entirely bottom-up in the sense that they occur within the lexicon without influence from other modules. However, in word priming which is textual by an assembly of text propositions, there is minimal a top-down component which is supported in a number of studies (e.g. Glucksberg, Kreutz, & Rho, 1986; Tabossi, 1988; Blutner & Sommer, 1988; Keenan, Golding, Potts, Jennings, & Aman, in press). Although, the empirical arguments currently present a muddy picture, the LD model was built partly out of engineering considerations and so shows *one* efficient way in which to model context effects. It is not argued here that it is the only way to model them. Nonetheless, by building an explicit alternative computational model with precise process predictions it is hoped that some of the issues can be resolved empirically. The model has recently been empirically compared to the Kintsch (1988) model and been shown to fit the data better (Sharkey and Sharkey, 1989).

THE LEXICAL DISTANCE MODEL

Traditionally the lexicon has been considered to be a store of information about words e.g. information about their meanings, syntactic class, orthography etc. In the current model, the lexicon consists of a set of units such that each unit corresponds to a microfeature. This leads to quite a different class of model than previous models of word recognition (c.f. Sharkey, 1989b, for a detailed comparison). In earlier models, a concept, where mentioned, is represented either as a single network node or similarly, as the contents of some addressed location in memory. The radical change here is that the concept associated with a word does not occupy a single location in memory. Instead, it is distributed across several different memory locations. Each concept is composed of a number of microfeatures which represent elements of its meaning (see Sutcliffe, 1988). Such meaning microfeatures may be thought of as propositional predicates (e.g. a stereotypical set of microfeatures for man might be: is male, is tall, is strong, can't cook, likes women etc.). In the present model meaning is not only represented by semantic microfeatures such as is-male, has-wings, etc. It is also represented by situational microfeatures which provide information about the activities or events that a word is involved in, or locations in which it may be found. The lexical net is illustrated in Figure 1. Moreover, each microfeature may appear in several concepts. Thus DOCTOR shares many situational microfeatures with NURSE - they are both persons and they have overlapping job roles. This distributed representation makes it difficult to maintain the old addressing metaphor because each lexical entry would occupy a number different addresses. Of course there is more to the lexicon than meaning microfeatures. There may also be phonemic, and syntactic microfeatures etc. (e.g. Kawamoto, in press). Meaning microfeatures are the main concern of the current model, but it is the graphemic microfeatures that are used to gain access to the lexicon.

SOME PROPERTIES OF THE MODEL

(i) Each microfeature in the lexicon may be thought of as having an activation value. Thus a lexical entry may be characterised as a vector of microfeature activations. And, more importantly, each vector of microfeature activations may be identified as a point in an n -dimensional energy landscape (called lexical space here), where n is the number of microfeatures in the lexicon.

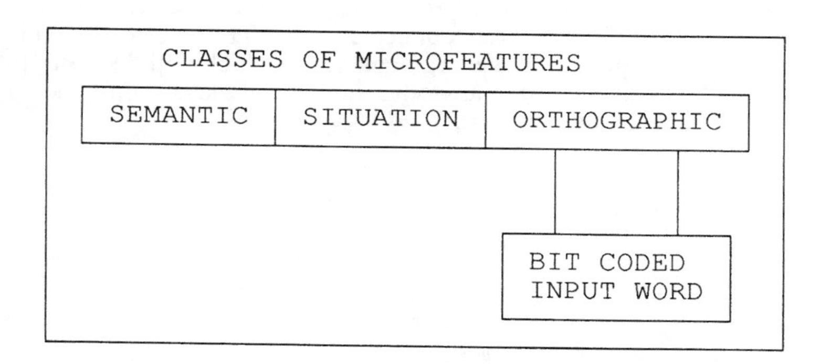

Figure 1. A diagramatic representation of the lexical net in the LD model showing three categories of microfeatures. A bit coded word activates the graphemic microfeatures in order to retrieve its appropriate meaning.

More formally, each collection of microfeatures representing a word's meaning and its visual characteristics (its lexical entry) is installed as a minimum of an energy function E (Hopfield 1982) given by:

$$E = -1/2 \sum_{i=j} s_i w_{ij} s_j + \sum_{j} s_j \theta$$

where s_i is the activation level of the ith unit, w_{ij} is the weight between the ith and j^{th} units.

This provides a new formalism with which to discuss the lexicon. Rather than considering a lexical entry as having a location or address in memory, it may now be considered as a point in an n-dimensional energy landscape created by the E function as shown in Figure 2. Each microfeature assembly is represented as a low point or basin in this landscape. Thus lexical access is characterised as a point moving through energy space to relax on appropriate assemblages of microfeatures. (Note that the new metaphor could be aligned with the old by saying that the unique point in n-dimensional space is a *location* for a lexical entry and that the vector of microfeature activations is the address of that entry).

(ii) Hopfield's (1982) *gradient descent* method is used to retrieve the meaning microfeatures which best fit the graphemic input constraints. Such a scheme is easy to implement on a parallel machine because an important property of Hopfield's formalism is that a given unit can locally compute the difference in energy a change in its state from 1 to 0 or vice versa will make. This is done simply by summing the total activity that a unit receives from all other active units in the network.

The change in energy for a unit is given by $\Delta E_{ij} = \sum_{i} s_i w_{ij}$.

The gradient descent rule is then simple. If the energy change results in a positive number, the unit adopts a +1 state, and if it results in a negative number the unit adopts a 0 state. Eventually the system will settle in a minimum of the energy function (one of the attractor basins as shown in Figure 2 i.e. a state which prevents the system from moving downwards in energy regardless of a change of state in any of the units. When the system relaxes in one of these stable states it is said to have retrieved that state i.e. the set of microfeatures corresponding to word meaning. One problem with gradient descent is that the system will only move in a downward direction. So when a new word in input, the system will be stuck in the minimum corresponding to the previous word's meaning. To overcome this problem, the pulse mechanism was employed here (c.f. Sharkey, Sutcliffe, Wobcke, 1986). Essentially, this means that when a new unit, not in the current microfeature set, comes on, it will pulse (switch off) all units to which it is negatively connected. This has the effect that the state of the lexical net jumps to a high point in the energy landscape which will be closer to the appropriate microfeature minimum than to any other minima in the net; only the microfeatures shared by the old and new pattern will stay active.

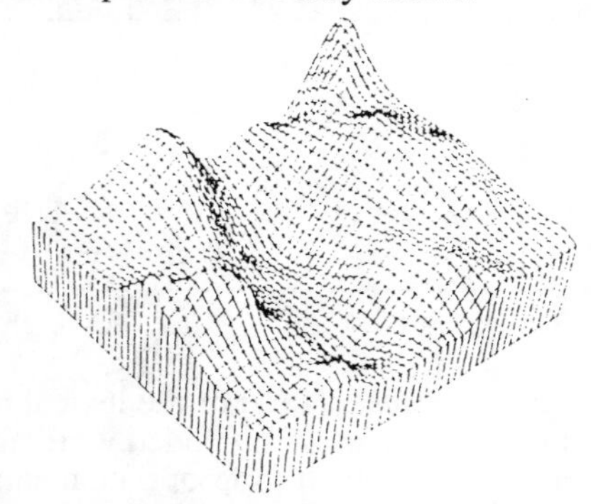

Figure 2: A three dimensional idealisation of an Energy landscape. The wells or minima are points representing lexical entries.

(iii). The relationship between the outside world and the lexicon in this model is via word units. These may be thought of as being like the outputs from McClelland and Rumelhart's (1981) interactive activation model. That is, in the simple simulation reported below, the output from the visual features of a word is represented as a single unit. The association between this unit and the graphemic microfeatures is learned using the delta rule. A property of this learning is that the weights for more frequently presented stimuli are stronger than the weights for less frequently occurring stimuli. (c.f. Sharkey, 1989 for a discussion of frequency and learning.

(iv). The activation values passed between the visual features and the graphemic microfeatures are incremental and continuous. The activity on a graphemic microfeature affects the probability of it adopting the +1 state during an update in the lexicon.

A SIMULATION OF CONTEXT EFFECTS

To model the experimental findings, a simulation was conducted for pairs of related words such as DOCTOR/NURSE, KNIFE/FORK, BREAD/BUTTER, DOG/BONE, and FOOT/SHOE. This simulation was exploratory and so ten microfeatures were arbitrarily assigned to each word in the lexicon. Four of these represented graphemic microfeatures, three represented semantic microfeatures and the other three represented situational microfeatures. The three situational microfeatures for each word were shared with its associate e.g. DOCTOR shared three situational microfeatures with NURSE.

Installing the meanings. The lexical microfeature sets, corresponding to lexical entries, were installed in the lexical net using an autoassociative version of the delta rule in combination with the pulse mechanism (Sharkey, Sutcliffe, & Wobcke, 1986). Briefly, the lexical entries of words were collated as patterns of microfeature activations to be learned by the system. The patterns were then presented to the system one at a time. Each pattern was used to activate a set of input-units. The states of these units were then propagated across a set of weights to produce values on a set of output-units. These output values were compared with the values of the corresponding input-units to produce an error vector **d**, where δ_i = (input-unit$_i$ - output-unit$_i$). The change in weights between the input-units is given by $\Delta\mathbf{W} = \eta\mathbf{di}$, where $\Delta\mathbf{W}$ is the weight change matrix, h is the learning rate parameter, and **i** is the vector of input-unit values.

Once the learning had been completed the system was started in one of two initial states; either (i) a stable state resulting from the presentation of a prime word, or (ii) an arbitrary state resulting from the presence of a neutral (e.g. a row of Xs). A prime word activates a set of microfeature units and sets the system on a downward descent in the energy function until a stable minimum has been reached. This minimum will be the lexical entry for the prime word. In contrast, when the target is preceded by a neutral instead of a prime, the resulting starting state will be arbitrary (and it may not be a minimum of E). Now, when a target word is presented, some new graphemic units are activated, and the system begins to move from the current state to a state which best fits the input.

Timing predictions. The metric used to derive the time predictions is the *distance* which must be traversed to get from an initial state to a target state in the lexicon, where distance, d, is defined as the length between two points in n-dimensional lexical space. To make this clearer, imagine two vectors of microfeature activations in the lexical space $\mathbf{L}^n$. Let these vectors represent the starting state of the system **s** and the required or target state **r**. Then the distance between the two points **s** and **r** is given by $\|\mathbf{s} - \mathbf{r}\|^{1/2}$, where length $\|\mathbf{v}\| = (\mathbf{v} \cdot \mathbf{v})^{1/2}$. A major assumption of the model is that the greater the distance from an initial state to a target state, the longer will be the recognition time for a target word.

Context effects. The model makes the correct time predictions for context effects because a target that shares a number of microfeatures with a prime (semantically and/or situationally related), will be closer to the prime than a word which shares no features (semantically and situationally unrelated). Thus, by definition, the state resulting from presentation of a related prime will be closer, in lexical space, to the target state than the state resulting from an unrelated prime. Figure 3 plots distance against energy for two pairs of words DOCTOR/NURSE and DOCTOR/FORK. For simplicity binary activation has been used here and so the graph shows the energy of the system as it moves from the initial DOCTOR state to the NURSE and FORK states. Note that FORK is much further from DOCTOR than NURSE is and that there is a much steeper ascent and descent to reach FORK. In the DOCTOR/NURSE graph, the first circle indicates the state of the system with only the shared microfeatures on, and second circle indicates the state after all of the graphemic microfeatures have come on and the pulse mechanism has been run. If the second circle is compared to the circle on the DOCTOR/FORK graph, it can be seen that NURSE is considerably closer than FORK to the initial state (DOCTOR). Therefore, the NURSE state will take less time to reach.

Lexical priming. This simulation presents a very simple and entirely bottom-up model of lexical context effects in which lexical priming is a measure of network distance from an initial to a decision state. The main factor in time to respond (e.g. Lexical Decision) is the relationship between the target and the initial state of the system. It is assumed that, overall, the target states are further away from the arbitrary Neutral state than from the Related prime states; but the target states may, on average, be closer to the Neutral states than to the Unrelated prime states.

Textual priming. It was shown that textual effects can be produced by exactly the same processes as the lexical effects i.e. through shared situational features. However, the different onset/offset properties of the two types of priming result from processes which operate externally to the lexicon. There is not space to delve into these processes here (but see Sharkey, 1989b and in press). Briefly, in reading text, the primary aim is to construct meaning propositions. In the Sharkey (1989b) model, once a proposition has been constructed, it activates a knowledge-net which results in a stable state of situationally related propositions. This stable state is maintained until cues from the text indicate otherwise (Sharkey & Mitchell, 1985). In order to explain the sustain of textual priming on word decisions in the current model, the stable state in the knowledge-net holds the situational microfeatures active in the lexicon. Moreover, the time taken to construct a proposition explains why the onset of textual priming is slower than lexical priming. Note that this minimal top-down view is different from previous top-down models. It is not claimed that particular lexical items are *expected*. Nor are particular words or visual features being anticipated. On the contrary, it is only the shared abstract contextual properties of

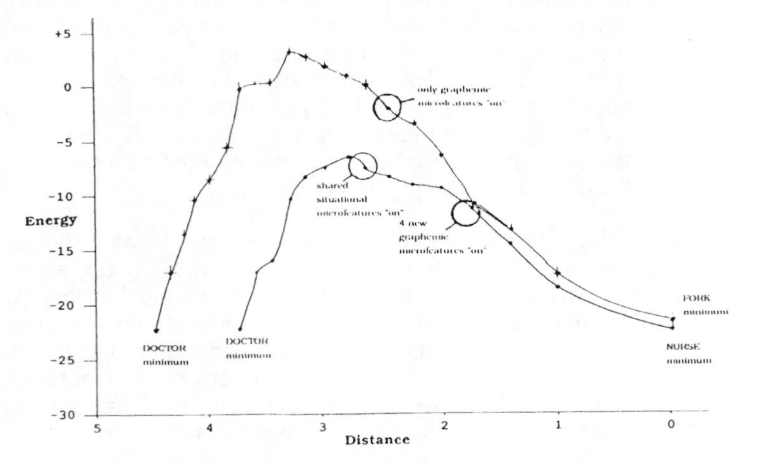

Figure 3: A graph of the movement in the lexicon from DOCTOR to NURSE and from DOCTOR to FORK. This is plotted as Distance against Energy. See the text for a discussion.

words (the situational microfeatures) which are held active. Thus the system is, in a sense, predisposed to receive certain contextual classes of words. This saves on the computational complexity of earlier models and serves the function of disambiguating word meaning[1]. However, before the utility of this model can be assessed, it is important to examine whether it accurately predicts the interaction of context effects with other variables such as word frequency and stimulus quality.

Rate of microfeature activation. In order to understand the predictions arising from the model on the combined effects of word frequency, context, and stimulus quality, the way in which the rate of graphemic microfeature activation affects movement from the initial to the target state is first examined. At time t_0, just before presentation of the target, and therefore before any new graphemic units have been activated, the distance from the start state **s** to the required or target state **r** is $\delta = \|\mathbf{s} - \mathbf{r}\|^{1/2}$. At time t_1, the presentation of the target will activate the word unit vector **v**, and at t_2 this activation will be broadcast across the weights **W** using the limiting function LIMIT[**Wv**] = **f**, where **f** is the vector of new graphemic microfeature activations. The the graphemic microfeatures are activated at t_3 by adding **f** to the initial lexical vector **s**. So the new state of the system, before update at t_4, will be **s** + **f**, and the distance will now be $\delta = \|(\mathbf{s} + \mathbf{f}) - \mathbf{r}\|^{1/2}$. Thus the magnitude[2] of the new microfeature activations, **f**, will affect the distance moved between the start state and the target states; the greater **f** the smaller the difference between **s** and **r**. The process described in these four time cycles continues to iterate until a stable state is attained.

Stimulus quality and frequency effects. Predictions concerning frequency effects rely on a property of learning to associate the visual features with the graphemic microfeatures. In delta rule learning, the weights for more frequently presented stimuli are larger than the weights for less frequently occurring stimuli. Now, as shown above, the distance moved by the system towards the target state depends on the magnitude of **f** which in turn depends on two factors: the structure of the weights **W** and the magnitude of word unit vector **v**. Since frequency is encoded in **W**, when the stimulus quality in **v** is held constant, low frequency targets take longer to maximise activation on the graphemic microfeatures than do high frequency targets. In other words, the stronger the connection between a set of graphemes and their lexical representation, the greater will be the rate of microfeature activation. Thus high frequency targets will be responded to faster than low frequency targets.

The effect of degrading the quality of a stimulus word is simulated in the model by varying the magnitude of **v** while holding frequency constant. It should be clear from the above analysis that the smaller the magnitude of **v** (stimulus quality), the smaller the magnitude of **f**, and consequently the longer it will take to maximise activation on the graphemic microfeatures. Thus the model predicts that degraded stimuli will take longer to recognise.

Combined effects of context, frequency and stimulus quality. The model predicts that both stimulus quality and frequency will interact with context. This is because the closer the initial state **s** is to the target state **r**, the less effect the magnitude of **f** will have on the movement of the system from **s** to **r**. An initial state close to a target state will reach the target state before the microfeature activations have been maximised. Because of the nature of update, the lexicon will in effect "clean up" degraded stimulus. These predictions have been supported empirically. Becker and Killion (1977) and Becker (1979) found context by frequency interactions, and interactions of context and stimulus quality have been demonstrated by Meyer, Schvaneveldt, and Ruddy (1975), and Becker and Killion (1977). Moreover, since frequency and stimulus quality effects are brought about by changes in the magnitude of **f**, our model predicts an additive effect of stimulus quality and frequency. However, demonstrations have had mixed results. Some research has shown frequency and stimulus

---

[1]By derivation from the Kawamoto (in press) model, the current model can also explain the lexical ambiguity effects (c.f. Sharkey, in press).

[2]For mathematical simplicity, it is assumed here that after initial activation, **f** does not change direction.

quality to be interactive (Stanner, Jastrzembski, and Westbrook, 1975) though the majority have found them to be additive (Norris, 1984; Becker & Killion, 1977).

It should be noted that the distance metric has parallels with the older Location Shifting model (e.g. Meyer, Schvaneveldt & Ruddy, 1972; Posner & Snyder, 1975). Both models accurately predict that associative priming effects can be disrupted by the presentation of an unrelated item between the prime and the target (e.g. Meyer, Schvaneveldt & Ruddy, 1972; Gough, Alford, & Holly-Wilcox, 1981; Foss, 1982; A.J.C. Sharkey, 1988). In both models, an unrelated intervening item would move the state/location of the system to a new state/location. And it is this new state/location which would be the initial state/location before the presentation of the target. Therefore, priming of the target would be disrupted. However, because we use the computational power of a distributed representation, it is not possible, as in Posner & Snyder (1975), to speak of *the* location for a concept; it may share meanings with other concepts in more than one location. Instead, location is discussed more abstractly in terms of n-dimensional energy space and Euclidean vector distance. In addition, the LD model makes prediction about textual priming which would not be possible from the older model.

CONCLUSIONS

It has been shown how a simple connectionist model can generate accurate predictions for both lexical and textual context effects and their interactions with frequency and stimulus quality. There are no hidden processes in this model and all of the associations are learned. The model provides an entirely bottom-up account of lexical effects which does not rely on fast spreading activation to contextually related concepts; recognition threshold adjustments; plausibility checks; or shortlist search. Indeed, it does not require any special purpose mechanisms to handle context effects; the effects fall naturally out of the normal operation of the lexicon during access. If the prime word is contextually related to the target word, in the restricted definition of sharing microfeatures, the lexicon will have less distance to travel in order to stabilise on the best fitting lexical microfeatures. Moreover, textual effects fall out of the same lexical processes as the lexical effects. The two types of priming differ only in processes that occur externally to the lexicon. For textual priming, the activation of a propositional knowledge-net holds active the situational microfeatures in the lexicon and thus provides a sustain of priming. Since the knowledge net is most responsive to propositional input, the time taken to construct propositions accounts for the slow onset of textual priming.

REFERENCES

Becker, C.A.(1979) Semantic context and word frequency effects in visual word recognition. Journal of Experimental Psychology: Human Perception and Performance, **5**, 252-259.

Becker, C.A. & Killion, T.M. (1977) Interaction of visual and cognitive effects in word recognition. Journal of Experimental Psychology: Human Perception and Performance, **3**, 389-401.

Blutner, R., & Sommer, R. (1988) Sentence processing and lexical access: The influence of the focus-identifying task. Journal of Memory and Language, 27, 359-367.

Foss, D.J. (1982) A discourse on Semantic Priming, Cognitive Psychology, **14**, 590-607.

Glucksberg, S., Kreuz, R.J. & Rho, S. (1986) Context can constrain lexical access: Implications for models of language comprehension. Journal of Experimental Psychology: Learning, Memory and Cognition, **12**, 323-335.

Gough, P.B., Alford, J.A., Jr., & Holley-Wilcox, P. (1981) Words and Contexts. In J.L. Tzeng & H. Singer (Eds.). Perception of print: Reading research in experimental psychology. Hillsdale, NJ: Erlbaum.

Hopfield, J.J. (1982) Neural Networks and Physical Systems with Emergent Collective Computational Abilities. Proceedings of the National Academy of Sciences, U.S.A., 79, 2554-2558.

Kawamoto, A.H. (in press) Distributed representations of ambiguous words and their resolution in a connectionist network. In S.L. Small, G.W. Cottrell and M.K. Tanenhaus (Eds) Lexical ambiguity resolution in the comprehension of human language.

Keenan, J. M., Golding, J.M., Potts, G.R., Jennings, T.M. & Aman, C.J. (in press) Methodological Issues in Evaluating the Occurrence of Inferences. In A. Grasser and G.H. Bower (Eds.) Learning and Motivation, Vol. 24. Academic Press.

Kintsch, W. (1988) The role of knowledge in discourse comprehension: A construction-integration model. Psychological Review, 95, 163-182.

Kintsch. W., & Mross, E.F. (1985) Context effects in word identification. Journal of Memory and Language, **24**, 336-349.

McClelland, J.L. & Rumelhart, D.E. (1981) An interactive model of context effects in letter perception: Part 1. An account of basic findings. Psychological Review, **88** , 375-407.

Meyer, D.E., Schvaneveldt, R.W., & Ruddy, M.G. (1972) Activation of lexical memory. Paper presented to the psychonomic society, St Louis, Mo.

Meyer, D.E., Schvaneveldt, R.W., & Ruddy, M.G. (1975) Loci of contextual effects on word recognition. In P.M.A. Rabbitt & S. Dornic (Eds) Attention and Performance V. New York: Academic Press.

Neely, J.H. (1976) Semantic priming and retrieval from lexical memory: Evidence for facilitatory and inhibitory processes. Memory and Cognition, **4**, 648-654.

Norris, D.G. (1984) The effects of frequency, repetition and stimulus quality in visual word recognition. Quarterly Journal of Experimental Psychology, **36A**, 507-518.

Posner, M.I., & Snyder,C.R. (1975) Attention and cognitive control. In R.L. Solso (Ed) Information processing and cognition: The Loyola Symposium. Hillsdale, N.J., Lawrence Erlbaum Associates.

Sharkey, A.J.C. (1989) Contextual mechanisms of text comprehension. Unpublished Ph.D. Dissertation, University of Essex.

Sharkey, A.J.C. & Sharkey, N.E. (1989) Lexical processing and the mechanism of context effects in text comprehension. The proceedings of the 11th Annual Conference of the Cognitive Science Society.

Sharkey, N.E. (1989 a) A PDP learning approach to natural language understander. In I. Alexander (Ed) Neural Computing Architectures. London: Kogan Page.

Sharkey, N.E.(1989 b) Connectionist Memory Modules for Text Comprehension, Research Report #170, Dept. Computer Science, University of Exeter.

Sharkey, N.E.(in press) A Connectionist Model of Text Comprehension. In D. Balota, G.B. Flores d'Arcais and K. Rayner (Eds.) Comprehension Processes in Reading.

Sharkey, N.E and Mitchell D.C. (1985) Word Recognition in a Functional Context: the Use of Scripts in reading. Journal of Memory and Language. **24** 253-270.

Sharkey, N.E., Sutcliffe, R.F.E. & Wobcke, W.R. (1986) Mixing Binary and Continuous Connection Schemes for Knowledge Access. Proceedings of the American Association for Artificial Intelligence.

Stanners, R.F., Jastrzembski, J.E. & Westbrook, A. (1975) Frequency and visual quality in a word-nonword classification task. Journal of Verbal Learning and Verbal Behavior, **14**, 259-264.

Tabossi, P. (1988) Accessing lexical ambiguity in different types of sentential contexts. Journal of Memory and Language, **27**, 324-340.

Till, R.E., Mross, E.F., & Kintsch, W. (1988) Time course of priming for associate and inference words in a discourse context. Memory and Cognition, **16** (4) 283-298.

Acknowledgements: I would like to thank Amanda Sharkey for comments on earlier versions of this paper, and the Leverhulme Trust (A/87/153) and ESRC (CO820015) for supporting this research.

A Cooperative Model of Intuition and Reasoning for Natural Language Processing – Microfeatures and Logic

Hideo Shimazu & Yosuke Takashima
C&C Information Technology Research Laboratories
NEC Corporation

ABSTRACT

This paper discusses problems of right retrievals of memory, preferential orderings, and script selection/withdrawal in natural language processing (NLP). **Atmosphere** is introduced to solve these problems. It works as a contextual indicator which roughly grasps what is being talked about. An implementation mechanism for **atmosphere** is presented inspired by artificial neural network researches. It is characterized by microfeature representation, a chronological FIFO (First-In First-Out memory), and threshold-based selection. The mechanism constructs an intuition module and works for NLP while cooperating with a logic module which uses TMS to check the justifications of preferential decisions done by the intuition module.

MOTIVATION

A problem solving task can be divided into two paradigms; *solving by reasoning* and *solving by intuition.* Natural language processing (NLP) is also divided into these two solving paradigms. Examples of *solving by intuition* in NLP are followings:

(Ex-1) **Right memory retrieval:**

While we talk about tennis if we call a name like Ron, we can extract a memory structure corresponding to the right *Ron* among many Rons we know.

(Ex-2) **Preferential ordering:**

S1. The astronomer married a star. She lived in Hollywood.

S1 is a modification of an example in [1]. When we read S1, we naturally interpret that a male astronomer married a movie star who lived in Hollywood. But there is another logically correct interpretation; a female astronomer living in Hollywood married a male movie star. Such a preferential ordering is what humans do and AI programs don't do.

Right memory retrievals and preferential orderings are important tasks in NLP. However, AI has not established a proper mechanism which deals with them. We introduce **atmosphere** to deal with them. **Atmosphere** is a contextual indicator which roughly grasps what is being talked about now. By introducing **atmosphere**, the followings are achieved:

- **Atmosphere-based memory retrieval:**
  Right memory retrievals and preferential orderings are achieved.

- **Atmosphere-based script selection/withdrawal:**
  Script [16] is an important knowledge structure to express contextual information. A difficult problem is to select/withdraw scripts at the right time and place. If each script is pre-defined its typical atmosphere, distances between the current contextual atmosphere and atmosphere definitions in each script can be calculated. If the atmosphere of a script is closely approximate to that of the current context, such a script can be thought of a proper script at the place and time. The comparison of atmospheres can also be used to decide when to withdraw scripts which are now being selected.

In the following section, the strategy and approach of our research are described. Next, a micro-feature based realization of **atmosphere** inspired by artificial neural network (ANN) researches is presented. Then, a cooperative model of an intuition module and a logic module is described. Finally, the implementation details of the model is presented.

STRATEGY AND APPROACH

Recently artificial neural networks (ANN) [15] are paid attention as the first rival against AI. Also in natural language processing fields, many researchers are doing researches using ANN [13][17] [9] [8]. ANN seems a good candidate to handle **atmosphere** since it has many good features AI does not have. For example, Rumelhart et al. proposed a completely new point of view towards schema definition [14]. However, ANN still has many hard problems, some of which can be dealt with by AI. They are variable bindings, schema/role bindings, recursive structures, instantiations, inheritance, one-shot learning, sequential input, etc [7].

In addition to these problems, from the practical implementation point of view, ANN is hard to develop practical programs at the current stage. A schema concept is abstract and does not have an explicit boundary as a module [14]. It is hard to define, modularize, maintain and change such knowledge structures. On the other hand, in AI programs since each knowledge structure has a concrete boundary, it is easier to develop and handle them. Such portability is important when we construct a practical NLP program. Our strategies are the followings:

- **To place right paradigms in the right places:**
  Our goal is to create a practical NLP model which handles **atmosphere** as well as other required features for NLP. Since ANN and AI have many contradictory characteristics, it is difficult to construct a unique NLP paradigm which contains all advantages of both approaches. Therefore, the model will be a cooperative model of AI and something which holds good features of ANN enough to handle **atmosphere**.

- **To extract good features of ANN and to create simpler mechanisms:**
  Presently ANN models can not be practical NLP programs because they still have many functional problems and development difficulties. However, it is possible to skim the needed features for expected functions from the ANN model and to create simpler mechanisms for them.

- **To add good features of ANN without destroying AI's knowledge structures:**
  Although ANN still adopts knowledge concepts like schema or script which AI once proposed, ANN destroys AI's conventional structural skeletons for such knowledge concepts [14]. Instead, ANN introduces microfeature based distributed representations. Our strategy is to

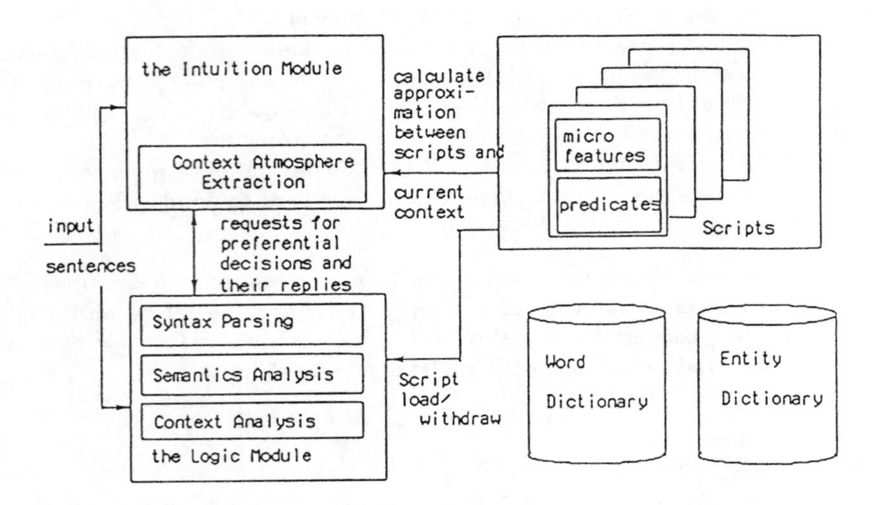

Figure 1: Overview of the Cooperative Model

keep the AI's various structural skeletons for such knowledge concepts and to stuff ANN based representations into such structural skeletons.

OVERVIEW OF THE COOPERATIVE MODEL

The cooperative model consists of two separate modules; a logic module and an intuition module. The logic module and the intuition module run in parallel. Both modules get the same input sentences. Figure 1 shows the overview of the cooperative model. The logic module does ordinary syntax parsing, semantic analysis and context analysis to input sentences. In addition to these, it checks for the justifications of various preferential decisions done by the intuition module. The intuition module extracts a current context atmosphere as analyzing input sentences word by word basis. By using the current context atmosphere, the intuition module makes preferential decisions according to the demands of the logic module like the preference of semantics for ambiguous words and the preference of memory retrieval, for example, like selecting appropriate *Ron* among many Rons. Further, the intuition module monitors scripts and notifies the logic module of the proper selection/withdrawal of scripts.

Each knowledge structure holds two different representations; predicate style knowledge for the logic module and microfeature style knowledge for the intuition module. Microfeature definitions are placed per each word definition, entity knowledge, and script. This dual definition has an advantage from the implementation point of view. Since each knowledge structure has its concrete skeleton, its development, modularity, maintenance, and partial change are easy, comparing with fully distributed representation like [14].

The Intuition Module

The intuition module keeps ANN's good features and is constructed by much simpler mechanisms. It is characterized by microfeature representation, chronological FIFO, and threshold-based script selection.

Microfeature representation [11] is well-suited to express **atmosphere** of a concept. **Atmosphere** at a specific situation is defined as a collection of **atmospheres** of words appearing lately in input sentences. For example, if there appear words like *a written oath*, *candle*, *ring* and *march*, an atmosphere like *as for marriage* will be suggested.

A simple **chronological FIFO** structure can be the container to store microfeature expressions of words appearing lately. Microfeature expressions of lately appearing words are pushed into the FIFO and each microfeature is calculated its number of appearances in the FIFO. The set of microfeatures whose number of appearances is more than the system defined threshold becomes the microfeature expression of **atmosphere** for the current situation. Microfeatures which become old in the FIFO are automatically abandoned. However, if a context proceeds in a same topic, the microfeature organization in the FIFO does not change rapidly because words appearing in a same topic must hold similar microfeature expressions.

The preferential decisions for lexical disambiguations or right memory retrievals are done by the comparison of distances between the microfeature expression of the current situation and microfeature definitions of candidate concepts or memories. For example, if a word has two different meanings, a meaning whose microfeature expression is closer to that of the current situation is chosen.

The selections of scripts are done in the similar manner. Each script is defined its characteristics with a microfeature expression. If the distance between the microfeature expression for a specific script and that of a current situation becomes smaller than the system defined threshold value, the script is regarded as a proper script for the current situation. If a script is selected, the script changes the microfeature organization in the FIFO. Each script is beforehand enumerated several keywords in it to express the characteristics of the script. Each keyword has its microfeature expression. If a script is chosen as a proper script, the microfeature expressions of enumerated keywords in the script are added into the FIFO. As the effect, many older microfeatures in the FIFO are chronologically abandoned and the contents in the FIFO become dominated by the newly entering microfeatures.

In AI based NLP programs, each typical situation is discretely defined like script. In order to make the discretions fine, various approaches have been proposed like a discrimination-net in FRUMP [4] or a hierarchical tree in ATRANS [12]. However, there sometimes happen situations which should be located between classifications. The **threshold-based script selection** approach achieves more continuous discrimination and selection of scripts than such conventional approaches. Instead of selecting only one fit script, it regards all scripts whose approximation to the current context are close enough as proper scripts, and adopts them.

The Logic Module

Since the logic module must find logical mistakes in the preferential decisions of the intuition module, justification mechanisms are necessary for the logic module. Therefore, Truth Maintenance System (TMS) [6] was introduced for the logic module. In TMS each predicate is followed by its justifications which support the predicate. If a conflict occurs between two predicates, TMS traces back along the justification links (dependency-directed backtracking) and discovers the causal predicate of the conflict. We add a new justification type, *by-preference* in TMS. This justification type is the weakest compared with other types of justifications. For example:

S2. Person: How is Ron going?

S3. System: He will be divorced next week.

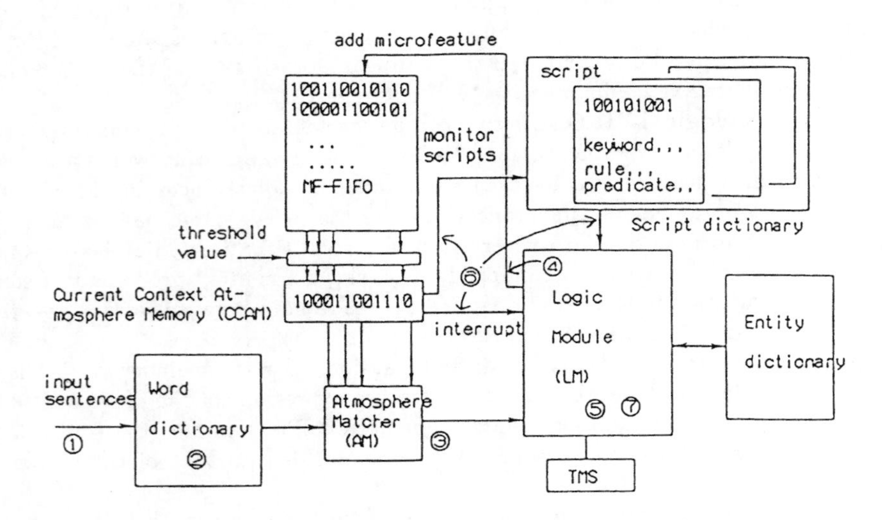

Figure 2: Configuration of the Cooperative Model

S4. Person: No, he is single.

After reading S2, the system searches its memory space and finds several memory entities each of which expresses a person named "Ron". Then, it calculates the distance between the microfeature expression of the current situation and the microfeature definition of each candidate memory entity. The system selects the most approximate entity to the current situation among them and regards it as *Ron* mentioned in S2. Then, it replys S3 to the person. After reading S4, TMS in the logic module of the system finds a logical conflict since the assumed *Ron* is not single. Then, TMS discovers a predicate which says that the memory entity for *Ron* was selected as *by-preference*. The predicate is removed and the preference is retried and a new entity for "Ron" is chosen again.

DETAILS OF THE SYSTEM

System Configuration

Figure 2 indicates the whole system configuration. The system consists of the following modules:

- Microfeature FIFO (MF-FIFO) and Current Context Atmosphere Memory (CCAM);
- Atmosphere Matcher (AM);
- Logic Module (LM), which is monitored by TMS;
- Script dictionary, Word dictionary, and Entity dictionary.

Word dictionary holds the meanings of words and phrases. Entity dictionary holds the memories of various entities like many Rons this system memorizes. Script dictionary holds scripts. Each word, entity and script has two different representations; microfeature representation and predicate representation. The microfeature representation is implemented as a fixed-sized bit vector. The following is the general form of a script in Script dictionary.

Script *script-name:*

Microfeature definition,

Keyword, keyword, keyword,...

Local rules available in this script,

Local predicates available in this script.

Each script holds several keywords which characterize the script, local rules which analyze sentences under the local domain of this script, and local predicates which describes the local domain of this script.

MF-FIFO, CCAM and AM construct the intuition module. MF-FIFO is a FIFO whose lengths are several dozens and whose widths are the same as that of microfeature bit vectors. CCAM calculates the number of ON (1) bit per microfeature in MF-FIFO, then selects microfeatures whose number of appearances is greater than the system defined threshold. The set of the selected microfeatures is also expressed in the form of a bit vector and is used as the current context atmosphere. The microfeature set in CCAM changes when a new input microfeature is added into MF-FIFO. AM gets an input in the form of microfeatures, then calculates the distance between the input and the state of CCAM.

LM is monitored by TMS. Justification links of TMS are made from predicates in LM to other predicates in LM. A justification is also linked from a predicate in LM to a bit vector in MF-FIFO if the bit vector was pushed into MF-FIFO by the predicate. It means that contents in MF-FIFO are also monitored by TMS.

Flow of the System

The typical flow of this model is described in the following sequence. Numbers from (1) to (7) in Figure-2 are corresponding to the following processes.

(1) A new input sentence is given to the system.

(2) Lexical meanings for each word in the sentence are taken from Word dictionary. Each meaning consists of two different representations; the predicate form of logical definitions and the bit vector form of microfeatures. If a word has two or more meanings, all lexical meanings are taken.

(3) AM receives the lexical meaning definitions. If there is only one meaning for a word, the meaning definition is soon passed to LM. If a word has two or more meanings, AM compares the microfeature definition of each meaning with that of CCAM. According to the degree of the approximation between each meaning and CCAM, preferences are given among the competing meanings. Then, all of them are passed to LM.

(4) LM employs the most approximate meaning to the current context atmosphere among competing meanings. The logical definitions of the employed meaning are loaded into LM in the form of predicates, and the microfeatures of the employed meaning are pushed into MF-FIFO in the form of bit vector. The bit vector in MF-FIFO is pointed from the corresponding predicate in LM by a dependency-directed link of TMS.

(5) Syntax parsing, logical semantic analysis and context analysis are done in LM. When a predicate is newly derived by logical inferences in LM and if the predicate has its microfeature definition, the microfeature definition is added into MF-FIFO.

(6) The system always measures the distance between CCAM and each script in Script dictionary. If a distance between CCAM and a script becomes smaller than the system defined threshold, CCAM

asynchronously sends an interrupt to LM and notifies that the script is proper to be selected as the current context. Local rules and local predicates of the script are taken from Script dictionary and loaded into LM. Keywords of the script are added into MF-FIFO in the form of microfeatures. If a distance between CCAM and a script which is currently loaded into LM becomes larger than the system defined threshold, CCAM asynchronously notifies the event to LM. Then, LM removes the local rules and the local predicates of the script from LM. If there exist bit vectors in MF-FIFO which were justified by the removed predicates, such bit vectors are also removed from MF-FIFO at the same time.

(7) If a contradiction occurs among logical predicates in LM, TMS finds its causal predicate by tracing back dependency links, then removes the causal predicate. If the causal predicate was justified by *by-preference*, LM employs another candidate according to the preferential orderings.

RELATED WORKS

Hendler [10] combines microfeature with the marker passing approach. While he unites microfeature and marker passing, we constructed a cooperative model of microfeature based module and logic based module. Wilks's preferential semantics [18] is similar to our intuition module. But his model does not have a logical justification mechanism for preferential decisions. Charniak [2] proposes the cooperation model of a marker passing module and a logic module. He relies on the marker passing mechanism and lets the mechanism do as many things as possible including higher level inferences. Our stance is the opposite. We regard the logic module is main and the intuition module is its assistant since the preferential decisions of the intuition module is doubtful. Charniak and Goldman [3] propose another model which is based on logic. They introduce ATMS [5] and use its justification mechanism. ATMS generates many assumptive interpretations. However, it is not sure how their model makes preferential decisions among such many interpretations.

CONCLUSIONS

In this paper, we have presented a *solving by intuition* method. We introduced **atmosphere** as an instance of *solving by intuition*. **Atmosphere** is useful for right memory retrievals, preferential orderings, and script selection/withdrawal in NLP. **Atmosphere** is realized by a microfeature based mechanism which was inspired by ANN researches. The mechanism can be seen as a simplified implementation of ANN. It is characterized by microfeature representation, chronological FIFO, and threshold-based script selection. The microfeature based mechanism works for NLP as an intuition module cooperating with a logic module. The logic module does syntax parsing, semantic analysis and context analysis. In addition to these, it checks for the justifications of preferential decisions done by the intuition module. The cooperative model can construct a practical NLP program since it is easy to develop, modularize, maintain, and change knowledge structures in the model.

ACKNOWLEDGEMENTS

The authors would like to express their appreciation for continuous encouragement from Kazumoto Iinuma and Takashi Araseki. One of the authors stayed at the Artificial Intelligence Laboratory, UCLA for the 1987-1988 academic year. He would like to thank Prof. Michael G. Dyer for giving him the opportunity to work at UCLA, and for his technical suggestions throughout the work. He thanks Ron Sumida for his technical assistance in NLP and ANN researches. He'd also like to thank other lab members. They thank to Shinji Yanagida for his support to install LaTeX.

References

[1] Charniak, E.C., "Passing markers: A theory of contextual influence in language comprehension.", Cognitive Science 7(3), July - Sep, 1983.

[2] Charniak, E.C., "A Neat Theory of Marker Passing", AAAI-86, 1986.

[3] Charniak, E.C. and Goldman, R., "A Logic for Semantic Interpretation", ACL, 1988.

[4] DeJong, G., "An Overview of the FRUMP system", in "Strategies for Natural Language Processing", Erlbaum, 1982.

[5] De Kleer J., "An Assumption-based TMS", Artificial Intelligence, Vol. 28, No. 2, 1986.

[6] Doyle, J., "A glimpse of Truth Maintenance", in "Artificial Intelligence: An MIT Perspective", MIT Press, 1979.

[7] Dyer, M.G., personal communications in his class at UCLA, 1988.

[8] Dyer, M.G., Flowers, M. and Wang, Y.A., "Weight Matrix = Pattern of Activation: Encoding Semantic Networks as Distributed Representations in DUAL, a PDP Architecture", Tech. Report UCLA-AI-88-5, AI Lab., UCLA, 1988.

[9] Feldman J.A. and Ballard, D.H., "Connectionist models and their properties", Cognitive Science, 6, 1982.

[10] Hendler, J., "Marker-passing and Microfeatures", IJCAI-87, 1987.

[11] Hinton, G.E., McClelland, J.L., and Rumelhart, D.E., "Distributed Representations", in "Parallel Distributed Computing Vol. 1", the MIT Press, 1986.

[12] Lytinen, S.L. and Gershman, A., "ATRANS: Automatic Processing of Money Transfer Message", AAAI-86, 1986.

[13] McClelland, J.L. and Kawamoto, A.H., "Mechanisms of Sentence Processing : Assigning Roles to Constituents of Sentences", in "Parallel Distributed Processing. Vol. 2", the MIT Press, 1986.

[14] Rumelhart, D.E., Smolensky, P., McClelland, J.L. and Hinton,G.E., "Schemata and Sequential Thought Processes in PDP Models", in "Parallel Distributed Processing. Vol. 2", the MIT Press, 1986.

[15] Rumelhart, D.E. and McClelland, J.L., "Parallel Distributed Processing Vol. 1 and 2", the MIT Press, 1986.

[16] Schank R.C. and Abelson, R. "Script, plans, goals and understanding", Erlbaum, 1977.

[17] Waltz, D. and Pollack J., "Massively Parallel Parsing", Cognitive Science, 9, 1985.

[18] Wilks Y., "An Intelligent Analyzer and Understander of English", CACM, Vol. 18, No. 5, 1975.

Reinterpretation and the Perceptual Microstructure of Conceptual Knowledge

Cognition Considered as a Perceptual Skill

Jeff Shrager
Xerox PARC
Palo Alto, California

Abstract

In this paper I argue that conceptual knowledge has significant perceptual content, based upon evidence from studies of theory formation and from recent experimental work on learning in complex physical domains. I outline a theory of "perceptually grounded" conceptual knowledge, and briefly outline a computational model of learning about lasers, in which student's "qualitative" understanding of lasers rests primarily upon his perceptual experience in the domain.

Introduction

The goal of this research is a detailed computational theory of conceptual representation and use. Previous theories (e.g., Schank & Abelson, 1977) have been based primarily on symbolic representational substructure. Pavio (1986) and others have argued for a mixed cognitive representational framework, but these theories still rely upon an independently meaningful symbolic representation. In this paper I argue from our studies of "reinterpretation" during theory formation that our conceptual knowledge must be *perceptually grounded*, and propose a theory of conceptual representation based upon such grounding.

Studies of Theory Formation

Shrager & Klahr (1986) gave college students a programmable toy vehicle called the "BigTrak" and asked them to "figure it out" without instructions or advice. In the course of about one-half hour, subjects undertake numerous steps of theory refinement and reformulation. In some of these events subjects seem to reformulate their theory of the BigTrak in ways that introduce new terms and representational principles.

Consider the segment of protocol in Table 1 (studied in detail in Shrager & Klahr, 1986). By programming the BigTrak with "$CLR, \rightarrow, 1, \uparrow, 2, GO$" (FC122-127) FC caused the toy to move six degrees clockwise and then two feet forward. From previous behavior we believe that FC thought that this would make the BigTrak move one foot to the right and then one foot forward. Figure 1 shows (a) what we think FC expected, and (b) what the BigTrak really did.

A reformulation step takes place at this point of mismatch between FC's expectation and the behavior of the BigTrak. Around FC127 we hypothesize that he does the following:

1. *Recognizes* that the behavior of the BigTrak matches his expectations when mediated by the concept of vector-addition;
2. *Introduces the concept* of vector-addition into his theory of the BigTrak, including "resultant" and "component" terms, and the associated representational principles; and

```
115:        Does it...I don't know maybe it remembers things or
116:        something so that...it just did the same thing I told it
117:        to do last time even though I pushed different buttons.
118: CLR
119: CLR    Alright.  I guess you can like oh I see (?) program
120:        steps into it or
121:        something like that. So if you push ummm...
122: CLR
123: →      right one
124: 1      then forward
125: ↑      two
126: 2
127: GO     Went straight and right a little bit.
{Here the BigTrak turns right 6 degrees and moves forward 2 feet.}
128:        Oh. I see that's the resultant
129:        thing maybe.  I don't know.
```

Table 1: A part of FC's BigTrak Instructionless Learning Protocol.

3. *Reformulates his knowledge* of the BigTrak and its operation in accord with the new terms and representational principles introduced in the preceding step.

This reformulation results in FC having a theory of the BigTrak which is a combination of his previous knowledge and his general knowledge of vector-addition. FC's introduction of vector-addition seems to be *rapid*; to apply *as a unit, without intermediate problem-solving*, to his understanding of the device; and to *augment* and serve as a *reorganizing principle* for his understanding of the device and its behavior.

Problems with Concept Use in Theory Formation

We previously proposed that theory changes of this sort involve a cognitive mechanism that we called "View Application" (Shrager, 1987), whose role was to *reinterpret one's knowledge in terms of newly uncovered abstractions* (i.e., "views"). Implementing View Application in a symbolic representational framework leads to two particular problems:

The Paradox of Recognition: How can views containing novel terms and relations be recognized as applicable to the current domain if some of those terms and relations are not *already* available in the learner's current theory? We seem to depend upon *prearticulated sensory data* for view selection, but we must wait for the perceptual framework given by a view in order to obtain these articulations.

The Framework Alignment Problem: How can semantic contact be made between terms and relations in the learner's current theory and those in a novel view without common terms shared between theory and view, or rules of translation between terms in the theory and those in the view? In the worst case, terms introduced by the new view may simply be incommensurable with those in the theory to be reformulated in accord with the new view.

Since, for instance, the vector-addition view is the locus of the vector and resultant terms and representations, the subject must have noticed these terms and this representation in the activity of the BigTrak *before* choosing the vector-addition view. However, I previously claimed that the view application step introduces these terms and representations into the learner's theory. This is an example of the paradox of selection.

The combination step of View Application suffers from the framework alignment problem. When the view applier begins to reformulate the learner's current theory according to the new view, it must make "representational contact" between aspects of the view (say, the individual vectors) and the aspects of the learner's current theory (say, movement commands). That is, *differently represented terms which are about the same real-world thing(s)* must be located and their relationship made available to the view applier.

These difficulties seem to stem from our tendency to think of views and theories in terms of schematic internal knowledge in the form of models composed of categorical terms and relations. These categorical entities (which when under interpretation are generally referred to as "symbols") are captured in computational models in the form of scripts, frames, schemas, views, etc. The connection that must hold between the world and the symbolic structures in order that they are *operational* is usually ignored or relegated to the "peripheral" roles of perception or motor activity. This over-reliance on internal and ungrounded knowledge has led theories of mental model formation to be overly rigid, entirely missing the ability to reinterpret experience as *experience per se is nowhere to be found!*

Perceptually Grounded Conceptual Knowledge

The theory of grounded representation rests upon the the following fundamental claim:

Perception and perceptual experience form the basis of conceptual knowledge.

Specifically, we replace symbolic representation in frames, views, scripts, etc, with a set of *"synchronization routines"* that mediate between traces in one modality (say echoic, visual, or motor traces) and traces in another (or the same) modality.[1] Knowledge thus consists of *skills* of *identifying* (and often *naming*) relevant features and concepts, and more importantly, *skills* for *acting* (i.e., executing appropriate actions) with respect to these entities.[2]

The basic approach to the framework alignment problem and the paradox of selection, provided by the grounded representation framework, is that knowledge that is "carried" in different representational frameworks can be compared by understanding how they differentially interpret the experiences that compose their grounding. A central cognitive role is given to experiences themselves (or to quasi-perceptual traces of experiences themselves).[3]) Not only is a picture worth ten-thousand words, but it may be described in perhaps ten different ways, at say a thousand words per description. If each of these thousand-word descriptions is "grounded" on the picture, then we can compare these different descriptions to one-another by reference to the picture itself.

[1] *Modalities* are the substrate of *representations*, but representational structures operate under interpretation. Both algebra and linguistic inference rules, for instance, might be represented in a quasi-linguistic modality; and both static images and physical animations might be represented in an iconic modality.

[2] This approach is reminiscent of the dual-coding approach of Pavio (1986), but Pavio proposes only associations between codes, whereas the present theory makes the stronger proposal of inter/intra-modality synchronization *procedures*. Our theory is a cognitive analog to the theory of visual routines proposed by Ullman (1984).

[3] By the term "quasi-perceptual traces" I mean some poorly-understood combination of deep motor representation and animated-imagery. However, as I haven't any real idea what this deep quasi-perceptual modality might be like, my computational implementations use bitmap animations (ala Funt, 1980). There is a difficult issue here of how a *procedure* or its input, output, or parameters exist such that they can be "examined".

The approach to paradox of selection, suggested by the present theory of grounded representation, is similar: As all knowledge is grounded to experience (or to traces, as above), one can find the desired features for selection in the experiences themselves (or the traces) – among one of the those thousand-word descriptions of our picture. Thus, we do not have to rely upon finding these terms in the learner's present theory.

Let us return to the event where FC's recognizes the BigTrak's movements as a vector resultant. Note that the triangle made by the two component arms (1a and 2a in Figure 1) and the resultant (2b) form approximately the "image" that most of us who have taken formal trigonometry associate with vector-addition. The claim is, then, that what we know of vector-addition includes a procedural recognizer for this image and that it is through this path that we come to "recognize" the possible use of the process of vector-addition in the BigTrak's activity.

To see how perceptual representation helps with framework alignment consider the process of introducing the notion of "memory" into one's theory of the BigTrak. This commonsense concept may be suggested by observing that the BigTrak "did the same thing I told it to do last time even though I pushed different buttons" (Table 1: FC115-118). The application of this view involves reunderstanding the procedure of pressing keys on the BigTrak as storing things in the memory, and the internal activity of the BigTrak as reading out the contents of that memory, and executing it. The quasi-perceptual nature of knowledge gives a straightforward account for this reinterpretation: The representation of these procedures, and of our understanding of what goes on inside the BigTrak's memory is "active" in a kinesthetic or animated sense (or, more likely, both – but certainly far from actual visual perception or physical motion). The BigTrak's mechanism is thus thought of as actively placing (iconic representations of) the BigTrak's actions into (iconic representations of physical) memory slots that have (quasi-perceptual) spatial organization with respect to one-another. Similarly, introducing vector-addition into FC's knowledge of the BigTrak entails bringing in the *procedural skills* of locating and reasoning with aspects of vector addition. (See Shrager, in press, for further details of this sort of model.)

Studying the Perceptual Content of Conceptual Knowledge

We are presently developing paradigms which will both help to reveal the specific quasi-perceptual content of conceptual knowledge, in accord with the above theory, and to provide support the theory. Here I describe a study of learning about laser physics (quantum optics) which serves both goals to some extent.[4]

Overview: We wish to observe the development of students' interpretation of quantum optics via learning about lasers. We wish to specify the "conceptual" (actually, in the present theory, quasi-perceptual) chunks and skills that the students pick up and use in learning and explanation in this domain. We employ a number of methods, ranging from eye-tracking during study and explanation, to reconstructive tasks (as Chase & Simon, 1973), mostly augmented by verbal protocols. In the present paper I report preliminary results from a reconstruction task.

Method: Undergraduates with little physics background were given approximately three hours of instruction in laser physics over four sessions one week apart, including reading textual materials with figures, and answering summary questions. At the end of each session the subject was asked to copy twenty 8.5x11 figures from the page on which they were drawn, onto the next page of the test booklet. The subject could look back as many times as necessary to complete the drawing, but was required to turn the pages fully either to draw or to look back. Complete protocols were

[4]This domain is a good one in many ways. Although everyone knows approximately what a laser is, and is interested in them, almost no one knows how they work. Furthermore, quantum physics is a rich domain but is relatively separate from real world experience and so is easily manipulated.

only collected for the first subject ("J"); here I will focus on her behavior.

Figure 2 shows the stimulus design and predictions from the copying task. Four of the figures in the copying task came directly from the textual materials that the subject had studied (all textual labels in the figures were deleted). Six were *analogs* of the figures in the laser text (drawn from a different textbook). The rest came from a book on computer vision, and were unrelated to laser physics.

Results: J is able to haltingly but correctly answer the relatively difficult questions after each session, sometimes by reference to the text figures. One study question (appearing after 46 minutes of study) asks: "In your own words explain what role the mirrors play in making a laser work. Do the same for stimulated emission." J says:

> We have this uh this discharge tube that has gases inside it...a gas mixture inside it and there are two mirrors on either end. One is like 100 percent reflective and the other is like 95 percent reflective or whatever. [...] Okay, they are spontaneously emitting photons and after a while they keep on doing this and eventually one will hit the mirror and it will bounce back ... it'll hit the mirror head on and it'll bounce back and it will keep on doing this and after a while um it'll start collecting other photons and like stimulating emission, creating them to give off more photons and then soon [...]"

Figure 3 contains the originals (left) and J's first copies (right) for one image from each category in the copying task. *A* is a portion of a figure from the text (less labels) showing a laser cavity in operation. *B* is an analogous representation of a laser cavity in operation, but one which J did not see in her reading. *C* is a figure taken from computer vision. J required 157 seconds and 2 page-turns to copy *A*, 195 seconds and 4 turns for *B*, and 166 seconds and 5 turns for *C*. The summary statistics in Figure 2 (from our preliminary analyses for J) confirm the expected trends.[5]

During her copying of *A*, J says: "Here we have d and e ... the photons and the mirrors. [...] This is an example of that stimulated emission and these [referring to some of the dots] are just spontaneous emission[...]." When she draws the mirrors she says: "Here we have mirror one and here was have another mirror [...]." At one point, when she draws the second from the left photon vector on part "d" of the figure, she says: "Oh no'd better make it look in another way to show uh spontaneity [...]." Most of her reference is in terms of laser dynamics: "photons" "stimulated emission", etc. She clearly recognizes the time sequence implicit in the ordering of the similar parts of the figure.

During her copying of *B*, J says: "[...] these look like springs or something. [...] There are two identical, I guess I identical [...] except for three lines here...wavy lines...c and b, I wonder if that has any significance whatsoever." At one point she says: "I guess I should draw some of the dots...I don't know why I just feel like without them this picture, I don't know if it would make much sense [....]" Most of her reference is in terms very close to the image structure: "wavy lines" "dots" "inside", etc.

During her copying of *C*, J says: " Oh, this looks like uh one of those games that you used to play where you have a bunch of marbles and you have to get em through [....] nebulous shape here [....] one circle going in here, one going off [....] going in through this hole [....]" Most of her reference is in terms very close to the image structure: "circles" "here" "holes", etc.

[5]There is much complexity in interpreting the quantitative results of this study. We must balance for figure complexity and repeated exposures. The analyses presented here are not so controlled and thus can only be considered preliminary.

Observations: From her explanation, J seems to have learned the "conceptual" material in the text. Also, although she recognized and "conceptually interpreted" figures that she had seen, but not a novel figure (unsurprisingly) or a close conceptual analog to one she had seen *even though she was trying to interpret these other figures in terms of lasers.* At several points during the copying tasks J says (in paraphrase): "I'm trying to figure out what this picture has to do with lasers."

From her verbal protocol it is clear that J recognized A as the laser cavity with a process of stimulated emission taking place, and that she did not recognize this for B, even though she was actively trying to interpret this figure. Her copy of A is a *"semantic" analog* rather than a close *visual analog*, whereas her copies of B and C are close visual analogs. (Note, the care with which B and C were copied, versus A.) This is supported, as well, by the fact that she refers to A mostly in (laser) meaningful terms, but not so B or C. Interestingly in later sessions, after she has learned that photons are sometimes (visually) represented in a wave-like way she refers to the "springs" of her verbalization above (B) as photons, but still does not interpret the figure as a laser cavity.

From her apparent conceptual understanding of the laser, her failure to "conceptually" interpret conceptual analogs, but the more efficient performance in their reconstruction (over out-of-domain figures), we can argue that much of what seems to be her "conceptual" knowledge has (quasi-) perceptual content. (Always remembering that I include in this *skills* of interpretation and action in the domain.)

Discussion: Cognition Considered as a Perceptual Skill

I have argued on theoretical and empirical grounds that perceptual content underlies our conceptual knowledge of the world. FC is able to "see" a vector-resultant (and the process of vector-addition) in the activity of the BigTrak; Although J seems to "conceptually" understand the operation of the laser, she is unable to interpret figures that were closely analogous to ones that she directly experienced (and which showed precisely the same "conceptual" information), even though she is clearly trying to impose an interpretation on them that would make them sensible in terms of lasers. The paradigms used in the present research may enable us to observe the fine perceptual substructure of what we call conceptual knowledge, and the details of its functioning in learning and interpretation.

A theory of the microstructure of category representation and use that retains content quite close to the perceptual exemplars from which we learn these concepts is not an entirely new theory of concept structure. It echoes exemplar-based theories (e.g., Medin & Schaeffer, 1978) and the dual-coding approach of Pavio (1986, see also Huttenlocher, 1968), however within a significantly more procedural framework.

Our current modelling efforts follow the reasoning in this paper. We have implemented "qualitative" simulation of laser processes which (a) learns about how lasers work using approximately the same information – particularly the figural information – that our experimental subjects have, and (b) which can reason about the lasing process (Shrager, in press). This model contains two "working memories" in different modalities: an iconic (bitmap) memory in which animations take place (ala Funt, 1980), and a "symbolic" (quasi-linguistic) memory in which explicit (rule-based) inference takes place. These are synchronized by inter-modality (inter-memory) "grounding" routines. Learning takes place by introducing routines specific to the application at hand, which serve to *label* the contents of the iconic memory (by making appropriate changes in the symbolic memory), and conversely, to make appropriate changes in the iconic memory whenever inference (or any other change in the symbolic memory) takes place.

Acknowledgments

Thanks go to the reviewers of this paper, and to many of my colleagues for comments on the paper and the research. I especially thank Sharon Lunt for helping me understand the details of quantum chemistry.

References

Chase, W.G. & Simon, H.A. (1973) Perception in Chess & The Mind's Eye in Chess. papers reprinted as chapters 6.4-6.5 (pp. 386-427) in Simon (1979) Models of Thought. Yale University Press; New Haven.

Funt, B. V. (1980) Problem-Solving with Diagrammatic Representations. Artificial Intelligence, 13, 201-230.

Huttenlocher, J. (1968) Constructing Spatial Images: A Strategy in Reasoning. Psychological Review, 75(6), 550-560.

Kosslyn, S.M. (1987) Seeing and Imaging in the Cerebral Hemispheres: A Computational Approach. Psychological Review, 94(2), 148-175.

Medin, D.L. & Schaeffer, M.M. (1978) A context theory of classification learning. Psychological Review, 85, 207-238.

Pavio, A. (1986) Mental Representations: A Dual Coding Approach. Oxford.

Schank, R. & Abelson, R. (1977) Scripts, Plans, Goals, & Understanding. Lawrence Erlbaum; Hillsdale, NJ.

Shrager, J. (in press) Commonsense Perception and the Psychology of Theory Formation. in Shrager & Langley (eds.) Computational Models of Discovery and Theory Formation. To appear from Lawrence Erlbaum; Hillsdale, NJ.

Shrager, J. (1987) Theory Change via View Application in Instructionless Learning. Machine Learning, 2: 247-276.

Shrager, J. & Klahr, D. (1986) Instructionless learning about a complex device: the paradigm and observations. Int. J. of Man-Machine Studies, 25, 153-189.

Ullman, S. (1984) Visual Routines. Cognition, 18, 97-159.

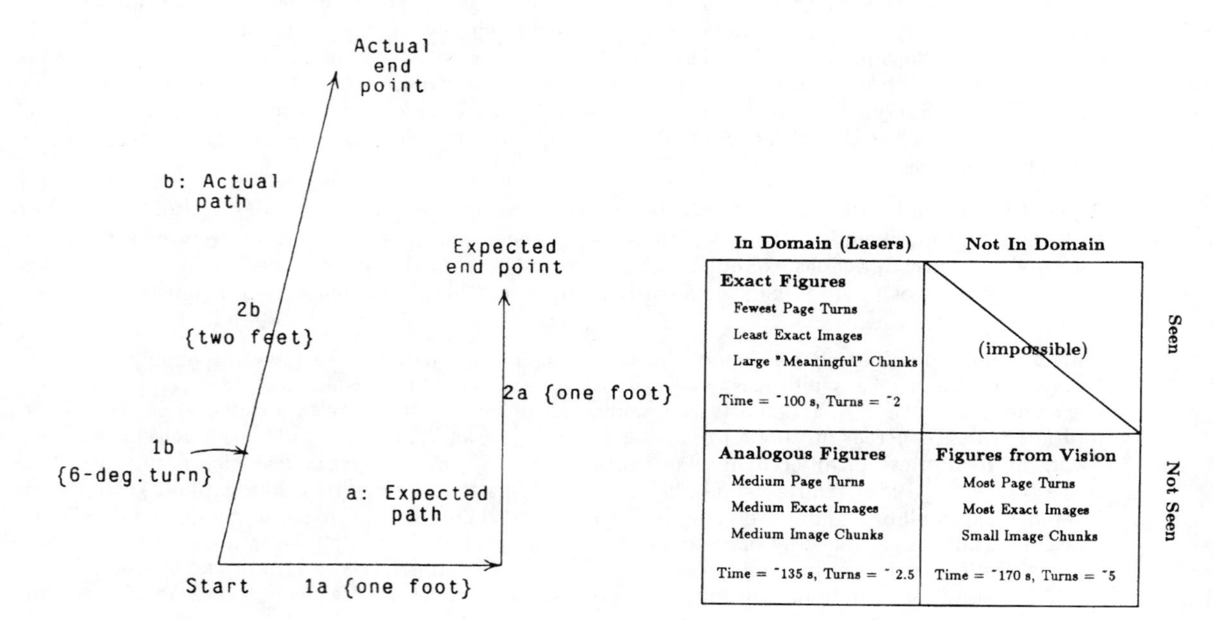

Figure 1: The BigTrak Actions (a) Expected by FC, and (b) That Actually Took Place at FC127.

Figure 2: Design, Predictions and Preliminary Summary Data

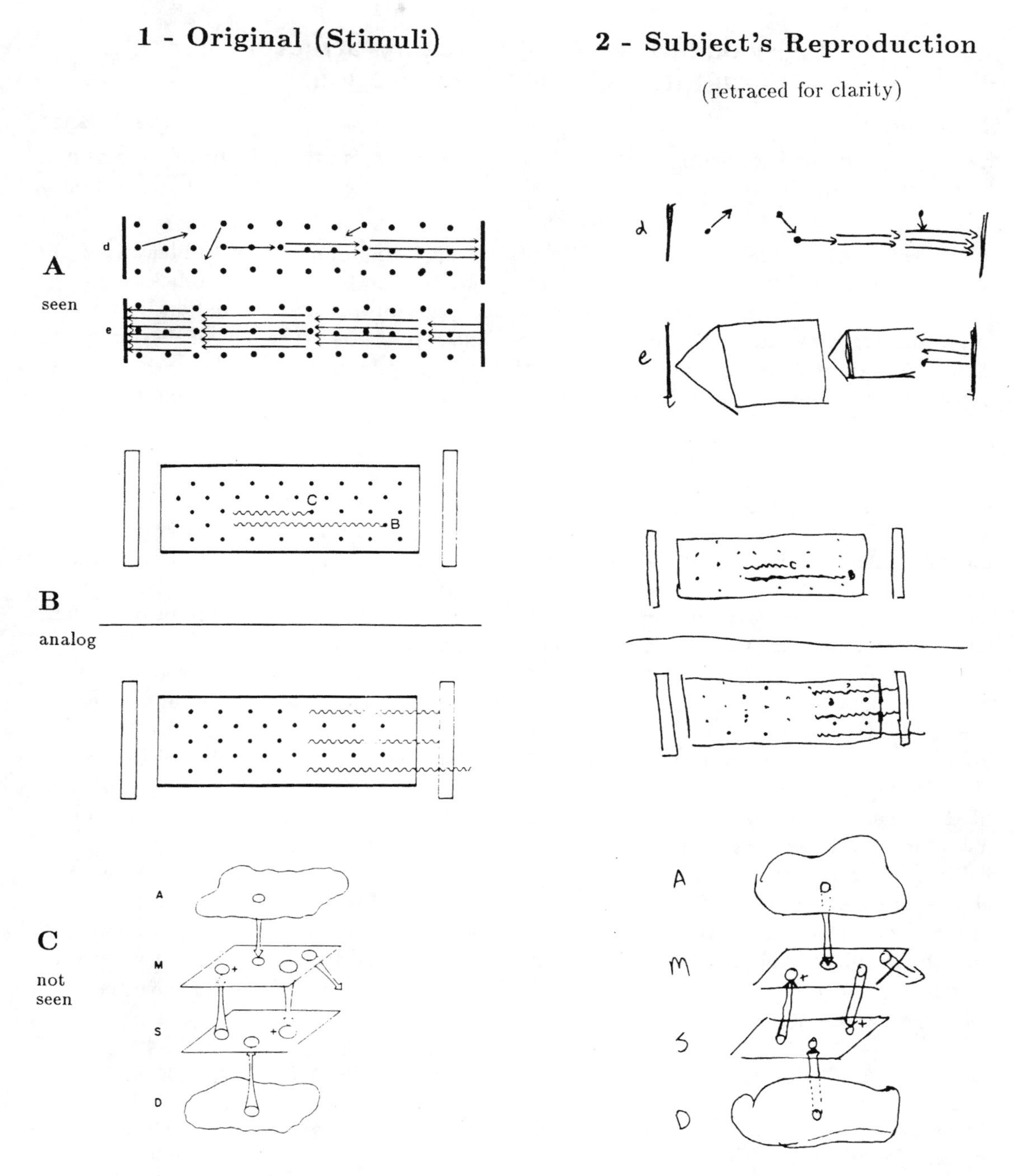

Figure 3: Selected Results from J's First Copying Task

A Model of Natural Category Structure and its Behavioral Implications[1]

Jane Silber
Management of Technology
Vanderbilt University

Douglas Fisher
Department of Computer Science
Vanderbilt University

Abstract: Fisher (1988) uses the COBWEB concept formation system to illustrate a computational unification of basic level and typicality effects. The model relies on probabilistic, distributed concept representations, and appropriate interaction between cue and category validity. We review this work and report a new account of the *fan effect*. This extension requires an additional assumption of parallel processing, but otherwise is explained by precisely the same mechanisms as basic level and typicality phenomena.

INTRODUCTION

Cognitive modeling fits general computational mechanisms to the constraints of psychological data. The problem of determining an initial starting point for cognitive modeling has been implicitly addressed by several authors. Anderson (in press) suggests a *rational analysis*, whereby a general class of behaviors (e.g., concept formation) are associated with a performance function to be optimized. The guiding assumption is that natural organisms are rational, albeit resource-bounded decision makers.

This paper traces the development of the COBWEB concept formation system (Fisher, 1987) from rational analyses by Gluck and Corter (1985), Kolodner (1983), and Lebowitz (1982). Gluck and Corter provide insights on the absolute quality of conceptual knowledge in their work on human basic level effects. Kolodner's CYRUS and Lebowitz's UNIMEM provide general mechanisms of indexing and classification that we engineer to fit the constraints of basic level effects. In Fisher (1988) the consistency of the resultant model is verified with respect to basic level effects. However, the model also accounts for typicality effects, which were not the focus of engineering. In fact, the model unifies these effects and suggests heretofore unexplored interactions between basic level and typicality phenomena. This paper extends the phenomenological basis of the model by accounting for the *fan effect* (Anderson, 1976). The extensions required for this account are natural, do not adversely affect earlier behavioral accounts, and suggest ways to improve the robustness of COBWEB's underlying learning mechanisms.

BASIC LEVEL EFFECTS AND RATIONAL CONCEPT FORMATION

Substantial experimental evidence suggests that there is a *basic* or preferred level of human classification (Rosch, Mervis, Gray, Johnson, and Boyes-Braem, 1976; Jolicoeur,

[1] Requests for reprints should be sent to Douglas Fisher.

Gluck, and Kosslyn, 1984). For example, when a subject is shown a picture of a collie and asked to name it, the response will typically be *dog*, not *collie*, *mammal*, or *animal.* Similarly, when asked to confirm that a pictured collie is a *collie*, *dog*, *mammal* and *animal*, subjects will respond more quickly for *dog* than the other categories. These tasks indicate that for a hierarchy containing {collie, dog, mammal, animal}, *dog* is the basic level concept.

Gluck and Corter (1985) formulated *category utility*, which presumes that the basic level maximizes 'predictive ability'. For example, very few correct predictions can be made about an arbitrary *animal*, but those that can be made (e.g., animate) apply to many objects. In contrast, knowing something is a *robin* assures many predictions, but they apply to much fewer objects. The basic level concept (e.g., *bird*) is where a tradeoff between the *expected* number of correct predictions (e.g., has-feathers, beaks, flies) and the proportion of the environment to which the predictions apply, $P(N_k)E(\#$ correct predictions$|N_k)$, is maximized. If $P(A_i = V_{ij}|N_k)$ is the probability that an attribute value will be predicted and this prediction is correct with the same probability then this measure can be further formalized as:

$$P(N_k)\sum_i \sum_j P(A_i = V_{ij}|N_k)^2. \qquad (1)$$

Category utility correctly predicts the basic level (as behaviorally identified by human subjects) in two experimental studies (Hoffman and Ziessler, 1983; Murphy and Smith, 1982).

Gluck and Corter's derivation of category utility is motivated by the same rational arguments made by Anderson (in press): good classes are those that maximize correct predictions that can be made about class members. Anderson develops a Bayesian heuristic function to guide concept formation. In contrast, Fisher's (1987) COBWEB uses category utility to guide the incremental formation of classification trees (Kolodner, 1983; Lebowitz, 1982). Fisher (1988) demonstrates that with an appropriate indexing scheme, COBWEB consistently classifies observations at the same intermediate or basic-level classes as human subjects (Hoffman and Ziessler, 1983; Murphy and Smith, 1982).

The indexing strategy is developed from category utility. In particular, (1) can be rewritten (using Bayes Rule) as:

$$\sum_i \sum_j P(A_i = V_{ij})P(A_i = V_{ij}|N_k)P(N_k|A_i = V_{ij}). \qquad (2)$$

Thus, category utility can be viewed as maximizing a weighted (by $P(A_i = V_{ij})$) tradeoff of *cue validity* (i.e., reflected in $P(N_k|A_i = V_{ij})$) and *category validity* (i.e., reflected in $P(A_i = V_{ij}|N_k)$). Indexing can be viewed as 'compiling' this similarity assessment process. Individual attribute value indices are weighted by $P(N_k|A_i = V_{ij})$ and are directed at nodes, N_k, that maximize $P(A_i = V_{ij}|N_k)P(N_k|A_i = V_{ij})$ (i.e., the *collocation* (Jones, 1983)) of the value with respect to ancestors and descendents of N_k. $P(A_i = V_{ij}|N_k)$'s are stored at nodes. Figure 1 illustrates that this strategy results in

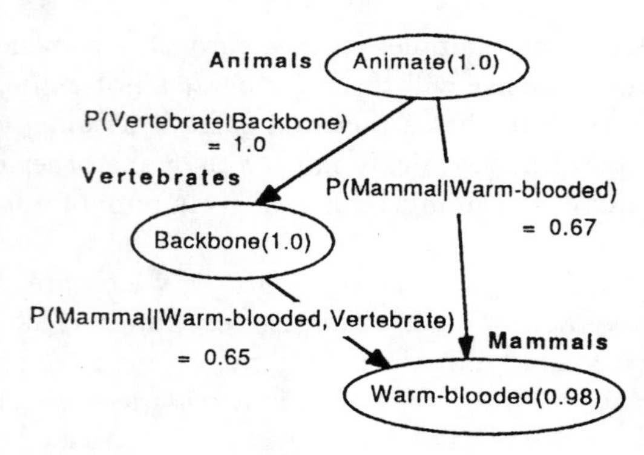

Figure 1: Opportunistic index placement (from Fisher, 1988).

opportunistic indexing [2] that may jump levels. An object is initially classified at that node, N_k, that maximizes the *total cue validity* (Rosch, 1978):

$$\sum_i P(N_k|A_i = V_{ij}), \qquad (3)$$

over the attribute values of the object that are used for indexing. Notice that because category *validity* helps determine index placement it impacts object classification, although it is not explicitly considered at classification time.

TYPICALITY EFFECTS

Importantly, COBWEB does not only account for basic level effects – the phenomena for which it was engineered – but the indexing/classification mechanisms also account for a second influential class of phenomena known as *typicality* effects (Mervis and Rosch, 1981; Smith and Medin, 1981; Rosch, 1978). Psychological studies indicate that some members of a class are treated preferentially or as more typical of a class. For example, in a target recognition task a *robin* will be recognized as a *bird* more quickly than will a *chicken*. In particular, Rosch and Mervis (1975) demonstrate that object typicality increases with the number of features shared with other objects of the same class and varies inversely with the number of features shared with members of contrasting classes.

COBWEB's indexing scheme accounts for typicality effects found by Rosch and Mervis (1975). These studies used letter strings like those of Figure 2a that were arranged into categories A and B and taught to subjects. Subjects were then asked to verify category membership of letter strings of A. Subjects consistently verified membership more quickly for those strings of category A that shared many symbols with other strings of A and shared little with members of category B. To account for this data COBWEB clustered over the collective letter strings of A and B. For example, Figure 2b shows a

[2] A term due to Bareiss, Porter, and Weir (1987).

	Letter String	Intra Over-lap	Letter String	Inter Over-lap	*Typi-cality*
	JXPHM	low	4KCTG	high	*low*
	QBLFS	"	GKNTJ	"	"
A	XPHMQ	med.	4KC6D	med.	*med.*
	MQBLF	"	HPNSJ	"	"
	PHMQB	high	HPC6B	low	*high*
	HMQBL	"	HPNWD	"	"
	CTRVG		8SJKT		
	TRVGZ		8SJ3G		
B	RVGZK		9UJCG		
	VGZKD		4UZC9		
	GZKDW		4UZRT		
	ZKDWN		MSZR5		
	(1a)		(1b)		

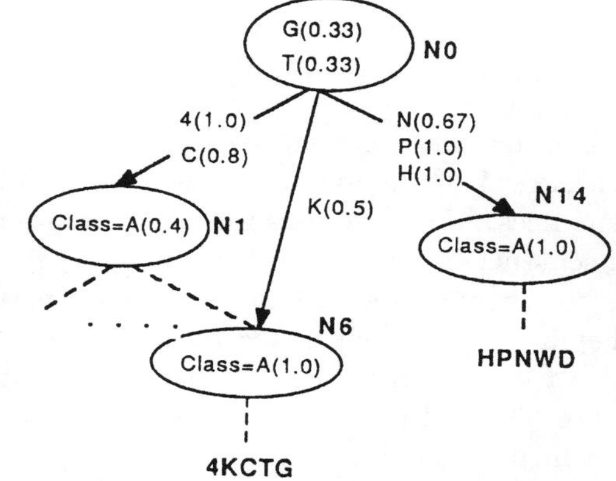

Figure 2: Letter strings and sample COBWEB tree (from Fisher, 1988).

partial tree over the strings of 1*b*. Because some members of category *A* may share more in common with members of *B* than with other members of their own class, class *A* strings are not necessarily localized at a single node. Rather, we assume that a string is recognized (verified) as a category A member by classifying it to a node for which $P(\text{Class}= A|N_k) = 1.0$. Verification time is simulated by the inverse of the total cue validity scores (i.e., 1/total-cue-validity) used to classify the object; we assume that the more an object predicts a node, the faster the object will be classified with respect to it. COBWEB's category-verification time is ordered in precisely the same manner as human subjects, regardless of intra- or inter- category overlap.

On the surface typicality and basic level effects appear to be disparate behaviors. However, Fisher (1988) demonstrates that while concept trees may equate classes with nodes (i.e., a local representation), members of a single class can also be 'distributed' throughout the tree. This enables a unified account of basic level and typicality effects because individual concepts (i.e., the scope of typicality) and concept hierarchies (i.e., the scope of basic level effects) are represented by the same tree-structured representation. This work provides the only computational account of any basic level phenomena that we know of. In addition, the distributed account of typicality effects (with respect to human data found in Rosch and Mervis (1975)) is novel. Finally, the model accounts for known interactions between basic level and typicality effects (Jolicoeur, Gluck, and Kosslyn, 1984) and predicts previously unexplored interactions.

FAN EFFECT

Work since (Fisher, 1988) has accounted for a third phenomena: the *fan effect* (Anderson, 1976). The fan effect has been demonstrated in sentence recognition tasks. Typically, simple sentences that consist of a person and a location are used:

(1-1) The doctor is in the bank. (1-2) The fireman is in the park.

(2-1) The teacher is in the church. (2-2) The teacher is in the park.

The sentences vary in the number of features associated with the subject of the sentences and the location in which the subject appears (e.g., 'teacher' appears in two sentences). The numbers following each sentence indicate the size of the fan: the number of sentences that contain the feature (person – location). After training on selected sentences, recognition experiments are performed; subjects must respond as to whether they have previously observed a sentence (true) or not (false). Recognition time increases with the frequency that a person and location is present in training sentences.

For COBWEB, sentences are encoded as attribute value pairs. The set of objects, each of which contains two attributes (i.e., person and location), is then used to create a concept tree. A test set is a mixture of items that appeared in the original training set ("trues"), and new sentences that have not been seen previously ("falses").

One key processing assumption was added to the basic classification model. Many studies in cognitive psychology have suggested that search through memory proceeds in a parallel fashion. Triggering nodes in memory will cause activation to spread among all related elements, perhaps with different degrees of strength or speed. The assumption of parallel search was added to the COBWEB model. Rather than only examining the path that maximizes total cue validity, all paths indexed by object (sentence) values are explored. The search ends when indices lead no further or when the test item is found in a node. For the "true" statements, COBWEB always locates the test object in a node, thus ending the search. The total simulated time required to reach that node is the resultant recognition time. The search for "false" test objects, on the other hand, will end when all paths have been explored as far as possible. In these cases the limiting factor is the time required to explore the *slowest* path. Our data compares favorably with experimental data, in cases of true (observed) and false sentences and across all feature frequencies. Figure 3 contains a portion of the tree produced by COBWEB when presented with a set of person-location sentences. The dotted lines in the diagram represent the indices that are used to recognize a test probe. In the training set, *doctor* and *church* each appear in only one sentence, while *park* appears in two. When the "false" probe *The doctor is in the church* is presented, COBWEB predicts that the search will simultaneously follow both the *doctor* index and the *church* index, leading from *N0* to *N3* and *N6*. Both of these paths are exhausted with a total time of 1 unit. In contrast, the "false" probe *The doctor is in the park* has a longer response time, because *park* appears in two sentences and has a larger fan. The search resulting from this probe proceeds from *N0* to *N3* along the *doctor* index, requiring 1 unit of time. However, the search simultaneously follows the *park* index from *N0* to *N2*, requiring 1 unit of time, and then from *N2* to *N7*, requiring another unit. Therefore, 2 units of time are required before *N7* is reached and the model can identify the probe as false.

Table 1a shows the mean recognition times for "true" and "false" statements in actual human experiments (Anderson, 1976). In comparison, the (unfitted) reaction times

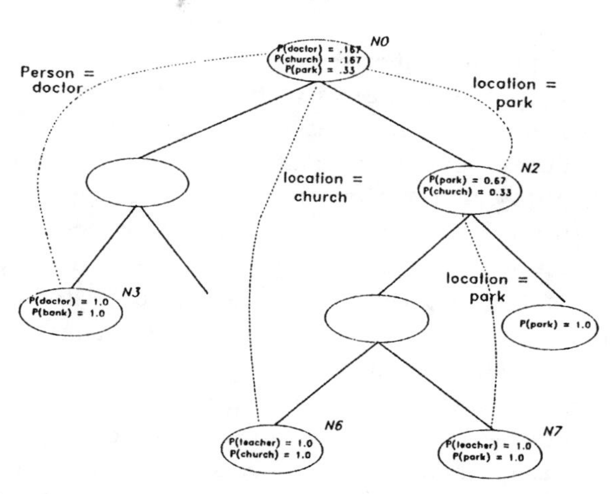

Figure 3: Concept tree for person-location experiment.

Table 1: Fan effect mean reaction times. Mean time for 'true' statements are shown above the mean time for 'false' statements.

(a)

Sentences / location	Sentences/person: *1*	*2*	*3*
1	1.11	1.17	1.22
	1.20	1.22	1.26
2	1.17	1.20	1.22
	1.25	1.36	1.29
3	1.15	1.23	1.36
	1.26	1.47	1.46

(b)

Sentences / location	Sentences/person: *1*	*2*	*3*
1	0.50	0.83	0.95
	1.00	1.50	2.25
2	1.47	2.30	2.25
	1.55	1.70	1.82
3	1.65	2.30	2.85
	1.62	1.97	2.07

predicted by the COBWEB model are displayed in Table 1b. COBWEB produced a concept hierarchy from the same training set used in human experiments; the data presented here are averaged over several trials. We expect systematic increase in time as the number of sentences per person and per location increase, comparisons of relative magnitude are most meaningful. In the recognition time tables, there are 36 possible comparisons of relative size (18 each for "trues" and "falses"). Human experiments and COBWEB simulations each resulted in 3 comparisons that are not in the expected direction.

There is great similarity between the COBWEB account of the fan and typicality effects. Typicality studies are generally based on target recognition tasks that require subjects to classify an instance as a member of a category. Instances with high inter-category similarity are associated with longer response times, while high intra-category similarity produces shorter response times. On the other hand, Anderson's (1976) ACT model predicts that instances with a large fan resulting from many associated propositions will have longer response times; ACT accounted well for the human data. This produces an apparent contradiction in that objects with features shared with many other objects (i.e., persons or locations appearing in many sentences) produce longer times in the fan effect, but are apparently more "typical", thereby resulting in shorter times according to the typicality effect. However, further examination of the learning task reveals that these two findings are consistent, and the explanation rests on the distinction between intra- and inter- category similarity. When propositions or sentences are learned in fan effect studies, each is remembered as an individual case, or category. Persons or locations that appear in a large number of sentences correspond to attributes that are common to more than one category, i.e., high inter-category similarity not intra-category similarity. Thus, the direct relationship between fan size and response time closely parallels the relation between typicality and inter-category similarity. The COBWEB model accounts for typicality and fan effects in the precisely the same manner; the fan effect emerges as a special case of typicality effects in which the classes being learned are singletons. Although the original COBWEB typicality studies were conducted without the parallel processing assumption (Fisher, 1988), similar results are obtained when parallelism is incorporated.

CONCLUDING REMARKS

We have extended the scope of behaviors accounted for by COBWEB. By our account, the fan effect is a special case of typicality phenomena. We are extending our research in several directions. First, computer experiments reveal that very early in concept formation our indexing scheme is very sensitive to the ordering of observations. Indexing is easily fooled and led astray. In general, our indexing procedure and tree structure are too inflexible. Early in training desirable classes can fluctuate wildly. Our work with the fan effect suggests that rather than placing (classifying) an object along a single best path, it may be more desirable to place (classify) it along a number of paths. In fact, the category utility indexing scheme is easily extensible to allow this – without the use of arbitrary thresholds that characterize other systems (Kolodner, 1983; Lebowitz, 1982). Classification along multiple paths leads naturally to a directed acyclic graph structure (DAG). A DAG is more robust in that is allows orthogonal classes to develop (e.g., mammal or reptile or bird or ... or fish *versus* carnivore or omnivore or herbivore). Classes that do not prove useful later in training can be pruned out. Thus, a rational analysis (Anderson, in press; Gluck & Corter, 1985) initially led to a model of certain psychological effects, but an inverse process is also valuable: modifications to the cognitive model suggest extensions that are primarily computational improvements.

REFERENCES

Anderson, J. R., *Language, Memory, and Thought*, Lawrence Erlbaum Associates, Hillsdale, NJ, 1976.

Anderson, J. R., "The Place of Cognitive Architectures in a Rational Analysis." In K. Van Lehn (ed.), *Architectures for Intelligence*, (in press).

Bareiss, E.R., Porter, B.W., and Wier, C.C. Protos: an exemplar-based learning apprentice. In *Proceedings of the Fourth International Workshop on Machine Learning*, Morgan Kaufmann, 1987, pp. 12–23.

Fisher, D., "A Computational Account of Basic Level and Typicality Effects," *Proceedings of AAAI-88: The Seventh National Conference on Artificial Intelligence*, Morgan Kaufmann, 1988, pp. 233-238.

Fisher, D., Knowledge Acquisition Via Incremental Conceptual Clustering, *Machine Learning*, 2, 1987, pp. 139-172.

Gluck, M. A. and Corter, J. E., "Information, Uncertainty, and the Utility of Categories," *Proceedings of the Seventh Annual Conference of the Cognitive Science Society*, Irvine, CA, Lawrence Erlbaum Associates, 1985, pp. 283-287.

Hoffman, J., and Ziessler, C., "Objectidentifikation in Kunstlichen Begriffshierarchien," *Zeitscrift fur Psychologie*, 16, 1984, pp. 43-275.

Jolicoeur, P., Gluck, M., and Kosslyn, S., "Pictures and Names: Making the Connection," *Cognitive Psychology*, Vol. 16, 1984, pp. 243-275.

Kolodner, J. L. (1983). Reconstructive memory: A computer model. *Cognitive Science*, *7*, 281–328.

Lebowitz, M. (1982). Correcting erroneous generalizations. *Cognition and Brain Theory*, *5*, 367–381.

Murphy, G., and Smith, E., "Basic Level Superiority in Picture Categorization," *Journal of Verbal Learning and Verbal Behavior*, Vol. 21, 1982, pp. 1-20.

Rosch, E. and Mervis, C., "Family Resemblances: Studies in the Internal Structure of Categories," *Cognitive Psychology*, Vol. 7, 1975, pp. 573-605.

Rosch, E., Mervis, C., Gray, W., Johnson, D. and Boyes-Braem, P. "Basic Objects in Natural Categories," *Cognitive Psychology*, Vol. 8, 1976, pp. 382-439.

Smith, E. and Medin, D., *Categories and Concepts*, Harvard University Press, Cambridge, MA, 1981.

Qualitative and Quantitative Reasoning About Thermodynamics

Gordon Skorstad and Ken Forbus
Qualitative Reasoning Group
Beckman Institute, University of Illinois

Abstract: One goal of qualitative physics is to capture the mental models of engineers and scientists. This paper shows how Qualitative Process theory can be used to express concepts of engineering thermodynamics. This encoding provides the means to integrate qualitative and quantitative knowledge for solving textbook thermodynamics problems. These ideas have been implemented in a program called SCHISM, which analyzes thermodynamic cycles, such as gas turbine plants and steam power plants. We describe its analysis of a sample textbook problem and discuss our plans for future work.

1 INTRODUCTION

A goal of qualitative physics is to capture the tacit knowledge engineers use to organize and control knowledge gained through formal training. The initial motivation for qualitative physics was to set up and guide the solution of textbook motion problems [6]. Since then, research has mainly focused on purely qualitative reasoning [2], and significant progress has been made. We believe the time is right to begin exploring the integration of qualitative and quantitative reasoning again. In particular, our long-range goal is to develop a system which can automatically perform engineering analyses of thermodynamic systems in a human-like way. This paper describes our first step towards that goal.

Studies of textbook problem solving have tended to focus on quantitative reasoning [1,4,14,15]. We begin instead with the view that qualitative models are the starting point for the accumulation and use of more sophisticated, quantitative models. This view is widely held in the mental models literature [11], and widely but less formally in the engineering community [16,17]. In problem-solving, the analysis begins by constructing a qualitative understanding of the situation. This initial understanding provides the framework for further analyses, such as deriving and solving sets of equations. Developing a correct qualitative understanding of the problem is essential to solving complex problems. Qualitative physics should provide the foundation for a more complete, formal account of human mental models, including how qualitative and quantitative knowledge interact.

This paper shows how Qualitative Process theory [8] can be used to encode fundamental concepts of engineering thermodynamics. This qualitative knowledge is used for problem solving in several ways. Qualitative simulation is used to verify that questions make sense by ensuring that the behavior mentioned can actually occur. The simulation also provides a framework for extracting equations. For example, heuristics for choosing appropriate control volumes are based on qualitative criteria. We have tested these ideas through implementation in a program called SCHISM, which solves textbook thermodynamics problems involving cycles.

The next section shows how a set of fundamental thermodynamic concepts can be encoded in QP theory. Section 3 describes how this encoding can be used as a basis for equation extraction and quantitative analysis. Section 4 describes SCHISM. Lastly, Section 5 demonstrates our ideas with an example of SCHISM analyzing the efficiency of a simple steam plant.

2 QP THEORY AND THERMODYNAMICS

Thermodynamics deals with transformations of energy from one form to another. The notion of process is central to thermodynamics, hence QP theory should be well-suited for representing it. Here we show how the following fundamental concepts of thermodynamics can be expressed in QP theory: *control volumes, closed cycles, equilibrium, steady state, phase changes, special processes,* and *point and path quantities.*

2.1 CONTROL VOLUMES

Every thermodynamic analysis starts by partitioning the universe into a *system* or *control volume* and its surroundings. A system is any macroscopic object or region of space selected for analysis. Systems are divided into three classes: *open*, *closed* and *isolated.* Open systems (such as the human body) exchange matter with their surroundings. Closed systems (e.g., the coolant in a refrigerator) allow energy but not matter to be exchanged with their surroundings. Isolated systems exchange neither mass nor energy with their surroundings.

Control volumes in a QP model correspond to individuals with the quantity `volume`, and contiguous collections of such individuals. The contained stuff ontology [12], used in our model, provides a natural partioning of an apparatus into macroscopic control volumes. "The coolant in the room coils of the refrigerator" is an example of a contained stuff. Our *Molecular Collection* (`MC`) ontology [5], which follows an infinitesimal piece of fluid through an apparatus, provides another useful control volume. An `MC` may be viewed as a closed control volume since its mass does not change. The `MC` control volume lets us describe properties of a fluid at a point in space.

In QP theory, open control volumes are easily identified as those which take part in some process that causes a mass transfer (such as `liquid-flow` or `boiling`). Closed control volumes are those which are not open but which participate in some work or heat transfer. Heat transfer and work transfer are indicated by participation in a `heat-flow` or `work-flow` process, respectively. A control volume is isolated if it does not participate in mass, work, or heat transfers.

2.2 CLOSED CYCLES

An important class of thermodynamic systems are *closed cycles.* In such systems, fluid continuously passes around a closed loop. Closed cycles are of great practical importance since they form the basis of heating, cooling and power generation systems. Indeed, whole books are written about the analysis of such systems [13]. Closed cycles are the first class of systems we have chosen for automated analysis by `SCHISM`.

The `MC` ontology provides a simple way to detect closed cycles, since a closed cycle directly corresponds to a cycle in the `MC` envisionment. Recognizing closed cycles allows `SCHISM` to select states of the envisionment that have the intended behavior as candidates for further analysis. (This also allows `SCHISM` to reject questions about impossible behaviors.)

2.3 PHASE CHANGES

Many engineering systems, such as refrigerators and steam plants, rely on phase changes to operate. These phase changes are modelled as processes in QP theory. `SCHISM` includes a model of boiling and of condensation. Unlike previous models, these processes include the thermal effects of mixing in the destination gas for boiling and the destination liquid for condensation.

2.4 EQUILIBRIUM

Equilibrium is the absence of certain processes acting. It is important enough to be explicitly represented, so we use views whose quantity conditions are the equality of driving forces. For example, the following view is active whenever two objects with a connecting heat path have the same temperature:

```
(defview (Thermal-Equilibrium ?src ?dst ?path)
    Individuals ((?src  :conditions (Quantity (Temperature ?src)))
                 (?dst  :conditions (Quantity (Temperature ?dst)))
                 (?path :conditions (heat-path ?path)
                                    (path-to ?path ?src ?dst)))
    Preconditions ((Heat-aligned ?path))
    QuantityConditions ((equal-to (A (temperature ?src))
                                  (A (temperature ?dst)))))
```

2.5 STEADY STATE

Another vital concept in thermodynamics is ***steady state***. An apparatus is said to be in steady state when all point properties are constant with respect to time. This is the normal mode of operation for continuous flow processes. For example, when your kitchen refrigerator is running continuously, the temperature of the coolant at any point along the room coils is constant. Engineering analyses of thermodynamic cycles focus on steady state behavior.

In the QP model, a steady state system is indicated when all time derivatives of point properties are zero. When performing a steady-state analysis, these derivative constraints are added to QPE's scenario model so that only steady-state behaviors are envisioned[1]. If the envisionment is empty under this constraint, steady state behavior is impossible given the qualitative description of the system. Sometimes there is more than one steady state behavior (for example, the same apparatus could be used as a gas turbine power plant or an air cycle refrigerator, depending on driving conditions). If there is more than one steady-state behavior, teleology is used to select the appropriate state for further analysis.

2.6 SPECIAL PROCESSES

Quantitative analyses of closed systems are greatly simplified when processes drive parameters through particular trajectories in state space. Thermodynamic analyses often approximate real systems by assuming processes follow such trajectories. These approximations include:

- constant volume, or *isometric*
- constant pressure, or *isobaric*
- constant temperature, or *isothermal*
- *adiabatic*, ie., no heat flow crosses the system boundary.

For example, boiling is generally approximated as an isothermal process. These exact distinctions can be drawn about the processes in the QP model. Isometric, isobaric, and isothermal processes can be recognized by noting the sign of the appropriate derivative. Adiabatic processes can be recognized by the absence of active heat flow processes between the system and its environment.

[1]QPE is an envisioner for QP theory. For details see [9].

2.7 POINT AND PATH QUANTITIES

Thermodynamics distinguishes between ***path-independent*** and ***path-dependent*** parameters. Path-independent parameters, also known as ***point properties*** or ***state functions*** of a substance, include temperature, pressure and volume. They can be determined directly from the current values of other parameters. For example, fixing the pressure and volume of a gas uniquely determines its temperature. Path-dependent parameters (often called "absolute flows") are integrals of flow rates. Examples include work, mass flow, and heat flow. Computing path-dependent parameters requires histories. For example, the amount of work required to compress a gas from state S_1 to S_2 depends on how the compression is done. Compression may occur isothermally, adiabatically or along some arbitrary path.

Path-independent parameters are always explicit properties of individuals in the QP domain model. Flow rates are always explicit properties of processes in the QP domain model (e.g., `mass-flow-rate`, `heat-flow-rate`). Since `SCHISM` currently focuses on steady-state problems, we have not yet implemented path-dependent properties.

3 EXTRACTING EQUATIONS

The interaction of qualitative and quantitative reasoning used in classical thermodynamic analyses is common in the interdisciplinary field called ***mathematical modelling***. Experts in the field regard math modelling as something of an art [16]:

> "It should now be apparent that an understanding of the scientific motivation of the problem and the ability to use heuristic reasoning, as *well* as manipulative skill, are essential to the practice of applied mathematics."

We claim mathematical modelling of physical phenomena begins with a qualitative model. Equations are extracted from the qualitative model until a tractable ***closed*** set is obtained. A closed set of equations is a set of n independent equations that contains n or fewer unknowns. If the equations are intractable, simplifying assumptions may be added to the qualitative model. An example of a simplifying assumption in thermodynamics is ***adiabaticity*** of a process.

The equations which can be extracted from a model can be divided into three classes. ***Domain principles*** P include fundamental laws and empirical correlations such as conservation of mass and equations of state. ***Domain definitions*** D introduce new quantities by defining them in terms of existing ones. An example is the efficiency of a system behaving as a heat engine, which is defined to be the rate of work flowing into the system divided by the rate of work flowing out. ***Qualitative identities*** I are equations that are derivable directly from relations in the qualitative model. For example, the qualitative model of a dammed river at steady state will include the relation that the flow rate of water into the lake equals the flow rate of water out.

In thermodynamics, extracting an equation from a qualitative state consists of two steps: (1) choosing a control volume v from the set of possible control volumes V, and (2) applying to that control volume a domain principle $p \epsilon P$, domain definition $d \epsilon D$, or qualitative identity $i \epsilon I$.

The number of possible equations that can be extracted from a given qualitative state is thus $|V \times (P \cup D \cup I)|$. This number can be enormous. In thermodynamics, choosing the right control volumes is crucial to the efficient search of the equation space. For example, instantiating the ideal gas law for a contained gas about which nothing is known introduces four new variables: the temperature, pressure, volume and mass of the contained gas. This moves us further from the goal of a closed set of equations.

While the qualitative model provides all possible control volumes, the subset which is actually useful tends to be small. We have developed a heuristic technique for ordering the possibilities. The control volumes are divided into lexicographically ordered classes using five essentially qualitative criteria:

1. *Boundary Conditions:* Prefer systems which border goal flow rate quantities.
2. *Geometry:* Prefer systems whose boundaries are crossed by fewer flows.
3. *Number of Knowns:* Prefer systems containing many known quantities.
4. *Boundary Homogeneity:* Prefer systems where only a single type of flow (e.g., only heat flow) crosses its boundary.
5. *Internal Complexity:* Prefer smaller, simpler control volumes.

In the example below, these heuristics enabled SCHISM to narrow its search to a small fraction of the total equation space.

4 HOW SCHISM WORKS

SCHISM is an approximately 7000 line lisp program consisting of three major parts that perform: (1) qualitative teleology analysis of program input, (2) equation space searching, and (3) symbolic math manipulations. It takes four inputs: (*i*) the intended function of the system, (*ii*) an envisionment of the system (generated by QPE), (*iii*) a set of quantitative facts and measurements of the system, and (*iv*) a goal quantity.

SCHISM begins an analysis by verifying that the apparatus behaves as intended. It does this by examining QPE's envisionment. Currently, SCHISM recognizes two classes of thermodynamic systems, heat-engines and heat-pumps. If the expected behavior is that of a heat-engine, SCHISM checks that some state in the envisionment satisfies the following three criteria: (1) it contains a closed MC cycle, (2) it has a net flow of work *out* of the system, and (3) it transfers heat from a hotter place to a colder place. Each of these properties can be determined directly by inspecting the qualitative situation. This increases SCHISM's robustness by allowing it to detect a class of nonsense questions.

SCHISM organizes its search through the equation space as an AND/OR tree[2] with the root goal node being to show that the goal quantity is known. To solve for the goal quantity, equations are extracted that contain the sought quantity. Closing these equations become the subgoals of the root. The unknown quantities in these subgoals are then sought at the next level of the tree, and so forth. During the search, SCHISM might choose to focus on a new control volume for each sought quantity, using the heuristics described earlier.

Once a closed set of equations containing the sought quantity is found, the equation space search halts. The final expression for the goal quantity is found by solving the set of equations via substitution. SCHISM's symbolic math package includes a canonical rational function manipulator to perform simplification of most mathematical expressions. The *isolation, collection* and *attraction* methods of Bundy [3] are used for extracting variables from equations.

5 AN EXAMPLE

The following example is taken from [13]. In the text, Haywood introduces the steam plant shown in figure 5 by describing its parts, structure and qualitative behavior. The steam plant consists of

[2] We use an extension of the AO-SOLVE system described in [10].

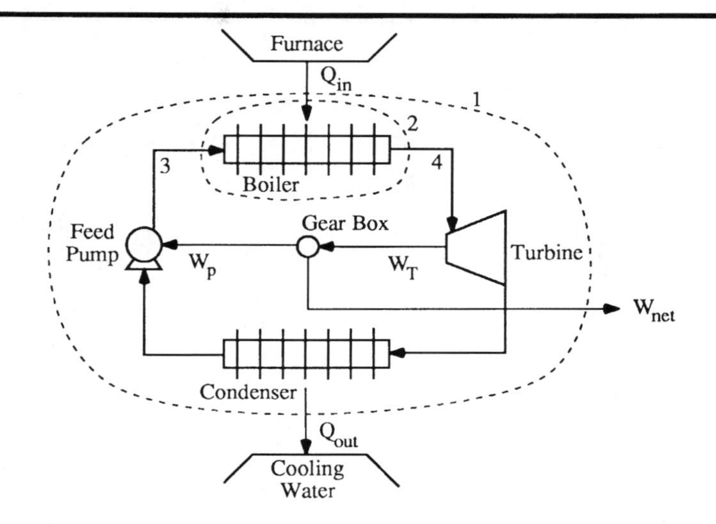

Figure 1: A Steam Plant

a turbine, condenser, feed pump, boiler, high temperature furnace, low temperature cooling water, and a gear box for splitting work output. Water enters the boiler at a low temperature and leaves as high-pressure steam. In the boiler, the fluid remains at approximately constant pressure while heat flows to it from the furnace. The steam flows through the turbine, dropping in pressure and temperature while producing work. The low temperature steam is then condensed at very nearly constant pressure while heat is transfered to the cooling water. The condensate is then pumped from the condenser into the boiler and the cycle repeats.

The problem statement is:

> **1.1.** In a test of a cyclic steam power plant, the measured rate of steam supply was 7.1 kg/s when the net rate of work output was 5000 kW. The feed water was supplied to the boiler at a temperature of 38°C, and the superheated steam leaving the boiler was at 1.4 MN/m^2 and 300°C. Calculate the thermal efficiency of the cycle.

From a QPE envisionment, SCHISM locates a contiguous set of control volumes (labelled 1 in figure 5) whose combined behavior does indeed match that of a heat engine. Since the goal quantity refers to a heat engine, this is the initial system choice from which equations are extracted.

A commonly used heuristic in the analysis of thermodynamic flow processes is ***plunking*** (as in [7]) of a system's mass flow rate. A plunked quantity is permitted to appear as a constant in the final solution. The plunking of a system's mass flow rate is equivalent to basing its analysis on the assumption of a unit mass flow rate. In this example, SCHISM infers that the closed cycle has a mass flow rate of 7.1 kg/s since that is the given flow rate of steam entering the turbine. Because the mass flow rate of the heat engine is known, SCHISM elects not to use the plunking heuristic.

SCHISM next initiates a search through the equation space. In our example, the control volume heuristic guides SCHISM to consider seven systems out of a possible 64. Two of the seven systems prove useful for extracting a set of closed equations.

(1)	$\rho_1 = \sum_1 Q_{in}/\sum_1 W_{out}$	(2)	$\sum_1 W_{out} = W_{net}$
(3)	$W_{net} = 5000$	(4)	$\sum_1 Q_{in} = Q_{in}$
(5)	$\sum_2 nH + \sum_2 Q + \sum_2 W = 0$	(6)	$\sum_2 Q = \sum_2 Q_{in} - \sum_2 Q_{out}$
(7)	$\sum_2 Q_{in} = Q_{in}$	(8)	$\sum_2 Q_{out} = 0$
(9)	$\sum_2 W = \sum_2 W_{in} - \sum_2 W_{out}$	(10)	$\sum_2 nH = \sum_2 (nH)_{in} - \sum_2 (nH)_{out}$
(11)	$\sum_2 W_{in} = 0$	(12)	$\sum_2 W_{out} = 0$
(13)	$\sum_2 (nH)_{in} = n_3 H_3$	(14)	$\sum_2 (nH)_{out} = n_4 H_4$
(15)	$H_3 = Table(H, water, liquid, T_3)$	(16)	$H_4 = Table(H, water, gas, T_4, P_4)$
(17)	$n_3 = n_1$	(18)	$n_4 = 7.1$
(19)	$n_1 = n_4$	(20)	$T_3 = 38$
(21)	$T_4 = 300$	(22)	$P_4 = 1.4$
(23)	$Table(H, water, liquid, 38) = 159$	(24)	$Table(H, water, gas, 300, 1.4) = 3041$

Notation: Thermodynamic symbols are defined below. Subscripts and summation indices refer to the control volumes and locations shown in figure 5. For example, $\sum_2 Q$ denotes the sum of the heat flow rates into and out of control volume 2 (the boiler). We use $Table(H, water, gas, T_4, P_4)$ to denote the tabulated intensive (ie., per unit mass) enthalpy value of water vapor at location 4.

Q	=	heat flow rate	W	=	work rate	n	=	mass flow rate
H	=	intensive enthalpy	T	=	temperature	P	=	pressure
ρ	=	efficiency						

Figure 2: Steam plant equations generated by SCHISM

SCHISM spawns a total of 56 equations, 24 of which form a closed set (see Figure 5). Substitution of equations is then performed on the closed set to produce a final expression for the sought quantity: 0.244 (i.e., 24.4%) which is the correct answer.

6 DISCUSSION

We have shown how the language of QP theory is well suited for representing qualitative knowledge in the domain of engineering thermodynamics, and can serve as a framework for organizing other kinds of knowledge. The qualitative model provides four essential functions: (1) recognition/verification of the system's intended behavior, (2) establishing the set of possible control volumes, (3) heuristic guiding of the selection of control volumes in equation extraction (4) establishing the set of qualitative identities which contribute equations to the closed set.

While we do not view SCHISM as a cognitive simulation per se, we believe that our model for how qualitative and quantitative knowledge interact can provide a richer framework for explaining psychological data. For example, "keywords in the [problem] statement" have been conjectured as the basis for ignoring variables or setting their values to zero [1], which in SCHISM falls out through qualitative analysis. Further psychological studies might reveal a novice-expert shift, with novices using surface features and experts relying on a generative qualitative analysis [4].

At present SCHISM has been successfully tested on three examples, all from Chapter One of [13]. Our plan is to continue working through the textbook, seeing how much of it we can master by augmenting the set of equations and domain model as necessary. An interesting question we hope to answer is how large a role each kind of knowledge plays in mastering these problems. For example, we currently suspect that the number of specialized equation-solving techniques will continue to grow with the number of examples, while the qualitative model will stabilize more quickly. As we extend the range of problems SCHISM can solve, we hope to compare its performance with human subjects.

7 ACKNOWLEDGEMENTS

Comments by Dedre Gentner and Janice Skorstad improved this paper. This research is supported by the National Aeronautics and Space Administration, Contract No. NASA NAG-9137.

References

[1] Bhaskar, R. and Simon, H. "Problem solving in semantically rich domains: An example from engineering thermodynamics" *Cognitive Science*, **1**, 193–215, 1977.

[2] Bobrow, D. (Ed.) *Qualitative reasoning about physical systems*, MIT Press, Cambridge, 1984

[3] Bundy, A. *The Computer Modelling of Mathematical Reasoning*, Academic Press, 1983

[4] Chi, M., Feltovich, P. and Glaser, R., "Categorization and representation of physics problems by experts and novices" *Cognitive Science* 5(2), 121-152.

[5] Collins, J. and Forbus, K. "Reasoning about fluids via molecular collections", Proceedings of AAAI-87, July, 1987.

[6] de Kleer, J. "Qualitative and quantitative knowledge in classical mechanics", TR-352, MIT AI Lab, Cambridge, Mass, 1975

[7] de Kleer, J. and Sussman, G. "Propagation of Constraints Applied to Circuit Synthesis", *Circuit Theory and Applications*, **8**, 1980

[8] Forbus, K. "Qualitative process theory" *Artificial Intelligence*, **24**, 1984

[9] Forbus, K. "QPE: A study in assumption-based truth maintenance" *International Journal of Artificial Intelligence in Engineering*, October, 1988.

[10] Forbus, K. and de Kleer, J. "Focusing the ATMS", Proceedings of AAAI-88, August, 1988.

[11] Gentner, D. and Stevens, A. (Eds.) *Mental Models*, Erlbaum Associates, Hillsdale, N.J., 1983.

[12] Hayes, P. "Naive Physics 1: Ontology for Liquids" in Hobbs, J. and Moore, B. (Eds.), *Formal Theories of the Commonsense World*, Ablex Publishing Corporation, 1985.

[13] Haywood, R. W. *Analysis of Engineering Cycles*, Pergamon Press, 1980

[14] Larkin, J., McDermott, J., Simon, D., Simon, H. Expert and Novice Performance in Solving Physics Problems. *Science* Vol. 208, 20, June 1980

[15] Larkin, J. Reif, F., Carbonell, J. and Gugliotta, A. "FERMI: A flexible expert reasoner with multi-domain inferencing." Technical report, Carnegie-Mellon University. 1985

[16] Lin, C. C., and Segel, L. A. *Mathematics Applied to Deterministic Problems in the Natural Sciences*, Macmillan Publishing Co, New York 1974

[17] Reynolds, W. and Perkins, H. (1977) *Engineering Thermodynamics*. McGraw-Hill Press, New York, New York.

An Approach to Constructing Student Models: Status Report for the Programming Domain

James C. Spohrer

Yale University
Computer Science Department
(As of Sept. '89, Apple Computer)

ABSTRACT

Student models are important for guiding the development of instructional systems. An approach to constructing student models is reviewed. The approach advocates constructing student models in two steps: (1) develop a descriptive theory of correct and buggy student responses, then (2) develop a process theory of the way students actually generate those responses. The approach has been used in the domain of introductory programming. A status report is provided: (1) Goal-And-Plan (GAP) trees have been developed to describe student program variations, and (2) a Generate-Test-and-Debug (GTD) impasse/repair architecture has been developed to model the process of student program generation.

INTRODUCTION: MOTIVATIONS AND GOALS

The long-term goal of the research reported here is to build computer-based applications that help students learn design skills (i.e., planning, constructing, evaluating, and debugging artifacts such as computer programs). Therefore, one purpose of this paper is to present a brief overview of a long-term research plan for building instructional systems. A key part of these systems is a student model. This paper provides a status report on the development of a student model for the domain of introductory programming.

Previously [SSP85], we have advocated an approach to constructing student models that decomposes the problem into two steps: (1) develop a descriptive theory of the alternative correct and buggy responses students generate, and (2) develop a process theory of the way students actually generate those responses. In [SSP85], we present a descriptive theory of correct and buggy student generated Pascal programs that is based on the notion of a Goal-And-Plan (GAP) tree. However, a descriptive theory provides only a systematic enumeration of what the alternatives are, and does not address the question of how the alternatives originate in the first place. In this paper, we present a model of the way different students write alternative programs. The problem solving behavior of students writing programs will be described in terms of a generate-test-and-debug (GTD) problem solving architecture in which impasse/repair knowledge plays a key role.

The paper will: (1) describe a long-term research plan for building instructional systems, (2) illustrate the important role of student models in the plan by arguing that limitations in existing instructional systems can be traced back to weaknesses in those systems' student models, (3) describe some alternative programs that real students generate, and finally (4) explain the process by which our student model generates these programs.

WHAT'S DMATA?

DMATA is an acronym for a long-term research plan aimed at developing and studying the development of computer-based applications, especially instructional systems.

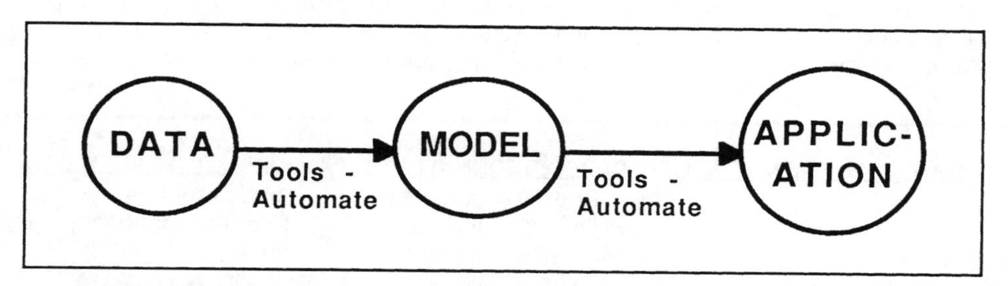

The DMATA plan advocates using Data from empirical studies to first construct Models of people performing problem solving in some domain, and then to use the models to build Applications that support human problem solving. However, we are also interested in developing Tools that help researchers construct models from data and that help researchers build applications from models. Eventually, we would like to Automate the data-model-application development path.

Some application builders would argue that it is unnecessary to construct separate models of human problem solving before building applications. In fact, constructing a separate model is no guarantee that a successful applications can then be built. Nevertheless, weaknesses in existing instructional systems for the programming domain can be traced back to limitations in their underlying student models, as described in the next section.

COGNITIVE REVERSE-ENGINEERING: APPLICATIONS -> MODELS

In general, computer-based applications for design domains incorporate, either explicitly or implicitly, a model of the way humans solve tasks in those domains. We term the process of extracting a model from an application "cognitive reverse-engineering" (see [CK89] for a related concept). For instance, the student model underlying the PROUST system [JS85] might be termed an *enumeration student model*, because to find bugs in student programs PROUST requires a large knowledge-base that enumerates alternative correct solutions (i.e., plan library) and incorrect solutions (i.e., bug library) for a programming task. Alternatively, the student model underlying the GREATERP system [ABR85] might be termed a *restriction student model*, because students are forced to follow in the "foot-steps" of an ideal student and tutorial advice is provided as soon as a student deviates from the restricted ideal solution path.

In sum, PROUST and GREATERP deal with the variability problem -- the problem of coping with alternative correct and buggy programs -- by an enumeration and restriction approach, respectively. Unfortunately, enumerating plans and bugs is very time consuming and can never be totally complete. However, restricting the possible solutions does not give students a chance to acquire skills for exploring and evaluating alternative designs. Thus, neither the enumeration or restriction student models are entirely satisfactory. For design domains, we argue that computational *generative models* [BV80] are the preferred type of model to use to guide the development of computer-based applications because they parsimoniously account for variability.

DESCRIPTIVE THEORY OF PROGRAMS: GAP TREES

Because real students generate so many different correct and buggy programs when asked to solve even simple introductory programming tasks, some way must be found to systematically organize and describe all the variations before attempting to build a generative student model. For instance, consider a programming task that must process a series of input values, stopping when a sentinel value is entered. Figure 1 shows some alternative pseudo-code solutions. The solutions are based on actual Pascal programs.

CORRECT (DUPLICATE INPUT)

```
input
while not-sentinel
 do begin
      calculate
      output
      input
    end
```

CORRECT (DUMMY INIT)

```
init-to-not-sentinel
while not-sentinel
 do begin
      input
       if not-sentinel
        then begin
               calculate
               output
             end
    end
```

CORRECT (MORE-DATA)

```
input(more-data)
while not-sent.(more-data)
 do begin
      input
      calculate
      output
       input(more-data)
    end
```

BUGGY (MISSING RE-INPUT1)

```
input
while not-sentinel
 do begin
      calculate
      output
    end
```

BUGGY (MISSING GUARD)

```
init-to-not-sentinel
while not-sentinel
 do begin
      input
      calculate
      output
    end
```

BUGGY (MISSING RE-INPUT2)

```
input(more-data)
while not-sent.(more-data)
 do begin
      input
      calculate
      output
    end
```

Figure 1: Example variability for an "alternate" type task.

These examples illustrate a few of the many alternative correct and buggy programs we have catalogued in the GAP tree for this particular type of programming task [SPL*85]. The alternatives illustrate three correct plans for the sentinel-controlled-input goal, as well as a single buggy version of each plan. Because a programming task is composed of several goals, and each goal has several plans, and each plan may have several bugs, a GAP tree with bugs indexed off plans provides a concise description of the programs that students generate. In the next section, we will present a generative student model that can account for some of the alternative programs that a GAP tree only enumerates.

PROCESS THEORY OF PROGRAMMERS: GTD IMPASSE/REPAIR MODEL

The development of the generative model (i.e., a process theory) could only occur after a systematic organization of the the alternative correct and buggy programs had been developed (i.e. a descriptive theory). In addition, thinking-aloud protocol data -- complete problem solving *behavior traces* of the verbally reported planning, implementation, and debugging steps involved in writing a program -- had to be collected and analyzed. Based on the previously developed descriptive theory and the additional thinking-aloud protocol data, a process theory has been developed that employs a *generate-test-and-debug (GTD) impasse/repair problem solving architecture* (see [Su75], [Ham86], [Si88], and also [BV80] [BS85] [NS72]). The three problem solving phases of the architecture are:

Generate Phase: During the generate phase, students use different generation mechanisms to write code to achieve the goals of the task specification. The students either (1) used previously acquired *programming knowledge* to write the code, or (2) created new programming knowledge by translating relevant *non-programming knowledge* (i.e., "commonsense" plans) into code. Non-programming knowledge (see [BS85] for a related concept) is a key part of the model and corresponds intuitively to knowledge that would allow a student to easily do a *hand calculation*. For instance, a student may be able to calculate the average of an arbitrary set of numbers by hand, but have a great deal of difficulty writing a program to do the same.

Test Phase: During the test phase, students use different program testing mechanisms to detect one of a few types of problems, or *impasses*. The students either (1) compared a simulation of their programs to a simulation of an internal representation (i.e., mental model) of the expected solution or (2) checked for specific commonly occurring bugs. Impasses in MARCEL might more appropriately be called expectations violations, because they are unlike the impasses caused by lack of domain knowledge as in [BV80] and [BS85]. However, because repairing the impasses in all these model can lead to bugs, we prefer the term impasse to expectation violation.

Debug Phase: During the debug phase, impasses are fixed using one of small set of *repairs*. Associated with each impasse are between two and six repairs that might be applied to fix the impasse. One way variability can arise in the model is when different repairs are used to fix the same impasse.

A simulation program, called MARCEL, implements the model, and can be used to simulate students writing both correct and buggy Pascal programs [S89]. In the remainder of this paper, we will focus on accounting for the generation of alternative correct and buggy programs in terms of impasse/repair knowledge.

PROGRAM VARIABILITY IN TERMS OF IMPASSE/REPAIR TREES

In this section, a small set of impasses and repairs which students appear to use will be described. As in the subtraction domain [BV80], we will see that a small set of impasses and repairs can give rise to a great deal of variability. However, because the amount of variability in the programming domain (a design domain) is enormous compared to variability in the subtraction domain (a procedural skill domain), we do not yet make specific quantitative claims about the coverage of our model, but instead support the model with short quotes or *snippets* from thinking aloud protocol data.

To understand the impasses and repairs used in the model one should begin by viewing a program as a consumer-producer system in which certain goals *consume* some objects and *produce* others (e.g., the calculation goal *consumes* the input objects and *produces* the output objects). Most of the impasses and repairs used in the model are domain-independent, and can be applied to a variety of consumer-producer systems (e.g., biological systems, economic systems, etc.). For instance, a coal company *produces* coal that is *consumed* by an electric company to *produce* smoke and electricity. If the coal contains impurities (i.e., BAD-KIND) that lead to too much pollution, then a number of repairs can tried: separate the impurity before the coal is burned (i.e., INSERT-SPLIT), or scrub the smoke (i.e., INSERT-CONSUMER).

In programs (or any other consumer-producer system) six types of impasses can occur:

I1. NOT-PRODUCED: An object is consumed before it has a value (before produced).
"If I just start with a WHILE-DO statement, the variable is not gonna have any value yet." (AAS7.15).

I2. BAD-NEXT-GOAL: The next goal is not the expected goal.
"I'm thinking what will happen if they put in less than zero [invalid], *and I still try to print out the answer* [on invalid should stop, not output]." *(AVM5.126).*

I3. DOUBLE-USE: A goal uses (consumes) the same value twice.
"...I had to put it in a place so it wouldn't be affected [by the same value again]..." *(JBH7.232).*

I4. BAD-SOURCE: An object's value is not from the user.
"I'd have to rewrite the first line instead of... automatically [dummy initialization]... *assigning to the value... I could prompt* [get value from user]" *(AVM6.415).*

I5. OVER-WRITE: A value is destroyed before it is used (consumed by a goal).
"Every time it goes through its gonna see sum gets zero...so maybe I'll put that outside the whole loop [sum initialization over-writes the update]." *(JBH7.111).*

I6. BAD-KIND: A value is inappropriate for the case.
"Everything is gonna have to deal with... wait it did say something about impossible values [the calculation almost got run on invalid values]." *(JBH5.62).*

The protocol data contain examples of impasse/repair episodes on average once every 2.5 minutes. Protocol snippets guided the development of the impasse/repair component of the model, and provide support for the cognitive plausibility of the model.

During the debug phase, a repair is selected for an impasse. All of the repairs involve simple operations (insert, delete, move, change, duplicate) on a few basic types of program elements (producer, consumer, expected, encountered, object, test, split), defined when a particular impasse is detected in a particular program context (see [S89] for details). For example, consider the small set of repairs that apply to the impasse NOT-PRODUCED:

Repairs to I1:NOT-PRODUCED: When a consumer goal tries to consume an object whose value has not yet been produced, try one of the following repairs:

R1:CHANGE-OBJECT - If the consumer of the not-produced object is a split, then try changing the object to an auxiliary object.
R2:INSERT-PRODUCER - If the producer is not in the program yet, then insert the producer directly before the consumer.
R3:MOVE-PRODUCER - If the producer is somewhere else in the program, then move the producer directly before the consumer.
R4:MOVE-CONSUMER - If the producer is somewhere else in the program, then move the consumer to directly after the producer.
R5:DELETE-CONSUMER - Delete the offending consumer.
R6:DUPLICATE-PRODUCER - If the producer is somewhere else in the program, then make a duplicate of the producer and insert it before the consumer.

Like the impasses, all of the repairs used in the model are derived from protocol snippets, and supported by additional snippets (see example below).

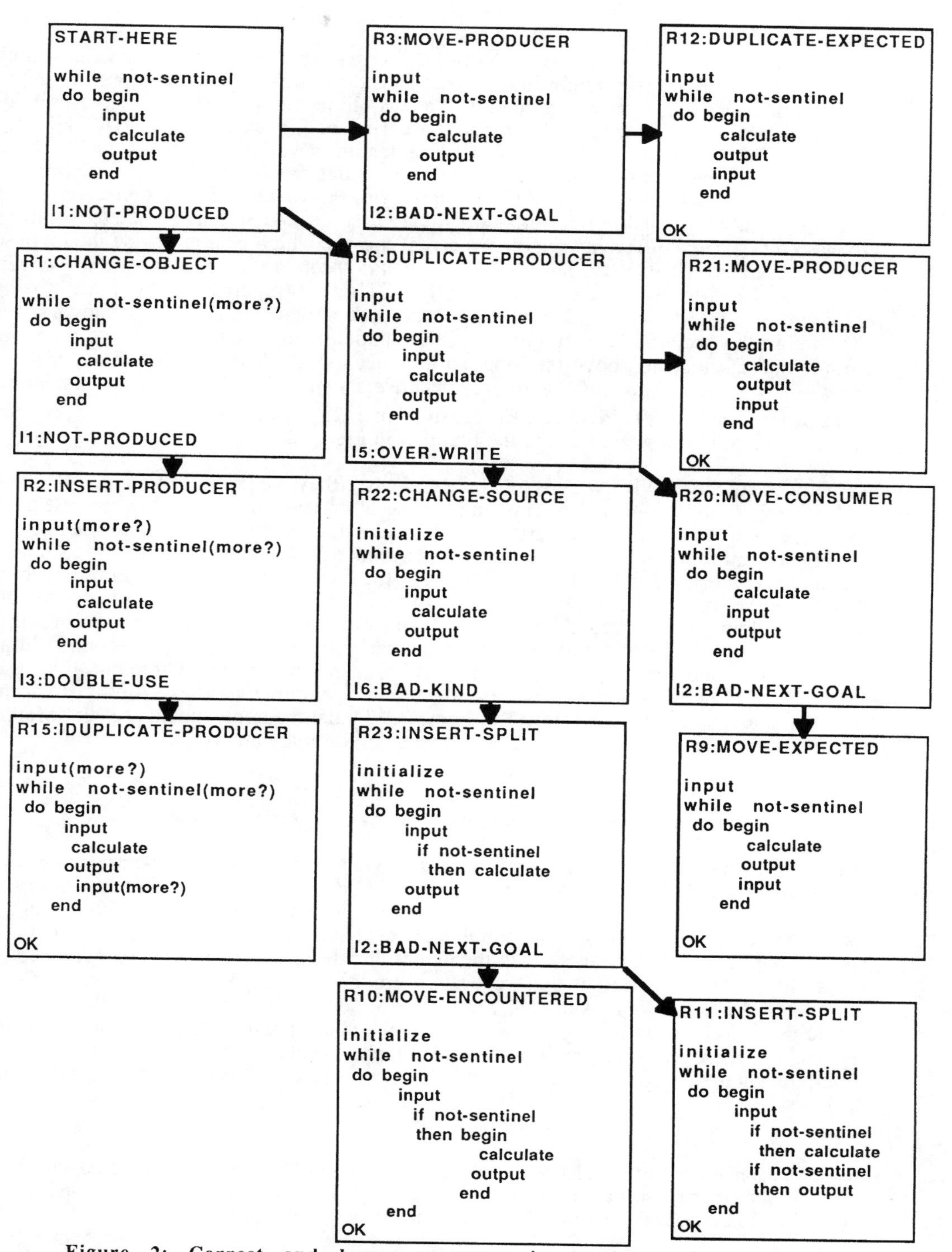

Figure 2: Correct and buggy programs in an impasse/repair tree.

Often when students tried to write a program to process a series of input values, they would start by saying something like -- what I need to do is a standard input-calculate-output, but with a loop wrapped around it. This would result in a program whose pseudo-code structure was like that in the upper left corner of Figure 2 (i.e., START-HERE). Since the "not-sentinel" test in the WHILE is testing a variable that has not yet been produced (the input is inside the loop), some students detect a NOT-PRODUCED impasse (e.g., *If I just start out with WHILE-DO statement, the variable is not gonna have any value yet." (AAS7.15).)* After detecting the impasse, some student may decide to repair the impasse by testing a different variable instead of the one which is input inside the loop, so they use a CHANGE-OBJECT repair (e.g.,*"I could create another variable and just say WHILE..."* (AVM6.59).) The CHANGE-OBJECT repair (repair R1 above), after being applied would result in a program whose pseudo-code structure was like that shown in the first box in the second row of Figure 2. Other students might decide to move the input from inside the loop to above the loop, so they use a MOVE-PRODUCER repair (e.g., *"that's gonna be outside of the loop... because its got to prompt before the loop." (AAS7.15)*). The MOVE-PRODUCER repair (repair R3 above) would result in a program like that shown in the second box in the first row in Figure 2.

Sometimes students add new bugs to a program when they are trying to fix a bug [GO86], and in a related phenomena repairing an impasse often leads to a new impasse. Because impasses can give rise to repairs that can give rise to new impasses, an impasse/repair tree is a convenient representational device for describing a large set of programs that students might conceivably generate. For instance, all of the correct and buggy programs of Figure 1 occur in the impasse/repair tree shown in Figure 2 ("duplicate input" third column and first row, "dummy init" second column and fifth row, "more data" first column and fourth row, "missing re-input1" second column and first row, "missing guard" second column and third row, and "missing re-input2" first column and third row). Three questions that remain are: How do students generate the initial program hypothesis? Why do some students detect an impasse, while others do not? Why do different students select different repairs for the same impasse? (see [S89] for some preliminary answers).

CONCLUDING REMARKS: MODEL -> APPLICATION

We have claimed that computational generative student models are to be preferred over enumeration or restriction student models when building computer-based applications to help students perform design activities and acquire design skills. Admittedly, this claim lacks convincing support until we complete the next stage of our research effort and build such an application. Nevertheless, to the extent that design domains are characterized by variability, and to the extent that generative models capture important aspects of that variability in a parsimonious model, we feel we are on the right track. If students can be explicitly and effectively taught how to detect the six impasses and apply the necessary repairs, then a programming environment that supports exploring and evaluating alternative programs via impasse/repair trees should help the students exercise and develop important design skills.

Acknowledgements: Elliot Soloway provided support and direction for this research. This work was supported in part by National Science Foundation Grant MDR-88-96240. I would like to thank David Littman for his comments on drafts of this paper.

REFERENCES

[ABR85] J.R. Anderson, C.F. Boyle, and B. J. Reiser. Intelligent tutoring systems. *Science*, 228(4698):456-462, 1985.

[BS85] J. Bonar and E. Soloway. Preprogramming knowledge: A major source of misconceptions in novice programmers. *Human-Computer Interactions*, 1(2):133-161, 1985. (Reprinted in [SS89]).

[BV80] J. S. Brown and K. VanLehn. Repair theory: a generative theory of bugs in procedural skills. *Cognitive Science*, 4:379-426, 1980.

[CK89] J.M. Carroll and W.A. Kellogg. Artifacts as theory-nexus: Hermeneutics meets theory-based design. *IBM Research Paper*. Yorktown Heights, NY.

[GO86] Leo Gugerty and Gary M. Olson. *Comprehension differences in debugging by skilled and novice programmers.* In Empirical Studies of Programmers, Soloway and Iyengar (Eds). Ablex: Norwood, NJ. 1986.

[Ham86] K.J. Hammond. *Case-Based Planning: An Integrated Theory of Planning, Learning, and Memory*. PhD Diss. CS TR 488, Yale, New Haven CT, Oct 1986.

[JS85] W.L. Johnson and E. Soloway. PROUST. *Byte Magaz.* 10(4) 179-192, 1985.

[NS72] A. Newell and H.A. Simon. *Human Problem Solving.* Prentice Hall,NJ, 1972.

[Si88] R. Simmons. A theory of debugging plans and interpretations. In *Proceedings of AAAI-88.* Saint Paul, MN. pp 94-99, Aug. 21-26, 1988.

[SS89] E. Soloway and J.C. Spohrer, Editors. *Studying the Novice Programmer.* Lawrence Erlbaum Publishers, Hillsdale NJ, 1989.

[SPL*85] J.C. Spohrer, E.Pope, M. Lipman, W. Sack, S. Freiman, D. Littman, W.L.Johnson, and E. Soloway. *BUG CATALOGUE: II,III, IV.* CS TR 386, Yale New Haven CT, May 1985.

[SSP85] J.C. Spohrer, E. Soloway, and E. Pope. A goal/plan analysis of buggy Pascal programs. *Hum.-Com. Inter.*, 1(2):163-207, 1985. (in [SS89]).

[S89] J.C. Spohrer. MARCEL: A GTD impasse/repair model of student program generation and individual differences. Ph.D. Diss. CS TR 687, Yale New Haven CT, 1989.

[Su75] G. Sussman. *A Computer Model of Skill Acquisition.* Elsevier: NY, 1975.

Processing Unification-based Grammars in a Connectionist Framework

Andreas Stolcke

Computer Science Division
University of California, Berkeley
and
International Computer Science Institute
Berkeley, California

ABSTRACT

We present an approach to the processing of unification-based grammars in the connectionist paradigm. The method involves two basic steps: (1) Translation of a grammar's rules into a set of structure fragments, and (2) encoding these fragments in a connectionist network such that unification and rule application can take place by spreading activation. Feature structures are used to constrain sentence generation by semantic and/or grammatical properties. The method incorporates a general model of unification in connectionist networks.

INTRODUCTION

In recent years connectionist models have achieved notable results in modeling various aspect of perception and cognition. Although natural language processing has not been among the most prominent of its applications, there are a fair number of connectionist models of both language analysis and generation (Charniak & Santos, 1987; Cottrell, 1985; Dell, 1985; Fanty, 1985; Gasser, 1988; Kalita & Shastri, 1987; McClelland & Kawamoto, 1986). However, most of these models have a very narrow coverage, and hardly any attempts to take into account current linguistic theories of grammar (other than the basic context-free framework), for the most part adopting some ad-hoc linguistic formalism.

This paper's connectionist approach to natural language is based on *unification-based grammar*, a formal framework which has gained wide acceptance within the linguistic community within the last decade through its various variants (Kay, 1984; Kaplan & Bresnan, 1982; Gazdar et al., 1985). Although it is legitimate to argue that, by their very natures, formal grammar and connectionist models have different objectives (being competence versus performance theories, respectively), this work is intended as a first step towards a reconciliation of the two paradigms.

UNIFICATION-BASED GRAMMARS

Lack of space does not allow a self-contained overview of the formal linguistic apparatus underlying this work (Shieber (1986) gives an excellent introduction). Instead, we will present the basic features of the formalism by way of a simple example, upon which further discussion can be based. The version of unification-based grammar used here is essentially the one found in the PATR-II system (Shieber et al., 1983).

Feature Structures

Unification-based grammar extends traditional context-free grammars by introducing additional structure to the language it describes. The usual tree-like phrase structure of a sentence (or sentential form) is referred to as its *c-structure*. Additionally, each node in the c-structure (i.e. each constituent) has assigned to it a matrix of feature-value pairs encoding grammatical properties, semantic content, etc., referred to as its *feature structure* or *f-structure*. Features and values can be any (mnemonically chosen) atomic labels.

For example, the propositional semantics used in the sample grammar below will be encoded as f-structures of the form shown in Figure 1a.

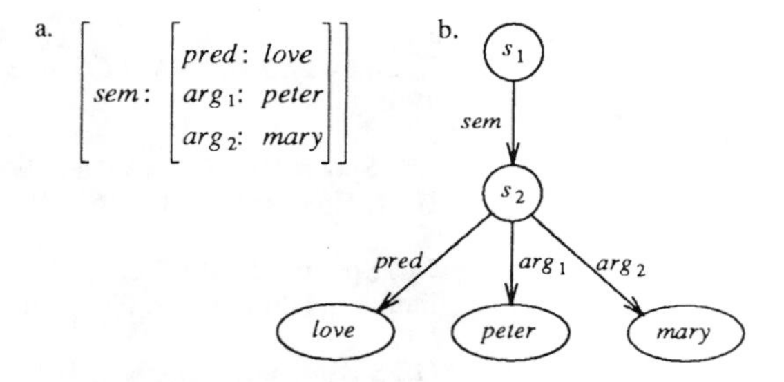

Fig. 1. F-structure representing *love(peter, mary)*.

sem is the main feature under which all semantic information is grouped. Feature *pred* contains the logical constant associated with a constituent, possibly with additional *arg*uments.

Note that the value of *sem* is a complex feature matrix, showing that f-structures may be embedded. Furthermore, feature values may be shared, i.e. the same subsidiary structure may be 'pointed to' by several features. These properties suggest that f-structures be represented as directed acyclic graphs (DAGs) with labeled edges, as in Figure 1b.

Finally, the concept of *unification* as used for terms in first-order languages can be applied to f-structures. Informally, unifying two or more structures means merging their feature-value pairs recursively. Thus Figure 1a could be obtained as the unification of

$$\left[sem: \begin{bmatrix} pred: love \\ arg_1: peter \end{bmatrix} \right] \text{ and } \left[sem: \begin{bmatrix} arg_1: peter \\ arg_2: mary \end{bmatrix} \right].$$

Unification might fail in case its operands contain incompatible features, such as if *peter* had been replaced with *john* in one of the structures above.

A Sample Grammar

We will now present a somewhat naive grammar generating simple active and passive constructions involving transitive verbs, such as "Peter loves Mary", "Peter is loved by Mary", etc.[1]

Consider the top-level structure of these sentences, as depicted in Figure 2.

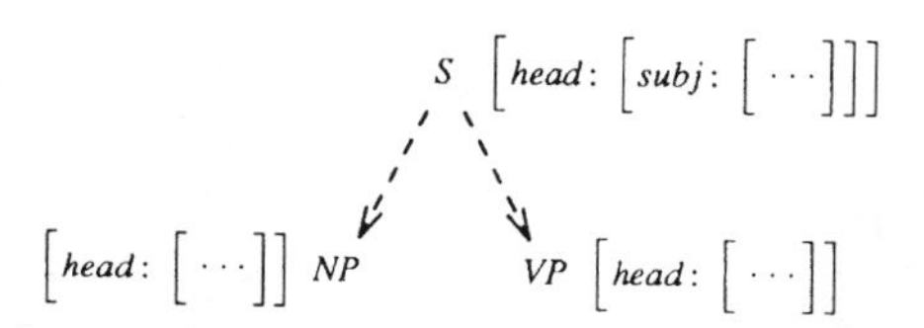

Fig. 2. C-structure and f-structure at sentence level.

The c-structure consists simply of three tree nodes, namely for the sentence (S) itself and its two subordinate constituents, noun phrase (NP) and verb phrase (VP). Attached to each of these is a piece of f-structure. By convention, the grammatical and semantic features of each c-structure node are grouped together under the *head* feature to be able to handle them as a whole. The *subj* feature in the S's *head* will be explained below.

Now consider the top-level rule for sentences, characterizing the structures shown in Figure 2. Grammar rules take the form of usual context-free rewriting rules, augmented with equations specifying that certain parts of the associated f-structures have to unify (failure to do so will render the rule inapplicable).

(R_S) $S \rightarrow NP\ VP$
$S.head = VP.head$
$S.head.subj = NP.head$

S.head designates the value of the *head* feature in the f-structure belonging to the S node. The dot notation may be extended to specify feature values buried deeper in the f-structure, as in *S.head.subj*.

The second rule describes how to further expand verb phrases.

(R_{VP}) $VP \rightarrow V\ NP$
$VP.head = V.head$
$VP.head.obj = NP.head$

[1] Here and in the following, note the distinction between the surface string "Mary" and its semantics, the logical constant *mary*.

The unification equations so far specify that the *head* structures of S, VP, and V all have to unify, i.e. can be merged and thus effectively shared. The *head* features of the subject and object NP, on the other hand, will be unified with the values of *subj* and *obj*, respectively, in the sentence's *head*, i.e. they are effectively 'assigned' to these features.

All that has to be added now, for the grammar to fulfill its humble purpose, are lexical rules for NP and V (verbs).

(R_{Peter}) $NP \rightarrow$ Peter
$NP.head.sem = peter$

(R_{Mary}) $NP \rightarrow$ Mary
$NP.head.sem = mary$

(R_{loves}) $V \rightarrow$ loves
$V.head.sem.pred =$ love
$V.head.sem.arg_1 = V.head.subj.sem$
$V.head.sem.arg_2 = V.head.obj.sem$

For the purpose of exposition, passives are handled in a very simple-minded way, assuming auxiliary + past participle + "by" as a single complex verb. Thus passives can be generated by a single additional lexical rule.

($R_{\text{loved-by}}$) $V \rightarrow$ is loved by
$V.head.sem.pred =$ love
$V.head.sem.arg_1 = V.head.obj.sem$
$V.head.sem.arg_2 = V.head.subj.sem$

This completes our sample grammar. Note how the assignment of grammatical roles (*subj*, *obj*) to semantic arguments (arg_1, arg_2) is neatly handled by unification equations, depending on the verb.

For simplicity, we have only considered the semantic features shown above; in a typical grammar additional equations would have to be included, such as

$NP.head.agree.person = 3rd$,
$V.head.agree = V.head.subj.agree$, or
$V.head.tense = pres$

to account for agreement, tense, etc.

There is one fine point about the rule notation which has been omitted so far: Category labels (S, VP, NP, etc.) are not really part of the c-structure, but are encoded as another standard feature at each node: *cat*. Thus, for convenience and to relate the notation to its context-free origins, a node designation such as VP is simply a shorthand for a generic node X with a category specification of $X.cat = VP$.

Grammar Rules As Fragments of Structure

In their usual interpretation unification equations function as declarative constraints on the f-structure assigned to a sentence's c-structure. Taking an alternative view, however, the rules can themselves be regarded as pieces of structure.

Besides being a very compact representation for rules, this interpretation will allow processing of rules using just one basic mechanism, namely unification. Thus, the goal of this transformation of rules into structure fragments is to have rule application translate precisely into unification of well-defined nodes in the corresponding fragments.

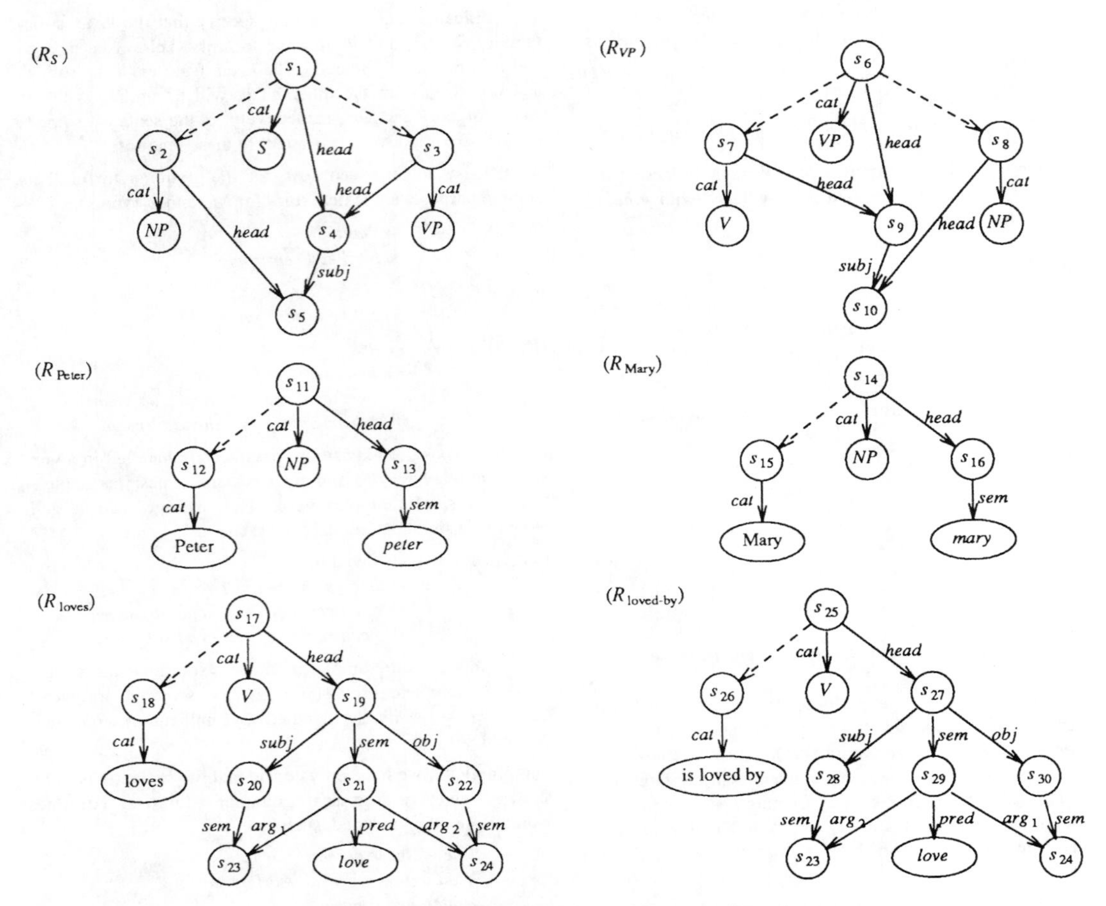

Fig. 3. Structure fragments derived from sample grammar.

The *c-structure fragment* derived from a grammar rule is rather obvious: Since the c-structure is just a tree, it can be obtained by 'pasting together' tree fragments of depth one, with a root node for the left-hand side part of the rule and one child node for each right-hand side element. For instance, rule (R_S) corresponds to a c-structure fragment consisting of an S node and two child nodes NP and VP. Likewise, rule (R_{VP}) has a VP root node and children V and NP. Applying (R_{VP}) to the VP in the right-hand side of (R_S) then corresponds to a simple 'merging' of the two VP nodes. Since c-structures are trees, we can view them as special cases of f-structures and interpret the node merging as a unification operation.[2]

The *f-structure fragment* corresponding to a rule is derived from its unification equations. We create a minimal DAG containing all the features and values mentioned in the equations, and encode equalities of values as reentrancies (shared nodes) in the DAG. We thus arrive at a DAG that can be interpreted as a somewhat generalized type of f-structure, since it contains not a single root node, but rather several 'root' or 'source' nodes, one for each element of the rule.

The result of applying this transformation to the sample grammar is depicted in Figure 3. Here c-structure fragments and f-structure fragments have been combined into a single structure by identifying a c-structure node with the root node of the f-structure assigned to it. C-structure edges are distinguished as dashed arrows, and internal nodes have been numbered for reference.

The critical point in the construction of f-structure fragments from rules is, again, that rule application maps directly to unification of corresponding nodes.[3] For example, both the c-structure and the f-structure of "Peter loves Mary" is obtained

[2] At this point it is crucial that, technically, c-structure nodes do not carry any category labels themselves. Rather, categories are encoded as *cat* values in the f-structures corresponding to c-structure nodes.

[3] We shall say that two f-structure *nodes* unify, iff the f-structures rooted in those nodes unify. In general, we use the root of a structure to designate the structure as a whole, whenever this is implied by the context.

by performing the following unifications ('~' denotes the 'unifies' relation):

$$s_2 \sim s_{11},\ s_3 \sim s_6,\ s_7 \sim s_{17},\ s_8 \sim s_{14}.$$

In our example, possible unifications are mainly restricted by category (*cat*) matching, but in a richer grammar agreement, selection restrictions, etc. would all be encoded in the f-structures and act as constraints.

F-structures As Sentence Specifications

One of the appealing features of unification-based grammars is that multiple levels of linguistic description can be accommodated within a single simple formal apparatus. Both syntax and semantics of a sentence can be encoded in f-structures and are generated by the rules if the grammar accounts for them. This is a very desirable property when the grammar is used in the context of sentence generation or parsing.

In generation, the semantics can be specified as a partially filled f-structure which automatically constrains the application of rules so as to produce sentences which conform to the specified semantics. Conversely, when parsing takes place based on the syntactic form of a sentence, its semantics are assembled as a side effect of f-structure construction by successive unifications.

The particular application experimented with in our research involved sentence generation; therefore the usage of f-structures as specifications for generation will be discussed in more detail. Suppose, e.g., we wanted to use the f-structure in Figure 1 to specify the semantics of the sentence to be generated. More formally, we want the f-structure of the root of the c-structure (i.e. the S node) to *unify* with

$$\left[head: \left[sem: \begin{bmatrix} pred: & love \\ arg_1: & peter \\ arg_2: & mary \end{bmatrix} \right] \right]$$

(For technical reasons, our grammar embeds *sem* features in the *head* values, hence the same embedding has to occur in the specification.)

It turns out, however, that specification by f-structures does not require any additions to our formal apparatus and its implementation. Alternatively, we can express the above constraint by adding to our grammar a new top-level category S', plus a rule of the form

$$(R_{S'}) \qquad \begin{array}{l} S' \rightarrow S \\ S'.head = S.head \\ S.head.sem.pred = love \\ S.head.sem.arg_1 = peter \\ S.head.sem.arg_1 = mary \end{array}$$

and generate sentences from S'.

This rule can then be transformed into a structure fragment as described before. As a result, sentence specifications can be incorporated in our framework in a natural way following the pattern shown above. This gives a set of structure fragments encoding the grammar, which is typically kept invariant within a certain context of application, plus a single varying f-structure encoding a sentence specification.

A CONNECTIONIST MODEL OF UNIFICATION

The previous section has shown that sentence generation in unification-based grammars can essentially be reduced to unification of structural fragments derived from the grammar. We will now describe how unification in turn can be efficiently implemented using the connectionist model of computation, i.e. a network of very simple processing units exchanging activation. This model of unification is by no means restricted to linguistic applications; connectionist unification is discussed in detail elsewhere (Stolcke, 1989). For the purposes of this paper an informal description will be sufficient.

Representing F-structures

Note that each f-structure, and hence the grammar as a whole can be represented as a set of edges, each characterized by a triple (node, feature, node). Each such triple is represented by a single so-called ***e-unit***, with an activation corresponding to the presence or absence of the corresponding edge. Units will be designated by enclosing their 'meaning' in angle brackets. Thus we have, e.g., that the activation of e-unit $\langle s_3.cat = VP \rangle$ equals 1 whenever feature *cat* has value *VP* in structure (node) s_3, and is 0 otherwise. All the units in the implementation will be simple linear threshold units operating with activations of either 0 or 1.

This representational scheme is essentially a localized version of the encoding of S-expressions in BoltzCONS (Touretzky, 1986). E-units can be visualized as residing in a 3-dimensional space, with two 'node' dimensions and one 'feature' dimension.

Representing Unifications

Unification of f-structures can be viewed as a merging of DAG nodes. For example, consider the structures representing rules (R_S) and (R_{VP}) in Figure 3. Suppose structures s_3 and s_6 are to be unified. This means node s_3 has to be merged (unified) with s_6, and, due to the features *head* and *subj* present in both structures, s_4 has to unify with s_9 and s_5 with s_{10}.

Again, we use a localist representation to encode the 'unifies' relation on nodes. Each possible unification $s_i \sim s_j$ is represented by a ***u-unit***, such that activation 1 on $\langle s_i \sim s_j \rangle$ indicates that the two nodes have been unified.

It is not sufficient, however, to just represent unifications; *non-unifiability* has to be dealt with explicitly, too. For example, suppose we wanted to unify s_7 in (R_{VP}) with s_{11} in (R_{Peter}). This will fail due to incompatible *cat* features *V* and *NP*, and will be represented in the network by turning on the *nu-unit* $\langle s_7 \not\sim s_{11} \rangle$. (Exactly how this takes place is the subject of the next section.)

Thus we have two spaces of units representing node unifications, u-units and nu-units, which can be thought of as organized along two 'node' dimensions. Obviously activations in these two sets of units have to be kept consistent. In particular, activity on corresponding u-units and nu-units should be mutually exclusive. The way the net is operated implies that u-units merely represent 'tentative' unifications which should always be overruled by the stronger 'evidence' from nu-units. Therefore the relationship is not symmetrical, and nu-units simply deactivate their corresponding u-units by strong inhibitory links, so-called *nu-links*.

Unification As Constraint Satisfaction

Using the representational scheme described above, we now have to implement the *operation* of unification within our connectionist framework, using appropriate link patterns. Broadly speaking, the link structure must connect e-units and u/nu-units such that the unifications represented conform to the edges present in the f-structures.

The approach taken here is formally justified by a characterization of unifications as a specially constrained class of equivalence relations on f-structure nodes. This gives rise to a reformulation of unification as a constraint satisfaction problem with a straightforward connectionist implementation. It is possible, however, to describe the implementation without going into the formal details, so we will try to convey a more intuitive understanding.

Node equivalence

The equivalence relation alluded to above informally corresponds to the 'unifies' relation on nodes, as used in the discussion so far; it should be obvious that this relation actually has to be reflexive, symmetrical and transitive. Therefore, the activity patterns on n/nu-units have to be constrained to actually have these properties.

Reflexivity and symmetry can be encoded implicitly using simple techniques. To ensure reflexivity, all u-units $\langle x \sim x \rangle$ are kept active all the time, while all nu-units $\langle x \not\sim x \rangle$ are clamped to be permanently inactive.[4] Similarly, symmetry can be implicitly accounted for by the net structure by collapsing symmetric u-units $\langle x \sim y \rangle$ and $\langle y \sim x \rangle$ (and likewise for nu-units).

Transitivity, on the other hand, has to be encoded explicitly in the link structure. For every group of three u-units $\langle x \sim y \rangle$, $\langle y \sim z \rangle$ and $\langle x \sim z \rangle$, activity of any two of them should cause activation of the third.

There is a similar constraint involving nu-units, which is not completely symmetrical: For every pair of nu-units $\langle x \not\sim y \rangle$ and $\langle y \not\sim z \rangle$, and each u-unit $\langle x \sim z \rangle$, activity of one of the nu-units plus the u-unit should activate the other nu-unit.

A link setup that implements this behavior is shown in Figure 4. Also shown are the inhibitory nu-links mentioned earlier.[5] The type of conjunctive activation needed for transitivity has been realized by a set of intermediate units (*t-units*) labeled A through E in the figure. These units behave conjunctively, i.e. their threshold is set up so that *all* their inputs have to be active for the unit itself to become active (hence their distinctive square shape). Other units (represented as ellipses) generally work disjunctively, meaning that one

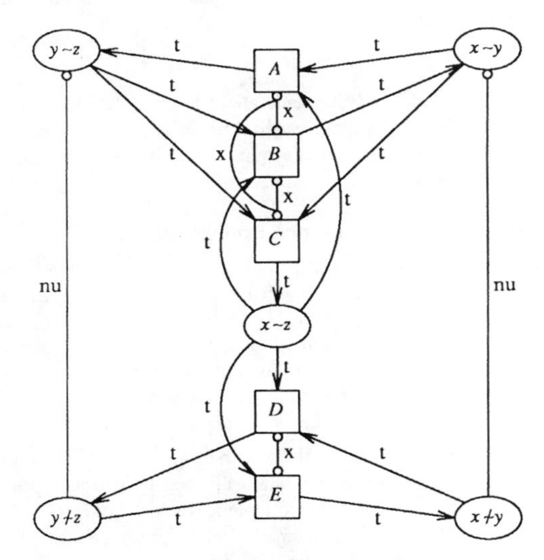

Fig. 4. Link structure enforcing transitivity.

active input is sufficient to exceed the unit's threshold turning it on.[6] Connections linking t-units to u-units and nu-units are called *t-links*.

For technical reasons, inhibitory *x-links* cause activation in t-units to be mutually exclusive, thus preventing stable coalitions (Feldman & Ballard, 1982) of u/nu-units.

Unification by spreading activation

We will now describe the link structure which forces node equivalence (represented by u/nu-units) to conform to the given set of f-structure edges (represented by e-units) and the definition of unification. Unification proceeds recursively, following the recursive composition of the f-structures being processed.

Specifically, when unifying two structures x and y containing the same feature f, say $x.f = x'$ and $y.f = y'$, we have to unify the values x' and y' recursively. In terms of node equivalence, this means that simultaneous presence of the edges $x.f = x'$ and $y.f = y'$ and the equivalence $x \sim y$ should induce the equivalence $x' \sim y'$. Again, this is implemented by a conjunctive pattern of activation, shown in the left half of Figure 5a. As for transitivity, an intermediate unit, A, is needed to realize the conjunctive behavior. A will become active only if all three of its inputs are active. The scheme causes activation representing equivalence to spread along co-occurring features top-down, i.e. from the root of the f-structures towards the leaves. Accordingly, the links and intermediate units transmitting this activation have been termed *td-links* and *td-units*, respectively.

A similar flow of activation occurs among the nu-units, since co-occuring features also transmit non-unifiability.

[4] As described later, these and other constant units can be eliminated by a simple space optimization. However, this optimization will be ignored here for clarity of exposition.

[5] Following connectionist convention, excitatory links are drawn as arrows, while inhibitory links carry small circles at their ends.

[6] Precise values for unit thresholds and link weights are ommitted here, focussing instead on the functionality of the net structure. Stolcke (1989) gives a complete specification.

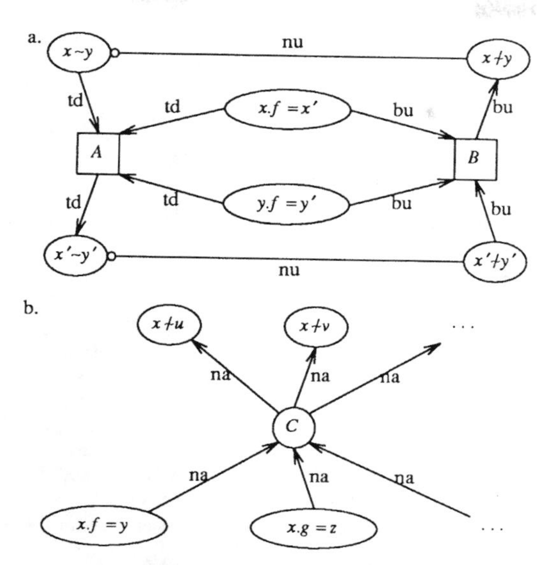

Fig. 5. Link structure performing unification.

Specifically, if the two values x' and y' are known to be non-unifiable, so are their parent nodes x and y. This gives rise to the link structure in the right half of Figure 5a, consisting of *bu-links* and the conjunctive *bu-unit* B. Thus activation representing non-unifiability flows in a bottom-up direction, possibly suppressing top-down activation via nu-links.

A question that remains is: Where does top-down and bottom-up activation originate? Top-down activation corresponds to an attempt to unify given f-structures, i.e. comes from some outside source, presumably some other network or input that uses the unification network as a 'subroutine'. In our case this initial activation is provided by a set of links that connect grammar rules to trigger the generation process, which will be described in the next section.

Bottom-up activation, on the other hand, originates in the f-structures themselves, generated by feature value mismatches at the leaves of the structures involved. A basic definitional property of unification is that non-identical atomic values can never unify. This implies that units like $\langle V \not\vdash NP \rangle$ are clamped to remain constantly active; bottom-up activation will spread non-unifiability to any pair of nodes x and y which has these unequal values in the same feature f, activating $\langle x \not\vdash y \rangle$, and so on further up the f-structure.

Another source of bottom-up activation comes from the fact that an atomic value can never unify with a complex one. Hence nodes with outgoing edges can never be equivalent to atomic nodes. This property is enforced by the link structure shown in Figure 5b. For every non-atomic node x, there is a disjunctive *na-unit* C which transmits activation from e-units to all nu-units $\langle x \not\vdash u \rangle$, u atomic, using *na-links*. The intermediate unit C merely avoids full connectivity between e-units and nu-units, thus saving links.

Connectionist Unification: Summary

The preceding section presents a general mechanism for f-structure unification by connectionist means. The overall procedure is as follows: Two or more f-structures are 'input' to the net by activating the corresponding e-units. Following this, any number of unifications can be attempted by activating the u-units representing equivalence of the roots of the respective f-structures. After a time proportional to the depth of the structures these u-units will either remain active, indicating successful unification, or be turned of by the corresponding nu-unit, thus indicating failure.

Processing is extremely fast, since it explores subordinate f-structures in parallel, while requiring a reasonable amount of network resources: The most expensive aspects of the network are the links realizing transitivity (cubic in the number of nodes) and td/bu-links/units (quadratic in the number of edges).

A significant optimization is possible in case certain f-structures are fixed. This is true for our application, since all the grammar rules are typically fixed with the exception of the inital rule encoding a sentence specification. This implies that all corresponding e-units and a portion of the u/nu-units have constant activation. All of the category mismatches in a grammar can be precomputed this way. For example, $\langle V \not\vdash NP \rangle$ is constantly 1 and implies the same for $\langle s_2 \not\vdash s_{17} \rangle$, $\langle s_2 \not\vdash s_{25} \rangle$, $\langle s_8 \not\vdash s_{17} \rangle$, and $\langle s_8 \not\vdash s_{25} \rangle$. In a second step, all units with constant activation (and the links incident upon them) can be eliminated from the network, resulting in savings of network resources and computation time.[7]

SENTENCE GENERATION

A traditional approach to sentence generation would use some top-level control structure to deal with rule selection, rule application, etc. Connectionist models lack the means to naturally implement global controlling instances and restrict themselves to purely local interactions of processing elements. This section describes how the model presented earlier can be extended to accomplish sentence generation.

Controlling Rule Application

Our approach to generation relies on parallel application of all the rules in the grammar whenever considering expansion of a non-terminal c-structure node. This is possible since the network holds all the rules of the grammar and allows parallel unification attempts to take place. The unification process itself will then single out those rules that are actually applicable, and incorporate the corresponding structure fragment into the structure generated so far.

To arrive at the link structure for this task, it is convenient to distinguish two special classes of nodes within the set of structures derived from the grammar rules. Those root nodes corresponding to left-hand side elements in rules are referred to as *L-nodes*, roots derived from right-hand side elements are

[7] Inactive units can be simply dropped. Active units can be eliminated after adjusting the thresholds of their neighbors according to the weights of the connections that are deleted in the process.

R-nodes. L-nodes in Figure 3 are s_1, s_6, s_{11}, s_{14}, s_{17}, and s_{25}; R-nodes are s_2, s_3, s_7, s_8, s_{12}, s_{15}, s_{18}, and s_{26}. Rule application corresponds to unification of R-nodes with L-nodes (L/R-unifications for short). Hence the approach of parallel rule application described above can be implemented by a link structure which attempts all possible L/R-unifications involving the R-nodes of a rule, once the L-node of that rule has been unified.

As an example, consider rule (R_{VP}), whose context-free component is $VP \rightarrow V\ NP$ with L-node s_6 and R-nodes s_7 and s_8. The link structure shown in Figure 6 triggers parallel rule application as follows:

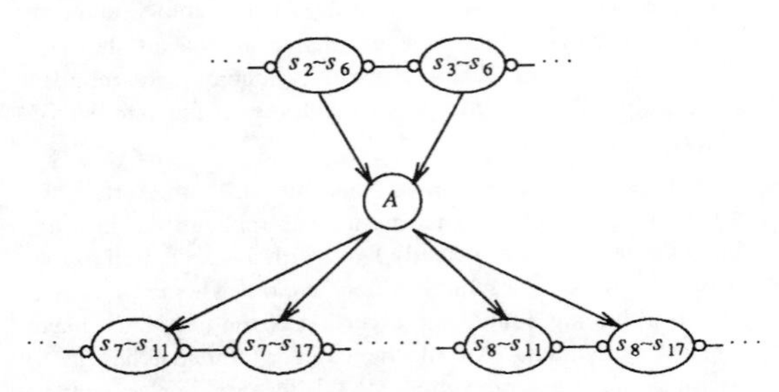

Fig 6. Link structure triggering rule application.

As soon as L-node s_6 unifies with any R-node (from any other rule), the intermediate disjunctive unit A transmits activation to the u-units responsible for unification of R-nodes s_{14} and s_{17} to other L-nodes.

Note that L/R-unifications involving the same L-node or R-node are mutually exclusive, since each right-hand side element can only be attached to exactly one left-hand side (and vice-versa). The mutally inhibitory links between u-units in Figure 6 implement this property.

Parallel rule application would in principle attempt any combination of L-nodes and R-nodes and include them in the schema shown in Figure 6. In practice those combinations resulting in category mismatches can be eliminated beforehand (e.g. $\langle s_7 \sim s_{11} \rangle$). Since categories are just *cat* feature values, however, this optimization would fall out as a by-product of the constant unit elimination process suggested earlier.

Implementing Specifications

Initial specification rules such as ($R_{S'}$) can be enoded as a degenerate structure fragment containing just a single R-node but no L-node (the R-node will be simply the root of the specifying f-structure). Accordingly, the schema from Figure 6 will be reduced to its bottom half. Assuming the root node of the specifying f-structure is s_0, this will give the links shown in Figure 7. Here the auxiliary unit A will serve the purpose of triggering the generation process as a whole.

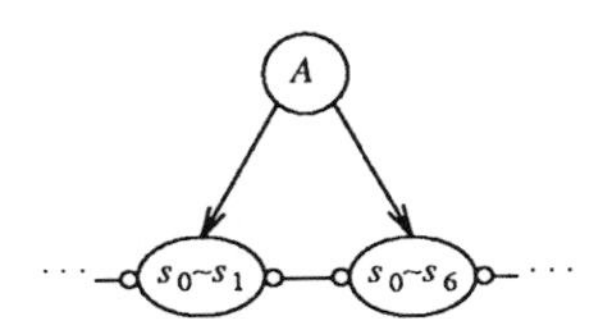

Fig 7. Links for initial rule application.

Experience and Shortcomings

We used simlation tools to implement our model and investigate its dynamic behaviour empirically, although the underlying software posed significant limits on the size of networks and hence grammars. The sample grammar and others of slighly higher complexity were encoded and used for generation to verify our method.[8]

One important property of the network is random selection of alternative formulations for a given semantics.[9] For example, given a *sem* structure as in Figure 1 as specification, the sample grammar will either generate an active ("Peter loves Mary") or a passive ("Mary is loved by Peter") construction. 'Priming' of either of these alternatives is possible by pre-specifying what the *subj* of the sentence should be, or by specifying an explicit *aspect* feature (and accounting for it in the grammar).

The most serious drawback encountered was the apparent inability of the generation process to 'backtrack'. In cases where the unsuitability of a rule becomes evident only after several steps of intermediate rules applied successfully, the network has no means to undo the unifications and try alternatives. To guarantee successful generation, then, the specification must be specific enough to avoid such dead-end paths; this requirement, however, is clearly not acceptable for many purposes.

A different perspective on this problem might indicate a way to its solution. Rule applications from which the system has to backtrack eventually, roughly correspond to local minima in the energy function generally used to describe and analyze the dynamics of connectionst systems (Hopfield, 1982), whereas the set of unifications resulting in a complete sentence should constitute a global energy minimum. There exist standard techniques to 'escape' such local minima (Hinton & Sejnowski, 1986), but they do not apply to networks with asymmetric links such as ours.

A less serious shortcoming of the current model involves recursive rule applications. The model handles recursiveness insofar as the depth of the structures generated is limited only by the size of the relevant unit spaces. Each rule application, however, 'consumes' that rule in the sense that the corresponding fragment is incorporated in the overall structure, thus becoming unavailable for reuse. To allow multiple rule application, say of the *VP* rule, a corresponding number of duplicates of that rule has to be included in the grammar. A mechanism that accomplished such rule duplication 'on the spot' would run into well-known problems of connectionist models, in particular the variable binding problem.

[8] Credit is due to Kai Zimmermann at TU Munich for designing and implementing the LOOPS-based interactive network simulator that was the basis for our experimental work.

[9] This randomness is rooted in the asynchronous model of operation of the units.

EXTENSIONS AND DIRECTIONS FOR FUTURE RESEARCH

One of the most obvious extensions to the model presented here is its application to sentence analysis (parsing). The same transformation of grammar rules into structure fragments could be used, with the same connectionist approach to f-structure representation and unification. A sentence to be parsed would be represented by the set of fragments corresponding to the lexical items constituting it. Parsing would proceed combining those lexical items with rule fragments, using essentially a link structure inverse to the one in Figure 6 (links point bottom-up and the intermediate unit operates conjunctively rather than disjunctively).

A fundamental feature of natural language neglected in our model is time-sequentiality. Although considerable parallelism is probably essential for natural language processing, sequentiality is still inherent in priming effects on sequencing and other psycholinguistic phenomena (Bock, 1982). As a first step in this direction, activation flow (progressing unifications) could be modified so as to follow a left-to-right pattern. Early segments would be generated first, thereafter constraining what follows in the sentence.

Another issue is how current theories of grammar can account for the wealth of ungrammaticality found in actual utterances, such as agreement violations and blending of constructions. These phenomena suggest that grammaticality is really a matter of degree, realized in actual speech according to limitations of processing resources and other constraints. By their nature, connectionist models seem to be better suited to model graded grammaticality, yet it is not clear how to integrate such a notion with our or other models of processing.

Finally, it would be nice if a model of processing also gave some perspective on how its language-specific structures can be efficiently acquired, i.e. learned. With respect to our model, it remains an open question whether any of the known connectionist learning procedures can be applied to accomplish this task.

CONCLUSION

We have shown that connectionist models of natural language processing can efficiently incorporate state-of-the-art linguistic formalisms. In particular, we view our model of sentence generation as a first step towards an integration of unification-based grammar with connectionist principles. Also, the work reported here seems to suggest several possible directions in which traditional linguistic theories may be extended and modified to accommodate performance models of natural language.

ACKNOWLEDGEMENTS

Many thanks are due to the members of the AI research group at TU Munich, who were of great help during the preparation of the Diploma thesis on which this work is based.

I would also like to thank Joachim Diederich, Jerry Feldman, Jim Hendler and Charles Rosenberg for their valuable comments of earlier versions of this paper.

REFERENCES

Bock, J. Kathryn (1982), "Toward a Cognitive Psychology of Syntax: Information Processing Contributions to Sentence Formulation". *Psychological Review* **89**(1): 1–47.

Charniak, Eugene & Santos, Eugene (1987), "A Connectionist Context-Free Parser Which is not Context-Free, But Then It is not Really Connectionist Either". In *Proceedings of the 9th Annual Conference of the Cognitive Science Society*, Seattle, Wash., pp. 70–77.

Cottrell, Garrison W. (1985), "A Connectionist Approach to Word Sense Disambiguation". Technical Report TR 154. Computer Science Department, University of Rochester, Rochester, N.Y..

Dell, Gary S. (1985), "Positive Feedback in Hierarchical Connectionist Models: Applications to Language Production". *Cognitive Science* **9**: 3–23.

Fanty, Mark (1985), "Context-Free Parsing in Connectionist Networks". Technical Report TR 174. University of Rochester, Rochester, N.Y..

Feldman, Jerome A. & Ballard, Dana H. (1982), "Connectionist Models and Their Properties". *Cognitive Science* **6**: 205–254.

Gasser, Michael E. (1988), "A Connectionist Model of Sentence Generation in a First and Second Language". Technical Report UCLA-AI-88-13. Artificial Intelligence Laboratory, University of California, Los Angeles, Calif..

Gazdar, Gerald, Klein, E., Pullum, G. K., and Sag, I. A. (1985), *Generalized Phrase Structure Grammar*. Cambridge, Mass.: Harvard University Press.

Hinton, Geoffrey E. & Sejnowski, Terrence J. (1986), "Learning and Relearning in Boltzmann Machines". In David E. Rumelhart, James L. McClelland (Ed.), *Parallel Distributed Processing: Explorations in the Microstructure of Cognition. Volume 1: Foundations*. Cambridge, Mass.: MIT Press, pp. 282–317.

Hopfield, J. J. (1982), "Neural networks and physical systems with emergent collective computational abilities". *Proceedings of the National Academy of Sciences USA* **79**: 2554–2558.

Kalita, Jugal & Shastri, Lokendra (1987), "Generation of Simple Sentences in English Using the Connectionist Model of Computation". In *Proceedings of the 9th Annual Conference of the Cognitive Science Society*, Seattle, Wash., pp. 555–565.

Kaplan, Ronald M. & Bresnan, Joan (1982), "Lexical Functional Grammar: A Formal System for Grammatical Representation". In Joan Bresnan (Ed.), *The Mental Representation of Grammatical Relations*. Cambridge, Mass.: MIT Press, pp. 173–281.

Kay, Martin (1984), "Functional Unification Grammar: A formalism for machine translation". In *Proceedings of the 10th International Conference on Computational Linguistics*, Stanford, Calif., pp. 75–78.

McClelland, James L. & Kawamoto, Alan H. (1986), "Mechanisms of Sentence Processing: Assigning Roles to Constituents of Sentences". In David E. Rumelhart, James L. McClelland (Ed.), *Parallel Distributed Processing: Explorations in the Microstructure of Cognition. Volume 2: Psychological and Biological Models*. Cambridge, Mass.: MIT Press, pp. 272–325.

Shieber, S. M., Uszkoreit, H., Pereira, F. C. N., and Robinson, J. J. (1983), "The Formalism and Implementation of PATR-II". In B. Grosz, M. Stickel (Ed.), *Research on Interactive Acquisition and Use of Knowledge*. SRI Final Report 1894. Artificial Intelligence Center, SRI International, Menlo Park, Calif..

Shieber, Stuart M. (1986), "An Introduction to Unification-Based Approaches to Grammar". CSLI Lecture Note Series. Center for Study of Language and Information, Stanford, Calif..

Stolcke, A. (1989), "A Connectionist Model of Unification". Technical Report TR 89-032. International Computer Science Institute, Berkeley, Calif..

Touretzky, David S. (1986), "BoltzCONS: Reconciling Connectionism with the Recursive Nature of Stacks and Trees". In *Proceedings of the 8th Annual Conference of the Cognitive Science Society*, Amherst, Mass., pp. 522–530.

A Discrete Neural Network Model for Conceptual Representation and Reasoning

Ron Sun
Computer Science Dept.
Brandeis University
Waltham, MA 02254

ABSTRACT

Current connectionist models are oversimplified in terms of the internal mechanisms of individual neurons and the communication between them. Although connectionist models offer significant advantages in certain aspects, this oversimplification leads to the inefficiency of these models in addressing issues in explicit symbolic processing, which is proven to be essential to human intelligence. What we are aiming at is a connectionist architecture which is capable of simple, flexible representations of high level knowledge structures and efficient performance of reasoning based on the data. We first propose a discrete neural network model which contains state variables for each neuron in which a set of discrete states is explicitly specified instead of a continuous activation function. A technique is developed for representing concepts in this network, which utilizes the connections to define the concepts and represents the concepts in both verbal and compiled forms. The main advantage is that this scheme can handle variable bindings efficiently. A reasoning scheme is developed in the discrete neural network model, which utilizes the inherent parallelism in a neural network model, performing all possible inference steps in parallel, implementable in a fine-grained massively parallel computer.

1. INTRODUCTION

The advances in neurobiology and connectionist modeling provide a whole set of possibilities in terms of implementing and extending AI ideas in conceptual representation and reasoning. Current connectionist models are only crude approximations of the real neural network. They are oversimplified in terms of the internal mechanisms of individual neurons and the communication between neurons. This oversimplification leads to the failure and/or inefficiency (at least as I have seen so far) of the models in addressing issues such as modeling biological neural networks([Selverston 1987]), representing high level data structures, rules, or concepts, developing inferential schemes, and extending the application domain of the connectionist models to domains involving symbolic processing (see [Pinker and Mehler 1988] for the necessity of explicit symbolic processing). What we are aiming at is a computational neural network model which is capable of simple, flexible representations of high level data structures and efficient performance of reasoning based on the data, i.e. an AI architecture based on a neural network model, drawing ideas from biological mechanisms in real neural networks.

Little progress has been made toward such an architecture. Among the few works that are reported are [Touretzky and Hinden 1987], [Touretzky 1986], [Barnden 1988], [Shastri and Feldman 1987], and [Smolensky 1987]. But in each of these schemes, parallelism is lost in some way, either because of the matching process of harhwired rules or a centralized working memory. For example, in [Touretzky and Hinton 1987], an elaborate pull-out network is designed to pick up a rule from a rule network and to match the data (triples) in the working memory. Although the mechanism is very elegant, it hinders the speed of reasoning by doing one match at a time. And it is possible to travel deep down a wrong path. In [Barnden 1988] scheme, the rules are wired in symbolic forms into a network in a grid form. Thus the problem is the symbolic manipulation necessary to match the rule against data, which is a slow and complicated process in a connectionist model. Because of that, only one rule can be matched at a time. The inherent parallelism is not fully utilized as a result. In [Shastri and Feldman 1987], a mathematical formalism is developed, and a network architecture is designed to implement the formalism. Many different types of neurons are devised and each has a special activation function specifically designed for that neuron. The scheme can handle property inheritance in a conceptual hierarchy but not rule encoding and rule based reasoning. Besides these, there are other shemes that employ different techniques for high level data or knowledge representation, for example, [Ballard 1986], [Fanty 1988], [Ackley 1987], and [Derthick 1988].

2. THE DISCRETE MODEL

Our aim is to devise a model more general than conventional PDP models and capable of explaining many intricate phenomena found in real neural networks. The generalization goes along several dimensions: internal states, different synaptic outputs, and temporal response. The resulting model can be used to attack several important problems in developing a reasoning scheme, i.e. rule matching, variable binding, and certainty factor propagation. The model seems to be a reasonable basis for an inference system and it is presented here as a first step towards a full fledged conceptual representation and reasoning system.

Basically, a discrete neural model is a 2-tuple

W=<N, M>

where

N={<S, A, I, IF, T, C>}

S= the set of all the possible states of a neuron,
A= the set of all the actions to be taken by the neuron,
I= inputs,
IF= input manipulation function: I --> I',
T= State transition function: S x I' --> S,
C= action function: S x I' --> 2^A,

and M is the connectivity among neurons in the set N.

In this model a set of discrete states is explicitly specified instead of a continuous activation function. Hopefully this can capture more accurately the biological information processing mechanisms built into a real neuron. The idea came from the modeling study of lobster stomatogastric ganglion neural networks (see [Sun et al. 1988]). Evidence from physiological data observed by biologist overwhelmingly points to a more powerful neural network model, which is capable of accounting for more phenomena than conventional models. In a real neuron, unlike in conventional connectionist models, there is no continuous input or output through synapses. Instead, an all-or-none action potential is generated if the cell is depolarized to a certain degree, which in turn causes the release of neurotransmitters. The input to the postsynaptic cell is dependent upon two factors: the type and the amount of neurotransmitters released ([Kandel and Schwartz 1984] and [Edelman 1987]). This powerful mechanism can not be captured by conventional neural network models. In a conventional neural network model, the continuous output is meant to represent the frequency in which the action potentials are generated, it is doubtful that the firing frequency is a primitive feature (not an emergent feature that is caused by other more primitive activities) in the neuronal information processing mechanism. On the contrary, we have shown in a simulation study [Sun et al 1988] that the firing frequency, as well as phase relationship, is an emergent property of the network created by the complex interaction of the components of the network, at least in lobster stomatogastric ganglions. The proposed discrete model can easily capture the neural information processing mechanisms through action functions and state transition functions by specifying a sequence of states to go through, and specifying actions associated with each state, namely

$s(t) = s(t\text{-}1) + 1 \bmod n$,
$C(t) = f(s(t), I1, I2, ..., Ik)$,
where f is a predetermined function such as weighted sum or Goldman Equation.

This formalism can explain many intricate phenomena found in real neural networks such as phase reponses, neuronal modulation and phasic relationship. These properties are important in terms of the functional capability and versitility of a network, as seen in many different domains (e.g. [Richmond & Optican 1987]).

Another issue is the importance of the membrane properties and, therefore, the endogenous firing of individual cells. According to our study [Sun et al 1988], the dynamics and emergent properties of a neural network can mostly be attributed to two factors: the endogenous firing (determined by membrane properties of the cell, which could be affected by current inputs and the input history) and the synaptic connectivity. Because of the physiological properties of the cell membrane, each cell is capable of firing endogenuously even when it is insulated from any external influence. The endogenous firings are important as a source of influences that help to shape the behavior of a network. This fact is indicated in many biological papers (e.g. [Selverston and Moulin 1987]). However, the importance of membrane properties and endogenous firings is overlooked in conventional connectionist models, because of the highly approximate nature of these models. In the discrete neural model, this feature can be captured by a state variable that represents the particular moment of internal changes. The mechanism works this way: using the formula specified above, s(t) now determines a particular endogenous firing curve, for example,

Suppose the weighted sum model is used (see [Sun et al 1988]),
C(t) = f(s(t), I1, I2, ... ,Ik) = w0*E(s(t)) +w1*I1(t) +w2*I2(t) + ... +wk*Ik(t) ,
where E(s(t)) = sin(s(t)) .

Yet another issue is the different presynaptic actions performed by the same cell at differnet sites of the axon. Different sites on the same axon can release different types of neurotransmitter (thus cause different types of reactions in postsynaptic cells) or different amount of transmitters of the same type. Some types of neurotransmitters may have long lasting effect, while others may act instantaneously. Each can cause a different reaction in a postsynaptic cells. The "action" taken by an individual postsynaptic cell is determined mainly, but not exclusively, by the following factors: the endogenuous properties of the cell, the type(s) and amount of transmitters it received, and the current that is injected into it in case of electric synapsis. The issue of different postsynaptic actions is not dealt with in conventional connectionist models either. In my model, the variaty in presynaptic actions can be modeled by A (the set of actions) and C (the action functions).

The equivalence property of this model to the more conventional models is studied. It is at least capable of the same computational power as well as expressive power. Beyond that, it has the advantage of generality and versatility. It is more general because it can accormodate the conventional connectionist models as special cases as discussed below. It is also more versatile because, by introducing state variables and a set of synaptic actions, the model can handle more elaborate processing at neuronal level.

To see how my model simulates other connectionist models, look at various neural network models. In general, neural network models can be classified into four classes:

continuous input/discrete activation models (e.g. linear threshold unit model),

discrete input/discrete activation models (e.g. Feldman and Ballard model),

continuous input/continuous activation models (e.g. McClelland and Rumelhart's interactive activation and competition model),

discrete input/continuous activation models (as another possibility).

All of them can be easily handled by my general formalism. To simulate a continuous input/discrete activation neural model (suppose using a uniform activation function a), let a dicrete neural network model be

<S,A,I,IF,T,C>
where
S={0,1},
A={do-nothing, output-1-to-all-postsynaptic-cells},
IF=$\sum w_i I_i$,
T= the original acivation function a,
C= a table specifying which action in A to perform (see Figure 1).

This model can simulate the original model and produce the same output: 0 if I'<ths and 1 if I'>=ths. The model will carry out the computation exactly as its conventioal counterparts.

In case of simulating a continuous activation model, we will have to discretize the output, i.e. C will be a table specifying a sequence of points sampled from the responce curve the neuron in the original model. If we sample enough points on the continuous output curve, we can approximate the behavior of the original model closely enough for any practical purpose. For example, Figure 2 shows the approximation of the model: output= potential+ $\sum(w_i i_i)$.

We also looked at ways of implementing this model with a multilayer conventional PDP model. The question is how to implement the state variable and the state transition function of a discrete neuron. It has been shown that a three layer network could do the job: the hidden layer represents the current state and each input/ouput value is explicitly represented by individual cells (cf. [Servan-Schreiber 1988] and [Allen 1988]). See Figure 3. The output from the hidden layer is fedback into the input layer to help decide, together with current inputs, which state to enter next.

There is one aspect of the model that may raise some questions. Usually in real neuron, one synapse can only release a certain type of transmitters (or a certain group of transmitters). But in my model each synaptic site can release different transimitters (i.e. different messages or synaptic actions). How do we resolve this contradiction? This contradiction can be easily resolved by realizing the fact that we can implement this dicrete neural network model using only the type of neurons in which each synaptic site can only release one type of transmitters, by adding a group of intermediate cells each of which represents a particular message and hook them together. See Figure 4.

The communication between cells can be viewed this way: each message sent is coded as (state, strength), where state means output state or symbol. This can be implemented, in the same sense as above, with the same kind of intermediate layer of units, connecting to source and target cells with certain strengths. See Fig 5.

3. LOGICAL OPERATIONS

A number of researchers have cited logical operations as an important factor in determining the adequency of a neural network model as a universal computational model ([Abu 1986],[Rumelhart 1986] etc.).

The discrete model can handle all logical operations very efficiently because of the nature of the state transition function and the action function. An AND operation of two inputs can be modeled by the following state transition/action function (see Figure 6). The other operations such as OR and NOT can be modeled exactly the same way.

Another advantage of the model is the ease with which we can model multiplicative connections. There is no need for an extra type of connections in the network. All of the connections can be accormodated in the same general framework. Yet this framework is kept simple and directly implementable.

4. DUALITY-CONNECTION ENCODING

A technique, called duality-connection encoding or DCE, has been developed for representing concepts in a neural network of the type mentioned above, which utilizes the connections to define the concepts and represents the concepts in both verbal and compiled forms. The main advantage is that this scheme can handle variable binding efficiently.

The main dilemma of reasoning in connectionist models is at which level we should incorporate symbols into the schemes. If we perform pure symbolic reasoning, the cost for representing symbols and performing the reasoning is too high, such as in Barnden's scheme (see [Barnden 1988]) or Touretzsky&Hinton's scheme (see [Touretzsky and Hinton 1985]) (even though it handles only a much simplified case). But if we eliminate symbols from the scheme, it will not be suitable for performing high level cognitive task. This model resolved this dilemma by introducing a dual coding technique, That is, encoding a concept by using two cell assemblies: one for linguistic(symbolic) representation and the other for non-linguistic representation suitable for reasoning and variable binding. This scheme ensures the efficiency of reasoning processes. Coarse coding can be used here to have the advantage of fault-tolerance. Another mechanism for fault tolerance is the replication of identical units, which is particularly suitable in this model. This mechanism is found in some small neural circuits in crustacean stomatogastric systems ([Selverston 1986]).

A concept is encoded in the network by the connections it has to the other cells. Those unidirectional connections help shape the concept as well as guide the reasoning. For example, Figure 7 shows how a concept is wired into a network.

In the reasoning assembly, there are k+1 cells: CF,c1,c2, ... ,ck. CF cell contains the certainty factors (or confidence, possibility, etc.) used in reasoning and connects to all other concepts related to it. The other k cells take care of variable bindings for a maximun of k variables. The set of states in the variable cell represents all possible bindings. The signal from CF cell tells the variable cell which input to take. See Figure 8. The formulas used are summarized below (just one simple case as an example):

For CF, $S(t) = f(CF(t\text{-}1), I1(t), I2(t), \ldots\ldots Ik(t))$.

f here is a mapping to a value which encodes two things: the activation level and the activation source. Because several other assemblies are connected to this one, f has to distinguish different sources by encoding it in its resulting value. CF(t-1) here is for keeping certain historical contextual information and $I_i s$ are outputs of other CF cells in other assemblies.

And for Ci, i=1,2,....k, $S(t) = fi(CF(t), I1(t), I2(t), \ldots\ldots In(t))$.

f_i here is a table specifying the state of C_i at time t based on inputs at that moment from the CF cell and c_i cells in other assembly. CF(t) is actually an instruction to $c_i s$, telling them which input to take and make that input state its activation state.

The linguistic (symbolic) assembly of a concept representation records the verbal form of a concept or a predicate which defines that concept. The information recorded can be recalled when the concept is invoked in reasoning.

The representation scheme actually can handle two things: concept representation and predicate representation. Predicate representation is a cell assembly containing one main connection cell determining CF and a set of variable cells for variable binding as described above. On the other hand, concept representation is a cluster (implemented with a cell assembly) with slots to be filled just like variable binding. Each cluster is a frame like structure consisting several parts: a control cell (CF) and a set of role cells. Cells in the latter two groups send signals to the control cell. Control cell also receive signals from other cell assemblies(spreading activation). The conceptual hierarchy is traversed based on spreading activation.

5. REASONING SCHEME

A reasoning scheme is developed in the discrete neural network model, which maximizes the inherent parallelism in a neural network model and performs all possible inference steps in parallel.

One of the major drawbacks of conventional connectionist model is its inability in handling deductive reasoning, i.e. deriving conclusions from existing facts. The explicit deductive reasoning (not intuition or subconscious reasoning) requires one to establish rules, store facts in working memory, and use rules to deduce new facts. In real world, facts are usually known with certain uncertainty. So a connectinoist inference engine has to take that into consideration too. Another problem is variable binding. In order to avoid crosstalk betweeen rules, we have to have an efficient mechanism for handling variable binding.

The basic architecture consists of three layers: input, processing and output, with additional modules attachable to them, each of which can handle learning and pre- and post-processing correspondingly.

The input information is processed in input layer and passed on to the processing layer. The processing layer can have complicated internal structures. The information passed to each cell is processed and propagated to all the post synaptic cells from each pre-synaptic cells. This scheme guaranttees a high degree of parallelism.

The calculus for dealing with uncertainty factor propagation was proposed in [Sun 1984, 1985]. The soundness and completeness under certain constraints were proven. It is capable of dealing with certain types of default reasoning. For exampple, if C1(X) and C2(X) and C3(X) then A(X), where X is the vector of variable bindings, can be coded as shown in Figure 8 in DCE. Cell A then combines the evidences by doing CF=w* $\sum I_i$. In case C3 is undetermined, based on partial information available, the system can still deduce A, with activation less strong than it would be if C3 is known. For contradictory propositions, there can be inhibitory connections between each pair of them, with strengths corresponding to the degrees of contradiction. When strict logical operations (AND, OR, and NOT) are required in the reasoning, the method described in section 3 is applied to achieve the desired effect. An interesting thing is that this scheme fits the 100 step rule well (see [Feldman 1986]). Besides this formalism, it can also implement schemes proposed in [Zadeh 1983] or [Shastri and Feldman 1987].

ATTENTIONAL MECHANISMS There are two attentional mechanisms in the model: A-area, the reasoning trace, and C-area, a mechanism for controlling the reasoning process directed by the goal of the system.

We assume that the activation is calculated with $\sum w_i i_i$, where $w_i = s_i m_i + l_i$. Usually $m_i = 0$. But when we want to concentrate on one area in the network (forming a C-area), the external intention control module can increase m_i . s_i is a predetermined value. So we might come up with results that can not be deduced otherwise (because of strong inhibitions or high thresholds).

7. CONCLUSION

Putting these components together, it forms a coherent system with various features and modules for various purposes. This discrete neural network model has the advantages of representational flexibility and expressive power with regard to high-level conceptual representation, and massive parallelism and real-time efficiency with regard to reasoning within this representational framework. Further work is needed to specify more details of conceptual representations and various rule codings. Several learning algorithms are currently under development.

ACKNOWLEDGEMENT I would like to thank David Waltz and Lawrence Bookman for the discussions and suggestions. This work was supported in part by the Defense advanced Research Projects Agency, administered by the US Air Force Office of Scientific Research under contract #F49620-88-C-0058.

REFERENCES

[1] Y. Abu-Mostafa, Neural Networks for Computing?, Neural Networks for Computing, 1986

[2] D. Ackley, Stochastic iterated genetic hillclimbing, Technical Report, TR CMU-CS-87-107, Carnegie-Mellon University, 1987

[3] R. Allen, Connectionist state machines, Technical Report, Bellcore, 1988

[4] D. Ballard, Parallel logical inference and energy minimization, Technical Report, TR 142, University of Rochester, 1986

[5] J. Barnden, The right of free association: relative-position encoding for connectionist data structures, 10th conf. of Cognitive Science Society, 1988

[6] M. Derthick, Mundane reasoning by parallel constraint satisfaction, Technical Report, TR CMU-CS-88-182, Carnegie-Mellon University, 1988

[7] G. Edelman et al, Synaptic Function, John Wiley & Sons, 1987

[8] M. Fanty, Learning in structured connectionist networks, Technical Report, TR 252, University of Rochester, 1988

[9] J. Feldman, Neural Representation of conceptual knowledge, Technical report 189, 1986

[10] G. Hinton, Connectionist learning procedures, Technical Report, University of Toronto, 1988

[11] J. Holland, Escaping brittleness, Machine Learning, Vol.2, 1986

[12] E. Kandel and J. Schwartz, Principle of Neural Science. 2ed. Elsevier, 1984

[13] S. Pinker and J. Mehler. Connections and Symbols. MIT Press, 1988

[14] B. Richmond and L. Optican, Temporal Encoding of Two-Dimensional Patterns by Single Units in Primate Inferior Temporal Cortex, Journal of Neurophysiology, Vol 57. No 1, January 1987

[15] D. Rumelhart and J. McClelland, Parallel Distributed Processing, MIT press, 1986

[16] A. Selverston and M. Moulins, eds. The Crustacean Stomatogastric System, Springer-Verlag, 1987

[17] D. Servan-Schreiber et al, Encoding sequential structure. Technical Report, CMU-CS-88-183, Carnegie Mellon University, 1988

[18] L. Shastri and J. Feldman. Evidential reasoning in semantic networks. 9th IJCAI, 1987

[19] P. Smolensky, On variable binding and representation of symbolic structure, Tech Report, University of Colorado, Boulder. 1987

[20] P. Smolensky, On the proper treatment of connectionism, Behavioral and Brain Sciences, 11, 1988

[21] R. Sun, The matrix representation of production rules with CF, 3rd Symp. of Discrete Mathematics in China, 1984

[22] R. Sun, The logic for approximate reasoning combining probability and fuzziness, 1st Congress of International Fuzzy System Association, 1985

[23] R. Sun, E. Marder and D. Waltz, The modeling of lobster stomatogastric ganglion, Technical Report CS-88-143, Brandeis University, 1988

[24] D. Touretzky, Representing and transforming recursive objects in a neural network, 1986

[25] D. Touretzky and G. Hinton, Symbols among neurons. 9th IJCAI, 1987

[26] L. Zadeh, Commonsense knowledge representation based on fuzzy logic, Computer, Vol.16, No.10, 1983

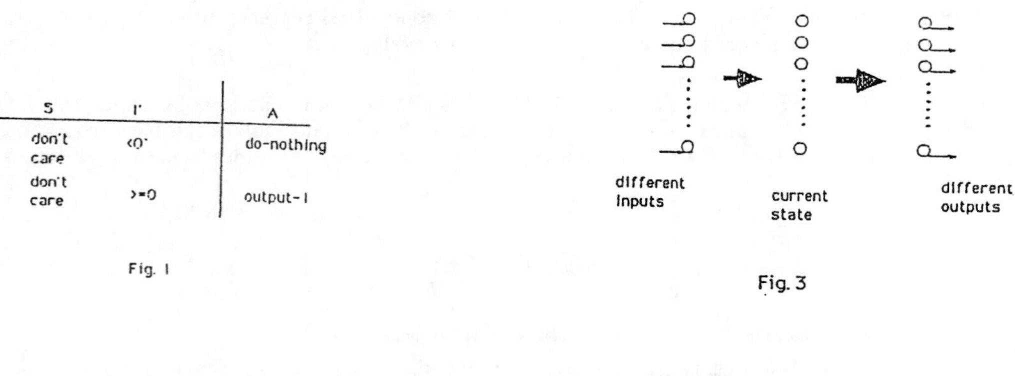

S	I'	A
don't care	<0	do-nothing
don't care	>=0	output-1

Fig. 1

Fig. 3

S	I'	A
0	0	0
0	0.1	0.1
0	0.2	0.2
......	......	......
0.1	0	0.1
0.2	0	0.2

Fig. 2

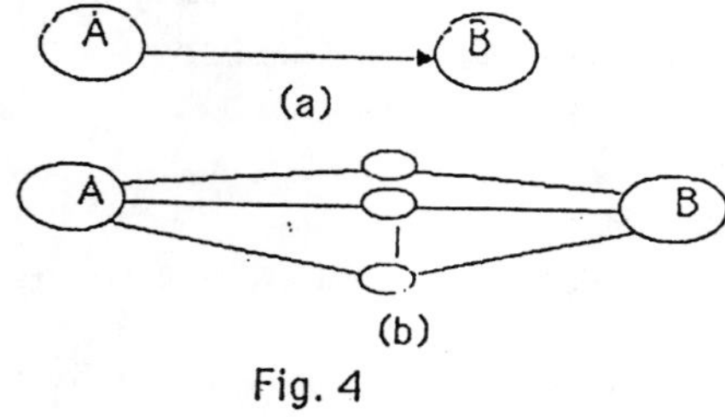

Fig. 4

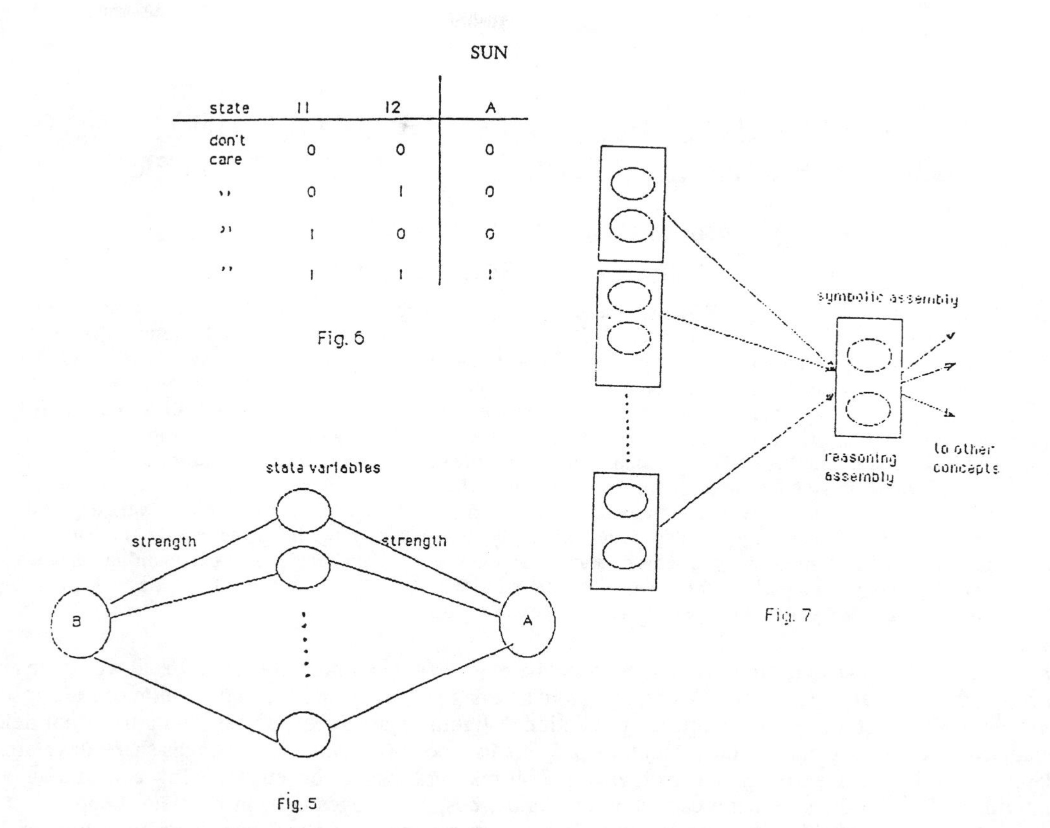

state	I1	I2	A (SUN)
don't care	0	0	0
,,	0	1	0
,,	1	0	0
,,	1	1	1

Fig. 6

Fig. 5

Fig. 7

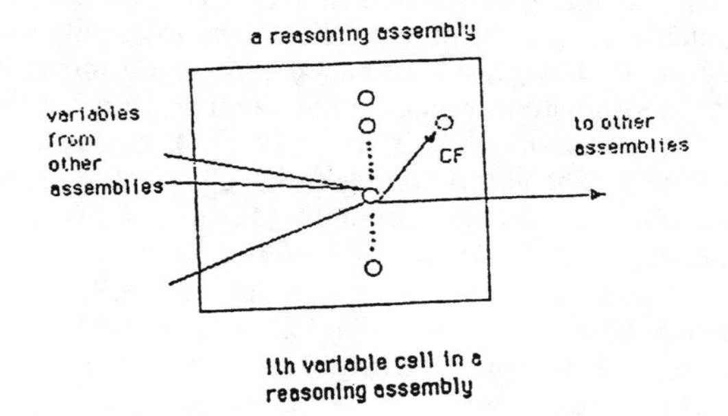

Fig. 8

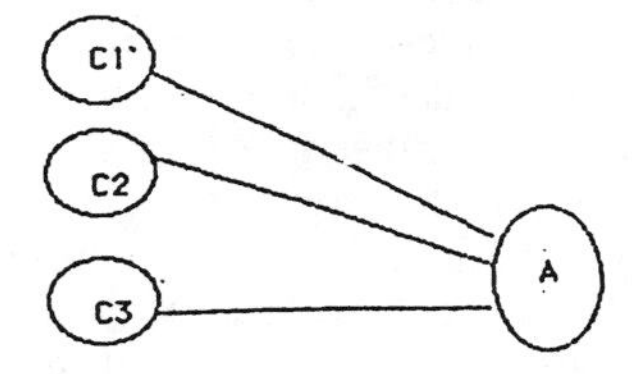

Fig. 9

PREATTENTIVE INDEXING AND VISUAL COUNTING: FINSTS AND THE ENUMERATION OF CONCENTRIC ITEMS

LANA TRICK AND ZENON PYLYSHYN
UNIVERSITY OF WESTERN ONTARIO

According to Pylyshyn's FINST hypothesis(in press) distinctive feature clusters, locations that pop out in search tasks (Treisman and Gellade, 1980), compete for a small number of spatial reference tokens or FINSTS. A FINST individuates a given feature cluster, making it distinct from others. Once assigned, a FINST remains attached to its respective cluster despite changes in the cluster's position. These spatial indices allow attentive processes to access selected clusters for further analysis though the retinal position of the cluster change through object or eye movement. It is argued that *subitizing*, the rapid apprehension of number in the 1-4 range, exploits this preattentive mechanism; therefore, subitizing should not be possible when the counting task is embedded in one in which subjects have to compute a spatial relation that requires the attentional focus, such as inside(Ullman,1984). Subjects were required to count either concentric rectangles, which implicitly entails computing the inside relation, or count rectangles of uniform or varying sizes spread across the screen. Trend analysis of the counting latencies revealed no sign of subitizing when subjects were required to count items that were one inside another, although subitizing emerged as usual in the other two conditions.

In constructing robots that can move and manipulate objects in a complex, dynamic visual world we are faced with a problem. The properties of objects in an image change from moment to moment as a result of changes in the object or in the object's projection or lighting: an objects's position in the visual field changes with object or camera movement; its projected shape may change if it changes shape or rotates in depth; its projected size may change as it grows or shrinks, approaches or retreats. How can an item be individuated from others so that it can retain its identity despite changes in its properties? People routinely solve this problem; we can easily pick out an item in an image and then move our retinal or attentional focus towards it, compensating even as the item changes position, shape or size. Moreover, we can do this even if we do not recognise the object. We appear to be able to keep track of objects automatically and effortlessly. This ability has been called *indexing*(Ullman,1984). The ability to index is prerequisite for visual motor coordination; we could not touch or capture the things we want to manipulate, or dodge the things we want to avoid if we could not distinguish a particular item from the rest, focus on it and keep track of it. The ability to index is also prerequisite for object description because spatial attention is thought necessary for combining features(Treisman & Gellade, 1980) and computing spatial relations between parts(Ullman, 1984). Without the ability to index a location it would not be possible to move the attentional focus to where we want it to go, since in order to move attention to a particular point we must first be able to specify *which* point. The objective of this research is to understand indexing by studying visual counting, a process that by its nature requires item individuation. First, however, it is necessary to discuss counting in the context of visual processing in general.

Visual processing is thought to have two stages. The first is an automatic *preattentive stage* that employs local parallel operations to derive features (eg. color, line orientation, depth). The second is a goal driven *attentive* stage that employs a serial spatial processing focus to combine features at a location (eg. combine "red" and "vertical" for a red vertical line, Treisman & Gellade,1980), and derive global relations such as inside and connected that cannot be computed by local parallel units(Ullman,1984). Coordination of parallel (preattentive) and serial (attentive) stages is assumed to involve a bottleneck; a small number of preattentively derived feature clusters must be individuated, assigned unique internal reference tokens (FINSTs, Pylyshyn, in press) so they can serve as destinations for the attentional focus. FINSTs, short for FINgers of INSTiation, provide a way of indexing, "pointing to", a cluster without specifying retinal coordinates or properties so that the cluster's identity could be preserved though the cluster moved and changed. Although items may be FINSTed automatically or in response to goals, according to the theory only FINSTed locations can be accessed by attentional or motor commands. A small number of feature clusters can be FINSTed simultaneously; for example, there is evidence that up to 5 independently moving targets can be tracked at once in a field of identical moving distractors(Pylyshyn & Storm, in press). The FINST mechanism is thus parallel but limited capacity; there are only a small number of reference tokens or FINSTs. Differential processing of small and large numbers of items is hence predicted. For this reason the research on subitizing and counting is important. It has been suspected for over a hundred years that the enumeration of small numbers of items employs different processes than the enumeration of large numbers(Jevons, 1871). *Subitizing*, the process of enumerating up to 4 items, is rapid (60 msec/item), effortless and accurate; *counting proper*, the process of enumerating more than 4 items, is slow (300 msec/item) effortful and error-prone. The question remains, however: Why are there two enumeration processes? Why can't we subitize any number of items? I would like to argue that subitizing is parasitic on FINSTS, the limited capacity preattentive indexing system, whereas counting proper involves moving the attentional focus as suggested by Ullman(1984).

One way to support this contention is to show that subitizing of small numbers of items cannot be accomplished in situations in which spatial attention is required to distinguish one item from others. One such situation is when subjects are required to count concentric items, items that are one inside another. Why would this be the case? Consider a display of white outline rectangles on a black background. Low level processing would deliver a representation in which illumination discontinuities were grouped into clusters on the basis of the Gestalt grouping principles(Marr, 1982), primarily proximity in this case. When objects are spread across the screen, as in the most counting experiments, these groupings would correctly reflect the number of objects. Edges that were closest typically come from the same object. Thus a FINST could be assigned to each cluster and subitizing could carry on as usual. If the rectangles were concentric this would not be possible. The edges that were closest together are inevitably from different objects when items are concentric, and moreover, these immediately adjacent edges and corners would also have the same orientation. Thus, there would be a tendency to group the wrong contours on the basis of both the proximity and similarity. Attention would be required to properly establish which edges belong to which objects. Of couse, this laborious process could be short cut if the subject simply moved the attentional focus outwards from the centre and counted edge crossings. Regardless, subjects need to move the attentional focus in order to count concentric objects. Consequently, subitizing should not be possible in this situation.

Given this prediction it is interesting that one of the few studies that failed to produce evidence of subitizing had subjects counting concentric circles (Saltzman and Garner, 1948). The characteristic "bend" in the reaction time curve caused by the change in slope after four, the trademark of the shift from subitizing to counting, was not evident in this study. Unfortunately, trend analysis was not in use at the time and the authors had different interests; this result was not pursued. At this point it is necessary to replicate their finding and establish why subitizing was not evident in their study. Their concentric circle task differed from typical dot enumeration tasks in three ways. First, subjects were presented with objects, circles, instead of points of light. Second, these objects were of different sizes. Third, the objects were concentric. I would like to argue that it is the fact that the items had a common centre, rather than that they were objects of different sizes, that made subitizing impossible in their study.

There were three conditions in the experiment. In the *Same size* condition subjects were required to count rectangles of the same size spread across the screen. The *Different size* condition was similar except at least one of the rectangles was a different size than the others. Finally, in the *Concentric* condition subjects were required to count concentric rectangles, thus implicitly computing the inside relation, which requires the focus of spatial attention, according to Ullman(1984). If subitizing is only possible when items were spread across the screen then there should be evidence of slope discontinuities between the 1-4 and 5-8 ranges in the *Same size* and *Different size* conditions but not the *Concentric* condition.

METHOD

Subjects

Twelve undergraduate psychology students participated in the study for course credit. Five were male. Each subject participated in every condition of the experiment.

Apparatus and Materials

An Apple II+ computer was used to generate the displays and record the data. Oral response latencies were measured using a Gerbrands G1341 voice activated relay.

Displays were comprised of up to eight white outline rectangles on a black background. There were three types of display. In the *Same size* condition all the items in the display were rectangles of the same size. There were three possible sizes. When subjects were seated 110 cm from the video screen the rectangles subtended .26 X .16, .60 X .42, or 1.01 X .78 degrees visual angle. Rectangles could be located in any of 24 positions. The closest horizontal and vertical neighbours were 1.2 and .94 degrees away from each other, respectively. The minimal distance between diagonal neighbours was .18 degrees, however. The maximal distance between items was 8.33 degrees for small squares in diagonal corners. At most, the entire display would occupy 8.02 X 5.97 degrees visual angle. The size of items and their positions were chosen randomly for each subject and display. In the *Different size* condition, at least one of the rectangles in the display was different in size from the others. Once again there were three possible sizes and 24 potential item locations. Item sizes and positions were chosen randomly for each display and subject. Subjects were required to count concentric rectangles centred at fixation in the *Concentric* condition. Rectangles came in 15 sizes, ranging from .26 X .16 to 7.25 X 5.71 degrees visual angle. For the inner six rings the minimal distance between items was .21 degrees horizontal and .16 degrees vertical. For the outer rings the distance was made larger because acuity decreases towards the periphery. Thus for the outer rings the minimal distance was .29 and .21 degrees respectively. The maximal distances between rings was 3.49 horizontal and 2.71 vertical degrees. The sizes of concentric rectangles were chosen randomly for each subject and display.[1]

Procedure

The experiment was conducted in a slightly darkened room. Subjects were seated 110 cm from a video screen, with a computer keyboard within easy reach. Their task was to say the total number of rectangles in each display as fast as they could, with accuracy. The latency of their vocal response was measured using the voice activated timer.

Each trial had four phases. First subjects were required to fixate on the central area of a white screen for 608 msec. The computer then beeped to indicate the start of the trial. The counting display came on 256 msec later with up to eight white rectangles. The display remained on the screen until the timer was activated, at which point the screen went white. Fourth, after a pause of 512 msec the subjects were prompted to type in the number they had said or an "X" if something had gone wrong in the trial. The "X" response was reserved for situations in which the timer failed to go off the first time a response was made, or went off before the response was made. These "misfire" trials were readministered at the end of each block.

There were 240 experimental trials. At the beginning of the session subjects were also given 24 practise trials.

---

[1]Recently this experiment has been replicated with an increase in the number of ring sizes, and thus maximal distance between contours, in the *Concentric* condition, and a decrease in the inter-item distances for the *Same size* and *Different size* conditions. The same basic results obtained although there was a relative inflation in the time to count 1 item in the *Concentric condition*.

RESULTS

The counting latency data was analyzed in three ways. First, analysis of variance was performed in order to determine if the configuration of the stimuli, *Concentric* as opposed to *Same size* and *Different size*, had an effect on counting latencies. Second, trend analysis on averaged and individual datasets was done in order to determine if there was evidence of subitizing in the counting latency function for the three conditions. Finally, slopes for the subitizing and counting functions were calculated using regression.

Analysis of variance revealed that condition had an effect ($F(2,22)=114.6, p<.001$) as did number of items ($F(7,77)=261.9, p<.001$). See figure 1. Newman Keuls analysis revealed that latencies for the *Concentric* condition were significantly greater than the other two conditions starting at 2($p<.05$). Finally, there was a significant interaction between condition and number($F(14,154)=13.2, p<.001$), with number having an overall greater effect on latencies in the *Concentric* condition than the other conditions.

Trend analysis over averaged data

The primary difference between the subitizing and counting processes is the speed with which they can be carried out; for subitizing the reaction time increase with number is slight whereas for counting the reaction time increase is substantial. For this reason it is important to look for slope changes in the function that relates counting latencies to the number of items. These slope changes are the principal evidence that different processes are being employed for small than large numbers of items. At points where slope changes occur, trend analysis will register significant deviations from linearity.

As predicted, number seemed to produce a more uniform effect on latencies in the *Concentric* condition than it did in the other two, as would be predicted if subjects could no longer subitize when objects were concentric. In order to determine more precisely if subitizing occured trend analysis was performed on the entire range (1-8) for the three conditions, to find out if significant non-linear trends emerged. If the reaction time function showed no significant deviation from linearity then it was assumed that subitizing did not occur. If there were significant deviations from linearity, however, it was necessary to find out where the trend emerged and if it was in the right direction. The point at which there was an upward turn in the latency curve and the function began to show significant deviations from linearity was judged to be the boundary of the subitizing range.

Trend analysis on latencies revealed significant linear trends in all conditions. Only the non-concentric conditions showed any significant deviations from linearity, however(non-linear deviation $F(6,88)=7.1$, $p<.0001$ and $F(6,88)=7.8$, $p<.0001$ for *Same size* and *Different size* conditions respectively as compared to $F(6,88)=1.5$, $p>.05$ for the *Concentric* condition). Given that non-linear trends indicate the change from one enumeration process to another, it would seem that the same enumeration process is being used for both small and large numbers in the *Concentric* condition. In fact, considering the magnitude of the latencies, it seems probable that counting proper is occuring.

Trend analysis over individual datasets

Given that there are individual differences in how high people can subitize(Akin and Chase, 1978), averaging across subjects could obscure slope changes in the latency functions. Consequently, the data for each subject were also analyzed separately. All subjects had non-linear trends in the in *Same size* and *Different size* conditions. (See table 1). Only three of the twelve subjects showed significant trends in the *Concentric* condition, however; this represents a significantly smaller proportion ($\chi^2(2)=6.0, p<.05$) than in the other two conditions. Further analyses were performed on the individual datasets to ascertain where the non-linear trend emerged. For both the *Same size* and *Different size* conditions, most subjects subitized to 4. Of the few that showed non-linear trends in the *Concentric* condition, most subitized to 3.

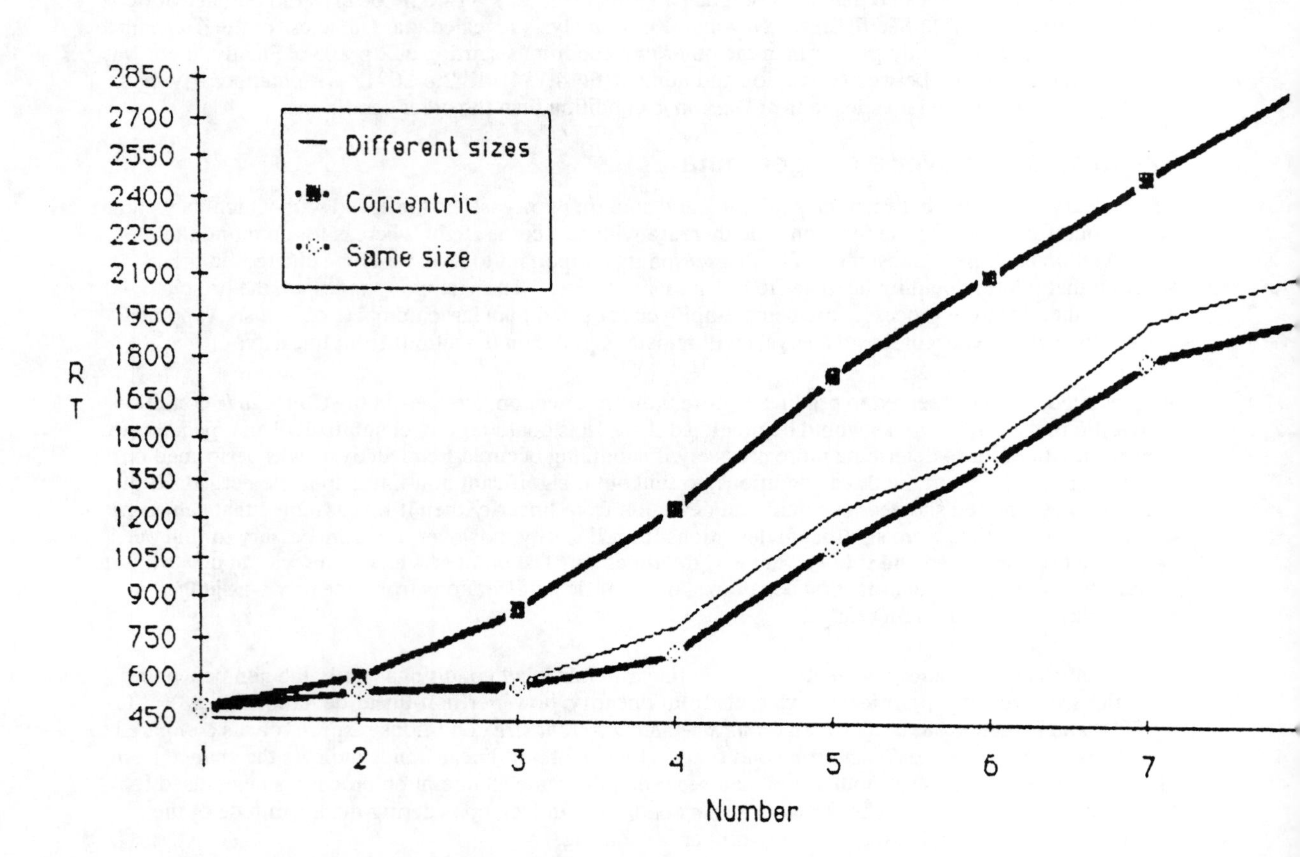

Figure 1: Counting latencies for Concentric study

TABLE 1

Trend analysis of individual datasets

Number of subjects showing evidence of subitizing

Same size	12/12
Different size	12/12
Concentric	3/12

Number of subjects subitizing to each number

	Same size	Different size	Concentric
Total	(N=12)	(N=12)	(N=3)
# subitizing to 2	1	3	1
# subitizing to 3	3	2	2
# subitizing to 4	7	6	-
# subitizing to 5	1	1	-

Regression analysis of averaged counting latencies

	Slope
SUBITIZING RANGE (1-3)	
Same size	55.6
Different size	66.3
Concentric*	198.8
(2-3)	276.2
COUNTING RANGE (5-8)	
Same size	300.7
Different size	330.3
Concentric(1-8)	346.3

*Only the data from subjects who showed evidence of subitizing were included in this analysis(N=3).

Slope analysis

Regression was performed on the averaged data in order to calculate slopes. Although most subjects subitized to 4 subitizing slopes were calculated in the 1-3 range to avoid inflating slopes with latencies from trials in which subitizing did not occur. As can be seen from table 1, the slopes for the 1-3 range were 55.6 and 66.3 for the *Same* and *Different* size conditions, respectively. The 95% confidence intervals for the slopes overlapped in these conditions so there were no significant differences, however. In contrast, for the three subjects that showed evidence of subitizing in the *Concentric condition* the slope in the 1-3 range fell outside these confidence intervals, at 198.8 msec/item. Notice that the slope in the 1-3 range of the *Concentric* condition is somewhat lower than for the 2-3 range; latencies to count 2 in this condition were atypical of the rest of the range. Perhaps subjects are more adept at counting 2 because of frequent exposure to concentric rectangles in objects such as picture frames. Slopes for the 5-8 range for the *Same size* and *Different size* conditions and the 1-8 range in the *Concentric condition* condition are in excess of 300 msec. All slopes fell within each others 95% confidence interval, and differed significantly from the slopes in the non-concentric conditions for the 1-3 range.

DISCUSSION

As predicted, subitizing was only evident when items were distributed across the screen. When subjects were required to enumerate concentric rectangles, the slope of the reaction time function was constant and high, suggesting first, that the same process was being used for both small and large numbers of concentric rectangles, and second, that the process was counting proper. The results of this study are consistent with Saltzman and Garner's(1948) and moreover show why their results were so different from those of dot enumeration studies. It was the fact that items had a common centre, rather than that they were objects of different sizes that produced the constant slope.

The results of this study are consistent with the idea that subitizing is only possible when items can be individuated on the basis of preattentive information. Subitizing was not possible in the *Concentric* condition because moving the attentional focus was required to discover which edge belonged to which object. Low level processing does not deliver the information necessary for enumeration in that condition; grouping on the basis of proximity and similarity will deliver the wrong number of clusters, perhaps four for the number of corners, or one for the centre of the radiating pattern.

In contrast, subitizing was evident in the *Same size* and *Different size* conditions because low level analysis delivered clusters each of which corresponded to an item. Edges relatively close to each other belonged to the same item, typically. Grouping by similarity was not in evidence because the similar corners were relatively far away from each other, thus proximity cues overode. Because low level grouping processes delivered a number of feature clusters that corresponded to the number of objects, the FINST mechanism could be exploited to accomplish enumeration of small numbers of objects. Consequently, moving the attentional focus from location to location in the proximal stimulus was not necessary in these cases. Enumeration could be accomplished simply by ascertaining the number of assigned reference tokens--performing a FINST role call.

REFERENCES

Akin, O. & Chase, W. (1978). Quantification of three dimensional structures. Journal of Experimental Psychology: Human Perception and Performance, 4(3), 397-410.

Jevons. W. (1871). The power of numerical discrimination. Nature, 3, 281-282.

Marr, D. (1982). Vision. San Francisco: W.H. Freeman and Company.

Pylyshyn, Z. (In press). The role of location indexes in spatial perception: A sketch of the FINST spatial index model. Cognition.

Pylyshyn, Z. & Storm, R. (In press). Tracking multiple independent targets: Evidence for both serial and parallel stages. Spatial vision.

Saltzman, I. & Garner, W. (1948). Reaction time as a measure of the span of attention. Journal of Psychology, 25, 227-241.

Treisman, A. & Gellade, G. (1980). A feature integration model of attention. Cognitive Psychology, 12, 97-136.

Ullman, S. (1984) Visual routines. Cognition. 18, 97-159.

Making Conversation Flexible [1]

Elise H. Turner and Richard E. Cullingford
School of ICS
Georgia Institute of Technology

Abstract

The goals of the speakers are the motivating force behind a conversation. The differences in these goals, and their relative priorities, account for many of the differences between conversations. In order to be easily understood, however, the resulting conversation must be constrained by the language conventions shared by speaker and hearer. In this paper we describe how the use of schemas for conversational control can be made flexible by integrating the priorities of a system's goals into the process of selecting the next utterance. Our ideas are implemented in a system called JUDIS (Turner & Cullingford, 1989), a natural language interface for an advice-giving system.

A characteristic feature of conversation is *flexibility*; the "topic" or "point" being pursued shifts unpredictably as the conversation proceeds. Clearly, the conversants adopt a series of communicative goals (Appelt, 1985; Cohen & Perrault, 1979; Grosz, 1977; Hobbs & Evans, 1980) and work cooperatively to achieve these goals. It is clear as well that an important component of conversation is convention (McKeown, 1985; Reichman, 1985). That is, we not only plan our utterances in the presence of perceived intentions, but we also, in a sense, recall how conventional conversations were conducted in the past to achieve similar ends. This paper describes an implemented conversational system, JUDIS, which applies a knowledge structure, the *conversation MOP*, to provide a means of combining intention and convention in discourse. The integration of problem solving goals and linguistic constraints has been shown to improve comprehension (Carberry, 1986; Litman & Allen, 1987) and to be important in determining discourse structure (Grosz & Sidner, 1986). Here, we focus on how these two essential aspects of conversation can be united to provide flexible generation. We present an example of the system processing a typical conversation with the user during a common kind of naturalistic conversational task, commonsense problem solving.

JUDIS

JUDIS (Julia's DIscourse System) provides the natural language interface for Julia (Cullingford & Kolodner, 1986), a highly interactive, advice-giving system being developed at the Georgia Institute of Technology. Julia is designed to perform such commonsense tasks as giving directions, advising consumers, and planning meals, its current task. It is comprised of several subsystems which include: a *from-scratch planner*, JUPITER (Hinrichs, 1988), which plans a meal using traditional methods from artificial intelligence; a *case-based reasoner*, JULIANA (Shinn, 1988), which uses previous experience in meal-planning to help solve the current problem; and the natural language interface, JUDIS (Turner & Cullingford, 1989). JUDIS handles conversational control, focusing on what should be included in the dialogue and when it should appear. This system uses an existing software system, the NLPTool (Cullingford, 1986), to generate English utterances from concepts and to analyze the utterances of the user.

[1] This research has been funded by NSF Grant IST-8608362. Thanks to Richard Billington, Janet Kolodner and Roy Turner for their helpful comments on earlier drafts of this paper.

J1: Would you like to serve guacamole as an appetizer?
U1: Yes.
J2: Would you like chili as a main course?
U2: Would we have to serve it in bowls?
J4: Yes.
J5: Do you have enough bowls?
U3: Yes.
J6: I remembered a meal where one of the guests couldn't eat guacamole because she was allergic to tomatoes.
J7: Do you know if any of your guests are allergic to tomatoes?
U5: No, they aren't.

Figure 1: Dialogue with Julia.

When the problem solving systems of Julia need to communicate with the user, they send a request to JUDIS in the form of a goal. JUDIS must respond to the request in a way that not only is understandable to the user, but also takes into account the urgency of the request, reflected by the goal's priority. Sometimes the request is so unimportant to the problem solver that it can be left out of the dialogue or brought into the conversation at a more natural time. Sometimes, JUDIS must interrupt the conversation to handle a request, such as when a piece of information is needed to allow a problem solver to continue an important task. Other times the request relates to a previous topic of conversation and JUDIS must interrupt the established order of the conversation and refer back to an earlier topic. Figure 1 shows a portion of an actual dialogue with Julia where such a request is handled in J6 – J7. To manage such infrequent requests effectively, JUDIS is guided by both the conventions of conversation and the needs of Julia.

REPRESENTING DISCOURSE STRUCTURE

JUDIS represents its knowledge of discourse structure in *conversation MOPs* (Kellermann et al., 1989; Turner & Cullingford, 1989). MOPs, or *memory organization packets* (Schank, 1982) are schematic structures used to organize long-term, conceptual, episodic memory. Conversation MOPs are much like other rhetorical schema (e.g., McKeown, 1985; Reichman, 1985). Each MOP contains an associated goal or goals which is achieved by the actions, or episode, specified in the MOP. The episode is divided into *scenes* which can be shared with other MOPs. An example of a MOP, one for conducting the problem solving portion of a conversation between a client and a caterer is shown in Figure 2. This MOP is itself a scene in the "complete-conversation-MOP", and the MOP's scenes are also MOPs. They are topic MOPs which in turn include the scenes "topic switch", "discussion", and "close topic".

In JUDIS, scenes can be either *executable acts* or MOPs. The scenes in MOPs can be either *mandatory scenes*, or *optional scenes* which are not necessary for the execution of the MOP but are often associated with it. The scenes may be actual utterances in the dialogue, or they may be other actions associated with those utterances. These other actions describe how an utterance affects the knowledge of the conversants. For example, a parse includes actions to update the knowledge base of the hearer, and a topic switch contains actions to update the focus of the dialogue. Although such actions are not fully implemented in the current version of JUDIS, those that affect conversational control have been included in the appropriate MOPs.

MOPs are formed when episodes are stored in a dynamic memory (Kolodner, 1984; Schank, 1982). When adding an episode, dynamic memory uses the salient features of the episode, called *predictive indices*, to find a place for it in memory. When this happens new MOPs are created which contain *generalized episodes* that reflect the similarities in the episodes.

Caterer's General MOP

goal: plan-meal
characters: caterer, customer
part-of: complete-conversation-MOP
predictive-features: problem-strategy
indices: problem solving strategy/chronological order → chronological-order MOP
problem solving strategy/main courses first → main-first MOP
activity: general info, dessert, appetizer, main-course
mandatory-scenes: general-info, dessert, appetizer, main-course

Chronological Order MOP

sequence of events: ((seq general-info appetizer) (seq appetizer main-course) (seq main-course dessert))

Main First MOP

sequence of events: ((seq general-info main-course)(seq main-course dessert)(seq main-course appetizer))

Figure 2: Caterer's MOP

Specializations of a generalized episode can be found by treating salient features that differ from the generalized episode's as predictive indices. For example, the "caterer's general MOP" has two specializations, each only differing from the more general episode because a scene ordering is specified (the only slot of these MOPs shown in Figure 2). Because the "caterer's general MOP" is associated with problem solving, its specializations are indexed by problem solving strategies such as planning the meal in chronological order or considering the main course first. The specializations for other MOPs may use different indices that are important to their purpose. For example, the topic switch MOP has specializations that relate to whether or not the scene has executed and the kind of change in topics that will take place. It also includes a specialization with no utterance that is indexed by the conditions that allow an explicit topic switch to be omitted from the conversation.

Knowledge of the discourse structure is important to JUDIS and cannot be built during the conversation, as in (Grosz & Sidner, 1986), for two reasons. First of all, like (McKeown, 1985), the schemas can be used as stored plans to make generation easier. Secondly, knowledge of how the discourse is likely to proceed allows JUDIS to decide when it can defer a system goal and wait for its topic to arise naturally in the conversation.

CONTROLLING CONVERSATION IN JUDIS

Conversation MOPs provide JUDIS with knowledge of conventional conversations. However, many conversations do not follow the norm, often due to the needs of the conversants. So, instead of simply following a schema for the current portion of the dialogue, JUDIS combines information about the priorities of its goals and the normal course of conversation to determine which MOP to follow at execution time. We will discuss how a MOP is selected for execution after a brief overview of processing conversation MOPs in JUDIS.

Overview

When a user begins a problem solving session with Julia, JUDIS knows that it is expected to hold a conversation with the user that includes planning a meal. JUDIS starts with the complete conversation MOP and finds the specialization of its scenes that fit the current situation. These

MOPs, called *active MOPs*, form the template for a conventional conversation in which JUDIS maintains the initiative; in other words, they form a high-level plan for the conversation.

JUDIS uses the expectations provided by the active MOPs to help satisfy the requests of the problem solvers within the confines of a coherent conversation. When JUDIS receives a request, it searches memory for a MOP to achieve the goal. It then tries to fit this MOP into the overall conversation by searching up part-of links for an active MOP which may, directly or indirectly, contain the new MOP. Since the MOPs represent conventions in conversation, finding the containing episode allows JUDIS not only to satisfy a goal, but to do it in such a way that is easy for the user to understand. The new MOP and the episodes on the path between it and the active MOP then become active MOPs. This mechanism allows JUDIS to observe conventions in conversation and maintain a coherent dialogue without explicitly planning to achieve these goals, as in (Appelt, 1985; Litman & Allen, 1987).

JUDIS selects a MOP for execution using the algorithm described below. If the selected MOP is an executable act that has been executed by JUDIS or can be inferred to have been executed by the user, it is marked "executed". A MOP is also marked "executed" if it is a MOP that has had all of its mandatory scenes executed. When a scene is executed, the episode which contains that scene is considered an *executing MOP*. The executing MOPs include not only the episode that this scene was chosen to help satisfy, but also any other MOPs which share that scene. These other MOPs are said to be *serendipitously executing*.[1] Serendipitously executing MOPs indicate options that are not part of JUDIS' original plan. For example, JUDIS may know that the problem solvers are following the "chronological order" strategy and select the corresponding "chronological order MOP", shown in Figure 2, as an active MOP. However, if only the "general-info" scene has been executed and one of the problem solvers has a question about the main course, JUDIS can pursue the serendipitously executing "main-first MOP" and ask the question, or it can choose to continue following the active "chronological order MOP".

Selecting a MOP for Execution

To determine which MOP should be executed, JUDIS must consider the conventions for the conversation and the goals of the system. In order to combine the effects of intention and convention, JUDIS relies on an activation metaphor. Activation is divided into two types: *goal-based activation* which reflects the importance of a MOP to the work of the system, and *MOP-based activation* which indicates how well a MOP fits the schema for conventional conversation.

Goal-based Activation

The goal-based activation of a MOP is determined by the priorities of the goals that the MOP can help to achieve. The goals associated with the MOP are considered to be achieved when the MOP is executed, so these goals contribute to the goal-based activation. Also, mandatory scenes inherit goals from their containing episodes because the execution of all mandatory scenes is necessary for an episode to be executed. Finally, any goals of scenes that are contained in the MOP and are not subsumed by the MOP's associated goals contribute to the goal-based activation. For example, if a discussion of a particular topic will include giving the user a useful piece of information and suggesting the dish to be served for a course, the priorities of these goals will be added to the goal-based activation for the topic. By allowing goal-based activation to accrue to the containing episode, JUDIS can move to the portion of the dialogue which satisfies a

[1] A MOP is not considered to be serendipitously executing unless its scenes have been executed in the order specified by the MOP.

large number of goals, even if none of the individual goals have a high priority.

MOP-based Activation

MOP-based activation is afforded to the MOPs which follow some rhetorical convention that is at play in the conversation. There are two types of MOP-based activation, reflecting the two types of MOPs, active and executing, that influence conversation. *Active MOP-based activation* is passed from the highest level active MOPs, usually the MOP for the overall conversation. Since active MOPs indicate the system's plan for the conversation, the value assigned to active MOP-based activation should express the extent to which JUDIS wishes to adhere to its original plan and to remain in control of the conversation. *Executing MOP-based activation* is passed from all executing MOPs. Since all MOPs that are executing represent an accepted schema for conversation, its value represents the system's commitment to following conversational conventions.

MOP-based activation is given to the appropriate MOPs and any of their scenes that are ready to execute. A scene is ready to execute if all of the mandatory scenes which precede it have executed and if no scene which it precedes has been executed. Optional scenes affect the way activation is passed depending on the type of MOP-based activation. For active MOP-based activation, an optional scene with an active associated goal is treated like a mandatory scene. Here, the optional scene can be executed to help JUDIS achieve a goal and so can be seen as part of the system's plan. However, optional scenes do not affect how well a dialogue adheres to convention, so those which are ready to execute and the mandatory scenes which they precede receive executing mop-based activation. When activation is passed in this way, optional scenes require a higher goal priority than mandatory scenes to be included in the dialogue. This is an extension of the work of McKeown (McKeown, 1985), where optional scenes are selected based on the focus of the dialogue and the availability of the knowledge the scene is to contain. In JUDIS, an optional scene that meets these criteria may be omitted from the dialogue if it is not important enough for inclusion. This allows JUDIS to leave out information that is often relevant, but may not be pertinent to the current situation.

Each time JUDIS needs to select a MOP for execution it chooses the MOP with the highest activation. If the selected MOP is not an executable act, JUDIS must choose one of its scenes to execute. JUDIS uses the method described above with the selected MOP serving as the sole active and executing MOP to pick a scene to execute.

INTEGRATING REQUESTS INTO A COHERENT DIALOGUE

The processing for conversational control described above allows JUDIS to produce a variety of conversational meanderings that are motivated by the goals of the system but moderated by the conventional structures of discourse. JUDIS uses the priority of system goals as the primary factor in determining what to say next, instead of relying mainly on pre-described discourse structures or rules of focus (Grosz, 1977; McKeown, 1985; Reichman, 1985; Sidner, 1983; Webber, 1983).[2] However, since JUDIS places requests from the problem solvers in conventional discourse structures, it is able to integrate them into a coherent dialogue that is also responsive to the import and urgency of the system's goals.

An example of a request forcing an interruption in the expected course of the dialogue is shown in Figure 1. In the interest of brevity, we will address only those active MOPs which play an interesting role in JUDIS' decision and ignore serendipitously executing scenes and component

[2] A useful extension to JUDIS would be to include focus to help determine when an opportunity may be lost to handle a request with ease. This would involve explicitly incorporating focus into MOP-based activation so that requests that are at a high level of focus (Reichman, 1985) can receive additional activation.

MOP	*executing act.*	*active act.*	*goal act.*	*total act.*
J5	40	20	10	70
Dessert	0	0	20	20
Appetizer	0	20	32	52

Figure 3a

MOP	*executing act.*	*active act.*	*goal act.*	*total act.*
Dessert	40	20	20	80
Appetizer	40	20	32	92
Topic switch with failure	40	20	2	62
Topic switch without failure	40	20	0	60
Discussion	0	0	30	30

Figure 3b

MOP	*executing act.*	*active act.*	*goal act.*	*total act.*
Topic switch with failure	40	20	2	62
Topic switch without failure	40	20	0	60
Discussion	0	0	30	30

Figure 3c

Figure 3: Activations for Example

scenes which are not important to the example. In this conversation JUDIS has a strong commitment to keeping the dialogue coherent, so the constant for executing MOP-based activation is 40. At the start of this example, the conversation MOP that has the "chronological order MOP" as a scene is a top-level active MOP. JUDIS follows the dialogue laid out by this MOP through J4 which causes the main course topic MOP to be "executing". Here, one of the problems solvers has noticed that people do not often have enough bowls and the associated question has been given a priority of 10.

Meanwhile, the case-based reasoner has requested JUDIS to find out if any guests are allergic to tomatoes. The goal of the request has a priority of 40 since if there are guests that are allergic, a new constraint will be added to the problem which may affect both future problem solving and past decisions. When JUDIS receives the request it inserts it into the template for the dialogue by noticing that a question is part of a discussion of a topic. The subject for this topic MOP will be the appetizer because that is the focus of the case-based reasoner at the time the request is made.[3] The appetizer topic MOP has already been executed, but since the topic is a scene in the caterer's MOP, a new appetizer topic MOP is formed and attached to the caterer's MOP. Because the topic MOP is being added, it has no preceding scenes and is immediately capable of receiving any mop-based activation passed from the caterer's MOP.

JUDIS follows the indices in the topic switching MOP to find the specialization which pertains to previously executed topics. This specialization contains its own specializations including many, such as "Let's go back to ...", which cannot incorporate telling the user about the failure. One specialization, "I remembered..." allows this information to be included.[4]

Now JUDIS must decide when to execute the request. The activations for the MOPs of interest are shown in Figure 3a. The MOP containing J5 has the highest activation. Although there was an active goal with a much higher priority, the fact that the main course scene was currently executing gave J5 enough activation to execute at this time. The main course topic is marked executed after J5 has executed. Now the caterer's MOP becomes the executing MOP and both the dessert and appetizer MOPs and their scenes receive activation from it as shown in Figure 3b. The new appetizer topic MOP is chosen for execution, but it is not an executable act.

[3] We do not address the complexities of finding the topic of a request. Instead, we rely on the focus of the problem solver to correspond to some topic MOP. This is adequate for JUDIS since the conversation MOPs closely follow the problem solving strategies in the system.

[4] For this type of topic switching, we allow only entities explicitly mentioned in the previous discourse to be used. Here, for example, JUDIS can refer to guacamole, but not to the tomatoes which it contains. This is a simplification which, once again, is adequate for our needs.

Using this topic MOP as both the active and the executing MOP, and repeating the selection algorithm, the topic switch scene is selected. The activation levels for this selection are shown in Figure 3c. The topic switch MOP that includes the failure is chosen. The other specializations will never be chosen because the topic switch scene in the appetizer topic MOP is marked executed and these MOPs cease to receive activation. Now the appetizer topic MOP is executing. Next the question MOP, which satisfies the request, is selected and executed in J7.

Other requests may be handled differently, depending on the priorities of their goals. A request with a very high priority, say 100, would cause the current topic to be interrupted immediately, without executing a topic switch. However, a low priority request that is part of a topic MOP which is not yet ready for execution will have to wait until its topic is executed in the expected course of the conversation.

CONCLUSION

This paper describes an approach to the control of conversation, as implemented in a system called JUDIS, and an implemented example of its use of conversation MOPs to flexibly manage an interaction with the user. We believe JUDIS and its MOPs provide a method for combining intention and convention to generate flexible discourse and a means to sequence the conversational activities requested by different problem solvers in a composite system

REFERENCES

Appelt, D. E. (1985). Planning English referring expressions. *Artificial Intelligence*, 26:1–33.

Carberry, S. M. (1986). Pragmatic modeling in information system interfaces. Technical Report 86-07, Department of Computer Science, University of Delaware. Ph.D. thesis.

Cohen, P. R. & Perrault, C. R. (1979). Elements of a plan-based theory of speech acts. *Cognitive Science*, 3:177–212.

Cullingford, R. E. (1986). *Natural language processing: A knowledge engineering approach.* Totowa, New Jersey: Rowan and Littlefield.

Cullingford, R. E. & Kolodner, J. L. (1986). Interactive advice giving. In *Proceedings of the 1986 IEEE International Conference on Systems, Man and Cybernetics*, pages 709–714, Atlanta, Georgia.

Grosz, B. J. (1977). The representation and use of focus in a system for understanding dialogs. In *Proceedings of the Fifth International Conference on Artificial Intelligence*, pages 67–76, Los Altos, California. William Kaufmann, Inc.

Grosz, B. J. & Sidner, C. L. (1986). Attention, intention, and the structure of discourse. *Computational Linguistics*, 12(3):175–204.

Hinrichs, T. (1988). Towards an architecture for open world problem solving. In *Proceedings of the DARPA Workshop on Case-Based Reasoning*, pages 182–189, Clearwater Beach, Florida.

Hobbs, J. R. & Evans, D. A. (1980). Conversation as planned behavior. *Cognitive Science*, 4(4):349–377.

Kellermann, K., Broetzmann, S., Lim, T.-S., & Kitao, K. (1989). The conversation mop: Scenes in the stream of discourse. *Discourse Processes*, 12(1):27–61.

Kolodner, J. (1984). *Retrieval and organizational strategies in conceptual memory.* Hillsdale, New Jersey: Lawrence Erlbaum Associates, Publishers.

Litman, D. J. & Allen, J. F. (1987). A plan recognition model for subdialogues in conversation. *Cognitive Science*, 11:163–200.

McKeown, K. R. (1985). *Text generation: Using discourse strategies and focus constraints to generate natural languauge text.* New York: Cambridge University Press.

Reichman, R. (1985). *Getting computers to talk like you and me: Discourse context, focus, and semantics (An ATN Model).* Cambridge, Mass: The MIT Press.

Schank, R. (1982). *Dynamic memory.* New York: Cambridge University Press.

Shinn, H. (1988). The role of mapping in analogical transfer. In *The Tenth Annual Conference of the Cognitive Science Society*, pages 738–744, Montreal, Quebec, Canada.
Sidner, C. L. (1983). Focusing in the comprehension of definite anaphora. In Brady, M. & Berwick, R., (Eds.). *Computational models of discourse.* Cambridge, Mass.: The MIT Press.
Turner, E. H. & Cullingford, R. E. (1989). Using conversation mops in natural language interfaces. *Discourse Processes*, 12(1):63–90.
Webber, B. L. (1983). So what can we talk about now. In Brady, M. & Berwick, R., (Eds.). *Computational models of discourse.* Cambridge, Mass.: The MIT Press.

When Reactive Planning is Not Enough: Using Contextual Schemas to React Appropriately to Environmental Change [1]

Roy M. Turner
School of ICS
Georgia Institute of Technology

Abstract

A problem solver operating in the real world must adapt its behavior to an unpredictable and changing problem-solving environment. It must react *appropriately* to changes in the situation, where what is appropriate depends to a large extent on the overall problem-solving context. In order to do this, the reasoner needs to have explicit knowledge about the context it is in. In our approach, the problem-solving context is represented explicitly as a *contextual schema*. When presented with a problem, the reasoner finds an appropriate contextual schema, then uses it to influence its problem-solving behavior. The reasoner uses the contextual schema to recognize important changes in the problem-solving situation and to respond appropriately to those changes

Our approach is implemented in the MEDIC program (Turner, 1988b; Turner, in preparation). MEDIC is medical diagnostic consultant whose domain is pulmonology.

A real-world problem solver solves problems in a world that is both unpredictable and changing. Such a reasoner cannot adopt the typical planning approach of creating a plan and then executing it—the problem is likely to change during execution, thus invalidating the remainder of the plan. Instead, the reasoner must react appropriately to unexpected changes in the state of the world.

Reactive planning research (e.g., Agre & Chapman, 1987) is concerned with reacting to change; however, no reactive planning approach explicitly represents the reasoner's notion of what the problem-solving *context* is. This is unfortunate, because the appropriate response to a change in the environment depends to a great extent on the problem-solving context. Consider the following examples:

Example 1. An appropriate response to a knock on the door when expecting friends is to open the door and say "Come in!"; this is not such an appropriate response in a different context: one in which an axe murderer is suspected to be in the neighborhood.

Example 2. While diagnosing a patient, a doctor sees a finding that makes him consider requesting that another diagnostic service examine his patient. Normally, he would go ahead and request the consultation. However, if he is at a hospital where the diagnostic service is very interested in trying a new, somewhat risky operating procedure, he would likely forego the consultation and attempt to diagnose the patient himself.

[1] This research has been funded in part by NSF Grants IST–831771 and IST–8608362 and by grant DTD 09–25–87 from the Lockheed AI Center.

Example 3. A woman hails a cab, then waits calmly as it darts across two lanes of traffic and screeches to a halt beside the curb where she is standing. In another situation, the woman is waiting to cross a street when a cab darts across two lanes of traffic towards the curb where she is standing—this time, she backs quickly away.

In each of these examples, the reasoner's response is not solely determined by the stimuli (e.g., a knock on the door). Instead, the entire *problem-solving context*—all of the information about the problem solver's goals and the problem's features—is used to help determine the response. So it is in most real-world situations: reactions that are perfectly appropriate in one context will be inappropriate or even dangerous in another. An accurate judgment of the problem-solving context is crucial to responding appropriately to changes in the world.

In our approach, the reasoner explicitly represents the problem-solving contexts it knows about as *contextual schemas*. Contextual schemas are stored in a *conceptual memory* (cf. Kolodner, 1984; Simpson, 1985) from which they can be retrieved based on the reasoner's goals and features of the problem-solving situation. When a new situation occurs, or when the situation changes significantly, the reasoner retrieves a contextual schema which characterizes the new or changed situation. Information from the contextual schema is used by the reasoner to respond appropriately to future changes to the environment.

In the remainder of this paper, we discuss contextual schemas and how they are used to respond appropriately to changes that arise during problem solving. We draw examples from MEDIC, the program that is the testbed for our approach. MEDIC is a *schema-based reasoner* (Turner, 1988a; Turner, 1988b; Turner, in preparation) whose domain is medical diagnostic consultations in pulmonology.

REPRESENTING THE PROBLEM-SOLVING CONTEXT

In order to respond appropriately to changes, a reasoner must have an explicit representation of what its current problem-solving context is. A representation of a problem-solving context should provide the reasoner with information to allow it to behave appropriately in that context. This information includes:

- predictions about changes to the situation
- appropriate goals to activate in response to changes in the situation
- actions or procedures that are likely to be useful for achieving goals in that context
- relative worth of goals likely to occur in the context—i.e., information which focuses the reasoner's attention on appropriate goals to pursue

In MEDIC, we represent this knowledge in *contextual schemas*. These schemas represent general knowledge about specific types of problem-solving situations. The contextual schema in Figure 1, for example, describes pulmonary consultations, i.e., times when a doctor has to diagnose a pulmonary disorder. Other contextual schemas we would expect a pulmonary specialist to have would include those representing "pulmonary consultations involving alcoholics," "consultations involving a nodule in the lung," and "consultations involving lung cancer."

A contextual schema has four parts. First, there is a description of the problem-solving *situation* represented by the schema, including a description of the patient, expected findings, etc. This is used by the reasoner to determine if the contextual schema represents the current situation, and it also provides a source of predictions about expected features of the problem-solving situation. Second, a contextual schema has information about *goals* that are likely to occur during problem solving, along with information about changes to the environment that should trigger those goals. Associated with each goal is information about that goal's relative worth in the context represented by the contextual schema. Third, a contextual schema

```
Situation:
    patient isa human, smokes (cf=:low)
    chief complaint = cough (cf=:moderate)
    findings = {dyspnea (cf=:low), cough (cf=:moderate),
             abnormal-chest-X-rays (cf=:very-low)}
    hypotheses = {pulmonary disease (cf=:high)}
Goals:
    G1: Diagnose a patient.
         priority: .3
    G2: Interpret finding of dyspnea
         trigger: finding of dyspnea added to STM
         priority: .4
         ...
    G5: Interpret a finding.
         trigger: finding is added to STM
         priority: .4
    G6: Confirm a hypothesis that pulmonary disease is present
         trigger: hypothesis of pulmonary disease is added to STM
         priority: .4
         ...
Scenes:
    main: S1
    S1: sc-consult ;; general consultation procedure
         goal: G1
    S2: sc-dyspnea ;; procedure tailored to interpret dyspnea
         goal: G2
         ...
    S5: sc-finding ;; general procedure for interpreting findings
    S6: sc-hypothesis ;; general procedure for evaluating hypotheses
         goal: G6, G7
         ...
Strategy:
    Hypothetico-deductive reasoning
```

Figure 1: Part of a contextual schema representing the context of a pulmonary consultation.

contains a description of *scenes* (Schank, 1982) that generally occur in situations represented by the schema: i.e., actions or procedures that are performed to achieve problem-solving goals. This information is used by the reasoner to find appropriate actions and procedures when similar goals occur in the current situation. Finally, a contextual schema contains information which suggests a possible problem-solving *strategy* to use; e.g., the schema in Figure 1 recommends the strategy of "hypothetico-deductive reasoning" for pulmonary consultations.[1]

A contextual schema can be viewed as a generalization of prior, similar problem-solving episodes. On this view, a schema provides information about: goals that have usually arisen in similar episodes, and what usually triggers them; past decisions about the relative worths of those goals; actions and procedures that are usually useful for achieving goals in similar situations; and previously-useful strategies.

USING CONTEXTUAL SCHEMAS TO RESPOND TO CHANGES

Knowledge about the problem-solving context is used several different ways to help the reasoner react appropriately to changes in its problem-solving situation:

1. contextual schemas contain information that helps the reasoner decide which changes are important;

[1]Strategies are represented as schemas in MEDIC, similarly to the way contexts are represented. For details, see (Turner, 1988b) or (Turner, in preparation).

2. contextual schemas contain information that helps the reasoner select a goal to activate when a change occurs;
3. the strategy suggested by the contextual schema, along with knowledge contained in the schema about the relative worth of goals in the context, allows the reasoner to choose between several active goals; and
4. contextual schemas contain information about useful actions and procedures for goals in that context; this information is used to help the reasoner select actions and procedures to use to achieve its goals.

Deciding Which Changes are Important

A reasoner should not react to every change in its problem-solving situation, but only to those that are important. Which changes are important depends on the problem-solving context. For example, if during a problem-solving session concerned with planning a meal the client tells the reasoner that he has a chronic cough, the new information constitutes an unimportant change in the problem-solving situation; however, in the context of diagnosing the client's pulmonary problem, the same information constitutes an important change in the situation, one that may impact the final diagnosis.

Contextual schemas provide the reasoner with information about important changes that are expected to occur in a problem-solving situation. For example, the contextual schema in Figure 1, which represents the context of pulmonary consultations, predicts that findings of cough, dyspnea,[2] and abnormal chest X-rays will occur; if any of these *do* occur in the reasoner's current situation, then the reasoner knows that the change, i.e., the occurrence of the finding, is important and should be responded to.

Activating Goals

Part of a reasoner's response to a change in its problem-solving situation has to do with the change itself: the reasoner must determine an appropriate goal to activate to ensure that the change is handled. Which goal should be activated depends on the reasoner's problem-solving context. For example, an appropriate goal for the event of being told about back pain when in a social context is *express sympathy*; in the context of a doctor's office, this same event will give rise to the goal of *interpret the finding of back pain.*

A contextual schema can help the reasoner select an appropriate goal for its context. Associated with most goals in a schema is information about environmental events that should trigger the goal. When a change occurs, the reasoner can use this information to determine which goal it should activate. The contextual schema in Figure 1, for example, suggests activating the goal *interpret finding of dyspnea* when a finding of dyspnea occurs.

Choosing a Goal to Pursue

Another part of a reasoner's response to changes in its problem-solving situation is deciding which of its active goals is appropriate to pursue, given the new, changed state of the environment. A problem solver will often have several goals active simultaneously. For example, a pulmonary consultant such as MEDIC might have goals such as *form a diagnosis*, *explain the finding of dyspnea*, *gather information about the patient's history*, and *evaluate the hypothesis that pneumonia is present*. Each goal may be difficult, and most or all of the reasoner's attention may be required to achieve it. The reasoner must have some way to choose which goal to focus on.

Contextual schemas provide a nice way of judging the relative worth of goals in context. First, a contextual schema suggests a reasoning strategy to use in the context. Strategies provide

[2]Shortness of breath.

information about the relative worth, or priority, of each goal when the strategy is being followed. For example, the strategy *hypothetico-deductive reasoning* gives goals related to hypotheses (e.g., *evaluate hypothesis*) greater priority than goals related to gathering information.[3] Second, each goal in a contextual schema provides information about its relative worth in that context. For example, in most consultations, a finding of anemia is important, and goals related to it should have a reasonably high priority. However, in consultations involving alcoholic patients, goals relating to anemia have low priority since anemia is a complication of alcoholism. In most contextual schemas (e.g., the one in Figure 1), goals relating to findings are given a high priority; if anemia occurs in contexts represented by these schemas, goals associated with it would be considered important. However, a contextual schema representing *pulmonary consultations involving alcoholic patients* would explicitly give a low priority to the goal of following up anemia, preventing the reasoner from wasting time on the unimportant goal in that context.

In MEDIC, information about the worth of a goal comes from the representation of the goal itself (i.e., all things being equal, some goals are more important than others), from the current strategy, and from the contextual schema. Information from each source is combined in a weighted sum to give the overall priority of the goal;[4] the goal with the highest priority is the one selected by the reasoner to pursue. When the situation changes, MEDIC re-evaluates its goals based on the new situation; this leads to different goals being pursued at different times during problem solving.

Selecting Actions

The third part of a reasoner's response to a change involves selecting an action or procedure to use to achieve the goal that was activated as a result of the change. This, too, depends on reasoner's problem-solving context, since some actions are more appropriate in one context than in another. For example, asking the question *How far can the patient walk before becoming short of breath?* is one way of gathering information about dyspnea from a patient; the answer can be used to determine the severity of the dyspnea. However, in another context, one in which the patient cannot walk, this action is inappropriate; instead, the reasoner should perhaps ask *How much activity can the patient perform before becoming short of breath?*.

A contextual schema provides the reasoner with a context-specific repertoire of ways to achieve goals. Contextual schemas contain information about useful actions and procedures for goals that they predict will arise. The reasoner uses this information as a source of actions and procedures to achieve goals in its problem-solving situation. For example, if the reasoner is working on the goal of interpreting dyspnea, then the contextual schema in Figure 1 would suggest achieving it by using the specialized procedure **sc-dyspnea.**[5] This procedure asks standard questions designed to elaborate what is known about the finding, including *How far can the patient walk before becoming short of breath?* If the problem-solving context is instead one in which the patient cannot walk, the contextual schema used will recommend a different procedure, one which does not ask questions about walking.

In MEDIC, procedures are organized in specialization hierarchies based on the goals they achieve and the features of situations in which they are useful. With no contextual schema, the specialization hierarchies must be searched for an appropriate procedure, which is computationally expensive. By using a contextual schema, however, the reasoner needs only to perform the equivalent of a table look-up within the schema to find an appropriate procedure. The reasoner may then either use the procedure or try to find a more specific one using the

[3]See (Turner, 1988b) for details.

[4]For details, see (Turner, in preparation).

[5]Procedures are represented in MEDIC as a kind of schema; see (Turner, 1988b) or (Turner, in preparation) for details.

procedure as a starting point to search the specialization hierarchies. In either case, the schema provides a short-cut to finding an appropriate procedure.

CHOOSING A CONTEXTUAL SCHEMA

Contextual information can only help a reasoner respond to changes if the context can be appropriately identified. In our approach, this means choosing an appropriate contextual schema for the reasoner's problem-solving situation. The contextual schema selected should be the most specific schema the reasoner knows that matches the problem-solving situation. For example, if the problem description is *diagnose a patient whose chief complaint is dyspnea*, the most specific contextual schema is one representing consultations involving cardiopulmonary problems, not one representing consultations in general, since dyspnea would be expected in the former and not the latter. There are three issues to resolve in finding an appropriate contextual schema:

1. retrieving schemas from memory;
2. choosing between competing schemas; and
3. switching contexts during problem solving.

Retrieval, in our approach, is from a *conceptual memory* (cf. Simpson, 1985) similar to CYRUS (Kolodner, 1984). In this scheme, contextual schemas representing general contexts, such as *diagnostic consultations*, index more specific similar contexts, such as *consultations involving cardiopulmonary problems*, using as indices the features that differentiate between them. Contextual schemas can be retrieved from the memory by presenting it with a description of the problem-solving situation: goals, findings, etc. The memory responds with the most specific schemas that match the situation.

This does not completely solve the problem of finding an appropriate contextual schema, however, since more than one schema may be returned by the memory. The reasoner needs some way of choosing between "competing" schemas.

Our approach is to make use of a set of *preferences* when selecting between competing schemas. These include:

- Favor schemas whose goals include all of the goals given in the initial problem statement.
- Choose a specialization of a contextual schema over its parent if
  - it matches the situation by some feature that is missing in the parent, or
  - it matches by a feature that is more specific in the child than the parent.
- Choose a parent over its specializations if all specializations match some feature to the same degree and otherwise match the situation no better than the parent.
- Compare contextual schemas based on the features of the situation matched, taking into account the degree of confidence each schema has in each predicted feature being present.

Often the reasoner cannot simply select a contextual schema at the start of problem solving, then use that schema throughout the problem-solving session. The reasoner's problem-solving situation will change as problem solving progresses, and, as this happens, the contextual schema in use may cease to be a good match for the situation. Some mechanism is needed for *switching contexts*: i.e., for re-evaluating the reasoner's notion of what the current context is.

In our approach, the reasoner remembers all contextual schemas it considers when selecting one as the current context. When its problem-solving situation changes, the reasoner re-evaluates its choice of context by re-examining these schemas. In addition, new candidate schemas are added to those the reasoner already is considering by a separate process called the *prober*. The prober monitors the reasoner's problem-solving situation and, when there is a change, tries to find a new contextual schema which fits the changed situation. If one is found, it is added to those the reasoner is already considered, and the reasoner is notified. When the reasoner re-evaluates its context, the new contextual schema will be available as a candidate.

CONTEXTUAL SCHEMAS AND OPPORTUNISM

Responding appropriately to changes is closely related to *opportunistic reasoning* (cf. Hayes-Roth & Hayes-Roth, 1979). The use of contextual schemas promotes opportunism in two ways. First, information from contextual schemas is used by the reasoner to recognize important changes and to activate goals to handle them. This allows the reasoner to take the opportunity of activating important problem-solving goals that might otherwise be activated much later or not at all. The importance of this is evident in diagnosis. When a finding is discovered, the reasoner responds by activating a goal to interpret that finding. Pursuing this goal will lead to the generation of hypotheses, which, in turn, serve to focus the reasoner's problem-solving behavior (cf. Patel et al., 1987). Second, contextual schemas provide information the reasoner uses to recognize an opportunity for pursuing a goal. This takes the form, in our approach, of information about a goal's priority in the context. If a situation changes, it may cause the reasoner to switch the contextual schema it is using; this, in turn, will provide a new estimate of the goal's priority, which may cause it to be pursued.

Other researchers studying *opportunistic reasoning* (e.g., Hayes-Roth & Hayes-Roth, 1979) have also had the goal of making their problem solvers respond appropriately to environmental change. However, as Hammond (Hammond, 1988) notes, most of this work "is a model of opportunism at planning-time rather than execution-time," and thus suffers the same shortcomings as more traditional planners: these planners ignore the effects of the planner's own actions on the environment.

Hammond's work in opportunistic reasoning deals with satisfying suspended goals as the opportunity to do so arises (Hammond, 1988). Unfortunately, both his model and that of Birnbaum (Birnbaum, 1986) seem to to make little provision for the activation of goals in the first place, but concentrate instead on their *reactivation* once blocked. Yet goal activation is a crucial part of both reactivity and opportunism. Perhaps combining the approach presented here with one of their approaches would be a reasonable step towards a more complete view of real-world problem solving.

CONCLUSION

Real-world problem solvers must not only react to changes when they occur, but they must react *appropriately*. The response that is appropriate depends heavily on the situation the reasoner is in; thus, if the reasoner is to respond appropriately to changes, it must have an explicit representation of its problem-solving context.

Our approach explicitly represents problem-solving contexts as contextual schemas. A contextual schema provides the reasoner with information it can use to respond appropriately to changes in a context represented by the schema. Specifically, a contextual schema provides: (1) predictions about changes likely to occur and that should be responded to; (2) goals that should be activated in response to changes in the situation; (3) actions that are useful for goals occurring in that context; and (4) strategies and other information the reasoner can use to assess the relative worth of goals in its current context, allowing it to focus on appropriate goals during problem solving.

Our approach is currently being tested by the MEDIC program in the domain of medical diagnostic consultations. However, we believe our approach is more general than this. It should be useful in any task in which the appropriate response to a change depends on the problem-solving context. This will include most real-world problem-solving tasks.

ACKNOWLEDGEMENTS

Thanks to Janet Kolodner, Elise Turner, and Mike Redmond for their helpful comments on earlier drafts of this paper.

REFERENCES

Agre, P. & Chapman, D. (1987). Pengi: An implementation of a theory of activity. In *Proceedings of the Sixth National Conference on Artificial Intelligence*, pages 268–272.

Birnbaum, L. (1986). *Integrated Processing in Planning and Understanding.* PhD thesis, Yale, Department of Computer Science. December, 1986, Technical Report YALEU/CSD/RR#480 (New Haven, CT).

Hammond, K. (1988). Opportunistic memory: Storing and recalling suspended goals. In *Proceedings of the DARPA Workshop on Case-Based Reasoning*, pages 154–168, Clearwater Beach, Florida.

Hayes-Roth, B. & Hayes-Roth, F. (1979). A cognitive model of planning. *Cognitive Science*, 2:257–310.

Kolodner, J. (1984). *Retrieval and Organizational Strategies in Conceptual Memory.* Lawrence Erlbaum Associates, Publishers, Hillsdale, New Jersey.

Patel, V., Arocha, J., & Groen, G. (1987). Domain specificity and knowledge utilization in diagnostic explanation. In *Proceedings of the Ninth Annual Conference of the Cognitive Science Society*, pages 195–202, Seattle, Washington.

Schank, R. (1982). *Dynamic Memory.* Cambridge University Press, New York.

Simpson, R. (1985). *A Computer Model of Case-Based Reasoning in Problem Solving: An Investigation in the Domain of Dispute Mediation.* PhD thesis, School of Information and Computer Science, Georgia Institute of Technology. Technical Report #GIT–ICS–85/23.

Turner, R. (1988a). Opportunistic use of schemata for medical diagnosis. In *Proceedings of the Tenth Annual Conference of the Cognitive Science Society*, Montreal, Canada.

Turner, R. (1988b). Using schemata for diagnosis. In *Proceedings of the Twelfth Annual Symposium on Computer Applications in Medical Care*, Washington, DC.

Turner, R. M. (in preparation). *Adaptive Reasoning in Medical Diagnosis.* PhD thesis, School of Information and Computer Science, Georgia Institute of Technology.

Search in Analogical Reasoning

Joseph P. Vybihal
School of Computer Science
McGill University

and

Thomas R. Shultz
Department of Psychology
McGill University

ABSTRACT

Analogical reasoning is the process of finding and adapting old solutions to solve new problems. Unlike most analogy work, which has emphasized mapping the analogy to the target problem, we focussed on search for the analogy. Experiments with humans doing analogical reasoning uncovered a search strategy which we call Lambda Search, because of its up and down shape through long-term memory. Lambda Search begins by generalizing on the properties of the target problem and then eventually specializing on the examples of some higher level concept. These ideas were implemented in a computer program named Lambda. Simulations demonstrated that search lessened, and in some cases solved, the problems of mapping and tweaking.

ANALOGICAL REASONING

Analogical reasoning is known to have four major steps: (1) problem representation, (2) search, (3) mapping (with tweaking), and (4) procedural adaptation (also with tweaking) (Holland, Holyoak, Nisbett, & Thagard, 1986; Novick, 1988).

Problem representation is a critical part of analogical reasoning. Novick (1989) observed that novices and experts interpret problems differently depending on how well they understand the problem domain. Experts' greater ability to interpret problems and convert them into a more useful form increases problem solving effectiveness. Analogy programs with the capacity to create and modify their own problem representations are rare (but see Hammond, 1988).

Search is presumably required to find the most useful analogies to the target problem. Little progress has been made on search for analogies in systems with realistic sized long term memories. A possibly promising approach is the connectionist analogy retrieval program of Thagard and Holyoak (1988). In contrast, we attempt a symbolic level approach to analogy search compatible with the symbolic level treatments of other aspects of analogical reasoning.

A series of psychological experiments by Gentner and her colleagues (Skorstad, Falkenhainer, & Gentner, 1987) have demonstrated that people typically use surface, rather that deep, information to find analogies, thus ensuring that the analogies they find are not terribly useful. In contrast, Faries and Reiser (1988) have presented evidence that people in a problem solving context ignore surface information and instead find and use deep analogies through goal information. This suggests that Gentner's subjects did not find deep analogies because her experiments were not conducted in a problem solving context. Our work attempts to integrate both surface information and goal information into a single, seamless algorithm, and thus unify the approaches of Gentner and Reiser.

Mapping is the process that selects and copies important analogical information from the source to the target. Mapping establishes correspondences between pieces of knowledge that contain some similarity. Gentner (1986) has claimed that only structural criteria govern analogical mapping: one-to-one mappings and mappings among connected systems of predicate relations. Her Structure Mapping Engine (SME) algorithm uses a bottom-up approach with predicate calculus to create analogies (Skorstad et al., 1987).

Tweaking is the modification of elements of information that have been mapped if they cause inconsistency in the analogy. There are three aspects of tweaking: (1) avoiding items that do not need to be tweaked, (2) identifying the portions of items that need to be tweaked, and (3) actually tweaking. An interesting finding of our research is that competent analogy search can routinely handle the first two aspects of tweaking, and sometimes can even accomplish the third aspect.

Procedural adaptation uses the computed analogy to solve the target problem. Any inconsistencies discovered during use must be tweaked again, and in this manner the last draft of the analogy is created.

PSYCHOLOGICAL EXPERIMENTS

We conducted a number of experiments to determine the search process used by humans doing analogical reasoning (Vybihal, 1989). All of these experiments had the purpose of inspiring our programming rather then providing a rigorous psychological demonstration. Two of these experiments are described here: one on goal-less search and another on goal-driven search.

Goal-less Analogical Search

Goal-less analogy tasks ask the subject to produce an analogy to something in the absence of any other problem solving goal. This is basically the technique used in Gentner's psychological experiments (Skorstad et al., 1987).

Method

Three university students were asked to give an analogy for two cars crashing together and to think aloud while doing so. We drew graphs from the taped protocols by drawing a node for each concept mentioned and drawing a directed arc from that concept to any other concept that directly descended from it in the protocol. For example, if the protocol read: "If x then y", a node was drawn for x, another node for y, and a directed arc from x to y. Then the directed arcs were arranged so that those referring to a generalization, abstraction, or categorization pointed upward, whereas arcs referring to events, instances, or specializations pointed downward. These are not diagrams of the structure of memory, but rather of the search process as reported by the subjects.

Results

Examination of these graphs indicated that people can perform goal-less analogies and that they do so using a characteristic search pattern. One subject's protocol is presented as a representative example: "mm ... mm ... sounds, impact, people inside injured, two moving objects crashing together ... two snooker balls ... no, no ... two potatoes smashing together ... because crushing."

This subject listed the problem's properties and then tried to match those attributes with some other event in memory. This is a two way hierarchical search that generalized over properties and then used those properties to specialize onto a solution. The other two subjects did this as well. Unlike the other subjects, this subject proposed a solution to the problem, and then rejected it for a better solution. The interesting result is that the better solution had an extra property that matched to it as compared to the properties that matched in the first solution. This suggests that solutions are evaluated on the basis of the number of properties that match, with a better solution possessing more matches.

Goal-driven Analogical Search

Goal-driven analogy tasks ask the subject to solve a problem that may be analogous to other, already solved problems. This is essentially what Faries and Reiser (1988) have done in their analogy experiments.

Method

Three university computer science students were each given 10 problems to solve in elementary Lisp programming. Then they were given a new Lisp problem and asked to solve it given what they had learned from the previous 10 problems. The new problem was superficially similar to 1 of the 10 previous problems, and similar in goal to 1 or 2 of the other 10 previous problems. While the subjects were solving the problems, they were asked to think aloud. Each subject was also asked to give a label or a title for each problem. Each problem was couched in a brief story with a distinct human interest context; this was to provide plenty of surface information.

The 10 initial problems were: (a) accounting firm - goal: display first item in a list, (b) family historian - goal: return ascending and descending version of a list, (c) political campaign - goal: return a list with the last element moved to the front of the list, (d) theologian - goal: insert an item into the second position of a list, (e) author - goal: test if a list is a palindrome, (f) librarian - goal: test if an item is in a list, if not add it to the list, (g) physicist - goal: count the elements in a list, (h) AIDS - goal: test if a list is empty; (i) math professor - goal: print out the Fibonacci number sequence given an input number, and (j) psychotic publisher - goal: remove the last element from a list.

The target problem: "An AIDS researcher detects HIV using a machine that monitors cell tissue every one-hundredth of a second. Each time the machine detects an HIV virus it increments a counter of all HIV's it has seen until it has counted to 100; then it concludes that the patient has AIDS. Write a LISP function that increments a counter every time it detects an element in a list (the element is an H for HIV detected) until 100 where it ceases to increment. The function is passed a list like (H H H H) for all HIVs detected."

Results

The protocols were diagrammed as in the previous experiment. The labels, solution, and protocol from one representative subject are presented here. The labels, in an order corresponding to that used above, are car, up&down, rotate_right, in_second, palindrome, set_add, cardinality, is_empty, fibonacci, shift_right.

Solution: (defun has_aids (l) (cond ((>= count_atoms (l) 100) t)(t f)))

Verbal Protocol: "Same as AIDS research (problem) ... rings (a) bell on (the) is-empty (problem - the AIDS problem) I think, yes, same type of problem ... no! ... counts number instead of saying found one ... ok ... (new problem counts to) 100 and then detects ... um ... look for something in a list and keep count of them to 100, then you stop ... ok ... (that means) get cardinality of list. If over 100 then ... if you want to use other functions .. use cardinality and simple test with respect to threshold of 100 ... so that's (the) count_atoms (problem) ... call it has_aids ... use the cond function and return true or false ... refer to Fibonacci for structure of COND."

This subject noticed that the problem was similar to problem (h) (the other AIDS problem) but failed to continue this line of search because the new problem's goal was not similar to the goal in the other AIDS problem. Then the subject defined the new problem's goal as using cardinality, which reminded him of the physicist problem (g) and a conditional test that, in turn, reminded him of the Fibonacci problem (i). Using these two pieces of information, he created his solution.

This subject solved the target problem using only goal information. Surface information was never even mentioned except at the beginning where the match failed because the analogous goal was not similar to the target goal. Goal information completely out-weighed surface information. The same pattern existed for the other two subjects.

Tweaking was observed in this protocol when the Fibonacci problem was used to complete this version of Count Atoms. The subject observed a difference between the target AIDS problem and the analogous physicist problem. Upon finding the Fibonacci problem that reduced this difference, the subject extracted only the critical part of the Lisp code needed to complete the Count Atoms solution. Finally, even that part of the solution needed to be tweaked slightly. Although it is not possible to ascertain from a verbal protocol alone whether or not tweaking involved search, it is true that the program described below accomplishes these first two tweaks (changing the physicist analogy by finding the Fibonacci problem, and extracting the critical part of the Fibonacci problem) by search alone, the last tweak requiring some still unspecified process.

In all of our experiments, we have 15/15 subjects who demonstrated at least part of this up and down search pattern through LTM. In some cases, the generalization part of the search may be omitted, due to a direct match between the target and the analogy. Because of its characteristic up and down shape, we call this pattern Lambda Search.

THE LAMBDA PROGRAM

The Lambda program was designed to implement the main ideas discovered in the preceding psychological experiments. The program takes as input a LTM database of concepts and a single WM problem concept. It then tries to solve the problem using the Lambda Search process. Lambda Search first tries a direct solution, which is then specialized if it is not exact. If a direct solution fails, a generalization search occurs until a sufficiently good match is found. This match is then specialized to improve the fit of the solution. When a solution is found or too many tries have occurred, the program terminates and displays both the solution to the problem (if any) and statistics concerning the various memory accesses made. Generalization search moves upward in the LTM hierarchy by using the properties slots of concepts, whereas specialization search moves downwards through this hierarchy by employing the examples slots of concepts.

Memory Structure

In our program, the structures of LTM and WM are centered on the idea of a *Concept*. The Concept is a data structure based on frames. It supports other familiar AI structures such as scripts and production rules in a uniform way.

Concept

An important part of the meaning of a concept is its relation to other concepts in memory (Lindsay & Norman, 1977). Concepts in the Lambda program contain the four features of name, class, properties, and examples. Each value contained within a feature is called an element. Each element is not only a descriptive value but also the name of another Concept, giving a recursive quality to a set of Concepts.

With Concepts, one can represent events and ideas and access and interrelate other events and ideas. Each idea can be accessed instantly given its name. Indexing and knowledge are united since the knowledge contained within a Concept can also be used as a key to another Concept. Information can be added or modified within a given Concept structure by simply adding or deleting the properties, examples, class, or name elements. Concepts can be used to form hierarchies of interrelated knowledge containing generic definitions (an entire Concept) and particular instances of generic definitions (indexed by the generic Concept's examples elements). In this manner, memory can be organized in a general to specific hierarchy.

Concept structures inherently create three types of hierarchies accessed through class, properties, and examples. These hierarchical paths have a restriction that they must not produce circuits and the properties paths do not include examples paths and visa versa. The class hierarchy produces a path of ancestors from the current Concept to some more general Concept from which information can be inherited. The properties and examples hierarchies produce paths to other related Concepts that help describe the current Concept, which therefore allows information contained in those Concepts to be inherited for expansion of the current Concept's description.

The Concept data structure is implemented using frames with a unique frame name and three slots for class, properties, and examples. All values and facets are represented with predicate calculus statements. A facet together with all its values, and any single value can be inserted or deleted from a Concept, thus giving Concepts a dynamic quality. Any number of facets can exist. The properties list is a more general description (category information) of the Concept while the examples list is a more specific description (specific instances, events and actions) of the Concept.

```
Concept Name = Tart(English)
        Class = pie
        pr = composed_of(crust(soft),apples), characteristics(small,baked).
        ex = example(tart(Joseph's),tart(mother's)).
end Concept.
```

In this example *pr* is the properties slot. *Composed-of* is a facet and *crust(soft)* and *apples* are two values of *composed-of.* The comma specifies that *characteristics* is another facet with two values. *Ex* is the examples slot and it contains one facet: *example.*

Within this formalism, a script (Schank, 1982) is a specialization of the Concept data structure. The script is represented by a Concept name, but prefixed by the key word *script.* The Concept class and property list are used normally, but the examples list is different, in that an event_sequence facet must be included within the slot along with any other information stored there. The order of the elements within the event_sequence facet indicates the order of their execution. Each element in the event_sequence facet is a line of code that will get executed in sequence unless a branching statement is encountered that directs control elsewhere. The elements are predicate clauses where the predicate is the name of a procedure and the clause's variables are the procedure's parameters. Scripts have an important use in the Lambda program. For example, Lambda Search is implemented using a script.

The power of the Concept data structure lies in four areas. It can add and delete values and facets which make the data structure dynamic. It uses predicate calculus to enable a complete and expressive language to represent knowledge. It possesses a built-in triple hierarchical memory structure that facilitates knowledge association and search. Lastly, the Concept structure can represent knowledge in chunks that are related to other chunks.

Working Memory

Working memory (WM) in Lambda has two parts: (1) an area that accepts new Concepts from the external world that are eventually stored in LTM, and (2) an area that accesses knowledge from LTM. WM is viewed as a list of pointers with an activation value (Anderson, 1983). As long as the activation value is greater than zero, the pointer holds onto the newly accepted Concept or the LTM Concept being pointed to. WM can be infinite in length except that it has a large overhead rehearsal factor (Lindsay & Norman, 1977). Decaying activation values conserve computational resources by limiting the size of WM.

Working memory (WM) has two control processes. One process is called *Maintenance Rehearsal* (Lindsay & Norman, 1977; Anderson, 1983). Its function is to maintain the activation of Concepts and to degenerate the activation of Concepts contained within WM according to a set of rules listed below. The other process is called *Elaborative Rehearsal* (Lindsay & Norman, 1977; Reiser, 1986); its purpose is learning. Learning is the storing of new information contained within WM into LTM. Learning is performed by *chunking*, which inserts one Concept's name into the properties or examples list of another Concept.

The following rules, similar to those used by Anderson (1983), govern Maintenance Rehearsal:

1. Activation of memory: A Concept is activated by attaching a pointer to it from WM. The Concept is given a maximum activation value of 1.0.

2. Maintenance of activation: A Concept is maintained as active in WM according to the following formula:

N(t) = 1.0, if Concept accessed in WM, or N(t) = N(t-1) - K, if Concept is not accessed

Where:

N(t) is a given Concept in WM at time t

t is the latency since the Concept was last accessed within WM

$K = 0.2^{(-t/10)}$ is a rapid decay function

0 >= N(t) <= 1

N(t) = 1.0 for maximum amount of activation

N(t) = 0.0 Concept is deactivated

3. Spread of activation: The Concepts are processed according to their activation order (N(t)) or by the execution of an activated script.
4. Conflict resolution: If more than one Concept has the same activation value, then the Concept closer to the head of the list is executed first.

Long-term Memory

LTM is a storage area in which any Concept contained there can be instantly accessed given the Concept's name. LTM is implemented with a two-three tree (Aho, Hopcroft, & Ullman, 1983) having Concept names as indices. LTM Concepts can also be accessed by obtaining an element within a Concept's slot and using it as a search index. LTM is monotonic and therefore Concepts once stored there cannot be deleted. Modifications or deletions to a Concept's properties or examples list element are permitted, but the deletion of an entire Concept is not permitted. If an entire Concept is to be changed, a new Concept should be installed. The old Concept is then labeled as modified. This leaves trace information in LTM concerning changes in state. This is similar to humans remembering an erroneous idea they used to hold.

Search

Lambda Search is a three stage cyclic search of memory structures. Each Concept currently being processed is a potential structure that may be used in the creation of a resultant analogy in WM. As each Concept is being processed, evaluations are made as to how appropriate it is to the currently developing analogy and whether it should be included in the analogy.

The matching criteria in Lambda Search are obtained from the input problem. The input problem's properties are scanned for a goal. If a goal is found, it is used as the matching criterion. If no goal is found, then the entire list of properties (i.e., surface information) is used as matching criteria.

Lambda Search follows three steps:

1. Direct Solution. Upon statement of the problem, a direct solution is attempted. If a direct solution is found by a match using all the parameters in the matching criteria, this is called an exact match and the search terminates. If a direct solution is found where only a majority of its parameters match with the given analogy problem, this is called an inexact match. If a direct, but inexact solution is obtained, then a specialization search is performed in an attempt to complete the partial solution (step 3). Up to the point of this specialization search, direct solutions are based on memory retrieval rather than on analogy.
2. Generalization Search. If there is a failure in finding an exact or inexact solution in step 1, then there is generalization on the problem across the properties of concepts. Previous failed attempts are used as guides in the generalization. This generalization of the problem continues until an exact or inexact match is found with the given matching criteria.

3. Specialization Search. Upon reaching a satisfactory level of generalization, where an exact or inexact match has been found, a solution is developed by specializing (traveling across the examples slot of concepts) to find the best fitting solution. This specialization search builds on the possible inexact solution of stage two and attempts to obtain the greatest proportion of matches with the matching criteria's parameters.

These three search steps are cyclic, in that, if the process fails at some point or when extra information is needed, the program redoes the steps at a new starting point. The new starting point is selected by a reconstruction of the goal involved in the problem.

PROGRAM PERFORMANCE

The program has been tested on 15 problems with a LTM that averaged 20 potential source analogs from a wide variety of domains. The program produced both goal-less and goal-driven analogies similar to those of our human subjects. In searches for analogies, it used goals when available and resorted to surface information when it had to. Following is an example of input and output for a version of the classic radiation problem (Holland et al., 1986). The target problem of destroying a tumor with a ray powerful enough to destroy intervening tissue may be solved by finding the analogy of dividing an army into small groups so as to avoid overloading fragile bridges.

Frame Name: problem, Frame Class: problem(input)
Properties List:
goal[destroy,tumor]
large(ray)
danger(tissue)
many(guns)
Examples List:
<<EMPTY>>

Returned Solution:

Frame Name: *ANALOGY, Frame Class: solution
Properties List:
goal[destroy,tumor] / goal[destroy,castle]
large(ray) / large(army)
danger(tissue) / danger(bridges)
many(guns) / many(bridges)
Examples List:
solution[divide(army),use(army),direction(multiple)]

In goal-directed search such as this, surface information is unimportant, but the goal is important. Therefore, this solution was chosen only because of its goal. The solution facet, in the examples list, was copied from the analogy as a solution. This solution needs to be tweaked if it is to be used as a solution for the tumor target problem. The tweaking, not yet implemented, would substitute *army* for *ray* in the solution facet of the examples list.

Lambda Search predicts that analogies will be found having no properties in common but the goal. In other words, an analogy to a problem may be selected only by a goal match, with none of the other predicates in the properties list matching. The radiation problem does not demonstrate this, but other test runs on analogies from the research literature did.

We also asked human subjects to evaluate the analogies generated by the program for similarity to human-generated solutions. Results indicated that more similarity was perceived when the program operated under goal-directed search than under goal-less search. Subjects also rated goal-directed solutions as being more effective than goal-less solutions. The program also generated better analogies when consistent goal information was provided, thus simulating Novick's (1988) data on expert-novice differences. It was assumed that experts would know more about the goals in a domain and would be less influenced by surface information than would novices.

CONCLUSIONS

Lambda search, working on the Concept data structure, simulated human analogical reasoning not only in solutions obtained but also in method. The program accomplished both goal-driven and goal-less tasks, thus unifying the approaches of Gentner and Reiser in a natural and seamless way. The Concept data structure proved to be versatile and easy to use for representing many problems and for storing hierarchies of knowledge relations.

ACKNOWLEDGEMENTS

This research is based on a Masters thesis submitted by Vybihal to the School of Computer Science of McGill University. The research was supported in part by grants to Shultz from the Natural Sciences and Engineering Research Council of Canada and IBM Canada. Please direct correspondence to Thomas R. Shultz, Department of Psychology, McGill University, 1205 Dr. Penfield Ave., Montréal, Québec, Canada H3A 1B1. Email: inoa@musicb.mcgill.ca

REFERENCES

Aho, A. V., Hopcroft, J. E., & Ullman, J. D. (1983) *Data structures and algorithms*. Reading, MA: Addison-Wesley.

Anderson, J. R. (1983). *The architecture of cognition*. Cambridge, MA: Harvard University Press.

Faries, J. M., & Reiser, B. J. (1988). Access and use of previous solutions in a problem solving situation. *Proceedings Cognitive Science Society*, **10**, 433-439.

Gentner, D. (1986). *Analogical inference and analogical access*. Unpublished manuscript, University of Illinois.

Hammond, K. J. (1988). Analogical reasoning as a by-product of problem-solving. *Proceedings Cognitive Science Society*, **10**, 302-303.

Holland, J. H., Holyoak, K. J. , Nisbett, R. E., & Thagard, P. (1986). *Induction: Processes of inference, learning, and discovery*. Cambridge, MA: MIT Press.

Lindsay, P. H., & Norman, D. A. (1977). *Human information processing*. New York: Academic Press.

Novick, L. R. (1988). Analogical transfer, problem similarity, and expertise. *Journal of Experimental Psychology: Learning, Memory, and Cognition*, **14**, 510-520.

Reiser, B. J. (1986). The encoding and retrieval of memories of real-world experiences. In J. Galambos, R. Abelson, & J. B. Black (Eds.) *Knowledge structures*, pp. 71-99. Hillsdale, NJ: Lawrence Erlbaum Associates.

Schank, R.C. (1982) *Dynamic memory: A theory of reminding and learning in computers and people*. New York: Cambridge University Press.

Skorstad, J., Falkenhainer, B., & Gentner, D. (1987). Analogical processing: A simulation and empirical corroboration. *Proceedings AAAI*, **6**, 322-326.

Thagard, P., & Holyoak, K. (1988). Analogical problem solving: A constraint satisfaction approach. *Proceedings Cognitive Science Society*, **10**, 299-300.

Vybihal, J. P. (1989). *Search and knowledge representation in analogical reasoning*. Unpublished Masters Thesis, McGill University.

Capturing Intuitions About Human Language Production

Nigel Ward

University of Tokyo, Faculty of Engineering
University of California at Berkeley, Computer Science Division

Abstract

Human speech is creative. Move specifically, it is an effortful process that starts from a rich input and creates new meaning. Speech is also incremental, as evidenced by pauses and false starts. Existing models of language generation have not adequately addressed these phenomena. This paper presents six principles which specify a design for a cognitively plausible generator, as follows: Be able to handle non-trivial inputs, Be able to access relevant words, Consider many words as candidates for potential inclusion, Produce an utterance incrementally, Use feedback from words, and Monitor the output. These principles can be implemented using spreading activation in a semantic network which includes lexical and syntactic knowledge. The prototype generation system FIG is such an implementation.

Introduction

The study of human language production is still in its infancy. No existing model approaches even descriptive adequacy. Many open problems are well known, such as problems of choosing a referring expression or choosing the correct position for an adjunct. But there are deeper problems, stemming from the failure to address some very basic issues in language production.

[0]Thanks to Dan Jurafsky, Terry Regier, Michael Gasser, Jim Martin, Y. Kuniyoshi, H. Inoue, Robert Wilensky, and Dekai Wu. This work was supported in part by a Monbusho Fellowship, by the Sloan Foundation via a grant to the Berkeley Cognitive Science Program, and by the Defense Advanced Research Projects Agency (DoD), monitored by the Space and Naval Warfare Systems Command under Contract N00039-88-C-0292.

In particular, human speech is creative and incremental. These two phenomena have received little attention, perhaps because they are hard to formalize. But it is worth the effort to explore their implications, for they place important constraints on cognitive models. This paper discusses these basic intuitions, proposes some qualities that a generator needs in order to capture them, and describes a generation program designed to exhibit these phenomena.

Phenomena

Speech is Creative

"Creative" is here a sort of umbrella term for some important intuitions about the nature of speech:

1. The "input" is much richer than the output. In Vygotsky's words, "thought, unlike speech, does not consist of separate units. When I wish to communicate the thought that today I saw a barefoot boy in a blue shirt running down the street, I do not see every item separately: the boy, the shirt, its blue color, his running, the absence of shoes" [Vygotsky 1982]. This points up the computational tasks of dividing and organizing the input.

Rich inputs cause another problem as well, that of selection. Imagine a peach moving in a stream towards a woman standing by the side of the stream. If you have formed a rich image of this scene, then you can think of many words that could be used in a sentence describing it, including perhaps *"water," "flow," "float," "in," "on," "downstream," "down," "towards," "to," "moving," "direction," "buoyant," "bobbing," "current," "with," "stream,"* and so on. No normal utterance will contain all these words, so a speaker must select which aspects of an input to express.

2. Speech creates meaning. Those having difficulty organizing an idea often use the strategy of verbalizing their thoughts, hoping to understand them better. This suggests that speaking involves creating new conceptual content, and is not merely a process of encoding existing thoughts. In Wittgenstein's words, it is a mistake to assume that "the thoughts are already there ... and we merely look for their expression" [Wittgenstein 1963].

3. Speech is effortful. As suggested by the common saying "he was so busy talking that he never noticed ...," even the folk theory of language includes the notion that speech imposes a cognitive load.

Speech is Incremental

Consider the following utterance:

> *Nigel, you've got such a we-ird answering machine message. - so anyway we need to know what time we can come and rehearse tomorrow, - a-nd, - we're assuming that, - ten o'clock in the morning we'll show up at your place, — and, — or or shortly thereafter, - and uh - if we - if we don't hear from you then we'll do that, if you - can't do that then leave a message on my machine ok? - thanks bye.*

Notation:

- \- short pause or lengthened word
- — longer pause
- ,.? clause boundaries, based on intonation

Now that you understand the content, a second reading will reveal:

1. Speech is full of *pauses,* including filled pauses such as *"uh"* and *"oh."* The obvious and pervasive explanation for this is that people think as they speak; in particular, that "deciding" what to say next requires thought. In other words, the "effort" of speaking is expended "on-line."

2. Speech exhibits *false starts,* that is, cases where the speaker utters a few words, "denies" them, and starts over. The obvious explanation for this is that speakers choose words without completely computing the consequences of what they are likely to say next. In Kempen's words, "speakers often ... initiate overt speech production after having worked out only a fragment of the conceptual content of the resulting utterance" [Kempen & Hoenkamp 1987].

Speech is Successful

For the sake of completeness it should be noted that people usually manage to say what they mean, and they do so more or less according to the rules of their language. Obeying the rules means producing an utterance which is not only grammatical but also consists of a consistent set of words. The complexity involved in being consistent can be seen by considering the many ways in which a preposition can be inconsistent with the other words in an utterance:

> *went* into *the hills to gather wood*
> **went* into *the hill to gather wood*
> (but *"to"* is ok)
> **went* into *the hillside to gather wood*
> (but *"gather wood* on *the hillside"* is ok)
> **?walked into the hills to gather wood*

Thus, the choice of a preposition can depend on a previous word, a latter word, the number of that word, and so on.

Trends in Generation Research

Human language production has received a fair amount of attention, but the phenomena of creativity and incrementality have been largely neglected. This section points out some broad trends in generation research and discusses the extent to which the results are plausible cognitive models. The strengths and weaknesses of specific models are discussed in later sections.

Psycholinguists' models of generation have not addressed creativity, nor, in general, incrementality. Instead, they generally target quantifiable data, such as pause durations and rates, speech errors, and response latencies. These are typically explained directly in terms of a speech "machine" and its phases, levels, modules, or stages (for a survey of many such models, see [Rosenberg 1977]). In general, much of this work seems prematurely concerned with details at the expense of the big picture, and also too willing to accept the Von Neuman computer as a model for cognition.

In the AI tradition "cognitive validity" usually refers to the use of data *structures* which plausibly reflect human knowledge. There has been less use of intuitions about *processing* aspects of language skills. There are exceptions, notably Kempen's work in incremental generation [Kempen & Hoenkamp 1987]. But even this seems mostly motivated by the goal of producing syntacticly correct output. The result is yet another tree-based syntactic engine, albeit one capable of generating even while the speaker's intention is changing.

Most researchers are not terribly concerned if their models cannot account for creativity. Generating successfully is usually given first priority. A typical viewpoint is "while there are creative aspects in speech, they should be handled separately from the basic generation process." Yet it seems wrong not to try for a unified model that can account for both creative aspects and more mundane aspects of generation.

Indeed, it may be that creativity and incrementality are not merely incidental phenomena but are intrinsic to the generation task: to the extent that thought is creative and unconstrained, so must language be; to the extent that language is concise, it must reflect a creative selection of elements from a thought; to the extent that speech is produced in real time and by a speaker situated in a changing world, it must be produced incrementally.

Principles for a Cognitive Model of Language Production

The following principles describe how a generator should operate if it is to be cognitively plausible. Taken together, they form a kind of "specification" for a generator.

Principle 1: Be Able to Handle Non-Trivial Inputs

A lot of things are "active in the mind" and affect the generation process, as illustrated by Vygotsky's example and by the telephone message. Pragmatic goals are also active in large numbers; in Hovy's words, "when we speak, we do not try to satisfy only one or two goals, and we operate (often, and with success) under conflicting goals for which no resolution exists" [Hovy 1987]. Indeed, generation can be affected by utterly extraneous thoughts [Harley 1984]. It may not be too much to say that the generator's input is the entire brain-state of the speaker. For this reason to use the word "input" is somewhat inappropriate, in so far as it evokes the image of a generation process running as an isolated module that is passed a few symbols and has no access to other components of thought.

Yet this is exactly the image that many generation researchers have adopted. They assume the "input" can be adequately modeled as a logical form, feature structure, conceptualization, set of propositions, or the like. As a consequence, the most widely used metaphor for generation, even in psychological circles, seems to be that of encoding a thought or a "meaning." The computational analog of this is to treat generation as a process of mapping one representation (a thought) onto another (a sentence). This is typically done by a matching or unification process or by a process that "traverses" the input structure. This metaphor assumes, and its implementations require, a simple, well-organized and contextless input, which makes them implausible as cognitive models.

Another common metaphor for generation is realizing a specification. This metaphor seems better suited for explaining the ability to handle non-trivial inputs. Yet the computational models based on this metaphor are also unsatisfactory. The first, syntax-driven generation, seems hard to reconcile with the creative, meaning-creating aspects of generation. The second is planning-based generation. Planning techniques seem, unfortunately, too general to cast much light on the specific task of language production.

Principle 2: Be Able to Access Relevant Words

In order to "say what it means" a generator must find words relevant to its input. Relevance is not always a straightforward relationship; many words may qualify as relevant [Ward 1988]. For example, to produce an utterance expressing something like *"Chang lived with his widowed mother"* a generator may need access to words like *"alone," "father," "without," "dead,"* and *"orphan."* This flexibility, sometimes called paraphrase ability, is one key to creativity.

A wealth of possible choices, however, is something that existing generation models (with the exception of planning and unification approaches) cannot cope with. This is because their basic algorithms are fundamentally serial. The problem of producing a grammatical, consistent, and appropriate utterance despite a wealth of choices is the primary topic of the remaining principles.

Principle 3: Consider Many Words as Candidates for Potential Inclusion

Recall the problem of making a consistent set of choices: a word choice which seems excellent in isolation may turn out to be inappropriate when the possibilities for neighboring words are considered. In order to have a good chance of finding a set of choices which are all individually reasonable and together form a consistent set, a generator must consider many alternative words. The previous principle says that a generator should have access to many words; this one says that it should actively consider them "at run time." That is, it should consider many alternative words in parallel. This allows it to represent all dependencies and "solve" them together.

Consideration of many possible words is necessary for another reason also: the huge number of available concepts if the input is non-trivial. A generator will typically directly express only a few of the possible concepts, as the *"floating peach"* example shows. Not until words are considered can a generator know which concepts it should select. Danlos has pointed out that, in general, "conceptual and linguistic decisions ... are all dependent on one another" [Danlos 1984]. (The distinction between strategy and tactics in generation [Thompson 1977] is an attempt to define this problem away.) In most generators, however, the input consists of a small set of propositions or nodes, in which case generation is a trivial matter of mapping each element or literal to an appropriate word.

Most models of generation do not include consider candidate words in parallel. On the contrary, it is common to treat word choice in terms of dictionary lookup, pointer following, or checklist evaluation, all of which generate only a few candidates. Of course, the lookup process is usually constrained by previous choices, but never by probable future choices. Alternatives are usually not considered unless a failure is detected, in which case special processing is started, such as backtrack or a search process to find another word.

It is worth noting that the goal of producing a consistent set of choices may conflict with the goal of using relevant words. That is, a speaker must sometimes make trade-offs between being faithful to his intention and sounding natural and fluent. To make these diverse goals be comeasurate a generator needs some "scoring" mechanism to enable it to determine what set of choices is the best compromise.

Principle 4: Produce an Utterance Incrementally

A cognitive model of generation should be incremental, or in other words, "on-line." That is, most of the processing relating to the output of a word should be done near the time when that word is output. Incremental generation stands in contrast to multi-pass generation and to top-down generation. Multi-pass generation is obviously useless for cognitive modeling — if speakers first planned the content then the syntactic form and then the words, and only then began to speak, there would be no explanation for false starts. Top-down generation also cannot serve as a cognitive model — a process that expands S to a surface string, preserving grammaticality at each step, can hardly account for disfluencies and false starts.

An incremental generator needs an explicit representation of the current state of the generation process at each moment. Most models of generation do without, maintaining state in pointers to sub-trees or lexical entries, or implicitly in the process state. An explicit representation allows straightforward explanation of errors. For example, false starts can be explained in terms of what is under consideration at each point in time, rather than in terms of buffer properties or architectural shortcomings.

There is a superficial contradiction between choosing words one by one and choosing a consistent set of word. There is no contradiction if a generator represents relevance in general, not just for the next output position. For example, if a generator has a representation of the fact that *"the hills"* is likely to emitted sometime soon, it can use this fact to infer that *"into"* is likely to be appropriate now. This, the need to represent future possible choices and their likelihoods, of course requires yet more parallelism.

Principle 5: Use Feedback from Words

"Speech creates meaning" in part because the availability of words during generation affects the thought of the speaker. More concretely, the retrieval of a word, for whatever reason, provides an opportunity to use the associated concept in thought. This is of course a weak version of the Sapir-Whorf hypothesis.

The incrementality principle and the feedback principle together have an interesting implication. Since most of the processing of a word is done just before that word is output, if feedback is present, then concepts associated with that word will become the "focus of processing." This accounts neatly for Chafe's idea of a "moving focus of attention" which successively "lights up" various parts of the input during the course of generation [Chafe 1980].

If the incrementality principle is taken to the extreme it leads to the claim that "there is nothing more to generation than successive choices of words," and that the word order, syntactic structure, and conceptual content of utterances are emergent. In other words, syntax and content are correctly formed without benefit of a mechanism to explicitly make syntactic or conceptual choices. On this view, meaning arises as side effect of the process of finding words.

Principle 6: Monitor the Output

A generator should exploit feedback from past word choices. This is especially important in an incremental generator because it is necessary to make sure that the generation process stays "on track." One thing feedback must ensure is that the system has a correct representation of what fraction of the input has been conveyed and what remains to be said. For example, after emitting *"there was a peach floating in the stream,"* it must realize that information has been conveyed implicitly; this prevents it from continuing redundantly with *"moving downstream"* or *"being moved by the current."* Feedback must also ensure a correct representation of the current syntactic state.

Feedback is necessary because the other principles require the generator to simultaneously satisfy many goals and subgoals. The generator must "want" to express all the input, to be concise, and to be grammatical. To the extent that these goals are all active at run time there must be processes to check and update the current status (satisfied or not) of each goal.

While monitoring is widely advocated, it is not actually very critical for conventional models of generation. For example, direct replacement generators produce an utterance isomorphic to the meaning structure they are given, and hence allow no possibility for creative word choice. Thus the output is guaranteed to (trivially) conform to the input — monitoring is not really needed. Similarly, syntax-driven generators never output a word without knowing in advance the implications for the sentence's syntactic structure. Everything is predictable so no monitoring is needed.

Implementation

Generating with Spreading Activation

The spreading activation framework is well suited for implementing the above principles. The basic ideas behind spreading activation are: a network represents knowledge, the activation levels of nodes in the network represent the process state, and flow of activation among nodes represents evidence. In generation, a node's activation level represents the degree to which it is relevant to the input or to the utterance under construction. Generation being an incremental process, the activation level of a node represents its relevance at the current time. A spreading activation model can embody the principles as follows:

1. The input is a (potentially large) set of activated nodes.

2. Activation flows in all directions, but in particular it flows from concepts to words, via paths comprised of links representing world knowledge and lexical knowledge. Activation flow across long paths corresponds to the chains of inference in order to "access" words that appear in other models. There is no need to separate lexical information into a special data structure; words are, like everything else, simply nodes in the net.

3. At any given time, many nodes have activation, including many which represent words. The network is designed so that its stable states represent consistent sets of choices. In order for it to settle in this way it has links among words that cooccur, and between compatible choices in general.

This basic mechanism is extended to handle syntax. This solution is based on Construction Grammar [Fillmore, Kay, & O'Connor, to appear], a framework in which the basic units of grammatical knowledge are constructions, such as the subject-predicate construction, the noun-phrase construction, the existential-there construction, and various comparative constructions. Constructions are encoded in the network, where their primary role is to transmit activation to words. At run time many constructions have activation, and they cooperate and compete, "trying" to influence which words get chosen. (This conforms nicely to analyses of speech error data which suggest that even normal speech is the result of competing "plans"[Baars 1980].) If the network is designed right, the states it settles into will represent sets of choices which are consistent from the syntactic point of view also.

It is very hard to prove that the output of this model will be grammatical, due to the massive parallelism. One can say that it strives for grammaticality, without being certain of acheiving it. This seems appropriate, since neither is human speech consistently grammatical. Despite this, other models of generation usually give special status to syntactic considerations. For example, syntax is often treated as a set of constraints, or a filter, or an engine. Other construction-based approaches employ some unification or matching process to arbitrate among or coordinate constructions, rather than having them compete at run time.

4. An utterance is produced by periodically selecting and emitting the most highly activated word-node. These are the only explicit choices; all other choices are emergent. Syntactic considerations, for example, manifest themselves only through their effects on the relative activation levels of nodes.

As a result this is a very open architecture. The generator doesn't know or care if extraneous considerations recently altered the activation level of some node. Moreover, it is robust in the face of such changes, that is, a reasonable output should always result, provided only that the network is given time to settle. Thus, like Kempen's IPG [Kempen & Hoenkamp 1987], it can operate in face of changing thoughts, since, no matter what, it just chooses the next word based on activation levels.

5. Activation flows in all directions, and in particular from words to concepts, thereby providing feedback. Since there is a unified knowledge representation, feedback is easy and pervasive.

6. A monitoring process updates activation levels after each word is emitted. This to ensure that activation levels always represent the current state of the generation process. Some of the specific things involved here are: updating the nodes representing the current syntactic state, zeroing out the activation of a word after it has been emitted (to ensure that it will not be selected again immediately), and zeroing out the activation of those nodes of the input which have been expressed.

FIG – A Flexible Incremental Generator

The above scheme has been implemented as a program called FIG (for "Flexible Incremental Generator"). It works in the domain of fairy tales, for no good reason. FIG's task is generating English in the context of machine translation. The above principles are, of course, most appropriate to spontaneous language production, but they are also relevant to machine translation. The ability to produce language is the most important component skill of the translator's art [Seleskovitch 1968]; and creativity, in particular, is necessary in order to produce natural translations [Ward 1989]. One advantage of studying generation in the context of translation makes it harder to "cheat." There is a temptation in generation research to start from inputs which are really just disguised English sentences. FIG generates directly from the output of a Japanese parser/understander, avoiding this temptation.

In connectionist terminology, FIG is a "localist" system. That is, there is a one-to-one correspondence between concepts and nodes. For example, **old-woman**, **long-ago**, **stream**, and **gather** are all nodes, as are words, such as **"woman"**. While systems with distributed representations have many advantages, localist systems are easier to implement, debug, and explain, and have most of the same characteristics.

The purpose of implementation is to identify the functionality needed for generation and to uncover ways to provide it using spreading activation. I make no claims for FIG as a program; I have little confidence in the details of representation (for example, the ontology of link types, or the heuristics for assigning link weights) or the details of processing (for example, the criteria to determine when the network has settled into a stable state). Experiments with FIG, however, are leading to an understanding of what kinds of knowledge are needed for generation and how they should interact. Some of the results on lexical knowledge and word choice are reported in [Ward 1988].

The remainder of this section gives some details to illustrate the FIG approach. Discussion focuses on syntax because it is not obvious how to handle it in a spreading activation framework.

A construction is represented as a node linked to nodes representing semantic and pragmatic contexts where it is appropriate, the syntactic environments in which it can appear, and its internal structure. For example, consider the existential-there construction [Lakoff 1987]. In the net there is the node **ex-there**, and from it links to nodes representing its constituents: **ex-there.first**, **ex-there.second**, and **ex-there.third**. From these constituents are links to, respectively, the word **"there"**, the category **stative-verb**, and the category **noun**. **ex-there** is also linked to **introductory-sentence**, representing that it is appropriate to use this construction when introducing a new person into the domain of discourse.

The current syntactic state is represented by the activation levels of the constituents of constructions. There is parallelism within constructions: "future" constituents all have some degree of activation, proportional to their imminence. (This is necessary to handle backwards dependencies, as in the *"into the hills"* example, and also to handle optional constituents and adjuncts.)

To see how this knowledge is used during generation, suppose that FIG is given an input including concept-nodes like **woman, old, live, poor, fairy-tale, introductory-sentence**, and **hovel**. Suppose further that FIG has already emitted *"once upon a time."* In this context **ex-there** receives activation from **woman**, indirectly, via a path consisting of **"woman"** (the word, not the concept), **noun,** and **ex-there.second**. It also receives activation from **introductory-sentence**. As a result **ex-there** becomes highly activated (relative to other constructions, such as **subject-predicate**, the construction responsible for normal SV order). A large fraction of this activation flows from **ex-there** via **ex-there.first** to **"there"** (since initially the first constituent of every construction is the most highly activated). As a result of this activation, **"there"** becomes the most highly activated of the nodes representing words, so *"there"* will be emitted next.

After *"there"* is output, activation levels are updated to represent the new syntactic situation. As a result **ex-there**'s second constituent, **ex-there.second**, is highly activated. Activation flows from **ex-there.second**, to the feature **stative-verb**, and from there to stative verbs. At this point the word **"live"** will have the highest activation of any word, because it receives activation from both syntactic sources (**stative-verb**) and semantic sources (the node **live**, a component of the input). Thus FIG will emit *"lived"* next. (There is a kludge for morphology).

This example illustrates several things: Activation flow from constituents to words helps determine which word gets chosen and emitted next. There is "bottom-up" activation which flows from words "up" to constructions they could be constituents for. Appropriate words are selected due to a sort of "cooperation" between syntactic and semantic considerations, since the activation level of a word is given by the sum of the amounts of activation received from all sources.

FIG's knowledge network currently includes about 100 nodes and 300 links. It produces utterances like *"Once upon a time there lived an old man and an old woman,"* and *"One day the old man went to the hills to gather wood."* To produce the latter takes about 21 seconds on a Sun 4/110.

Related Work

FIG builds on other connectionist and activation-based models of generation. Dell [1986] developed a connectionist model of the phonetic realization of words. He emphasized the role of bottom-up feedback (in his case from phonemes to words), and realized that activation levels should represent relevance in general, as well as appropriateness for the very next output position. Stemberger [1985] proposed a similar model for lexical access and word order. Gasser [1988] implemented such a model, CHIE, and noted numerous advantages, including robust word choice. Compared with CHIE, FIG is less top-down, more incremental, and relies more on parallelism and emergents.

Directions

While FIG implements the principles for a cognitive model for language production, it does not fully capture the intuitions about language production. It is incremental, often successful, but never yet creative. To make FIG become more successful, I am gradually extending its knowledge network. On the agenda are investigations of how to handle specific topics, such as morphology, phonology, agreement, and ellipsis, within the spreading activation framework. To make FIG exhibit creativity will be harder. This will require massively scaling up the network so that there are an abundance of choices. One difficulty will be that it takes a fair amount of computer time to do experiments, even for small networks. Another is that it takes a lot of effort to extend the network; at some point a learning algorithm will be needed.

References

[Baars 1980] Baars, Bernard J., The Competing Plans Hypothesis: an heuristic viewpoint on the causes of errors in speech, in *Temporal Variables in Speech,* Hans W. Dechert and Manfred Raupach (eds.), Mouton, 1980.

[Chafe 1980] Chafe, Wallace L., The Deployment of Consciousness in the Production of a Narrative, in *The Pear Stories,* Wallace L. Chafe (ed.), Ablex, 1980.

[Danlos 1984] Danlos, Laurence, Conceptual and Linguistic Decisions in Generation, *Coling-84*, 1984.

[Dell 1986] Dell, Gary, A Spreading-Activation Theory of Retrieval in Sentence Production, *Psychological Review* 93, 283-321, 1986.

[Fillmore, Kay, & O'Connor, to appear] Fillmore, Charles J., Paul Kay, and M. C. O'Connor, Regularity and Idiomaticity in Grammatical Constructions: The Case of Let Alone, *Language,* to appear.

[Gasser 1988] Gasser, Micheal, A Connectionist Model of Sentence Generation in a First and Second Language, PhD Thesis, also Technical Report UCLA-AI-88-13, Computer Science Department, University of California, Los Angeles, 1988.

[Harley 1984] Harley, Trevor, A Critique of Top-down Independent Levels of Speech Production: Evidence from Non-Plan-Internal Speech Errors, *Cognitive Science*, 8, 1984.

[Hovy 1987] Hovy, Eduard, Generating Natural Language Under Pragmatic Constraints, PhD Thesis, also Technical Report YaleU/CSD/RR #521, 1987.

[Kempen & Hoenkamp 1987] Kempen, Gerard, and Edward Hoenkamp, An Incremental Procedural Grammar for Sentence Formulation, *Cognitive Science*, 11, 201-258, 1987.

[Lakoff 1987] Lakoff, George, *Women, Fire, and Dangerous Things*, University of Chicago Press, 1987.

[Rosenberg 1977] Rosenberg, Sheldon, Semantic Constraints on Sentence Production: An Experimental Approach, in *Sentence Production,* Sheldon Rosenberg (ed.), 195-228, Erlbaum, 1977.

[Seleskovitch 1968] Seleskovitch, Danica, *L'intèrprete dans les conférences internationales,* Minard, Paris, 1968.

[Stemberger 1985] Stemberger, Joseph Paul, An Interactive Activation Model of Language Production, in *Progress in the Psychology of Language, Volume 1*, Andrew W. Ellis (ed.), Erlbaum, 1985.

[Thompson 1977] Thompson, Henry, Strategy and Tactics: A Model for Language Production, *Proceedings of the Chicago Linguistics Society*, 13, 1977.

[Vygotsky 1982] Vygotsky, Lev S., *Thought and Language* MIT and Wiley, 1962

[Ward 1988] Ward, Nigel, Issues in Word Choice, *Proceedings of Coling-88*, Budapest, 1988

[Ward 1989] Ward, Nigel, A Model for Natural Machine Translation, *Jouhou Shori Gakkai Dai38kai Zenkoku Taikai*, Tokyo, 1989.

[Wittgenstein 1963] Wittgenstein, Ludwig, *Philosophical Investigations,* Blackwell, Oxford 1963.

Learning Semantic Relationships in Compound Nouns with Connectionist Networks

Stefan Wermter
Department of Computer and Information Science
University of Massachusetts

Abstract

This paper describes a new approach for understanding compound nouns. Since several approaches have demonstrated the difficulties in finding detailed and suitable semantic relationships within compound nouns, we use only a few basic semantic relationships and provide the system with the additional ability to learn the details of these basic semantic relationships from training examples. Our system is based on a backpropagation architecture and has been trained to understand compound nouns from a scientific technical domain. The test results demonstrated that a connectionist network is able to learn semantic relationships within compound nouns.

Introduction

Understanding compound nouns plays an important role in understanding natural language. In the past, different approaches for understanding compound nouns have been investigated in artificial intelligence, linguistics, and cognitive science ((Marcus 80) (Finin 80) (McDonald 82) (Lehnert 86) (Arens 87) (Dahl 87)). Most approaches relied on a representation of the words in compound nouns as frames or semantic features and contained fixed control structures which determined the semantic relationships between the words. For example, Finin (Finin 80) used frames to predict the semantic relationships between words and a hierarchy of rules to identify the best relationship. McDonald's system (McDonald 82) is based on Fahlman's parallel semantic network (Fahlman 79) and used marker passing to find the semantic relationships between word concepts.

These approaches try to understand compound nouns by coding as much knowledge as possible about the words, semantic relationships, and control structures. In this paper we investigate a different approach for understanding compound nouns consisting of two words. We use only a few basic semantic relationships and provide the system with the ability to learn the details of the basic semantic relationships from training examples. Instead of encoding knowledge structures and control structures for understanding compound nouns, basic semantic relationships in compound nouns are learned using a connectionist architecture.

The Domain and the Basic Semantic Relationships

Compound nouns are frequently used in almost every domain. Our domain is the NPL[1] corpus (Sparck-Jones 76) which contains abstracts and queries from the physical sciences. From this corpus

[1]National Physics Laboratory

we randomly chose 108 compound nouns consisting of two words, e.g. "heat effect". Each word is represented as a binary vector of 16 semantic features, which were extracted by using the NASA thesaurus (NASA 85). For a more detailed description of the process of feature extraction see (Wermter and Lehnert 89). Figure 1 illustrates the semantic features for the compound nouns.

Semantic Features	Examples
MEASURING-EVENT	Observation, Investigation, Research
CHANGING-EVENT	Amplification, Acceleration, Loss
SCIENTIFIC-FIELD	Mechanics, Ferromagnetics
PROPERTY	Intensity, Viscosity, Temperature
MECHANISM	Experiment, Technique, Theorem
ELECTRIC-OBJECT	Transistor, Resistor, Amplifier
PHYSICAL-OBJECT	Earth, Crystal, Vehicle, Room
RELATION	Cause, Dependence, Interaction
ORGANIZATION-FORM	Layer, Level, Stratification, F-Region
GAS	Air, Oxygen, Atmosphere, Nitrogen
SPATIAL-LOCATION	Antarctic, Earth, Range, Region, Source
TIME	June, Day, Time, History
ENERGY	Radiation, Ray, Light, Sound, Current
MATERIAL	Aluminium, Water, Carbon, Vapour
ABSTRACT-REPRESENTATION	Note, Data, Equation, Term, Parameter
EMPTY	Cavity, Vacua

Figure 1: Semantic Features of the Nouns and Examples

To represent basic semantic associations between words we use 7 basic semantic relationships. We specify a **Basic Semantic Relationship** as a preposition paraphrase (see figure 2). For example, a "room experiment" has the basic semantic relationship IN-P since the experiment is "in" a room, and an "excitation mechanism" has the basic semantic relationship FOR-P since it is a mechanism "for" excitation. Each compound noun can have different basic semantic relationships; for instance, a "feedback circuit" is a "circuit FOR-P feedback" or a "circuit WITH-P feedback". Each basic semantic relationship can have several meanings; for instance, the IN-P is different for "storage IN-P computer" and "disturbance IN-P atmosphere".

Basic Semantic Relationships	Examples for the Basic Semantic Relationships
BY-P	Impurity Conduction
FOR-P	Excitation Mechanism
FROM-P	Space Vehicle
IN-P	Room Experiment
OF-P	Oxygen Emission
ON-P	Skin Effect
WITH-P	Amplifier Circuit

Figure 2: The Basic Semantic Relationships

We consider the basic semantic relationships as a first step to differentiate semantic relationships according to their main properties. This general concept of classifying semantic relationships according to preposition paraphrases has been found useful in several studies on compound nouns (e.g., (Lee 60) (Levi 78) (Finin 80)), since preposition paraphrases contain general relationships; e.g., FROM-P expresses a source, FOR-P expresses a purpose, and IN-P expresses inclusion. Our goal here is to specify basic semantic relationships as preposition paraphrases and to build a system which learns the underlying semantic relationships from training examples.

The Architecture

The architecture for learning semantic relationships is a backpropagation network with three layers (see figure 3). The bottom layer consists of 32 binary input units for the semantic features of the two words in the compound noun. The hidden layer is a 7 x 12 array of hidden units, 12 hidden units for each of the 7 basic semantic relationships. The top layer consists of 7 real-valued output units, one for each of the 7 basic semantic relationships.

Each output unit is connected only to all hidden units of the same basic semantic relationship. All hidden units are connected to all input units. This modular organization has two advantages: (1) training and testing for each basic semantic relationship can be done independently, and (2) adding, deleting and modifying a basic semantic relationship does not require retraining the whole network.

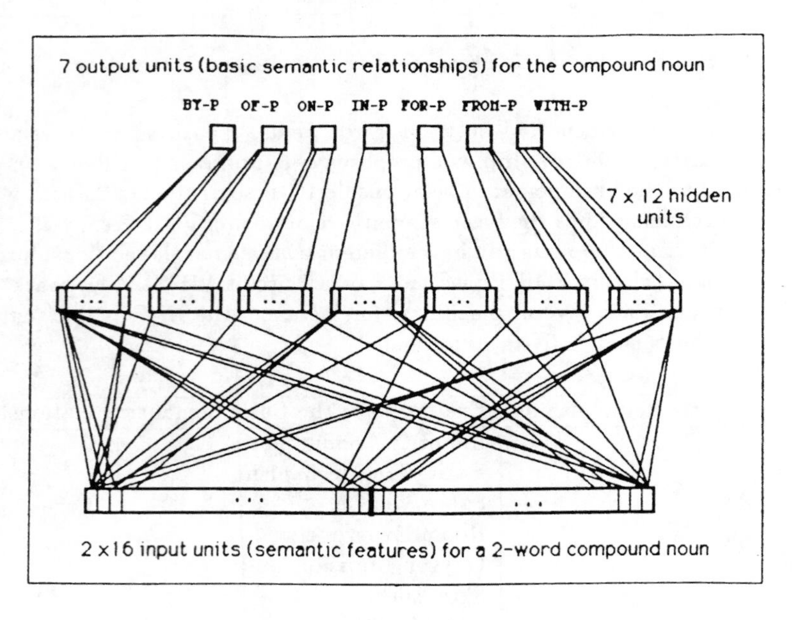

Figure 3: The Structure of the Backpropagation Network

Training the Network

First, 108 compound nouns consisting of two words were randomly selected from the NPL corpus. Each compound noun was represented with 32 binary features, 16 for each word. The 108 compound nouns were divided into 88 compound nouns for a training set and 20 compound nouns for a test set. Because of the modular architecture the network can be trained in separate modules for the different basic semantic relationships. For each of the 7 basic semantic relationships the feature representations of the 88 compound nouns were presented as the input together with a desired binary plausibility value as the output. The plausibility value indicates if the basic semantic relationship between the two words is plausible (value 1) or not plausible (value 0). The following example shows two of the 88 training examples for the basic semantic relationship IN-P: "Plasma layer" in the sense of "layer IN-P plasma" is plausible, while "sunspot number" in the sense of "number IN-P sunspot" is not plausible.

```
PLASMA LAYER        ->      LAYER IN-P PLASMA        1
SUNSPOT NUMBER      ->      NUMBER IN-P SUNSPOT      0
```

For each of the 7 basic semantic relationships the semantic features and plausibility values of the 88 compound nouns were presented for 800 cycles (that is 70400 training examples). The backpropagation algorithm (Rumelhart et. al. 86) was used to learn the plausibility of each basic semantic relationship[2]. To be independent of the random start initialization of the network, three different runs (each with the 70400 training examples) were conducted for each of the 7 basic semantic relationships. Within this learning phase the average of the total sum squared error for all training examples over all 21 runs decreased from 23.2 at the start of the training to 1.4 at the end of the training.

Evaluation of the Test Results

After training, the network was tested on the training set of 88 compound nouns and the test set of 20 compound nouns. The semantic feature representation of the compound nouns in the test set had not been part of the training set. The network was tested by presenting the feature representation of a compound noun, and the system computed the plausibility value for each basic semantic relationship. A basic semantic relationship is considered correct, if the computed plausibility value deviates less than 0.49 from the desired value 1 for a plausible basic semantic relationship and from the desired value 0 for an implausible basic semantic relationship.

[2]The learning rate η was set to 0.01, the weight change momentum α was 0.9 for all experiments.

Basic Semantic Relationships	Correct in the Training Set	Correct in the Test Set
BY-P	94%	83%
FOR-P	97%	73%
FROM-P	94%	82%
IN-P	96%	73%
OF-P	93%	77%
ON-P	98%	95%
WITH-P	98%	88%

Figure 4: Basic Semantic Relationships in Training Set and Test Set

Figure 4 illustrates the overall system performance on the training set and on the test set for each basic semantic relationship. The average percentage of correctly learned training examples for the three different learning runs is between 93% and 98%, the percentage of correctly generalized test examples is between 73% and 95%.

Figure 5 shows a more detailed interpretation of representative examples from the test set of new compound nouns. Each compound noun is shown with the computed plausibility values for each basic semantic relationship[3]. We say that a basic semantic relationship for a compound noun exists if the computed plausibility value is greater than or equal to 0.5.

Compound Nouns	BY-P	FOR-P	FROM-P	IN-P	OF-P	ON-P	WITH-P
Heat Exchange	0.3	0.0	0.0	0.3	0.9	0.0	0.0
Transistor Life	0.0	0.4	0.0	0.1	1.0	0.0	0.1
Writing Method	0.0	0.8	0.1	0.0	1.0	0.0	0.0
Wing Motion	0.0	0.1	0.3	1.0	0.5	0.0	0.0
Waveform Solution	0.1	0.4	0.0	0.1	0.4	0.1	0.0
Earth Satellite	0.0	0.0	0.9	0.9	0.0	0.0	0.7
Transport Theory	0.3	0.1	0.0	0.0	0.9	0.6	0.1
Water Vapour	0.0	0.0	0.6	1.0	0.4	0.0	0.6
Wave Propagation	0.1	0.0	0.2	0.7	0.7	0.1	0.0
Microwave Emission	0.7	0.1	0.0	0.0	1.0	0.0	0.0

Figure 5: Examples for the Interpretation of Compound Nouns (see text for explanation)

In the first two examples in figure 5 a single basic semantic relationship exists between the two words in the compound noun: "heat exchange" is interpreted as "exchange OF-P heat", and "transistor life" as "life OF-P transistor" (only these basic semantic relationships have a plausibility value greater or equal 0.5).

[3]Again, as in figure 4, the plausibility values shown are the averages over the three different runs for each basic semantic relationships.

Although only one basic semantic relationship exists in the first two examples, most test examples have more than one existing basic semantic relationship. For instance, "writing method" has the existing relationships "method FOR-P writing" and "method OF-P writing". The other basic semantic relationships for "writing method", like "method BY-P writing" and "method FROM-P writing", do not exist. Another example of multiple basic semantic relationships is "wing motion" (as in airplanes) which is interpreted as "motion OF-P wing" and "motion IN-P wing". This example illustrates ambiguous interpretations and context is needed to determine if the wing is the object which is moving (motion OF-P wing) or the location of a motion (motion IN-P wing).

The plausibilty values in Figure 5 indicate unsure interpretations as well. For instance, the plausibility values of the compound noun "waveform solution" are lower than 0.5 for all basic semantic relationships. The network can not find a basic semantic relationship because similar relationships had not been in the training set. The results show examples with some incorrect basic semantic relationships as well. For instance "water vapour" is interpreted with 3 existing relationships: "vapour FROM-P water", "vapour WITH-P water", and "vapour IN-P water". While the first two relationships FROM-P and WITH-P are plausible, the third is not plausible.

Although our corpus is still fairly small our test results demonstrate the extent to which the learned basic semantic relationships generalize for new compound nouns. The basic semantic relationships in our network generalize well for compound nouns whose first and second noun are characterized with subsets of the following semantic features: Noun1: ENERGY PROPERTY ORGANIZATION-FORM and Noun2: CHANGING-EVENT PROPERTY MECHANISM. Examples for this class of compound nouns are "heat exchange" and "wave propagation". Another class of compound nouns with good generalizations are subsets of the following features: Noun1: ELECTRIC-OBJECT PHYSICAL-OBJECT and Noun2: TIME PROPERTY, like in "transistor life".

Besides these classes of compound nouns with good generalizations, compound nouns with subsets of the following features do not generalize well: Noun1: PHYSICAL-OBJECT SPATIAL-LOCATION MATERIAL and Noun2: PHYSICAL-OBJECT GAS MATERIAL. Examples with subsets of these feature combinations are "earth satellite" and "water vapour". The reason for the decrease in the generalization performance for this last class is the restricted use of only 16 semantic features. To generalize relationships between two physical objects more features are needed. For instance, a network with a SIZE feature could generalize the WITH-P relationships between physical objects so that "earth satellite" could not be interpreted as "satellite WITH-P earth" since the earth has a bigger size than a satellite. The identification of these incorrectly generalized basic relationships is important for deciding which semantic features and basic semantic relationships might be modified. We make no claim for a "right" classification of semantic features and basic semantic relationships for our domain but we claim that the adaptive process of identifying better suitable semantic features and semantic relationships is supported by the learning ability and the modular architecture.

Related work

Comparing the performance of our system with existing systems for compound noun analysis is somewhat difficult, because the techniques, the level of the semantic relationships, and the domains are fundamentally different. McDonald reports about 54% to 64% correct interpretations for his compound noun system (McDonald 82) using detailed semantic relationships and fixed control strategies. The performance of Finin's system is similar to McDonald's system. Our system determines plausible basic semantic relationships for unknown compound nouns. Although our basic semantic relationships are not as detailed as McDonald's or Finin's, our basic semantic relationships are automatically acquired. As far as we know there is currently no system which has the ability to *learn* the semantic relationships between compound nouns.

Our system has the advantage of learning knowledge for the semantic relationships, while this knowledge is difficult to acquire in other compound noun systems (e.g. (Finin 80) (McDonald 82) (Arens 87) (Gay 88)). The knowledge about semantic relationships is represented uniformly in modular networks. On the other hand, these systems allow compound nouns with more than two words while we need additional mechanisms to understand longer compound nouns. Currently, we are investigating the use of recursive autoassociative network architectures ((Pollack 88), (St John 88)) and relaxation networks (Wermter 89) to understand compound nouns of arbitrary length.

Conclusions

One way to approach compound noun analysis is the use of extensive knowledge engineering, as demonstrated in several computational models. Because of the difficulties of identifying the semantic relationships and control structures, we presented a new approach for understanding compound nouns. Using a modular connectionist architecture we showed that basic semantic relationships within compound nouns can be learned. The general concepts of basic semantic relationships, learning, and modular network architectures demonstrate how uniform memory models can be built for natural language understanding.

Acknowledgements

I would like to thank Wendy Lehnert, Steve Bradtke, Claire Cardie, and Ellen Riloff for discussions and comments on earlier drafts of this paper. This research was supported by the Advanced Research Projects Agency of the Department of Defense, monitored by the Office of Naval Research under contract #N00014-87-K-0238, the Office of Naval Research, under a University Research Initiative Grant, Contract #N00014-86-K-0764 and NSF Presidential Young Investigators Award NSFIST-8351863.

References

1. Arens Y., Granacki J.J., Parker, A.C. 1987. Phrasal Analysis of Long Noun Sequences. *Proceedings of the ACL 87.*

2. Fahlman S.E. 1979. *NETL: A system for representing and using real-world knowledge.*

3. Finin T.W. 1980. *The semantic Interpretation of Compound Nominals.* PhD Thesis. University of Illinois at Urbana-Champaign.

4. Dahl A.D., Palmer M.S., Passonneau R.J. 1987. Nominalizations in PUNDIT. *Procedings of the ACL 1987.*

5. Gay L.S. 1988. *Interpreting Nominal Compounds for Information Retrieval.* Internal Report, GE Research and Development Center.

6. Lee R.B. 1960. The grammar of English Nominalizations. *International Journal of American Linguistics, Vol. 26, 3.*

7. Lehnert W.G. 1986. The analysis of compound nouns. *VERSUS, December, 1986.*

8. Levi J.N. 1978. The syntax and semantics of complex nominals.

9. Marcus M.P. 1980. *A theory of syntactic recognition for natural language.*

10. McDonald D.B. 1982. *Understanding Noun Compounds.* PhD thesis, Carnegie Mellon University.

11. NASA Thesaurus 1985.

12. Pollack J. 1988. Recursive Auto-associative Memory: Devising Compositional Distributed Representations. *Proc. of the Tenth Annual Conference of the Cognitive Science Society.*

13. Rumelhart D.E., Hinton G.E., Williams R.J. 1886. Learning Internal Representations by Error Propagation. In: McClelland J.L., Rumelhart D.E. (Ed.) *Parallel Distributed Processing Vol 1.* MIT Press.

14. Sparck-Jones K., VanRijsbergen C.J. 1976. Information Retrieval Test Collections. *Journal of Documentation, vol 32, no 1.*

15. St.John M.F., McClelland J.L. 1988. Applying contextual constraints in sentence comprehension. *Proc. of the Tenth Annual Conference of the Cognitive Science Society.*

16. Wermter S., Lehnert W.G. 1989. Noun phrase analysis with connectionist networks. In: Sharkey N., Reilly R.: *Connectionist Approaches to Language Processing.* (in press).

17. Wermter S. 1989. Integration of semantic and syntactic constraints for structural noun phrase disambiguation. *Proc. of the Eleventh International Joint Conference on Artificial Intelligence 89.*

The Role of Intermediate Abstractions in Understanding Science and Mathematics

Barbara Y. White

BBN Laboratories
10 Moulton Street
Cambridge, MA 02138

Abstract

Acquiring powerful abstractions -- i.e., representations that enable one to reason about key aspects of a domain in an economical and generic form -- should be a primary goal of learning. The most effective means for achieving this goal is not, we argue, the "top-down" approach of traditional curricula where students are first presented with an abstraction, such as **F=ma**, and then with examples of how it applies in a variety of contexts. Nor do we advocate the "bottom-up" approach proposed by situated cognition theorists. Instead, we argue for a "middle-out" approach where students are introduced to new domains via intermediate abstractions in the form of mechanistic causal models. These models serve as "conceptual eyeglasses" that unpack causal mechanisms implicit in abstractions such as **F=ma**. They are readily mappable to a variety of real-world contexts since their objects and operators are generic and causal. Intermediate abstractions thus give meaning to higher-order abstractions as well as to real-world situations, provide a link between the two, and a route to understanding.

Proponents of the theory of "situated cognition" argue that abstractions are an inherently impoverished and inert knowledge form, and that to be meaningful, knowledge must be contextualized in real-world situations. The following quotation exemplifies this position: "A situated theory of knowledge challenges the widely held belief that the abstraction of knowledge from situations is the key to transferability. An examination of the role of situations in structuring knowledge indicates that abstraction and explication provide an inherently impoverished and often misleading view of knowledge" (Brown, Collins, & Duguid, 1989).

In this paper we support the contrary position: Real-world situations are inherently complex and confusing -- The key to powerful cognition lies in acquiring knowledge in an abstract form, and in understanding the form and utility of abstraction. This position is consistent with the generally accepted view of mathematical and scientific knowledge, and this perspective is implicitly embedded within most existing math, science, and engineering curricula. The failure of many of these curricula, we argue, is not due to this belief in the importance of abstraction, rather, it is due to the way in which abstractions are introduced to students. In this paper, we will argue for the need to start curricula with "intermediate abstractions" in the form of models that (1) map readily to real-world contexts, (2) yet possess many of the properties of higher-order abstractions, and (3) unpack the meaning of higher-order abstractions, thereby providing a bridge to acquiring and using such abstractions. These intermediate abstractions serve as "conceptual eyeglasses" that enable students to make sense out of physical domains and mathematical formalisms.

The Meaning of Abstraction

If one looks up the word "abstraction" in the dictionary (The Second College Edition of the American Heritage Dictionary), one is presented with a variety of nuances for the term:

1. "Thought without reference to a specified instance". Abstract representations incorporate generic objects and operators. For instance, they reason about forces being applied to objects, rather than about kicks being applied to balls. Using such representations, one can reason about generic, abstract cases rather than about specific objects and situations. In this way, students can evolve knowledge in a form that can be mapped onto many different situations. The claim (supported by the research of Bassok & Holyoak, in press) is that such generic representations facilitate the transfer of knowledge to multiple contexts.
2. "The concentrated essence of a larger whole". One interpretation of this nuance is that abstract representations typically attempt to model only certain aspects of a domain. This is particularly true of abstractions, like F=ma and V=IR, employed in scientific disciplines. They enable one to achieve an economy of thought by simplifying the situation and thereby reducing the cognitive load. Yet, if one abstracts the key properties of the domain, powerful inferences can be made from such economical simplifications. Another interpretation of this nuance has to do with the form of the representation itself. For instance, V=IR is a more compact form for expressing the relationship between voltage, current, and resistance than is a dynamic, causal model of electrical circuit behavior. The quantitative law, V=IR, takes less space to represent than the causal model, and can be employed in algebraic, constraint-based reasoning. This form of reasoning, enabled by the form in which the law is represented, allows the efficient generation of certain inferences about the properties of any given circuit (see White & Frederiksen, 1987). Thus the phrase "concentrated essence" can refer to the economy of both the content and the form of what is being represented.
3. "Meaningless or difficult to understand". Many students have had the experience of being presented with laws in physics class and of finding them difficult to comprehend. Yet, one of the primary goals of learning is to acquire such powerful abstractions that apply across a range of contexts (i) to generate explanations and (ii) to solve many different types of problems. In this paper, we argue that these abstractions need not be meaningless or difficult to understand, if they are introduced via "intermediate abstractions".

Examples of Intermediate Abstractions

Proponents of the theory of situated cognition argue for a "bottom-up" approach to education: Knowledge structures that are widely applicable (which they term generalizations[1]) should be gradually induced from exposure to many real-world instances (Brown, Collins, & Duguid, 1989). This is a viewpoint shared by many case-based reasoning proponents (e.g., Spiro, Coulson, Feltovich, & Anderson, 1989). Traditional curricula typically embody a more "top-down" approach to education: Students are first presented with general principles in the form of abstract formalisms, and are then given examples of how the principles apply in real-world situations. In contrast to both of these viewpoints, we argue for a "middle-out" approach to education. Students should first be presented with intermediate

[1]Generalizations, they argue (Brown, Collins, & Duguid, 1989), differ from abstractions in that generalizations are analogous to fables, whereas, abstractions are analogous to the moral of the fable.

abstractions, in the form of dynamic causal models, that share many properties of both the real-world and of higher-order abstractions. To foster their acquisition, these models can be made interactive and articulate by embedding them in a computer simulation. When internalized by students in the form of a mental model, they enable students to (i) interpret real-world situations and (ii) give meaning to higher-order abstractions like F=ma and V=IR. They provide a more efficient and effective route, we will argue, to understanding and utilizing powerful abstractions. In this section we present three examples of intermediate abstractions: one from mathematics, one from engineering, and one from physics.

Example #1: Understanding place-value notation and arithmetic: The first illustration presents an abstraction that is intermediate between concrete situations, such as working with Dienes blocks, and higher-order abstractions, such as working with arabic numbers and formal arithmetic. It incorporates a "bin model" for representing place value notation and the arithmetic operations of addition and subtraction. When embodied in a computer system, this model displays bins on the screen: a ones bin, a tens bin, a hundreds bin, and a thousands bin (see Figure 1). The students can give commands, such as ADD 386 or SUBTRACT 79, and the program will cause the appropriate numbers of icons to be added or subtracted from the appropriate bins in a manner analogous to the standard procedures for addition and subtraction. When a bin overflows, the process of carrying is animated. Similarly, when the student is subtracting and there are not enough icons in the appropriate bin, the model visually portrays the process of borrowing. While doing so, the computer explains what it is doing and why to the student using computer generated speech. When students worked with and began to assimilate this model, we found that their understanding of place notation and its relationship to the processes of addition and subtraction improved (Feurzeig & White, 1983). Once assimilated, the model was used as a foundation for introducing the standard arithmetic procedures that operate on arabic numbers, and for modelling alternative real-world situations. (See Resnick & Omanson (1987) for a discussion of Dienes blocks as a bridging abstraction for understanding arithmetic.)

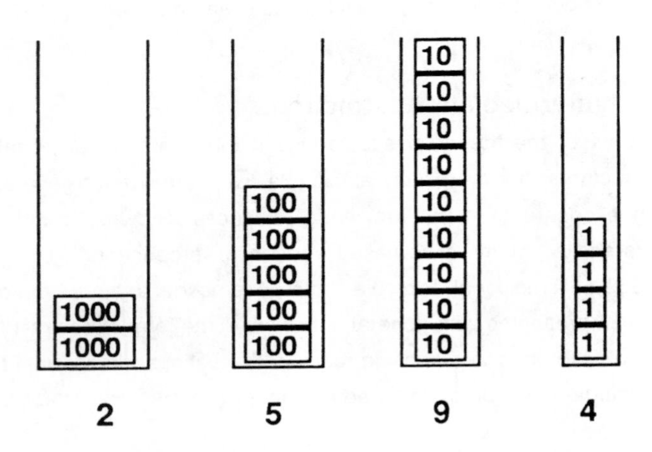

Figure 1. The bin model.

Example #2: Understanding how electrical circuits work: The next example is a generic model of a transport mechanism that represents the aggregate behavior of particles (see Frederiksen & White, in press; White & Frederiksen, in press). It is more abstract than a model of the movement of individual particles, and less abstract than models based on steady-state principles such as V=IR. In this model, there are objects that contain "stuff" (where stuff can represent, for instance, collections of electrically charged particles). If two such objects are connected together, and if they contain different amounts of stuff, then stuff will flow from one to the other (see Figure 2). In each time increment, the flow of stuff between adjacent objects depends on the "stuff gradient" (i.e., the difference in the amount of stuff). The explanation for why stuff flows is reductionistic and is based upon the motion of particles and their interactions (e.g., attraction & repulsion). The aggregate transport model provides an introductory representation for many physical processes such as (1) the distribution of electrical charge, (2) the diffusion of gases, and (3) the flow of heat. If one creates a model of a physical system using this transport process, such as a model of an electrical circuit, one can see how the steady-state laws (such as Ohm's law and Kirchhoff's laws) are emergent properties of a system that incorporates this process (see Figure 3). The model thus links the behavior of individual particles with the steady-state system equations. It is interesting to conjecture that there may be a few such physical-process models that can potentially play a crucial role in understanding physical systems. These process models may be key because (1) they facilitate the understanding of a wide range of systems, (2) they are relatively easy to interpret since they can be explained in terms of concepts and processes, like attraction and repulsion, derived from common experiences with the every-day world, and (3) they provide a mechanistic origin for the steady-state laws that are so useful in predicting the behavior of physical systems.

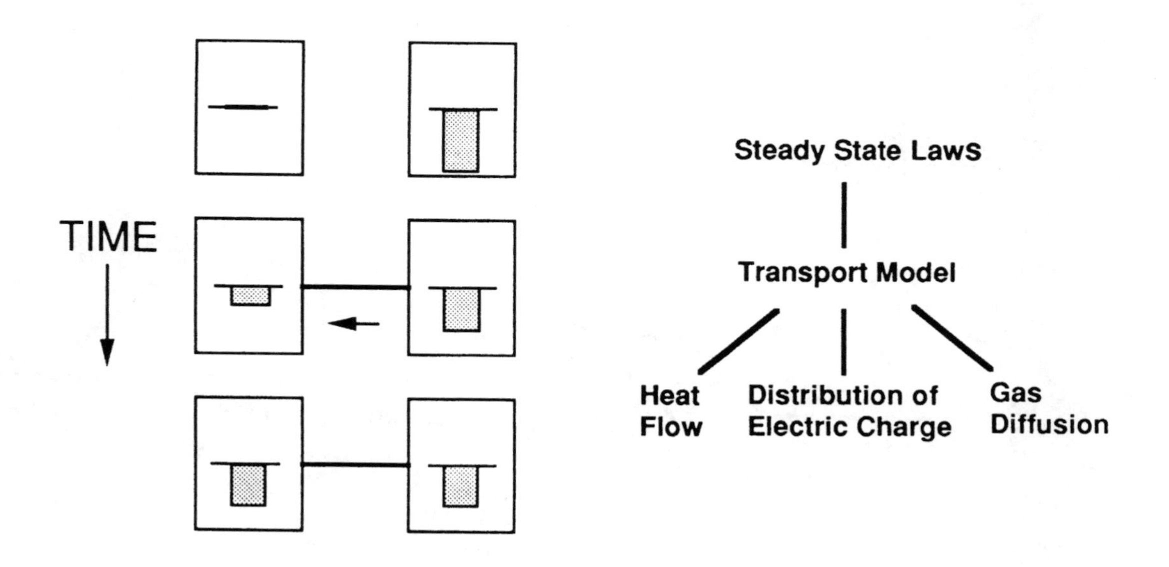

Figure 2. The transport model.

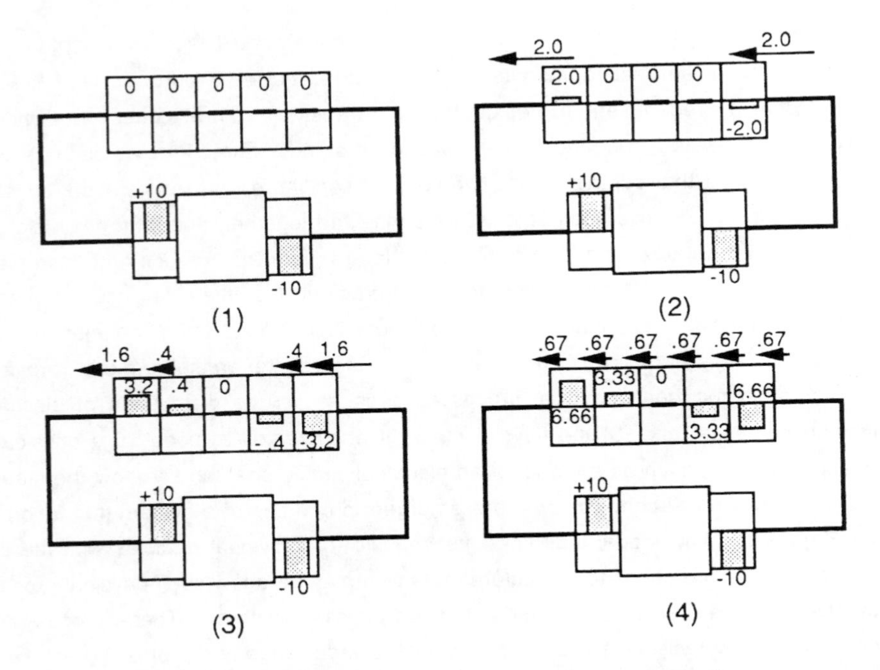

Figure 3. An electrical circuit with a resistor and a battery.
At steady state, current flows are equal and charge densities form a stable gradient.

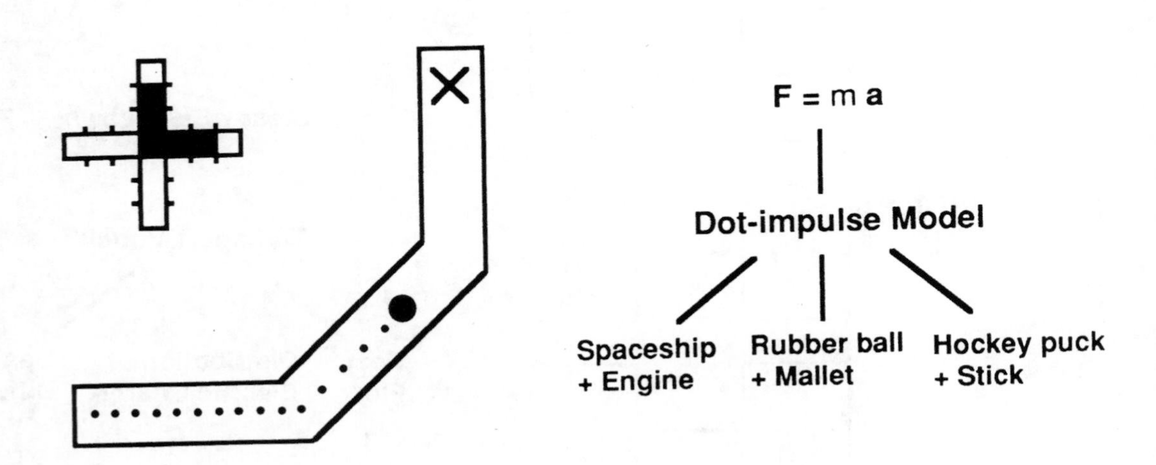

Figure 4. The dot-impulse model.

In the task displayed above, the student is controlling the motion of the large dot in order to make it navigate the track and stop on the target X. The small dots indicate the history of the large dot's motion, and the cross at the upper left indicates the large dot's orthogonal velocity components.

Example #3: Understanding Newtonian mechanics: This final example describes an intermediate abstraction that has proven useful in helping middle school students understand force and motion (see White & Horwitz, 1988; White; 1988). When presented with the computer embodiment of this causal model, students engage in tasks such as attempting to control the motion of an object by applying impulses to it via a joystick (see Figure 4). The students are not asked to think of this object as a spaceship with a rocket engine, nor as a billiard ball controlled by a stick. Instead they are asked to think of it as a generic object (which is simply referred to as the "dot") being controlled by impulses (i.e., forces that act for a short time). The students' task is to determine the physical laws underlying this model. They formulate principles such as "whenever you apply an impulse to the dot, it changes its speed". These qualitative laws form the foundation for understanding more abstract laws such as F=ma. Further, the generic quality of the students' laws plays a role in enabling them to transfer and apply the principles underlying this model to real world contexts (see White, 1988).

Properties of Intermediate Abstractions

These three examples of intermediate abstractions share some common properties that we conjecture are crucial to their success in fostering understanding:

1. Useful: They model and generate explanations relevant to key aspects of a domain. For instance, example #1 presents a model of place value notation and its implications for the design of arithmetic procedures. Example #2, when instantiated in the context of electrical circuits, presents a model for the concept of voltage drop, and for how voltages and currents change when the conductivity of devices within circuits change. Example #3 presents a model for forces and how they affect the motion of objects. These models thus enable one to predict, envision, and explain the behavior of systems. They can thereby foster the acquisition of difficult domain concepts and processes that are crucial to domain understanding.

2. Transferable: The objects and actions in intermediate abstractions are represented in a decontextualized form -- they embody generic objects and forces. For instance, the tens icon in example #1 is just a generic icon which, in the course of problem solving, can be instantiated to represent anything from ten jelly beans to a ten dollar bill. Similarly, the "stuff" in example #2 can be thought of as generic stuff, and can be instantiated to represent anything from electrical charge to gas molecules. Further, the "dot" in example #3 is just a generic object which can map onto anything from a spaceship to a hockey puck. Presenting generic icons, operators, and processes might play a key role in enabling students to readily map these intermediate abstractions to different real-world situations, and to thereby give higher-order abstractions meaning in many contexts.

3. Meaningful: Intermediate abstractions are meaningful and relatively easy to understand because they build on intuitive notions of causality and mechanism. They parse the behavior of a system into a sequence of discrete causal events, and introduce a sense of mechanism. Further, they are grounded in primitive abstractions (akin to diSessa's (1983) phenomenological primitives). That is, they are constructed from conceptual and process abstractions, like *resistance* and *balancing*, which students derived as children from experiences with the everyday world. For instance, in example #1, adding more objects causes a container to overflow. In example #2, a change in connectivity or amount of stuff causes stuff to change location. And, in example #3, impulses cause changes in objects' velocities. All of these are easy to understand, and link abstractions, like V=IR and F=ma, to mechanistic causal phenomena. Intermediate abstractions thus provide a bridge that gives meaning to higher-order abstractions (such as arabic numbers and arithmetic, steady-state circuit laws, and Newton's laws of motion). They also provide a causal theory for interpreting real-world situations.

Acquiring Intermediate Abstractions

Despite the fact that intermediate abstractions incorporate primitive abstractions, they are, nonetheless, a more abstract and sophisticated knowledge form. They include graphical representations, such as the cross shown in Figure 4 (which represents the orthogonal velocity components of the dot), and principles for operating on those representations to predict system behavior. When reified in a computer microworld, they become formal models whose properties can be discovered and debated.

When students first interact with computer microworlds that embody these intermediate abstractions, they typically induce principles that are overly situation specific. For instance, when exposed to the dot-impulse model of example #3, they formulate rules such as "If the dot is moving to the right at one unit of speed and you want it to stop, apply an impulse to the left". In order to help students to internalize these models in a more useful form, instructional techniques need to be developed that center around interacting with the microworlds. For instance, in research with the dot-impulse model (see White & Horwitz, 1988), we developed techniques that include getting students to evaluate alternative laws proposed for the microworld. The laws vary in correctness, generality, and parsimony in order to foster discussions about the properties of a good scientific law. Such techniques help students to evolve mental models in a generally applicable form. They also foster an awareness about the form of scientific knowledge. Only after students have assimilated the intermediate abstraction are they asked to consider its application to real-world situations: Does it apply in a given context and is it useful? And, only after they have internalized the model do they use it to derive higher-order abstractions. The model thus forms the "conceptual eyeglasses" for interpreting both the real-world and higher-order abstractions.

Conclusions

Intermediate abstractions, we have argued, can enable students to understand physical domains and mathematical formalisms. They provide a medium for exploring the form and utility of abstractions: What are models, how do they evolve, and why are they useful? The challenge for cognitive scientists and instructional designers is (1) to determine the properties that effective intermediate abstractions must possess, (2) to create models that possess these properties, and (3) to devise interesting projects for students that require the acquisition and use of these models. Such projects could include designing electrical circuits, or constructing a theory of force and motion. Thus, intermediate abstractions, when appropriately designed and embodied as interactive articulate microworlds, can provide tools not only for developing understanding, but also for introducing students to the practices of engineering and scientific inquiry.

Acknowledgements

This research was funded by the Army Research Institute under contract MND-90387C0545, and by the National Science Foundation under grants DPE-8400280 and SED-8012481. The author is grateful to Allan Collins and John Frederiksen for their comments on a draft of this paper.

References

Bassok, M. & Holyoak, K. (in press). Interdomain transfer between isomorphic topics in algebra and physics. The Journal of Experimental Psychology: Learning, Memory, and Cognition).

Brown, J., Collins, A., & Duguid, P. (1989). Situated Cognition and the Culture of Learning. BBN Report No. 6886, BBN Laboratories, Cambridge, Massachusetts.

diSessa, A. (1983). Phenomenology and the evolution of intuition. In D. Gentner & A. Stevens (Eds.), Mental Models, Hillsdale, NJ: Lawrence Erlbaum.

Feurzeig, W., & White, B. (1983). Development of an Articulate Instructional System for Teaching Arithmetic Procedures. BBN Report No. 5484, BBN Laboratories, Cambridge, Massachusetts.

Frederiksen, J., & White, B. (in press). Mental models and understanding: A problem for science education. In New Directions in Educational Technology. E. Scanlon & T. O'Shea (Eds.). New York: Springer Verlag.

Resnick, L., & Omanson, S. (1987). Learning to understand arithmetic. In Glaser, R. (Ed.). Advances in Instructional Psychology (Vol. 3). Hillsdale, NJ: Erlbaum.

Spiro, R., Coulson, R., Feltovich, P., & Anderson, D. (1988). Cognitive flexibility theory: Advanced knowledge acquisition in ill-structured domains. In the Proceedings of the Tenth Annual Meeting of the Cognitive Science Society. Hillsdale, NJ: Erlbaum.

White, B., & Frederiksen, J. (in press). Causal models as intelligent learning environments for science and engineering education. Applied Artificial Intelligence.

White, B., & Frederiksen, J. (1987). Causal Model Progressions as a Foundation for Intelligent Learning Environments. Report No. 6686, BBN Laboratories, Cambridge, Massachusetts. To appear in Artificial Intelligence.

White, B., & Horwitz, P. (1988). Computer microworlds and conceptual change: A new approach to science education. In Improving Learning: New Perspectives. P. Ramsden (Ed.), Kogan Page, London.

White, B. (1988). ThinkerTools: Causal Models, Conceptual Change, and Science Education. Report No. 6873, BBN Laboratories, Cambridge, Massachusetts. To appear in Cognition and Instruction.

Learning From Examples: The Effect of Different Conceptual Roles

Edward J. Wisniewski
Psychology Department
University of Illinois

Many studies of category learning have emphasized a single role of the concept that is learned --namely, the concept as a mechanism for classifying objects and discriminating them from members of other categories. Recently, researchers have noted that concepts have many purposes besides classification--prediction, communication, explanation, goal attainment, and so on. This paper presents a study that varied the roles of concepts during a classification learning task. Specifically, one group of subjects (the discrimination group) was given standard instructions to learn about pairs of categories. A second group of subjects (the goal group) was given these instructions but also informed about the functions of the categories. The results of the study suggest that the two groups formed different concepts, even though they saw the same examples of the categories. The concepts of the discrimination group were based on those features in the examples that had predictive value--features with high cue and category validity. In contrast, the concepts of the goal group were based on predictive features and features that were important to the function of the category (called "core" features). Relative to the discrimination group, the goal group placed less emphasis on predictiveness. The results are discussed in terms of their implications for standard classification tasks in psychology and explanation-based and similarity-based approaches in machine learning.

INTRODUCTION

In many category learning tasks, the experimenter presents examples of two or more categories, and subjects learn concepts that allow them to discriminate members of one category from those of others. These tasks provide insight into the general nature of people's concepts (e.g., Reed, 1972; Rosch, Simpson, & Miller, 1976; Medin, Wattenmaker, & Michalski, 1987; Nosofsky, Clark, & Shin, 1989).This paradigm is similar to the similarity-based learning paradigm in machine learning. In similarity-based learning, a program examines a number of examples of different categories and creates generalized descriptions (concepts) of those categories. The descriptions enable the program to identify new category members (see Dietterich & Michalski, 1983; Fisher & Langley, 1985, for overviews of these systems).

There are at least two problems with this approach, however. First, it focuses people and programs on forming concepts that emphasize only one of many roles that concepts can have (i.e., classification or discrimination). The importance of the concept is for accurately classifying category members. However, concepts must represent information about a category other than that used to identify its members. Otherwise, why have concepts? In the real world, people don't form concepts solely to use them to identify objects. Object classification is just one of many roles of a concept. Other roles of concepts include using them to attain goals, construct explanations, make predictions, and so on (Schank, Collins, & Hunter, 1986; Matheus, Rendell, Medin, & Goldstone, 1989). Second, the approach focuses people and programs on forming concepts that are based only on information that is explicit in the training examples (but see Stepp & Michalski, 1986). As a result, it ignores the effect of background knowledge on concept formation. In the real world, people inductively learn about categories by integrating background knowledge with the information provided in the examples. Some of this background knowledge includes people's basic, common sense theories of the world (Murphy & Medin, 1985; Medin & Wattenmaker, 1986; Murphy & Wisniewski, in press; Pazzani & Schulenburg, 1989).

In general, by emphasizing only the classification role that concepts play and by ignoring the importance of background knowledge, these learning tasks may obscure the nature of people's concepts and the processes that they use to form them. This paper examines differences in conceptual structure that result when different roles of concepts and different kinds of background knowledge are emphasized. The results of an experiment suggest that: i) people form different concepts from the same set of training examples, when different roles of the concept are emphasized, and ii) people represent information about a category other than that used to identify its members (e.g., information relevant to achieving goals).

EXPERIMENT 1

Undoubtedly, our concepts of objects contain a large amount of information about the functions of objects (Barsalou, 1982). This information is important in achieving goals. As an example, consider one's concept of washing machine and its function "to clean clothes." To achieve the goal of cleaning clothes, we know that clothes, soap, and water must be placed in the machine, it must be turned on, various dials must be set, and so on. While these features are important in achieving a particular goal, any one of the features may not be particularly predictive of category membership. For example, the feature "contains water" is a property of many things and could not be used to classify an object as a washing machine. Yet, the feature is crucial to our understanding of washing machines. This reasoning suggests that when learning about categories, providing people with their functions may induce them to search for features that are relevant to those functions and to incorporate them into their conceptual representations. Providing these functions emphasizes the goal-achievement role of a concept.

In the following experiment, different conceptual roles were emphasized by either informing or not informing subjects about the functions of the categories that they were learning about. In this study, one group of subjects was only instructed to learn the categories (the "classification" group). Because these instructions emphasize the classification role of concepts, we reasoned that subjects might look for features that identify the members of a given category and exclude those of other categories. What will make a feature important is that it have high cue and category validity. Cue validity is the probability that given a particular feature, an object belongs to a category. Category validity is the probability that given an object belonging to the category, it has the feature. So, for example, if the feature of color allows one to discriminate all members of one category from another (a feature with perfect category and cue validity), then that feature will be incorporated into a person's concept. On the other hand, subjects who are informed about the functions of the categories (the "goal" group) should also look for features that are relevant to achieving the category function. So, for example, given the function "used for underwater public transport," subjects might consider the features, "has a propeller" and "emits sonar" as important for achieving the function.

Method

Subjects. Subjects were 24 students at the University of Illinois who participated in the experiment as part of course credit.

Materials. Three category pairs were used. Each category was given a two-syllable nonsense name such as mornek or donker. Four types of features were used to construct the training examples of a category. A feature could be classified as predictive or non-predictive and core or superficial. A predictive feature was one with high cue and category validity (see definitions above). All of the examples that contained a predictive feature were members of the category (high cue validity) and 80% of the category members had the feature (high category validity). Non-predictive features occurred equally often in the examples of both categories of a given pair. Specifically, they occurred in 80% of the members of both categories. Besides being predictive or non-predictive, a feature was either core or superficial. A core feature was one that was especially relevant to the category's function. For example, the function of one category was "for killing bugs." A core feature of the category was "contains poison." A superficial feature was one that was not particularly relevant to the category's function. For example, the feature "manufactured in Florida" is not particularly relevant to the function "for killing bugs." Table 1 lists the features that were used to construct the examples of the category pairs, along with their functions. The structure of each category contained three superficial features (two predictive and one non-predictive) and two core features (one predictive and the other non-predictive). One of the superficial-nonpredictive features of a category was the core-nonpredictive feature of its contrast category (see Table 1).

The training examples that were presented to subjects consisted of all possible combinations of four of the five features from each category. In addition, two "random" features were added to each example. These features appeared equally often with examples of both categories in a pair. To make the random features, two stimulus dimensions with two values each were selected for each category pair. For example, the two dimensions selected for the donker/oostap category pair were "color" (with the values gray and blue) and "developed by" (with the values Japanese company and American company). A value from each dimension was then randomly selected for each example. There were 15 training examples (consisting of six features) from each category. Each exemplar was represented as an alphabetized list of features on an index card. Subjects in the function group also saw the function of each category typed in bold-face above each learning example.

There were 10 test examples from each category, divided into four types. The superficial-core* type contained the two superficial-predictive features of the category and the two core features of the (other) contrast category. Four test examples of this type were constructed by adding a different combination of two random features to the core and superficial features. There were two test examples of the core type, consisting of the two core features of the category and different combinations of two random features. There were two test examples of the superficial type, consisting of the two superficial-predictive features of the category and different combinations of two random features. Finally, there were two test examples of the superficial-core type. Each of these examples consisted of the three superficial features and two core features of the category and one random feature. Table 2 shows an example of each type for the mornek category. Notice that none of the test examples are ambiguous in that they all contain more predictive features of one category than the other.

Procedure. Subjects read instructions telling them that they were to learn various categories of objects by reading descriptions of individual objects. The instructions also mentioned that they would see new examples of the objects and that they would have to decide which kind of object each example was. The task was introduced by way of example. Subjects were told to imagine that they did not know what cars and airplanes were. They would be shown some examples of cars and airplanes and had to figure why the examples of car were cars and why the examples of airplane were airplanes. Then, they would see new examples and have to decide whether they were cars or airplanes. In addition, the function group was told that knowing what an object is used for (its function) is helpful in learning about that object. They were also told that they would see descriptions of each category's function.

For practice, subjects first learned two categories (unrelated to the experimental categories) to give them an idea of the difficulty of the task. Next, the experimental categories were taught. The randomized examples of the two contrast categories were presented on index cards, and subjects

Table 1. Features used to construct examples of the category pairs and their functions.

Mornek

Function: for killing bugs
sprayed on plants **C-P**
contains poison **C-NP**
contains a sticky substance **S-NP**
stored in a garage **S-P**
manufactured in Florida **S-P**

Plapel

Function: for wallpapering
sprayed on walls **C-P**
contains poison **S-NP**
contains a sticky substance **C-NP**
stored in a basement **S-P**
manufactured in Ohio **S-P**

Ardon:

Function: warns people about leaking gas
has a red flashing light **C-P**
makes a loud noise **C-NP**
has a vacuum chamber **S-NP**
box-shaped **S-P**
turned on by a dial **S-P**

Carpel:

Function: used to suck up water
has a rubber hose **C-P**
makes a loud noise **S-NP**
has a vacuum chamber **C-NP**
barrel-shaped **S-P**
turned on by a button **S-P**

Donker:

Function: reads printed text to people
emits word sounds **C-P**
contains speakers **C-NP**
has a propeller **S-NP**
made of platinum **S-P**
costs thousands of dollars **S-P**

Oostap:

Function: underwater public transport
emits sonar **C-P**
contains speakers **S-NP**
has a propeller **C-NP**
made of steel **S-P**
costs millions of dollars **S-P**

C-P: core predictive
C-NP: core non-predictive
S-P: superficial predictive
S-NP: superficial non-predictive

Table 2. Examples of the test items for the mornek category.

superficial-core*
stored in the garage **S-P**
manufactured in Florida **S-P**
contains a sticky substance **C-NP***
sprayed on walls **C-P***
best if used within 1 year **R**

core
contains poison **C-NP**
sprayed on plants **C-P**
best if used within 5 years **R**
came in a 32-ounce container **R**

superficial
stored in a garage **S-P**
manufactured in Florida **S-P**
best if used within 1 year **R**
came in a 16-ounce container **R**

superficial-core
stored in a garage **S-P**
manufactured in Florida **S-P**
contains a sticky substance **S-NP**
contains poison **C-NP**
sprayed on plants **C-P**
best if used within 1 year **R**

S-P: superficial predictive
C-P: core predictive
C-P*: core predictive (of contrast category)
R: random
S-NP: superficial non-predictive
C-NP: core non-predictive
C-NP*: core non-predictive (of contrast category)

were given 12 sec to study each item. A timer beeped every 12 sec to mark the time. Subjects learned about three pairs of contrast categories. All possible orders of the pairs were presented and order was counterbalanced across subjects. After subjects had learned all three category pairs, they classified the 60 test examples (10 from each category), presented in random order. Each item consisted of a list of features followed by a rating scale, and each was presented on a separate sheet. The rating scale asked subjects to indicate which of the two contrast categories they thought the object was in and to indicate their confidence on a 1 to 7 scale. A 1 was the most confident value for one category of the pair and a 7 was the most confident value for the other. Subjects were instructed to use the other numbers of the scale to indicate intermediate degrees of confidence. It was assumed that certainty rating is closely related to the typicality of the example to the category (see Murphy & Wisniewski, in press). The whole experiment took about 45 minutes to complete.

Results and Discussion

The mean confidence ratings for the types of test examples are shown in Table 3. Recall that none of the test examples were ambiguous in that they all contained more predictive features of one category than its contrast category. In the table, the higher the rating, the more confident subjects were that a test example was a member of this more predictable category. All of the statistical analyses reported are t-tests for paired comparisons.

Table 3. Confidence ratings for test examples.

	Function	Discrimination
superficial-core*	4.00	5.02
core	6.16	5.93
superficial	6.04	6.36
superficial-core	6.43	6.54

There were several important findings. First, compared to the discrimination group, the goal group was more confident that the superficial-core* items belonged to the less predictable category. These items contained only one predictive feature of this category (a core feature) compared to two predictive features of its contrast category (both superficial). The mean certainty score was 4.00 for the goal group compared to 5.02 for the discrimination group. In fact, the goal group rated all 24 of the superficial-core* items lower than the discrimination group. This difference was highly significant, $t(23) = 11.96$, $p < .001$, in the item analysis. The rating difference was also considerably larger than any other differences between item types among the two groups. Second, the discrimination group rated the superficial items higher than they rated the core items (6.36 versus 5.93). This difference was significant, $t(11) = 2.33$, $p < .05$, in the subject analysis. In contrast, the goal group rated the core items slightly higher than they rated the superficial items (6.16 versus 6.04), although this difference was not significant. Finally, the discrimination group rated the superficial items higher than the goal group (6.36 versus 6.04), a difference that was significant, $t(11) = 2.48$, $p < .05$, in the item analysis. In contrast, the goal group rated the core items slightly higher than the discrimination group (6.16 versus 5.93), although this difference was only marginally significant, $t(11) = 1.84$, $p < .10$, in the item analysis.

Taken together, the results suggest that the goal and discrimination groups formed different concepts, despite being presented with the same examples of a category. The discrimination group, given standard instructions to learn categories, formed concepts that were based on predictive features. Two results support this conclusion. First, the discrimination group rated the superficial items as better examples of their category than the core items. The superficial items contained more predictive features than the core items (two versus one). Second, given items containing two predictive features of one category and one predictive feature of its contrast category (the superficial-core* items), subjects rated the items as better members of the predictive category.

On the other hand, the goal group, provided with information about the category function, formed concepts that emphasized both predictive features and features that were relevant to the function (the core features). Clearly, the core features were important in the conceptual representations of the function group. Compared with the discrimination group, subjects in this group rated the superficial-core* items as more typical of the less predictable category. Presumably, subjects had represented the core features of these items as important information about the function of the less predictable category. Furthermore, the goal group rated the core items as slightly better examples of the category than the superficial items--even though the superficial items contained more predictive features and one of core features of each core item was nonpredictive.

GENERAL DISCUSSION

The strategies used by the subjects in this experiment are somewhat similar to explanation-based learning or EBL (Dejong & Mooney, 1986). When provided with category functions, people incorporated features from the training examples into their concepts that were relevant to those functions. Most likely, people used their intuitive theories of the world to determine the relevant features (see also Murphy & Medin, 1985; Medin & Wattenmaker, 1987). For example, when informed that the category members were used "for killing bugs," people may have used their basic knowledge of the world that poison kills animate things and that insects inhabit plants and often destroy them, to determine that the features "contains poison" and "sprayed on plants" are important aspects of the category members. People's use of theories is similar to an EBL program that uses its domain theory to explain why a training instance is an example of some high-level concept (often functional in nature). On the other hand, people's strategies were different from EBL in several ways. First, many EBL programs construct a deductive proof (explanation) for why a single example fits a high-level concept. They then inductively generalize this explanation to form a new concept. Features are not included in the new concept if they are not part of the explanation. In contrast, subjects in the goal group probably constructed plausible explanations (as opposed to deductive proofs) for why category members fit their functions. They also incorporated non-explanatory (but predictive) features into their concepts. Current EBL programs discard such features.

The results of this study have implications for several areas of cognitive science. In psychology, the findings suggest that the standard classification learning paradigm provides a limited view on the nature of concepts and the processes that are used to construct them (see also Schank, Collins, & Hunter, 1986). Researchers have generally focused on one purpose or role of concepts--namely, their role as representations that allow one to classify or discriminate objects.
As with the classification paradigm in psychology, many similarity-based approaches in machine learning primarily focus on this role. Yet, concepts have a number of different purposes (Matheus, et al. provide a useful taxonomy). It is important to study concept acquisition and use in contexts that highlight these purposes. In fact, different purposes of a concept may interact with its purpose as a classification mechanism. Thus, standard classification tasks may be further limited in their emphasis on the classification role to the exclusion of other roles. To take a simple example, it might be the case that some combination of simple features (i.e., a higher-order feature) achieves an object's function and that the combination is also predictive of category membership. In a standard classification task, finding such a combination might be extremely difficult, given the problem of combinatorial explosion. However, the search for such a combination can be constrained by knowing the function of the category.

REFERENCES

Dejong, G., & Mooney, R. J. (1986). Explanation-based learning: An alternative view. Machine Learning, 1, 145-176.

Fisher, D., & Langley, P. (1985). Methods of conceptual clustering and their relation to numerical taxonomy. University of California Irvine Technical Report 85-26.

Matheus, C. J., Rendell, L. R., Medin, D. L., & Goldstone, R. L. (1989).Purpose and conceptual functions: A framework for concept representation and learning in humans and machines. In The Seventh Annual Conference of the Society for the Study of Artificial Intelligence and Simulation of Behavior.

Medin, D. L., & Wattenmaker, W. D. (1987). Category cohesiveness, theories, and cognitive archeology. In U. Neisser (Ed.), Concepts and conceptual development: The ecological and intellectual factors in categorization. Cambridge: Cambridge University Press.

Medin, D. L., Wattenmaker, W. D., & Michalski, R. S. (1987). Constraints in inductive learning: An experimental study comparing human and machine performance. Cognitive Science, 11, 319-359.

Murphy, G. L., & Medin, D. L. (1985). The role of theories in conceptual coherence. Psychological Review, 92, 289-316.

Murphy, G. L., & Wisniewski, E. J. (in press) Feature correlations in conceptual representations. In G. Tiberghien (Ed.) Advances in Cognitive Science, vol 2, John Wiley & Sons.

Nosofsky, R. M., Clark, S. E., & Shin, H. J. (1989). Rules and exemplars in categorization, identification, and recognition. Journal of Experimental Psychology: Learning, Memory, and Cognition, 15, 282-304.

Pazzani, M. J., & Schulenburg, D. (1989). The influence of prior theories on the ease of concept acquisition, to appear in The Proceedings of the Eleventh Annual Conference on Cognitive Science.

Reed. S. K. (1972). Pattern recognition and classification. Cognitive Psychology, 3, 382-407.

Rosch, E., Simpson, C., & Miller, R. S. (1976). Structural bases of typicality effects. Journal of Experimental Psychology: Human Perception and Performance, 2, 491-502.

Schank, R. C., Collins, G. C., & Hunter, L. E. (1986). Transcending inductive category formation in learning. Behavioral and Brain Sciences, 9, 639-686.

Stepp, R. E., & Michalski, R. S. (1986). Conceptual clustering: Inventing goal-oriented classifications of structured objects. In R. S. Michalski, J. G. Carbonell, and T. M. Mitchell, (Eds.), Machine Learning, vol 2, Los Altos, CA: Morgan Kaufmann Publishers

Wattenmaker, W. D., Dewey, G. I., Murphy, T. D., & Medin, D. L. (1986). Linear separability and concept learning: Context, Relational properties, and concept naturalness. Cognitive Psychology, 18, 158-194.

Active Acquisition for User Modeling in Dialog Systems

Dekai Wu*
Computer Science Division
University of California at Berkeley

Bettina Horster
FB Informatik
University of Dortmund, West Germany

ABSTRACT

A *user model* in a natural language dialog system contains knowledge about particular users' beliefs, goals, attitudes, or other characteristics. User modeling facilitates cooperative adaptation to a user's conversational behavior and goals.

This paper proposes *active* strategies for acquiring knowledge about users. Current systems employ *passive* acquisition strategies, which build a model of the user by making inferences based on passive observation of the dialog. Passive acquisition is generally preferable to active querying, to minimize unnecessary dialog. However, in some cases the system *should* actively initiate subdialogs with the purpose of acquiring information about the user. We propose a method for identifying these conditions based upon maximizing expected utility.

INTRODUCTION

Consider the following dialog with a route consultant system:

User:	Is there an inexpensive motel close to Fisherman's Wharf?
System:	Yes, but they are usually full at this time of the year.
	You might try the Ponderosa Inn, which is about a mile from Fisherman's Wharf.
	There is a cable car stop less than two blocks away.
U:	How do I get there?
S:	Go down the street, then turn right on Powell, at the third light.
	There is a sign on the left-hand-side after half a block.

The system's responses are cooperative, in that they help the user achieve his goals. Not only does the system directly answer the user's queries, but in addition, responds at a useful level of detail and expertise, and volunteers pertinent information that was not specifically requested. This example is representative of the kind of cooperative dialog behavior at which current research efforts are directed [Wilensky et al. 1988, Chin 1988, Mayfield 1989, Wahlster et al. 1983, Kobsa 1985].

Generating cooperative responses involves making many different types of inferences. Some of the inferences needed to produce the responses in the example above are:

- The user has the goal of knowing an inexpensive motel close to Fisherman's Wharf.
- The user assumes the system has this knowledge, and wants the system to communicate it to him.
- The user has the goal of staying in the motel today.
- The user wants to be as close as possible to Fisherman's Wharf.
- The user wants to be able to reach Fisherman's Wharf as conveniently as possible.
- The user's budget constraints outweigh his desire to stay close to Fisherman's Wharf.
- The user has the goal of knowing how to reach the motel.
- The user is driving a car (because he asked for a motel).
- The user does not live in the area, and is probably a tourist.
- The user does not know the area well, and requires detailed directions.

---

* This research was sponsored in part by the Defense Advanced Research Projects Agency (DoD), monitored by the Space and Naval Warfare Systems Command under Contract N00039-88-C-0292, the Office of Naval Research, under grant N00014-80-C-0732, and the Sloan Foundation, under grant 86-10-3.

Inferences such as these fall in the area of *user modeling*, because they involve inferring and utilizing knowledge about the user's beliefs, goals, attitudes, or objective characteristics. Wahlster and Kobsa [1986] have given the following definition:

> A user model is a knowledge source in a natural-language dialog system which contains explicit assumptions on all aspects of the user that may be relevant for the dialog behavior of the system.

To some extent, determining the user's goals and beliefs is an intrinsic part of understanding an utterance; for example, to understand "Is there an inexpensive motel close to Fisherman's Wharf?" the hearer must recognize the speaker's information acquisition goal, and must recognize the presupposition that the hearer knows the information. Other inferences are made only when needed; for instance, the planning stage requires the inference that the user's budget overrides other constraints.

User modeling affects most tasks performed in a dialog system. Some aspects of user modeling merely improve "user-friendliness", while others are absolutely crucial to communication. The user model helps the system understand the deictic reference in "How do I get there?" because knowing that the user has the goal of staying in the motel makes "Ponderosa Inn" a more plausible referent than "cable car stop". The system can only build an appropriate plan for the user if it knows the user's goals—to find accommodations convenient to Fisherman's Wharf—and constraints—a limited budget. It generates a response at the appropriate level of detail and expertise, assuming the user is a tourist. Thus, the user model improves the system's cooperativeness by influencing understanding, planning, and generation tasks.

Now consider the following interchange:

U1: How do I get to the center of the bay?
S2: Why do you want to go there?
U3: I want to take a picture of the skyline.
S4: Is it sufficient to drive to Treasure Island, or is it necessary to take a cruise?
U5: No, I don't want to take the picture from Treasure Island.
S6: Then you can take a bay cruise tour from Fisherman's Wharf.

This is an example of dialog behavior that is beyond most existing dialog systems. It involves *active* acquisition on the system's part, because the system seeks additional user model information by directly querying the user. With S2, the system initiates a subdialog to determine a more specific user goal, and with S4, the system initiates a subdialog to determine the user's preference between two plans. In contrast, all of the knowledge about the user in the earlier example was *passively* acquired by making inferences from observing the dialog, without intentionally altering the course of the dialog.

Usually, passive acquisition is preferable to active, because unnecessary querying wastes time. However, as the example shows, active acquisition is sometimes useful. A passive system would respond like this:

U1: How do I get to the center of the bay?
S2: You can drive to Treasure Island.
U3: But I don't want to be on land.
S4: Then you can charter a yacht.
U5: But I don't have the money.

and so on. Alternatively, the system could suggest all known options:

S2/b: You can drive to Treasure Island, charter a yacht, rent a windsurfer, swim in a wetsuit, take a bay cruise tour, buy a rowboat, scuba dive, hop on the ferry, or hire a helicopter.

Clearly, neither passive approach is satisfactory.

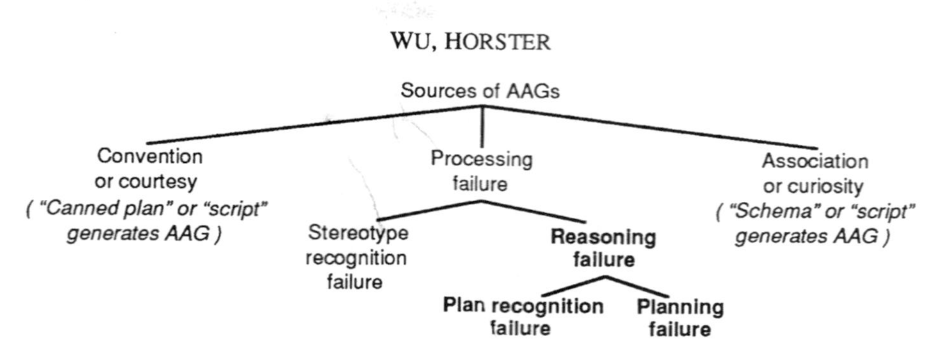

Figure 1. Sources of AAGs.

Dialog systems lack principled means for detecting situations that call for active acquisition during the course of a dialog. Early user modeling systems relied too heavily on active acquisition. GRUNDY [Rich 1979] asks the user a "canned" set of questions at the beginning of a session, and builds a user model from the answers. "Canned" active approaches are valid only for highly restricted domains with little conceptual variation from one dialog to another. Because of this limitation, later systems such as KNOME [Chin 1988], PAGAN [Mayfield 1989], and TRACK [Carberry 1988] concentrate on passively inferring models of the user, an approach that inherently ensures the user model is tied to the particular dialog context. However, although the ideal agent relies primarily upon passive acquisition to meet efficiency and appropriateness considerations, the same considerations dictate occasional *motivated* use of active acquisition.

This work is heavily related to plan recognition research [Allen and Perrault 1980, Litman and Allen 1984], but differs in emphasis. Plan recognition techniques only *recognize* the correlations between discourse structure and conversants' plans; they do not *predict* the most plausible continuation of a dialog given the conversants' plans.

ACTIVE ACQUISITION GOALS

As a useful conceptual notion, we define an *active acquisition goal* (AAG) as a goal held by a dialog agent to actively acquire knowledge about the dialog partner. We assume that in normal operation a dialog system builds a model of the user through passive acquisition, but occasionally adopts an AAG, and therefore initiates an information-seeking subdialog. Thus, the issues to be addressed are: (1) under what conditions should AAGs be generated, and (2) once generated, what are the criteria for adopting or rejecting AAGs?

A broad classification of reasons for generating AAGs is given in Figure 1. Our analysis is limited to the categories in boldface, but there are other potential sources of AAGs. In particular, systems employing stereotypes may generate AAGs in the event that no satisfactory stereotype is recognizable.[1]

Plans for achieving AAGs involve *speech acts* in Austin's [1962] sense that utterances are produced by actions. The most straightforward type of plan initiates a *clarification subdialog* by verbalizing a direct request for information. Subtler plans for actively acquiring information use *indirect speech acts* [Searle 1969] or ask a question whose answer can then be used to infer the desired information.

There are two ways to interpret AAGs. In one view, there are only ordinary acquisition goals—in themselves neither passive nor active—for which some plans involve active speech acts and others involve passive means. According to this view, there are active acquisition *plans*, but AAGs are merely a conceptual shorthand that help us focus on a particular phenomenon. On the other hand, AAGs can be seen as a real class of goals that circumscribe a narrower class of plans than ordinary acquisition goals; that is, the existence of a separate class of AAGs constitutes compiled indexing information for retrieving plans from memory. We take no position on this distinction, in the absence of empirical psychological data.

---

[1] Some cases where this might happen are: (1) if the only matching stereotypes are over-abstract (i.e., superordinate rather than basic-level categories [Rosch et al. 1976]), (2) if mutually exclusive stereotypes are equally plausible, or (3) if a stereotype is a very close but imperfect match.

Plan recognition failure
Plan recognizer produces no plan of acceptable utility explaining user's speech act
1a → *Generate AAG to identify unknown user goal*
1b → *Generate AAG to identify (and/or correct) unknown user misconception*
Plan recognizer produces more than one "maximum utility" plan explaining user's speech act
-or- Plan recognizer lacking information needed to compare plan utility
2 → *Generate AAG to disambiguate user's intention*
Domain planning failure
Domain planner lacking information needed to compare plan utility
3a-b → *Generate AAG to ascertain needed information*
Domain planner produces more than one "maximum utility" plan
4 → *Generate AAG to determine the user's preference*
Dialog planning failure
Dialog planner lacking information needed to compare plan utility
5 → *Generate AAG to ascertain needed information*

Figure 2. Taxonomy of failure conditions under which to generate AAGs.

REASONING FAILURES AS A SOURCE OF AAGS

Our analysis concentrates on AAGs generated in response to failures or exceptions in a dialog system's normal reasoning processes. This is a highly productive source of AAGs and accounts for dialogs like the example given earlier. We assume three major types of normal reasoning processes in a dialog system: plan recognition, domain planning, and dialog planning. The following paragraphs briefly sketch how failures in any of these processes can lead to AAGs. We then discuss how the failures can be detected, and give rules for generating AAGs in response to specific failure types. Figure 2 summarizes the general failure types.

Plan recognition: The system performs plan recognition to explain the user's speech acts by inferring his underlying plans and goals; as such, plan recognition is an important form of passive acquisition. If, however, the system is unable to construct any plan to explain the user's actions, the system may hypothesize one of two possible causes: (1) an unknown user goal, or (2) an unknown user misconception. In either case, it may then generate an AAG to identify the unknown. On the other hand, if the system can produce two or more plausible explanations for the user's speech act but cannot decide between them, it may generate an AAG to determine some fact that would eliminate all but one explanation.

Domain planning: The system performs domain planning in its area of expertise to produce a solution for the user's goals (e.g., a route plan). If the system is unable to evaluate the utility of the plans it produces because it lacks information about the user, it may generate an AAG to obtain the information. If it produces multiple plans of high utility, an AAG to determine the user's preference may be generated.

Dialog planning: Dialog planning is performed to determine the system's own actions, particularly its speech acts. In some cases where the system is unable to evaluate the expected utility of alternative plans, an AAG to obtain relevant information may be generated.

Detecting Reasoning Failure Conditions

The foregoing failure conditions all involve evaluating or comparing the utility of plans. The dialog-planning cases involve the system's own potential plans, whereas the plan-recognition cases involve plans which the system hypothesizes the user holds, and the domain-planning cases involve hypothetical plans for the user. Thus, to define failure criteria requires a metric for plan utility.

For current purposes, we use a 3-tuple measure, where plan utility is broken down into the following independent attributes:

(1) *Difficulty*: The difficulty of a plan has to do with the difficulty (effort or time required) of the individual steps of the plan, as well as the difficulty of achieving the preconditions (if they are not already satisfied). Estimating the difficulty of a plan, without actually executing the plan, requires some sort of statistical

expectation based on experience.

(2) *Degree of goal conflict*: Any plan satisfies the goal that was planned for, but may also have unintended consequences as side-effects. The side-effects may conflict with other goals. Some goal conflicts may be acceptable, while others may not.

(3) *Over-specificness of the plan's consequences*: Even if side-effect consequences do not conflict with any other goals, a plan should have as few extra consequences as possible, because extra consequences unnecessarily constrain future actions.

These attributes are meaningful only in relation to a particular agent, in the context of his goals and constraints. The utility of a plan cannot be measured in absolute terms.

Given these definitions, the failure condition "plan recognizer produces no plan of acceptable utility explaining the user's speech act" can be detected by establishing minimum standards for each attribute, so that a failure occurs if no plan meets the standards in all three dimensions.

The failure conditions "plan recognizer produces more than one 'maximum utility' plan" and "domain planner produces more than one 'maximum utility' plan" are detected when two plans' utility measures are *non-comparable*. This can occur because a 3-tuple measure of utility establishes only a partial ordering of plans, since two utilities can only be ranked if one is better than or equal to the other in all three attributes. A "maximum utility" plan must be at least equally good as every other plan in all three attributes, and better than every other plan in at least one attribute (not necessarily the same attribute for each plan). If no plan meets the "maximum utility" criteria, a failure condition holds.

Finally, the system may lack information needed to determine values for utility attributes. For example, if the achievability of some precondition is unknown, the difficulty of a plan cannot be computed. This accounts for the remaining failure conditions above. (Note that it is sometimes possible to compare plans even when it is not possible to determine individual utility attribute values. If, for instance, a precondition status is unknown, but both of the plans being compared require the precondition, then the status of the precondition does not affect the comparison.)

Generating AAGs

We now enumerate the rules for generating AAGs in response to reasoning failures.

- *Rule 1a*: If it is not possible to produce a plan of acceptable utility explaining the user's speech act, then generate an AAG to identify an unknown user goal.

- *Rule 1b*: If it is not possible to produce a plan of acceptable utility explaining the user's speech act, then generate an AAG to identify (and/or correct) an unknown user misconception.

These rules are responsible for S8/1a or S8/1b in the following example. The system cannot produce a plan of acceptable utility to explain U7, and adopts an AAG assuming either an unknown user goal or misconception.[1]

U1: How do I get to the center of the bay?
S2: Why do you want to go there?
U3: I want to take a picture of the skyline.
S4: Is it sufficient to drive to Treasure Island, or is it necessary to take a cruise?
U5: No, a cruise isn't necessary.
S6: Then you should drive to the Bay Bridge and take the Treasure Island exit.
U7: What about Angel Island?

[1] Rule 1b is only one case of suspecting a user misconception; detecting and correcting misconceptions is an orthogonal issue which many researchers have addressed [e.g., McCoy 1988, Chin 1988].

S8/1a: Why do you ask?
U9/1a: I also want to visit Angel Island.

S8/1b: There is no bridge to Angel Island, you must take a ferry.

- *Rule 2*: If the highest-utility plans explaining the user's speech act are non-comparable, or the plan recognizer lacks information needed to compare plan utility, then generate an AAG to disambiguate the user's intention.

Rule 2 is responsible for S4 in the following dialog. The system cannot determine whether the user utters U3 to request directions or to convey a wish to eat in Chinatown, because it lacks the information needed to determine the speech act's appropriateness for the user's overall goals.

U1: Where can we eat a good Chinese meal tonight?
S2: There is a good restaurant called Mandarin House on Clement.
U3: Is that in Chinatown?
S4: No, do you want to eat in Chinatown?
U5/a: Yes.
S6/a: The Red Chamber on Jackson is quite good.

U5/b: No, that doesn't matter.
S6/b: To get to Clement, you can take Geary down to 30th and then go north one block.

The following rules are subcases of the general situation where the domain planner lacks information necessary for comparing the plans with the highest expected utilities. The subcases involve different plan utility attributes.[1]

- *Rule 3a*: If, while comparing the over-specificness of the highest-utility domain plans, no plan closely matches the specificness of the known user goals, and the plans have mutually exclusive consequences, then generate an AAG to determine a more specific user goal.

Rule 3a accounts for the following exchange:

U1: How do I get to the center of the bay?
S2: Why do you want to go there?

The system is able to build a number of plans, including driving to Treasure Island, chartering a yacht, taking a bay cruise tour, and windsurfing. Each plan's consequences are over-specific in comparison with the known goal of the user, which is to get to the center of the bay; thus, each plan strongly constrains the possible future actions. Moreover, each plan constrains future actions differently; one results in the user being on Treasure Island, another results in the user being on a boat, and so on. Since the user presumably has a particular purpose for getting to the center of the bay, the plan selected should be the one whose constraints most closely match his specific goal. However, because the system does not know the user's specific goal, it is unable to evaluate which plan's consequences provide the best match.

- *Rule 3b*: If, while comparing the difficulty of the highest-utility domain plans, some plans have a precondition that others do not, and the precondition is neither known to hold nor assumable by default, then generate an AAG to determine the ease of achieving the precondition.

The following example illustrates rule 3b:

U1: How do I get to the Marina?
S2: Do you drive?

[1] There is no subcase for the degree of goal conflict attribute because, if the system has no information about a conflicting goal, it is assumed that no conflict exists.

The system needs to discover whether the user can satisfy the precondition of a plan, in order to select the easiest plan.

- *Rule 4*: If the highest-utility domain plans are non-comparable, then generate an AAG to determine the user's preference.

For example, the system asks "Is it sufficient to drive to Treasure Island, or is it necessary to take a cruise?" because the Treasure Island plan is superior in the difficulty attribute, but the cruise plan is superior in the goal conflict and/or over-specificness attributes since taking the picture from the water constrains the angle less than the island.

- *Rule 5*: If the dialog planner lacks information to compare the highest-utility dialog plans, then generate an AAG to obtain the needed information.

In the following example, the system builds several different plans for expressing a location, but cannot judge their difficulty until it ascertains whether the user's knowledge satisfies the plans' preconditions.

U1: Where is Cafe Rigoletto?
S2: Do you know where Symphony Hall is?
U3: Yes.
S4: Cafe Rigoletto is in the alley across the street from Symphony Hall.

EVALUATING AND SELECTING AAGS

The rules above will generate too many AAGs, and most should be rejected for one reason or another. The problem of evaluating and selecting AAGs is a subcase of the same goal selection problem faced by any general dialog planner. The utility criteria discussed above thus also apply to comparing and selecting plans for satisfying AAGs.

If a failure that generates an AAG is encountered, processing continues as normally as possible. In this way, all AAGs potentially relevant to the user's utterance are collected before any decisions are made. The motivation for this delayed-commitment strategy is as follows. The AAGs selected are those which maximize expected utility *with regard to the system's top level goals*, i.e., cooperative goals such as briefness, comprehensibility, and relevance. The maximum-utility AAG (or set of AAGs) cannot be determined *a priori*; this is especially obvious in cases where a single plan satisfies multiple AAGs. For example, S2 in

U1: Do you know good restaurants in this neighborhood?
S2: Yes, are you interested in a particular style of cuisine?

satisfies the AAG to determine whether the user's specific goal is to discover the system's breadth of knowledge or to discover good restaurants (rule 2), as well as the AAG to determine information needed to compare the utility of various restaurant-going plans (rule 3a). S2 is a better response than "Yes, do you want to know some?" or "What style of cuisine?" which satisfy only one or the other AAG.

Moreover, many AAGs are not worth satisfying because the expected utility is lower than that of an alternative non-active-acquisition plan. For example, it is often easier to correct a suspected misconception rather than take the trouble to verify whether the user actually believes it. Another case occurs when the system produces two non-comparable plans for the user, and simply verbalizes both plans briefly, rather than determining the user's preference. Thus, AAGs are evaluated against all the system's goals and not just against themselves.

To collect the set of candidate AAGs, it is useful to maintain a dependency graph that reflects which AAG plans subsume or exclude others. The dependency graph may also include plans for the system's other goals. In this way, poorer courses of action can be immediately pruned when the utilities are comparable, and the subset that subsumes the most goals can be selected.

CONCLUSION

We have presented the beginnings of a theory of active acquisition for building the user model, as an extension of current theories of cooperative dialog planning and plan recognition. The dialog system generates such AAGs in response to failures detected during utility comparisons in its normal reasoning processes. Plans to achieve an AAG are executed when the expected utility exceeds that of alternative courses of action. Although the classification of active acquisition goals is by no means comprehensive, it covers a large proportion of cases where active acquisition is desirable. The communicative efficiency and naturalness of existing dialog systems can be substantially enhanced by the addition of AAG generation and selection capabilities.

Further work to refine the utility metric is needed. One open issue is the computation of the individual plan utility attributes; numeric values will almost certainly be needed, the source of which must be justified. Possibly, n-tuples with more sophisticated attributes are necessary. The definition of utility also needs to be expanded for the case of plans that partially satisfy goal-sets comprising multiple goals.

Another issue is how to reduce spuriously generated AAGs. Rule 5, for example, must be triggered sparingly to avoid recursive application. Sharper appropriateness conditions should be found for the rules.

ACKNOWLEDGEMENTS

The authors would like to thank Prof. Robert Wilensky, Prof. Armin B. Cremers, and Rainer Waschkowski.

REFERENCES

Allen, James F., and Raymond C. Perrault. [1980]. "Analyzing intention in utterances". *Artificial Intelligence* 15: 143-178.

Austin, J. L. [1962]. *How to do things with words.* London: Oxford University Press.

Carberry, Sandra. [1988]. "Modeling the user's plans and goals". *Computational Linguistics* 14(3): 23-37.

Chin, David. [1988]. *Intelligent agents as a basis for natural language interfaces* (Ph.D. Thesis). Comp. Sci. Div., Univ. of California at Berkeley, Report No. UCB/CSD 88/396.

Kobsa, Alfred. [1985]. "VIE-DPM: A user model in a natural-language dialogue system". In J. Laubsch (ed.), *GWAI-84, 8th German Workshop on Artificial Intelligence.* Berlin: Springer-Verlag.

Litman, Diane J., and James F. Allen. [1984]. *A plan recognition model for subdialogues in conversation.* Dept. of Comp. Sci., Univ. of Rochester, TR 141.

Mayfield, James. [1989]. *Goal analysis: Plan recognition in dialogue systems* (Ph.D. thesis). Comp. Sci. Div., University of California at Berkeley, report forthcoming.

Rich, Elaine. [1979]. *Building and exploiting user models.* Ph.D. Thesis, Comp. Sci. Dept., Carnegie-Mellon Univ.

Rosch, E., C. B. Mervis, W. D. Gray, D. M. Johnson, and P. Boyes-Braem. 1976. "Basic objects in natural categories". *Cognitive Psychology* 8: 382-439.

Searle, J. R. [1969]. *Speech acts: An essay in the philosophy of language.* Cambridge: Cambridge University Press.

Wahlster, W., H. Marburger, A. Jameson, and S. Busemann. [1983]. "Over-answering yes-no-questions: Extended responses in a NL interface to a vision system". *Proc. IJCAI-83*, 643-646.

Wahlster,W., and A. Kobsa. [1986]. *Dialog-based user models.* Dept. of Comp. Sci., Universitaet des Saarlandes, West Germany, XTRA Report No. 3.

Wilensky, Robert, David Chin, Marc Luria, James Martin, James Mayfield, and Dekai Wu. [1988]. "The Berkeley UNIX Consultant project". *Computational Linguistics* 14(4): 35-84.

9780805806847.